Symbol	Description	Page

LATIN SYMBOLS

Symbol	Description	Page
s_X^2	sample variance	87
$s_{Y_{next}}$	estimator of standard deviation: of Y_{next}	513
$s_{\overline{Y}_X}$	of $\overline{Y}_X$	508
$s_{Y.X}$	estimator: of $\sigma_{Y.X}$	496
$s_{Y.X_1X_2}$	of $\sigma_{Y.X_1X_2}$	531
S_0	prior standard deviation of μ_X	463
S_1	posterior standard deviation of μ_X	465
S_*	S value for sample information	470
t	slope of loss function	469
	t-distribution value	250
V_1	test statistic: for χ^2 tests	416
V_2	for analysis of variance	430
w	exponential smoothing weight	734
X_a	midpoint of any class	102
$\overline{X}$	sample mean:	
	grouped data	81
	ungrouped data	79
$\overline{\overline{X}}$	overall sample mean	427
$\overline{X}_j$	treatment sample mean	427
$\overline{X}_{st}$	stratified sample mean	291
Y_{next}	next value of Y for given X	512
$\overline{Y}_X$	estimator of $\mu_{Y.X}$	493
$\overline{Y}_{X_1X_2}$	estimator of $\mu_{Y.X_1X_2}$	530
z	standard normal deviate	148
z_I, z_{II}	specified z values	358, 361

GREEK SYMBOLS

Symbol	Description	Page
α	regression intercept	487
β	regression slope, simple	487
β_1, β_2	regression parameters, multiple	529
δ	parameter of χ^2-distribution	416
δ_1, δ_2	parameters of F-distribution	431
μ_d	mean: of d	287
μ_D	of D	281
$\mu_{\bar{p}}$	of $\bar{p}$	217
μ_X	of population	108
	of probability distribution	130
$\mu_{\overline{X}}$	of $\overline{X}$	194
$\mu_{Y.X}$	of distribution of Y given X	486
μ_0	specified μ value	358
μ_I, μ_{II}	specified μ values	358, 361
π	constant, about 3.142	148
σ_b	standard deviation: of b	516
σ_d	of d	288
	standard deviation:	
σ_D	of D	281
$\sigma_{\bar{p}}$	of $\bar{p}$ (finite population)	218
	of $\bar{p}$ (infinite population)	218
σ_X	of population	108
	of probability distribution	131
$\sigma_{\overline{X}}$	of $\overline{X}$ (finite population)	195
	of $\overline{X}$ (infinite population)	196
$\sigma_{Y.X}$	of Y given X	486
σ_X^2	variance of probability distribution	131
Σ	single summation operation	79
$\Sigma\Sigma$	double summation operation	427
χ^2	chi-square distribution value	416

OTHER SYMBOLS

Symbol	Description	Page
$\binom{x}{y}$	number of combinations	212
$\lvert\ \rvert$	absolute value	469
$!$	factorial	144
$\leq$	less than or equal to	
$\geq$	greater than or equal to	

Fundamental Statistics
for Business and Economics

4th edition

Fundamental Statistics

for Business and Economics

4th edition

JOHN NETER
Professor of Quantitative Analysis
School of Business Administration
University of Minnesota

WILLIAM WASSERMAN
Professor of Business Economics and Statistics
School of Management
Syracuse University

G. A. WHITMORE
Associate Professor
Faculty of Management
McGill University

Allyn and Bacon, Inc. Boston

470 Atlantic Avenue, Boston

Library of Congress Catalog Card Number: 72–87656

Printed in the United States of America

to Dorothy, Cathy, and Lonnie

CONTENTS

Preface **xiii**

Chapter **1 Introduction** **1**

1.1 What is statistics? 1.2 The expanding role of statistics 1.3 Statistics for business and economics 1.4 Focus of this book

Unit **I DATA HANDLING**

Chapter **2 Data** **11**

2.1 Internal data 2.2 Published external data 2.3 Surveys and experiments 2.4 Methods of obtaining information 2.5 Construction and use of schedules and questionnaires 2.6 Variables 2.7 Classification and tabulation

Chapter **3 Frequency distributions** **45**

3.1 Variation and its significance 3.2 A case study of variation 3.3 Additional case illustration: variation in manufactured product 3.4 Frequency distributions 3.5 Construction of frequency distributions 3.6 Graphic presentation of frequency distributions 3.7 Cumulative frequency distributions

Chapter **4 Characteristics of frequency distributions** **71**

4.1 Shortcuts to description of frequency distributions 4.2 Calculation of arithmetic mean 4.3 Calculation of median and percentiles 4.4 Calculation of standard deviation 4.5 Coefficient of variation 4.6 Pearson's coefficient of skewness

Chapter **5 Additional topics in data handling** **101**

5.1 Calculation of mean from grouped data 5.2 Calculation of standard deviation from grouped data 5.3 Chebyshev inequality

Unit II **PROBABILITY**

Chapter 6 **Probability and random variables** 107

6.1 Finite and infinite populations 6.2 Probability distributions 6.3 Meaning of probability 6.4 Basic probability concepts 6.5 Basic probability theorems 6.6 Random variables

Chapter 7 **Probability distributions and applications** 141

7.1 Bernoulli probability distributions 7.2 Poisson probability distributions 7.3 Normal probability distributions 7.4 Exponential probability distributions 7.5 Applications of probability theory

Chapter 8 **Additional topics in probability** 166

8.1 Chebyshev inequality 8.2 Continuous random variables

Unit III **SAMPLING AND SAMPLING DISTRIBUTIONS**

Chapter 9 **Statistical sampling** 175

9.1 Populations and samples 9.2 Reasons for sampling 9.3 Simple random sampling

Chapter 10 **Sampling distribution of $\overline{X}$** 188

10.1 Sample data and sampling distributions 10.2 Significance of sampling distribution of $\overline{X}$ 10.3 Properties of sampling distribution of $\overline{X}$ 10.4 Use of theory concerning sampling distributions of $\overline{X}$ 10.5 Effect of sample size on sampling distribution of $\overline{X}$ 10.6 Effect of population variability on sampling distribution of $\overline{X}$ 10.7 Need for sample information about sampling distribution of $\overline{X}$

Chapter 11 **Additional topics: sampling distribution of $\overline{p}$** 211

11.1 Exact functional form of sampling distribution of $\overline{p}$ 11.2 Characteristics of sampling distribution of $\overline{p}$ 11.3 Use of theory concerning sampling distribution of $\overline{p}$

Unit IV **STATISTICAL ESTIMATION**

Chapter 12 **Estimation of population mean** 229

12.1 Some typical estimation problems 12.2 Point estimation of population mean 12.3 Interval estimation of population mean—large simple random sample case 12.4 Interval estimation of population mean—small simple random sample case

Chapter **13 Sampling procedures and applications** **261**

13.1 Probability samples, judgment samples, and chunks 13.2 Probability sampling procedures 13.3 Applications of statistical estimation

Chapter **14 Additional topics in statistical estimation** **278**

14.1 Estimation of difference between two population means—large simple random sample case 14.2 Estimation of population proportion—large simple random sample case 14.3 Estimation of difference between two population proportions—large simple random sample case 14.4 Design and evaluation of stratified random sample

Unit **V STATISTICAL DECISION-MAKING (CLASSICAL)**

Chapter **15 Introduction to decision-making** **303**

15.1 What is a decision problem? 15.2 Decision-making under conditions of certainty 15.3 Decision-making under competitive conditions 15.4 Decision-making under conditions of uncertainty 15.5 Decision-making under conditions of risk 15.6 Summary 15.7 Statistical decision-making

Chapter **16 Statistical decision-making** **329**

16.1 Nature of statistical decision problem 16.2 Statistical decision rules 16.3 Classical statistical decision-making 16.4 Act probabilities 16.5 Error probabilities 16.6 Appropriate type of decision rule 16.7 Effect of change in action limit on power curve of rule 16.8 Effect of change in sample size on power curve of rule 16.9 Control of error probabilities

Chapter **17 Statistical decision-making concerning population mean** **353**

17.1 Construction of decision rule to control Type I errors 17.2 Construction of decision rule to control Type II errors 17.3 Control of both types of risks through sample size determination 17.4 Lower-tail decision problems 17.5 Two-sided alternative decision problems 17.6 Specification of acceptable risk levels

Chapter **18 Additional topics I: population means and proportions** **385**

18.1 Decision-making concerning population mean—small simple random sample case 18.2 Decision-making concerning difference between two population means—large simple random sample case 18.3 Decision-making concerning population proportion—large simple random sample case 18.4 Decision-making concerning difference between two population proportions—large simple random sample case 18.5 Statistical control charts and acceptance sampling

Chapter **19 Additional topics II: chi-square tests and analysis of variance** **412**

19.1 Tests of goodness of fit 19.2 Contingency tables 19.3 One-way analysis of variance

Unit **VI STATISTICAL DECISION-MAKING (BAYESIAN)**

Chapter **20 Introduction to Bayesian decision-making** **443**

20.1 Bayes' Theorem 20.2 Bayesian decision-making with prior probabilities only 20.3 Bayesian decision-making with prior probabilities and sample information 20.4 Determination of optimal sample size 20.5 Expected payoff with perfect information 20.6 Expected value of perfect information 20.7 Objective and subjective approaches to prior probabilities

Chapter **21 Additional topic: Bayesian decision-making with normal prior and sampling distributions** **462**

21.1 Decision-making with prior probabilities only 21.2 Decision-making with prior probabilities and sample information 21.3 Expected value of perfect information 21.4 Expected value of sample information 21.5 Determination of optimal sample size 21.6 Additional comments

Unit **VII REGRESSION AND CORRELATION**

Chapter **22 Introduction to regression and correlation** **479**

22.1 Introduction 22.2 Relation between two variables 22.3 Basic concepts in regression analysis 22.4 Point estimation of parameters of regression model 22.5 Coefficients of correlation and determination

Chapter **23 Inferences in regression analysis** **507**

23.1 Interval estimate of conditional mean $\mu_{Y.X}$ 23.2 Prediction of next value of Y for given X 23.3 Interval estimate of β 23.4 Additional considerations in the use of regression analysis

Chapter **24 Additional topics in regression and correlation** **524**

24.1 Cases of regression and correlation applications 24.2 Derivation of least squares estimators 24.3 Multiple regression analysis 24.4 Curvilinear regression analysis

Unit **VIII DATA ANALYSIS AND PRESENTATION**

Chapter **25 Ratios** **539**

25.1 Ratios as an aid to analysis 25.2 Typical uses of ratios in administration and economic analysis 25.3 Considerations in the compilation and use of ratios

Chapter **26 Cross-classification** **560**

26.1 Classification and cross-classification 26.2 Study of statistical relationships between two variables 26.3 Need to consider several variables simultaneously 26.4 Study of causes and effects by cross-classification

Chapter **27 Presentation** **580**

27.1 Functional parts and construction of statistical tables 27.2 Additional concepts and procedures in tabular presentation 27.3 Graphic presentation 27.4 Bar charts 27.5 Time series line graphs 27.6 Ratio or semilogarithmic graphs 27.7 Some general guides for the construction of graphs

Unit **IX INDEX NUMBERS AND TIME SERIES ANALYSIS**

Chapter **28 Index numbers** **621**

28.1 Compilation of price indexes 28.2 Compilation of quantity indexes 28.3 Some typical uses of index numbers in administration and analysis 28.4 Problems and procedures in the construction and use of index numbers

Chapter **29 Trend analysis** **650**

29.1 A brief survey of forecasting 29.2 Secular trend 29.3 Patterns of secular trend in economic and business activity 29.4 Calculations in time series analysis 29.5 Trend projections and forecasting 29.6 Case illustrations of long-term forecasting

Chapter **30 Cyclical fluctuations** **678**

30.1 Cyclical fluctuations and short-term forecasting 30.2 Business indicators 30.3 Use of regression analysis in forecasting 30.4 Some additional forecasting examples

Chapter **31 Seasonal variation** **699**

31.1 Nature and causes of seasonal variation 31.2 A conceptual framework for measuring stable patterns of seasonal variation 31.3 Applications of seasonal indexes 31.4 Computations for estimating indexes of seasonal variation by the method of ratio to moving average

Chapter **32 Additional topics in time series analysis** **729**

32.1 Shortcut method of fitting linear trend 32.2 Adaptation of annual linear trend equation 32.3 Alternative models in time series analysis 32.4 Exponential smoothing

APPENDIX TABLES

Table A-1	Table of areas for standard normal probability distribution
Table A-2	Poisson probabilities
Table A-3	Probabilities in right tail of exponential probability distribution
Table A-4	Binomial probabilities
Table A-5	Table of t-distribution
Table A-6	Table of χ^2 distribution
Table A-7	Table of F-distribution
Table A-8	Table of unit normal loss
Table A-9	Five-place logarithms
Table A-10	Squares, square roots, and reciprocals 1–1000

Answers to selected problems **763**

Index **773**

PREFACE

Fundamental Statistics for Business and Economics is intended for use in basic statistics courses offered to students of business and public administration and economics, as well as for people already engaged in these fields who desire an introduction to statistical methods. It is designed to give the reader an understanding of the uses of statistical methods as tools of decision-making. Sound decision-making depends not only on the statistical decision-making procedure but also on the quality and organization of the data and on the criteria employed. Therefore, we have developed in this introductory text both the modern methods of statistical inference and also some of the important related topics that are an integral part of the general decision-making process, such as collection, organization, and evaluation of quality of statistical data.

Great stress is placed on fundamental statistical ideas. Explanation of the important principles and concepts in each chapter precedes the discussion of detailed statistical techniques. To facilitate still further an understanding of basic statistical principles and their applications, some of the less important and less useful topics sometimes included in an introductory work have been omitted. Generally, only the most basic calculational procedures are explained in the chapter proper; where alternative computational procedures exist, they are presented as optional topics in "Additional Topics" chapters.

We believe that an introductory statistics book for business and economics must help the reader understand statistical methods and their uses as tools of management rather than merely train him in the manipulation of data in formulas. Therefore, we have used many actual case applications in explaining the statistical methods, so that these methods can be understood in terms of their actual uses. Furthermore, we hope that these case examples will also serve as forceful demonstrations of the usefulness of statistical methods in the fields of business and economics.

Our presentation requires only a knowledge of high school algebra. We have found that the basic ideas underlying modern statistical inference can be presented quite simply, and that in an introductory book this approach may lead to a greater appreciation of the uses of statistical methods than a highly mathematical one. For a few optional topics, we have included in "Additional Topics" chapters a limited amount of material which requires calculus, so that readers who have studied calculus can strengthen their understanding of basic concepts. Those readers who wish to continue their study of statistics and who therefore must learn more of the particulars about statistical methods, including the mathematical basis of statistics, should find this book a good foundation upon which they can build.

Many questions and realistic problems are included at the end of each chapter to help the reader understand the principles discussed and to enable him to apply statistical techniques in practical situations. These questions and problems offer a valuable means of learning by doing.

The fourth edition differs from the third in a number of important ways. Above all, the exposition has been reorganized to facilitate development of topics and an understanding of the relations between them. The chapters are grouped into nine units, to clarify the structure of the book as to content and to show the relation of parts to the whole. Chapters are shorter than in the third edition, so that a chapter can be read in an effective time span. Each unit of chapters contains one or more foundation chapters and (except for one unit) one or more "Additional Topics" chapters. Optional material has been placed in these "Additional Topics" chapters so that the instructor and reader can see clearly the main track of development and the relation of optional topics to the main track. Since the main development is self-contained, additional topics can be chosen as interest and time permit. Also, wide freedom of choice exists in the selection and sequencing of main-track content.

A key change in the sequence of topics made in the fourth edition is that material on data analysis and presentation (ratios, cross-classification, and statistical presentation) has been placed later in the text to facilitate taking up probability and statistical inference as soon as possible, if this is desired.

Finally, important formulas and definitions have been set out in a distinctive fashion for easier reference.

Numerous changes in the development of materials have been made. Some optional discussion of continuous random variables, requiring calculus, has been added in an "Additional Topics" chapter. The presentation of Bayesian statistical decision-making has been expanded into two chapters, one of which is devoted to the case of a normal prior probability distribution and normal sampling (this chapter is an optional "Additional Topics" chapter). The material on regression and correlation has been largely rewritten. We have strengthened the intuitive, descriptive aspects of regression before turning to the development of a formal probability model, and have unified the inferential elements by considering from the start the small sample case. We have also expanded the discussion of multiple regression and curvilinear regression.

In addition to these changes, we have made many revisions to improve the clarity of the presentation as well as to bring materials up-to-date. The problems at the end of each chapter have been revised, and the number has been increased wherever we have expanded the coverage in the chapters. Answers for selected problems are given in the back of the book, so that the student can check his results immediately. These problems are identified by an asterisk placed before the problem number.

This book can be used for a one- or two-quarter or one- or two-semester introductory statistics course for students in business or public administration or in economics. The organization of the book permits its use in a variety of such courses. A one-quarter or one-semester course which emphasizes statistical inference may use the principal chapters of the following units:

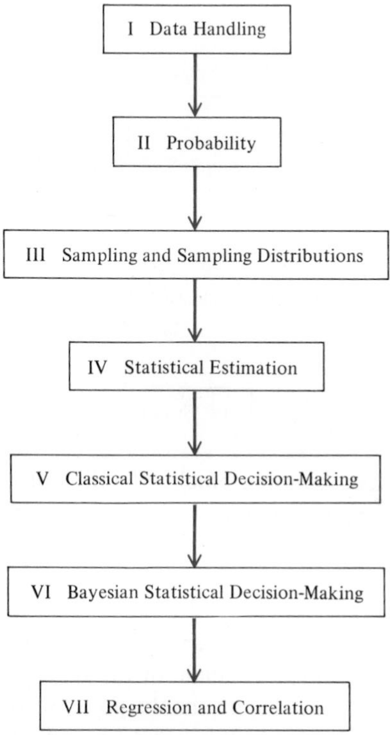

If time permits, some of the special topics in Units I–VII or, perhaps, some of the material from Unit IX, Index Numbers and Time Series Analysis, may be covered.

A two-quarter or two-semester course emphasizing statistical inference could follow the basic structure described above, and cover most if not all of the special topics in Units I–VII.

A one-quarter or one-semester course emphasizing statistical decision-making could use the principal chapters of Units I–VI, as well as many of the special topics in Units V (Classical Statistical Decision-Making) and VI (Bayesian Statistical Decision-Making). If time permits, the principal chapters of Unit VII (Regression and Correlation) may also be included in the course.

A one-quarter or one-semester course stressing statistical description, with a limited introduction to statistical inference, might use the principal chapters of the following units:

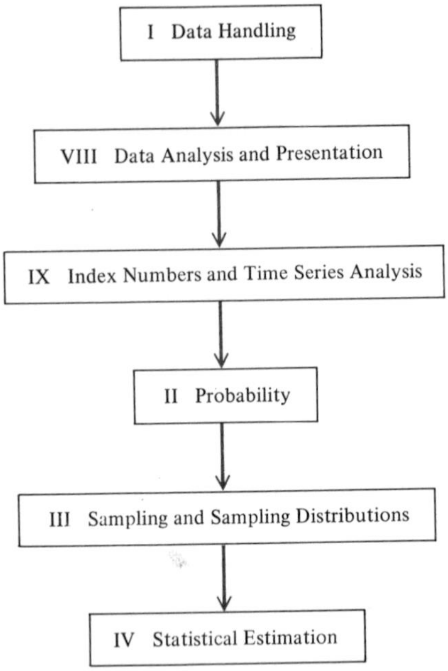

Given the basic building blocks of nine units, together with nine "Additional Topics" chapters from which any or all special topics can be selected, a wide variety of introductory statistics courses can be served by this book.

We are greatly indebted to the many individuals and organizations who have so generously furnished us with case illustrations. In some instances, specific acknowledgment is made in the text; in others, the source must be kept confidential. Our sincere thanks go to all who have helped us illustrate the usefulness of statistical methods in administration and in economic analysis.

Many persons have made helpful suggestions on the past editions, including our colleagues and reviewers of the manuscript, for which we are most grateful. We particularly wish to acknowledge our appreciation to Professor Jack Hayya of the College of Business Administration at Pennsylvania State University and Professor Paul R. Merry of the College of Business Administration at the University of Denver, who kindly prepared detailed comments for the fourth edition. Anthony Frayne and Marvin L. Zimmerman were most helpful in working with us on checking the manuscript. Allyn and Bacon, our publishers, helped us in many ways.

We also are indebted to the Literary Executor of the late Sir Ronald A. Fisher, F.R.S., Cambridge, to Dr. Frank Yates, F.R.S., Rothamsted, and to Messrs. Oliver and Boyd Ltd., Edinburgh, for permission to reprint Tables III and IV from their book *Statistical Tables for Biological, Agricultural and Medical Research.*

John Neter
William Wasserman
G. A. Whitmore

Chapter

1

INTRODUCTION

1.1

WHAT IS STATISTICS?

The influence of statistics pervades life so widely today that almost everyone has heard of the word *statistics,* is exposed to statistics, and uses statistics. The word *statistics* refers in common usage to numerical or quantitative data. Vital statistics, for example, are numerical data on births, deaths, marriages, divorces, and communicable diseases. Business and economic statistics are numerical data on employment, production, prices, sales, and so forth. In short, *statistics* often refers to information about any activity expressed in numbers.

Statistics has an additional meaning that is more specialized. In this second sense, *statistics* refers to the body of techniques, or methodology, that has been developed for the collection, presentation, and analysis of quantitative data, and for the use of such data. The notions that "figures speak for themselves" and that "figures don't lie" are widely distrusted, and properly so. Unless quantitative data are accurate, properly presented, and correctly analyzed, numerical information may be dangerously misleading. Since we all are "consumers" of statistics, it is important for all of us, not only professional statisticians, to know about statistical methodology.

The word *statistician* also has several meanings. It can refer to: (1) a person who performs clerical operations involving statistical data; or (2) an analyst who is highly trained in statistical methodology and who uses this methodology in the collection and interpretation of numerical data; or finally, (3) an applied mathematician who utilizes advanced mathematics to develop new and powerful statistical methods. Statisticians at each of these levels are needed so that maximum usefulness can be obtained from numerical information.

1.2 THE EXPANDING ROLE OF STATISTICS

Statistical data have been used for many centuries by governments as an aid in administration. In antiquity, statistics usually were compiled to ascertain the number of citizens liable for military service and taxation. Governments in Western Europe after the close of the Middle Ages were interested in vital statistics because of the widespread fear of devastating epidemics and the belief that population size could affect political and military power. As a result, data were compiled from registrations of christenings, marriages, and burials. In the sixteenth through eighteenth centuries, when mercantilistic aspirations set nation-states in search of economic power for political purposes, data began to be collected on such economic subjects as foreign trade, manufactures, and food supply. Not surprisingly, many of the data collected during this period were treated as state secrets.

Today, statistical data are collected in comprehensive, though frequently informal, "intelligence systems" to supply the quantitative information that governments, businesses, private groups, and individuals require for carrying out their activities. This tremendous expansion in the collection of statistical data has been accompanied by the rapid development of the methodology of statistics, which has exercised a profound influence in almost every field of human activity. Statistical concepts have been incorporated into the basic principles of such sciences as physics, genetics, meteorology, and economics. Statistical methods have been used to improve agricultural products, to determine the design of telephone equipment, to plan traffic control, to forecast epidemics, and to aid in achieving better management in business and government. Students of the natural sciences study statistics to become better scientists; students of economics study statistics to become better economists; students of business or public administration study statistics to become more effective administrators. Truly, the development of the statistical point of view and its adoption in various fields of activity has been a most significant characteristic of recent times.

1.3 STATISTICS FOR BUSINESS AND ECONOMICS

Some knowledge of statistics is essential today for people pursuing careers in business and public administration or in economics. Not only are increasingly comprehensive networks of quantitative data available in these areas to serve as a basis for drawing sound conclusions and making decisions, but the purpose in assembling the data has shifted from record-keeping to evaluation and action, based on the most timely information. Until quite recently, business and economic statistics were collected primarily as a record of past events. Although such statistics were analyzed to gain insights into current problems, the emphasis was essentially backward-looking. Today, the collection of numerical information for the record still takes place, but because of managements' needs for improved planning and control, data-collection systems have been designed to provide data that are as up-to-date as possible. Statistical analysis has in turn been carried to the point where it is chiefly concerned with the present and the future. As Mills and Long have written in a report to the Commission on Organization of the Executive Branch of the Government (the Hoover Commission):

> Experiments are designed, samples are selected, statistics are analyzed with reference to decisions that must be made, controls that must be exercised, judgments that entail action. The tremendous forward movement in the arts of statistical analysis and inference that has occurred within the last two decades involves, essentially, the use of observations in making decisions, in choosing among alternative lines of action. . . . Current reports on national income, the nation's economic budget, the production of goods, the level of wages, living costs and prices, consumer expenditures, savings, outlook estimates in agriculture, the construction of housing, the size of inventories, the profits of corporations enter into the thinking and the decisions of public officials and of private citizens as they did not twenty-five years ago. (Ref. 1.1, p. 7; *see references at end of each chapter.*)

The increasing use of statistics in administration is part of the trend toward basing administrative decisions on as objective and scientific a foundation as possible. Modern managements more and more depend upon statistical data to obtain required factual information about their internal operations and the wider fields of business and economic activity. Statistical data are concise, specific, capable of being analyzed objectively with powerful formal procedures, and well-suited for making comparisons. Hence, they are especially useful in such key administrative functions as setting goals, evaluating performance, measuring progress, and locating weaknesses.

Organizations collect data on their internal operations through the accounting system as well as through other data-reporting systems. Data on entire industries, economic sectors, and the like are collected and published by both governmental and private organizations. In either case, the masses of collected data often have little meaning until they are processed and condensed into some significant form. Thus, measures and devices that summarize masses of statistical data in a form useful to management have become essential. Such statistical concepts as averages, ratios, index numbers, and frequency distributions aid in the interpretation of masses of quantitative data. As summarizing techniques, they are employed in answering such questions as:

1. What was the rate of return on investment during the last quarter, and how did this rate compare with the rates of previous quarters?
2. What are the labor costs per unit of output?

3. What proportion of items produced today were defective?
4. What is the income distribution of the families living in this market area?

These questions and similar ones can be answered concisely with the aid of the statistical techniques discussed in this text.

Challenging issues arise in determining which, if any, of the available summarizing techniques is most applicable for processing a set of data pertaining to a given problem. This determination is an important step in decision-making based on such data; yet it is hardly an end in itself. The summary measures that have been obtained by processing the data must be analyzed to determine the appropriate course of action. It is in the area of analyzing quantitative data for reporting, diagnosis, and decision-making that the use of statistics as an objective, scientific management tool has made the most significant strides in recent years. In fact, the very nature of the questions asked by management has been affected by statistical developments; that is, the statistical point of view has been incorporated into the approaches management has taken to many problems.

The modern statistical point of view is characterized by the use of formal probability theory in collecting and analyzing data. Suppose, for example, a consultant is asked to estimate how many members of a large trade association of retailers favor certain proposed federal legislation. It is neither feasible nor necessary to contact all the members to obtain this estimate. Statistical procedures based on probability theory enable the consultant to obtain a highly reliable, sufficiently precise estimate at relatively low cost from a sample of all the members.

This example relates to *statistical estimation.* Another use of statistical methods involves *statistical decision-making*. Consider an inspector who receives a large shipment of springs that are to be used in making cigarette lighters. He must decide whether to pass the shipment directly into production or to screen the shipment first to cull any substandard springs. The characteristic of interest is the proportion of substandard springs in the shipment. If this proportion is low, it is better to pass the shipment, but if the proportion is high, it is better to screen the shipment first. Statistical methods based on probability theory enable the inspector to make a decision from a sample of the springs, with the risks of incorrect decisions controlled at specified levels.

Applications of statistical estimation and statistical decision-making arise in all areas of business. Here are a few more examples to show the range of applications:

1. Yesterday, 3 per cent of the items produced were defective; today, the defective rate was 5 per cent. Note how a statistical measure summarizes information on the quality of production yesterday and today. Statistical theory is needed, however, in deciding whether this increase in the proportion of defective items indicates a basic deterioration in the quality

of the production process that requires remedial action, or whether it is simply the result of normal day-to-day quality variability.

2. A company makes steel bars of specified length. The bars turned out by the production process inevitably vary in length. Management must determine the average length for which the process should be set so that the total scrap—that resulting from trimming long bars plus that resulting from scrapping the short ones—is at a minimum. This type of problem requires statistical theory for a solution.
3. A mail order firm re-opens some packages before they are mailed to check on the accuracy with which its packagers fill orders. Since it is impractical to re-open every package, a sample of each packager's output is taken to determine whether or not the packager is exceeding the allowable error rate. There are risks of failing to recognize a packager's unsatisfactory performance or of erroneously condemning a packager's satisfactory performance on the basis of the per cent of errors found in a sample. Statistical theory enables management to take samples and to draw conclusions from the error rates in the samples by a procedure that holds both types of risks at satisfactory levels.
4. A manufacturer of chinaware wishes to use a manual dexterity test to predict the speed with which prospective employees will be able to paint designs on chinaware after a period of on-the-job training. Statistical methods enable management to determine how well a test will give predictions of useful accuracy.

Statistical concepts are so woven into the methodology of the management sciences and economics that boundary lines between the disciplines tend to become meaningless. A case in point is the use of statistical estimation and decision-making in the implementation of operations research and econometric models. For example, suppose that a market research analyst is interested in predicting the number of automobile batteries that will be sold next year. He reasons that sales of such batteries depend essentially on two types of demand: batteries installed in new cars and replacement sales. The number of batteries demanded for new cars depends upon the number of cars that will be made next year, whereas replacement sales depend primarily upon the ages and numbers of batteries now in use. Thus the analyst might develop the following model for the phenomenon of interest (number of batteries to be sold next year):

$$X = W + aY + bZ$$

where X is the number of batteries to be sold next year; W is the number of batteries required for new cars next year; Y is the number of batteries now in use that are under three years old; Z is the number of batteries now in use that are three or more years old; and a and b are numbers that have values between 0 and 1 inclusive.

This model, like other models in business and economics, is a simplified representation of reality, in which some real-world phenomenon is reduced to its essential features for the problem at hand. To make the model specific so that it can be used for prediction, the analyst must obtain the appropriate values for a and b. Thus, he might conduct a study to answer the following questions: What is the probability that a battery now in use that is under three years old will be replaced next year? What is the probability that a battery now in use that is three or more years old will be replaced next year? These probabilities, once estimated, become values for a and b in the model, since they indicate the proportions of all batteries in the two groups that will be replaced. Thus, the term aY gives the replacement sales that can be anticipated next year for batteries in the first group, and bZ gives the corresponding estimate for the second group.

Having estimated a and b statistically, the analyst will then test his model with new data to determine whether it makes adequate predictions. He may revise his estimates of a and b, or he may add additional terms to the model, or he may abandon the model entirely and construct a different representation of the real-world phenomenon in which he is interested. By going through this sequence of obtaining additional information, testing the model, and revising it, the analyst will improve the model until it makes adequate predictions.

The analyst will require statistical methods even after a suitable model has been developed. Current estimates of W, Y, and Z are required, and tests are needed to decide whether the values used for a and b continue to be realistic. Thus, the employment of statistical methods is a continuing feature in the construction and implementation of the model.

1.4 FOCUS OF THIS BOOK

A variety of topics are covered in this introductory statistics book. The first group of chapters discusses the handling of statistical data and covers such topics as data sources, data collection and classification, and frequency distributions and their characteristics. Next, six groups of chapters are devoted to an explanation of modern statistical ideas, based on probability and the methods of statistical estimation and decision-making that are finding ever-widening areas of application in all phases of management. Terms currently becoming more and more significant to management—such as probability, confidence interval, decision rule, expected payoff, Bayes act, acceptance sampling, statistical quality control, and regression analysis—will take on meaning for the readers of these chapters.

The eighth group of chapters introduces additional concepts and procedures in the analysis of statistical data, in particular, the use of ratios and cross-classification in data analysis and presentation of statistical data through tables and graphs. The last group of chapters covers index numbers and time series analysis. Index numbers are extensively used for presenting and analyzing economic data and are useful as well in the interpretation of internal data for individual firms. Time series analysis is employed both in forecasting and planning future operations and in controlling current ones.

We believe that the best way to impart an understanding of fundamental statistical concepts and their applications is to discuss these in connection with concrete, representative situations. Hence, many case examples drawn from actual experiences of business firms and public agencies are presented. We hope that this approach will enable the reader to understand the basic statistical concepts and their applications in management, to appreciate the power of statistical tools, and most important, to recognize the types of situations in which alert managements can make effective use of these tools.

Cited reference

1.1 Mills, Frederick C., and Clarence D. Long, *The Statistical Agencies of the Federal Government* (A Report to the Commission on Organization of the Executive Branch of the Government). New York: National Bureau of Economic Research, Inc., 1949.

Unit

I

DATA HANDLING

Chapter

2

DATA

Data are the raw material of statistics. Statistical analysis cannot proceed until the necessary data are collected and evaluated for accuracy, applicability, and completeness. In this chapter, we first discuss data that are readily available for the analysis of business and economic problems. Such data include the routine information collected by organizations on their own operations, as well as the multitude of data on the economy and its various sectors that are collected by governmental agencies and private organizations. We then take up some important considerations pertaining to statistical data that are relevant both when the data are readily available and already collected and when special studies need to be made to obtain these data. Among the topics taken up are the distinction between data collected under experimental conditions and data collected under nonexperimental conditions, and some of the methods whereby statistical data are collected and processed for use in analysis and decision-making.

2.1 INTERNAL DATA

Distinction between internal and external data

Many of the statistical data required by management in planning and guiding the affairs of an organization are *internal data*—that is, data on the organization's own production, sales, and other operations. These internal data are compiled in the many basic records of an organization and provide management with a wealth of detailed information.

A firm's management also requires data on matters that are outside the scope of purely internal activity. To determine whether the firm is maintaining its sales position in the industry, for example, management needs data on industry sales to compare against company sales performance. Such industry-wide data are *external data* from the point of view of the management of a company.

External data can often be obtained from reports or publications of governmental statistical agencies, of trade associations, and of other data-compiling organizations. At other times, statistical surveys and experiments must be conducted to compile information not available in published sources, such as consumer reactions to a new or proposed product.

Internal records

The internal records that a firm produces in carrying out its operations—such as purchasing, receiving, selling, payroll preparation, and billing—are a prime source of information for management. Maintaining internal records and processing them for reports is often greatly facilitated by mechanical or electronic tabulating equipment, a subject discussed in Section 2.7. From the mass of data contained in internal records, the pertinent facts that enable management to plan, direct, and control operations are collected and presented systematically in internal reports.

Internal reports

Several types of internal reports are usually required to provide management with a comprehensive picture of operations. These are conventionally designated as *financial reports, operating reports,* and *special reports.*

Financial reports. The most important company financial report is the balance sheet, which shows the financial status of the business at a given point in time. It generally is supplemented with other financial reports such as cash reports, accounts receivable reports, and capital expenditures reports.

Operating reports. Operating reports present data on company operations, which may be classified according to company function, product, territory, and so on. A basic operating report is the profit and loss statement (which may also be considered a financial report), in which the incomes and expenses of a business during the fiscal period are measured. Other operating reports are sales reports, production reports, and purchasing reports. Some of these reports are accounting documents providing dollar data; others, however, provide a wide variety of nonaccounting information required for the direction and control of such activities as sales, production, and purchasing.

Special reports. From time to time, recurrent reports reveal conditions requiring additional analysis; also, special new problems arise that cannot be analyzed with the information presented in the recurrent reports. Hence, a firm's system of routine reports must be supplemented by nonrecurrent or special reports in which particular problems are considered at length. Each special report tends to be a unique presentation in which a given problem is investigated thoroughly and clear-cut recommendations for management action developed. Frequently these special reports require the analysis of internal operating data in ways different from the treatment in the routine accounting system. They often make use of external data and extended statistical analysis as well.

2.2 PUBLISHED EXTERNAL DATA

A great variety of external data is available to the businessman who requires information about the industry and the general economy in which his firm operates. Quantitative data for the economy and many industries are published by agencies of federal, state, and local governments as well as by private groups such as trade associations, business firms, and specialized research organizations.

In the following sections, we take up some important considerations in the use of published external data.

Primary and secondary sources

Sometimes the data published by an organization are also collected by it; publications containing such original data are called *primary sources* of statistical data. Other organizations report data initially collected and published by another agency; publications containing such data are called *secondary sources*. Many publications are primary sources of some data and secondary sources of others.

In general, it is better to obtain statistical data from the primary source than from a secondary one. In the first place, the data in primary sources tend to be more complete than those in secondary sources; for example, detailed breakdowns of the data in primary sources are often omitted when the same data are reported in secondary sources. Secondly, in a primary source the statistical data are often supplemented with pertinent information about collection methods and changes made in definitions. Such supplementary information, which aids greatly in the evaluation and interpretation of the data, is frequently condensed or even entirely omitted when the data are republished in secondary sources. Finally, the possibility always exists that errors not contained in the primary source will be introduced into secondary sources because of clerical and typographical mistakes made in transcribing the data.

However, secondary sources are sometimes convenient to use when they bring together related data dispersed in a number of primary sources. For example, the *Statistical Abstract of the United States,* published annually by the Department of Commerce, contains data compiled from a variety of governmental and nongovernmental primary sources. When data from several of these primary sources are required for the analysis of a given problem, it may be more convenient to obtain them from a single volume such as the *Statistical Abstract* than from the individual primary sources. Furthermore, comprehensive secondary sources such as the *Statistical Abstract of the United States* may also be used to locate quickly the primary sources of the desired data.

Cautions in the use of published data

When using published data, one must take care to become acquainted with all their limitations. These limitations include errors caused by the use of imperfect or improper techniques in collecting the statistics, such as improper question-phrasing in schedules or questionnaires, unintentional or intentional bias of interviewers, and faulty recollections by respondents. There may also be errors from clerical and typographical mistakes made in processing and presenting the data. Since the problem of evaluating the accuracy of statistical data is fundamental in statistical analysis, we shall discuss pertinent aspects of this problem in forthcoming sections.

One must also determine whether the definitions employed in compiling the data are appropriate to the purposes for which the data are needed. It is important to check whether changes in concepts, definitions, data-collection methods, and the like have occurred in data collected over a period of time and, if so, to determine the effect of these changes on the data.

We cannot overstress the importance of studying all comments on the data contained in the source; if explanatory comments are not available in a secondary source, one should refer to the primary source for this discussion. Statistical data must not be used blindly. Only a thorough study of all limitations of the data will lead to intelligent use of published statistics.

2.3 SURVEYS AND EXPERIMENTS

Many times, of course, data are needed that are not readily available. Furthermore, intelligent use of readily available data requires an understanding of the problems in collecting statistical data so that the limitations of the data can be recognized. For both these reasons, we shall now discuss the major problems in collecting and processing statistical data, whether this is done routinely or for special studies.

Distinction between surveys and experiments

First we shall take up the distinction between survey data and experimental data.

(2.1) The term *survey* is used by statisticians to refer to the collection of data about characteristics of existing things, with no special control over any of the factors influencing the variable of interest.

Suppose the variable of interest is the productivity of employees of a certain plant. If one collects data on the productivity of the employees during the past week and also information on the employees' ages, education, and similar characteristics, these data are survey data. On the basis of these, certain relationships, such as the relation between amount of education and productivity, may be studied in order to obtain an understanding of the factors affecting productivity. Note, however, that no control is exercised over, say, the amount of education of an employee.

Other examples of survey data are:

1. Data on characteristics of families who attend concerts frequently, and of those who attend infrequently.
2. Data on sex, age, income, and distance between home and store for customers of a store.
3. Data on unit costs and lot sizes for job lots during the past year.
4. Routinely collected operating data for a company.

(2.2) The term ***experiment*** is used by statisticians to refer to the collection of data when control is exercised over one or more factors to determine the influence of these on the variable of interest.

For instance, management may wish to know whether additional training increases productivity. An experiment to investigate this problem might consist of selecting half the employees at random and having them participate in a training program, letting the other half continue without further training, and then comparing the productivity of the two groups.

Other examples of experimental data are:

1. Data on store sales of a product when each store in the study was randomly assigned one of three different product displays.
2. Data on consumer preferences after each consumer in the study was exposed to one of four different sets of advertisements, the selection being made on a random basis.

Both surveys and experiments can be extremely useful for studying the effects of one or more factors on the variable of interest. Experiments, however, provide stronger evidence of these effects than surveys. In our earlier illustration, for instance, a survey of the plant employees might find that employees with higher education were the most productive ones. This does not necessarily imply, however, that education increases productivity.

Ambitious employees might seek more education and also work harder on the job regardless of the amount of education. In the experiment, on the other hand, it would be decided by a random mechanism whether an employee is to be given more training or not, so that one would not need to be concerned whether the more ambitious employees would also be more likely to volunteer for training programs.

Thus, experimental data are stronger, or more convincing, than survey data. Nevertheless, much of statistical analysis in business and economics is based on survey data. In the first place, most of the readily available data are survey data, such as internal data on company operations and published external data on the economy, consumer behavior, and the like. Secondly, it is often not feasible to exercise the controls required by experiments. For instance, suppose that an economist is interested in the effect of family size on the proportion of income the family saves. The economist certainly is not in a position to select a group of newlyweds and tell each of them to have a family of certain size. Survey data on existing families, on the other hand, can give useful information on family size, income, and expenditures, from which the relation between size of family and proportion of income saved can be studied.

Statistical surveys

As noted earlier, statistical surveys provide data about the characteristics or properties of existing things. Surveys may be conducted to collect information about persons, families, shipments of raw materials, finished products, plant equipment, business firms, and many other subjects.

Censuses and samples. A survey is always concerned with some particular group of persons, firms, farms, or the like.

(2.3) The totality of persons, firms, farms, or other items under study is called the ***population.***

(2.3a) The listing of all elements in the population is called the ***frame.***

In some surveys, it is possible to obtain information about every element in the population. For example, a small company may contact every one of its employees in a survey to obtain information on employees' reactions to a proposed pension program.

(2.4) A survey that includes every element in the population under study is called a ***census.***

In most cases, though, it is too costly and time-consuming to obtain information by means of a census. For instance, an automobile manufacturer who wishes to determine which aspects of current advertising are remembered by people cannot contact every member of the population to obtain this information. Rather, he can contact only a sample of persons and from a study of this sample make inferences about the population.

(2.5) A *sample* is a part of the population under study selected so that inferences can be made from it about the entire population.

Sampling is a key procedure in many data-collection surveys as well as in many administrative and control activities. In fact, modern statistical sampling procedures are so important that a fuller discussion of sampling is reserved for later chapters. Here, sampling will be treated only briefly and in the particular context of statistical surveys.

Reasons for sampling in statistical surveys. There are a number of cogent reasons for using samples rather than censuses in statistical surveys, which will be discussed more fully in Chapter 9. A brief list follows:

1. Ordinarily, a sample can provide reliable and useful information at much lower cost than a census.
2. A sample provides more timely data than a census, because fewer data have to be collected, and the smaller amount of data can then be processed more quickly.
3. A sample often will provide more accurate information than a census. Many types of errors in survey data can be controlled more effectively in sample surveys than in censuses; for example, more careful training and supervision of interviewers is possible with sample surveys than with censuses, because the former are smaller-scale undertakings.
4. Frequently, more time can be spent in probing each respondent's attitudes and motivations and in getting more detailed information when a sample rather than a census is taken.

Use of censuses. We do not wish to imply that samples are always preferable to censuses. If the population is small, and precise information is needed concerning it, a census may be appropriate. Again, if precise information is needed not only about the total population but also about small components of the population, a census may be appropriate.

Continuous and changing samples. Surveys are often undertaken periodically to determine current consumer expectations and attitudes, current employment status, and other characteristics for which it is important to study changes taking place over time. The question then arises as to whether the sample in each time period should be made up of the same individuals or whether a new sample should be selected each time. Frequently, more precise information can be obtained on changes in income, attitudes, and expectations if the sample in successive time periods consists of the same individuals. This technique, involving a *continuous panel* or fixed sample of respondents, is often used to collect data from consumers on their purchasing patterns, reactions to new products, responses to advertising, and similar subjects where it is important to recognize changes over time. Obviously, a panel should remain essentially intact during its operating life; hence a major problem in the use of panels is to prevent panel members from dropping out because of loss of interest.

Use of continuous panels, however, presents some difficulties. If continued too long, the panels may no longer be representative of the population. After a period of time, for example, a panel of firms will contain no newly established firms. Also, panel members may become conditioned in their attitudes or even in their behavior by belonging to the panel. To avoid some of these disadvantages, panels may be set up so that a member stays on the panel only for a limited number of successive surveys, with part of the panel being replaced each time. In this way, the overlapping members of the panel help to provide more precise information on changes over time in attitudes and expectations, while the newly sampled persons or firms keep the panel up-to-date.

Statistical experiments

As noted earlier, an experiment involves the collection of data when control is exercised over one or more factors, such as the type of training, the type of product display, or the type of advertisement. We now consider in more detail the essential parts of a statistical experiment.

Treatments. The different training programs being compared, or the different product displays being compared, or the different advertisements being compared are called the *treatments*. The particular problem determines the specific treatments that are to be studied.

Experimental units. In an experiment, a treatment is applied to an *experimental unit*. The experimental unit might be an employee when the treatment is a particular type of training program, a store when the treatment is a particular type of product display, or a family when the treatment is a particular type of cake mix.

Randomization. A statistical experiment requires that assignment of the particular treatment to a given experimental unit be made *at random*. The process of assigning treatments to experimental units in this manner is called *randomization*. One of the major advantages of randomization is that it eliminates potential bias. For instance, in the experiment to study the effect of a training program on productivity, randomization guards against the possibility that low-productivity employees would tend to be assigned more frequently to the group receiving additional training if foremen were to make the assignments subjectively. In effect, randomization provides that the toss of a balanced coin decides whether a particular employee is to receive the additional training or not. In Chapter 9, we shall discuss tables of random digits, which can be used to make assignments of treatments on a random basis.

Sampling. Generally, the experimental units in an experiment are a sample of all possible experimental units that might be employed. For instance, a study of different types of drug-product displays would usually be undertaken only in a sample of drugstores in a city or in a sample of cities. Again, a study of different types of cake mixes generally would be based only on a sample of consumers.

Some limitations of experiments. Statistical experiments have some limitations. As mentioned earlier, it is often not possible to assign treatments of interest (family size) to experimental units (newlyweds). Also, the very act of experimentation may affect the behavior observed, so that conclusions from the experiment may be misleading. For instance, in an experiment studying the effect of lighting on employee productivity, employees may work harder in the experiment regardless of the new type of lighting tested. Systematic errors may thus be present in experimental data as well as in survey data. We shall discuss these types of errors in data shortly.

Need for planning surveys and experiments

A survey or experiment must be designed carefully and conducted competently if it is to provide accurate and useful data. A statistical survey or experiment undertaken or sponsored by an organization usually begins with the recognition by management of a problem whose solution requires quantitative information. Frequently, the problem posed by management is a broad one that must first be translated into a series of specific questions before meaningful answers can be obtained. For example, let us say that management in an automobile manufacturing firm wishes to determine the points to be stressed in advertising next year's models. In order to obtain useful information about this broad subject, a series of more specific questions has to be studied. These questions may include the following: Which features in the current models are most attractive to buyers? How much are buyers paying for various used models of our cars? What aspects of current advertising are remembered by people?

After the initial analysis of the broad problem has led to the formulation of specific questions, the next problem is whether the data needed to answer the specific questions are already available or whether they must be obtained by a statistical survey or experiment. Before deciding to undertake a survey or experiment, a careful study should be made to determine if the required information is already available. If it is necessary to conduct an experiment or a survey, any previous investigations pertaining to the same problem should be studied as an aid in planning.

The decision whether to undertake an experiment or a survey usually depends on a number of factors. These include:

1. The nature of the problem.
2. The feasibility of an experiment or a survey.
3. The length of time available to obtain the needed information.
4. The costs of a survey and an experiment.
5. The need for definitive answers to the problem at hand.

In planning any survey or experiment, problems arise as to the most effective means of obtaining the information, the extent and cost of the study, and similar matters. After these have been solved, questionnaires or other data-collection forms must be developed, supervisors, interviewers, and other personnel may have to be trained, the actual collection of the data must be carefully undertaken, the data obtained must be checked for accuracy and consistency, and finally the data must be processed so that they can be analyzed effectively for adopting a course of action. Each of these steps must be carefully planned so that the study will provide reliable and useful results.

Planning may take from a few weeks for a small undertaking to several years for the large statistical surveys made by the federal government.

Errors in statistical data

The accuracy of statistical data is clearly an important requisite to their successful use in the analysis of business and economic problems. Before considering how accuracy of statistical data can be achieved through appropriate data-collection procedures, we take a brief look at the general problem of errors in statistical data.

Errors in survey data. One can distinguish between two types of errors in survey data:

(2.6) ***Sampling error*** is the difference between the result obtained from a sample survey and that which would have been obtained from a census of the population conducted under the same procedures as the sample survey.

(2.7) ***Non-sampling errors*** are all those errors that can arise in any survey, whether it is based upon a census or a sample.

The sampling error, then, measures solely the discrepancy arising from an incomplete enumeration of the population. Note that the sampling error is measured against the result that would have been obtained had the same survey methods used for the sample been applied to the entire population.

(2.8) The result that would be obtained if the same survey methods used for the sample were applied to the entire population is called the ***equal complete coverage.***

Consider, for instance, a survey of tax returns to determine the average income from dividends. The equal complete coverage here is the average income from dividends that would be obtained by a study of all tax returns, using the same survey methods as in the sample study. This equal complete coverage may not, however, be the quantity sought. If, for example, persons understate substantially their income from dividends, then the equal complete coverage is in error even though it does not contain any sampling error. This error in the equal complete coverage is a non-sampling error.

Many causes can be responsible for non-sampling errors. For example, these errors may arise in a survey because the population has not been defined carefully or because it does not correspond to the population that should be studied. Consider, for instance, a company that wishes to study certain attitudes held by the population of a city. For convenience, a telephone directory is to be used as the basis of selection in the survey. Bias can enter the survey results because the people who do not have telephones are omitted from the survey, whereas they should be included according to the purpose of the study. In other words, the *target population*—the population to be studied—is not the same as the *sampled population*—the population actually sampled.

Non-sampling errors can enter a survey because questions are not worded properly or because of biases and mistakes on the part of interviewers. They may also occur because the respondent does not furnish accurate information, refuses to furnish information, or is not available to be interviewed. Still other non-sampling errors can occur in the editing, coding, tabulating, and calculating stages of a survey.

Non-sampling errors can be a serious cause of difficulty. An illustration may help to reinforce this caution. In one study of non-sampling errors, some 250 respondents were asked if they had redeemed any U.S. savings bonds recently (Ref. 2.1). About 17 per cent of the respondents indicated that they had not recently redeemed any bonds. It so happened that the respondents were selected, unknown to them, because each of them had redeemed U.S. savings bonds within the last seven days. Thus, this study clearly indicates that a substantial proportion of respondents gave inaccurate replies.

The final accuracy of survey results depends on the extent of both non-sampling and sampling errors. Therefore, both types of errors need to be controlled. Given that an efficient sampling procedure is already being used, sampling errors can be reduced only by increasing the size and/or complexity of the sample. Control of non-sampling errors may require such steps as extensive testing of questionnaires or schedules, thorough training of interviewers, the use of three or more call-backs to reduce nonresponses of persons not at home, and the use of a follow-up sample to check on the execution of the fieldwork. Since funds, personnel, and other economic resources available for a study are always limited, the problem is how to balance the control of sampling and non-sampling errors so that the available economic resources will yield the greatest possible accuracy. Finding this economic balance is difficult, since no ready theory is available yet.

Errors in experimental data. Experimental data are also subject to sampling and non-sampling errors. The earlier discussion of errors in survey data is relevant here also.

2.4 METHODS OF OBTAINING INFORMATION

A variety of methods of obtaining desired information are employed in statistical surveys and experiments. The characteristics of the more important ones and their advantages and limitations will now be discussed. Since the most difficult problems usually arise in collecting information about people, data collection of this type will be emphasized.

Observation

Data may be gathered by direct observation. In an experiment on family decision-making, for instance, the experimenter may observe (and record) the interactions between husband and wife as they decide on the brand of refrigerator to buy.

The observation method is a direct means of studying many phenomena without relying on people's recollections. It requires suitable instruments for recording the information, preferably simultaneously with the observation. One limitation of this method is the possibility of observer bias. For instance, an observer may tend to concentrate on one type of phenomenon and miss the occurrence of some others. Usually observers require thorough training so that they will record accurately as they observe, and so that all observers, when a number of them are used, will record the same events in the same way.

Personal interviews

Personal interviews are used to obtain information in many surveys and experiments. A survey of households in a city may utilize personal interviews to obtain information on family size, income, appliances owned, and so on. Similarly, an experiment on preferences between different types of soft drinks may utilize personal interviews to ascertain which kind of soft drink is preferred, the reasons why, and so on.

In the interviewing procedure most frequently used, an interviewer asks prepared questions that are printed on a *schedule* form and records the respondent's answers in designated spaces on the form. Part of a typical interview schedule used in a survey is shown in Figure 2.1; note that this

CONFIDENTIAL - The National Health Survey is authorized by Public Law 652 of the 84th Congress (70 Stat. 489; 42 U.S.C. 305). All information which would permit identification of the individual will be held strictly confidential, will be used only by persons engaged in and for the purposes of the survey and will not be disclosed or released to others for any other purposes (22 FR 1687).

BUDGET BUREAU NO. 68-R620-S4.5
APPROVAL EXPIRES JULY 31, 1965

FORM **NHS-HES-2**
(11-13-63)

U.S. DEPARTMENT OF COMMERCE
BUREAU OF THE CENSUS
ACTING AS COLLECTING AGENT FOR THE
U.S. PUBLIC HEALTH SERVICE

NATIONAL HEALTH SURVEY

1. Questionnaire ________ of ________ Questionnaires

2. (a) Address or description of location (include city, zone, and State)

3. Identification code | 4. PSU number | 5. Segment number | 6. Serial number

E If this questionnaire is for an "EXTRA" unit in a B or NTA Segment, enter:

Serial No. of original Sample Unit	Item No. by which found	If in NTA Segment, also enter for FIRST unit listed on property	
		Segment List	
		Sheet No.	Line No.

2. (b) Mailing address if not shown in 2(a) **OR** ☐ Same as shown in 2(a)

2. (c) Name of special dwelling place | Code

7. Type of living quarters *(Check one box)*
☐ Housing unit ☐ Other unit

L Ask items 8 and 9 only if "Rural" box is marked
1 ☐ Rural 2 ☐ All other *(Skip to Item 10)*

8. **Do you own or rent this place?**
1 ☐ Own *(Ask 9(a))* 2 ☐ Rent *(Ask 9(b))* 3 ☐ Rent free *(Ask 9(a))*

9. (a) If Own or Rent free, ask - **Does this place have 10 or more acres?**
(b) If Rent, ask - **Does the place you rent have 10 or more acres?**
1 ☐ Yes 2 ☐ No

(c) **During the past 12 months did sales of crops, livestock, and other farm products from the place amount to $50 or more?**
1 ☐ Yes 2 ☐ No

(d) **During the past 12 months did sales of crops, livestock, and other farm products from the place amount to $250 or more?**
1 ☐ Yes 2 ☐ No

ALL segments (ask if Item 2(a) address identifies a SINGLE-UNIT structure).
10. **Are there any occupied or vacant living quarters BESIDES YOUR OWN --**
-- in the basement? .... ☐ Yes--S______ L______ ☐ No
-- on this floor? .... ☐ Yes--S______ L______ ☐ No
-- on any other floor of this building? .... ☐ Yes--S______ L______ ☐ No
(Fill Table X for each quarters NOT listed)

ALL segments (ask if Item 2(a) identifies entire floor or unnumbered part of floor in a MULTI-UNIT structure).
11. **Are there any occupied or vacant living quarters BESIDES YOUR OWN --**
If Item 2(a) identifies entire floor
-- on this floor?
If Item 2(a) identifies part of the floor, specify part
-- in the -- of this floor?
☐ Yes--S______ L______ ☐ No
(Fill Table X for each quarters NOT listed.)

TA and NTA segments (ask at all units EXCEPT APARTMENT HOUSES).
12. **Is there any other building on this property for people to live in - either occupied or vacant?**
☐ Yes--S______ L______ ☐ No
(Fill Table X for each quarters NOT listed.)

13. **What is the telephone number here?**
Telephone No. ______ **OR** ☐ No telephone

(INTERVIEWER): If eligible child in household enter child's name, segment, serial, and column number on Medical History Form.
(READ TO RESPONDENT)
In addition to the information you have already given me, I would like to leave this form to be filled out about -- . The form is self-explanatory. A representative of the U.S. Public Health Service will come by to pick up the form in a week or so. *(Ask Item 14)*

14. **What would be the best time of day for the representative to come?** ....

Medical histories left for--	Person with whom form left--
Column No(s).	Column No. and relationship

15. RECORD OF CALLS AT HOUSEHOLD

Item		1	Com.	2	Com.	3	Com.	4	Com.	5	Com.
Entire household	Date										
	Time										

16. REASON FOR NON-INTERVIEW

TYPE	A	B	C	Z
Reason:	☐ Refusal *(Describe in footnotes)* ☐ No one at home--repeated calls *(Go to 17)* ☐ Temporarily absent *(Go to 17)* ☐ Other *(Specify)*	☐ Vacant--non-seasonal ☐ Vacant--seasonal ☐ Usual residence elsewhere ☐ Other *(Specify)*	☐ Demolished ☐ In sample by mistake ☐ Eliminated in sub-sample ☐ Other *(Specify)*	**Interview not obtained for** Cols. ___ ___ ___ ___ ___ because:

17. TYPE A FOLLOW-UP PROCEDURE
If final call results in a Type A non-interview (except Refusals) take the following steps:
1. Contact neighbors (caretakers, etc.) until you find someone who knows the family.
2. Find out the number of people in the household, their names and approximate ages; if names of all members not known, ascertain relationships. Record this information in the regular spaces inside the questionnaire.

18. Signature of interviewer

19. Code

Courtesy U.S. Department of Commerce, Bureau of the Census

Figure 2.1. Example of part of a survey schedule

form contains some instructions to the interviewer, the questions to be asked, and the spaces for recording the answers.

Both the advantages and limitations of securing data through personal interviews arise from the fact that direct personal contact is made between the respondent and the interviewer. In a survey, most people will respond when they are approached directly; hence the personal interview method usually yields a relatively high proportion of usable returns from those persons who are contacted. Also, this direct contact generally enables the interviewer to clear up any misinterpretations of questions by the respondent, to observe the respondent's reactions to particular questions, and to collect relevant supplementary information—in an experiment, for example, whether the respondent made some comments on a subject not covered by the schedule.

The interviewer is a potential source of errors in surveys and experiments. In a survey, for instance, he may not follow directions for selecting respondents; if he interviews a member of the family other than the one designated by the statistical sampling procedures, as an example, he may introduce a bias into the sample results. He may influence the respondent by the manner in which he asks questions or by other actions; a slight inadvertent gesture of surprise at an answer, for example, can exert subtle, unrecognized pressures on the respondent. Finally, the interviewer may make errors in recording respondents' answers.

The personal interview is sometimes a relatively expensive method of collecting data as compared with other available methods.

Telephone interviews

In some surveys, the interviews are conducted over the telephone. It is possible with this method to obtain information on the behavior of the respondent at the exact moment of the call. This characteristic of the telephone interview method has been utilized, for example, by C. E. Hooper, Inc., in the *coincidental method* of radio and television audience research, in which respondents are asked about their activities at the moment of interview in order to minimize errors due to faulty memory. With this procedure, persons are called by telephone and asked a series of questions, such as the following ones (Ref. 2.2, p. 157):

1. Were you listening to your radio just now?
2. To what program were you listening, please?
3. What station, please?
4. What is advertised?
5. How many men, women, and children in your home were actually listening?

Note the shortness and impersonal nature of the questions, as well as the brevity of the entire interview. While telephone interviews are usually brief and impersonal in order to obtain the cooperation of the respondent, some telephone surveys are being made in which the respondent's interest is held through 25 questions or more.

The collection of data by telephone interviewing is usually less expensive than by direct interviewing conducted in respondents' homes because of savings in interviewers' time and transportation costs. The interviewers can also be supervised more closely when they operate from telephones located in a single room in the presence of the supervisor than when they interview in individual respondents' homes.

A serious limitation of the telephone interview method arises from the fact that many homes do not have telephones. Since telephone subscribers tend to belong to higher income classes and/or to particular socioeconomic groups, it is frequently impossible to obtain data representative of the entire population from a survey based solely upon telephone contacts. In some surveys, though, the population of telephone subscribers may closely coincide with the population relevant to the study.

Self-enumeration

Self-enumeration, where the respondent (a person, a company, a family) is provided with a form or questionnaire to fill out, is frequently used in experiments and surveys. Note that we distinguish between a *schedule,* which is completed by the interviewer in a personal interview, and a *questionnaire,* which is completed by the respondent himself.

In most surveys utilizing questionnaires, the forms are distributed to the respondents by mail, although other methods of distribution may be used as well. For example, employees in a company may be given questionnaires to fill out anonymously; or warranty cards containing questions on income and method by which the purchaser first heard of the product may be enclosed in the products; these in turn are mailed in by the purchaser.

Questionnaires must be designed carefully so as to invite the cooperation of the respondent. Specialists in questionnaire construction have studied the effects of question-structure, layout, order of questions, type and color of paper used, and other factors upon the rates of response. It has been found, for instance, that questions in mail questionnaires should be so constructed that the respondent can easily answer them in a few words or by making check marks in appropriate spaces. Figure 2.2 shows part of a page from the questionnaire used in the 1971 Canadian census, containing various types of questions that are easy to answer.

Both the chief advantages and limitations of the questionnaire method spring from the fact that it does not require the use of interviewers. The elimination of interviewers serves to avoid the types of interviewer errors discussed under *Personal interviews.* Also, this method is frequently cheaper than personal interviewing. On the other hand, the absence of interviewers creates two serious problems in obtaining responses in surveys. First, when a questionnaire sent to a household or other group is completed

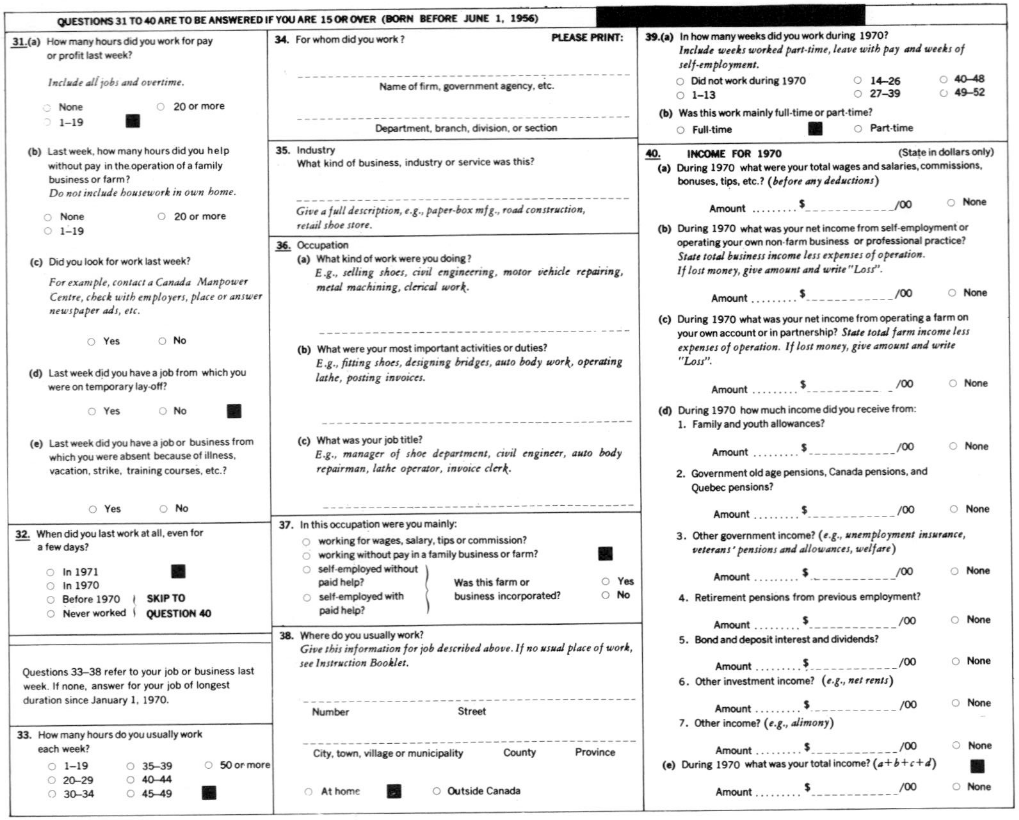

QUESTIONS 31 TO 40 ARE TO BE ANSWERED IF YOU ARE 15 OR OVER (BORN BEFORE JUNE 1, 1956)

31.(a) How many hours did you work for pay or profit last week?

Include all jobs and overtime.

○ None ○ 20 or more
○ 1–19

(b) Last week, how many hours did you help without pay in the operation of a family business or farm?
Do not include housework in own home.

○ None ○ 20 or more
○ 1–19

(c) Did you look for work last week?

For example, contact a Canada Manpower Centre, check with employers, place or answer newspaper ads, etc.

○ Yes ○ No

(d) Last week did you have a job from which you were on temporary lay-off?

○ Yes ○ No

(e) Last week did you have a job or business from which you were absent because of illness, vacation, strike, training courses, etc.?

○ Yes ○ No

32. When did you last work at all, even for a few days?

○ In 1971
○ In 1970
○ Before 1970 } SKIP TO
○ Never worked } QUESTION 40

Questions 33–38 refer to your job or business last week. If none, answer for your job of longest duration since January 1, 1970.

33. How many hours do you usually work each week?

○ 1–19 ○ 35–39 ○ 50 or more
○ 20–29 ○ 40–44
○ 30–34 ○ 45–49

34. For whom did you work? **PLEASE PRINT:**

Name of firm, government agency, etc.

Department, branch, division, or section

35. Industry
What kind of business, industry or service was this?

Give a full description, e.g., paper-box mfg., road construction, retail shoe store.

36. Occupation
(a) What kind of work were you doing?
E.g., selling shoes, civil engineering, motor vehicle repairing, metal machining, clerical work.

(b) What were your most important activities or duties?
E.g., fitting shoes, designing bridges, auto body work, operating lathe, posting invoices.

(c) What was your job title?
E.g., manager of shoe department, civil engineer, auto body repairman, lathe operator, invoice clerk.

37. In this occupation were you mainly:
○ working for wages, salary, tips or commission?
○ working without pay in a family business or farm?
○ self-employed without paid help?
○ self-employed with paid help?
} Was this farm or business incorporated? ○ Yes ○ No

38. Where do you usually work?
Give this information for job described above. If no usual place of work, see Instruction Booklet.

Number Street

City, town, village or municipality County Province

○ At home ○ Outside Canada

39.(a) In how many weeks did you work during 1970?
Include weeks worked part-time, leave with pay and weeks of self-employment.

○ Did not work during 1970 ○ 14–26 ○ 40–48
○ 1–13 ○ 27–39 ○ 49–52

(b) Was this work mainly full-time or part-time?

○ Full-time ○ Part-time

40. **INCOME FOR 1970** (State in dollars only)

(a) During 1970 what were your total wages and salaries, commissions, bonuses, tips, etc.? *(before any deductions)*

Amount .... $ ________ /00 ○ None

(b) During 1970 what was your net income from self-employment or operating your own non-farm business or professional practice?
State total business income less expenses of operation.
If lost money, give amount and write "Loss".

Amount .... $ ________ /00 ○ None

(c) During 1970 what was your net income from operating a farm on your own account or in partnership? *State total farm income less expenses of operation. If lost money, give amount and write "Loss".*

Amount .... $ ________ /00 ○ None

(d) During 1970 how much income did you receive from:
1. Family and youth allowances?

Amount .... $ ________ /00 ○ None

2. Government old age pensions, Canada pensions, and Quebec pensions?

Amount .... $ ________ /00 ○ None

3. Other government income? *(e.g., unemployment insurance, veterans' pensions and allowances, welfare)*

Amount .... $ ________ /00 ○ None

4. Retirement pensions from previous employment?

Amount .... $ ________ /00 ○ None

5. Bond and deposit interest and dividends?

Amount .... $ ________ /00 ○ None

6. Other investment income? *(e.g., net rents)*

Amount .... $ ________ /00 ○ None

7. Other income? *(e.g., alimony)*

Amount .... $ ________ /00 ○ None

(e) During 1970 what was your total income? $(a+b+c+d)$

Amount .... $ ________ /00 ○ None

Courtesy Government of Canada, Dominion Bureau of Statistics

Figure 2.2. Example of part of a survey questionnaire

and returned, one does not know which member of the group really answered the questions. Thus, the mail questionnaire method may be satisfactory in a survey obtaining general household data, but not in a survey where it is important that the questions be answered by a particular member of the household. Second, the absence of interviewers usually leads to substantially lower response rates. Sometimes, only 10 to 20 per cent of the questionnaires are answered in a private mail questionnaire survey. This partial response is a source of bias in the survey results, because the persons who *do* answer the questionnaires are seldom representative of the entire group contacted with respect to the subject matter of the survey. Hence, in most well-conducted mail questionnaire surveys, some or all of the nonrespondents are contacted as a routine procedure. Nonrespondents may be contacted by means of "reminder" letters (which are sometimes sent by special delivery mail for added impact), telephone calls, special personal interviews, other devices, or combinations of these. The use of a mail questionnaire combined with a follow-up on a sample of nonrespondents can, when properly conducted, avoid the bias possible when the nonrespondents are simply ignored, and still often retain cost advantages over the personal-interview method of collecting information.

Registration

Some survey data are collected by a procedure in which persons with the required information register this information at predesignated locations. For example, data on births and on motor vehicles in operation are collected by registration. Since legal compulsion or strong respondent interest is required to collect data successfully by registration, this method of collecting data is useful primarily to governmental bodies.

2.5 CONSTRUCTION AND USE OF SCHEDULES AND QUESTIONNAIRES

Interview schedules and self-enumeration questionnaires are the basic data-collection forms in many surveys and experiments. We now examine some important considerations in designing and using a schedule or questionnaire so that accurate, unbiased data will be obtained.

Designing the schedules and questionnaires

Types of questions. Several types of questions are used in questionnaires and schedules. The most important types are the *two-way, multiple-choice,* and *free-answer* questions. Each type of question has characteristics that make it best suited under certain conditions.

The *two-way,* or *dichotomous,* question requires the respondent to choose between alternatives such as "yes" or "no," and "good" or "bad." The following example illustrates two-way questions:

> In your opinion, does the XYZ Corporation make reliable products?
> ( ) Yes ( ) No ( ) No opinion

The two-way question reduces issues to their simplest terms, and according to its advocates, comes closest to duplicating the types of decisions that people are most accustomed to making. It is useful for investigating issues on which people are divided into two distinct groups.

When opinion is not sharply divided on a subject, and/or when a variety of answers is possible, a *multiple-choice* question is more appropriate. The following example is typical of multiple-choice questions:

> How would you categorize your opinion of the Blank Company's management?
> ( ) Very favorable
> ( ) Favorable
> ( ) Uncertain
> ( ) Unfavorable
> ( ) Very unfavorable

Multiple-choice, or "cafeteria," questions give the respondent a greater range of possible answers than two-way questions. The alternatives in a multiple-choice question should be clear-cut, mutually exclusive, and when dealing with an issue, more or less evenly distributed on both sides of the issue. Ideally, the choices should cover all answers likely to arise in response to the question; if too many alternatives are presented, however, they may not be clear-cut enough for the respondent to make a meaningful selection. One disadvantage of multiple-choice questions is that they tend to suggest an answer to the respondent in terms of the alternatives stated when actually he would have answered the question differently if no choices had been suggested to him.

This danger is avoided by another type of question, the *free-answer* or *open-end* question, which elicits answers in the respondent's own words. The following question is of the free-answer type:

> In your opinion, what things are good or bad about the Blank Company as a place to work?

In requesting answers in the respondent's own words, the free-answer question yields a multitude of replies that must be classified into groupings of similar answers before statistical analysis can be undertaken. This classification becomes a difficult task when thousands of replies to a free-answer question have been received, since the wording of each reply must be interpreted carefully. Hence, free-answer questions are usually used only in small-scale surveys and experiments or in the exploratory stages of large-scale ones to determine the patterns into which the responses to a question tend to fall. The information obtained through the use of exploratory free-answer questions in the early stages of a large-scale survey or experiment then is frequently used to construct the two-way and multiple-choice questions utilized later for the bulk of the data collection.

Order of questions. A schedule or questionnaire consists of a battery of questions arranged *in a certain order*. The first questions should establish rapport with the respondent, and all early questions should be simple. Where several topics are involved, it is usually best to complete one topic before going to another rather than to jump back and forth. The order of questions often affects the answers given by the respondent, because questions inevitably draw the respondent's attention to a particular complex of thoughts or feelings, in the context of which he answers the later questions. In market research surveys, for example, questions mentioning a specific product or firm tend to bias answers to questions that follow; consequently, such identifying questions should be placed toward the end whenever possible.

Directness of approach. Many respondents are prone to rationalize or to exaggerate in their replies when they are questioned directly about their motives, accomplishments, or other subjects involving their prestige or self-esteem. This is true even when the respondent's identity will remain unknown to persons utilizing the replies. In order to avoid biased data, an indirect approach is often taken in framing "prestige questions." For example, instead of asking, Did you complete high school? interviewers might be instructed to ask, What grade did you complete when you left school? In the latter question an attempt is made to avoid implications adverse to a respondent who did not graduate from high school.

Sometimes *projective* techniques are employed to obtain information on attitudes or motives. These involve an indirect approach where the respondent indicates his attitudes or motives indirectly in response to specially constructed situations. Examples of projective techniques include word-association tests, where the respondent is asked to mention the first word that comes to mind as the interviewer reads each word on a list, and sentence-completion tests, where the interviewer begins a sentence and the respondent is asked to complete it in the first way that comes to mind.

Need for clarity in questions. A question used in a survey or experiment must have approximately the same meaning for all respondents if the data obtained from the replies are to be meaningful. Vaguely defined terms should be avoided in framing questions, since such terms will be interpreted differently by different persons. In addition, questions should be stated simply. If long and involved questions are asked, there usually will be some respondents who do not interpret them correctly.

Need to avoid bias in question-framing. The replies of respondents are frequently influenced in a one-sided manner by the way in which survey questions are phrased. One type of question that tends to produce biased replies is a *leading question*—that is, one suggesting a particular answer. The question, Wouldn't you agree that the extra quality obtained in this brand is well worth the few extra pennies in cost? so obviously suggests a particular answer that few people would take the replies seriously. In many instances, though, the suggestive quality of a question is less easy to recognize. In some cases, one suggestive word so qualifies a question as to suggest the response. Words such as "absolutely," "completely," and "reasonable" frequently have this effect.

The answers to two-way and multiple-choice questions may not only be influenced by the wording used but also by the order in which the alternative answers appear. To counteract this influence, a *split-ballot* technique is sometimes used. With this technique, a given answer in, say, a two-way question is placed first on half of the schedules or questionnaires and last on the other half. The alternative answer-sequences are then presented to similar groups of respondents to control the influence exerted by the positions of the choices.

Value of pre-testing. Once a schedule or questionnaire has been designed for a survey or experiment, it is often pre-tested in a preliminary small-scale study. Pre-testing, usually involving between a few dozen to several hundred respondents, brings out unforeseen difficulties, such as the layout of the questionnaire, arrangement and wording of the questions, and even the clarity of instructions to the interviewers when interviewing is used. The difficulties can then be corrected before the large-scale survey or experiment is begun.

Editing the schedules and questionnaires

As errors and omissions are frequently made in filling out schedules and questionnaires, it is necessary to edit or check each form for accuracy and completeness. In small-scale surveys and experiments, this control usually is relatively easy to achieve. On the other hand, in large-scale operations a substantial amount of effort may be required for the editing task.

In large-scale field surveys and experiments utilizing interviewers, schedules are usually edited initially in the field. This makes it possible both to correct interviewers' mistakes before too many faulty interviews have been conducted and to maintain effective supervision over interviewers. Detailed editing of the interviewers' schedules, as well as all editing of mail questionnaires and similar data-collection forms, is usually undertaken in headquarters.

Some of the errors encountered in editing arise from simple clerical mistakes made by interviewers or respondents. For example, a dollar sign or a decimal point may be omitted from a figure entered on a schedule. Many of these clerical errors can be recognized at a glance. Less obvious errors may be brought to light by checking the answers on each form for internal consistency. As a case in point, a schedule entry stating the respondent's age is often checked against other entries, such as the ages of other family members mentioned in the schedule and occupation of the respondent. In some cases *check questions* are purposely included in the schedules or questionnaires to facilitate checking and evaluation of the entries. In one simple type of check question, the same information is requested as in a previous question, but in a different form. Thus, a respondent may be asked his age and, later in the interview, his date of birth. When the two answers differ, incidentally, it is usually the date of birth that is correct.

Tabulating equipment, discussed in Section 2.7, can be used in *mechanical editing* to identify cases where inconsistent answers are received. In recent censuses of manufactures, for instance, an electronic computer calculated the ratio between costs of materials and value of shipments reported by each firm and classified these results in such a way that firms with unusual ratios could be identified for further checking and, if necessary, correction. Many other such types of checks were programmed and used. Each of these essentially involved a check for reasonableness and consistency in the responses.

One of the most important purposes of editing each schedule or questionnaire is to make sure that it has been filled out as completely as possible. In some cases, the proper reply for an unanswered question can be determined from the other answers; the sex of a respondent, for example, can usually be ascertained from the respondent's name. In other cases, a schedule or questionnaire may have to be returned to the interviewer or respondent to be completed. In still other cases, the editor may simply enter the notation NR (not reported) in the blank space if the unanswered question is only of secondary importance.

Finally, an editor must decide whether the data on a given schedule or questionnaire are sufficiently reliable and complete to be utilized in the study, or whether this set of data should be discarded. Sound judgment and objectivity are required in this decision if the results are not to be biased either by the unwarranted exclusion of unfavorable replies or by the inclusion of erroneous and incomplete information.

2.6 VARIABLES

After data have been collected, they must be organized suitably for purposes of description or analysis.

Generally, the factors under study can take on different possible values or outcomes.

(2.9) A factor under study that can take on different possible values or outcomes is called a ***variable.***

For instance, the sex of a customer is a variable; it can be either male or female. Again, the rating of a new product by consumers (expressed as 1, 2, or 3) is a variable.

Quantitative and qualitative variables

We say that a variable is *quantitative* if the possible outcomes of the variable can be expressed numerically. Examples of quantitative variables are the per cent of defective items in outgoing shipments from a plant and the number of breakdowns per week in a computer. On the other hand, a variable is said to be *qualitative* if the possible outcomes are not expressed numerically. An example of a qualitative variable is the evaluation of an employee's performance by his supervisor where the possible ratings are "excellent," "very good," and so on.

For particular purposes a quantitative variable can be converted into a qualitative one by grouping the possible numerical values into non-numerical classes. Thus, with eggs for retail sale, the quantitative variable weight as measured in grams is converted into a qualitative variable by partitioning all possible weights into groupings or classes designated as "extra large," "large," and so on. Quantitative variables are converted into qualitative ones to facilitate reporting (as with eggs) or to simplify analysis.

Dependent and independent variables

In analysis of data, the term *dependent variable* designates the phenomenon or factor of fundamental interest. The other variables in the study are called *independent variables.* For example, suppose an analyst is interested in studying the saving of trading stamps and, in particular, wishes to determine whether certain factors such as type of household and income of household influence stamp-saving. Information about these variables is obtained by a survey of households. One of the questions asked in the survey is, Are trading stamps regularly saved in your household? The answers are classified as "yes" or "no." The saving of trading stamps then is a variable because an observation made on this phenomenon in a household can have different possible outcomes ("yes" or "no"). Since stamp-saving is the phenomenon of basic interest, it is the dependent variable. Type of respondent's household and income of household would function as other relevant variables, and these would be independent variables in the stamp-saving study.

The terms *dependent* and *independent* do not necessarily imply that the dependent variable depends in a literal sense on the independent variable or variables. If, for example, a large department store requires a quick estimate of the number of orders received in the mail each morning and obtains the estimate by weighing the mail, the number of orders received is the dependent variable in the analysis. The weight of the mail is the independent variable. Yet the weight of the mail on a given morning depends to a large extent on the number of orders received that morning.

2.7 CLASSIFICATION AND TABULATION

Description or analysis of data usually requires setting up classification systems and determining the number of cases falling into each class.

Classification

To a large extent, the classification system must be determined before any data are ever collected. For instance, suppose that a survey is to be undertaken to study the effect of various independent variables, such as age, sex, and income, on a person's readership of a particular national magazine. Given that purpose, the survey must find out from each person in the study if he is a reader, his age, sex, income, and so on. Hence, the desired classification systems dictate the kinds of information to be obtained.

Given the systems of classification, the question still remains of breakdowns or classes to be used within each system. As noted above, these classes are defined either quantitatively or in terms of attributes. In a survey of households, for instance, age of the household head might be classified quantitatively as follows: under 30 years, 30–39 years, etc., while refrigeration status might be classified in terms of attributes: have mechanical refrigeration, buy ice, have no refrigeration.

The decision about the particular classes to be used within each system of classification depends again on the purposes and method of the study. When two-way or multiple-choice questions are used, the classes are usually chosen at the time the questions are formulated, since the alternative answer-choices usually correspond to the classes to be used in tabulating the results. On the other hand, the classes into which replies to free-answer questions are tabulated usually are not determined until at least some of the replies have been examined.

Formal requirements. Certain formal requirements also should be considered in setting up systems of classification.

1. Generally, the classes within a system should be mutually exclusive. There are exceptions to this principle, as when a respondent might give several different reasons for preferring one style of packaging to another.
2. Classes should be set up so that each person, firm, farm, or item in the study can be placed in some classification category. This means that a

"no answer" class must be set up in cases where not all respondents may answer a question.

3. A given class should not mix together outcomes that have different implications for the analysis. Thus the class "defective" would be too coarse for recording inspection results for a production item if it is important for analysis and control to distinguish between defects caused by faulty material and those caused by poor workmanship.

It is not always easy to strike a proper balance in the number of classes to be employed in a system. With too few classes the description is too gross, and relationships may not be recognized because significant facts have been lost in the few large aggregates into which the data have been classified. With too many classes, meanings and relationships become obscured by details and by chance factors affecting the distribution of items in the relatively large number of classes. We shall say more about this subject in later chapters.

Coding

Tabulation is often facilitated if the basic information to be processed is first coded. In coding, numbers or symbols are used to represent the actual information. For example, the names of the states could be coded as follows:

State	*Code Number*
Alabama	01
Alaska	02
.	.
.	.
.	.
Wyoming	50

The name of any state may then be recorded conveniently and quickly on, for instance, a punchcard by punching two holes representing the digits of the code number for that state. Such a punchcard used in machine summarization is shown in Figure 2.3.

Answers to two-way and multiple-choice questions are coded by assigning a number or symbol to each possible answer. For instance, note how the following multiple-choice question has been coded:

> What was the principal reason for which this drainage enterprise was organized? (Check which)
>
> (1) ☐ Reclamation or improvement of land
> (2) ☐ Protection of land against overflow
> (3) ☐ Removal of alkali or seepage from irrigated land

An answer to this question can then be recorded on a punchcard by punching a hole at the appropriate location—1, 2, or 3—in the column reserved on the card for the answer to this question.

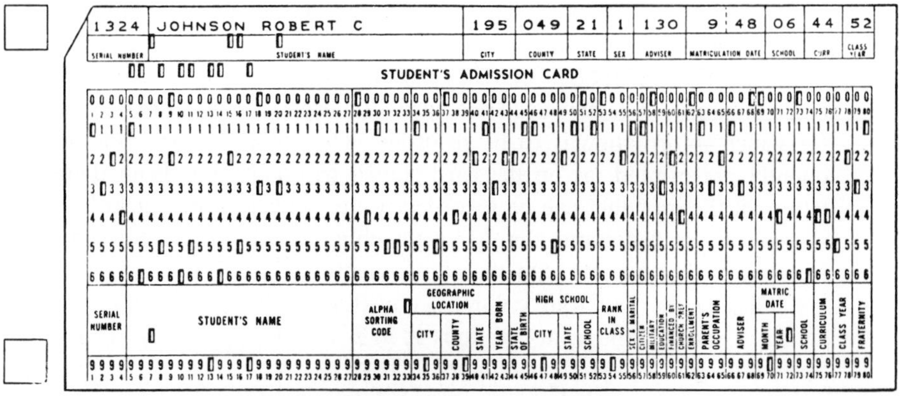

Courtesy International Business Machines Corporation

Figure 2.3. Example of a punchcard

Two-way and multiple-choice questions on schedules and questionnaires are often *pre-coded* to facilitate subsequent tabulation. This is done by assigning in advance code numbers or other symbols to the alternative choices in each question and printing these next to the choices, as in the above example. Replies to free-answer questions, on the other hand, can be classified and coded only after the answers have been received.

Machine tabulation

After the classification systems have been set up and data not already pre-coded have been coded, there still remains the big task of determining the number of cases falling into each class. This step involves, in other words, the tabulation of the data according to the classification systems used. One basic type of tabulating procedure, which is widely used for complicated, repetitious, and/or large-scale tabulating operations, requires the employment of punchcards and specialized tabulating machinery.

Preparation of punchcards. A typical 80-column punchcard is shown in Figure 2.3. Each of the 80 columns of this card has 12 punching positions. Eight of these positions are marked by the large printed digits, 0–6 inclusive and 9, which appear in each column. Two other positions, corresponding to locations 7 and 8 in each column, are unmarked on this particular card. Finally, there are two additional unmarked positions above the digit 0 in each column. A hole can be punched at a given location whether or not the location is explicitly marked. Altogether this card contains 12 punching positions in each of the 80 columns, or 960 positions in all.

Information from a source document—in this case, a student's admission form—is recorded by punching holes at appropriate locations on the card.

The punching positions must be organized into a definite arrangement, since the locations of the holes are the bases of subsequent sorting, counting, and other operations utilizing the cards. A *field,* consisting of one or more columns, is reserved on the cards for each question or other subject for which information is to be recorded. The labels of the fields are frequently pre-printed, as on the card shown in Figure 2.3. Both digits and letters of the alphabet can be recorded in the fields of a punchcard. A digit is recorded in a column simply by punching a hole at the corresponding location in that column. On the above-mentioned card, for instance, there are holes in the first four columns, constituting the field reserved for the student's serial number, at locations 1, 3, 2, and 4 respectively. Thus, these holes represent the student number 1,324.

Letters of the alphabet are recorded by punching two holes in each column. One of these holes is at a location corresponding to one of the digits from 1 through 9 inclusive, while the other hole is at one of the top three locations in the column—that is, at the location marked 0 or at one of the two unmarked locations above 0. For example, the letter *J* is recorded on the card in Figure 2.3 by two holes in the first column of the field reserved for the student's name. One hole is at the unmarked location immediately above 0, while the other hole is at location 1.

Note that the information on the student's home state, county, and city is not recorded by alphabetic punchings on the card but rather by code numbers. Use of coding makes it possible to record all this information with only eight digits.

Tabulating machines. The holes in punchcards, such as the ones shown in Figure 2.3, enable electric contacts to be made by which stacks of cards can be sorted and/or processed in other ways. Specialized equipment is available for this purpose. *Card punch* machines permit an operator to punch the holes into the cards, *sorters* can sort stacks of cards into sequences or groups at high speeds, and still other types of machines can count cards, perform calculations, and print out desired results.

Electronic data processing

High-speed processing of business data by electronic computers is a development of the 1950's and 60's. Today, computers are operating throughout the country. Electronic data processing has become established as a field by itself. Evidence of this is the existence of specialized programs in computer science, data processing, and management information systems at many universities and colleges.

Computers are capable of handling masses of data recorded on punchcards (discussed earlier), magnetic tapes, and magnetic disks. High-speed printers and visual-display screens are two of the common devices used for presenting the results of computerized data analysis. Frequently, computers are accessed from remote computer terminals where data input and output, and instructions for the computer, are transmitted to the central computing facility via communication lines.

The computer's ability to read, store, and display data and to perform logical operations on data makes it capable of performing more extensive tabulations and statistical analyses than was ever possible before. Standardized computer programs exist for performing many of the more common statistical analyses. Large-scale statistical problems requiring massive amounts of data storage and computation are handled with relative ease by these programs. As a result, a larger range of statistical problems are now computationally tractable and new statistical techniques are evolving which would not have been feasible before the advent of computers.

Computers have extended man's capacity to deal with statistical problems in yet another dimension. They facilitate the automation of information acquisition, storage, and retrieval within organizations. This centralization of information in organizations allows greater use of statistical planning and control procedures. In addition, the existence of large computer data banks or data repositories means that large pools of data are now available for tackling many contemporary management problems using statistical techniques.

Manual tabulation

A relatively large amount of set-up and other overhead work is required for conventional punchcard machine tabulation and for electronic data processing. In large-scale, complicated, or repetitive operations the overhead work of wiring and verifying tabulating machines, editing machine runs, or writing and testing programs for electronic computers is more than balanced by the greater speed and efficiency with which machines process the data. In small-scale undertakings, however, the processing operations often are not extensive enough to warrant the use of machines; in such cases, manual tabulation is used.

Schedules or questionnaires can be manually sorted into groups according to particular answers. For instance, in a survey conducted to study the relationship in a metropolitan area between automobile availability and shopping habits, the schedules first might be sorted into two groups according to car availability. Each group of schedules would then be sorted into subgroups based on answers to questions about shopping habits. The schedules in each subgroup would then be counted to provide comparative data on the relative numbers of shoppers with and without automobiles indicating particular types of shopping behavior.

This straightforward method is convenient when the number of groups into which the schedules are finally divided is not too large. When schedules are difficult to handle and/or when a relatively large amount of sorting according to a variety of classifications must be undertaken, it is often worthwhile to transfer the data on each schedule to a file card and to sort and count these cards. Coding of the data will facilitate their transfer from schedules to cards, since only simple code notations will then have to be entered on the cards. Mechanical aids to manual sorting and counting may be employed with specially designed cards.

Cited references

2.1 Hyman, Herbert, "Do They Tell the Truth?" *Public Opinion Quarterly,* Winter 1944, pp. 557–559.

2.2 Blankenship, Albert B., ed., *How to Conduct Consumer and Opinion Research.* New York: Harper and Brothers, 1946.

QUESTIONS AND PROBLEMS

2.1. Briefly explain or describe each of the following:

a. Schedule
b. Frame
c. Continuous consumer panel
d. Leading question
e. Editing
f. Experimental unit
g. Treatment
h. Follow-up of nonrespondents

2.2. Distinguish between:

a. Continuous panel and panels with overlapping membership
b. Self-enumeration and personal interviews
c. System of classification and classes
d. Multiple-choice question and free-answer question
e. Questionnaire and schedule
f. Quantitative and qualitative variable
g. Independent and dependent variable

2.3. Discuss each of the following statements:

a. Internal data need not be tabulated.
b. A secondary source is not as reliable as a primary source.
c. Neither two-way, multiple-choice, nor free-answer questions are ideally suited to the purposes of a survey.
d. Pre-testing of questionnaires or schedules is only needed when the persons who designed them are not experts.
e. Data collected in censuses are automatically free of errors.
f. The systems of classification to be used need not be considered in advance when collecting internal data.

2.4. Contrast the purposes of routine reports and special reports.

2.5. Distinguish between internal and external data. Do the same or different problems arise in the collection of the two types of data? Explain.

2.6. For *each* of the published sources of statistical data in Group I *and* for assigned published sources in Group II, provide the following information:

a. Who publishes the source?

b. How often is the source published?
c. Are the statistical data contained in the source monthly data, quarterly data, or annual data, or a combination of these?
d. Does the source contain only statistical data in tables or does it also contain articles and/or other textual presentations?
e. Cite three *specific* items of statistical information for *each* source selected that are found in that source. For example:

Source X:

1. The number of persons unemployed in the United States in September 1969 was ______.
2. The average hourly earnings of production workers in the aircraft industry in 1969 was ______.
3. At the end of 1968, ______ per cent of the assets of life insurance companies in the United States were invested in public utility bonds.

Group I (select all)

1. *Statistical Abstract of the United States*
2. *Survey of Current Business*
3. *Federal Reserve Bulletin*

Group II (select as assigned)

4. *Monthly Labor Review*
5. *Quarterly Summary of Foreign Commerce of the United States*
6. *Construction Review*
7. *Agricultural Statistics*
8. *International Financial Statistics*
9. *Minerals Yearbook*
10. *Employment and Earnings*
11. *Statistical Handbook of Civil Aviation*
12. *The Economic Almanac*
13. *Transport Statistics in the United States*
14. *Automobile Facts and Figures*
15. *Life Insurance Fact Book*
16. *Moody's Industrial Manual*
17. *Iron Age*
18. *Automotive Industries*
19. *Printers' Ink*
20. *Housing Statistics*
21. *Moody's Transportation Manual*

22–24. Supplements to *Survey of Current Business*

- 22. *U.S. Income and Output*
- 23. *Business Statistics, 19— Biennial Edition* (select current edition)
- 24. *Personal Income by States Since 1929*

25. *Sales Management*, Annual issue: *Survey of Buying Power*
26. *Petroleum Facts and Figures*
27. *Economic Indicators*
28. *U.S. Census of Population* (select any volume)
29. *U.S. Census of Housing* (select any volume)
30. *U.S. Census of Agriculture* (select any volume)
31. *U.S. Census of Business* (select any volume)
32. *U.S. Census of Manufactures* (select any volume)

(Continued)

33. *Canadian Statistical Review*
34. *Monthly Bulletin of Statistics* (Statistical Office of the United Nations)
35. *Economic Bulletin for Asia and the Far East* (United Nations, Secretariat of the Economic Commission for Asia and the Far East)
36. *Business Conditions Digest*

2.7. Distinguish between experimental and survey data. What is the significance of this distinction? Is randomization an essential element in the distinction? Discuss.

2.8. A company recently developed a new low-calorie soft drink and has shipped it in bottles to supermarkets and in cans to other stores. It is now examining sales data to see which type of container is preferred by customers.
a. Why are these sales data survey data?
b. How could you set up an experiment to study consumer preferences as to type of container? Explain.

2.9. The Antwerp Company ran the same advertisement in two cities; the cities were very similar in many respects. In the period after the advertisement was placed, sales increased in one city but decreased in the other.
a. Are the sales data experimental or survey data? Explain why.
b. How is it possible that opposite sales results were obtained in the two similar cities?
c. How could you set up an experiment to study effectively the impact of the advertisement on sales? Explain.

2.10. For each of the following, indicate whether it is a quantitative or qualitative variable:
a. Number of persons in the labor force in a given month.
b. The color of an automobile.
c. The annual sales of a manufacturing firm.
d. The marital status of an individual.
e. The rank of a state by population size.

2.11. **a.** In many studies, statistical tables are set up during the planning stage and the data are then filled in after the study has been completed. What advantage is there in setting up the tables during the planning stage of the study? Can this always be done? Explain.
b. Do the statistical tables set up during the planning stage serve as specifications for tabulating the collected data? Discuss.

2.12. In each of the following situations, discuss whether a census or a sample would be preferable to obtain the desired information; also discuss whether personal interviews or self-enumeration would be preferable:
a. A manufacturer of appliances wishes to determine consumers' color preferences for electric refrigerators.
b. A regional association of 25 universities wishes to obtain current data on enrollments in the member institutions.
c. A company which has 3,000 employees wishes to determine the employees' attitudes toward the company.

2.13. **a.** Distinguish between sampling errors and non-sampling errors. What is meant by the equal complete coverage of a study?
b. Are non-sampling errors eliminated when a census of the population is undertaken? Are sampling errors eliminated?

c. Can sampling errors be reduced if more care is taken in the execution of the study? Can non-sampling errors be reduced in this way? Discuss.

d. Can sample results ever be more accurate than census results? Explain.

2.14. **a.** A sample survey of households in a city was taken to ascertain the work skills available in the city. Information developed from the sample survey did not agree with earlier information obtained from other sources. Investigation indicated that many persons in certain job classifications did not have a chance to be included in the sample survey because they were out of the city on vacation at the time of the survey. Did the exclusion of these persons give rise to a sampling error or to a non-sampling error in the survey? Explain.

b. Investigation also revealed that an appreciable number of persons misunderstood certain questions and furnished incorrect information. Did this give rise to sampling or non-sampling errors? Explain.

2.15. A department store selected a sample of 1,000 customers with charge accounts from its 50,000 charge-account customers. A mail questionnaire was sent to the selected customers, and replies were received from 40 percent of them.

a. What are the target population and the sampled population in this case?

b. Is there a danger of bias here, because the sampled population is not identical with the target population? Explain. Would the danger of bias be serious if the response rate had been 99 per cent? Discuss.

2.16. A professional association conducted a sample survey of its members to study how the members liked the journal of the association. Subsequently, it was noted that the response rate for older members was much higher than that for younger members. Is there a danger that this differential response rate will introduce a bias into the sample survey results? Explain carefully; you may wish to construct hypothetical examples to illustrate your point.

2.17. It is frequently stated that errors in response are not too serious because they will tend to balance out. Metz (*Accuracy of Response Obtained in a Milk Consumption Study*, Cornell University Agricultural Experiment Station, 1956) conducted a sample survey based on 1,893 households to study the nature of response errors. He compared responses as to the number of quarts of milk bought through home-delivery for each of the seven preceding days with the records of the milk dealers. The results were as follows for the seven-day period:

		Average Quantity of Milk Purchased (Quarts)	
Respondent Statement	*% of Respondents*	*Dealer Record*	*Respondent*
Accurate	37	9.5	9.5
Overstated	47	8.2	11.8
Understated	16	11.8	9.2

a. Analyze these results and write a paragraph presenting your findings.

b. Did response errors balance out? What is the overall relative bias in average milk purchases through home-delivery as stated by household respondents?

c. What factors might account for the bias in responses? Discuss.

2.18. For each set of data in parts **a** through **f**, state which method of data collection (self-enumeration, personal interview, or some other method) would be most appropriate for obtaining the information, and justify your choice. Consider cost, need to obtain respondents' cooperation, need for consistent interpretation of definitions, and any other factors that you believe are relevant.

a. Quarterly data from employers on the number of employees who worked at any time during the quarter, and taxable wages paid them during the quarter.
b. Data from persons in a national register of scientists concerning field of specialization, nature of present employment, academic training, and foreign language and area knowledge.
c. Data on family backgrounds and education of migratory farm workers in the northeastern region of the United States.
d. Data on height, weight, and blood pressure of persons in a national sample of the population of the United States.
e. Data on food prices in a sample of outlets in various cities.
f. Data on public utility rates in a sample of cities.

2.19. A student in an education course described a term project in which he intended to survey student study habits by sending mail questionnaires to a representative group of 250 students. A classmate pointed out that, if past experience was any guide, only about 25 per cent of the prospective respondents could be expected to answer. The student describing the project admitted that he had not considered this fact, but stated that it posed no serious problem, because he would simply send questionnaires to a representative group of 1,000 students to obtain replies from 250 of them.
a. Do you agree that the student's plan is an adequate solution to the problem posed? Explain.
b. Should the report of a survey indicate the proportion of intended respondents from whom no information was obtained? Discuss.

2.20. Identify at least one major fault in each of the following questions designed to obtain information from respondents, and re-word the question to eliminate the fault. Indicate any assumptions you make when re-wording the question and explain the need for the assumptions.
a. How many cakes of soap did you buy during the past 24 months?
b. Does the name of the Blank Company or some other company come to mind first when the word "refrigerator" is mentioned?
c. When you graduate from school and go to work, would you rather go into business for yourself?
d. Is your family income high, average, or low as compared with the incomes of other families in this block?
e. Indicate which you prefer to drink — whole milk or skimmed milk — and give three reasons for your preference.

2.21. Consider the following two alternative questions for ascertaining information on consumer buying plans: (1) Which of the following products do you plan to buy within the next year? (2) Which of the following products do you plan to buy within the next year, and how certain are you of these plans?
a. Which question do you think will yield more useful information? Explain fully.
b. Do you think it is better to ask about buying plans "within the next year" or "over the next 12 months?" Explain the basis for your answer.

2.22. In a public-opinion poll on a coming election, the question was asked: If you were to vote today, would you vote for candidate A or B? In a market research survey to investigate the location of a supermarket, the question was asked: If the ABC Company opens a supermarket at the corner of Spruce and Pine Streets, would you patronize the store?

a. For each of these two cases, define the equal complete coverage of the survey.
b. Identify for each of the two cases several types of non-sampling errors likely to be present in the equal complete coverage.
c. For each of the two cases, would you expect sampling errors or non-sampling errors to be more troublesome? What implications does your answer have for determining how the available resources for the study should be allocated between controlling sampling errors and controlling non-sampling errors? Discuss.

2.23. The market research department of a company was designing a schedule for an interview-survey, and developed two alternative question wordings for obtaining the respondent's age. One was, How old are you? The other was, In what year were you born?
a. What criteria should be used for deciding which question wording is better? Discuss.
b. Explain how you might study which of the two question wordings is better according to your criteria in part **a**.

2.24. A survey is to be undertaken to collect data required in analyzing a local housing market. At what stage in the conduct of the survey must a decision be made on categories appropriate for tabulating the collected data? Explain.

2.25. The following question and tabulation of replies appeared in a published study of consumer intentions: Do you plan to buy a new automobile within the next 24 months?

Reply	*Number*	*Per Cent*
Yes	215	14
No	480	31
Don't know	864	55
Total	1,559	100

Suppose the following tabulation had appeared instead:

Reply	*Number*	*Per Cent*
Yes	215	31
No	480	69
Total	695	100

a. Would you have drawn the same conclusion from the two tabulations? Explain.
b. What formal requirement concerning classification is suggested by your answer to part **a**?
c. When would the second tabulation be appropriate? What heading should then be used for the tabulation? Discuss.

2.26. Must information necessarily be coded before it can be recorded on a punchcard? Explain.

2.27. Refer to Figure 2.3.
a. Has all the information punched into the card been "interpreted"? Explain.
b. What was the student's rank in his class?
c. Can you tell from the card alone in which city is the student's home? Explain.
d. Why are two holes needed in column 6 to record the letter O?

2.28. Major periodicals publish studies of their "readership." These studies contain data on such subjects as number of readers and age and income distributions of the readers, and are sent to advertisers and other interested persons. Technical appendices are frequently included in the studies; these contain descriptions of the methods used in collecting the data and cover such topics as sample design, questions used, interviewing techniques, and tabulating procedures. Can the inclusion of such technical material in a "readership" study issued by a periodical serve any practical purpose for the periodical's advertisers? Explain.

2.29. A survey of elementary schools was undertaken to determine the dental health of children and the influence of various factors upon it. In addition to individual dental health data, information about each child's age, personal health habits, medical and dental attention received, and family circumstances was obtained.

a. Which is the dependent variable in this study? Explain.

b. Which are the independent variables?

2.30. A survey of single-family dwellings in a city provided data for each dwelling on location, age, approximate market value, and amounts of any unpaid mortgages. Can the dependent variable in this survey be identified without additional information about the purpose of the survey? Explain.

Chapter

3

FREQUENCY DISTRIBUTIONS

3.1
VARIATION AND ITS SIGNIFICANCE

Variation is found throughout life. People have different aptitudes and earn different incomes, machines turn out parts that are not perfectly identical, the per cent of employees absent on any day because of sickness varies from day to day — this list could be extended almost indefinitely. Thus, managers and administrators must reach conclusions and make decisions in a world where variation, rather than uniformity, prevails. The statistical approach, which we shall begin to discuss in this chapter, can be a unique and powerful aid in drawing reasonable conclusions and making sound decisions when confronted with the welter of variation found throughout the range of business activity.

In this chapter, we study variation in characteristics that can be expressed *quantitatively*. We examine the significance of patterns of variation and study methods of analyzing these patterns. Succeeding chapters then will show how statistics can help management draw sound conclusions and make appropriate decisions from quantitative data, despite the prevalence of variation in these data.

3.2
A CASE STUDY OF VARIATION

Background

The Exeter Corporation, a manufacturer of aircraft parts, has one plant in which about 7,500 production workers are employed. During 1969 there were no major changes in the plant facilities, in the types of machines used, in the kind of personnel employed, or in the type of safety program carried out during the year. Yet the number of injuries per thousand manhours in the plant was not the same from week to week. Table 3.1 shows that a substantial amount of variation existed in the weekly accident rates during the year. This variation, which occurred even though no changes took place in the underlying conditions affecting the incidence of accidents, is of basic interest to us right now, because it can cause serious problems in drawing sound conclusions from available data.

Table 3.1 Exeter Corporation, Weekly Number of Injuries per Thousand Manhours—1969

Week of			*Week of*			*Week of*		
Jan.	6	3.0	May	5	4.0	Sept.	1	2.4
	13	3.2		12	3.9		8	3.3
	20	3.7		19	4.4		15	4.6
	27	3.7		26	3.2		22	3.3
Feb.	3	2.8	June	2	3.8		29	4.3
	10	3.7		9	4.7	Oct.	6	2.1
	17	3.3		16	2.3		13	3.5
	24	4.0		23	4.3		20	4.0
Mar.	3	3.2		30	4.2		27	3.6
	10	3.9	July	7	3.0	Nov.	3	3.2
	17	2.9		14	2.9		10	2.5
	24	3.8		21	3.5		17	3.4
	31	3.3		28	3.1		24	3.4
Apr.	7	3.1	Aug.	4	3.1	Dec.	1	3.5
	14	1.8		11	2.7		8	3.7
	21	5.3		18	2.8		15	3.6
	28	2.6		25	3.4		22	3.5
							29	2.6

Pattern of variation

Experience tells us not only that variation is prevalent throughout nature even though the basic causal conditions have remained the same, but also that this type of variation follows some kind of pattern. To study the pattern of variation in the weekly accident rates for the Exeter Corporation, we classify these rates according to their magnitude. This is done in Table 3.2. For instance, one class includes all those weekly accident rates for which the number of injuries per thousand manhours was from 1.5 to 1.9. Table 3.1 reveals that one week showed an accident rate of this magnitude. In the same manner, we determine that there were three weeks during 1969 when the injuries per thousand manhours were between 2.0 and 2.4, and so on. The total of the table must be 52, since 52 weekly accident rates are classified according to their magnitude. Problems relating to the choice of the classes will be taken up later.

The classification of Table 3.2 is called a *frequency distribution,* and the number of weeks falling into a class is called the *frequency* of that class. Note how the frequency distribution reveals the pattern of variation in the

Table 3.2 Exeter Corporation,
Frequency Distribution of Weekly Accident Rates — 1969

Number of Injuries per Thousand Manhours	*Number of Weeks*
1.5–1.9	1
2.0–2.4	3
2.5–2.9	8
3.0–3.4	16
3.5–3.9	14
4.0–4.4	7
4.5–4.9	2
5.0–5.4	1
Total	52

weekly accident rates. Most of the weeks during the year had somewhere between 2.5 and 4.4 injuries per thousand manhours. There were four weeks that had less than 2.5 injuries per thousand manhours and three weeks with 4.5 or more injuries per thousand manhours.

The frequency distribution of Table 3.2 also cán be presented graphically, as by the right-hand polygon in Figure 3.1. This graph, called a *frequency polygon,* gives a more effective picture of the pattern of variation than the table. On the X axis of a frequency polygon we plot the magnitude of the accident rate, and on the Y axis the class frequency — that is, num-

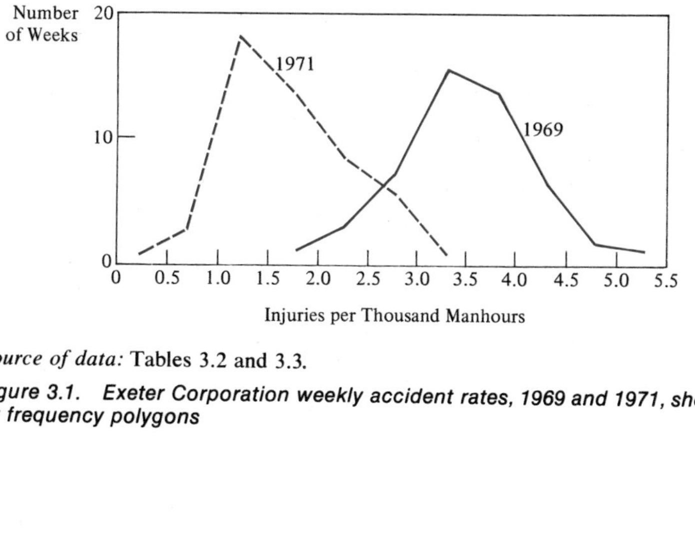

Source of data: Tables 3.2 and 3.3.

Figure 3.1. Exeter Corporation weekly accident rates, 1969 and 1971, shown by frequency polygons

ber of weeks. Note that the frequency of any one class is plotted corresponding to the middle of that class. Thus, the three weeks that had somewhere between 2.0 and 2.4 injuries per thousand manhours are plotted as a point corresponding to 2.2 injuries per thousand manhours. These points then are connected by a series of straight lines.

The polygon on the right in Figure 3.1 tells the same story as Table 3.2, though more easily. Remember that the variation in the weekly accident rates shown in the frequency distribution did not result from any changes in the basic conditions affecting the incidence of accidents. *This type of variation, which exists when the underlying causal factors have remained the same, is called variation inherent within a constant cause system.*

Changes in pattern of variation

Should there be a change in the underlying causal factors, the entire pattern of variation may change. An example of this type of change occurred in the Exeter Corporation during 1970. Early in that year, the Board of Directors elected a new president who began at once to attack various problems, among them plant safety. As a result, numerous safety measures and procedures were applied in the plant, production personnel were given a training program in plant safety, and new employees were required to complete a similar program before they could begin their jobs. These radical changes were completed by about the end of 1970.

One would expect that the pattern of variation in weekly accident rates would be affected by this safety program, and indeed it was. Table 3.3 shows the frequency distribution of weekly accident rates for 1971. Note that variation in the weekly accident rates still occurred, although the underlying causal conditions were fairly constant during that year.

Table 3.3 Exeter Corporation,
Frequency Distribution of Weekly Accident Rates — 1971

Number of Injuries per Thousand Manhours	*Number of Weeks*
0– .4	1
.5– .9	3
1.0–1.4	18
1.5–1.9	14
2.0–2.4	9
2.5–2.9	6
3.0–3.4	1
Total	52

The change in the pattern of variation can be seen most easily by comparing the frequency distributions for 1969 and 1971 on the same graph.

This is done in Figure 3.1. Note that the shape of the distribution has remained fairly much the same. However, the entire distribution for 1971 has shifted to the left of that for 1969. It is in this sense that we say the company has been able to reduce the incidence of plant accidents. While there were still some weeks in 1971 that had higher accident rates than certain weeks in 1969, most of the weekly accident rates in 1971 were lower than those of most of the weeks in 1969.

To summarize: (1) The frequency distributions of weekly accident rates for each of the two years reflect the variation that was present despite the fact that the underlying causal conditions affecting plant accidents were fairly constant within each period. (2) The difference in the basic conditions between the two years, resulting from the energetic safety program in 1970, is reflected in the shift of the frequency distribution. *The distinction between variation inherent within a constant cause system and changes in the pattern of variation arising as a result of changes in the underlying causal conditions is basic for much of our later work.*

3.3 ADDITIONAL CASE ILLUSTRATION: VARIATION IN MANUFACTURED PRODUCT

Units of a manufactured product may appear to be identical as they come off the production line, but they are not. Variation in such quality characteristics as thickness, hardness, breaking strength, and weight of products is of great importance to a manufacturer. In the first place, many products are assembled from parts. If these assemblies are to be mass-produced, the parts of a given type must be interchangeable. Interchangeability of parts really means uniformity of these parts with respect to given quality characteristics. Uniformity of product is also important to a manufacturer so that his customers know precisely what they are buying. While uniformity alone is not enough, of course, as a company can turn out uniformly poor products, even a company that supplies predominantly good products cannot afford any inconsistency in quality without risking the loss of customers' confidence.

The saving feature in this demand for uniformity is that perfect uniformity is not required. Rather, variation to a certain degree is tolerable. The extent of this permissible variation is embodied in product specifications. The problem of a manufacturer, then, becomes one of producing his product with sufficient uniformity so that most of the units meet the quality specifications, and achieving this uniformity as economically as possible.

We now shall consider a case in which variation in the product was excessive and study the methods whereby it was reduced. Bristol Laboratories, which is engaged in the manufacture of drugs, produces a tablet for which the thickness is an important quality characteristic (Ref. 3.1). To study the thickness of the tablets being produced, 200 tablets were selected from the production stream and the maximum thickness of each measured. The frequency distribution of the thicknesses of the tablets is presented in Table 3.4, and the graph of the distribution is shown on the left in Figure 3.2. Note that the classes are specified in a somewhat different manner

Table 3.4 Thicknesses of Tablets From Production Stream Before and After Adjustment of Machines

Thickness (Maximum Diameter in Inches, Measured to Nearest Thousandth)	*Number of Tablets*	
	Before Adjustment	*After Adjustment*
.238	2	1
.239	13	10
.240	32	20
.241	29	53
.242	18	71
.243	21	36
.244	20	7
.245	22	2
.246	22	
.247	13	
.248	3	
.249	0	
.250	1	
.251	1	
.252	0	
.253	1	
.254	0	
.255	2	
Total	200	200

Source: Reference 3.1, pp. 7–8.

from that of the earlier examples. Actually, the difference is only in appearance. Since the thickness is measured to the nearest thousandth of an inch, the first class really includes all tablets with a thickness anywhere between .2375 and .2385 inches. In other words, .238 inches, which specifies the class, is simply the midpoint of the class whose width is .001 inches. Figure 3.2 indicates clearly that the tablets are not being produced with uniform thickness. While most of the tablets have a thickness somewhere between .239 and .247 inches, a few are as thick as .255 inches.

The marked lack of symmetry in the distribution, as well as the fact that the distribution reached a peak at .240 inches and also near .246 inches, was unexpected and called for analysis. Previous experience indicated that a manufacturing process of this nature should turn out tablets whose frequency distribution of thicknesses is symmetrical, with only a single point

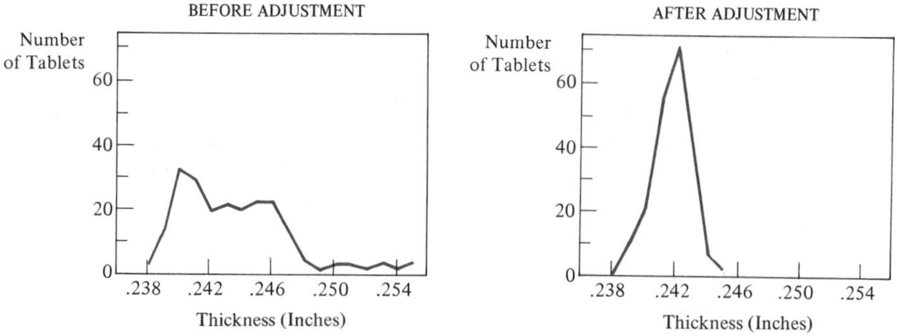

Source of data: Table 3.4.

Figure 3.2. Thicknesses of drug tablets selected from production stream before and after adjustment of machines

around which the thicknesses of the tablets cluster — in other words, with only one peak. Yet from Figure 3.2 there appear to be *two* peaks.

There are two major reasons that could account for the frequency distribution being asymmetrical and two-peaked. The first is that adjustments were made on one or more machines during the time the 200 tablets were selected from the production stream. This would mean that the underlying conditions affecting the thickness of the tablets had not remained the same during that time, so that the sample of 200 tablets would not represent the results from a constant cause system. The other possible reason is that the machines in the battery were not adjusted uniformly. Thus, each machine could turn out tablets whose thicknesses form a symmetrical frequency distribution with a single peak, but the distributions would not be centered on the same thickness. Therefore, a selection of 200 tablets from a battery of the machines would not yield a frequency distribution that looks anything like the distributions for the individual machines.

As a result of this type of analysis, the machines were adjusted and synchronized; then, another 200 tablets were selected from the production stream. The frequency distribution of the thicknesses of these tablets is shown also in Table 3.4 and on the right in Figure 3.2. Note that the distribution is now fairly symmetrical and, particularly, that there is much less variation in the thicknesses than before.

3.4 FREQUENCY DISTRIBUTIONS

We now define a frequency distribution formally:

(3.1) A ***frequency distribution*** is the classification of a group of items by some quantitative characteristic.

For instance, for the frequency distribution of 200 drug tablets, the quantitative characteristic employed was thickness in inches. Mutually exclusive (non-overlapping) classes were set up such that each tablet fell into one of these classes. Similarly, we presented distributions of weekly accident rates classified by number of injuries per thousand manhours.

The concept of a *distribution* is not limited to classification by a quantitative characteristic. Thus one can have a distribution of technical employees in a firm by mutually exclusive occupational classes—namely machinist, carpenter, plumber, pipefitter, electronic technician, and so on—such that each technical employee falls into one and only one class. The distribution of employees by occupational class is not a frequency distribution because it involves classification by a qualitative characteristic. This type of distribution frequently is called a *qualitative distribution* to distinguish it from a frequency distribution, which involves classification by a quantitative characteristic.

Frequency distributions may be constructed either in terms of *absolute frequencies* or *per cent frequencies.* In both cases, the pattern of variation shown is identical, as this pattern depends only on the relation of any one class frequency to the others. For example, on the left of Table 3.5 is shown

Table 3.5 Absolute and Per Cent Frequency Distributions of Readers' Ages

Age (Years)		*Number of Readers*	*Per Cent of Readers*
10–19		5,927	18.5
20–34		7,389	23.1
35–44		5,987	18.7
45–54		5,375	16.8
55 or more		7,337	22.9
	Total	32,015	100.0

the age distribution of 32,015 readers of a national magazine expressed in absolute frequencies. On the right of Table 3.5 is shown the same age distribution expressed in per cent frequencies. Here, for instance, 5,927 out of 32,015 readers, or $(5{,}927/32{,}015)100 = 18.5$ per cent, are between 10 and 19 years old; $(7{,}389/32{,}015)100 = 23.1$ per cent are between 20 and 34 years old; and so on. For certain types of problems the per cent frequency distribution is to be preferred to one expressed in absolute frequencies. For instance, in situations where two frequency distributions with unequal total number of frequencies are to be compared, the comparison is facilitated if both distributions are expressed in per cent frequencies. Of course, if the total number of frequencies in each distribution is the same, the comparison also can be made readily from the distributions containing the actual frequencies.

3.5 CONSTRUCTION OF FREQUENCY DISTRIBUTIONS

The main problem in constructing a frequency distribution of a given group of items is to determine the classes according to which the data are to be classified. This determination is largely an arbitrary decision. In general, no definite rules can be laid down as to how the frequency distribution should be constructed. We shall, therefore, simply point out the most important phases that should be considered in the construction of a frequency distribution as well as some of the dangers inherent in various procedures.

Number of classes

The larger the number of classes used in a frequency distribution, the more detail can be shown. If the number of classes is too large, though, the classification loses its effectiveness as a means of summarizing data. Furthermore, we shall see in later chapters that one is often not warranted in drawing conclusions about detailed aspects of a frequency distribution if the number of observations is not large. For that reason, it usually is suggested that a large number of classes be used only if the number of observations also is large. Too few classes, on the other hand, condense the information so much as to leave little insight into the nature of the pattern of variation. Both of these extremes will be demonstrated below. The number of classes in a frequency distribution is usually somewhere between 4 and 20.

Width of classes

The choice of the class width or class interval is related to the determination of the number of classes. It is generally best if all the classes have the same width. When class intervals are not equal, the interpretation of the distribution is more difficult. If the classes are not equally wide, one often cannot tell readily whether differences in class frequencies are due mainly to differences in concentration of items or to differences in the class widths.

Sometimes one must use unequal class intervals. Consider the construction of a frequency distribution of annual salaries of employees in a medium-size company. Assume that the annual salaries range from $2,500 to $75,000 and that about eight classes are to be used in the distribution. If equal class intervals are used, they each would have to have a width of about $10,000. Thus, the first class might be $0–under $10,000, and so on. This grouping provides equal class intervals but destroys the usefulness of the classification. Most of the employees earn less than $10,000 and hence would be lumped in the first class. Thus, no information would be provided about the distribution of salaries of the majority of the employees except that they earned less than $10,000. Subsequent classes would not provide much revealing information either, since relatively few officials earn over $10,000 in this company, yet seven of the eight classes would be devoted to a classification of their salaries.

In cases of this nature, unequal class intervals are usually used. For instance, equal class intervals of, say, $2,000 in width might be used for the range wherein most of the salaries fall, after which the interval might increase to, say, $20,000. In fact, when all but a few of the salaries have been classified, an open-end interval might be used to account for the remainder.

(3.2) An ***open-end interval*** is one that has only one limit, either upper or lower.

Thus, if only three officials in the company earned over $40,000, the last class might be $40,000 and more; in this way, only one class is needed to account for these top three officials. The use of an open-end interval has the disadvantage—or advantage, as the case may be—of not revealing the magnitude of the top salary in the company. Open-end classes may be necessary at the upper end of the distribution, as just illustrated, sometimes at the lower end of the distribution, and occasionally even at both ends.

Class limits

Still another problem is the choice of class limits. Calculations from a frequency distribution often make use of the midpoint of each class to represent all of the items in the class.

(3.3) The ***midpoint*** of a class is the value halfway between the two class limits.

Thus, the midpoint is determined by the class limits. In order to make the calculations discussed in the next chapter as accurate as possible, it usually is suggested that the class limits be chosen in such a way that the midpoint of each class is approximately equal to the arithmetic average of the items that fall in that class. In most cases, this condition will be fairly well satisfied even though one pays little attention to this principle in setting the limits. In some cases, where the values tend to be bunched at certain periodic points throughout the range of the data—for example, rents are often multiples of $2.50 or $5.00—one may have to experiment somewhat in deciding upon class limits for which each midpoint will approximately equal the arithmetic average of the items in that class.

In stating class limits, one should be careful to be unambiguous. For instance, the limits $30–$40, $40–$50 are not clear because one cannot be sure in which class $40 is included. Stating limits as $30–$39, $40–$49 is clear, provided that data are expressed in dollars only. When they are, the midpoint of the first class is [(30 + 39)/2] = $34.50, and so on.

If data are expressed to cents, the above limits are not clear. But, if the limits are stated as $30.00–$39.99, $40.00–$49.99, there can be no doubt into which class an item falls. In that case, the midpoint of the first class is [(30.00 + 39.99)/2] = \$34.995, or for all practical purposes \$35, and so on.

The limits \$30–under \$40, \$40–under \$50 are clear; however, without additional information it may not be possible to determine the midpoints accurately. If no additional information is provided, the midpoint of the first class is considered to be [(30 + 40)/2] = \$35, and so on.

Example

To make the above comments on the construction of frequency distributions more specific, we will construct a frequency distribution of the weekly accident rates in 1969 for the Exeter Corporation. The basic data were given in Table 3.1 (p. 46). By scanning the data in that table, we note that the weekly accident rates range from 1.8 to 5.3 injuries per thousand manhours. Arranging the data into an array often can be quite helpful in constructing the distribution.

(3.4) An ***array*** is a listing of the items in ascending or descending order of magnitude.

An array of the weekly accident rates is given in Table 3.6. We can easily find the extreme values from the array; also, by examining the array we can discern that the distribution will not require unequal class intervals. Since there are only 52 observations and since an interval from 1.8 to 5.3 must be covered, seven or eight classes of width .5 probably should be satisfactory. The choice of limits can be made fairly arbitrarily here, because Table 3.6 reveals no special periodic concentrations throughout the range of the data. Hence, round numbers are preferable as the class limits to make the distribution simple to read. In our case, 1.5–1.9 suggests itself as the first class, 2.0–2.4 as the second class, and so on.

Table 3.6 Array of Weekly Number of Injuries per Thousand Manhours During 1969 — Exeter Corporation

1.8	2.8	3.2	3.4	3.7	4.2
2.1	2.9	3.2	3.5	3.7	4.3
2.3	2.9	3.2	3.5	3.8	4.3
2.4	3.0	3.3	3.5	3.8	4.4
2.5	3.0	3.3	3.5	3.9	4.6
2.6	3.1	3.3	3.6	3.9	4.7
2.6	3.1	3.3	3.6	4.0	5.3
2.7	3.1	3.4	3.7	4.0	
2.8	3.2	3.4	3.7	4.0	

Once the classes have been decided upon, we next determine the number of items that fall into each class. Table 3.7 presents a form that is convenient to use when tallying the data to see how many cases fall into each class; it also gives a rough graphic picture of the pattern of variation once the tally has been completed.

Table 3.7 Tally Table for Constructing Frequency Distribution of Weekly Accident Rates in 1969 — Exeter Corporation

Number of Injuries per Thousand Manhours	*Tally*	*Number of Weeks*
1.5–1.9	/	1
2.0–2.4	///	3
2.5–2.9	~~////~~ ///	8
3.0–3.4	~~////~~ ~~////~~ ~~////~~ /	16
3.5–3.9	~~////~~ ~~////~~ ////	14
4.0–4.4	~~////~~ //	7
4.5–4.9	//	2
5.0–5.4	/	1
	Total	52

Table 3.8 contains a frequency distribution that is obtained if only 3 classes are used in the above case, and one if 13 classes are used. Note that the distribution with only 3 classes shows almost no detail of the pattern of variation, while the distribution with 13 classes contains so much detail that it becomes somewhat difficult to see the pattern.

Table 3.8 Weekly Accident Rates During 1969 for Exeter Corporation, Tabulated According to Three and Thirteen Classes

Three Classes		*Thirteen Classes*	
Number of Injuries per Thousand Manhours	*Number of Weeks*	*Number of Injuries per Thousand Manhours*	*Number of Weeks*
1.0–2.4	4	1.7–1.9	1
2.5–3.9	38	2.0–2.2	1
4.0–5.4	10	2.3–2.5	3
Total	52	2.6–2.8	5
		2.9–3.1	7
		3.2–3.4	11
		3.5–3.7	10
		3.8–4.0	7
		4.1–4.3	3
		4.4–4.6	2
		4.7–4.9	1
		5.0–5.2	0
		5.3–5.5	1
		Total	52

3.6 GRAPHIC PRESENTATION OF FREQUENCY DISTRIBUTIONS

Frequency polygon

(3.5) A *frequency polygon* is a line graph of a frequency distribution.

Construction. In Section 3.2 we explained how to construct frequency polygons, such as the ones in Figure 3.1 (p. 47). Each class frequency simply is plotted corresponding to the midpoint of that class. The plotted points are then connected by a series of straight lines.

Note from Figure 3.1 that the X scale is an ordinary arithmetic scale and that only convenient points, not necessarily the class limits in the frequency distribution, are labeled. The X scale need not begin at zero since we are concerned only with the pattern of variation as described by the distribution.

If the frequency distribution is expressed in per cent form, the procedure for constructing a frequency polygon is exactly the same as already described, except that the Y scale will represent per cent of total frequencies.

The procedure for constructing a frequency polygon just described is appropriate only if the class intervals are of equal width. Should that not be the case, adjustments must be made in graphing the distribution.

Comparison of frequency polygons. Two or more frequency polygons can be readily compared if they have the same class intervals and contain the same total number of frequencies. This was the case for the comparison of the two frequency polygons in Figure 3.1. If the distributions being compared do not have the same total frequencies, one should first express them in per cent form since otherwise it is difficult to compare the frequency polygons.

If the two distributions being compared do not have the same class intervals, one sometimes can combine classes within one or both of the frequency distributions, so that the class intervals in the two distributions will be the same. Another method of proceeding under such circumstances is to graph the cumulative distributions, a procedure that will be discussed in Section 3.7.

Histogram

A second graphic method of presenting a frequency distribution is by means of a histogram.

(3.6) A ***histogram*** is a bar graph of a frequency distribution.

Construction. The histogram for the weekly accident rates in 1969 for the Exeter Corporation is shown in Figure 3.3. Note that the X scale again represents the weekly accident rates and the Y scale the number of weeks.

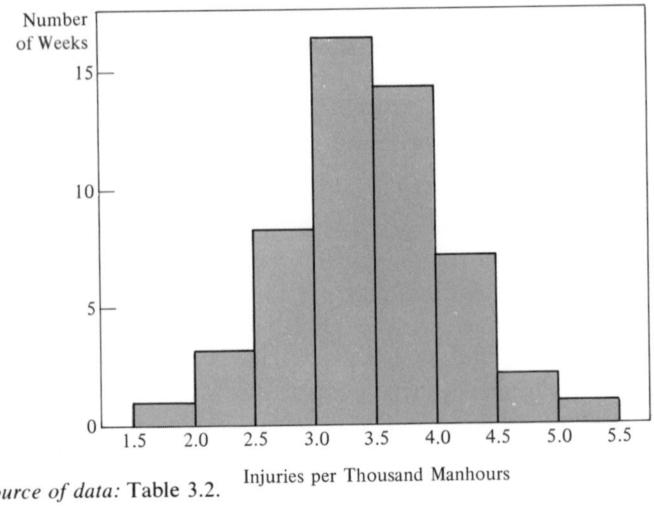

Source of data: Table 3.2.

Figure 3.3. Exeter Corporation weekly accident rates, 1969, shown by histogram

The *X* scale is a regular arithmetic scale that need not begin at zero. Only convenient points need be labeled. Bars are drawn with a width spanning the class interval and a height corresponding to the frequency of that class. A histogram thus shows the frequency of each class more clearly than a polygon. A polygon, on the other hand, often presents a more effective picture of the pattern of variation.

If the frequency distribution is expressed in per cent form, the histogram will be constructed as was previously described, except that the *Y* axis will represent per cent of total frequencies rather than number of items or cases.

The procedure explained above for plotting a histogram is applicable only if the class intervals are equal. Adjustments will have to be made if the intervals are unequal.

Comparison of histograms. It is quite difficult to obtain an effective comparison of patterns of variation by superimposing two histograms. Two frequency polygons, on the other hand, can be readily superimposed on the same graph for purposes of comparing them. Hence, graphic comparisons of several frequency distributions should ordinarily be made by means of frequency polygons.

3.7 CUMULATIVE FREQUENCY DISTRIBUTIONS

"Less than" distribution

In some situations, information about the pattern of variation is desired in a form that is a modification of the frequency distribution already discussed. For instance, in a study of the life of vacuum tubes before failure due to heater burnout, interest may center chiefly on the number or proportion of tubes that lasted less than any given number of hours. Table 3.9 presents the frequency distribution, in per cent form, of the life of 149

Table 3.9 Frequency Distribution of Life of 149 Vacuum Tubes Under Normal Operating Conditions

Number of Hours Before Failure Due to Heater Burnout	*Per Cent of Tubes*
100–under 200	2.7
200–under 300	5.4
300–under 400	7.3
400–under 500	16.1
500–under 600	12.8
600–under 800	13.4
800–under 1,000	10.1
1,000–under 1,200	11.4
1,200–under 1,400	9.4
1,400–under 1,600	3.3
1,600–under 1,800	2.1
1,800–under 2,000	2.6
2,000–under 2,200	0.7
2,200–under 2,400	0
2,400–under 2,600	0.7
2,600–under 2,800	1.3
2,800–under 3,000	0
3,000 and over	0.7
Total	100

Note: Data are disguised.

Source: Reference 3.2, p 27.

vacuum tubes tested. Table 3.10 presents the same data in the form of a cumulative frequency distribution, indicating what per cent of the tubes lasted less than a given number of hours. Since no tubes lasted less than 100 hours and 2.7 per cent of the tubes lasted between 100 and less than 200 hours, 2.7 per cent of the tubes lasted less than 200 hours. An additional 5.4 per cent of the tubes lasted between 200 and less than 300 hours, so that altogether 8.1 per cent of the tubes failed in less than 300 hours. The remainder of the cumulative distribution was calculated in the same manner.

"More than" distribution

The cumulative distribution also could have been computed to indicate the per cent of tubes that lasted a given number of hours or more. To show this "more than" distribution, we would have set up the cumulative frequency distribution in the following form:

Number of Hours Before Failure Due to Heater Burnout	*Cumulative Per Cent of Tubes*
100 hours or more	100
200 hours or more	97.3
300 hours or more	91.9
etc.	etc.

Table 3.10 Cumulative Frequency Distribution of Life of 149 Vacuum Tubes Under Normal Operating Conditions

Number of Hours Before Failure Due to Heater Burnout	*Cumulative Per Cent of Tubes*
Less than 100	0
Less than 200	2.7
Less than 300	8.1
Less than 400	15.4
Less than 500	31.5
Less than 600	44.3
Less than 800	57.7
Less than 1,000	67.8
Less than 1,200	79.2
Less than 1,400	88.6
Less than 1,600	91.9
Less than 1,800	94.0
Less than 2,000	96.6
Less than 2,200	97.3
Less than 2,400	97.3
Less than 2,600	98.0
Less than 2,800	99.3
Less than 3,000	99.3

Note: Data are disguised.

Source: Reference 3.2, p. 27.

Absolute or per cent distribution

A cumulative frequency distribution can be constructed in per cent form, as above, or in terms of the absolute number of observations. The method of construction in either case is exactly the same.

Ogive

(3.7) A graph of a cumulative frequency distribution is called an ***ogive.***

Construction. An example is presented in Figure 3.4. The X axis represents the life of the vacuum tubes and contains an ordinary arithmetic

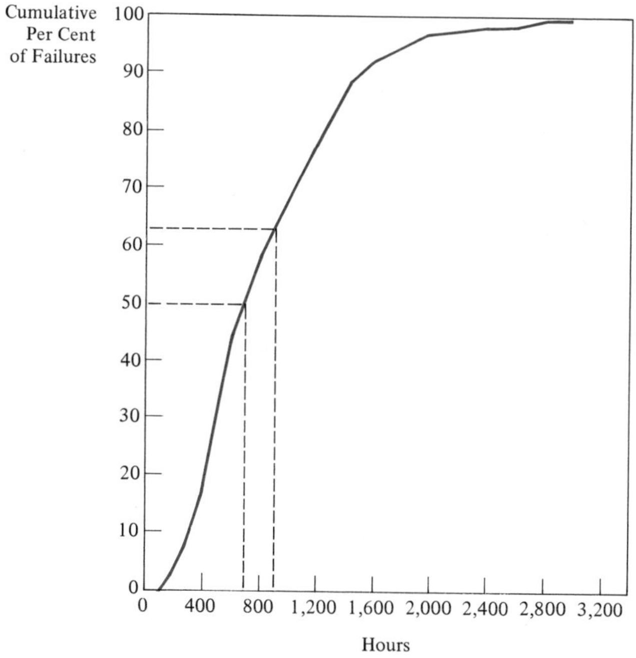

Source of data: Table 3.10.

Figure 3.4. Per cent of vacuum tubes lasting less than specified number of hours before failure due to heater burnout

scale, while the Y axis represents the cumulative per cent of tubes. Thus, since no tubes lasted less than 100 hours, a point corresponding to $Y = 0$, $X = 100$ is plotted. Similarly, 2.7 per cent of the tubes lasted less than 200 hours, so that a point corresponding to $Y = 2.7$ per cent, $X = 200$ is plotted. After all the points have been plotted, they are connected by a series of straight lines. Note that the graph in this instance does not reach the 100 per cent height, representing all the tubes, because the last class in the frequency distribution is an open-end class and we therefore do not know the maximum life of all the tubes.

From Figure 3.4 one can read, for instance, that half the tubes lasted less than about 685 hours (median number of hours), or that about 63 per cent of the tubes lasted less than 900 hours. To be sure, such statements are correct only to some degree of approximation, because the use of straight lines to connect the series of known points is only an approximation to the distribution of the items within any given class. Nevertheless, this approximation is sufficiently good in many cases.

The ogive also can be plotted for a cumulative distribution that is constructed on a "more than" basis. Similarly, ogives can be plotted for cumulative distributions stated in terms of actual number of cases. In neither of these two instances do any new problems arise.

Unequal class intervals. In plotting the ogive in Figure 3.4, no problem was encountered, despite the unequal class intervals of the distribution. We simply plotted points corresponding to those hours for which we had information telling us the per cent of tubes that burned out by that time. Since the X scale is a regular arithmetic scale and the Y scale represents cumulative frequencies, this plotting automatically adjusts for unequal class intervals.

Comparison of ogives. Several ogives can be compared readily on the same graph. Class intervals of the respective distributions need not be the same. If the total frequencies in each of the distributions is not the same, it is best to convert each to a per cent distribution first, to facilitate the comparison of the ogives. Otherwise, differences in the total frequencies will make it difficult to compare the patterns of variation shown by the ogives.

Cited references

3.1 Noel, Roland H., and Martin A. Brumbaugh, "Applications of Statistics to Drug Manufacture," *Industrial Quality Control,* September 1950, pp. 7–14.

3.2 Guild, Richard D., "Correlation of Conventional and Accelerated Test Conditions for Heater Burnouts by the Logarithmic Normal Distribution," *Industrial Quality Control,* November 1952, pp. 27–30.

QUESTIONS AND PROBLEMS [1]

3.1. Explain briefly each of the following:
- **a.** Frequency distribution
- **b.** Ogive
- **c.** Histogram
- **d.** Class limits
- **e.** Array

3.2. Explain the distinction between a frequency distribution and a qualitative distribution. In analysis why is it helpful to distinguish between these two types of distributions? (*Hint:* What is the significance of an average for each of these two types of distributions?)

3.3. **a.** Explain whether each of the three distributions on p. 63 (I, II, III) is a frequency distribution. Justify your answer.

b. Must a frequency distribution always contain absolute frequencies or can it contain either absolute or relative frequencies? Explain.

c. Must a class in a frequency distribution be designated by a pair of limits? Can it be designated by a single number? Can it always be designated by a single number?

d. What are the advantages and disadvantages of presenting a pattern of variation

[1] Answers are provided at the back of the book for problems preceded by an asterisk.

in terms of a frequency distribution with absolute frequencies? With relative frequencies?

Table I. Civilian Labor Force of the United States, April 1971

Status	*No. of Persons (Thousands)*
Employed in agriculture	3,558
Employed in nonagricultural industries	75,140
Unemployed	5,085
Total civilian labor force	83,783

Source: Federal Reserve Bulletin, May 1971, p. A64.

Table II. Family Income in the United States, March 1969

Family Income	*Per Cent of Families*
\$ 0–\$999	1.8
\$ 1,000–\$1,999	3.4
\$ 2,000–\$2,999	5.1
\$ 3,000–\$3,999	6.1
\$ 4,000–\$4,999	6.0
\$ 5,000–\$5,999	6.9
\$ 6,000–\$6,999	7.6
\$ 7,000–\$9,999	23.4
\$10,000 and over	39.7
All families	100.0

Source: U.S. Bureau of the Census, *Statistical Abstract of the United States: 1970.* Washington, D.C., 1970, p. 324.

Table III. U.S. Families by Size, March 1969

Size of Family	*No. of Families (Thousands)*
2 persons	17,392
3 persons	10,514
4 persons	9,642
5 persons	6,245
6 persons	3,510
7 or more persons	3,206
All families	50,509

Source: U.S. Bureau of the Census, *Statistical Abstract of the United States: 1970.* Washington, D.C., 1970, p. 38.

3.4. a. What is meant by variation under a constant cause system? Distinguish this type of variation from that arising with a change in the basic conditions underlying a process. Illustrate by an example.

b. Why is it important for management to distinguish between these two types of variation when using statistical data for control purposes?

3.5. a. Combine the frequency distributions in Tables 3.2 and 3.3 (pp. 47, 48) into one frequency distribution.

b. Graph this combined frequency distribution in the form of a frequency polygon.

(Continued)

c. Does the pattern of variation of weekly accident rates for 1969 and 1971 combined resemble the patterns for each of the individual years? Why, or why not?

d. Does Figure 3.1 or your graph of the combined frequency distribution provide more meaningful information for administrative purposes about accident rates in 1969 and 1971? Explain fully.

e. What does this problem suggest to you concerning the data to be included in a frequency distribution?

3.6. The new safety program in the Exeter Corporation (see p. 48) was accomplished by the end of 1970. Management was anxious to evaluate the new program as soon as possible. The weekly accident rates during the first four weeks of 1971 were:

Week of	*Number of Injuries per Thousand Manhours*
January 3, 1971	1.7
January 10, 1971	2.1
January 17, 1971	2.4
January 24, 1971	1.8

Compare these results with the distribution of accident rates for 1969 (p. 47). What conclusion does this comparison suggest? Can you be certain about your conclusion? Explain fully.

3.7. The following passage is quoted from the annual report of a certain corporation: "The following table shows the distribution of stock according to the number of shares held. That ______ Company stock is widely held is indicated by the fact that more than 90 per cent is owned by stockholders having 100 shares or less."

Number of Shares Held	*Percentage of Total Number of Stockholders*
1– 25	46.61
26– 50	23.13
51–100	22.25
101–500	6.94
Over 500	1.07
	100.00

Do you agree with this interpretation of the data? Explain fully.

3.8. In a committee discussion on a company's sales potential, a committee member stated that it is a misconception to believe that persons in younger age groups account for a relatively high number of sales of one of the company's major products. To support his contention, the committee member cited the following data on customers' ages, based on a recent market research study:

Age Group	*% of Customers*	*Age Group*	*% of Customers*
Under 16	1	26–29	14
16–17	6	30–39	19
18–19	8	40–49	25
20–21	7	50 and over	8
22–25	12		
		Total	100

The committee member pointed out that the per cents of customers in the age groups between 30 and 49 years are substantially greater than the per cents in the younger age groups. "In fact," he noted, "persons aged 40 to 49 are the best customers of the product."

Do you agree with this interpretation of the data? If so, support the contention by citing specific figures. If not, explain specifically why you take issue with the committee member's interpretation.

3.9. **a.** A frequency distribution of monthly rental payments in a metropolitan area is to be constructed. It has been decided to use class intervals having a width of $5 each. What class limits would you suggest as most appropriate? Explain the reasons for your choice.

b. Criticize each of the following systems of designating class intervals:

(1)	(2)	(3)
5–10	5–14	5–under 10
10–15	10–19	11–under 15
etc.	15–24	16–under 20
	etc.	etc.

3.10. The lifetimes in hours of a sample of forty-watt 110-volt internally frosted incandescent lamps in quality control forced-life tests were as follows:

Item Lifetimes

1,310	1,262	1,234	1,104	1,105	1,243	1,204	1,203
944	1,343	932	1,055	1,303	1,185	759	1,404
1,248	1,324	1,000	984	1,381	816	1,067	1,252
1,093	1,358	1,024	1,240	1,220	972	1,022	956
1,690	1,302	1,233	1,331	1,157	1,415	1,385	824
1,229	1,079	1,176	1,173	1,109	827	1,209	1,202
609	985	1,233	985	769	905	1,490	918
1,028	1,122	872	826	985	1,075	1,240	985

Source: D. J. Davis, "An Analysis of Some Failure Data," *Journal of the American Statistical Association,* June 1952, p. 142.

a. Construct a frequency distribution of the lifetimes of the lamps in the sample.
b. How many classes did you use in your frequency distribution? Justify your choice of the number of classes.
c. Did you use equal or unequal class intervals? Why?
d. Did you have any special problems in choosing the class limits? Explain.
e. Convert your frequency distribution into a cumulative frequency distribution of the "less than" type, so that it may be charted.
f. Chart the ogive of your cumulative frequency distribution.
g. Did you plot the absolute cumulative distribution or the per cent cumulative distribution? Explain your choice.
h. Analyze your graph and write a brief paragraph to present your findings.

3.11. The unemployment percentages in 1969 for each of the 50 states and the District of Columbia were as follows:

State	*Unemployment Percentage*	*State*	*Unemployment Percentage*	*State*	*Unemployment Percentage*
Ala.	3.9	La.	5.1	Ohio	2.7
Alaska	8.7	Me.	4.6	Okla.	3.4
Ariz.	2.9	Md.	3.0	Ore.	4.4
Ark.	4.2	Mass.	3.8	Penn.	2.9
Calif.	4.4	Mich.	4.1	R. I.	3.7
Colo.	3.0	Minn.	2.9	S. C.	4.0
Conn.	3.8	Miss.	4.2	S. D.	2.8
Dela.	3.1	Mo.	3.2	Tenn.	3.5
Fla.	2.5	Mont.	4.5	Texas	2.7
Ga.	2.9	Neb.	2.2	Utah	5.2
Hawaii	2.7	Nev.	4.4	Vt.	3.2
Idaho	4.0	N. H.	2.3	Va.	2.7
Ill.	2.9	N. J.	4.4	Wash.	4.8
Ind.	2.7	N. M.	4.9	W. Va.	6.4
Iowa	2.6	N. Y.	3.5	Wisc.	3.4
Kan.	3.0	N. C.	2.9	Wyo.	4.1
Ky.	3.6	N. D.	3.9	D. of C.	2.3

Source: U.S. Bureau of the Census, *Statistical Abstract of the United States: 1970*. Washington, D.C., 1970, p. 217.

a. Construct a frequency distribution of the percentages shown.
b. How many classes did you use in your frequency distribution? Justify your choice of classes.
c. Did you use equal or unequal class intervals? Why?
d. Did you use open-end classes? Why, or why not?
e. Did the fact that the percentages are rounded to the nearest one-tenth complicate or simplify your setting of class limits or did it make no difference? Explain.
f. Present your frequency distribution in the form of a frequency polygon or histogram.
g. Analyze your graph and write a brief paragraph presenting your findings.
h. Suppose that you had constructed a distribution of the unemployment percentages for all counties in the U.S. How would you expect this distribution by counties to compare with the corresponding distribution by states that you constructed in part **a**? Explain. What generalization does this suggest?
i. Does your frequency distribution indicate anything about the characteristics of states with very low or very high percentages? Why would a labor economist be interested in studying these characteristics? Discuss.

3.12. Refer to Problem 10.19. Freight bills 000 to 149 inclusive were issued during a three-day period in November 1971.
a. Construct a frequency distribution of the amounts due Crandell Motor Freight, Inc., during this three-day period.
b. How many classes did you use in your frequency distribution? Justify your choice of the number of classes.
c. Did you use equal or unequal class intervals? Why?
d. Did you have any special problems in choosing the class limits? Explain.
e. Is the frequency distribution of the freight charges symmetrical? Explain.

f. Analyze your frequency distribution and write a brief paragraph describing the main features of its pattern of variation.

3.13. In a weaving mill, observations were taken on a section of 400 looms at random times during three periods of the day for 20 days to determine the number of looms working at any given time. The results on the number of looms working were:

	Period of Day				*Period of Day*		
Day	1	2	3	*Day*	1	2	3
1	366	362	352	11	371	365	364
2	369	361	360	12	362	364	374
3	366	356	360	13	374	364	347
4	371	357	365	14	367	366	340
5	365	355	361	15	359	362	359
6	353	364	349	16	362	344	361
7	366	366	356	17	370	369	367
8	362	353	361	18	362	366	348
9	358	356	358	19	366	373	354
10	369	368	366	20	364	360	367

a. Construct a frequency distribution of the number of looms working at any given time, based on all 60 observations.
b. How many classes did you use in your frequency distribution? Justify your choice of the number of classes.
c. Did you use unequal or equal class intervals? Why?
d. Did you have any special problems in choosing the class limits? Explain.
e. Analyze your frequency distribution and write a brief paragraph describing the main features of the pattern of variation in the number of looms working at any given time.

3.14. The Northern Electric and Gas Corporation had 2,856 employees in 1970. Of this number, 1,306 employees had ten or more years of service with the company. The lengths of service of the 1,306 employees with ten or more years of service in 1970 were as follows:

Length of Service (Years)	*No. of Employees*
10–under 15	209
15–under 20	277
20–under 25	450
25–under 30	243
30–under 35	93
35–under 40	23
40–under 45	10
45–under 50	1

a. Present this frequency distribution graphically as a frequency polygon.
b. On another chart, present the frequency distribution graphically as a histogram.
c. Is the distribution symmetrical? Explain.
d. If a frequency distribution of lengths of service of all 2,856 employees of the firm were presented as a frequency polygon, would this polygon have the same general shape as your polygon in part **a** above? Explain. *(Continued)*

e. If the frequency distribution of the lengths of service of employees with ten or more years of service in 1975 were plotted, would it have the same location and pattern of variation as the 1970 distribution? Discuss.

3.15. The number (in millions) and per cent of passenger cars in use in the United States, classified by age of car, as of July 1, 1941 and 1968 were:

	1941		*1968*	
Age (Years)	*Number*	*Per Cent*	*Number*	*Per Cent*
0–under 4	10.49	38.2	32.08	42.6
4–under 8	10.39	37.8	25.57	34.0
8–under 12	4.27	15.5	11.66	15.4
12–under 16	2.34	8.5	4.47	5.9
16–under 20	0	0	1.52	2.1
Total cars	27.49	100.0	75.30	100.0

Source: Adapted from Automobile Manufacturers Association, *Automobile Facts and Figures, 1969 Edition,* p. 24; data compiled and supplied by R. L. Polk and Company. Further reproduction prohibited without Polk permission.

a. Plot the age distributions of passenger cars in 1941 and 1968 on the same graph, using frequency polygons.

b. Did you use the absolute or the per cent distributions in plotting the polygons? Why?

c. Would it have been equally effective to have plotted two histograms on the same graph to compare the distributions? Why, or why not?

d. Briefly describe the differences in the two age distributions. Are these differences substantial?

3.16. Refer to Problem 3.13.

a. Construct a frequency distribution of the number of looms working at any given time for each of the three periods of the day. Use five equal class intervals in the distributions, and use the same class intervals for all three distributions.

b. Plot the three frequency distributions on one graph, using frequency polygons.

c. Why was it unnecessary to convert the frequency distributions into per cent distributions so that they could be compared effectively?

d. Analyze your graph and write a brief paragraph summarizing your findings. In particular, does the period of day seem to affect the number of looms working at any given time and, if so, how? Why can you not be certain of your conclusion?

3.17. Refer to Table 3.5 (p. 52).

a. Why is the analysis of the pattern of variation made difficult by the unequal class intervals? Explain.

b. Assume that the ages of the readers in each class are spread out uniformly within the class. In that case, how many of the 7,389 readers 20–34 years old would fall into any ten-year interval within that class (e.g., 20–29 or 25–34)?

c. On the basis of the frequencies per ten-year class intervals, can you now obtain a better picture of the pattern of variation of the ages of readers? Explain. Briefly describe the pattern of variation.

d. Could the same type of adjustment have been made for the per cent distribution in Table 3.5? Why, or why not?

e. Could the same type of adjustment have been made for the open-end class as for the class 20–34 years? Why, or why not?

***3.18.** Refer to Problem 3.15.

a. Plot the two age distributions as "more than" ogives on one chart so that the two ogives can be compared easily.

b. Did you use the absolute or per cent distributions? Why?

c. Did you plot the cumulative data corresponding to the lower limit, midpoint, or upper limit of each class? Explain.

d. From an examination of your graph, would you conclude that the two age distributions differ in location? Explain.

e. What other significant changes in the ages of passenger cars in use are indicated by your graph?

f. From your graph of the ogives, read the answers to the following questions:

(1) In 1968, 50 per cent of the cars were how many years old or older?

(2) In 1941, 50 per cent of the cars were how many years old or older?

(3) In 1968, 80 per cent of the cars were less than how many years old?

3.19. Two frequency distributions are presented below. One shows the per cent distribution of individual stockholders of a large corporation, classified by income of stockholders. The other shows the per cent distribution of shares held by individual stockholders, also classified by income of stockholders.

Income of Stockholders (Dollars)	*Per Cent of Stockholders*	*Per Cent of Shares Held*
0– 3,999	6	1
4,000– 7,999	12	6
8,000–11,999	22	14
12,000–15,999	20	20
16,000–19,999	15	17
20,000–23,999	8	12
24,000 and over	17	30

a. Answer the following questions on the basis of the above distributions:

(1) How many classes are in each distribution?

(2) Do these distributions contain open-end classes? Why do you think they were constructed in this manner?

b. Convert each of the above distributions to a "more than" cumulative frequency distribution. Use classes: $0 or more, $4,000 or more, etc.

c. Plot your cumulative frequency distributions as "more than" ogives on the same graph so that they can be compared easily.

d. Answer the following questions from your graph:

(1) Did your ogives reach the zero line on the vertical scale? Explain.

(2) Approximately what per cent of the stockholders had incomes of $15,000 or more?

(3) What per cent of the shares were held by stockholders having incomes of $15,000 or more?

(4) The 25 per cent of the stockholders with lowest incomes held what per cent of the stock?

(5) What does your chart indicate about the distribution of the company's stock among individual stockholders in the different income groups? Would you expect that this is a typical pattern of distribution of a corporation's stock among individual stockholders? Explain.

(6) Under what conditions would the two ogives plotted in your graph coincide?

3.20. U.S. retail establishments in 1967 are classified in the following distribution by number of paid employees; the total sales of retail establishments in each class also are given:

Number of Paid Employees	*Number of Establishments (Thousands)*	*Sales (Billion Dollars)*
0– 3	1,243	63.8
4– 7	199	34.1
8–19	144	52.7
20 or more	84	148.8
All retail establishments	1,670	299.4

Source: U.S. Bureau of the Census, *Statistical Abstract of the United States: 1970.* Washington, D.C., 1970, p. 737.

a. Why do you think that unequal class intervals were used in these distributions?

b. Calculate the per cent distributions of number of establishments and of sales, by number of paid employees.

c. Convert each of the per cent distributions to a "less than" cumulative frequency distribution. Use classes: less than 0, less than 4, less than 8, etc.

d. Plot your cumulative per cent frequency distributions as "less than" ogives on the same graph so that they can be compared readily.

e. Answer the following questions from your graph:

(1) Did your ogives reach the 100 per cent line on the vertical scale? Explain.

(2) Approximately what per cent of retail establishments had less than 15 paid employees?

(3) What per cent of total U.S. retail sales was accounted for by retail establishments with less than 10 paid employees?

(4) The largest 10 per cent of retail establishments (in terms of number of paid employees) accounted for what proportion of total U.S. retail sales?

(5) What does your chart indicate about the 1967 distribution of retail establishments by number of paid employees? Would you expect this pattern of variation to be typical of frequency distributions for business and economic phenomena? Explain.

Chapter

4

CHARACTERISTICS OF FREQUENCY DISTRIBUTIONS

In the previous chapter, it was shown that a frequency distribution is a system of classification that describes the pattern of variation of a phenomenon. Many problems in administration and economics involve frequency distributions. If, for instance, one is concerned with consumer income in a geographic area, the distribution of annual incomes of spending units would be important. Often, however, it is rather cumbersome to work with the complete frequency distribution. Instead, measures are used to summarize certain important characteristics of the frequency distribution. In the following sections, we shall study some of these measures, their uses and limitations, and how they are calculated.

4.1
SHORTCUTS TO DESCRIPTION OF FREQUENCY DISTRIBUTIONS

Measures of location

Arithmetic average as measure of location for single distribution. The measure most commonly used to describe a frequency distribution is some kind of *average*. Everyone is familiar with an arithmetic average.

(4.1) An ***arithmetic average*** or ***mean*** of a group of items is defined as the sum of the values of the items divided by the number of items.

In what sense, however, does an arithmetic average describe a frequency distribution? Figure 4.1 presents the frequency distribution of the number of minutes required by employee A to perform a certain work operation on a turret lathe. Note that the employee was not able to perform this operation in a uniform time. We find that as usual a pattern of variation occurs

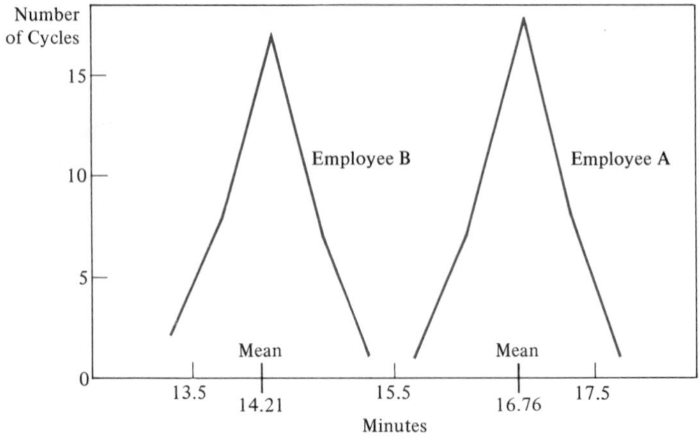

Figure 4.1. Time requirements for 35 cycles of work operation on turret lathe by employees A and B

in the operation times. Altogether, 35 cycles of the same work operation were timed, with the mean time being 16.76 minutes. (The calculation of arithmetic averages will be discussed in Section 4.2.) Note from Figure 4.1 that the arithmetic average in this instance falls at the center of the distribution, where most of the observations are clustered. Thus, the arithmetic average tells us here that employee A required, most of the time, somewhere near 16.76 minutes to perform the particular operation. In this instance, therefore, the arithmetic average can be considered as a measure of the *location* of the distribution. In other words, the *central tendency* or clustering in the distribution is around 16.76 minutes. Note, however, that the arithmetic average does not signify that employee A always required 16.76 minutes to perform this operation.

Arithmetic average as measure of location in comparing frequency distributions. Another use of the arithmetic average is to serve as a measure of location in comparing two or more frequency distributions. Figure 4.1 illustrates this use by presenting also the frequency distribution of the time requirements for 35 cycles of the same work operation for employee B. The mean time required by employee B for this work operation was 14.21 minutes, as compared to 16.76 minutes for employee A. In this case, the difference between the two arithmetic averages indicates that the two distributions differ in location, employee B's distribution being to the left of employee A's. This difference in location implies that employee B tends to require less time to perform this work operation than employee A.

Arithmetic averages can serve as useful measures of location in comparing two or more frequency distributions, even if the distributions being compared are not as concentrated or symmetrical as those in Figure 4.1, provided that the shapes of the distributions are similar. This is illustrated by

Figure 4.2, where the difference in the two means again clearly indicates the difference in the locations of the two distributions, even though both distributions are quite variable and asymmetrical.

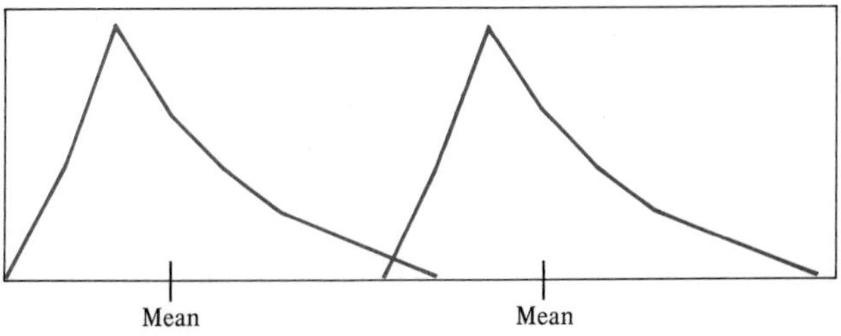

Figure 4.2. Arithmetic averages as measures of location when distributions are variable and asymmetrical

Limitations of any type of average. We now study the limitations of averages as measures of location by continuing our earlier example. Figure 4.3 presents the frequency distribution of the number of minutes required by employee C to perform the same work operation that was timed for employee A; it also contains the distribution for employee A shown previously in Figure 4.1. Again, 35 cycles of this work operation were timed for employee C; his mean time was the same as for employee A—16.76 minutes. One might be tempted to conclude from this fact that both employees were equally proficient. A glance at the two frequency distributions indicates, however, that C was much less consistent—or much more erratic—in his performance than A. Furthermore, one may question the significance of the mean time for C as a measure of central tendency in view of the fact that for many of the 35 cycles he needed either relatively much more or much less time than 16.76 minutes. Finally, one may question the usefulness of the arithmetic average as a measure for comparing the locations of the two distributions in this example. While both distributions have

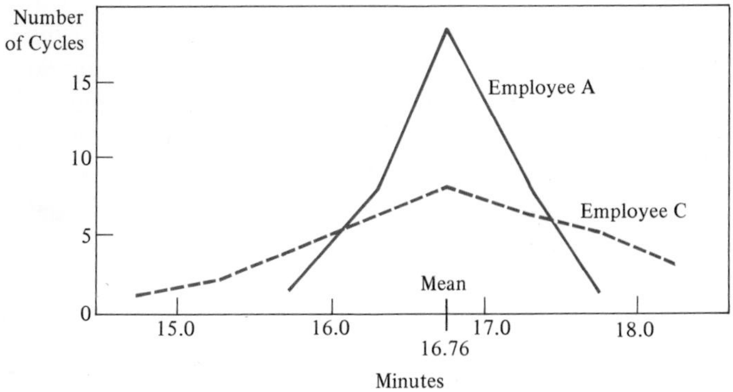

Figure 4.3. Time requirements for 35 cycles of work operation on turret lathe by employees A and C

the same average, their "locations" differ because C's distribution is so much more spread out than that of A.

The discussion so far has only involved one type of average, the arithmetic average. Nevertheless, the three important conclusions that can be drawn from the above example apply to all types of averages.

1. *An average can act as a measure of central tendency only if there is a substantial amount of concentration in the frequency distribution—i.e., if the variation is not too great.* An average alone does not, however, disclose the extent of variation in the frequency distribution. Hence, whenever we are presented simply with an average, we cannot be sure whether or not it is a meaningful measure of central tendency.
2. *An average serves as a useful measure of location for comparing two or more frequency distributions only if the distributions being compared have approximately the same shapes.* Again, one cannot tell from the averages alone whether they can serve as useful measures of location.
3. *An average should not be used as a summary of the entire frequency distribution when interest centers on the entire distribution.* Proficiency of a worker, in our example, is not only reflected by the average time required to perform the operation but also by his consistency on the job. An average does not provide any information about the consistency or uniformity of an employee's performance. It is, therefore, usually wise to define the problem at hand explicitly and not to rush ahead and compute an average at once. Too often, problems involve questions that must be answered on the basis of the entire frequency distribution and not just on the basis of an average.

Arithmetic averages in skewed distributions. Another type of situation in which an arithmetic average may not provide a useful measure of central tendency, even for the majority of the items, occurs when the frequency distribution is markedly asymmetrical. To see why, we turn to an illustration cited in the previous chapter. At one plant of Sylvania Electric Products, Inc., a test was made on 149 vacuum tubes of a certain type to determine how long they would function under normal operating conditions before failure due to heater burnout. Figure 4.4 presents the results of this test in the form of a per cent frequency distribution of the life of the tubes. Note again that the life of this type of vacuum tube is not uniformly long. Note also that this distribution, like some others presented previously, is not symmetrical. *A pattern of variation that is not symmetrical is called a skewed frequency distribution.* In this case, the distribution is said to be skewed to the right because the pattern has a "tail" to the right; in other words, a few tubes lasted particularly long before failure. A distribution with the tail to the left is said to be skewed to the left.

The mean life of the 149 tubes was about 842 hours (data disguised). Note that the arithmetic average in this case is not located where most of

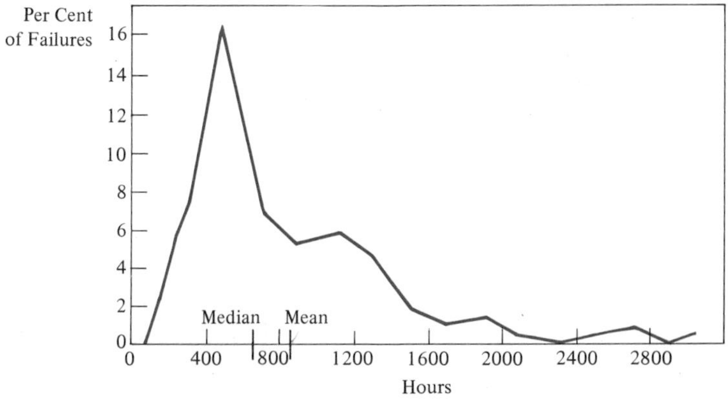

Note: Data are disguised. The source of data is Table 3.9.

Figure 4.4. Life of 149 vacuum tubes under normal operating conditions before failure due to heater burnout

the items are clustered, but to the right of this area. The reason for this location stems from the definition of an arithmetic average. Since it is defined as the sum of the values of all the items divided by the number of items, the few tubes that lasted a very long time pulled the arithmetic average up, so to speak. Students are quite familiar with the opposite effect. If a student did well on three examinations but extremely poorly on one, the mean grade is pulled down substantially. This profound influence of extreme items on the arithmetic average implies that this average frequently will not provide a meaningful measure of central tendency—that is, indicate a point near which most of the items are located—if the distribution is markedly skewed.

Median. In such cases of marked skewness, another type of average is often used. This average is called the median.

(4.2) The ***median*** of a group of items is the value of the middle item when all the items are arranged in either ascending or descending order of magnitude.

Thus, if the number of hours that each of 149 tubes lasted were arranged in ascending order, starting with the tube that had the shortest life and ending with the tube that had the longest life, the life of the middle tube—the 75th tube—would be called the median life. In this case, the median life was 685 hours. The median life, besides being used as a measure of central tendency, has the interpretation in this case that about one-half of the tubes lasted less than 685 hours before failure due to heater burnout while about one-half lasted longer than this number of hours. (The calculation of medians will be discussed in Section 4.3.)

Note that the median value is located more directly in the cluster of the distribution than is the mean value. Hence, the median may be better than

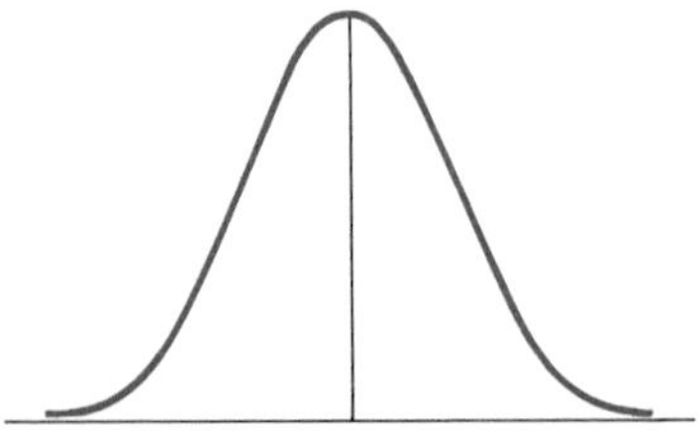

Figure 4.5. Examples of symmetrical and skewed unimodal frequency distributions and typical locations of mean, median, and mode

the mean as an indicator of central tendency of the majority of the tubes included in the distribution. A median is not influenced so much by extreme values because it is determined simply by the value of the middle item. As long as the 75th tube, when the 149 tubes are arranged by magnitude of life, lasted 685 hours, it does not matter whether the 149th tube lasted 1,500 hours or 3,000 hours. The values of the other items, aside from the fact that they are smaller or larger than the value of the middle item, do not affect the median. The mean, on the other hand, is determined from the values of all the items and is thus influenced by extreme values.

Another instance when the median may be a more meaningful measure of central tendency because of skewness in the distribution is in connection with income distributions. These distributions are highly skewed, with a few people having very large incomes. For this reason, the median is commonly used as a measure of central tendency of income distributions rather than the arithmetic average.

While the median *may* be more appropriate than the mean as a measure of central tendency for a skewed distribution insofar as the majority of the items are concerned, this does not imply that the median always will be sufficiently valid to be useful. We cannot stress enough that the meaning of *any* average as a measure of central tendency of the entire distribution is suspect if the variation in the distribution is great.

Mode. Another type of average, the mode, is seldom used in management.

(4.3) The ***mode*** refers to that value in a frequency distribution that occurs most often.

Thus, since the most prevalent family size in the United States in 1969 was two persons, we would say that the modal family size was two. Figure 4.5 indicates the location of the mode, and also that of the mean and median, in several types of frequency distributions.

Measures of skewness

We already have noted the distinction between symmetrical and asymmetrical frequency distributions. Figure 4.5a is an example of a symmetrical

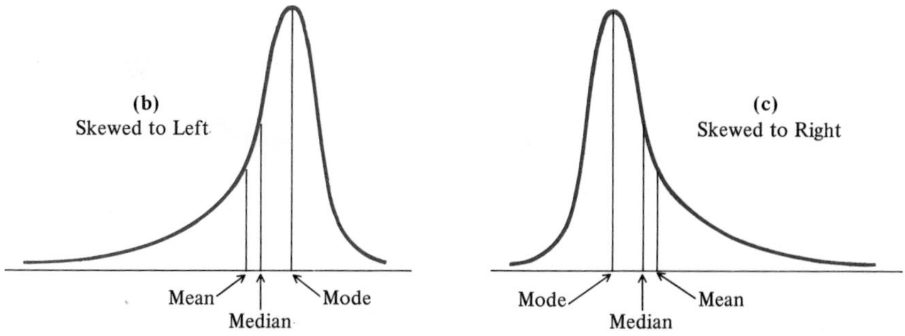

frequency distribution. The values of the mean and median in any symmetrical frequency distribution are identical. The distribution in Figure 4.5a is not only symmetrical but also unimodal. *A distribution with a single peak is called unimodal.* Note that if the distribution is symmetrical and unimodal, the value of the mode is the same as that of the mean and median.

A skewed frequency distribution is one which is not symmetrical. Figure 4.5b shows an example of a unimodal frequency distribution skewed to the left, or skewed negatively, and Figure 4.5c shows a unimodal frequency distribution skewed to the right, or skewed positively.

Figures 4.5b and 4.5c show the relationship typically existing between the mean, median, and mode in unimodal frequency distributions that are moderately skewed. In both the negatively and the positively skewed distributions, the mean is furthest out toward the tail of the distribution, while the median is between the mean and the mode.

In certain cases one may wish to measure the degree of skewness of a frequency distribution. The measure whose calculation we shall discuss later is called *Pearson's coefficient of skewness.* It makes use of the fact that the mean and median have the same value in a symmetrical distribution but differ in value in a skewed distribution. Other ways to measure the degree of skewness exist, but since a need for measures of skewness does not arise too frequently, we shall not discuss these here.

Measures of variation

Standard deviation. An important characteristic of frequency distributions is the extent of variation or dispersion of the distribution. *The measure of the extent of variation in a frequency distribution most commonly used in statistical analysis is the standard deviation.* The definition of this measure and its calculation are discussed in Section 4.4. Here, it is sufficient to state that the standard deviation is a measure that considers how far from the mean each of the items in a frequency distribution is located. The more spread out the distribution, the larger the standard deviation; the more concentrated the distribution, the smaller the standard deviation. Hence, the smaller the standard deviation of a frequency distribution, the more meaningful an average usually will be as a measure of central tendency for that distribution.

Range. Another measure of variation, quite familiar from everyday use, is the range.

(4.4) The ***range*** is the difference between the extreme items in a group of items.

Thus, the range in hourly temperature readings during the past 24 hours may have been: $82 - 51 = 31$ degrees. Often, the actual extreme values are stated, rather than the difference between them. For instance, the stock market page in a newspaper indicates the high and low quotations during the trading period for different stocks.

A difficulty in using the range, or the actual extreme values, as a measure of variation of the entire frequency distribution is that this measure depends only on the values of the extreme items and does not consider any of the other items in the distribution. Thus, a distribution might occur in which the values of all the items are quite close to each other with the exception of one extreme item on each end of the distribution. Despite the concentration of almost all of the items in the distribution, the range would be large since it is based only on the two extreme items.

Another difficulty in using the range as a measure of variability is that it depends on the number of items on which it is based. The larger the number of items, the larger the range is apt to be.

Nonetheless, under certain conditions the range can be most useful as a means of indirectly estimating the standard deviation. The range is used in this way in quality control work (discussed in Chapter 18), partly because it is much simpler to calculate the range than the standard deviation.

4.2 CALCULATION OF ARITHMETIC MEAN

In explaining the calculation of the various measures of central tendency and of dispersion, we shall use simple examples. This will help the reader to learn the basic steps involved in the calculations without getting bogged down in too much arithmetic. It should be noted that *the data in the examples are data based on samples, and the various measures of central tendency and dispersion to be discussed take account of this.* In Chapter 6, we will consider corresponding measures for universes or populations.

We shall discuss the calculations of measures of central tendency and dispersion separately for ungrouped and grouped data.

(4.5) ***Ungrouped*** data consist of the individual data for each element; ***grouped*** data are data that have been arranged in a frequency distribution.

An example of ungrouped data can be seen in Table 3.1, p. 46. Table 3.2, p. 47, presents these data in grouped form—i.e., as a frequency distribution.

Ungrouped data

Recall from definition (4.1) that the arithmetic mean is the sum of the values of the items divided by the number of items. Thus, if an employee in a sample of three successive cycles of a work operation takes 23, 25, and 24 seconds, his mean time is $(23 + 25 + 24)/3 = 24$ seconds.

The arithmetic average, denoted by $\overline{X}$ (read: X bar), may be written symbolically as:

(4.6) $$\overline{X} = \frac{\Sigma X}{n}$$

Here X refers to the values of the individual items, Σ (Greek letter, capital sigma) means that these values are to be summed, and n refers to the number of items.

It is a property of the arithmetic mean that the sum of the deviations around it is zero. In the example of the employee who performs a certain work operation in 23, 25, and 24 seconds, we have:

$$(23 - 24) + (25 - 24) + (24 - 24) = 0$$

Thus, we may think of the arithmetic mean as a balancing point for the individual observations, such that the individual observations X deviate from the mean $\overline{X}$ in a balanced fashion, namely:

(4.7a) $$\Sigma(X - \overline{X}) = 0$$

Another important property of the arithmetic mean is obtained by rearranging (4.6). We obtain:

(4.7b) $$\Sigma X = n\overline{X}$$

In other words, *the sum of the values of the items is equal to the mean multiplied by the number of items.* In our simple illustration, we have: $3 \cdot 24 = 72$, which is the total time required for the three work cycles in the sample.

Grouped data

When an average or a standard deviation is to be computed from internal company data, the values of the original items are usually available so that the procedures for ungrouped data can be followed, often by means of machine tabulation. Sometimes, however, the frequency distribution is used to speed calculations, or may be the only data available. In such cases, special problems arise.

Table 4.1 presents a frequency distribution of annual salaries of 20 employees in a sample. If the actual salaries of the 20 employees were known, there would be no problem in computing the average salary. Since this information is not available from a frequency distribution, we shall have to resort to an assumption in order to approximate the average that we would have obtained had the original data been available.

Table 4.1 Calculation of Arithmetic Average From Frequency Distribution

Annual Salary (Dollars)	*Number of Employees* f	*Class Midpoint* X	*Total Earnings* fX
2,000–under 4,000	7	3,000	21,000
4,000–under 6,000	11	5,000	55,000
6,000–under 10,000	2	8,000	16,000
Total	20		92,000

$$\text{Mean Earnings} = \frac{\$92{,}000}{20} = \$4{,}600$$

The basic approach is the same as that for ungrouped data. The mean salary is the sum of the salaries divided by the number of persons. In order to obtain the sum of the salaries, we work class by class. *For each class we assume that the midpoint of the class is approximately equal to the mean of the items included in that class.* This assumption leads in many cases to a reasonable approximation of the figure that would have been obtained for the average had the original data been available.

Given the assumption that each class midpoint is approximately equal to the mean of the items in that class, we utilize the property of an arithmetic mean reflected in (4.7b) to obtain an estimate of the total salaries earned by persons included in each class. Thus, if the mean salary of the 7 persons in the first class is $3,000 by our assumption, their total earnings are $21,000. Similarly, total earnings for the 11 persons in the second class would be estimated as $55,000, and finally, the total earnings of the 2 persons in the last class would be about $16,000. Now we can obtain the total earnings of all 20 employees by summing these class totals. Total earnings are $92,000, which are then divided by 20 in order to obtain the mean salary of $4,600.

The calculation of the mean of a frequency distribution may be represented symbolically as:

(4.8) $$\overline{X} = \frac{\Sigma fX}{n}$$

Here X represents a class midpoint, f the frequency in that class, Σ states that the products of midpoints times respective class frequencies for all classes should be summed, and n refers to the total number of items—that is, $\Sigma f = n$.

Note that the unequal class widths of the frequency distribution in our example did not affect the computation. If the distribution had been an open-end one, however, it would have been impossible to calculate the arithmetic average without additional information; there would have been no midpoint for the open-end class that could have been used as an approximation to the average of the values of the items in that class.

While the above discussion brings out the conceptual aspects of the calculations most clearly, it will often be useful to employ shortcut calculational methods in order to simplify the computational work. One such shortcut method is discussed in the next chapter.

Weighted arithmetic mean

At times, we need an arithmetic average in cases where the items to be averaged require different weights. For instance, if a student receives grades of 84 and 91 on tests during the semester and 87 on the final examination, which is to count twice as much as each of the other tests, his average grade would be 87.25, as follows:

Grade	*Weight*	*Product*
84	1	84
91	1	91
87	2	174
	4	4/349 = 87.25

In a weighted average, the items to be averaged are multiplied by their respective weights, the products are summed and then divided by the sum of the weights.

Weighted averages are required for averaging ratios and are also important in the construction of index numbers. These topics will be discussed in Chapters 25 and 28 respectively.

Weighted averages are used as well in averaging arithmetic means. For instance, if the mean time lost last year for the first shift in a plant was 7.4 days per employee, while for the second shift it was 5.7 days, the average number of days of lost time per employee for both shifts combined must be obtained by weighting each average. Specifically, the mean number of employees on each shift could be used as weights. Only if the number of employees on each shift was the same would a simple average of the two averages yield the correct result, as given by the weighted average.

4.3 CALCULATION OF MEDIAN AND PERCENTILES

Median

Ungrouped data. Recall from definition (4.2) that the *median* of a group of items is the value of the middle item when all items are arranged in either ascending or descending order of magnitude. If last month's sales of five salesmen were \$40,000, \$35,000, \$50,000, \$37,000, and \$29,000, respectively, we would arrange the sales in order of magnitude, say:

\$29,000
35,000
37,000
40,000
50,000

and then determine the value of the middle item. In this example, the median sales per salesman were \$37,000.

If there had been an even number of salesmen, say, six, with sales of:

\$29,000
35,000
37,000
40,000
42,000
50,000

the median amount of sales per salesman would usually be taken as the arithmetic average of the middle two items when all are arranged according to magnitude. In this instance, it would be the average of \$37,000 and \$40,000, so that the median sales per salesman would have been \$38,500.

In general, to find the median for ungrouped data, remember that the middle item in any set of ungrouped data arranged according to magnitude is the $(n + 1)/2$ item, where n equals the number of items. The median then is the value of the $(n + 1)/2$ item.

Grouped data. When data are presented in a frequency distribution, the median is still the value of the middle item when all items are arranged in order of magnitude. Since the values of the individual items are not known when data are presented only in the form of a frequency distribution, an assumption is made in order to approximate the figure that would have been obtained for the median if the original data had been available. *The assumption made is that the items in the median class—the class in which the middle item is located—are spread evenly throughout that class.* In many instances, this assumption leads to a quite accurate approximation.

Thus, the first step is to determine the class containing the middle item. In order to find this median class, we cumulate the frequencies; this is done in Table 4.2, which presents the same distribution of salaries used for calculating the arithmetic mean. A total of 20 frequencies exists. We want to find the salary of the middle person, so we must locate the 10th, (20/2), item in the distribution. Note that we use $n/2$ to locate the middle of the distribution rather than $(n + 1)/2$ as we did for locating the middle item for ungrouped data. Under the assumption for calculating the median stated earlier, the middle of the distribution as obtained by $n/2$ corresponds to the middle item as obtained by $(n + 1)/2$.

Table 4.2 Calculation of Median From Frequency Distribution

Annual Salary (Dollars)	*Number of Employees*	*Cumulated Number of Employees*
2,000–under 4,000	7	7
4,000–under 6,000	11	18
6,000–under 10,000	2	20
Total	20	

$$\text{Median} = L + \frac{n_1}{n_2}(i)$$

$$\text{Median Salary} = \$4{,}000 + \frac{3}{11}(\$2{,}000) = \$4{,}545$$

since:

$$\text{Middle Item} = \frac{20}{2} = 10$$

$$n_1 = 10 - 7 = 3$$

$$n_2 = 11$$

$$i = \$6{,}000 - \$4{,}000 = \$2{,}000$$

From the cumulated frequencies in Table 4.2, it is evident that the 10th item falls in the class \$4,000–under \$6,000. Hence, the median salary must be somewhere within that class. Seven items preceded the median class. Consequently, we must continue by going into the median class for 3 more items in order to find the middle, or 10th, item. Since we assume that the items in the median class are spread evenly, and since there are 11 items in the median class, the 10th item in the distribution must be $\frac{3}{11}$ of the way from \$4,000 to \$6,000. Hence, the value of the middle item must be: $\$4{,}000 + \frac{3}{11}(\$6{,}000 - \$4{,}000) = \$4{,}545$. We would say, then, that the median salary for the 20 employees is \$4,545.

The calculation of the median of a frequency distribution may be expressed symbolically as:

(4.9) $$\text{Median} = L + \frac{n_1}{n_2}(i)$$

Here L is the lower limit of the median class; n_1 is the number of frequencies that must be covered in the median class in order to reach the middle item; n_2 is the number of frequencies in the median class; and i is the width of the median class.

Note that the unequal class intervals in this example did not affect the computation of the median. Also note that the median could be calculated even if either of the end classes had been open-ended. In contrast, we would not be able to calculate a mean from an open-end distribution unless we had additional information. Only if the median class itself were the open-end class could we not interpolate for the median, because we would not know the range of the frequencies in the class.

Percentiles

Interpretation of median as percentile. The median may be thought of as the 50th percentile. *The 50th percentile is that value such that the values of half of the items are less than it.* Frequently, the interpretation of the median as the 50th percentile is only approximately correct. For instance, the median salary of the five salesmen discussed earlier was such that two of the salesmen (40 per cent, not 50 per cent) had lower salaries, and two had higher salaries. Of course, the larger the number of items in the group for which the median is being computed, the less the usual interpretation of the median is affected. Hence, we shall say that the median is such a value that *about* 50 per cent of the items have smaller values than it and *about* 50 per cent of the items have higher values than it.

A more extreme situation exists, however. Here, the median cannot even be interpreted as the value such that about 50 per cent of the items have smaller values, even if the number of items in the group is large. Consider the following distribution:

Size of Family	*Number of Families*
2	32,800
3	21,900
4	20,700
5	12,400
6 or more	12,200
Total	100,000

The median family size is three. Yet 32.8 per cent, not 50 per cent, of the families were smaller than the median family size of three. This substantial difference from 50 per cent arises here because the number of different possible values (number of members in family) is very small and each value has a substantial frequency. When we consider an income distribution, on the other hand, in which income may range anywhere from zero to millions of dollars, it is most unlikely that we would obtain a median value for which the usual interpretation is grossly inapplicable.

Quartiles. The 25th percentile is called the first quartile. Subject to the qualifications discussed in connection with the interpretation of the median, we may say that about one-fourth of the items in the group of items have a value smaller than the first quartile. The same method of interpolation is used to find the first quartile as was used to find the median.

Thus, to calculate the value of the first quartile of the salary distribution in Table 4.2, we first determine the item located one-fourth into the array when all items are arranged in order of ascending magnitude. For the distribution in Table 4.2, this is the 5th, ($\frac{1}{4} \cdot 20$), item. The 5th item is located in the class $2,000–under $4,000. Hence, the first quartile or 25th percentile must be somewhere within that class. Again, we assume that the items in the class of interest are spread evenly. There are 7 items in the class, so that the 5th item should be located $\frac{5}{7}$ of the way from $2,000 to $4,000. In other words, the value of the 5th item is $\$2{,}000 + \frac{5}{7}(\$4{,}000 - \$2{,}000) = \$3{,}429$. The first quartile, then, is $3,429, which means that about one-fourth of the employees earned less than that amount.

The 75th percentile is called the third quartile. The reader should test himself by finding the third quartile of the frequency distribution in Table 4.2. It is $5,455. Since about 75 per cent of the employees earned less than $5,455, and since it was estimated previously that about 25 per cent of the employees earned less than $3,429, about half of the employees must have had annual salaries between $3,429 and $5,455. *The range between the first and third quartiles is called the interquartile range and contains about the middle 50 per cent of the frequency distribution.*

Other percentiles. The value of any other percentile may be obtained by the same method used for the median and quartiles. Limitations on the interpretation of these percentiles are the same as for the median and quartiles.

4.4 CALCULATION OF STANDARD DEVIATION

Ungrouped data

Earlier discussion within this chapter explained that the standard deviation is a measure of the extent of variation in a group of items. Suppose that we wish to measure, by means of the standard deviation, the variation in the daily output of a certain item in a plant. The production in a sample of four recent days is shown in Table 4.3. In the calculation of the standard deviation, we use the arithmetic average as the benchmark from which variation is measured. Thus, the first step is to determine the mean output, which is 75 units. Now, we calculate how much each of the daily outputs differed from this average output. This calculation is shown in Table 4.3. For instance, the output of day 1 differed by 0 units from the average output, the output of day 2 was 4 units less than the average output, and so on. As was pointed out earlier, the sum of these deviations must be zero.

Table 4.3 Calculation of Standard Deviation — Ungrouped Data

Daily Output X	*Deviation From Mean* $X - \bar{X}$	*Deviation Squared* $(X - \bar{X})^2$
75 units	$75 - 75 = 0$	0
71 units	$71 - 75 = -4$	16
78 units	$78 - 75 = 3$	9
76 units	$76 - 75 = 1$	1
	Total 0	26

$$s_X^2 = \frac{26}{3} = 8.67$$

$$s_X = \sqrt{8.67} = 2.94 \text{ units of output}$$

In calculating the standard deviation, we shall use the squared deviations, rather than the deviations themselves, as a measure of variability; squaring, of course, eliminates the minus signs. We thus obtain four squared deviations in Table 4.3, which measure how far each of the daily outputs was from the mean output for the four-day period. It seems reasonable, then, to use the average of the squared deviations in constructing an overall measure of variability among the items. For reasons to be explained later, we shall divide by $n - 1$ rather than by n for obtaining the average.

The sum of the squared deviations in our example is 26, which is divided by $n - 1$, or 3. Hence, the average squared deviation is 8.67 (approximately, because we divided by 3, not 4). This average is in units of output squared. To return to our original units, we extract the positive square root, which is 2.94 units of output. This square root of the average of the squared deviations is called the standard deviation. Thus:

(4.10) The ***standard deviation***, s_X, is defined as:

$$s_X = \sqrt{\frac{\Sigma(X - \bar{X})^2}{n - 1}}$$

The subscript X to the standard deviation s is used to remind us that we are measuring the extent of variation in X. In our illustration, X represented daily output.

Formula (4.10) indicates the intuitive reasons why the standard deviation is defined as it is in order to measure the extent of variation in a group of items. For purposes of calculation, however, (4.10) is frequently awkward, especially if $\overline{X}$ is not some nice round number like 75 in our illustration. For this reason it will be advantageous to use an alternative formula:

$$s_X = \sqrt{\frac{\Sigma X^2 - \frac{(\Sigma X)^2}{n}}{n-1}} \tag{4.11}$$

This is algebraically identical to (4.10). Table 4.4 shows the calculation of the standard deviation by this alternative formula for the same example discussed before. The result is exactly the same, as it must be except for rounding. Frequently, the easiest method of obtaining the X^2 terms is by use of a table of squares, such as Table A-10 in the appendix.

Table 4.4 Calculation of Standard Deviation for Ungrouped Data — Alternative Method

Units of Daily Output X	X^2
75	5,625
71	5,041
78	6,084
76	5,776
$\Sigma X = 300$	$\Sigma X^2 = 22{,}526$

$$s_X = \sqrt{\frac{\Sigma X^2 - \frac{(\Sigma X)^2}{n}}{n-1}} = \sqrt{\frac{22{,}526 - \frac{(300)^2}{4}}{3}} = \sqrt{8.67} = 2.94 \text{ units of output}$$

At times the square of the standard deviation is used as a measure of variability.

(4.12) The square of the standard deviation, s_X^2, is called the ***variance.***

In our earlier example, the variance was 8.67. The larger the variability among the items, the larger is the standard deviation s_X and consequently the larger also is the variance s_X^2.

Grouped data

When data are presented in the form of a frequency distribution so that the values of the individual items are not known, an assumption is made in order to calculate the standard deviation. *The assumption that is made is that all items in a class have a value equal to the midpoint of that class.* Thus, in calculating the standard deviation of the frequency distribution in Table 4.2, we would assume that all employees included in the first class earned \$3,000 each, those in the second class earned \$5,000 each, and so on. This assumption may appear somewhat crude, but in many instances it yields a result quite close to the standard deviation that would have been obtained if the original data had been available.

Once this assumption is made, there are really no new problems in calculating the standard deviation of a frequency distribution. Since the deviations from the mean for all employees in any one class are the same, so are the squared deviations. Hence, we need to determine the squared deviation for an entire class only once and then multiply it by the number of employees in that class to get the sum of the squared deviations for that class. Table 4.5 presents the calculation of the standard deviation of the distribution of salaries for the 20 employees, using this procedure. Note, incidentally, that the deviation column in Table 4.5 will not total to zero. If each deviation is weighted by the class frequency, however, the weighted deviations around the mean do balance out.

Table 4.5 Calculation of Standard Deviation — Grouped Data

Annual Salary (Dollars)	*Number of Employees* f	*Class Midpoint* X	*Deviation* $X - \overline{X}$	*Deviation Squared* $(X - \overline{X})^2$	*Class Total of Squared Deviations* $f(X - \overline{X})^2$
2,000–under 4,000	7	3,000	−1,600	2,560,000	17,920,000
4,000–under 6,000	11	5,000	400	160,000	1,760,000
6,000–under 10,000	2	8,000	3,400	11,560,000	23,120,000
Total	20				42,800,000

$\overline{X} = \$4{,}600$ (from Table 4.1)

$$s_X = \sqrt{\frac{\Sigma f(X - \overline{X})^2}{n - 1}} = \sqrt{\frac{42{,}800{,}000}{19}} = \$1{,}501$$

The calculation of the standard deviation of a frequency distribution may be expressed symbolically as:

$$s_X = \sqrt{\frac{\Sigma f(X - \overline{X})^2}{n - 1}} \tag{4.13}$$

Here f is the frequency in the class; X is the midpoint of the class; $\overline{X}$ is the arithmetic average of the distribution; and $n = \Sigma f$ is the number of items in the distribution.

Just as an arithmetic average usually cannot be computed from an open-end frequency distribution, so the standard deviation cannot be computed in that case since the arithmetic average is required in order to calculate the standard deviation. Also like the arithmetic average, the calculation of a standard deviation is not affected by unequal class intervals in a frequency distribution. In fact, the example cited contained unequal class intervals.

Formula (4.13) makes clear how the calculation of the standard deviation of a frequency distribution corresponds to the calculation of a standard deviation for ungrouped data. Frequently, however, (4.13) would be more laborious to use than some algebraically identical shortcut formulas. One such shortcut formula is discussed in the next chapter.

4.5 COEFFICIENT OF VARIATION

The standard deviation is a measure of the *absolute variability* in a frequency distribution. For a number of problems, however, the *relative variability* in a frequency distribution is a more significant measure. The most commonly used measure of relative variability is the coefficient of variation.

(4.14) The ***coefficient of variation,*** denoted by $C.V.(X)$, is the ratio of the standard deviation to the mean expressed as a per cent:

$$C.V.(X) = \frac{s_X}{\overline{\overline{X}}} \cdot 100$$

For the frequency distribution in Table 4.5 the coefficient of variation is:

$$C.V.(X) = \frac{\$1{,}501}{\$4{,}600} \cdot 100 = 32.6 \text{ per cent}$$

The coefficient of variation is frequently used in sample survey work. Suppose one wants to estimate the mean income of spending units on the basis of a sample survey and requires that the estimate should be within 5 per cent of the true mean income. Then one would use the coefficient of variation of spending unit income, because the required accuracy is stated in relative terms.

Another use of the coefficient of variation is in comparing the relative variability in two distributions that are not expressed in the same units. For instance, one may study whether the distribution of income is more variable than the distribution of intelligence test scores for the same group of persons. One could not compare the standard deviations in this case, as one standard deviation would be expressed in dollars while the other would be expressed in points. The coefficients of variation, on the other hand, are not expressed in any units because the units are canceled out when one divides the standard deviation by the arithmetic mean. This permits a comparison of the relative variability between the two distributions.

The coefficient of variation can also be used to compare the relative variability in several distributions expressed in the same units—for example, to study the relative variability in the prices of two stocks, one of which is low-priced and the other high-priced.

4.6 PEARSON'S COEFFICIENT OF SKEWNESS

Pearson's coefficient of skewness is defined as:

$$\text{Skewness} = \frac{3(\overline{X} - \text{Median})}{s_X} \tag{4.15}$$

Note that the coefficient expresses the difference between the mean and median relative to the standard deviation of the frequency distribution. If the distribution is symmetrical, the mean and median will be identical and the coefficient will be zero. If the distribution is skewed to the left, as in Figure 4.5b, the mean will be less than the median and the coefficient will be negative. If the distribution is skewed to the right, as in Figure 4.5c, the mean will be greater than the median and the coefficient will be positive.

Refer again to the frequency distribution of Table 4.5. We know already that $\overline{X} = \$4{,}600$, Median $= \$4{,}545$, and $s_X = \$1{,}501$. Hence, the coefficient of skewness for this distribution is:

$$\text{Skewness} = \frac{3(\$4{,}600 - \$4{,}545)}{\$1{,}501} = +.11$$

QUESTIONS AND PROBLEMS

4.1. Briefly explain each of the following:

- **a.** Measure of location
- **b.** Skewness
- **c.** Median
- **d.** Coefficient of variation
- **e.** Mode
- **f.** Variance
- **g.** Interquartile range

4.2. An arithmetic average may not be a meaningful measure of location. Why not? When is the arithmetic average a meaningful measure of central tendency?

4.3. What types of information are provided by the frequency distribution that are not given by an average?

4.4. In a unimodal frequency distribution skewed moderately to the right, why is the arithmetic mean greater than the median? Why is the median greater than the mode? Explain carefully.

4.5. Give three examples of business and economic data in which you would expect the frequency distribution to be skewed, and state which type of skewness you would expect to be present.

4.6. **a.** Describe two administrative problems in which knowledge of the average of a frequency distribution is insufficient and in which additional information about the frequency distribution is required. Be explicit.

b. Describe an administrative problem in which knowledge of the average of a frequency distribution is sufficient and additional information about the frequency distribution is not essential. Be explicit.

4.7. In each of the following cases, explain whether the description applies to the mean, median, or both:

a. Can be calculated from frequency distribution with open-end intervals.

b. Can be calculated from frequency distribution with unequal class intervals.

c. The values of all items are taken into consideration in the calculation.

d. The values of extreme items do not influence the average.

e. In a distribution with a single peak and moderate skewness to the right, it is closer to the concentration of the distribution.

4.8. a. It has been reported that the average urban dweller spends the equivalent of three working weeks per year commuting between his home and place of employment. This finding also could have been stated as follows: The average amount of time urban dwellers spend commuting between their homes and places of employment is the equivalent of three working weeks per year.

Which of these two statements is preferable, and why, if the average used is (1) A mean? (2) A median? (3) A mode?

b. It has been reported that the average family owns 1.10 automobiles. What type of average must have been used? Would some other type of average have been more meaningful here? Discuss.

c. The modal number of children in families in the U.S. in March 1969 was zero. Can we conclude from this that most families had no children?

***4.9.** Refer to Problem 3.10 (p. 65). Use the 24 observations in the first three columns only.

a. Calculate the mean lifetime of lamps in the sample.

b. Calculate the median lifetime of lamps in the sample.

c. What does a comparison of the mean and median suggest about the symmetry of the distribution of lifetimes of lamps? Explain.

d. Can the median lifetime be interpreted here to indicate that one-half of the lamps in the sample lasted less than this number of hours? Explain.

e. Would you expect another sample of lamps from the same process to have the same mean as this one? Why, or why not?

***4.10.** Refer to Problem 3.10. Use the 24 observations in the first three columns only.

a. Calculate the range of the lifetimes of lamps in the sample.

b. Calculate the standard deviation of the lifetimes of lamps in the sample. In what units is the standard deviation expressed?

c. Since both the range and the standard deviation are measures of dispersion, should the standard deviation be approximately equal to the range? Why, or why not?

d. If the sample were enlarged to include three times as many lamps, would the range likely be smaller or larger than the one in part **a**? Would the standard deviation likely be smaller or larger than the one in part **b**? Explain.

e. Calculate the coefficient of variation of the lifetimes of lamps in the sample. In what units is the coefficient of variation expressed?

f. If the process became more variable, though still centered at about the same level as before, what effect would this have on the coefficient of variation?

4.11. Refer to Problem 10.19. Freight bills 250 to 264 inclusive were issued on November 16, 1971.

a. Calculate the mean amount of the freight charges in the freight bills issued on November 16.

(Continued)

b. Calculate the median amount of the freight charges in the freight bills issued on November 16.

c. Can the median amount be interpreted to indicate that half of the freight bills issued on November 16 were for less than this amount? Explain.

d. Would it be reasonable to use the modal amount of the freight charges on November 16 as an average of the charges for that day? Explain.

4.12. Refer to Problem 10.19. Freight bills 150 to 164 inclusive were issued on November 9, 1971. The mean and median of the freight charges in these freight bills are \$2.50 and \$1.72 respectively.

a. From which of these two averages can the total amount of freight charges on November 9 be obtained? Explain how this is done, and calculate the total amount of the freight charges from the relevant average.

b. If you were to calculate the mean or median amount of the freight bills for subsequent days, would you expect to obtain the same amounts as for November 9? Why, or why not?

c. What factors could account for changes in the average amount of the freight bills over a period of several years? Explain.

d. For freight bills 150 to 164 inclusive, calculate the deviation of each amount of freight charge from the mean, and sum these deviations. What do you find?

e. What property of the arithmetic average is illustrated by your finding in part **d**? Use this property to explain the meaning of an arithmetic average.

f. Calculate the deviation of each amount of freight charge from the median, and sum these deviations. What do you find?

4.13. Refer to Problem 10.19. Freight bills 250 to 264 inclusive were issued on November 16, 1971.

a. Calculate the range of the amounts of freight charges on November 16.

b. Does this range indicate the central tendency of the frequency distribution of the amounts of freight charges? The skewness of this distribution? Explain.

c. Are changes in the range of the amounts of the freight bills issued on each day affected more by variations in the small freight bills, in the freight bills of medium amounts, or in the large freight bills? Explain by referring to the data on the amounts of the freight bills that are presented in Problem 10.19.

4.14. Refer to Problem 10.19. Freight bills 250 to 264 inclusive were issued on November 16, 1971.

a. Calculate the standard deviation of the amounts of freight charges on November 16.

b. In what units is this standard deviation expressed?

c. If the standard deviation of the freight charges for November 17 were substantially greater than that of the freight charges for November 16, what would this indicate about the two distributions of the amounts of freight charges?

d. Calculate the coefficient of variation of the amounts of freight charges for November 16. Explain the meaning of this number.

e. What factors could bring about a change in the magnitude of this coefficient of variation? Explain.

4.15. Refer to Problem 3.13. Use the ungrouped data consisting of all 60 observations.

a. Calculate the mean number of looms working at any given time.

b. Calculate the median number of looms working at any given time. What interpretation can be given to this median?

c. What does a comparison of the mean and median suggest about the symmetry of the distribution of number of looms working at any given time?

d. If 60 additional observations had been made, would you expect their mean to be the same as the present one? Why, or why not?

4.16. Refer to Problem 3.13. Use the ungrouped data consisting of all 60 observations.

a. Calculate the range of the number of looms working at any given time in the sample of 60 observations.

b. Calculate the standard deviation of the number of looms working at any given time in the sample of 60 observations. In what units is the standard deviation expressed?

c. Do either the range or standard deviation provide any information about the central tendency of the distribution? About the skewness of the distribution? Explain.

d. Calculate the coefficient of variation of the number of looms working at any given time in the sample. In what units is the coefficient of variation expressed?

e. If we wished to compare the variability in the number of looms working at any given time in the section of 400 looms with another section that had 800 looms, would the standard deviation or the coefficient of variation be a more meaningful measure? Explain.

4.17. Refer to Problem 3.13. Use the ungrouped data.

a. To study whether the period of day has any effect on the number of looms working at any given time, calculate for each period of the day: the mean, standard deviation, and coefficient of variation for the 20 observations.

b. Write a paragraph summarizing your findings on the effect of the period of day on the number of looms working at any given time. Can you be certain of your conclusions? Why, or why not?

4.18. Robert Ferber conducted a survey ("On the Reliability of Purchase Influence Studies," *Journal of Marketing*, January 1955, pp. 225–232) to study the influence of different household members in the purchase of various types of goods and to determine how accurately such information could be obtained. For instance, the husband was asked what influence his wife plays in the purchase of a family car and to state this roughly in per cent terms. The wife was then asked independently about her evaluation of her influence in the purchase of a car. The husband might say, for example, that the wife has a 30 per cent influence, and the wife might state she has a 40 per cent influence. Ferber then averaged these two to get an approximate measure of 35 per cent as the wife's influence in the purchase of a family car. This would mean that the husband (in a husband-wife family) has the major influence in this decision.

a. Ferber found in his survey that the mean influence of wives in the purchase of cars was 31 per cent. Assuming that this study yielded valid data on relative influences, should automobile manufacturers then direct their advertising exclusively to husbands? Discuss fully.

b. The study indicated that in 30 per cent of families, the wife had the major influence in the purchase of cars (in other words, over 50 per cent influence). How can this be consistent with the earlier findings on average influence? Explain. What relevance does this finding have for automobile advertising?

c. In the purchase of radios, the mean influence of wives was found to be 44 per cent; yet in 60 per cent of families the wife's influence exceeded 50 per cent. What does this indicate about the distribution of wives' influence ratings? Would a different type of average have been more appropriate here than the mean of the ratings for all families? Discuss.

4.19. Refer to Problem 3.3, Table III. Consider the mean, median and modal number of persons per family for these data.

a. For each type of average, indicate whether it can be calculated from these data, explaining in each case why it can or cannot.

b. Suppose sufficient information were available to calculate each type of average. For each type of average, indicate whether it would necessarily be a whole number, explaining in each case why it would or would not.

***4.20.** Refer to Problem 3.3, Table III.

a. Calculate the median family size. If you had to make any assumptions in the calculation, explain them.

b. Can the median be interpreted here as indicating that half of the families had fewer persons than the median number, and half more? Explain fully.

c. Calculate the third quartile. How can it be interpreted here?

d. What is the modal number of persons per family?

4.21. The following data show the age, to the nearest birthday, of 136 boys who were recruited into a door-to-door magazine-selling campaign in a certain city:

Age, to Nearest Birthday	*Number of Boys*
15	13
16	27
17	51
18	39
19	6
	136

a. In the above distribution, what is the class specified by 19? Explain fully.

b. Will the mean age necessarily be a whole number? Explain.

c. What is the mean age of the 136 boys? State any assumptions that you had to make in your calculation.

d. Will the median age necessarily be a whole number? Explain.

e. What is the median age? State any assumptions that you had to make in your calculation.

f. How can the median age be interpreted in this case? Explain.

***4.22.** Refer to Problem 3.15.

a. Calculate the mean age of passenger cars in 1941 and also in 1968. State any assumptions you made in your calculations.

b. Did you use the per cent distributions in your calculations or the distributions of the actual number of cars? Why?

c. Are the two means in this case useful measures for comparing the locations of the two distributions? Discuss.

***4.23.** Refer to Problem 3.15.

a. Calculate the median age of passenger cars in 1941 and also in 1968. State any assumptions you made in your calculations.

b. Explain how the medians can be interpreted in this case.

c. What is the interquartile range for each of the two distributions? What information is provided by this measure about the two distributions?

d. What is the 90th percentile for each of the two distributions? Explain the meaning of this percentile.

***4.24.** Refer to Problem 3.15.

a. Can you determine whether the range in the ages of passenger cars was greater in 1941 or 1968? Explain.

b. Calculate the standard deviation for each of the two distributions. State any assumptions you made in your calculations.

c. Calculate the coefficient of variation for each of the two distributions.

d. How do the two distributions compare in absolute variability? In relative variability? Discuss.

e. Which distribution is more skewed, as measured by Pearson's coefficient of skewness?

4.25. At the end of last year, straight-time hourly earnings of two classes of production employees of a certain company were as follows:

Hourly Earnings	*Class A (Per cent)*	*Class B (Per cent)*
\$2.30–under \$2.50		9.7
\$2.50–under \$2.70		14.2
\$2.70–under \$2.90	7.7	23.7
\$2.90–under \$3.10	15.8	52.4
\$3.10–under \$3.30	43.2	
\$3.30–under \$3.50	21.8	
\$3.50–under \$3.70	10.0	
\$3.70–under \$3.90	1.0	
\$3.90–under \$4.10	.5	
All employees	100.0	100.0
Number of employees	830	2,075

a. For each class of employees, calculate the mean and median hourly earnings.

b. What assumptions did you make in each of the previous calculations? Do these seem to be reasonable here?

c. Are the two means in this case useful measures for comparing the locations of the two distributions? Discuss.

d. For each distribution, compare the mean and median. What information do you obtain about the symmetry of the two distributions? Explain.

4.26. Refer to Problem 4.25.

a. For Classes A and B, calculate the first and third quartiles of hourly earnings.

b. What is the interquartile range of hourly earnings for each of the two classes of employees? What information is provided by this measure about the two distributions?

c. How can the quartiles be interpreted in this case?

d. What is the 46th percentile for each of the two distributions? Explain the meaning of this percentile.

4.27. Refer to Problem 4.25.

a. Can you determine the exact range of the hourly earnings for each of the two distributions? Explain.

b. Can you determine which of the two distributions has the greater range? Explain.

(Continued)

c. Calculate the coefficient of variation for each of the two distributions. State any assumptions you made in your calculations.

d. Were hourly earnings of Class A or Class B employees relatively more variable? Discuss.

e. How do the two distributions compare in absolute variability? Explain.

f. Calculate Pearson's coefficient of skewness for each of the two distributions. On the basis of this measure, which distribution is more skewed? Are both distributions skewed in the same direction? Discuss.

4.28. The S. F. Eliot Company, as part of a program to improve the profitability of its operations, studied the size of orders placed by its customers. The size of the orders during the past fiscal year were:

Size of Order	*Number of Orders*
Under $10	958
$10–under $25	943
$25–under $50	1,117
$50–under $100	687
$100–under $250	254
$250–under $500	471
$500–under $1,000	630
All orders	5,060

a. Calculate the mean order size. What assumptions did you make in your calculation? Do they seem to be reasonable here? Did the unequal class intervals cause any complications in your calculations?

b. Calculate the median order size. What assumptions did you make in calculating the median order size? Do they seem to be reasonable here?

c. Are the mean and median order sizes approximately the same? Why, or why not?

d. Is the distribution of order sizes similar to one of the distributions in Figure 4.5? What problems do the unequal class intervals create in the analysis of the pattern of variation?

e. From which average—the mean or median order size—can the total sales for the year be determined? Explain.

4.29. Refer to Problem 4.28.

a. Calculate the first and third quartiles of the distribution. How can they be interpreted in this case?

b. Calculate the interquartile range. What does this range show?

c. Calculate the 19th percentile.

d. What assumptions did you make in calculating the quartiles and percentile?

4.30. Refer to Problem 4.28.

a. Calculate the total sales, and determine the amount of sales accounted for by the orders in each class.

b. Calculate the per cent distribution of sales by size of order; also calculate the per cent distribution of number of orders by size of order.

c. Analyze the per cent distributions and write a paragraph summarizing your findings.

d. The accounting department estimated that the direct cost of handling an order is about $5. Would the mean or median order size provide any indication of the proportion of orders received that are unprofitable to handle? Discuss.

e. What other types of information would be required to enable management to assess the implications of small orders?

4.31. Refer to Problem 4.28.

a. Can you determine the exact range of the order sizes from the data presented? Explain.

b. Calculate the standard deviation of the sizes of the orders. State any assumptions you made in your calculation.

c. Calculate the coefficient of variation of the distribution of orders by size of order. In what units is this coefficient expressed?

d. Does the coefficient of variation provide any information about the location of the distribution? Explain.

e. Would you expect the coefficient of variation of the size of orders for another firm with ten times the sales volume of the S. F. Eliot Company to be about the same as the one here? Explain.

f. Calculate Pearson's coefficient of skewness. What is the significance of its sign? Explain.

***4.32.** Refer to Problem 3.14.

a. Calculate the mean length of service of the employees who have ten or more years of service with the company.

b. Calculate the standard deviation for this distribution, and obtain the coefficient of variation. Would you say that this distribution is relatively variable? Discuss.

c. In what units is the standard deviation expressed? The coefficient of variation?

d. Does the coefficient of variation provide any information as to whether the mean of the distribution is a valid measure of central tendency? Discuss.

e. Calculate Pearson's coefficient of skewness for the distribution of length of service of employees with ten or more years of service. In which direction is the distribution skewed?

f. The mean length of service of the 1,550 employees with less than ten years of service is 3.75 years. Calculate the mean length of service of all the employees of the company. Explain the basis of your calculations.

4.33. Refer to Problem 3.20.

a. Calculate the mean sales per retail establishment.

b. Why were you able to obtain the mean sales, when you cannot calculate the mean number of paid employees per retail establishment from the data in Problem 3.20? Discuss.

c. What is the median number of employees per retail establishment? State any assumptions which you made in your calculation.

d. What interpretation can be assigned to the median number of employees in this case?

e. For the distribution of retail establishments by number of paid employees, calculate (1) first quartile; (2) 80th percentile.

f. How can the percentiles in part **e** be interpreted here?

g. The largest 10 per cent of retail establishments in terms of number of paid employees accounted for what proportion of all U.S. retail sales? Explain how you arrived at your answer.

***4.34.** In a survey of family health insurance, the following data on family income, health insurance coverage, and age of family head were obtained:

Family Income	*Per Cent of All Families*	*Per Cent of Families with Health Insurance*	*Mean Age of Family Head*
Under $10,000	55	22	30
$10,000–under $15,000	20	58	38
$15,000–under $25,000	13	83	51
$25,000 and over	12	91	57

a. What per cent of all families had health insurance?
b. What was the mean age in all families of the head of the family?
c. How is it possible that the mean age can be calculated in part **b**, but the mean income of all families cannot because of the open-end class?
d. How does the median income of heads of families with health insurance compare with the median income of all families? Make specific reference to the data to support your answer.

4.35. In calculating the mean and standard deviation from grouped data, certain assumptions must be made. Is the assumption for calculating the standard deviation stated in the text more or less restrictive than the one stated for calculating the mean? Explain. If the assumption for calculating the standard deviation were used for calculating the mean, would this have any effect on the value obtained for the mean? Explain.

4.36. Post Office researchers divided a number of mail sorters into two groups, such that sorters in each group were approximately comparable. Each group employed a different sorting technique. The researchers, in an effort to evaluate the effectiveness of the two techniques, studied the sorting rates of the individuals and obtained the following results:

	Technique A	*Technique B*
Mean pieces sorted per hour	1,058	1,005
Median pieces sorted per hour	998	1,113

a. Assuming that the variations found reflect differences in the effectiveness of the sorting techniques and not differences between sorters in the two groups, and assuming that the results obtained will also hold in the future, which of the two sorting techniques will lead to a larger number of sorted pieces per hour? Explain your answer fully.
b. Assuming that each of the two frequency distributions of pieces sorted per hour is moderately skewed with a single peak, what is implied by the different directions of skewness in the distributions for the two sorting techniques? Explain.

4.37. Refer to Problem 4.25. The mean hourly earnings for Class A and Class B employees are $3.23 and $2.84 respectively.
a. Using the mean hourly earnings for Class A and Class B employees, calculate the mean hourly earnings for the two classes of employees combined.
b. Did you use a weighted or unweighted arithmetic average? If you did not use weights, why not? If you did use weights, what were they and why did you use them?

4.38. A sample survey in a community disclosed that 73 per cent of all women 18 years of age or older heard a certain radio advertisement sometime during the week, while only 21 per cent of all men 18 years of age or older heard the same advertisement. Since about 53 per cent of all persons 18 years of age or older in this community are women, what per cent of all persons 18 years of age or older in the community are estimated to have heard the advertisement?

4.39. Refer to Problem 3.11. Data are presented there on the unemployment percentages in 1969 for each of the 50 states and the District of Columbia.

a. To determine the unemployment percentage for the U.S., why would a weighted average of the 51 percentages be required?

b. What would be the appropriate weights to use to obtain the unemployment percentage for the U.S.? Explain.

4.40. A market research analyst made a survey of 1,000 families and obtained, among other things, information on their incomes for 1970 and 1971. He constructed a frequency distribution of the 1971 incomes and calculated the mean, standard deviation and coefficient of variation for this distribution. He also calculated the change in income between 1970 and 1971 for each family. Then he constructed a frequency distribution of these income changes, and calculated the mean, standard deviation and coefficient of variation for this distribution of income changes.

a. Since some of the changes in family incomes were increases while others were decreases, would there be any special problems in calculating the mean and standard deviation of the distribution of income changes? Explain fully.

b. The mean of the distribution of income changes was near zero; in other words, the increases in income almost balanced the decreases in income. Can the coefficients of variation for the 1971 income distribution and for the distribution of income changes between 1970 and 1971 be compared meaningfully under these conditions to study which distribution is relatively more variable? Explain.

4.41. In one of the production departments of the Harrison Corporation, the mean daily output was 394.3 units per operator, and the standard deviation of the daily outputs per operator was 36.7 units. A training program was conducted for the less efficient operators. Subsequently, the mean daily output was 451.6 units per operator, and the standard deviation of the daily outputs per operator was reduced to 28.3 units.

a. Describe the changes in the frequency distribution of daily outputs per operator that probably took place. Explain the bases for your answers.

b. Was the frequency distribution of daily outputs per operator after the training program less variable or more variable than that of the outputs before the training program? Which measure of variability did you utilize in your answer and why did you do so?

4.42. In a community, the distribution of the population by age had a mean of 35.4 years and a standard deviation of 19.3 years, while the distribution of the families in that community according to income had a mean of $4,575 and a standard deviation of $4,139. Which of the two distributions contains greater variability? Explain the basis for your answer.

4.43. In a study of the variability of filling machines in filling containers with food products, the following results were observed:

	Net Weight	
Product	*Mean*	*Standard Deviation*
Peas	8 oz.	.13 oz.
Whole kernel corn	12 oz.	.30 oz.
Juice	6 oz.	.06 oz.
Soup	8 oz.	.11 oz.
Baby food	6 oz.	.04 oz.
Applesauce	5 oz.	.03 oz.

Source: Adapted from C. B. Way, "Fill Control in the Canning Industry," *American Society for Quality Control Convention Transactions, 1955,* p. 507.

a. In evaluating the performance of the machines, why should management be interested in both the means and standard deviations?

b. Analyze the absolute and relative variability in the net weights for the different products, and write a paragraph containing your findings and conclusions.

Chapter

5

ADDITIONAL TOPICS IN DATA HANDLING

In this chapter, three additional topics in data handling are discussed. The first two topics were mentioned in the previous chapter and relate to shortcut calculational methods in frequency distribution analysis. The last topic is the Chebyshev inequality, an extremely useful statistical tool.

5.1 CALCULATION OF MEAN FROM GROUPED DATA

The mean of a frequency distribution with equal class intervals may be readily computed from:

(5.1) $$\overline{X} = X_a + \frac{\Sigma fd}{n} i$$

Table 5.1 Calculation of Mean by Shortcut Method for Distribution of 100 Sales Invoices by Amount

Amount of Invoice (*$*)	*Number of Invoices* f	*Class Midpoint* X	*Unit Deviation From* X_a d	fd
0–under 10.00	34	5.00	−1	−34
10.00–under 20.00	45	15.00	0	0
20.00–under 30.00	17	25.00	1	17
30.00–under 40.00	4	35.00	2	8
Total	100			−9

$$\overline{X} = X_a + \frac{\Sigma fd}{n} i = 15.00 + \frac{(-9)}{100}(10) = \$14.10$$

Here X_a is the midpoint of any class, n is total frequencies, and i is the class width, and for any class, f is the class frequency and d is the unit deviation of class midpoint from X_a.

This procedure is demonstrated in Table 5.1. Note that X_a there is \$15, and that the class width is \$10. If a frequency distribution has unequal class intervals, the above approach must be modified.

5.2 CALCULATION OF STANDARD DEVIATION FROM GROUPED DATA

The standard deviation of a frequency distribution may be calculated from the following formula, if there are equal class intervals in the distribution:

$$s_X = i\sqrt{\frac{\Sigma fd^2 - \frac{(\Sigma fd)^2}{n}}{n-1}} \tag{5.2}$$

Here the notation is the same as in (5.1). This procedure is illustrated in Table 5.2 for the same frequency distribution as used in Table 5.1. If the frequency distribution has unequal class intervals, the above approach must be modified.

Table 5.2 Calculation of Standard Deviation by Shortcut Method for Distribution of 100 Sales Invoices by Amount

Amount of Invoice (\$)	*Number of Invoices* f	*Class Midpoint* X	*Unit Deviation From* X_a d	fd	fd^2
0–under 10.00	34	5.00	−1	−34	34
10.00–under 20.00	45	15.00	0	0	0
20.00–under 30.00	17	25.00	1	17	17
30.00–under 40.00	4	35.00	2	8	16
Total	100			−9	67

$$s_X = i\sqrt{\frac{\Sigma fd^2 - \frac{(\Sigma fd)^2}{n}}{n-1}} = 10\sqrt{\frac{67 - \frac{(-9)^2}{100}}{99}} = \$8.18$$

5.3 CHEBYSHEV INEQUALITY

The standard deviation was described in Chapter 4 as a measure of variation of a frequency distribution. One of its uses is with the Chebyshev inequality.

(5.3) The ***Chebyshev inequality*** states that, in any frequency distribution, no matter what the nature of the pattern of variation, the proportion of items falling beyond k standard deviations from the mean is at most $1/k^2$.

To illustrate the use of the Chebyshev inequality, consider the distribution of annual salaries in a small firm. Suppose we know that the mean salary is \$4,600 and that the standard deviation of salaries is \$1,500. Then, the Chebyshev inequality tells us, for instance, that the proportion of employees whose earnings fall below $\$4{,}600 - 2(\$1{,}500) = \$1{,}600$ or above $\$4{,}600 + 2(\$1{,}500) = \$7{,}600$ is at most 1/4, since in this case $k = 2$.

As another example, consider the case of a drug company that found that the mean thickness of tablets in a sample was .243 inches and the standard deviation was .001 inches. Then we would know at once from the Chebyshev inequality that the proportion of tablets in the sample whose thicknesses fell outside the range, say, .240 to .246 inches (here $k = 3$) could not exceed 1/9.

QUESTIONS AND PROBLEMS

***5.1.** Refer to Problem 3.15.

a. Calculate the mean and standard deviation of the age distribution of passenger cars in 1941 using the shortcut calculational methods described in this chapter.

b. Did you use the per cent distribution in your calculations or the distribution of the actual number of cars? Would the shortcut calculational methods yield the same results for both of these distributions? Explain.

5.2. Refer to Problem 4.25.

a. Calculate the mean and standard deviation of the hourly earnings distribution of Class A employees using the shortcut calculational methods described in this chapter.

b. Could the shortcut calculational methods be used if the class intervals of the hourly earnings distribution were unequal? Explain.

***5.3.** Refer to Problem 3.10 and consider the 24 observations in the first three rows. The mean and standard deviation of these observations are 1,153 and 176 hours respectively.

a. From the Chebyshev inequality, what is the maximum proportion of lamps in the sample with lifetimes beyond ± 2.5 standard deviations from the mean?

b. What fraction of the 24 lamps in the sample actually fell outside these limits? Does the Chebyshev inequality provide a close estimate of the actual fraction in this case? Is this result surprising?

5.4. The number of admissions to the emergency ward of a hospital between 6 and 8 P.M. during a period of 50 consecutive days is as follows:

3	0	4	0	1	4	1	0	3	5
1	2	3	2	2	1	1	3	5	2
2	1	2	4	1	0	3	2	1	2
2	3	5	2	2	2	4	4	2	3
4	5	2	3	0	6	2	3	3	2

a. The mean and standard deviation of these 50 observations are 2.4 and 1.5 admissions respectively. From the Chebyshev inequality, what is the minimum proportion of the 50 observations that are within ± 3 standard deviations from the mean?

b. What fraction of the 50 observations actually fall within these limits?

c. Is the validity of the proportion obtained in part **a** affected by the fact that the data are whole numbers in this case? Explain.

5.5. An inspector reported to his supervisor that in a sample of 50 meat packages, the mean weight per package was 16.80 ounces and the standard deviation was .27 ounces. When asked about the fraction in the sample weighing between 16.30 and 17.30 ounces, the inspector was unable to answer since the original data had been discarded. Can you help the inspector by providing a lower limit for the desired proportion?

5.6. A market researcher for a large resort found in a report by a competing resort that the mean income of its clientele is $20,000 and that the standard deviation of these incomes is $4,000. The market researcher was anxious to learn the proportion of the competitor's clientele with incomes between $10,000 and $30,000, but this information was not provided.

a. Find a lower limit for the desired proportion.

b. Is this lower limit valid even if the income distribution is highly skewed? Discuss.

c. Is the validity of the limit affected by the magnitude of the competitor's clientele? Discuss.

Unit

II

PROBABILITY

Chapter

6

PROBABILITY AND RANDOM VARIABLES

It was shown in Chapters 3 and 4 that variation is present in many phenomena and that this variation follows some kind of pattern. For instance, we noted the pattern of variation in weekly accident rates for the Exeter Corporation, and the pattern of variation in the thickness of drug tablets.

Problems arising from variation face administrators and economic analysts continually. In handling such problems, a statistical point of view, or method of approach, has been found to be extremely useful. This approach is built upon the concept of probability. To understand the statistical point of view, we therefore must examine probability and some of its implications.

6.1 FINITE AND INFINITE POPULATIONS

Finite populations

The aggregate or totality of items under consideration in connection with a specific problem is called the population under study. For example, the Exeter Corporation undertook to study employee attitudes toward the company in 1970 after a new president was elected by the board of directors. The 10,000 employees of the Exeter Corporation constituted the population for this particular study. As another example, consider the study of 1971 sales invoices by a department store to determine the proportion of sales accounted for by its branch store in a suburban shopping center. In this case, the totality of 1971 sales invoices constituted the population.

Note from the above examples that the population under study is intimately related to a specific problem. Also note that each of the populations mentioned above is of a definite, limited size.

(6.1) A population that is of limited size is called a ***finite population.***

We study a finite population because we are interested in one or more characteristics of the elements of the population. The characteristic may be a qualitative variable, such as whether the sales invoice represents a sale at the main store or at a branch store, or whether an employee works in production, office, or sales; or the characteristic of interest may be a quantitative variable, such as the amount of a sales invoice or the age of an employee.

Characteristics of finite populations

If one is interested in a quantitative characteristic of the elements in a finite population, one can utilize measures such as the mean and standard deviation to describe properties of this population. For one part of the study of employee attitudes toward the Exeter Corporation, the ages of the employees were an important characteristic. There is a mean associated with the population of 10,000 employee ages. It is called the population mean.

(6.2) The ***population mean*** is defined as:

$$\mu_X = \frac{\Sigma X}{N}$$

Here the symbol μ_X (Greek mu with subscript X) denotes the population mean, and N is the population size. Similarly, there is a standard deviation of the 10,000 employee ages, which is called the population standard deviation.

(6.3) The ***population standard deviation*** is defined as:

$$\sigma_X = \sqrt{\frac{\Sigma(X - \mu_X)^2}{N}}$$

Here the symbol σ_X (Greek sigma with subscript X) denotes the population standard deviation. The subscript X in μ_X and σ_X reminds us that the mean and standard deviation pertain to the variable X (age, in our example).

We use Greek symbols to refer to the population mean and standard deviation to distinguish these from the mean and standard deviation calculated from a sample. In Chapter 4, the symbols $\overline{X}$ and s_X were used for the sample mean and standard deviation, respectively. These refer to instances in which the mean and standard deviation are calculated from sample data, such as from the sample data of the 200 drug tablets selected from the production process. Thus, μ_X and σ_X are the "*true*" or population values, and $\overline{X}$ and s_X, based upon a sample from the population, are the *sample mean* and *sample standard deviation*, respectively.

This leads us to the distinction between parameters and statistics:

(6.4) Characteristics of the population, such as μ_X and σ_X, are called ***parameters.***

(6.5) Sample characteristics, such as $\overline{X}$ and s_X, are called ***statistics.***

Note the complete correspondence between the definition of the population mean in (6.2) and the sample mean in (4.6) on p. 79. The definition of the population standard deviation in (6.3) corresponds almost exactly to the definition of the sample standard deviation in (4.10) on p. 86. The only difference is that the population standard deviation has *N,* the population size, in the denominator, while the sample standard deviation is defined with $n - 1$, the sample size minus 1, in the denominator.

In working with populations classified by qualitative characteristics, the concepts of population mean and population standard deviation are not directly applicable.

Illustration of an infinite population

While many problems, as we have seen, involve finite populations, there are many other problems in which an infinite population is the population of relevance.

(6.6) An ***infinite population*** is one that is indefinitely large.

As in the case of finite populations, we may be interested either in a quantitative or a qualitative characteristic of the elements in an infinite population. To study the types of problems that involve infinite populations, we use an example involving a quantitative characteristic. Once more, we refer to the production process that turns out drug tablets. After the battery of machines had been adjusted and synchronized, 200 tablets were selected from the production stream. These tablets had been produced under a constant cause system, because the causal factors that affect the thickness of the tablets—such as the machine setting—had remained about the same during the production run. Despite this fact, the 200 tablets showed variation in their thickness, as illustrated in Figure 3.2 (p. 51).

This figure, to be sure, merely indicates the pattern of variation of these particular 200 tablets. Our real interest is in the *process* turning out the tablets. We might, therefore, reasonably ask: If the production process continued to operate under the same causal conditions, what would be the pattern of variation of 1,000 or 1,000,000 tablets? In fact, the statistical approach to the study of a process leads us to ask what would be the pattern of variation in the thickness of tablets if the production process continued to operate *indefinitely* under the given causal conditions—that is, if the process produced an indefinitely large number of tablets, all manufactured under the same operating conditions. We shall call the group of tablets that could be produced by the manufacturing process operating indefinitely under essentially constant conditions the *infinite population,* and the 200 tablets that were actually produced by the process under these operating conditions a *sample* from this infinite population.

6.2 PROBABILITY DISTRIBUTIONS

Infinite populations as probability distributions

In the example cited above, the infinite population consists of the indefinitely large number of tablets produced under the given operating conditions. The relative frequency distribution of the thicknesses of these tablets might look something like the one in Figure 6.1 or it might be substantially different. Note that the distribution in Figure 6.1 is similar to a frequency polygon that has been smoothed out.

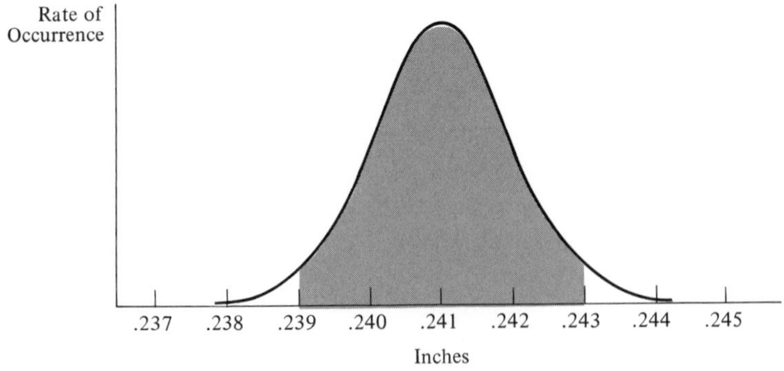

Figure 6.1. Probability distribution of thicknesses of drug tablets

The relative frequency distribution of the thicknesses of the indefinitely large number of tablets produced under the same operating conditions is considered to be a probability distribution. A probability distribution may be unimodal, as the one in Figure 6.1, or may have more than one mode. It may be symmetrical or skewed; it may have much variability or little. Any given state of the operating conditions pertaining to the manufacture of the drug tablets has associated with it a probability distribution of the thickness of tablets. If there is a change in the process, such as the introduction of a new type of machine, a new probability distribution is associated with the modified process. The tablets produced by the new type of machine are then considered a sample from the population of all tablets that would be produced by the process operating under the new conditions if it continued to operate indefinitely.

Main classes of probability distributions

Probability distributions may be classified according to whether they pertain to quantitative characteristics (for instance, length of life of a radio tube) or qualitative characteristics (for instance, sex of employee).

Quantitative characteristics. There are two main classes of probability distributions involving quantitative characteristics—continuous and discrete distributions.

(6.7) A ***continuous probability distribution*** is one where any value in an interval can occur.

For instance, the probability distribution illustrated in Figure 6.1 is continuous, since the thickness of a tablet might be any value on the scale. In contrast:

(6.8) A ***discrete probability distribution*** is one where only separated values on a scale can occur.

Consider a production process wherein four automobile tires are molded at one time. Suppose that we are concerned with the quantitative characteristic—number of defective tires in a batch. The probability distribution corresponding to this process might look something like the one in Figure 6.2. Note that the only possible outcomes are 0, 1, 2, 3, and 4 defective tires in a batch. Hence, the probability distribution is drawn as a series of separate bars to indicate that only particular values on the scale can occur and that intervening values (e.g., 1/3 defective tire) cannot occur.

Qualitative characteristics. Probability distributions involving qualitative characteristics are frequently encountered. For instance, in the manufacture of cabinets for high-fidelity sound equipment, one of the characteristics of interest might be whether or not the surface of a cabinet is scratched. Here, the probability distribution might contain three outcomes: not scratched, minor scratches, major scratches.

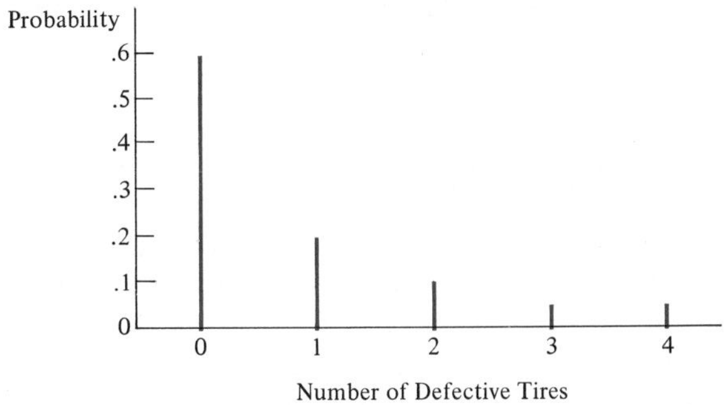

Figure 6.2. Illustration of a discrete probability distribution

Characteristics of probability distributions

For probability distributions of either continuous or discrete type, one can define a mean μ_X and a standard deviation σ_X. These are defined analogously to the corresponding measures for finite populations and have the same meaning. For instance, we can tell by inspection that the mean of the probability distribution in Figure 6.1 is .241 inches, because the distribution is symmetrical around that point. Similarly, the mean number of defective tires for the probability distribution in Figure 6.2 turns out to be .75 tires. Later in this chapter, we shall illustrate how the mean and standard deviation are obtained for probability distributions of the discrete type. In Chapter 8, we shall illustrate the calculation of these measures for probability distributions of the continuous type.

Interpretation of probability distributions

The meaning of a probability distribution can best be explained with reference to an example. Consider the discrete probability distribution in Figure 6.2 first. Here, the height of a bar indicates the probability of the particular number of defective tires in a batch. For instance, the probability of one defective tire in a batch is .2. Note that the sum of the heights of the bars is 1.

In a continuous probability distribution, such as the one in Figure 6.1, the height of the curve refers to *rate of occurrence,* not probability. For such distributions, the area under the probability distribution plays the same role as does the height of bars in a discrete probability distribution. The total area under any continuous probability distribution is, by definition, equal to 1. Further, referring specifically to Figure 6.1, the area under the probability distribution between any two values of thickness denotes the probability that a tablet will have a thickness between these two values. For instance, the probability that a tablet will have a thickness of more than .241 inches is .5 because half of the area of this symmetrical distribution lies to the right of .241 inches. As another example, the shaded area in Figure 6.1 denotes the probability that a tablet will have a thickness between .239 and .243 inches. Thus, *area under a continuous probability distribution corresponds to probability.*

Finite populations interpreted as probability distributions

Finite populations may also be interpreted as probability distributions. To see how, consider Table 6.1, which presents the population of the 10,000 employees of the Exeter Corporation in 1970, classified by age. For simplicity, Table 6.1 does not contain the individual ages of all 10,000 employees, but merely the distribution of employees' ages by convenient age groups. Table 6.1 also presents the age distribution expressed in terms of relative frequencies. This latter distribution is of interest to us now, because it may be interpreted as a probability distribution.

Table 6.1 Age of Employees of Exeter Corporation

Age (Years)	*Number of Employees*	*Relative Frequency*
Under 34	3,000	.30
34–54	6,000	.60
55 or more	1,000	.10
Total	10,000	1.00

Suppose that one employee was to be selected at random from the 10,000 employees. *By a random selection of one element from a finite population, we mean a selection procedure is used that gives each element in the population an equal chance to be selected.* Practical procedures whereby this can be accomplished will be discussed in Chapter 9. For the time being, assume that such a procedure is available. Then, any relative frequency in Table 6.1 indicates the probability that an employee selected at random will come from the corresponding age class, and the entire relative frequency distribution corresponds to a probability distribution. As does any such probability distribution, the relative frequency distribution indicates all the possible outcomes, together with the probabilities of each of these possible outcomes. We would say, for instance, that the probability is .3 that an employee selected at random is under 34 years of age.

When a finite population for which a quantitative characteristic is of interest is interpreted as a probability distribution, it is always of the discrete type. This follows, since only a limited number of values can occur. For instance, if a lot of 5,000 drug tablets is the population of interest, only 5,000 different thicknesses are possible. Frequently, however, very large finite populations are treated for convenience as if they were infinite populations.

6.3 MEANING OF PROBABILITY

In the preceding section, we employed the word *probability* in explaining a probability distribution. What is the meaning of this word? It is used often in our daily life, doubtless by many who are not quite clear as to its meaning. Indeed, the word *probability* has been defined in different ways and thus has been given various meanings.

The problem concerning the meaning of probability is not mainly at the mathematical level. Mathematicians have developed a formal structure whereby certain properties of probability are defined, and from which numerous important consequences then flow. This formal structure, however, is abstract, and one still needs to know how to interpret probability as it applies to the real world. It is largely in this area of interpreting how the mathematical probability model applies to the everyday world that differences in point of view exist. We present below an interpretation of probability that is widely used by statisticians and that is easy to convey.

Common interpretation of probability: objective probability

Consider the following probability statement with reference to an infinite population: The probability is .5 that the thickness of a tablet is more than .241 inches. We interpret this probability statement to mean that in a long production run, the proportion of tablets whose thickness is more than .241 inches will approach one-half, as more and more tablets are produced under the same conditions. Thus, *we interpret probability as relative frequency in the long run under a constant cause system.*

If the probability that an event will happen is extremely small, we interpret this to mean that the event will rarely, if ever, happen. For instance, in Figure 6.1 there is a very small area under the probability distribution to the left of .238 inches. It is so small, however, that the graph doesn't even show it. This means that a tablet with a thickness of less than .238 inches will rarely, if ever, be turned out by the given manufacturing process.

If an event cannot happen at all, we say that the probability of its occurrence is 0. If an event is certain to happen, we say that the probability of its occurrence is 1. Thus, probability is a number somewhere between 0 and 1.

Our interpretation of probability with reference to a finite population corresponds to that for an infinite population. Consider the statement based on Table 6.1 that the probability is .3 that an Exeter Corporation employee selected at random is under 34 years of age. We interpret this to mean that in a long sequence of random selections of one employee from the population, the proportion of employees selected who are under 34 years of age will approach .3 as more and more trials are made. Thus, probability is here interpreted as *relative frequency in a long series of trials.* Note how the series of random selections from the *same* finite population, to which we referred in the interpretation of probability, corresponds to a process operating under a constant cause system.

The interpretation of probability in terms of relative frequency in the long run is sometimes called *objective probability.* It is intimately related to repeatable events, such as the manufacture of a drug tablet, the testing of the effect of temperature on an alloy, or a series of random selections from the same finite population. According to this interpretation of probability, it does not make sense to talk about the probability of a unique event. For instance, from this point of view one would not talk about the probability that John Jones, aged 40, will die during the next year; he either will or won't. If he survives the year, his age will be 41; if he dies during the year, he is "out of circulation." In either case, John Jones' 41st year is not a repeatable event. But it does make sense, according to this interpretation of probability, to say that a male of age 40 has a probability of .002 of dying during the next year. This is interpreted to mean that among a large number of males of age 40, about two per thousand will die during the next year. It is not known, though, which specific men will die. Thus, probability is interpreted here with reference to a large number of events, not to specific ones.

Personal probability

A different interpretation of probability relates probability to *degree of belief*. This approach is called *personal probability* or *subjective probability*. It is not restricted to repeatable events but applies also to unique events. Thus, under this approach one would be willing to consider the probability that John Jones, aged 40, will die this year, or the probability that John Jones answered the questions in his application for life insurance truthfully. For these events, probability cannot be interpreted as relative frequency in the long run, since these events are unique.

Personal probability is intimately related to the person making the probability evaluation. Thus, two insurance examiners who have identical information about John Jones might still arrive at different personal probabilities that John Jones will die during his 41st year. Indeed, each insurance examiner might revise his probability assessment upon more reflection or with additional information. Even with reference to a repeatable event, such as the manufacture of drug tablets, two individuals might assess the probabilities differently, depending on the information each has, how this information is evaluated, hunches, and so on. On the other hand, the objective probability school of thought would hold here that the probabilities are determined by the conditions of the production process and do not depend on the amount of information available or on other such considerations.

As can be seen from this discussion, the personal probability school of thought applies probability concepts to a much wider class of phenomena than the objective probability school. The personal probability school will consider the probability that Congress will pass a tax reduction bill next year, the probability that the Acme Department Store will be purchased by a large chain of department stores during the coming year, and the probability that sales of a new soap product about to be launched in the market will exceed one million cases during the first budget period.

In later chapters, we shall discuss how personal probability can be used in statistical decision-making. In the main, however, we shall follow the common interpretation of probability as relative frequency in the long run.

6.4 BASIC PROBABILITY CONCEPTS

Now that we have discussed what is meant by probability and probability distributions on an intuitive level, we shall examine these concepts more formally.

Sample space

(6.9) Any process that leads to results for which probability concepts are applicable is called a ***random experiment.***

Thus, the selection of one employee at random from the population of 10,000 Exeter Corporation employees is a random experiment. So is the manufacture of four tires in a batch or the testing of a water sample for purity.

In any random experiment, one may be interested in a number of possible results. For instance, in the experiment of selecting one Exeter Corporation employee at random, one might be concerned with the employee's sex, age, I.Q., earnings, or number of dependents. The purpose of the experiment usually dictates the characteristic or characteristics of interest.

(6.10) The different possible results of interest in an experiment constitute the ***basic outcomes.***

For instance, suppose the random experiment consists of selecting an employee from a population of employees, and the characteristic of interest is the sex of the employee. There would then be two basic outcomes: male, female.

(6.11) The set of all possible basic outcomes in the experiment constitutes the ***sample space*** of the experiment.

Thus, Table 6.2a shows the sample space for the experiment in which concern is with the employee's sex. If, on the other hand, we are interested in the employee's age by broad categories, the sample space might consist of the basic outcomes shown in Table 6.2b.

If the random experiment is the production of tires in batches of four and the characteristic of interest is the number of defective tires, the sample space would consist of the basic outcomes shown in Table 6.2c.

Note that *the basic outcomes in a sample space do not overlap;* in other words, they are mutually exclusive. Also, *the outcomes in a sample space*

Table 6.2 Illustrations of Sample Spaces

		Univariate			
(a)		**(b)**		**(c)**	
O_1	Male	O_1	Under 34 years	O_1	No defective tire
O_2	Female	O_2	34–54 years	O_2	1 defective tire
		O_3	55 years or more	O_3	2 defective tires
				O_4	3 defective tires
				O_5	4 defective tires
		Bivariate			
		(d)			
O_1	Male and under 34 years			O_4	Female and under 34 years
O_2	Male and 34–54 years			O_5	Female and 34–54 years
O_3	Male and 55 years or more			O_6	Female and 55 years or more

include every possibility. Thus, the result of a random experiment is characterized by one and only one of the basic outcomes in the sample space.

There is no unique sample space associated with a random experiment. As we pointed out, there may be many possible characteristics that could be of interest. Even given one characteristic, such as age of the selected employee, we might be interested in age to the nearest year, or in age by ten-year age brackets, or in age by very broad age brackets. The purpose of the experiment will determine how the sample space is to be defined.

Univariate and bivariate sample spaces

In each of the sample spaces discussed in the previous section, only one characteristic was of interest, such as the sex of the employee, or the age of the employee, or the number of defective tires in a batch.

(6.12) A sample space in which the basic outcomes refer to a single characteristic is called a ***univariate sample space.***

Often, two or more characteristics are of interest.

(6.13) A sample space in which the basic outcomes refer to two characteristics is called a ***bivariate sample space.***

For instance, in the random experiment of selecting an Exeter Corporation employee, both his age and sex may be of interest. In this case, the sample space might consist of the six basic outcomes shown in Table 6.2d. Note that each of the six basic outcomes now refers to both sex and age, that they are mutually exclusive, and that they account for all possibilities.

At times, more than two characteristics are of interest.

(6.13a) A sample space in which the basic outcomes refer to more than two characteristics is called a ***multivariate sample space.***

Probability postulates

We shall denote the basic outcomes of a random experiment by O_1, O_2, . . . , O_k. Further, we shall write the probability associated with the basic outcome O_i as $P(O_i)$. We read $P(O_i)$ as the probability that O_i will be the outcome of the experiment. Thus, with reference to the experiment in Table 6.2b, $P(O_1)$ represents the probability that the selected employee is under 34 years old.

Mathematicians have developed three postulates on which probability theory is based. We shall discuss each of these in turn.

(6.14) ***Postulate 1.*** Each probability $P(O_i)$ must satisfy the relation:

$$0 \leq P(O_i) \leq 1$$

Here the symbol $\leq$ signifies "less than or equal to." In other words, the probability of a basic outcome cannot be less than 0 nor greater than 1. Table 6.3 contains the probability distribution of Exeter employees' ages that was discussed earlier. Here, the probability of the basic outcome "under 34 years" is .30, which falls between 0 and 1. The same is true of the probabilities of the other basic outcomes.

Table 6.3 Univariate Probability Distribution

Basic Outcome		*Probability*
O_1 Under 34 years		.30
O_2 34–54 years		.60
O_3 55 years or more		.10
	Total	1.00

Source of data: Table 6.1.

(6.15) ***Postulate 2.*** Given that there are k basic outcomes, the probabilities $P(O_i)$ must satisfy:

$$P(O_1) + P(O_2) + \cdots + P(O_k) = 1$$

Thus, the probabilities of all basic outcomes must add to 1. This is obviously satisfied in the illustration of Table 6.3.

(6.16) ***Postulate 3.*** For any two basic outcomes O_i and O_j in the sample space, it is defined that:

$$P(O_i \text{ or } O_j) = P(O_i) + P(O_j)$$

Here $P(O_i \text{ or } O_j)$ denotes the probability that either O_i or O_j will be the outcome.

To illustrate this postulate with reference to the sample space of Table 6.3, it is defined that:

$$P(O_1 \text{ or } O_2) = .30 + .60 = .90$$

Thus, the probability that an employee selected at random is either under 34 years old or between 34 and 54 years is .90 by definition.

Events

After a random experiment and the basic outcomes constituting the sample space have been defined, it often happens that interest will center on outcomes that are broader than the basic outcomes of the sample space. We therefore define the term event as follows:

(6.17) An ***event*** consists of one or more basic outcomes of the sample space.

We shall utilize the symbol E to denote an event.

To illustrate this concept, consider the sample space of Table 6.2c. The event E might be "two or fewer defective tires in the batch." Thus, E would consist of the basic outcomes O_1, O_2, O_3. On the other hand, E might simply be "no defective tire in the batch." In that case, E would consist only of the basic outcome O_1.

Probability of an event. From the probability postulates stated earlier, it follows that:

(6.18) The ***probability of an event*** E is the sum of the probabilities of the basic outcomes constituting E.

To illustrate this, let E be the event "age of employee is 34 years or more," with reference to the sample space in Table 6.3. Thus, the event E consists of the basic outcomes O_2 and O_3, and we have:

$$P(E) = P(O_2) + P(O_3) = .60 + .10 = .70$$

Mutually exclusive events.

(6.19) Two events are ***mutually exclusive*** if they do not contain common basic outcomes.

With reference to the sample space in Table 6.2d, let E_1 be the event "male and under 55 years" and E_2 be the event "female and 55 years or more." Thus, E_1 consists of basic outcomes O_1 and O_2, while E_2 consists of basic outcome O_6. Since E_1 and E_2 do not contain any common basic outcomes, we call them mutually exclusive events. In the next section, we shall present an important probability theorem for mutually exclusive events.

Figure 6.3 provides a symbolic illustration of two mutually exclusive events. Note that there is no overlap between the two mutually exclusive events, since they have no basic outcomes in common.

Complementary events.

(6.20) The ***complementary event*** "not-E" to the event E consists of all the basic outcomes in the sample space that are not contained in E.

For instance, let the event E be "two or fewer defective tires in a batch," with reference to the sample space in Table 6.2c. Then, the complementary

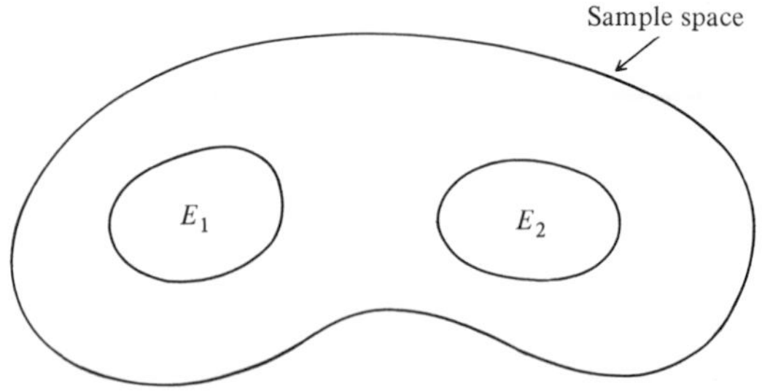

Figure 6.3. Symbolic representation of mutually exclusive events

event "not-E" consists of the basic outcomes O_4 and O_5. In other words, "not-E" is the event "more than two defective tires in a batch."

From the probability postulates given, it follows that:

(6.21) $$P(\text{not-}E) = 1 - P(E)$$

Thus, if the probability of two or fewer defective tires in a batch is .9, it follows at once that the probability of more than two defective tires is .1.

A complementary event is illustrated symbolically in Figure 6.4, where the complementary event to event E is shaded and labeled "not-E." Note that the shaded area is the entire sample space excluding event E.

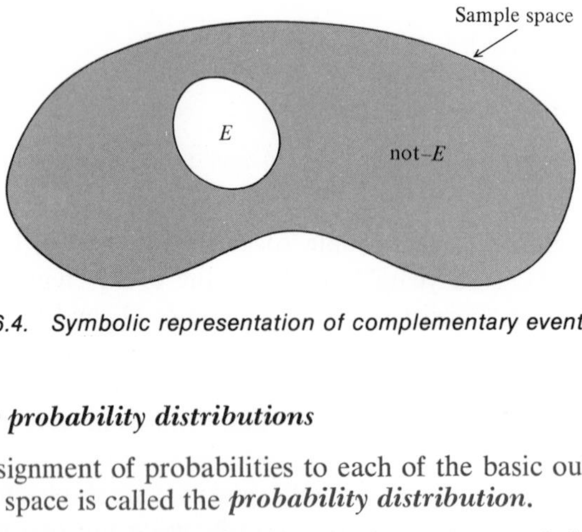

Figure 6.4. Symbolic representation of complementary event

Univariate probability distributions

(6.22) The assignment of probabilities to each of the basic outcomes in the sample space is called the ***probability distribution.***

Thus, Table 6.3 indicates the three basic outcomes of the sample space, together with the corresponding probabilities. The probability distribution in Table 6.3 is called a *univariate probability distribution* because it is based on a univariate sample space.

Bivariate probability distributions

When a probability distribution is based on a bivariate sample space, it is called a *bivariate probability distribution.* This type of distribution will be illustrated with reference to the finite population in Table 6.4, consisting of the 10,000 Exeter employees classified according to both age and sex.

Table 6.4 Age and Sex of Employees of Exeter Corporation

Age	*Sex* Male B_1	Female B_2	*Total*
A_1 Under 34 years	2,100	900	3,000
A_2 34–54 years	4,200	1,800	6,000
A_3 55 years or more	700	300	1,000
Total	7,000	3,000	10,000

The sample space for this experiment has been shown in Table 6.2d. Here, however, we shall adopt a new notation. A_1, A_2, and A_3 denote the three age classes, and B_1 and B_2 the two sex classes. Thus, the fundamental outcomes O_i of Table 6.2d are represented in the new notation as follows:

Old	*New*
O_1	A_1 and B_1
O_2	A_2 and B_1
etc.	etc.

The new notation indicates more clearly that the fundamental outcomes are *joint outcomes* involving both sex and age.

The probability of a joint outcome is called a *joint probability,* because a specification on two characteristics has been made. We shall write the joint probability that an employee selected at random comes from both classes A_1 and B_1 as $P(A_1 \text{ and } B_1)$. Thus $P(A_1 \text{ and } B_1)$ is the probability of randomly selecting a male worker under 34 years old, and this probability is $2{,}100/10{,}000 = .21$. Similarly, all the other joint probabilities can be obtained, and these are shown in Table 6.5.

Table 6.5 Bivariate Probability Distribution

Age	*Sex* Male B_1	Female B_2	*Total*
A_1 Under 34 years	.21	.09	.30
A_2 34–54 years	.42	.18	.60
A_3 55 years or more	.07	.03	.10
Total	.70	.30	1.00

Source of data: Table 6.4.

The probability distribution in Table 6.5 is bivariate, indicating the probability of each possible age-sex outcome. Again note that the basic age-sex outcomes are mutually exclusive and that the sum of the probabilities is 1.

Marginal probabilities and marginal probability distributions

Often when the sample space is bivariate, interest also exists in each of the two characteristics by itself. Each characteristic can be studied separately by summing over the other characteristic. If we sum over either one of the classifications in Table 6.5, we obtain *marginal probabilities* and a *marginal probability distribution.* For instance, the marginal probability that an employee selected at random is 55 years old or older is denoted by $P(A_3)$ and is $.07 + .03 = .10$. Of course, $P(A_3)$ could also have been obtained directly from Table 6.4 by taking $(700 + 300)/10{,}000$. The marginal probability distribution of sex of employees is:

Sex	*Probability*	
Male	$.21 + .42 + .07 =$	.7
Female	$.09 + .18 + .03 =$	.3
	Total	1.0

Note that the marginal probabilities are given in the total column and the total row ("margins" of the table) in Table 6.5, and have been boxed in for emphasis. Thus, the term *marginal* here means that one or more methods of classification have been summed over or ignored.

Note also that the marginal probability distribution of age in Table 6.5 is identical to the univariate probability distribution of age in Table 6.3. Whether this probability distribution of age is regarded as a marginal one or as an ordinary univariate distribution depends upon our original interest —in other words, whether we started from a bivariate or univariate sample space.

Conditional probabilities and conditional probability distributions

Frequently, one needs a probability of the type: Given that the person selected is a male, what is the probability that the person is under 34 years old? Such a probability is called a *conditional probability.* Note from Table 6.4 that the probability in question refers to the subpopulation of 7,000 males. It is natural to define this conditional probability as:

$$P(A_1|B_1) = \frac{2{,}100}{7{,}000} = .30$$

where $P(A_1|B_1)$ is read as: probability of person selected belonging to A_1, given that he belongs to B_1. Note that $P(A_1|B_1)$ can be expressed in the following form:

$$P(A_1|B_1) = \frac{2{,}100}{7{,}000} = \frac{2{,}100}{10{,}000} \div \frac{7{,}000}{10{,}000} = \frac{P(A_1 \text{ and } B_1)}{P(B_1)}$$

In general:

(6.23) If we have any events E_1 and E_2 based on a sample space, the ***conditional probability*** of E_1, given E_2, is defined as:

$$P(E_1|E_2) = \frac{P(E_1 \text{ and } E_2)}{P(E_2)}$$

where it is assumed that $P(E_2)$ does not equal 0.

To illustrate this with one more example, for the bivariate probability distribution in Table 6.5 we have:

$$P(B_2|A_1) = \frac{.09}{.30} = .30$$

A complete conditional probability distribution can be obtained by finding all the relevant conditional probabilities. For instance, the conditional probability distribution of age for male employees is:

Age	*Conditional Probability*
Under 34 years	$\frac{.21}{.70} = .3$
34–54 years	$\frac{.42}{.70} = .6$
55 years or more	$\frac{.07}{.70} = .1$
Total	1.0

Note that this conditional probability distribution has the attributes of any ordinary probability distribution—namely, it involves probabilities between 0 and 1 and the probabilities total to 1. Also note that this conditional distribution could have been obtained directly from Table 6.4 by applying the definition of a random selection of an employee to the subpopulation of male employees.

Other conditional probability distributions (for instance, sex distribution for given age) can be obtained from the bivariate probability distribution in Table 6.5 in the same manner as discussed.

6.5 BASIC PROBABILITY THEOREMS

Addition theorem

General case. Suppose that with reference to the sample space in Table 6.5 we wish to know the probability that a person selected at random is *either* under 34 years old *or* male. The "or" is interpreted inclusively—

that is, it includes the case of a person who is both under 34 and male. We write the desired probability symbolically as $P(A_1 \text{ or } B_1)$.

The addition theorem, which is an immediate consequence of the probability postulates, is applicable to this case. It states that for any two events E_1 and E_2 defined on a sample space:

$$P(E_1 \text{ or } E_2) = P(E_1) + P(E_2) - P(E_1 \text{ and } E_2) \tag{6.24}$$

For our example, we would have:

$$P(A_1 \text{ or } B_1) = P(A_1) + P(B_1) - P(A_1 \text{ and } B_1) = .3 + .7 - .21 = .79$$

Actually, this probability could have been obtained directly from Table 6.4. Persons who are either under 34 years old or male constitute $(2{,}100 + 4{,}200 + 700 + 900)/10{,}000 = .79$ of the total population. Note that by adding $P(A_1)$ and $P(B_1)$, we are counting persons who are *both* male *and* under 34 twice; hence they are subtracted once in (6.24).

Figure 6.5 gives a symbolic representation of the addition theorem. Figure 6.5a shows the event "E_1 or E_2," for which the probability is desired, as the shaded part of the sample space. The double-counting illustrated by the earlier example is associated with the event "E_1 and E_2," which is shown in Figure 6.5b as the cross-hatched area. This area represents the basic outcomes which are added twice when $P(E_1)$ and $P(E_2)$ are added. Hence,

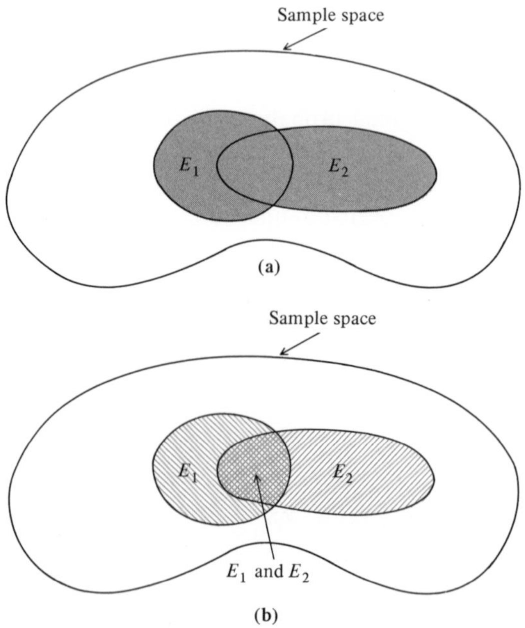

Figure 6.5. Symbolic representation of addition theorem: $P(E_1 \text{ or } E_2) = P(E_1) + P(E_2) - P(E_1 \text{ and } E_2)$

the probability of the basic outcomes common to the two events E_1 and E_2, $P(E_1 \text{ and } E_2)$, must be subtracted once to obtain the required probability, $P(E_1 \text{ or } E_2)$.

Mutually exclusive events. Suppose we were to apply the addition theorem to find the probability $P(A_1 \text{ or } A_2)$ with reference to the sample space in Table 6.5. We would have:

$$P(A_1 \text{ or } A_2) = P(A_1) + P(A_2) - P(A_1 \text{ and } A_2) = .3 + .6 - 0 = .9$$

Note that a person cannot be both under 34 years old and between 34 and 54 years old. Hence $P(A_1 \text{ and } A_2) = 0$.

Thus, if events E_1 and E_2 are mutually exclusive, $P(E_1 \text{ and } E_2) = 0$, and the addition theorem simplifies to:

(6.24a) $$P(E_1 \text{ or } E_2) = P(E_1) + P(E_2)$$

The addition theorem for mutually exclusive events is illustrated in Figure 6.6. The event "E_1 or E_2" is represented by the shaded area in the sample space. Since there is no overlap between the mutually exclusive events E_1 and E_2, no problem of double-counting arises here.

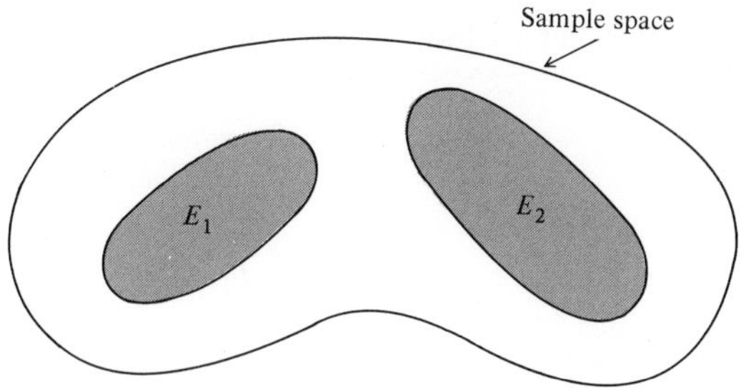

Figure 6.6. Symbolic representation of addition theorem for mutually exclusive events: $P(E_1 \text{ or } E_2) = P(E_1) + P(E_2)$

Multiplication theorem

General case. The joint probability of any two events E_1 and E_2 occurring together can be found from the multiplication theorem:

(6.25) $$P(E_1 \text{ and } E_2) = P(E_1)P(E_2|E_1) = P(E_2)P(E_1|E_2)$$

This theorem is an immediate consequence of the definition of conditional probability in (6.23).

Suppose we wish to find $P(A_1 \text{ and } B_1)$ with reference to the sample space in Table 6.5. We have from the multiplication theorem:

$$P(A_1 \text{ and } B_1) = P(A_1)P(B_1|A_1) = (.3)(.7) = .21$$

where $P(B_1|A_1)$ is the conditional probability that the person selected belongs to B_1, given that he belongs to A_1.

The joint probability $P(A_1 \text{ and } B_1)$ could have been obtained directly from Table 6.5, of course, but the multiplication theorem enables us to obtain it merely from knowledge of marginal and conditional probabilities.

The usefulness of the multiplication theorem in this regard can be illustrated by considering the following problem. A manufacturer receives shipments of parts, which he screens before letting them enter his production process. Let:

E_1 = Part is defective
E_2 = Inspector classifies part as acceptable

From past experience, the manufacturer knows that the probability that a part is defective is $P(E_1) = .05$. He also knows that the probability of a defective part being missed in the receiving inspection is $P(E_2|E_1) = .10$. Note that the latter is a conditional probability, since it is contingent upon the part being defective. The manufacturer wishes to know the probability that a part is defective and will be missed in the receiving inspection. Thus, he wishes to find $P(E_1 \text{ and } E_2)$. From the multiplication theorem, we have:

$$P(E_1 \text{ and } E_2) = P(E_1)P(E_2|E_1) = (.05)(.10) = .005$$

Independence. The probability distribution in Table 6.5 is of a special type. To see this, let us look at the conditional probabilities of age, given sex:

Age		*Conditional Probability of Age, Given:* Male B_1	Female B_2	*Marginal Probability of Age*
A_1	Under 34 years	.30	.30	.30
A_2	34–54 years	.60	.60	.60
A_3	55 years or more	.10	.10	.10
	Total	1.00	1.00	1.00

Note that for both sexes, the conditional probabilities of any age class are the same. Thus, it does not matter whether the person selected is male or female; the probability of this person coming from any specific age class is the same and is equal to the marginal probability. The same result would be found if we looked at the conditional probabilities of sex, given the age of the person selected. We therefore intuitively feel that age and sex in this population are independent.

To study some of the implications of independence more thoroughly, consider any joint probability in Table 6.5. Since, for instance, we have $P(A_1|B_1) = P(A_1)$, it follows from the multiplication theorem that:

$$P(A_1 \text{ and } B_1) = P(B_1)P(A_1|B_1) = P(B_1)P(A_1)$$

Thus, independence implies that the joint probability of A_1 and B_1 is simply the product of the two marginal probabilities.

Independent events. It is therefore natural to define that:

(6.26) Two events E_1 and E_2 are statistically independent if:

$$P(E_1 \text{ and } E_2) = P(E_1)P(E_2)$$

Statistical independence of E_1 and E_2 implies, by reversing the previous argument, that $P(E_2|E_1) = P(E_2)$ and $P(E_1|E_2) = P(E_1)$. In fact, we could define statistical independence in this latter fashion also.

Thus, we can see that with reference to the sample space in Table 6.5, A_2 and B_2 are independent events, since:

$$P(A_2 \text{ and } B_2) = .18$$

and

$$P(A_2)P(B_2) = (.60)(.30) = .18$$

As another illustration, suppose that two switches operate independently in the statistical sense. Let E_1 be the event "switch 1 working," and let E_2 be defined correspondingly for switch 2. If the probability of each switch working is .9, the probability of both switches working together is:

$$P(E_1 \text{ and } E_2) = P(E_1)P(E_2) = (.9)(.9) = .81$$

It also follows that the probability of neither switch working is:

$$P(\text{not-}E_1 \text{ and not-}E_2) = P(\text{not-}E_1)P(\text{not-}E_2) = (.1)(.1) = .01$$

Independent variables. As is evident from Table 6.5, age and sex are independent in that population, since the conditional age distribution for males is the same as the conditional age distribution for females, and both conditional age distributions equal the marginal age distribution. This implies that the joint probability of any two events A_i and B_j is equal to the product of the respective marginal probabilities, so that these are all statistically independent according to the definition in (6.26).

We therefore define that:

(6.27) Two variables (age and sex in our example) are statistically independent if for all joint probabilities $P(A_i \text{ and } B_j)$:

$$P(A_i \text{ and } B_j) = P(A_i)P(B_j)$$

Note that *all* joint probabilities must equal the product of their corresponding marginal probabilities for the two variables to be statistically independent.

In many populations, statistical independence is not present. For instance, Table 6.6 indicates that in the Exeter Corporation, sex and type of work are not statistically independent. This can be seen quickly, since the joint probability of a person being, say, male and working in production is .6, while the product of the probability of a male worker (.7) and the probability of a production worker (.75) is .525. This means that the conditional probability of a production worker for males (.86) is not the same as the conditional probability of a production worker for females (.5), so that sex does affect the conditional probability that the person selected is a production worker.

Table 6.6 Sex and Type of Work of Exeter Corporation Employees

	Type of Work			
Sex	*Production*	*Office*	*Sales*	*Total*
Male	6,000	700	300	7,000
Female	1,500	1,300	200	3,000
Total	7,500	2,000	500	10,000

6.6 RANDOM VARIABLES

Definition

To illustrate the concept of a random variable, consider a plant that has three loading docks. Trucks arrive at 7 A.M. and unload for several hours. Table 6.7a presents the probability distribution of the number of docks occupied in the morning. Note that the probability distribution involves a quantitative characteristic and that it is discrete because only four different outcomes are possible, namely 0, 1, 2, and 3 docks occupied. If x represents the number of docks occupied, x is a variable, since the actual outcome may be one of a number of values (0, 1, 2, 3 here). It is not a usual type of variable, however, since the values it assumes are associated with probabilities. We shall call x a random variable. Roughly speaking:

(6.28) A ***random variable*** is a variable whose value is determined by a random experiment.

Other illustrations of random variables are x—the number of defective tires in a batch, and x—the time required to perform a work operation.

In our example, the random variable x can assume the possible values $X = 0, 1, 2, 3$. Note that we use small x to denote the random variable, and capital X to represent the actual outcome or value. Later, when there is little danger of confusion, we shall not make this distinction in notation.

Functions of random variable

Often, we shall be interested in a function of a random variable. Suppose 2 persons are required at each dock for unloading. If y is the number of persons required for unloading in the morning, we have $y = 2x$. The probability distribution for y is shown in Table 6.7b. Note the correspondence in probabilities for x and y, since, say, 0 persons are required only if 0 trucks arrive.

Table 6.7 Probability Distributions for Random Variable and Two Functions of It

(a) Random Variable x		(b) $y = 2x$		(c) $z = 3 - x$	
Number of Occupied Docks X	*Probability*	*Number of Persons Required* Y	*Probability*	*Number of Empty Docks* Z	*Probability*
0	.1	0	.1	0	.2
1	.4	2	.4	1	.3
2	.3	4	.3	2	.4
3	.2	6	.2	3	.1
	1.0		1.0		1.0

If z is the number of empty docks, we have $z = 3 - x$. The probability distribution of z is shown in Table 6.7c. Note the correspondence of probabilities in this case. If one dock is used, for instance, then two are empty.

Expectation of random variable

Consider again the probability distribution in Table 6.7a. Suppose we are asked what is the mean number of occupied docks for this probability distribution. Intuitively, one would proceed by arguing that 0 occupied docks occur 10 per cent of the time, 1 occupied dock occurs 40 per cent of the time, and so on. Hence, a weighted average of the possible X values (0, 1, 2, 3), with the probabilities used as the weights, should provide the mean number of occupied docks. This is exactly how the mean of a probability distribution is defined.

We denote the mean of the probability distribution of x by $E(x)$, which is read "expected value of x." If $P(X)$ indicates the probability that a particular value X will occur, we define $E(x)$ as follows:

(6.29) $$E(x) = \Sigma XP(X)$$

Thus for the probability distribution in Table 6.7a, we have:

$$E(x) = (0)(.1) + (1)(.4) + (2)(.3) + (3)(.2) = 1.6$$

The expected value of x therefore is 1.6 docks.

Note that $E(x)$ simply stands for the mean of the probability distribution of x and that this mean is nothing but a weighted average of the possible outcomes with the probabilities used as weights. Since the sum of the weights is 1, division by the sum of the weights is not shown explicitly in (6.29).

We interpret $E(x)$, with reference to our example, as follows: Over a long run of operations of this unloading process, the mean number of docks occupied is 1.6. Thus, we interpret the expected value of x as the average value that the random variable x will assume in a long series of trials.

The mean of a probability distribution is also denoted by μ_X, which corresponds to our notation for the mean of a finite population. In fact, it is easy to see that the definition of a finite population mean in (6.2), p. 108, is a special case of the definition of a mean of a probability distribution in (6.29). If each of the N population values has equal probability of being selected, namely $(1/N)$, then (6.29) at once reduces to (6.2).

As another illustration, suppose that a person is selling subscriptions to two magazines in a house-to-house sales campaign. On a subscription to magazine A, he makes a profit of \$.60; on a subscription to magazine B, he makes a profit of \$.50. Further, suppose that the probability of selling a subscription to magazine A is .2, that of selling a subscription to magazine B is .1, and that of not selling any subscription (making a profit of \$0) is .7. Note that the probability of selling to the same customer more than one subscription of a magazine or subscriptions to both magazines is zero. The random variable x is the gain per call and takes on the possible values $X = \$0$, \$.50, and \$.60. By definition, the expected gain per call is:

$$E(x) = (\$.60)(.2) + (\$.50)(.1) + (\$0)(.7) = \$.17$$

Thus, $E(x)$ here is the weighted average of the three different profit possibilities, with the probabilities of these profit possibilities serving as weights. The expected gain is interpreted as the average profit per call in the long run. Over a long period of time about 20 per cent of the calls will lead to a profit of \$.60, about 10 per cent of the calls to a profit of \$.50, and about 70 per cent of the calls to a profit of \$0.

Consider one more illustration. A company has a \$100,000 executive airplane. The probability of loss by accident (which is assumed to be a complete loss) during the year is .001. Let x be the loss during the year. We have the probability distribution:

X	$P(X)$
\$0	.999
\$100,000	.001

and:

$$E(x) = (\$0)(.999) + (\$100{,}000)(.001) = \$100$$

The expected loss of \$100 for the year is an important consideration, though not the only one, when the company decides whether to purchase insurance on the airplane or to self-insure.

Expectation of function of random variable

Frequently, one is interested in functions of a random variable, such as the ones illustrated in Tables 6.7b and 6.7c. In that event, one may not have to obtain first the new probability distribution in order to find the expected value of the new random variable. Two helpful theorems state:

(6.30) If $y = kx$, then $E(y) = kE(x)$

(6.31) If $z = x + c$, then $E(z) = E(x) + c$

Here k and c are constants. Pulling these two theorems together, we have:

(6.32) If $w = kx + c$, then $E(w) = kE(x) + c$

Consider $y = 2x$ in Table 6.7b. From (6.30), and knowing that $E(x) = 1.6$, we can find immediately: $E(y) = 2E(x) = (2)(1.6) = 3.2$. Thus, the mean number of persons required for unloading is 3.2. Calculation of $E(y)$ directly from the probability distribution in Table 6.7b leads, of course, to the same result.

As another illustration, consider $z = 3 - x$ in Table 6.7c. We have from (6.32): $E(z) = 3 - E(x) = 3 - 1.6 = 1.4$. In other words, the mean number of unoccupied docks is 1.4.

Variance of random variable

In Section 6.1, we discussed the population standard deviation as a measure of the variability of the elements in a finite population. The population variance, which is the square of the population standard deviation, was defined there as the mean of the squared deviations, where the deviations are taken around the population mean; see (6.3) on p. 108. Correspondingly, the variance of a probability distribution is defined as the weighted mean of the squared deviations, where the deviations are taken around the mean of the distribution, and the probabilities are used as weights.

Thus, the variance of a random variable is defined as:

(6.33) $\sigma_X^2 = \Sigma(X - \mu_X)^2 P(X)$

Since the sum of the weights is 1, no explicit divisor for the sum of the weights appears.

The standard deviation σ_X of a probability distribution is simply the square root of the variance σ_X^2. Thus, we define:

(6.34) $\sigma_X = \sqrt{\Sigma(X - \mu_X)^2 P(X)}$

Note how the definition of the standard deviation for a finite population in (6.3) follows from (6.34) when $P(X)$ is replaced by $1/N$.

To find the variance of the probability distribution in Table 6.7a, we proceed as follows:

$$\sigma_X^2 = (0 - 1.6)^2(.1) + (1 - 1.6)^2(.4) + (2 - 1.6)^2(.3) + (3 - 1.6)^2(.2) = .84$$

Consequently, the standard deviation of the probability distribution is $\sigma_X = \sqrt{.84}$, or .92 docks.

Variance of function of random variable

When one is interested in a function of a random variable, it is often possible to find the variance of the new variable without first deriving the probability distribution of this variable. Two theorems of relevance in this instance are:

(6.35) If $y = kx$, then $\sigma_Y^2 = k^2\sigma_X^2$

(6.36) If $z = x + c$, then $\sigma_Z^2 = \sigma_X^2$

The second theorem states that adding a constant to a variable does not change the variance. This is intuitively clear, since adding a constant to a variable shifts the location of the distribution but does not affect the variability of the distribution.

Combining the two theorems, we have:

(6.37) If $w = kx + c$, then $\sigma_W^2 = k^2\sigma_X^2$

Applying these theorems to the random variables in Table 6.7, where we know $\sigma_X^2 = .84$, we obtain:

$$\sigma_Y^2 = (2)^2(.84) = 3.36$$
$$\sigma_Z^2 = (-1)^2(.84) = .84$$

Standardized variable

It is frequently helpful to consider a standardized variable z instead of the random variable x.

(6.38) A *standardized variable* z is defined as:

$$z = \frac{x - \mu_X}{\sigma_X}$$

Note that z is the deviation of x from its mean, with the deviation expressed in units of standard deviations.

By applying theorems (6.32) and (6.37), it can readily be shown that $\mu_Z = 0$ and $\sigma_Z^2 = 1$. Thus, z is a random variable with a mean of 0 and a standard deviation of 1. We shall later explain how standardized variables are useful.

Sums and differences of random variables

One is often interested in a random variable that is the sum or difference of two random variables. For instance, the preparation of an invoice may involve a typing operation and a checking operation. Let x be the time required for the typing, and y the time required for checking. If one is interested in the total required time $x + y$, the following two theorems can be utilized to obtain information about $x + y$ from the two component elements:

(6.39) $\mu_{X+Y} = \mu_X + \mu_Y$

(6.40) If x and y are statistically independent, $\sigma^2_{X+Y} = \sigma^2_X + \sigma^2_Y$

Thus, the means are additive when two random variables are added, and so are the variances if the random variables are statistically independent.

If we are concerned with the difference between two random variables, we have:

(6.41) $\mu_{X-Y} = \mu_X - \mu_Y$

(6.42) If x and y are statistically independent, $\sigma^2_{X-Y} = \sigma^2_X + \sigma^2_Y$

To illustrate these theorems, suppose we have the following information concerning the invoicing operation:

	Typing x	*Checking* y
Mean	3 minutes	1 minute
Variance	.4	.1

We then know at once that $\mu_{X+Y} = 3 + 1 = 4$ minutes. Further, if the checking time does not depend on the typing time, we have $\sigma^2_{X+Y} = .4 + .1 = .5$, or σ_{X+Y} is about .7 minutes.

QUESTIONS AND PROBLEMS

6.1. Explain briefly each of the following:

a. Probability

b. Sample space

c. Population mean

d. Finite population

e. Random variable

6.2. Distinguish between finite and infinite populations. Describe a problem in which a finite population is of relevance. Describe another problem in which an infinite population is of relevance.

6.3. What is the distinction between a parameter and a statistic? Give several examples of each. Why is it important to distinguish between the two?

6.4. Distinguish between continuous and discrete probability distributions. Describe a problem in which a continuous probability distribution is relevant. Describe another problem in which a discrete probability distribution is relevant.

6.5. For each of the following situations, discuss whether it is amenable to an objective probability approach, a personal probability approach, or both:

a. Probability that a certain type of fanbelt will fail within 1,000 hours after installation.

b. Probability that the John Smith household will purchase a new automobile next year.

c. Probability that the market price of C. A. Williams common stock will advance $8 per share during the next week.

d. Probability that a shipment contains no defective items.

6.6. Refer to Problem 6.5.

a. For each situation that is amenable to an objective probability approach, describe how one could obtain information about the magnitude of the objective probability involved.

b. For each situation that is amenable to a personal probability approach, discuss the types of factors that might be considered in forming a judgment about the magnitude of the personal probability involved.

6.7. An advertising agency has determined that the probability that a person can answer a particular question for a television quiz program within one minute is one-sixth.

a. Does this mean that if six persons are selected, one will correctly answer the question within one minute? Discuss, explaining fully the interpretation you attach to the probability statement.

b. How could you estimate through an experiment the probability of a correct answer within one minute? Could you ask the same person different questions? Discuss.

c. Would it be easier to estimate through an experiment the probability that a particular coin lands heads? Why, or why not?

6.8. Management of the General Products Company was considering the introduction of a new product on the market. The sales manager stated: "Chances are three out of four that this new product will succeed if introduced."

a. How do you think that the sales manager obtained this probability information?

b. Since the introduction of this particular product by the General Products Company is not a repeatable event, what interpretation can be given to the sales manager's probability statement?

c. The manager of market research estimated that the probability is .25 that the new product will succeed if introduced. How do you explain the discrepancy between this number and the sales manager's probability? Which figure should management now use: .25? .50? .75? Some other number? Explain how you arrived at your answer.

d. Suppose that 15 per cent of products of the kind the General Products Company is considering have been successfully introduced in the past. Is this probability information of relevance to management in deciding whether to introduce the new product? Discuss.

6.9. Explain why a store chain with a large number of stores may be willing to self-insure them against fire losses, while a concern in the same line of activity that has only one store may not be willing to self-insure it against fire losses.

6.10. An appraiser is to rate the suitability of a site for the location of a new plant. The rating is an integer from 0 (very poor) to 10 (outstanding).

a. Develop three alternative sample spaces that might be used to describe the possible outcomes of this evaluation of the site.

b. Is any one of three sample spaces you developed "better" than the other two? Discuss.

c. For each of the three alternative sample spaces you developed, describe a situation when this sample space would be appropriate.

d. Are the sample spaces you developed univariate or bivariate? Explain.

6.11. An assembly consists of three components. An inspector checks to determine the number of components in the assembly that are defective. Independently, a second inspector makes a similar check.

a. Develop a sample space to describe the possible outcomes of the joint inspection.

b. Is this sample space univariate or bivariate? Explain.

c. Label your basic outcomes in the sample space O_1, O_2, etc. If E_1 is the event that at least one inspector finds no components defective, what basic outcomes constitute E_1? What basic outcomes constitute not-E_1?

d. If E_2 is the event that both inspectors find the same number of components defective, what basic outcomes constitute E_2?

e. Are E_1 and E_2 mutually exclusive? Complementary? Explain.

6.12. A canal has a single lock. Ships may be waiting upstream or downstream.

a. Develop a sample space to describe the number of ships waiting upstream and the number waiting downstream. Assume that the number waiting on a given side never exceeds 3.

b. Is your sample space a univariate or bivariate one? Explain.

c. Label your basic outcomes O_1, O_2, etc. If E_1 is the event that no more than one ship waits upstream and no more than one waits downstream, what basic outcomes constitute E_1? What basic outcomes constitute not-E_1?

d. If E_2 is the event that at least two ships wait upstream and/or at least two wait downsteam, what basic outcomes constitute E_2?

e. Are E_1 and E_2 mutually exclusive? Complementary? Discuss.

f. Suppose we wish to consider the total number of ships waiting on both sides of the lock. Describe each of the events of interest, and state the basic outcomes of which it is composed.

6.13. Colossal Supermarkets operates 250 stores throughout the United States in cities of various sizes, as follows:

Population of City		*Number of Stores*
Under 20,000		25
20,000–under 50,000		50
50,000–under 100,000		75
100,000 and over		100
	All cities	250

a. An experimental sales promotion is to be tried in one of the stores. If this store is selected at random, what is the probability that it will be located in a city of 50,000–under 100,000?

b. Explain fully how you interpret this probability statement.

c. What is meant by "selection of one store at random"? Explain.

d. What difficulties do you encounter in interpreting the probability statement and explaining random selection?

e. What is the probability that the store selected at random will be located in a city of less than 100,000 population? Explain how you arrived at your answer.

f. Develop the complete probability distribution for this random experiment. Is it a univariate or bivariate probability distribution? Explain.

***6.14.** Colossal Supermarket stores are located throughout the United States as follows:

Population of City	North-east B_1	South-east B_2	Cen-tral B_3	North-west B_4	South-west B_5	U.S.
	Geographic Area					
A_1 Under 20,000	3	5	6	5	6	25
A_2 20,000–under 50,000	5	11	16	9	9	50
A_3 50,000–under 100,000	29	12	3	7	24	75
A_4 100,000 and over	63	12	10	4	11	100
All cities	100	40	35	25	50	250

a. What is the symbolic notation for the probability that a store selected at random to participate in an experimental program is located:
(1) In a Southwestern city under 20,000 population?
(2) In a city in the Central U.S. with population 20,000–under 50,000?
(3) In the Southeast?
(4) In a city with population less than 50,000?
(5) In the Northwest, given that the experimental store is to be in a city with population 20,000–under 50,000?

b. Explain in words the probability designated by each of the following symbolic forms: (1) $P(A_3|B_4)$; (2) $P(A_3 \text{ and } B_4)$; (3) $P(A_1)$.

c. Determine each of the probabilities in part **a**.

d. Determine each of the probabilities in part **b**.

e. How do you interpret any of your probability statements in parts **c** and **d**?

f. Which of the probabilities in part **a** is a joint probability? A marginal probability? A conditional probability?

g. Develop the complete probability distribution for this random experiment. Is it a univariate or bivariate probability distribution? Explain.

h. Derive the marginal probability distribution by size of city. Explain the meaning of this distribution.

i. Derive the conditional probability distribution by geographic area, given that the size of the city is 50,000–under 100,000. Interpret your distribution.

6.15. Refer to Problem 6.14.

a. Find the following probabilities by the multiplication theorem or the addition theorem and then verify your answers by obtaining each required probability directly from the joint probability distribution: (1) $P(A_2 \text{ or } B_3)$; (2) $P(A_2 \text{ and } B_4)$; (3) $P(B_1 \text{ or } B_3)$; (4) $P(A_1 \text{ and } A_4)$.

b. Are the two variables (size of city and geographic area) statistically independent in the population of 250 stores? Explain fully how you arrived at your answer.

c. If the two variables are independent, of what significance is this? If they are not independent, what is the nature of the relationship between them?

6.16. A lot of 10,000 parts, produced on four machines, was graded according to three grades. The results were:

Grade	W B_1	X B_2	Y B_3	Z B_4	All Machines
	Machine				
A_1 Satisfactory	3,200	800	2,400	1,600	8,000
A_2 Re-work	600	150	450	300	1,500
A_3 Scrap	200	50	150	100	500
All grades	4,000	1,000	3,000	2,000	10,000

a. One of the parts is to be selected at random from the lot. What is the probability that it was produced by machine Y and should be re-worked? What is the meaning of this probability statement?
b. What is meant by "selecting a part at random"?
c. What difficulties do you encounter in interpreting the probability statement and explaining random selection?
d. What is the symbolic notation for the probability that a part selected at random:
(1) Was produced by machine X?
(2) Was produced by machine Z and is satisfactory?
(3) Was produced by machine Y and needs to be re-worked?
(4) Needs to be scrapped?
(5) Needs to be scrapped, given that it was produced by machine X?
e. Explain in words the probability designated by each of the following symbolic forms: (1) $P(A_2 \text{ and } B_3)$; (2) $P(A_1)$; (3) $P(B_3|A_1)$.
f. Determine each of the probabilities in part **d**.
g. Determine each of the probabilities in part **e**.
h. Which of the probabilities in part **d** is a joint probability? A marginal probability? A conditional probability?
i. Develop the complete probability distribution for this random experiment. Is it a univariate or bivariate probability distribution? Explain.
j. Derive the marginal probability distribution by grade of parts. Explain the meaning of this distribution.
k. Derive the conditional probability distribution by machine, given that the part needs to be re-worked. Explain the meaning of this distribution.

6.17. Refer to Problem 6.16.
a. Find the following probabilities by the addition theorem or the multiplication theorem and then verify your answers by obtaining each required probability directly from the joint probability distribution: (1) $P(A_2 \text{ and } B_4)$; (2) $P(A_3 \text{ or } B_2)$; (3) $P(A_1 \text{ and } A_3)$; (4) $P(B_1 \text{ or } B_2)$.
b. Are the two variables (machine and grade) statistically independent in the population of 10,000 parts? Explain fully how you arrived at your answer.
c. If the two variables are independent, explain the significance of this. If they are not independent, explain the nature of the relationship between them.

***6.18.** Given:
A_1 Family has car
A_2 Family does not have car
B_1 Income of family is under \$4,000
B_2 Income of family is \$4,000–\$9,999
B_3 Income of family is \$10,000 or more

and that in the population under study:

$$P(A_1) = .70 \qquad P(A_1|B_2) = .85$$
$$P(B_1) = .45 \qquad P(A_1|B_3) = .90$$
$$P(B_3) = .08$$

a. Find $P(A_1 \text{ and } B_3)$. What probability is designated by this symbolic form?
b. Find $P(A_1 \text{ or } B_3)$. What probability is designated by this symbolic form?
c. Find $P(B_3|A_1)$. What probability is designated by this symbolic form?
d. Develop the joint probability distribution. Are car possession and family income independent in this population? Explain.

6.19. Given: A_1 Person reads magazine A
A_2 Person does not read magazine A
B_1 Person is male
B_2 Person is female

and that in the population under study:

$$P(A_2) = .60 \qquad P(B_1|A_2) = .60$$
$$P(B_1) = .45$$

a. Find $P(A_2 \text{ and } B_1)$. What probability is designated by this symbolic form?
b. Find $P(A_2 \text{ or } B_1)$. What probability is designated by this symbolic form?
c. Find $P(A_2|B_1)$. What probability is designated by this symbolic form?
d. Develop the joint probability distribution. Are readership and sex independent in this population? Explain.

***6.20.** The credit department of a large bank has found from past experience that the probability of a borrower's defaulting on his personal loan is .04. It also has found that, given that the loan is defaulted, the probability is .40 that it was made to finance a vacation trip. In addition, the bank's experience has shown that the probability that a borrower will default on his loan is the same whether he is a government employee or not.

a. What is the probability that a borrower borrows to finance a vacation trip and defaults on his personal loan?
b. If the probability that a personal loan is made to a government employee is .20, what is the probability that a borrower is a government employee and defaults on his personal loan? Are these two events statistically independent? Explain.

6.21. An assembly is made up of parts C and D. The probability that part C is defective is .01 and the probability that part D is defective is .05. Assume that the assembly operation mates the two parts so that they are statistically independent in the assembly.

a. Set up the bivariate probability distribution for the assembly operation.
b. What is the probability that the assembly is not defective (i.e., neither part is defective)?
c. What is the probability that both parts in the assembly are defective?

6.22. a. Demonstrate that the following two probability statements are valid for any pair of events E and F: (1) $P(E \text{ or } F) \leq P(E) + P(F)$; (2) $P(\text{not-}E \text{ and not-}F) = 1 - P(E \text{ or } F)$.
b. The probability that a household has an air conditioner is .15 and the probability that it has a dishwasher is .10. Consider the probability that a household has neither an air conditioner nor a dishwasher. Employing the probability statements in part **a**, determine the smallest value that this probability can have.

***6.23.** Let x be the number of defective tires in a batch of four molded at one time. The probability distribution of x is:

X	$P(X)$
0	.80
1	.10
2	.05
3	.03
4	.02

a. Find the expected value of x. What does this number signify?
b. Find the variance of x. Find the standard deviation of x,
c. Suppose a defective tire represents a loss of \$20. Let $y = 20x$. What does y represent?
d. Find the expected value of y.
e. Find the variance of y.

***6.24.** Refer to Problem 6.23. Let x_1 and x_2 be the number of defective tires in two successive batches, and assume that they are independent random variables with the same probability distribution given in Problem 6.23. Let $z = x_1 + x_2$ and $w = 20z$.
a. What does z represent? What does w represent?
b. Find the expected value of z. Does this result depend upon the assumption of statistical independence?
c. Find the variance of z. Does this result depend upon the assumption of statistical independence?
d. Find the mean and variance of w.

6.25. Let x_1 and x_2 respectively be the number of units sold in a day on two successive days. The two random variables are statistically independent and have the identical probability distribution:

X	$P(X)$
12	.5
14	.3
16	.2

The sale price is \$2 per unit.
a. Find the expected value of x_1. What does this number signify?
b. Find the variance of x_1. Find the standard deviation of x_1.
c. Let $y_1 = 2x_1$. What does y_1 represent?
d. Find the expected value and variance of y_1.
e. Let $z = 2(x_1 + x_2)$. What does z represent?
f. Develop the probability distribution of z and find its mean and variance.
g. Suppose that the numbers of units sold on each of five successive days are statistically independent and follow the above probability distribution. Find the mean and variance of t, the total sales in the five successive days, without first obtaining the probability distribution of t. (*Hint:* Formulas (6.39) and (6.40) extend in an obvious way for more than two variables.)

6.26. The number of operations performed in a hospital operating theatre in an eight-hour period is denoted by x. The expected value of x is 4.5 and the variance is 1.5. Assume that the numbers of operations performed in each of three theatres follow this probability distribution and are statistically independent. Find the mean and variance of the total number of operations performed in the three theatres in an eight-hour period. (*Hint:* Formulas (6.39) and (6.40) extend in an obvious way for more than two variables.)

***6.27.** Near the top of p. 130 an example of the calculation of expected gain is presented. Suppose that the probability distribution had been as follows:

Probability of selling no subscription	.50
Probability of selling a subscription to magazine A	.20
Probability of selling a subscription to magazine B	.15
Probability of selling a subscription to both magazines	.15

Suppose also that the cost of a call is \$.10 (the profits stated on p. 130 are the gross commissions and do not include the cost of the call).

a. What is the expected gain per call under these conditions?

b. Would the salesman be wise to give a \$.15 discount on magazine A out of his commission, assuming that this would increase the probability of selling a subscription to magazine A to .25 and the probability of selling a subscription to both magazines to .20, while reducing the probability of no sale to .40.

6.28. In the forthcoming harvest, a potato producer faces the following probability distribution for the grade of his potato crop:

Grade	*Probability*
A	.40
B	.50
C	.10

Grade *A* potatoes sell for \$1.20 per bushel, Grade *B* for \$1.00, and Grade *C* for \$.80.

a. What is the producer's expected revenue per bushel? What is the meaning of the expected revenue you have calculated?

b. If the yield of the crop will be 40,000 bushels, what is the producer's expected revenue from the crop? Is this the actual amount of revenue that will be received? Discuss.

c. By harvesting earlier, the probability distribution for the grade of the potato crop is changed to: $P(A) = .40$, $P(B) = .60$, and $P(C) = 0$, but the yield is reduced to 38,000 bushels. Is earlier harvesting recommended if the producer wishes to maximize expected revenue?

6.29. If the probability of a man aged 50 to live another year is .99, how much should he pay for \$30,000 of insurance for the next year (excluding administrative costs, profits, etc., of the insurance company)? In answering this question, consider what the expected gain for this type of transaction should be.

Chapter

7

PROBABILITY DISTRIBUTIONS AND APPLICATIONS

There are indefinitely many probability distributions associated with infinite populations. Each of these probability distributions differs from the others in one or more respects, such as central tendency, symmetry, and dispersion. It has been found, however, that a limited number of *types* or *families* of probability distributions can be successfully employed in a wide range of problems. We shall discuss a number of these types, namely the *Bernoulli,* the *Poisson,* the *normal,* and the *exponential* probability distributions. Each of these is considered here in the context of a single trial of an experiment, such as measuring the width of a part selected from a production process or observing the number of persons arriving in a five-minute period at a bank. In Chapter 9, we consider the case of more than one observation from a probability distribution.

7.1 BERNOULLI PROBABILITY DISTRIBUTIONS

Description of Bernoulli probability distributions

The *Bernoulli probability distribution* is an important family of probability distributions. It is encountered when the characteristic of interest is qualitative and when only two possible outcomes can occur. For instance, the calculation of a payroll check may be considered correct or incorrect, a manufactured product may be classed as acceptable or defective, and a consumer may or may not remember the sponsor of a TV program.

To quantify these qualitative outcomes, one outcome is assigned the value 0, the other the value 1. Which outcome is assigned the value 0 and which the value 1 is arbitrary. For instance, we might have:

0 — Correct	0 — Acceptable	0 — Recalls sponsor
1 — Incorrect	1 — Defective	1 — Does not recall sponsor

Thus, Bernoulli distributions involve a random variable x that can take on only two values, 0 and 1. Bernoulli distributions are therefore discrete. The Bernoulli probability distribution is given by:

(7.1) $$P(X) = p^X q^{1-X} \qquad X = 0, 1$$

Here $P(X)$ is the probability that X is the outcome, and $q = 1 - p$. In other words, the Bernoulli distribution has only one parameter, namely p.

Note that:

$$P(0) = p^0 q^1 = q$$
$$P(1) = p^1 q^0 = p$$

Thus, p is the probability that $X = 1$, and q is the probability that $X = 0$.

Characteristics of Bernoulli probability distributions

Skewness. Figure 7.1 shows Bernoulli distributions for three values of p. Note that this probability distribution is skewed to the right when p is less

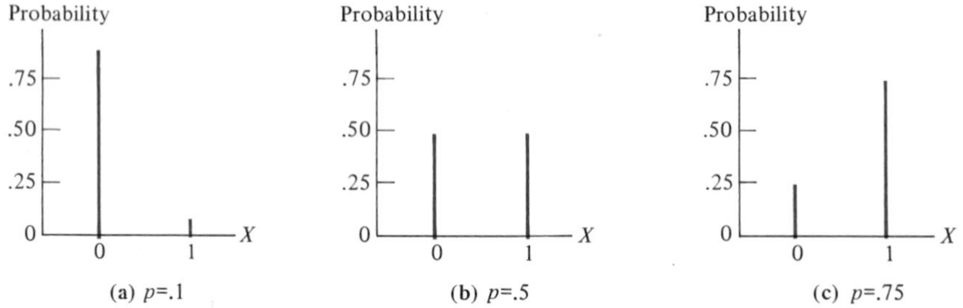

Figure 7.1. Three Bernoulli probability distributions

than .5, and to the left when p is greater than .5. Only if $p = .5$ is the Bernoulli distribution symmetrical.

Mean. The mean of a Bernoulli distribution can be found readily. Since we have:

X	$P(X)$
0	q
1	p

we obtain by using (6.29), p. 129: $E(x) = \mu_X = (0)(q) + (1)(p)$, or:

(7.2) $$\mu_X = p$$

Note what this result means: We needn't calculate the mean of a Bernoulli distribution each time; (7.2) indicates that the mean is always equal to p.

Standard deviation. The standard deviation and variance can also be obtained readily. Utilizing (6.33), p. 131, we have:

$$\sigma_X^2 = (0 - p)^2(q) + (1 - p)^2(p)$$

After some algebraic simplification, we obtain:

(7.3) $$\sigma_X^2 = pq$$

Consequently, the standard deviation is:

(7.3a) $$\sigma_X = \sqrt{pq}$$

Consider the Bernoulli distribution in Figure 7.1a. Let $X = 0$ if a part is acceptable, and $X = 1$ if the part is defective. The probability of a defective part is $p = .1$. Then the mean of this Bernoulli distribution is $\mu_X = p = .1$, and the standard deviation is $\sigma_X = \sqrt{pq} = \sqrt{(.1)(.9)} = .3$.

7.2 POISSON PROBABILITY DISTRIBUTIONS

Another important family of probability distributions that have been found applicable in many circumstances is the *Poisson probability distribution.* This distribution has been applied to many processes involving demands for service, such as the number of telephone calls received at a switchboard per five-minute period, the number of machines in a large plant that break down during any one day, the number of units of a particular item sold from stock during a day, and the number of persons arriving at a bank teller per quarter hour.

Note that in each of the illustrations mentioned, the outcomes possible are 0, 1, 2, and so on. For instance, there may be no telephone calls in a five-minute period, one call, and so on. The Poisson random variable x can in fact take on the values 0, 1, 2, 3, . . . , ad infinitum. Thus, the Poisson distribution is a discrete distribution, like the Bernoulli one, but with an infinitely large number of possible outcomes.

A common feature of each of the examples is that they involve some rate per time period, such as the number of phone calls received at a switchboard per five-minute period. It can be shown that if this five-minute time period is composed of small subperiods, such as a second, with the properties that:

1. The probability of a phone call in a second is small and the same throughout the five-minute period;
2. The probability of more than one phone call in a second is very small;
3. The number of phone calls received in a second is independent of the outcomes in the other subperiods;

then the number of phone calls received in a five-minute period follows the Poisson distribution.

The Poisson distribution has also been applied to phenomena that do not involve time, such as the number of typographical errors on a page, the number of defective solder connections in an electrical assembly, or the number of "stones" (small pieces of refractory or other nonglassy inclusions) in a glass bottle. In the last example, for instance, the subunits consist of the great many non-overlapping sub-areas into which the total area of a glass bottle can be divided. Experience indicates that for each sub-area there is only a small probability that it will contain a stone and a very small probability that it will contain more than one stone, that the number of stones in any one of these small sub-areas is independent of the number of stones in any other sub-area, and that the probability of the occurrence of a stone in a sub-area is the same for all sub-areas.

Description of Poisson probability distributions

As stated earlier, the Poisson distribution involves a random variable x, which takes on values $X = 0, 1, \ldots,$ ad infinitum. The probability that exactly X number of occurrences will happen is, according to the Poisson probability distribution:

$$P(X) = \frac{(\mu_X)^X e^{-\mu_X}}{X!} \tag{7.4}$$

Here μ_X is the mean number of occurrences, e is the base of natural logarithms and is equal to about 2.71828, and $X!$ (read: X factorial) is:

$$X! = (X)(X-1)(X-2)\cdots(2)(1)$$

Thus, $3! = (3)(2)(1) = 6$. By definition $0!$ is equal to 1.

Note that the Poisson distribution has only one parameter, μ_X, and that this parameter is in fact the mean of the probability distribution.

To illustrate the computation of probabilities, suppose that the number of stones in a particular type of glass bottle follows the Poisson distribution and that the mean number of stones per bottle is $\mu_X = .3$. We then can use (7.4) to compute the probability that a bottle contains any number (X) of stones. The calculations are facilitated by the use of logarithms (presented in Table A-9).

To compute the probability that a bottle contains no stones under the above conditions, we substitute in (7.4):

$$P(0) = \frac{(.3)^0(2.71828)^{-.3}}{0!} = (2.71828)^{-.3} \qquad [\text{Remember } 0! = 1]$$

Now:

$$\begin{aligned}\log (2.71828)^{-.3} &= (-.3) \log 2.71828 \\ &= -(.3)(.43429) \\ &= -.130287 \\ &= 9.869713 - 10 \\ (2.71828)^{-.3} &= .7408\end{aligned}$$

Hence:

$$P(0) = .7408$$

Thus, under the conditions assumed, there is a probability of .7408 that a bottle does not contain any stones. Similarly, we can compute the probability that a bottle will contain one, two, or any other number of stones. We shall indicate the calculations of two of these probabilities.

(a) *Probability that bottle contains one stone:*

$$P(1) = \frac{(.3)^1(2.71828)^{-.3}}{1!} = (.3)(.7408) = .2222$$

(b) *Probability that bottle contains two stones:*

$$P(2) = \frac{(.3)^2(2.71828)^{-.3}}{2!} = \frac{(.09)(.7408)}{2 \cdot 1} = .0333$$

Table 7.1 contains the Poisson distribution for $\mu_X = .3$ and includes, of course, the probabilities that we just obtained. Note that the probability that a bottle contains five stones is already so small that the probabilities of six stones or of still more stones are not even shown in Table 7.1. In other words, under the above conditions there will almost never be a bottle with more than five stones.

Table 7.1 Poisson Probabilities for 0 to 5 Occurrences ($\mu_X = .3$)

Number of Occurrences X	*Probability* $P(X)$
0	.7408
1	.2222
2	.0333
3	.0033
4	.00025
5	.000015

Table of Poisson probabilities

Tables such as those in Reference 7.1 are available, where Poisson probabilities have been computed for a large number of mean values. Use of such a table can, of course, save a large amount of time that otherwise would be spent in calculating the probabilities. Table A-2 in the appendix contains Poisson probabilities for selected values of μ_X. To illustrate the use of this table, suppose that the number of persons entering a store in a ten-minute period follows a Poisson distribution with $\mu_X = 2$. Then Table A-2 shows readily that the probability that two persons enter the store in a ten-minute period is .27. The probability that two or fewer persons enter the store in a ten-minute period can also be obtained from Table A-2 by adding the relevant probabilities, and the desired probability is .68.

Characteristics of Poisson probability distributions

Skewness. Figure 7.2 contains the Poisson probability distribution for $\mu_X = .3$. Note that this distribution is highly skewed to the right. In fact, all Poisson distributions are skewed to the right, although they become more symmetrical as the mean value becomes larger.

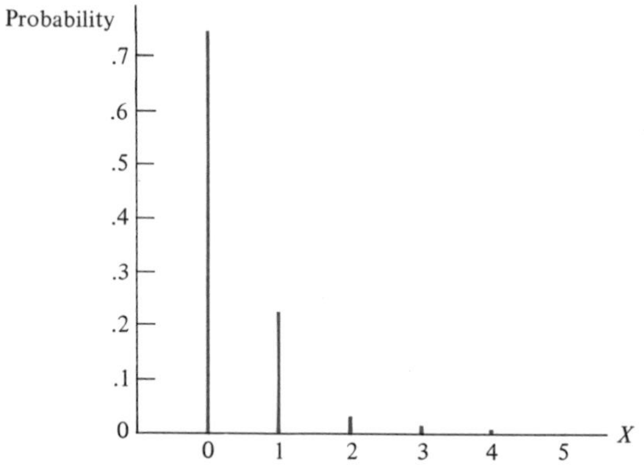

Figure 7.2. Poisson probability distribution, $\mu_X = .3$

Mean. The mean of a Poisson distribution can be calculated from (6.29), p. 129. We simply state now that the mean of a Poisson distribution is μ_X, the parameter appearing in (7.4). Thus, μ_X must already be known before any Poisson probabilities can be calculated.

Standard deviation. The standard deviation of a Poisson distribution can be calculated from (6.34), p. 131. Here, we state that for any Poisson distribution, the standard deviation is:

(7.5) $$\sigma_X = \sqrt{\mu_X}$$

Thus, for the Poisson distribution in Table 7.1, where the mean is .3, the standard deviation of the distribution of the number of stones in a bottle is:

$$\sigma_X = \sqrt{.3} = .55 \text{ stones}$$

7.3
NORMAL PROBABILITY DISTRIBUTIONS

Importance of normal probability distributions

The *normal probability distribution* is a particularly useful and important type of probability distribution. Let us say at once that no value judgment is implied by the name. Many phenomena seem to follow a pattern of variation characterized by a normal distribution. For instance, the height of persons, the thickness of tablets, the tensile strength of iron bars, the weight of cans—all these phenomena have been analyzed from the statistical point of view by considering them to follow normal distributions. In brief, all these phenomena have been considered to be normally distributed. Also, the normal distribution is often encountered when reaching conclusions and making decisions based upon sample data, as will be seen in later chapters.

Characteristics of normal probability distributions

Figure 7.3 contains a number of normal distributions. As this figure suggests, normal distributions are all bell-shaped; they are symmetrical and have a single peak at the center of the distribution. They vary, however, in the location of the average (center of the distribution) and in the extent of variability. For instance, one normal distribution may have a mean of \$500 and a standard deviation of \$10; another may have a mean of 10 pounds and a standard deviation of 2 pounds.

Also note from Figure 7.3 that the random variable associated with a normal distribution is a continuous one, since it can assume any value on the scale. While the normal distribution extends from $-\infty$ to $+\infty$, Figure 7.3 makes it clear that the area in the tails of the normal distribution becomes practically zero within a limited range.

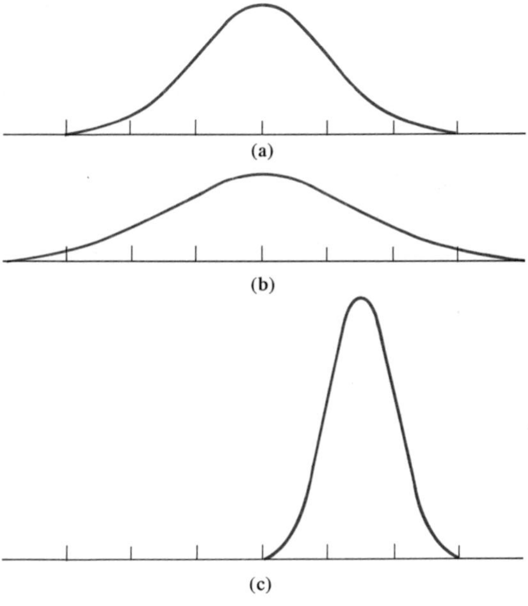

Figure 7.3. Three normal probability distributions

The normal probability distribution is given by:

$$f(X) = \frac{1}{\sqrt{2\pi}\sigma_X} e^{-\frac{1}{2}\frac{(X-\mu_X)^2}{\sigma_X^2}} \tag{7.6}$$

Here $f(X)$ is the ordinate of the curve at X, π is a constant (about 3.142), e is a constant (about 2.718), and μ_X and σ_X are the two parameters of the distribution.

The mean of the normal distribution is equal to the parameter μ_X; that is why the parameter was denoted as μ_X in the first place. The standard deviation of the normal distribution is equal to the parameter σ_X. Once these two parameters are given, the normal distribution is completely defined. Below, we show how to use these two quantities.

Table of areas for normal probability distributions

Reduction to standard normal distribution. We pointed out earlier that the area under a continuous probability distribution indicates probability. Thus, to determine a desired probability for a normal distribution, we might laboriously calculate the required area under the distribution. These calculations can be avoided by using a table of areas applicable to the entire family of normal distributions. This table is reproduced as Table A-1.

Table A-1 gives the *area between the mean and any other specified value* for the standard normal distribution, that is, for the normal distribution with a mean of 0 and a standard deviation of 1. Recall from (6.38), p. 132, that a standardized variable z is defined by:

$$z = \frac{x - \mu_X}{\sigma_X} \tag{7.7}$$

Recall also that the distribution of z has a mean of 0 and a standard deviation of 1. It can be proved that if x is normally distributed, z is also normally distributed. Hence, any normal distribution can be reduced to the standard normal by transforming the variable to a standardized one. When z refers to the normal distribution, it is frequently called a *standard normal deviate.*

To illustrate the use of Table A-1, we refer to Figure 7.4. The normal distribution shown there refers to the weight of cotton bales produced by the Windsor Company. The mean of the distribution is $\mu_X = 520$ pounds and the standard deviation is $\sigma_X = 11$ pounds. Suppose we wish to determine the probability that a bale of cotton, produced under the conditions for which the probability distribution in Figure 7.4 applies, has a weight between 520 and 531 pounds. The desired probability is shown as the shaded area in Figure 7.4. In order to use Table A-1, we express the distance between the mean and the other specified value in units of standard deviations. We can readily determine that 531 pounds is 11 pounds above the mean, and since the standard deviation is 11 pounds, 531 pounds is 1 standard deviation above the mean.

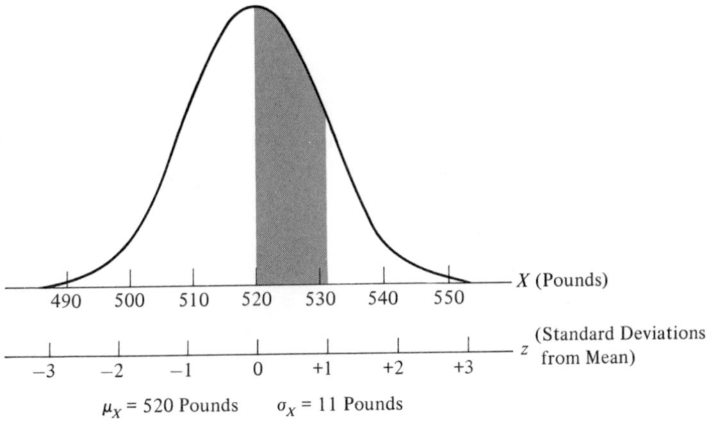

Figure 7.4

Table A-1 gives the area under the standard normal probability curve between the mean 0 and any given value of z. Note that the left column in Table A-1 presents the z value to one decimal place and the captions to the other columns give the second decimal place of the z value. Each figure in the body of the table indicates the area between the mean 0 and the corresponding z.

To determine the probability that a bale weighs between 520 and 531 pounds, we must find the area between the mean of the distribution and a z of 1.00 since the standardized value of 531 pounds is 1.00. Table A-1 indicates that this area is .3413 (out of a total area of 1.0000). Hence, we state that the probability that a bale will weigh between 520 and 531 pounds is .3413. This means loosely that if the process operates for a long time under the given conditions, about 34.13 per cent of the bales produced will have a weight between 520 and 531 pounds.

Since normal distributions are symmetrical, it does not matter that Table A-1 gives only the areas to the right of the mean. Areas to the left of the mean correspond to those to the right. If we want to know the probability that a bale will weigh between, say, 509 and 520 pounds, we first determine that the z value of 509 pounds is -1.00; in other words, 509 is 1 standard deviation below the mean. In entering Table A-1, we disregard the minus sign of the z value and find that the probability that a bale will weigh between 509 and 520 pounds is .3413.

The probability that a bale will weigh between 509 and 531 pounds is the sum of the separate probabilities: .3413 (that it will weigh between 509 and 520 pounds) plus .3413 (that it will weigh between 520 and 531 pounds). The two probabilities refer to mutually exclusive events, so that the probability that either event will happen is simply the sum of the two probabilities. Thus, the probability is .6826 that a bale will weigh between 509 and 531 pounds.

Similarly, we can determine a probability of .4772 that the weight of a bale will be between 520 and 542 pounds; note that the z value of 542 pounds is 2.00. It follows from the earlier example that the probability of a bale weighing between 498 and 542 pounds is about .954, since the probability of the weight being between 498 and 520 pounds is also .4772. Thus, this process, operating under the given conditions for a long time, will turn out all but about 4.6 per cent of the bales with a weight between 498 and 542 pounds.

The reader should check for himself that the probability that a bale will weigh between 487 and 553 pounds is about .997. While there is a probability that a bale's weight will be less than 487 pounds or more than 553 pounds, this probability is so small that we conclude that the process operating under the given conditions will rarely turn out such bales.

Three important area relationships. The probability statements just made on the basis of Table A-1 can be generalized as follows:

1. The area under the normal distribution between the mean ± 1 standard deviation is about .683 out of a total area of 1.
2. The area under the normal distribution between the mean ± 2 standard deviations is about .954 out of a total area of 1.
3. The area under the normal distribution between the mean ± 3 standard deviations is about .997 out of a total area of 1.

These relationships are shown graphically in Figure 7.5. They are often adequate for quick analysis without need of the entire table of areas under

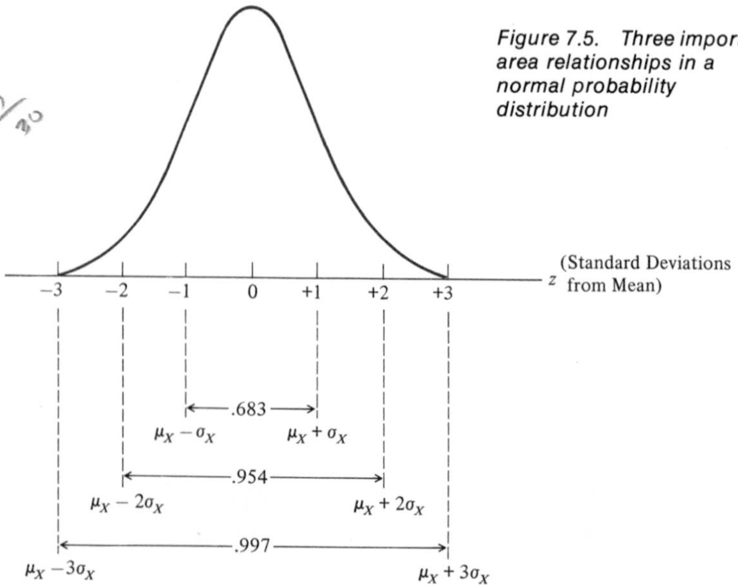

Figure 7.5. Three important area relationships in a normal probability distribution

the normal distribution. For instance, if interest should center in the area "mean ±2.75 standard deviations," we would know from the second and third relationships above that the desired area is fairly close to 1.

Examples of different types of probability calculations with Table A-1. We now illustrate the use of Table A-1 for a few additional types of probability statements; all examples refer to the previous normal distribution of the weight of cotton bales, with the parameter values being $\mu_X = 520$ pounds and $\sigma_X = 11$ pounds, respectively.

(a) *Probability that bale will weigh between 531.0 and 536.5 pounds:* It usually helps to draw a diagram such as that in Figure 7.6a. The desired area can be obtained from Table A-1 by finding the area between 520.0 and 536.5 pounds and subtracting from it the area between 520.0 and 531.0 pounds. Keep in mind that Table A-1 always refers to an area that begins at the mean of the distribution.

X	z	*Area Between Mean and z*
536.5 pounds	1.50	.4332
531.0 pounds	1.00	.3413
Area between 531.0 and 536.5 pounds		.0919

Hence, the probability that the weight will be between 531.0 and 536.5 pounds is .0919.

(b) *Probability that bale will weigh more than 536.5 pounds:* The desired area is indicated in Figure 7.6b. Table A-1 gives only areas that begin at the mean. We know, however, because of the symmetry of the normal distribution that half the total area is to the right of the mean. Since we further know from the previous example that the area between the mean and 536.5 pounds is .4332, we conclude that the probability that a bale will weigh more than 536.5 pounds is .0668, (.5000 − .4332).

(c) *Probability that bale will weigh between 512.0 and 525.5 pounds:* We must divide this problem into two parts again because Table A-1 provides only areas that begin at the mean. The two desired areas are shown in Figure 7.6c.

X	z	*Area Between Mean and z*
512.0 pounds	−.73	.2673
525.5 pounds	.50	.1915
Area between 512.0 and 525.5 pounds		.4588

Hence, the probability that the weight of a bale will be between 512.0 and 525.5 pounds is .4588.

(d) *Central 95 per cent probability limits for weight of bales:* Here, we want to determine two weight limits so that (1) the probability is .95 that the weight of a bale falls within these two limits, and (2) these limits are centered at the mean of the normal distribution. This requires that we use Table A-1 in reverse. Figure 7.6d indicates the area under consideration.

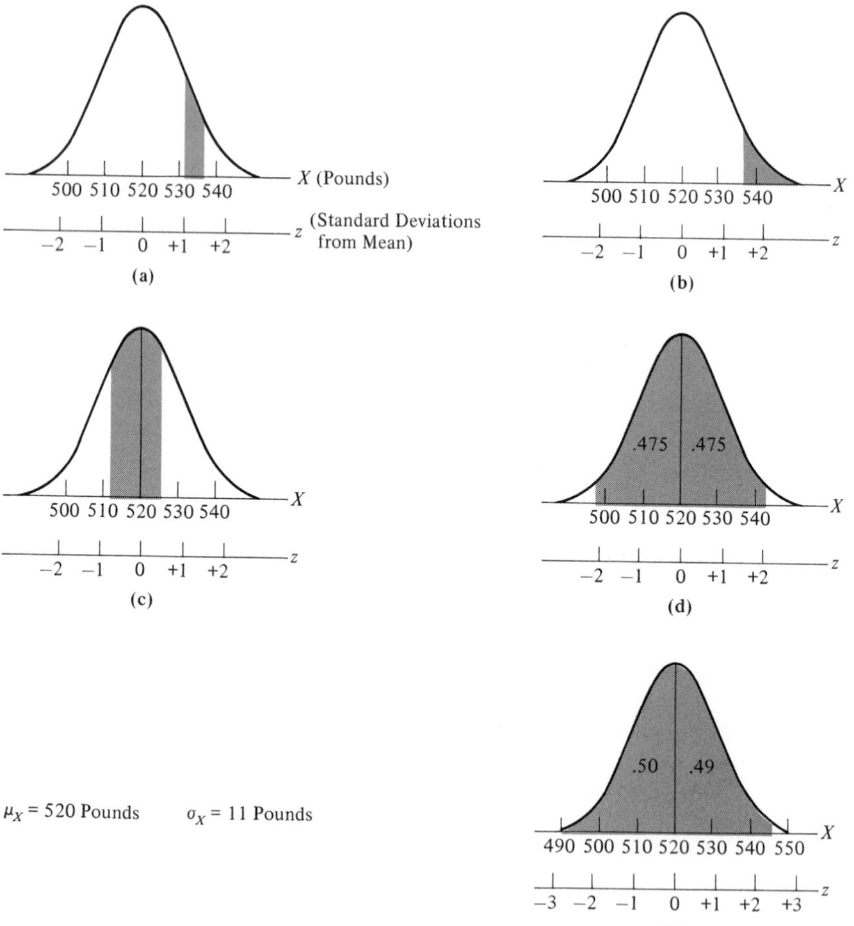

Figure 7.6

Because of the symmetry of the normal distribution, the desired area on each side of the mean is .475. Studying the data in the body of Table A-1, we note that the z value associated with an area from the mean of .475 is 1.96. Since the standard deviation of the distribution is 11 pounds, a z value of 1.96 represents a distance of 21.56 pounds, (1.96)(11), from the mean. Hence, the probability is .95 that a bale will weigh between 498.44 pounds, (520.00 − 21.56), and 541.56 pounds, (520.00 + 21.56).

(e) *99th percentile:* Here, we want to complete the following statement: The probability is .99 that the weight of a bale is less than ______ pounds. The area under consideration is shown in Figure 7.6e. Since we know that half the area in a symmetrical distribution is to the left of the mean, we must determine the z value associated with the area of .49 to the right of the mean. Table A-1 indicates that this z value is 2.33. Hence, it represents a distance of 25.63 pounds, (2.33)(11), above the mean. Therefore, the probability is .99 that the weight of a bale will be less than 545.63 pounds, (520.00 + 25.63).

7.4 EXPONENTIAL PROBABILITY DISTRIBUTIONS

Another important family of continuous probability distributions is the *exponential probability distribution.* This distribution has been used to describe the length of life of electronic components, the length of life of relays and transformers, and the length of time required to service a customer at a store. Note that each of these cases involves a length of time, which must be zero or greater. In fact, the random variable for the exponential distribution can take on any value between 0 and $+\infty$, though the probability of an extremely high value—an extremely long period of time—is very small.

The exponential distribution is applicable to describe the life of a component, such as a transformer, when the main cause of failure is a random occurrence as distinct from gradual wear and tear. Mechanical systems that are subject to wear and tear may still follow the exponential distribution if replacement of components and other preventive maintenance is performed.

The exponential distribution is also used to describe the length of time between two random events, such as between the arrival of two customers in a store, or between two successive breakdowns of a machine. In fact, it can be shown that if the random events (for instance, breakdowns in a machine, or arrivals of customers) follow a Poisson process, then the length of time between any two events follows an exponential distribution.

Description of exponential probability distributions

Exponential distributions involve a continuous random variable *x,* which, as noted, may take on any value between 0 and $+\infty$. The exponential distribution is given by:

$$f(X) = \frac{1}{\mu_X} e^{-\frac{X}{\mu_X}} \tag{7.8}$$

Here e is a constant (about 2.718) and μ_X is the parameter.

Mean. It can be shown that the mean of the exponential distribution is equal to the parameter μ_X of the distribution; hence, the notation μ_X for the parameter was used in the first place.

Standard deviation. It can also be shown that the standard deviation of the exponential distribution is:

(7.9) $$\sigma_X = \mu_X$$

Note that the standard deviation is a function of the mean, as is the case also in the Poisson distribution.

Skewness. Figure 7.7 illustrates the shape of the exponential distribution. Note that the distribution is always skewed to the right. This implies, for instance, that a transistor whose life follows the exponential distribution may last far beyond the mean life, but that the probability of this is small.

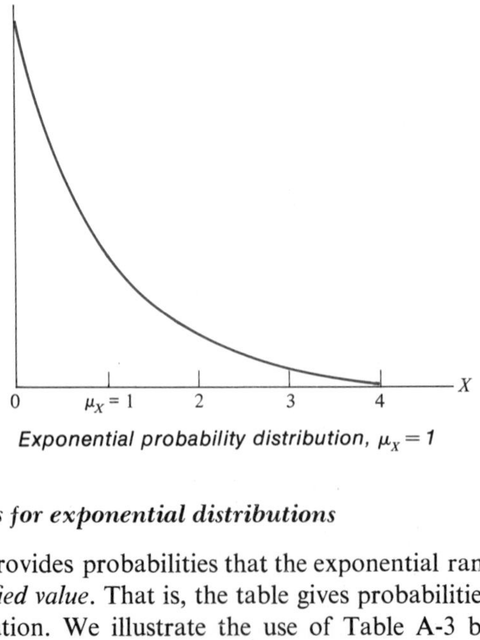

Figure 7.7. Exponential probability distribution, $\mu_X = 1$

Table of areas for exponential distributions

Table A-3 provides probabilities that the exponential random variable will *exceed a specified value*. That is, the table gives probabilities for the right tail of the distribution. We illustrate the use of Table A-3 by considering the length of life of a certain type of radio tube, where this variable follows the exponential distribution with mean $\mu_X = 500$ hours.

Suppose we wish to find the probability that a tube lasts more than 1,000 hours. To enter Table A-3, we must first express $X = 1{,}000$ as a multiple of the mean $\mu_X = 500$. Since $X/\mu_X = 1{,}000/500 = 2$, we find from the table that the probability is .135 that a tube will last more than 1,000 hours.

To find the probability that a tube will last more than 500 hours, we determine that $X/\mu_X = 500/500 = 1$. Then Table A-3 indicates that the probability that a tube will last more than 500 hours is .368. Note the indication of skewness here, since the probability is only .368 that a tube will last longer than the mean life.

If we wish to find the probability of a tube lasting less than, say, 400 hours, we use theorem (6.21) on complementary events. First, we determine that the probability of a tube lasting more than 400 hours is .449; we then know from the theorem that the probability of a tube lasting less than 400 hours is $1 - .449 = .551$.

7.5 APPLICATIONS OF PROBABILITY THEORY

We now discuss three applications of probability theory to show its uses in administrative problems.

Critical path application

In the planning, scheduling, and controlling of large-scale projects, such as the construction of a factory or the development of a new rocket, *critical path analysis* has proven to be a powerful tool for the efficient determination of manpower, material, and capital requirements. Essentially, a project is broken down into basic activities and these are incorporated into a network showing the interrelationships among them. From an analysis of this network, one can ascertain which activities are the critical ones for getting the job done on schedule. Management can then concentrate on these critical activities as the project is carried out.

To illustrate these ideas by a simple example, consider a marketing research agency that has been given a contract for a consumer survey. For the sake of simplicity, we shall consider only three activities of the project:

A Develop questionnaire
B Train interviewers
C Select sample households

The sample selection may be done at the same time as the questionnaire development. However, interviewer training cannot begin until the questionnaire has been developed. The network for this project is shown in Figure 7.8.

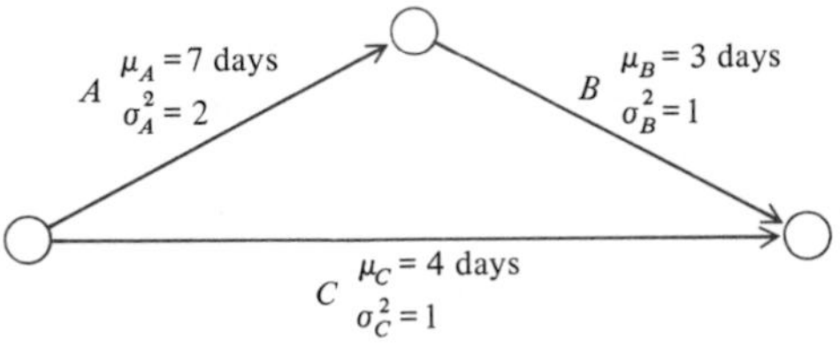

Figure 7.8

We assume that the length of time required for each of the three tasks is a normally distributed random variable, and that these times are independent of each other. The mean time and variance for each of the three tasks are shown in Figure 7.8. In this simple example, it is quite clear that the *A-B* path is likely to be the critical one in terms of requiring a longer time than *C*. To see this specifically, an important theorem is required:

(7.10) The sum (or difference) of two independent normal random variables is also normally distributed.

Let *A* denote the time required for designing the questionnaire, *B* the time for training the interviewers, and *C* the time for sample selection. The theorem just stated tells us then that $(A + B)$ is normally distributed since *A* and *B* are independent normal variables. We also know from (6.39), p. 133, that:

$$\mu_{A+B} = \mu_A + \mu_B = 7 + 3 = 10 \text{ days}$$

and from (6.40), p. 133, that:

$$\sigma^2_{A+B} = \sigma^2_A + \sigma^2_B = 2 + 1 = 3$$

Hence, the total time for questionnaire design and interviewer training is a normally distributed random variable, with mean 10 days and standard deviation $\sqrt{3} = 1.73$ days.

Now we know from Table A-1 that the probability that *C* exceeds 7 days is only .001 ($z = 3$ here). At the same time, the probability that $(A + B)$ will take less than 7 days is only .04 ($z = -1.73$). It is thus clear that the probability is extremely small that *C* will take longer than *A* and *B*, and it is in this sense that the *A-B* path is the critical one.

As one final example of probability calculations here, suppose that the contract calls for the survey to get under way within 14 days. The probability that $(A + B)$ exceeds 14 is .01 ($z = 2.31$), and the market research agency would probably feel fairly secure in being able to meet this contract specification. If, on the other hand, the contract calls for the project to begin within 12 days, management might feel that the probability .12 ($z = 1.16$) of failing to meet the deadline is too high. It then could analyze the critical path further to ascertain the best course of action, such as scheduling overtime on questionnaire design.

While our example dealt with a project at its beginning, it should be noted that critical path analysis is used throughout the life of a project. Periodic updating of the critical path analysis enables the manager always to know where to focus his attention and where to shift additional resources or funds. It should also be noted that in our illustration, the mean times and variances were assumed known. In actuality, these must usually be estimated.

Reliability engineering application

In recent years, much stress has been placed on *reliability engineering*. Reliability engineering is concerned with the proper functioning of systems, such as electronic computers, rockets, automated machinery, washing machines, and automobiles. An important part of reliability engineering is the determination of efficient means of obtaining the required reliability of the system.

To illustrate by a simple example how probability concepts aid reliability engineering, consider a complex system that requires a temperature control subsystem. Suppose that the life of the temperature control system follows the exponential distribution, with a mean of 300 hours. Suppose further that it is crucial that the temperature control system function for at least 90 hours. From Table A-3, we can ascertain that the probability is .74 that the temperature control system functions at least 90 hours.

In this instance, the reliability of the temperature control system was deemed unsatisfactory, and consideration was given to increasing the reliability. One way of doing this is to redesign the system, using better components and more controls on the workmanship. Many times, this approach to increased reliability must be followed, even though it may be very costly.

At times, however, it may be more efficient to use *redundancy* to increase reliability. Redundancy may take the form of overdesign, use of alternate backup systems, and variations of these. To illustrate a simple form of redundancy, consider the use of two temperature control subsystems in such a way that the entire system functions if either subsystem functions. Let A denote "temperature control subsystem functions at least 90 hours." We know then that $P(A) = .74$, and $P(\text{not-}A) = .26$.

Assuming that the two temperature control subsystems function independently, we have by (6.26), p. 127:

$$P(\text{not-}A_1 \text{ and not-}A_2) = (.26)(.26) = .0676$$

so the probability of neither subsystem working is .0676. Now the complement of neither subsystem working is that at least one of the subsystems is working. Hence, $P(A_1 \text{ or } A_2)$, the probability that at least one of the two subsystems is working, is $1 - .0676 = .9324$. Of course, this probability can also be obtained by using (6.24), p. 124.

Note how redundancy has increased the reliability of the temperature control subsystem from .74 to .93 without any change in technology. There are added costs, of course, with redundancy, including the cost of the additional subsystem and the cost of possible redesign of the entire system because of added space and weight requirements. At times, however, these costs are less than those required to improve the technology, and there are also instances when the technology has reached the limits of existing capability and further technological improvements are not readily attainable.

Waiting line application

As a final application of probability theory, we consider a waiting line problem. Waiting lines are found almost everywhere. People wait at a ticket office to purchase a concert ticket, autos wait at a tollgate to cross a bridge, airplanes wait in a stack to land, a machine waits to be repaired by a mechanic. Waiting line problems are concerned with finding an optimum balance between the costs connected with waiting or delay and the costs connected with idle time of the service facilities. In the process of determining this optimum balance, such characteristics of the waiting line as average length of wait and average length of the waiting line become of interest.

To study the behavior of a waiting line, one must first ascertain:

1. How the units arrive and get into a waiting line.
2. How many stations for service there are.
3. How the units are served—for instance, first come, first served.
4. How long the service takes.

As a specific example, we consider the complaint desk at a department store. One employee is assigned to handle complaints. If a customer comes to the complaint desk and finds another customer already there, he must wait until his turn comes. Thus we assume a first come, first served service policy.

Assume now that the number of customers arriving in an hour at the complaint desk (denoted by n) follows a Poisson distribution with mean $\mu_n = 3$. Furthermore, assume that the length of time it takes to handle the complaint (denoted by s) once the customer reaches the complaint desk follows an exponential distribution with mean $\mu_s = .1$ hour (or 6 minutes). Thus, on the average, 3 customers arrive per hour and require .1 hour each to be taken care of. It can be shown that the complaint desk employee is busy .3 hour (18 minutes) per hour, on the average. The latter quantity (.3) is called the traffic intensity or *utilization factor* and is an important characteristic for waiting line problems. Clearly, if the utilization factor is greater than 1, the waiting line would just keep on building up, as customers could not be handled as quickly as they arrive.

On the basis of the information provided, one can study the characteristics of the waiting line at the complaint desk. We are here concerned with the characteristics once the waiting line process has become stabilized. It can be shown that the probability that a customer arriving at the complaint desk will find no waiting line is:

$$\text{Probability of no wait} = 1 - (\mu_n)(\mu_s) \tag{7.11}$$

For our example, we have:

$$\text{Probability of no wait} = 1 - (3)(.1) = .7$$

The average length of the waiting lines that are formed from time to time is given by:

$$\frac{1}{1 - \mu_n\mu_s} \tag{7.12}$$

For our example, the mean length of waiting lines that are formed is:

$$\frac{1}{1 - (3)(.1)} = 1.43$$

The average waiting time of an arrival who has to wait is:

(7.13) $$\frac{\mu_s}{1 - \mu_n \mu_s}$$

For our example, the mean wait of customers who have to wait is:

$$\frac{.1}{1 - (3)(.1)} = .143 \text{ hours}$$

or 8.6 minutes.

On the basis of this type of analysis, management became concerned because some customers have to wait considerably before being served at the complaint desk. Since the customers come to complain in the first place, management was not anxious for them to become still more disaffected with the store. Note that the problem concerns only a relatively small fraction of complaining customers, since 70 per cent of them are served at once without waiting.

In order for management to decide whether to improve service at the complaint desk—for instance, by placing a second employee there, or by shifting another employee to the complaint desk whenever two or more persons are in line—information on costs of the improved service are needed, as is information on the costs of customer dissatisfaction.

While we cannot go into further details here, the illustration should make it clear that waiting line problems are important, and that probability concepts are basic to the formulation of these problems.

Cited reference

7.1 Molina, E. C., *Poisson's Exponential Binomial Limit.* New York: D. Van Nostrand Company, 1949.

QUESTIONS AND PROBLEMS

7.1. For each of the following Bernoulli variables, explain what the parameter p stands for:

a. $X = 0$ Customer recalls advertisement
$X = 1$ Customer does not recall advertisement

b. $X = 0$ Booth occupied
$X = 1$ Booth unoccupied

c. $X = 0$ Container underfilled
$X = 1$ Container not underfilled

*7.2. Refer to Problem 7.1a. Assume $p = .1$.

a. Calculate the expected value of x and the variance of x from the Bernoulli probability distribution.

b. Do the results agree with those obtained from formulas (7.2) and (7.3)?

7.3. Refer to Problem 7.1b. Assume $p = .7$.

a. Calculate the expected value of x and the variance of x from the Bernoulli probability distribution.

b. Do the results agree with those obtained from formulas (7.2) and (7.3)?

7.4. Cite two examples in which you expect the Poisson probability distribution to be applicable and explain why.

7.5. A study at the emergency ward of a hospital indicated that the mean number of admissions between 6 and 8 P.M. on a Monday is 2.5. Assume that the Poisson probability distribution is applicable.

a. Obtain the probability distribution of the number of emergency admissions between 6 and 8 P.M. on a Monday.

b. Present your probability distribution on a chart.

c. Is the probability distribution skewed? Is this typically the case for Poisson distributions?

d. What are the mean and standard deviation of the probability distribution?

e. Is it likely that more than 7 emergency admissions will occur between 6 and 8 P.M. on a Monday? Explain.

f. Would you expect the probability distribution of the number of emergency admissions between 6 and 8 P.M. on a Monday to differ from the distribution for the period 2 to 4 A.M. on a Monday? Explain.

7.6. The mean number of service calls per typewriter during the year is 2.0 for a certain type of machine. Assume that the Poisson probability distribution is applicable.

a. Obtain the probability distribution of the number of service calls per machine during a year.

b. Present your probability distribution on a chart. Justify your method of presentation.

c. Is the probability distribution skewed? Is this typically the case for Poisson distributions?

d. What are the mean and standard deviation of the probability distribution?

e. Suppose that the cost of a service call is \$10. What is the expected cost of service calls per machine during a year? Explain the basis for your answer.

f. What is the probability that the annual cost of service calls for a typewriter will exceed \$30?

*7.7. The average number of machines under repair during any day in a plant is 5. Assume that the Poisson probability distribution is applicable.

a. What is the probability that on any day there are two or less machines under repair? Ten machines under repair?

b. How many spare machines are needed if it is desired that the probability of not having a spare machine available to replace a machine under repair during the day be at most .01? Assume that a machine under repair is out of service all day. Explain how you arrived at your answer.

7.8. A wholesale firm analyzed the number of orders received per day for a certain stock-item and found the mean number of orders per day was 3.5. Assume that the Poisson probability distribution is applicable.

a. What is the probability that more than 4 orders are received in a day for the stock-item?

b. What is the probability that no orders are received in a day for the stock-item?
c. What is the probability that 6 or 7 orders are received in a day for the stock-item?
d. If the mean number of orders per day were 7, would the relative variability of the distribution of the number of orders per day be smaller or larger than if the mean is 3.5 orders per day? Explain.
e. Would you expect the mean number of orders per day to change over a period of time? Discuss.

7.9. A normal distribution is symmetrical and unimodal; this indicates that the mean, median, and mode of the distribution coincide. Can this statement also be interpreted to mean that all symmetrical distributions are normal? That all distributions whose mean, median, and mode coincide are normal?

7.10. Is it possible for two normal distributions to have the same arithmetic means, but different standard deviations? Can two normal distributions have the same standard deviations, but different arithmetic means?

7.11. The monthly accident rate in the factory of the Universal Joint Company is normally distributed. There are usually an appreciable number of days in every month, though, when no accidents occur at all. Is it reasonable to expect that the daily accident rate in the company also would be normally distributed? Explain.

***7.12.** The Standard Investors Company maintains a pool of typists in order to answer its mail correspondence. The number of letters received each week by the company requiring replies utilizing the pool's services is normally distributed, with mean $\mu_X = 3{,}500$ letters and standard deviation $\sigma_X = 200$ letters.
a. During what per cent of the weeks does the firm receive more than 3,500 letters?
b. During what per cent of the weeks does the firm receive less than 3,300 letters?
c. During what per cent of the weeks does the firm receive between 3,300 and 3,900 letters?
d. During what per cent of the weeks does the firm receive between 3,100 and 3,300 letters?
e. Is it possible that the firm receives less than 2,900 letters during a week?
f. Find the 38th percentile of the distribution. What is the meaning of this percentile?
g. Would your answers to questions **a** through **f** necessarily still apply if the number of letters received each week were not normally distributed?
h. What is the probability that the firm will receive more than 3,700 letters each week for three successive weeks? Assume that the numbers of letters received in successive weeks are statistically independent.

7.13. The number of manhours required by the Worth Construction Company to assemble and finish its Model S prefabricated home is normally distributed, with mean $\mu_X = 400$ manhours and standard deviation $\sigma_X = 40$ manhours.
a. What is the probability that the assembling and finishing of a home will take between 380 and 425 manhours? Explain your interpretation of this probability statement.
b. What is the probability that the assembling and finishing of a home will take less than 370 manhours?
c. What is the probability that the assembling and finishing of a home will take more than 450 manhours?
d. The probability is .90 that the assembling and finishing of a home will take less than how many manhours?

(Continued)

e. Fifty per cent of the homes will require between ___ and ___ manhours to assemble and finish? Use symmetrical limits around the mean.

f. Find the 70th percentile of the distribution. What is the meaning of this percentile?

g. If the company were able to reduce the standard deviation to half its present value without affecting the mean assembling and finishing time, what would be the probability that the assembling and finishing of a home would take more than 450 manhours?

7.14. The lengths of steel bars produced by the Morgan Steel Company are normally distributed with mean $\mu_X = 31.6$ feet and standard deviation $\sigma_X = .45$ feet.

a. What is the probability that a steel bar is less than 31.0 feet long? Explain the meaning of your probability statement.

b. What is the probability that a steel bar is between 31.5 and 32.5 feet long?

c. What is the probability that a steel bar is more than 32.0 feet long?

d. What is the probability that a steel bar is between 32.0 and 32.5 feet long?

e. The probability is .75 that a steel bar will be more than how many feet long?

f. Fifty per cent of the steel bars are between ___ and ___ feet long? Use symmetrical limits around the mean.

g. Find the 69th percentile of the distribution. What is the meaning of this percentile?

7.15. On a piece-work operation, the Jackson and Sons Company pays a bonus if an employee processes 300 or more acceptable pieces in a day. The daily number of acceptable pieces processed by Wilbur White and Lawrence Halverson, two employees in the department, are normally distributed with the following characteristics:

Employee	*Mean*	*Standard Deviation*
White	280 pieces	10 pieces
Halverson	270 pieces	20 pieces

a. On what per cent of the days will White get the bonus?

b. On what per cent of the days will Halverson get the bonus?

c. Is the bonus plan a "fair" one with respect to White and Halverson? In answering this question, consider the total number of acceptable pieces processed over a period of time and the advantages and disadvantages of uniform production rates. Assume, for purposes of this discussion, that the per cent of all pieces processed that are acceptable is the same for both employees.

d. Assume that the outputs of White and Halverson are statistically independent. What distribution does their combined daily output follow? Why?

e. What proportion of the time does Halverson's daily output of acceptable pieces exceed White's? Explain how you arrived at your answer.

7.16. The location of a new fire station has been narrowed to a choice between two possible sites — A and B. The important characteristic of a site is the probability distribution of response time, that is, the time required to answer a fire call in the region if the fire station is located at that site.

a. An analysis of the sites indicates that the mean response times for sites A and B would be 10.8 and 12.0 minutes respectively. Does this mean that A is the better site? Explain your answer, making clear what you mean by the term "better."

b. The analysis also shows that the probability distributions of response times for both sites would be approximately normally distributed with the means given in part **a** and standard deviations for sites A and B of 3.1 and 2.0 minutes respectively. Which site would provide more uniform response times? Explain how you reached this conclusion.

c. It is considered important that response times be less than 15 minutes. What proportion of the response times would be less than 15 minutes for each of the two sites?

d. On the basis of the foregoing information, which site should be selected? Outline briefly your reasons for this choice and indicate any implicit assumption that may be contained in your decision.

e. What other factors in addition to response time would you consider in making a choice between the sites?

***7.17.** Refer to Problem 7.14. Assume that steel bars 30 feet long are desired.

a. What is the probability of an under-length bar?

b. Over-length bars have to be trimmed to the desired length. What is the approximate average waste in steel (in feet) from trimming over-length bars? Explain why your answer is an approximation.

c. To what length should the process mean be shifted (assuming that the standard deviation remains the same) so as to reduce the waste from trimming over-length bars, subject to the restriction that the probability of an under-length bar be at most .001? What is the approximate average waste then from trimming over-length bars?

d. Could the waste from trimming over-length bars also be reduced if the process variability could be reduced? Explain fully.

e. Suppose that the process standard deviation could be reduced to $\sigma_X = .30$ feet. If the probability of an under-length bar is still to be .001 at most, by how much approximately could the waste from trimming over-length bars be reduced if the process mean is shifted to its optimum location? Explain fully how you arrived at your answer.

f. Since under-length bars must be scrapped completely, would it be desirable for management to insist that the process mean be kept at a level that would assure no under-length bars? Discuss.

7.18. The Mainline Canning Corporation uses a filling machine to fill cans of size No. 303 with peas. The can label states that the net weight of the peas is 17.0 ounces. The net weights of the cans are normally distributed with mean μ_X and standard deviation σ_X. The mean net weight of the peas placed in the cans is controlled by altering the setting of the filling machine. The standard deviation cannot be altered by the company, as it reflects the inherent machine capability to provide uniform fillings. This standard deviation is known from past experience to be $\sigma_X = .18$ ounces.

a. Assume that the company wishes to turn out no more than .5 per cent of the cans with a net weight less than that stated on the label. For what mean net weight of peas per can should the filling machine be set so that this requirement is met with the least possible amount of fill? Explain carefully how you arrived at your answer.

b. By how much, relatively, would the average fill be reduced if the company only insisted that no more than 1 per cent of the cans have a net weight less than that stated on the label?

c. Suppose that the net weights of the peas with a filling machine of a different make are also normally distributed, that the mean of this distribution also can be controlled by the setting of the filling machine, but that the standard deviation of this distribution is only .14 ounces. *(Continued)*

(1) Assume that the company wishes to turn out no more than .5 per cent of the cans with a net weight less than that stated on the label. For what mean net weight of peas per can should the filling machine be set, so that this requirement is met with the least possible amount of fill?

(2) How much more or less average fill, relatively, is required in this instance with the second filling machine than with the first one?

***7.19.** The length of time required to service a car at a gasoline station is exponentially distributed, with a mean of 4.0 minutes.

a. What proportion of cars are serviced within 1 minute?

b. What proportion of cars are serviced within 5 minutes?

c. What proportion of cars are serviced within 2 to 8 minutes?

d. Graph the cumulative probability distribution, using a less-than ogive. Is the distribution skewed? How can you tell?

7.20. The life of an electronic component (number of hours before failure) is exponentially distributed, with a mean of 550 hours.

a. What is the probability that a component fails prior to 375 hours?

b. What is the probability that a component fails prior to 1,000 hours?

c. What is the probability that a component fails somewhere between 500 and 1,200 hours?

d. Graph the cumulative probability distribution, using a more-than ogive. Is the distribution skewed? How can you tell?

7.21. Indicate the type of probability distribution (normal, exponential, Poisson) that you would expect to be most applicable in each of the following instances:

a. The pattern of variation in the number of typographical errors per typed sheet when the typist averages 1.5 errors per sheet.

b. The pattern of variation in the temperature readings of thermometers produced under a constant cause system and then exposed to the same temperature of 98.6°F.

c. The pattern of variation in the length of time required to process a traveler at an airline ticket counter.

7.22. A system contains two batteries in series so that the system will only work if both batteries work. Suppose that the probability that a battery will work is .95 and that the batteries operate independently in the statistical sense.

a. Construct the bivariate probability distribution of the joint outcomes. What is the probability that the system will work?

b. If the system is to have a probability of .99 of working, what would the probability have to be that a battery will work?

c. Suppose that batteries cannot be produced with a reliability of more than .95. To improve the reliability of the system, a second pair of batteries is placed into the system in parallel so that the system will fail only if both pairs of batteries fail. Construct the bivariate probability distribution of the joint outcomes. (Assume that the pairs of batteries operate independently in the statistical sense.) What is now the probability that the system will work? Discuss the implications of this.

7.23. In a construction project, excavation must precede foundation work, which in turn must precede structural steel erection. Suppose that the lengths of time (in days) required to perform each of the three activities are statistically independent and normally distributed with the following characteristics:

Activity	*Mean*	*Standard Deviation*
Excavation	25	2
Foundation	20	5
Structural steel	35	3

a. What is the probability that the foundation work is completed within 45 days from the start of the project?

b. What is the probability that the structural steel work is completed within 90 days from the start of the project?

c. Suppose the foundation work has been completed on the 50th day of the project. What is the probability that the structural steel work is completed by the 90th day? Explain how you arrived at your answer.

7.24. The number of television sets received per hour at a repair service store follows a Poisson distribution, with a mean of 1.0 per hour. One employee repairs the sets on a first come, first served basis. The length of time needed to service a set, once repairs are begun, follows an exponential distribution, with a mean of .8 hours.

a. What is the probability that when a set is received, it can be serviced at once?

b. What is the mean number of sets in waiting lines that are formed?

c. What is the mean number of working hours that a set which has to wait for repairs is actually waiting?

d. What is the utilization factor for this waiting line problem?

Chapter

8

ADDITIONAL TOPICS IN PROBABILITY

8.1 CHEBYSHEV INEQUALITY

One use of the standard deviation as an indicator of dispersion in a probability distribution is with the Chebyshev inequality. We discussed this inequality in Chapter 5 in connection with sets of sample data. The corresponding theorem for probability distributions is:

(8.1) In any probability distribution, the probability of an item falling beyond k standard deviations from the mean is at most $1/k^2$.

This theorem states, for example, that for *any* probability distribution, the probability is at most 1/9 that an observation will fall beyond 3 standard deviations from the mean.

Consider as an illustration the probability distribution of the number of customers entering a store in a day. If $\mu_X = 200$ and $\sigma_X = 25$, then no matter what the pattern of variation of the distribution, the probability that the number of customers entering on any day is less than 150 or more than 250 ($k = 2$) is at most 1/4.

8.2 CONTINUOUS RANDOM VARIABLES (Calculus Needed)

In this section, we illustrate the use of integral calculus in determining for continuous probability distributions: (1) desired probabilities (i.e., areas under the continuous probability distribution), and (2) the mean and variance of continuous random variables.

Areas under continuous probability distributions

In Chapter 6, we stated that area under a continuous probability distribution corresponds to probability. In Chapter 7, we applied this concept in our study of normal and exponential probability distributions by utilizing tables of areas. The general problem is illustrated in Figure 8.1 where

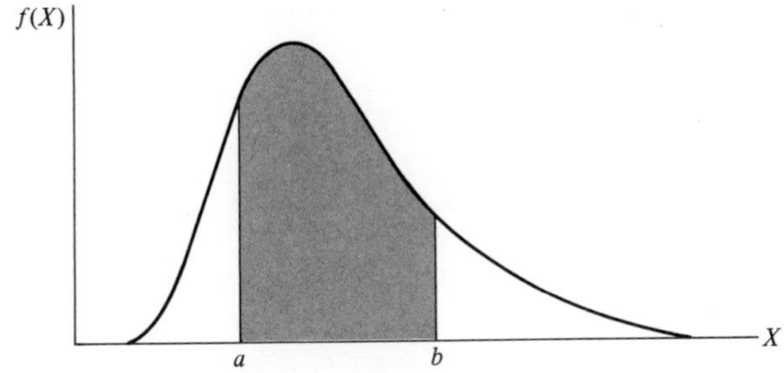

Figure 8.1. Area under continuous probability distribution

the probability that random variable x falls between the values a and b is to be obtained. In other words, we are to determine the shaded area under the continuous probability distribution. If $f(X)$ is the ordinate of the probability curve at X, we therefore have:

(8.2) $$P(a \leq x \leq b) = \int_a^b f(X)\, dX$$

To obtain the desired probability, we thus need to evaluate the definite integral on the right.

Example 1. Consider the right-angled continuous probability distribution shown in Figure 8.2. The probability curve of this continuous probability distribution has the formula:

(8.3) $$f(X) = 1 - \tfrac{1}{2}X \qquad 0 \leq X \leq 2$$

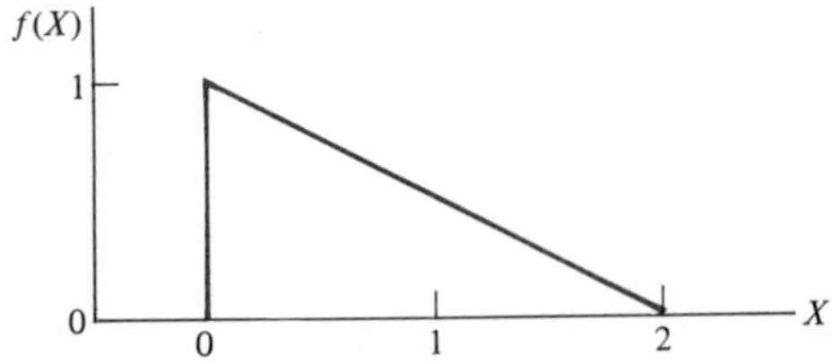

Figure 8.2. Right-angled continuous probability distribution

Suppose it is desired to find the probability that random variable x will take on a value between 0 and 1. The definite integral to be evaluated in this case is:

$$P(0 \leq x \leq 1) = \int_0^1 (1 - \tfrac{1}{2}X)\, dX = \left[X - \frac{X^2}{4}\right]_0^1 = .75$$

Hence the desired probability is .75.

Example 2. Suppose it is desired to find the probability that a radio tube will last 1,000 hours or more when the length of life for that type of tube has an exponential distribution with mean $\mu_X = 500$ hours. The formula for the exponential probability curve is given in (7.8), p. 153. In this case, the definite integral to be evaluated is:

$$P(1000 \leq x < +\infty) = \int_{1000}^{+\infty} \frac{1}{500} e^{-\frac{X}{500}}\, dX = \left[-e^{-\frac{X}{500}}\right]_{1000}^{+\infty} = e^{-2} = .135$$

Note that because the exponential random variable can take on any positive value, the upper limit of the definite integral was set equal to $+\infty$. The resultant probability .135 is, of course, identical to that obtained on p. 154 by using the table of areas for the exponential distribution in Table A-3.

Example 3. The area under any continuous probability distribution must be 1. To check that this is true for the right-angled probability distribution in Figure 8.2, we evaluate the integral:

$$\int_0^2 (1 - \tfrac{1}{2}X)\, dX = \left[X - \frac{X^2}{4}\right]_0^2 = 1$$

Mean of continuous random variable

Formula (6.29), p. 129, describes how to obtain the mean or expected value of a discrete random variable. Integral calculus provides an analogous formula for the mean or expected value of a continuous random variable, namely:

(8.4) $$\mu_X = E(x) = \int_{-\infty}^{+\infty} Xf(X)\, dX$$

For the sake of generality, the limits of integration in (8.4) have been shown as $-\infty$ and $+\infty$. However, where the sample space of x has finite bounds, these finite bounds replace the limits shown in (8.4).

The similarity between formulas (8.4) and (6.29) is obvious. The expression $f(X)\, dX$ represents the approximate probability that x will lie in the infinitesimal interval dX with midpoint X, and hence corresponds to $P(X)$ in (6.29). Since integration is analogous to summation, the $\int$ in (8.4) corresponds to Σ in (6.29).

Example. Consider again the right-angled distribution shown in Figure 8.2. To determine the mean of this continuous probability distribution, we substitute its probability curve (8.3) in (8.4) and evaluate the resulting definite integral, as follows:

$$\mu_X = \int_0^2 X(1 - \tfrac{1}{2}X)\,dX = \left[\frac{X^2}{2} - \frac{X^3}{6}\right]_0^2 = \tfrac{2}{3}$$

The limits of integration are 0 and 2 because these are the bounds of the sample space of x.

Variance of continuous random variable

The variance of a continuous random variable can be obtained by means of integral calculus using a formula that is similar to (6.33), p. 131, its counterpart for discrete random variables. The appropriate formula is:

$$\sigma_X^2 = \int_{-\infty}^{+\infty} (X - \mu_X)^2 f(X)\,dX \tag{8.5}$$

As usual, the standard deviation is the positive square root of the variance.

Example. We wish to find the variance of the right-angled distribution of Figure 8.2. Its probability curve is given in (8.3), and we have determined already that $\mu_X = \frac{2}{3}$ for this distribution. Substituting for μ_X and $f(X)$ in (8.5) and evaluating the resulting definite integral gives:

$$\sigma_X^2 = \int_0^2 (X - \tfrac{2}{3})^2(1 - \tfrac{1}{2}X)\,dX = \left[-\frac{X^4}{8} + \frac{5X^3}{9} - \frac{7X^2}{9} + \frac{4X}{9}\right]_0^2 = \tfrac{2}{9}$$

Hence, the variance of the distribution is $\sigma_X^2 = \frac{2}{9} = .22$. The standard deviation of the distribution is $\sqrt{.22} = .47$.

QUESTIONS AND PROBLEMS

***8.1.** The number of forest fires that occur in a certain region during July has a probability distribution with a mean and variance both equal to 7.0.
- **a.** From the Chebyshev inequality, what is the maximum probability that the number of fires in the region during July will be less than 2 or more than 12?
- **b.** If the number of forest fires that occur in the region during July actually has a Poisson distribution with a mean of 7.0 (and hence a variance with the same value), what is the probability that less than 2 or more than 12 fires will occur?
- **c.** Compare the probabilities obtained in parts **a** and **b**. Does the Chebyshev inequality provide a close estimate of the actual probability in this case? Is this result surprising?

8.2. A bank is studying the mid-month balances of personal checking accounts of a certain class of customer. The study indicates that the balances follow a probability distribution with a mean of \$190 and a standard deviation of \$56.
- **a.** From the Chebyshev inequality, what is the minimum probability that the mid-month balance of an account is between \$50 and \$330?

(*Continued*)

b. The probability distribution of mid-month balances is skewed to the right and, of course, large negative balances do not occur. Do either of these facts affect the validity of the probability bound computed in part **a**? Explain.

c. Consider the probability distribution of end-of-month balances for these same accounts. Would the probability bound for balances between \$50 and \$330 that was computed in part **a** apply to these end-of-month balances? Explain.

8.3. The time required for a shipload of ore to travel between two ports follows a probability distribution with a mean of 90 hours and a standard deviation of 3 hours. The ship's captain claims he will arrive in the other port between 80 and 100 hours after departure from the first port. What is a lower limit on the probability that the captain's claim is correct?

***8.4.** (Calculus needed) Consider a continuous probability distribution with probability curve $f(X)$ where the sample space of random variable x is the interval from 0 to 10. Let event E denote the set of outcomes of x in the interval from 0 to 5 and event F denote the set of outcomes of x in the interval from 3 to 8. Express the following as definite integrals:

a. $P(E)$

b. $P(\text{not-}E)$

c. $P(E \text{ and } F)$

d. $P(E|F)$

e. μ_X

8.5. (Calculus needed) Consider a continuous probability distribution with probability curve $f(X)$ where the sample space of random variable x is the interval from -1 to $+1$. Let event E denote the set of outcomes of x in the interval from $-.5$ to $+.5$ and event F denote the set of outcomes of x in the interval from 0 to $+1$. Express the following as definite integrals:

a. $P(\text{not-}F)$

b. $P(E \text{ or } F)$

c. $P(E \text{ and not-}F)$

d. σ_X^2

***8.6.** (Calculus needed) Assume that if an accident occurs in a uniform 10-mile segment of a highway, it is equally likely to be at any point in the segment. The location of an accident is therefore a random variable with a continuous probability distribution described by the following probability curve, where X denotes the distance along the highway segment in miles:

$$f(X) = \tfrac{1}{10} \qquad 0 \leq X \leq 10$$

a. Draw the probability curve on a chart.

b. Verify both by calculus and geometry that the total area under the probability curve is one.

c. Employ calculus to determine the probability that if an accident occurs, it will occur: (1) in the first 4 miles; (2) between the 5th and 8th miles; (3) in the last 6 miles.

d. From the geometry of the probability curve, what is the mean of the probability distribution? Verify this by calculus.

e. What are the variance and standard deviation of the probability distribution?

f. Given that an accident has occurred in the last 6 miles of highway, what is the probability that it occurred somewhere in the last 3 miles?

8.7. (Calculus needed) If a company defaults on an issue of its bonds, the bondholder may eventually recover a certain fraction of his principal and interest, the fraction varying from nothing to complete recovery. Suppose the default recovery experience of a certain type of bond follows a continuous probability distribution with the following probability curve, where X denotes the fraction of principal and interest recovered:

$$f(X) = 12X^2(1 - X) \qquad 0 \leq X \leq 1$$

a. Draw the probability curve on a chart.
b. Verify by calculus that the total area under the probability curve is one.
c. Employ calculus to determine the probability that the fraction of principal and interest that would be recovered in the case of default is: (1) more than .8; (2) less than .5; (3) between .3 and .9.
d. What is the expected fraction of principal and interest that would be recovered in the case of default?
e. What are the variance and standard deviation of the probability distribution?
f. If the probability of no default before the bonds mature is .95, and if recovery of principal and interest when default occurs follows the probability distribution given in this problem, what fraction of his principal and interest can the bondholder expect to receive?

8.8. (Calculus needed) The median of a continuous probability distribution is that value of the random variable which divides the area under the probability curve in half, that is, there is an equal probability that an outcome of the random variable will be on either side of the median. For the continuous probability distributions represented by the following probability curves, show that they have the median values indicated:

a. $f(X) = \frac{1}{10} \qquad 0 \leq X \leq 10$ — Median = 5
b. $f(X) = 1 - \frac{1}{2}X \qquad 0 \leq X \leq 2$ — Median = .586
c. $f(X) = \frac{1}{500} e^{-\frac{X}{500}} \qquad 0 \leq X < \infty$ — Median = 347 (*Note:* $e^{-.693} = .5$)

Unit

III

SAMPLING AND SAMPLING DISTRIBUTIONS

Chapter

9

STATISTICAL SAMPLING

In introducing probability in Chapter 6, it was noted that one often lacks exact knowledge about the population under consideration. Such exact knowledge is always unavailable when an infinite population or process is under consideration. Even when the population under study is finite, however, there are still many instances when exact knowledge about it is lacking and cannot be easily obtained. In all these cases, one must rely on sampling of the population to provide required information about the population.

Sampling and sample data play a central role in business administration and economics. Sample data may be used to estimate population characteristics, such as the average inventory per dealer or the proportion of consumers who saw a particular advertisement. These types of problems involve techniques of *statistical estimation*. Sample data may also be used for making decisions, such as whether to accept or reject a shipment from a supplier, or whether to conclude that an experiment supports the contention that consumers are insensitive to small price changes for a particular product. Techniques of *statistical decision-making* are employed in these latter problems.

Before one can study statistical estimation and decision-making, one must first understand sampling and characteristics of sample data. In this chapter, therefore, we consider the meaning of sampling and the major advantages of sampling methods. We define a random sample and discuss how such a sample can be selected.

9.1 POPULATIONS AND SAMPLES

(9.1) *Sampling* may be defined as the selection of part of an aggregate or totality, on the basis of which a judgment or inference about the aggregate or totality is made.

For example, the aggregate or totality may consist of all the iron ore transported on a Great Lakes ore boat during a passage. A part of this ore is examined for natural iron content in order to draw a conclusion about the natural iron content of the entire shipment. The part of the ore thus examined constitutes a sample of the shipment. Since the judgment or inference about the shipment is made on the basis of a part of the shipment only, we say that it is based upon incomplete or sample information.

Every person uses incomplete or sample information in daily life as a basis for action. A housewife tastes a grape at the fruit dealer's store, on the basis of which she decides whether or not to buy the bunch. A person, after reading the first few pages of a book, concludes that he does not wish to read this book. After having bought a suit of a certain brand and found it to wear well, a man decides to purchase this brand in the future. The list could be extended almost indefinitely.

(9.2) The aggregate or totality about which an inference is made on the basis of a sample is called the *population* or *universe*.

The concepts of finite and infinite populations were encountered in Chapter 6. *Infinite populations,* according to our point of view, are associated with processes. For instance, the population associated with the manufacture of drug tablets under given operating conditions consists of the indefinitely large number of tablets that would be turned out by the manufacturing process if it continued to operate indefinitely under these conditions. Since the population associated with any process is indefinitely large, according to our conceptual framework, we call it an *infinite* population. The only type of information we can obtain about an infinite population must of necessity be based on a sample, because no process in this world has operated indefinitely under the same conditions.

Populations of limited size are called *finite populations*. The shipment of iron ore on a Great Lakes ore boat, previously mentioned, may be considered a finite population. So may the population of the United States, the total number of accounts receivable of a company, the total number of trucks registered in the State of Minnesota, or a lot of ball bearings shipped by a manufacturing concern to one of its customers.

The particular population to be studied depends, of course, upon the problem at hand. For instance, if a company wishes to know how the present owners of one of its appliances like the performance of this product, the population to be considered consists of all the current owners of this particular appliance. If, however, the company must make a decision affecting future sales of the appliance on the basis of consumer preferences, the population to be considered consists of all potential consumers of this particular product.

The dependence of the population to be studied on the problem at hand also can be seen in another way. The same aggregate that is treated as a population for one purpose may be viewed as a sample for another purpose. Consider, for instance, a lot of ball bearings shipped by a manufacturing concern to one of its customers. The customer may be interested simply in the quality of this particular lot, in which case the shipment is the population. On the basis of a sample of ball bearings from this lot, the customer then draws a conclusion about the quality of all the ball bearings in the shipment.

However, if the customer is interested in the quality performance of the manufacturer's production process, the entire shipment of ball bearings would be considered a sample from the manufacturing process of the producer. A sample of the lot then would be a sample of a sample of the production process. The crucial distinction as to whether the lot is to be considered a population or a sample depends upon what type of decision is to be made: one about the quality of this particular lot or one regarding the quality of the manufacturing process of the supplier.

9.2 REASONS FOR SAMPLING

We have already pointed out that the only type of information that can be obtained about a process is based upon sampling. This stems from the fact that we consider the population corresponding to a process to consist of all the outcomes that would be generated by the process if it operated indefinitely under the same conditions. Thus, there is no choice about getting sampling information concerning an infinite population.

For a finite population, however, it is possible to obtain complete information by a 100 per cent examination of all the items in the population. Recall that a complete examination of a finite population is called a *census*. Why then should a sample, which provides only incomplete information about the population, be used when a census will provide complete information? In Chapter 2 we mentioned briefly the chief reasons why sampling is often used in statistical surveys, and we will elaborate on these now.

Cost

A sample, in which only a part of the entire population is examined, is usually much less expensive than a census. Many types of data required by organizations would be prohibitively expensive if collected by censuses.

For instance, a company wishing to study the television-viewing habits of the population of the United States by means of a census would find the cost of such an undertaking stupendous. As a matter of fact, the federal government only undertakes a census of the population of the United States every ten years. Many problems in business and public administration, to be sure, involve universes whose magnitude is not as great as that of the population of the United States. Even in these instances, however, cost can be an important factor.

In stressing the smaller costs of samples, we must be careful not to base the argument for sampling on cost alone. After all, one can always reduce the cost of a survey by sacrificing the quality of the results. Cost is an argument in favor of sampling because frequently a sample can furnish data *of sufficient accuracy,* and at much smaller cost, than a census.

For many problems in administration, complete accuracy is not required. For instance, a marketing decision on packaging will usually be the same whether the per cent of consumers preferring one type of package to another is 70 per cent or 75 per cent. Whenever sampling can furnish information within the necessary degree of accuracy at less cost than a census, a cogent reason for sampling exists.

Accuracy

The results obtained by sampling are often almost as accurate and sometimes even more accurate than those obtained from a census. This statement may be somewhat startling, and it is true that the element of incompleteness does cause an error in sample results that is not present in results from a census. However, as we discussed in Chapter 2, there are other errors that enter any investigation, whether it is a sample or a census. Errors occur because of faulty interviewing, incomplete returns, inaccurate information, and mistakes in processing of the survey results. It has been found that much better control over these types of errors can be exercised with sampling than with a census, because a sample is a smaller-scale undertaking. For instance, in a sample survey one usually can obtain better supervision and training of the staff, and more care in interviewing, examining the returns, tabulating, and the like. Consequently, the final result from a sample may be more accurate than the result from a census.

An excellent illustration of this point occurred after World War II, when France conducted a census of industrial and commercial enterprises (Ref. 9.1). By definition, the census was to include each and every one of such firms. Results from the census revealed certain anomalies, however, and it was decided to check on the accuracy of the census. A carefully controlled sample of industrial and commercial enterprises was taken which indicated that in the large cities 20 to 27 per cent of the enterprises had been overlooked in the general census. The reason for this high percentage of enterprises missed in the census was attributed to "negligence on the part of the census enumerators" (Ref. 9.1, p. 379). This case clearly shows that an intention to get a census is not necessarily the equivalent of obtaining a census. Control and supervision are essential in any survey and often are more effective with a small-scale sample than with a complete census. The mere fact that one undertakes to conduct a census is no guarantee of accurate results. Indeed, the U.S. Bureau of the Census has been using sampling to check on the accuracy of its censuses. It might be added that because of the inaccuracies in the French census, the results were not published.

Timeliness

Another major advantage of a sample over a census is that the sample usually produces information faster. This is particularly important in problems in which speed is of the essence—for instance, when a company whose employees have just gone on strike wishes to determine the community's reaction to the strike, or when information about consumer expectations in a given week is to be obtained.

A sample provides faster information for two important reasons. First, a sample usually takes less time to complete than a census because it is a smaller-scale undertaking. Second, editing, coding, punching, and tabulating the survey results usually take less time for a sample than for a census. Any survey provides usable information only after the data have been compiled and tabulated. Thus, the time required for tabulating the results is important in comparing the timeliness of sample and census information.

Amount of information

More detailed information can often be obtained from a sample survey than from a census, because a sample in many instances takes less time, is less costly, and permits more care to be taken in its execution. Indeed, in certain areas—such as accounting—needed information may not be obtained because it would be too costly to do the job by complete examination of the populations, and managers are not yet aware that such information can be obtained at reasonable costs by sampling methods. An example of this anomalous situation may be found in the compilation of certain railroad statistics by the railroads. As the Director of Research for the Erie Railroad stated:

> Accountants, by training, have a natural aversion to anything less than a 100 per cent collection of data. Yet, in many instances, the volume and the cost of collecting railroad statistics either leads to methods that produce results of no greater accuracy than sound sampling would provide at far less cost, or desirable and needed data are not collected. (Ref. 9.2)

The Bureau of the Census in its census of the population uses sampling to obtain additional or more detailed information. For instance, information about personal income has been obtained by asking 25 per cent of all households for data concerning this subject.

Destructive tests

When a test involves the destruction of the item under study, sampling must be used. Consider, for instance, a manufacturer who wishes to test the quality of vacuum tubes in a production lot by subjecting them to a life-test—that is, burning them until failure. If he were to test each and every tube in the lot, he could be sure of the quality of the lot but would have no tubes left to sell. Given the costs of testing and the losses arising from the sale of tubes of poor quality, statistical methods can be used to decide what the optimal number of tubes to be tested is.

9.3 SIMPLE RANDOM SAMPLING

In order to be able to utilize statistical estimation and decision-making techniques, it is necessary that the sample elements be selected according to known probabilities. The most basic type of sample in this category is a *simple random sample,* often merely called a *random sample*. We shall use either of these terms when there is no danger of confusion.

Definition of simple random sampling

Finite population. Consider a population of five employees, denoted by A, B, C, D, and E. Suppose that a sample of three employees is to be selected from this population. What are the various combinations of three employees that could be selected for the sample? We can enumerate them as follows:

A, B, C	A, D, E
A, B, D	B, C, D
A, B, E	B, C, E
A, C, D	B, D, E
A, C, E	C, D, E

(9.3) ***Simple random sampling from a finite population*** is a method of sample selection that gives each possible sample combination an equal probability of being chosen.

This definition refers to *sampling without replacement,* that is, once an element from the population has been selected for the sample, it no longer is eligible to be selected again. *Sampling with replacement,* which is used only under special circumstances, differs in that the element selected for the sample is returned to the population before the next sample element is selected. Throughout this book, we shall assume that simple random sampling from a finite population is always without replacement.

Note that simple random sampling does *not* imply haphazard selection, such as selecting a sample of the inhabitants of a community by standing at a downtown street corner and interviewing persons who pass by during some period of the day. Nothing could be further from simple random sampling. There is nothing haphazard about such sampling. When we speak of a simple random sample, we use *random* interchangeably with *probability,* not with *haphazard.* We must have positive controls, not haphazard selection, to give each possible sample combination an equal probability of being chosen, if we are to meet the requirements of simple random sampling.

Infinite population. If the population sampled is an infinite one, such as when a process is sampled, the definition of a simple random sample parallels the above definition for a finite population. A simple random sample from an infinite population may be visualized by considering this population to be made up of an indefinitely large number of elements. A simple random sample consists, then, of a selection of elements such that at each stage of sampling, every element in the population has an equal probability of being included in the sample. Of course, this interpretation is simply illustrative, since infinite populations do not have any physical existence.

To state the definition of simple random sampling from an infinite population more technically:

(9.4) ***Simple random sampling from an infinite population*** requires that all sample observations be statistically independent.

Thus, the outcome of any sample observation must have no effect on the outcomes of the other sample observations.

Characteristics of simple random sampling

We discuss now some of the implications of simple random sampling. *It is a property of simple random sampling that this type of selection gives each element in a finite population an equal probability of getting into the sample.* However, a sample is not a simple random one if only this condition is met. Consider the following procedure for selecting a 10 per cent sample: Divide the population into ten equal groups, and select one of these groups as the sample by giving each group an equal probability of being chosen. This method would give each element in the population an equal probability of entering the sample, but it would not give each possible sample combination equal probability of selection. For instance, combinations consisting of persons from two or more groups would have probability zero of being selected. Hence, this method would not meet the requirements of simple random sampling.

Note then that *equal probability of selection for each individual element in a finite population is a necessary requirement of simple random sampling, but not a sufficient one.* Therefore, any sample selection that does not give each element in the population an equal chance of being chosen is automatically not a simple random one; but if we only know that the method of sample selection gives each population element an equal chance to be selected, we cannot conclude that the sample meets the requirements of simple random sampling.

It now should be clear why persons who pass a downtown corner during a given period of the day are not a simple random sample of all persons in that community. All persons in a community do not pass a given corner with equal frequency; hence they would not have an equal probability of being selected for the sample with this haphazard method.

Selection of simple random sample: finite population

In most applications of sampling from finite populations, the number of possible sample combinations is fantastically large, running into billions and billions. Hence, it is necessary to employ selection procedures that meet the requirements of simple random sampling but do not require the actual enumeration of all possible sample combinations. It is a characteristic of simple random sampling from a finite population that the requirements of this type of sampling are automatically met by the following procedure:

1. Select the first sample element by giving each population element equal probability of being chosen.
2. Select the second sample element by giving each of the remaining population elements equal probability of being chosen.
3. Continue this procedure until all sample elements have been selected.

It can be shown that this procedure gives each possible sample combination equal probability of selection and thus meets the requirements of simple random sampling. Note then that a simple random sample from a finite population can be selected without an enumeration of all sample combinations, merely by giving the population elements remaining in the population at each stage of the sample selection equal probability of being chosen next.

To illustrate one procedure of selecting a simple random sample from a finite population in this fashion, consider a population consisting of 950 retail stores in a community, from which a simple random sample of ten stores is to be selected. We can write the names of the 950 stores on chips or slips of paper and place these in a bowl. After shuffling the contents of the bowl thoroughly, one chip or slip is drawn by a blindfolded person; a thorough shuffling of the remaining chips or slips then takes place, followed by another blindfolded drawing. This procedure is continued until ten different stores have been selected. Experience indicates that if the shuffling at each stage of the drawing is extremely thorough, the results of this procedure will satisfy the requirements of simple random sampling—namely, that each store remaining in the population has an equal probability of getting into the sample at each stage of the selection process, and therefore that each possible sample combination has an equal chance to be selected.

Table of random digits. Shuffling chips is not a very convenient device, especially if the population is large. Furthermore, if the shuffling is not extremely thorough, the results may not meet the requirements of simple random sampling. Another device, better and much more practical, is known as a *table of random digits;* one page of such a table is reproduced as Table 9.1. Two of the more commonly used tables of random digits are the Rand Corporation tables (Ref. 9.3) and the Interstate Commerce Commission tables (Ref. 9.4).

Tables of random digits could be constructed by numbering ten chips 0, 1, . . . , 9 respectively, drawing a chip at random after shuffling, recording the number, replacing the chip and reshuffling the ten chips, again drawing a chip, and so on. Actually, more time-saving and effective procedures are used for constructing a table of random digits (for instance, electronic computers are used), but the principle involved still is the same.

Once the random digits are generated, they are assembled in tables. Table 9.1 is an excerpt from one of these. To illustrate the use of this type of table, we return to our problem of selecting a sample of ten retail stores from a population of 950. Assume that a list of these 950 stores has been obtained from the local Chamber of Commerce. This list constitutes the *frame*. As we explained in Chapter 2, the frame is a listing of all of the units in the population to be sampled. The first task, then, is to number each store; for convenience, the numbering might as well be done consecutively from 1 to 950. Since the population size is 950, we shall need to look up a sequence of three random digits, constituting three-digit numbers. *The sequence of three random digits must be selected in some predetermined, systematic manner to avoid the introduction of any bias.* If this is done, the method by which a table of random digits is constructed assures us that any three-digit number has an equal probability of appearing next, no matter which previous three-digit numbers have already been found. Thus, any store remaining in the population will have an equal chance of being chosen next for the sample, no matter which other stores already have been selected. A sample selected by use of a table of random digits, therefore, meets the requirements of simple random sampling.

Suppose that we decide to use the first three columns in Table 9.1 to provide the three-digit numbers and that we shall read downward consecutively. The first number is 132; therefore, the store numbered 132 is to be included in the sample. The next store to be included in the sample is the one numbered 212. The next number is 990; since there is no store with

Table 9.1 Sample Page From a Table of Random Digits

Line	*(1)–(5)*	*(6)–(10)*	*(11)–(15)*	*(16)–(20)*	*(21)–(25)*	*(26)–(30)*	*(31)–(35)*
101	13284	16834	74151	92027	24670	36665	00770
102	21224	00370	30420	03883	94648	89428	41583
103	99052	47887	81085	64933	66279	80432	65793
104	00199	50993	98603	38452	87890	94624	69721
105	60578	06483	28733	37867	07936	98710	98539
106	91240	18312	17441	01929	18163	69201	31211
107	97458	14229	12063	59611	32249	90466	33216
108	35249	38646	34475	72417	60514	69257	12489
109	38980	46600	11759	11900	46743	27860	77940
110	10750	52745	38749	87365	58959	53731	89295
111	36247	27850	73958	20673	37800	63835	71051
112	70994	66986	99744	72438	01174	42159	11392
113	99638	94702	11463	18148	81386	80431	90628
114	72055	15774	43857	99805	10419	76939	25993
115	24038	65541	85788	55835	38835	59399	13790
116	74976	14631	35908	28221	39470	91548	12854
117	35553	71628	70189	26436	63407	91178	90348
118	35676	12797	51434	82976	42010	26344	92920
119	74815	67523	72985	23183	02446	63594	98924
120	45246	88048	65173	50989	91060	89894	36036
121	76509	47069	86378	41797	11910	49672	88575
122	19689	90332	04315	21358	97248	11188	39062
123	42751	35318	97513	61537	54955	08159	00337
124	11946	22681	45045	13964	57517	59419	58045
125	96518	48688	20996	11090	48396	57177	83867
126	35726	58643	76869	84622	39098	36083	72505
127	39737	42750	48968	70536	84864	64952	38404
128	97025	66492	56177	04049	80312	48028	26408
129	62814	08075	09788	56350	76787	51591	54509
130	25578	22950	15227	83291	41737	59599	96191
131	68763	69576	88991	49662	46704	63362	56625
132	17900	00813	64361	60725	88974	61005	99709
133	71944	60227	63551	71109	05624	43836	58254
134	54684	93691	85132	64399	29182	44324	14491
135	25946	27623	11258	65204	52832	50880	22273
136	01353	39318	44961	44972	91766	90262	56073
137	99083	88191	27662	99113	57174	35571	99884
138	52021	45406	37945	75234	24327	86978	22644
139	78755	47744	43776	83098	03225	14281	83637
140	25282	69106	59180	16257	22810	43609	12224
141	11959	94202	02743	86847	79725	51811	12998
142	11644	13792	98190	01424	30078	28197	55583
143	06307	97912	68110	59812	95448	43244	31262
144	76285	75714	89585	99296	52640	46518	55486
145	55322	07598	39600	60866	63007	20007	66819
146	78017	90928	90220	92503	83375	26986	74399
147	44768	43342	20696	26331	43140	69744	82928
148	25100	19336	14605	86603	51680	97678	24261
149	83612	46623	62876	85197	07824	91392	58317
150	41347	81666	82961	60413	71020	83658	02415

Source: Reference 9.4.

that number, we simply disregard it and continue. The next number is 001, which is store number 1. This procedure is continued until ten stores are selected. Should a number already selected ever be repeated, we merely would pass on to the next number, since the store corresponding to the repeated number is already in the sample.

We could have used any three columns or rows in the table, including columns and rows from different parts of the table, and could have read upward or diagonally for selecting the sequence of three random digits. As long as some predetermined systematic procedure is followed for obtaining the random numbers, the result will be a sample that meets the requirements of simple random sampling.

This method of selecting a simple random sample with a table of random digits is a relatively easy one. Note that it requires that each item in the population can be assigned a number. When a frame for the population exists, such as the list of the 950 retail establishments provided by the local Chamber of Commerce in our previous example, no problem arises. In fact, sometimes the elements of the population already have been serially numbered as, for instance, payroll vouchers and sales invoices.

Frequently, it is not even necessary to number each element of the population in advance. For instance, suppose that we wish to select a sample of 200 accounts receivable from a population of 8,700 accounts receivable. The 8,700 accounts receivable are in 87 files containing 100 accounts each. We then could number each of the 87 files from 1 to 87 and select the random numbers in the usual manner; we would need to look up a sequence of four random digits, since the population size is 8,700. After the random numbers have been selected, the corresponding accounts can be found by counting. For example, account number 0817 would be the 17th account in file 8, account number 6,482 would be the 82d account in file 64, account number 2,300 would be the 100th account in file 22, and so on. Note that we conceptually assigned each account a unique number in this last example, even though we actually did not write out a list of accounts and then number them.

Selection of simple random sample: infinite population

When the population is infinite, the process associated with the infinite population simply provides sample observations. For instance, the process producing drug tablets just provides drug tablets with particular thicknesses. For the observations to constitute a simple random sample, two conditions must hold:

1. The process must be *stable* during the time the observations are produced, so all observations come from the *same* infinite population.
2. The sample observations must be *statistically independent*.

There is no way in which one can prove that a sample from an infinite population is a simple random one. The case for making this assumption must rest on the usefulness of the results obtained by making it. Statistical tests are available to help one decide whether or not to conclude that a series of observations from a process constitute a simple random sample. One such test is discussed in Section 18.5.

Cited references

9.1 Chevry, Gabriel, "Control of a General Census by Means of an Area Sampling Method," *Journal of the American Statistical Association,* September 1949, pp. 373–379.

9.2 Root, E. S., "Utilization of Transportation Flow Data by Carriers," Paper read at 1952 Annual Meeting of the American Statistical Association.

9.3 Rand Corporation, *A Million Random Digits with 100,000 Normal Deviates.* New York: Free Press of Glencoe, 1955.

9.4 *Table of 105,000 Random Decimal Digits.* Interstate Commerce Commission, Bureau of Transport Economics and Statistics, May 1949.

QUESTIONS AND PROBLEMS

9.1. Explain briefly each of the following:
- **a.** Population
- **b.** Table of random digits
- **c.** Census
- **d.** Simple random sampling

9.2. Distinguish briefly between:
- **a.** Finite and infinite populations
- **b.** Sampling with and without replacement
- **c.** Simple random sampling from finite and infinite populations

9.3. Describe a situation in which a stack of punchcards punched by a particular operator would be taken as a population, and a situation in which this same stack of cards would be considered a sample, for purposes of obtaining information about the accuracy of the card punching.

9.4. In recent years, sampling procedures have been applied to analyze and control department store operations. In the following cases, was the population under study finite or infinite?
- **a.** Management installed a sampling plan to control the quality of the wrapping and packaging department's work. Under this plan, samples of packages wrapped by the department were selected at random time intervals and the packages in the samples were opened and inspected.
- **b.** A department store studied the shopping habits of a sample of its charge account customers in order to obtain data on the extent to which a nearby branch store currently was cutting into the sales of the main store.

9.5. The following argument was made by an administrator: "Samples are to be preferred to censuses because they cost less."
- **a.** Why is this argument incomplete?
- **b.** When may a census be preferable to a sample?

9.6. A sample of employees of a company was selected in such a way that each employee had equal probability of being included in the sample. Does it necessarily follow that the sample of employees was a simple random one? Refer explicitly to the definition of simple random sampling.

9.7. A city planning commission has a card file of all addresses in the community. Each card contains one address, though more than one family may live there.

a. Explain carefully how you would proceed to select a simple random sample of addresses from this file.

b. Would the families included in the simple random sample of addresses be a simple random sample of the families in the community? Explain.

c. Suppose that for each address included in the simple random sample of addresses, one family is selected at random from the families living there. Is the resulting sample of families a simple random sample of families living in the community? Explain.

9.8. Explain how you would proceed to select a simple random sample of:

a. 100 credit card holders from the 12,000 credit card holders of Friedland's Department Store.

b. 275 members from the 3,500 members of a trade union.

c. 250 inhabitants from the 22,000 inhabitants of a community.

9.9. A sample of families with children attending elementary schools in the area is to be selected. It is suggested that a simple random sample of children attending elementary schools in the area be selected first, since a listing of this population is readily available; then all families whose children are included in the simple random sample of school children would constitute the sample of families with children attending elementary schools.

a. Why is this sample of families not the equivalent of a simple random sample of families with children attending elementary schools in the area?

b. How can the listing of school children in elementary schools in the area be used to select a simple random sample of families with children attending these schools? Explain.

***9.10.** In a table of random digits, what is the probability that three successive digits are the same? That three 2's are found in succession? Explain how you arrived at your answers, indicating the probability principles employed.

9.11. Purchase orders numbered serially from 6991 to 7063 were issued on March 15 by the Marquette Paper Company. It is desired to select a simple random sample of five of these purchase orders. Use Table 9.1 to select the sample. Which serial numbers did you select? Describe and justify your method of selection.

9.12. The following hospitals have agreed to participate in a joint research program aimed at improving nursing services. A simple random sample of three hospitals is to be selected for an initial research study.

Franklin General	Northmount
Lewis General	Southhill
Maple Valley	Washington
Mercy	Westchester

a. Equal probability of selection for each element in a finite population is a necessary requirement of simple random sampling. What is the probability that Mercy Hospital will be selected for the sample?

b. Use Table 9.1 to select a simple random sample of three hospitals. Which hospitals did you select for the sample? Describe and justify your method of selection.

Chapter

10

SAMPLING DISTRIBUTION OF $\bar{X}$

Once a sample has been selected, the sample data may be used to calculate the mean, the median, the range, the standard deviation, and other statistics based on the sample observations. In this chapter, we shall examine some of the key properties of such sample statistics when they are the result of random sampling. After the general concepts are introduced, we shall concentrate on one of the most important sample statistics, the sample mean, and its properties.

10.1 SAMPLE DATA AND SAMPLING DISTRIBUTIONS

Population to be sampled

As a vehicle for discussion, suppose that the manager of a company is concerned with the age characteristics of the employees and that he is going to sample the company records to obtain information about these. To simplify the problem, assume that there are only five employees in the company—in other words, the population size is $N = 5$. The ages of the five employees are given in Table 10.1.

Some of the major characteristics of the population are also shown in Table 10.1. The calculations of the population mean and standard deviation presented in this table follow the definitions in Chapter 6.

Of course, one would not normally use a sample in this instance; one might just as well take a census, since only five employees are involved. Remember that we are oversimplifying a situation in order to bring out as clearly as possible the implications of random sampling.

Table 10.1 Population of Five Employees and Some Key Population Characteristics

Employee	Age (Years) X	$X - \mu_X$	$(X - \mu_X)^2$
A	27	−7.8	60.84
B	39	4.2	17.64
C	30	−4.8	23.04
D	36	1.2	1.44
E	42	7.2	51.84
Total	174	0	154.80

$$\mu_X = \frac{\Sigma X}{N} = \frac{174}{5} = 34.8 \text{ years}$$

$$\sigma_X = \sqrt{\frac{\Sigma(X - \mu_X)^2}{N}} = \sqrt{\frac{154.8}{5}} = \sqrt{30.96} = 5.6 \text{ years}$$

Population median = 36 years

Proportion under 35 = .4

Sample statistics

The manager might be interested in any number of different age characteristics of the employees. For the sake of simplicity, we consider only the following three sample statistics: sample median; sample mean; proportion of employees under 35 years old in sample. Assuming that a sample of three employees is to be selected, the sample might consist of employees A, B, and C. Their ages are 27, 39, and 30 years respectively. Hence, the sample mean, denoted by $\bar{X}$, would be 32 years; the sample median, denoted by M_e, would be 30 years; and the proportion of employees under 35 years old in the sample, denoted by $\bar{p}$ (read: p bar), would be 2/3. Similarly, it can be determined that if employees A, B, and D comprise the sample of three employees, we would have $\bar{X} = 34$, $M_e = 36$, and $\bar{p} = 1/3$.

In this fashion, we can ascertain for each of the three statistics the result that would be obtained for any combination of three employees. Table 10.2 contains the ten different sample combinations of three employees that can be formed from the population of five employees and shows the ages of each of the sample employees. In addition, Table 10.2 shows the value of the sample mean, sample median, and sample proportion for each of the sample combinations.

Sampling distributions

Table 10.2 makes it abundantly clear for each of the three statistics that different sample combinations will lead to different values of the statistics. For instance, the sample mean might be as low as 31 years or as high as 39 years, depending upon the sample combination chosen.

Table 10.2 Possible Sample Combinations and Three Different Sample Measures for Each

Combination	*Sample Elements*	*Sample Observations*	$\overline{X}$	M_e	$\bar{p}$
1	A, B, C	27, 39, 30	32	30	$\frac{2}{3}$
2	A, B, D	27, 39, 36	34	36	$\frac{1}{3}$
3	A, B, E	27, 39, 42	36	39	$\frac{1}{3}$
4	A, C, D	27, 30, 36	31	30	$\frac{2}{3}$
5	A, C, E	27, 30, 42	33	30	$\frac{2}{3}$
6	A, D, E	27, 36, 42	35	36	$\frac{1}{3}$
7	B, C, D	39, 30, 36	35	36	$\frac{1}{3}$
8	B, C, E	39, 30, 42	37	39	$\frac{1}{3}$
9	B, D, E	39, 36, 42	39	39	0
10	C, D, E	30, 36, 42	36	36	$\frac{1}{3}$

Suppose now that the sample is to be selected by simple random sampling. In fact, *throughout this chapter, we assume that simple random sampling is the sampling procedure used.* In that event, each sample combination must have a probability of .10 of being the one selected. Remember that there are ten possible sample combinations here, and that simple random sampling requires each of these to have an equal probability of selection.

If each sample combination has a probability of .10 of being selected, then we can derive the probability that any particular value of the sample statistic will be observed. For instance, two sample combinations (6 and 7) lead to a sample mean of 35 years. Since these two outcomes are mutually exclusive and each has probability of .10 of occurring, it follows that if a simple random sample of three employees is selected, the probability is .20 that the sample mean will be 35 years. Similarly, the probability is .20 that the sample mean will be 36 years, since sample combinations 3 and 10 provide this result.

Thus, we can derive a probability distribution that indicates all the possible values which the sample mean $\overline{X}$ can assume, together with the probabilities of each of these outcomes occurring. In a similar fashion, we can obtain a probability distribution for M_e, the sample median, and for $\bar{p}$, the sample proportion. These three probability distributions are shown in Table 10.3.

Note that the probability distributions in Table 10.3 have the required features of any probability distribution: All the possible outcomes of the random experiment (here, the experiment is the sample selection) are given, together with the corresponding probabilities. The only distinction from the probability distributions discussed in Chapter 6 is that the possible outcomes in Table 10.3 refer to the results of a simple random sample rather than to the selection of one element from the population. It is for this reason that the probability distributions in Table 10.3 are called sampling distributions.

(10.1) A *sampling distribution* is a probability distribution where the possible outcomes are the different values a sample statistic may assume.

Thus, we speak of the *sampling distribution of the mean,* or more briefly, of the *sampling distribution of* $\overline{X}$. Similarly, we refer to the *sampling distribution of* $\bar{p}$. In each case, the term *sampling distribution* refers to a probability distribution of sample results.

Table 10.3 Three Sampling Distributions

(a) Sampling Distribution of $\overline{X}$		(b) Sampling Distribution of M_e		(c) Sampling Distribution of $\bar{p}$	
Sample Mean $\overline{X}$	Probability $P(\overline{X})$	Sample Median M_e	Probability $P(M_e)$	Sample Proportion $\bar{p}$	Probability $P(\bar{p})$
31	.1	30	.3	0	.1
32	.1	36	.4	$\frac{1}{3}$	.6
33	.1	39	.3	$\frac{2}{3}$	.3
34	.1		1.0		1.0
35	.2				
36	.2				
37	.1				
39	.1				
	1.0				
$\mu_{\overline{X}} = 34.8$		$\mu_{M_e} = 35.1$		$\mu_{\bar{p}} = .4$	
$\sigma_{\overline{X}} = 2.3$		$\sigma_{M_e} = 3.6$		$\sigma_{\bar{p}} = .2$	

A sampling distribution is interpreted like any other probability distribution. For instance, consider the statement, "The probability is .20 that the sample mean will be 35 years." We interpret this to mean that if a great many simple random samples of three employees are selected from the population, in about two-tenths of these the sample mean will be 35 years.

From any sampling distribution, we can determine the probability that the sample statistic will fall in a specified interval. For instance, from Table 10.3 we can determine the probability that the sample median age is, say, between 35 and 40 years inclusive. The sampling distribution of M_e indicates that this probability is .7.

Since sampling distributions are probability distributions, one can calculate the mean and standard deviation of a sampling distribution according to the definitions in Chapter 6. The only difference is that the variable now is $\overline{X}$, or M_e, or $\bar{p}$, rather than X. Thus $\mu_{\bar{p}}$ stands for the mean of the sampling distribution of $\bar{p}$, $\sigma_{\overline{X}}$ stands for the standard deviation of the sampling distribution of $\overline{X}$, and so on. The mean and standard deviation of each of the sampling distributions under discussion are shown at the bottom of Table

10.3. We shall discuss the calculation of these measures later in this chapter and in the next chapter. Now, however, we shall take a closer look at the three sampling distributions in Table 10.3.

Sampling distribution of $\bar{X}$. Note that the possible values of $\bar{X}$ range from 31 to 39. Also note that the distribution is centered around 34.8 years. This value is the same as the population mean, shown in Table 10.1. It is no coincidence that the sampling distribution of $\bar{X}$ is centered around the population mean; we shall discuss this property in detail later.

It is also interesting to note that the sampling distribution of $\bar{X}$ is not as variable as the population sampled. We have $\sigma_{\bar{X}} = 2.3$ years, while $\sigma_X =$ 5.6 years. This again is characteristic; the sampling distribution of $\bar{X}$ is always less variable than the population sampled.

Sampling distribution of M_e. While only three different outcomes are possible in our example for the sample median, in general there will be many more possible outcomes when the population and sample sizes are larger. Note that the sampling distribution is centered around 35.1, which differs from the population median age of 36 years. Thus, *not every sampling distribution is centered around the corresponding population characteristic.*

Also note that the sampling distribution of M_e is more variable than that of $\bar{X}$. While both the sample median and the sample mean are measures of central tendency, the sample median will vary more from sample to sample than the sample mean. The relative variability of the sampling distribution of $\bar{X}$ is 6.6 per cent, (2.3/34.8), while that of the sampling distribution of M_e is 10.3 per cent. This difference in variability from sample to sample is an important consideration in choosing the sample statistic to be utilized in a study. We shall consider this problem at greater length in Chapter 12.

Sampling distribution of $\bar{p}$. Similar to the sampling distribution of $\bar{X}$, the sampling distribution of $\bar{p}$ is centered around the corresponding population characteristic—namely around the population proportion .4. Note that the relative variability of the sampling distribution of $\bar{p}$ is 50 per cent, which is much greater than that of either of the other two sampling distributions. Intuitively, this greater variability may be ascribed to the fact that $\bar{p}$ ignores the actual ages of the sample employees and considers only whether or not they are under 35 years old.

Recapitulation. We have now shown that for any given sample statistic based on simple random sampling of a particular size from a specified population, there is a sampling distribution of that sample statistic. This sampling distribution indicates:

1. All the various possible values of the sample statistic that can be obtained from all the different possible random samples of given size from the population.
2. The probabilities that these values of the sample statistic will occur.

Note especially that any sampling distribution always refers to:

1. A specific population that is being sampled.
2. A specific random sample size.

If either the population or the random sample size is changed, we obtain a new sampling distribution.

10.2 SIGNIFICANCE OF SAMPLING DISTRIBUTION OF $\overline{X}$

As we have noted, any sample statistic based on a simple random sample is a random variable with an associated probability distribution, called a sampling distribution. We now concentrate on one of these sampling distributions, namely the sampling distribution of $\overline{X}$, in order to examine more thoroughly the properties and significance of sampling distributions. In the next chapter, we shall examine some other sampling distributions.

The sampling distribution of $\overline{X}$ is based on all possible random samples of given size that can be selected from a population. Yet in practice only one random sample is taken. In that case, is the sampling distribution of $\overline{X}$ a useful concept? The answer is emphatically "yes." We now know, when one random sample of given size is selected from the population and the sample mean calculated, that the value of the sample mean actually obtained is merely one out of many possible values that the sample mean could assume. The question then is whether the particular sample mean obtained is close to the population mean.

How does the sampling distribution of the mean help to answer this question? The sampling distribution of $\overline{X}$ in Table 10.3a reveals that no sample mean will differ from the population mean by more than 4.2, (39.0 − 34.8), years—that is, the possible error due to sampling is at most about 12 per cent, $[(4.2/34.8) \cdot 100]$. Furthermore, there is a high probability (.80) that the sample mean will not differ from the population mean by more than 2.8 years (about an 8 per cent error). Thus, we can be fairly confident that any one simple random sample of three employees will indicate the population mean age with an error of not more than about 8 per cent. It is in this way that the sampling distribution of $\overline{X}$, containing the results of all possible random samples, enables us to assess the precision with which we can estimate the population mean on the basis of any one simple random sample.

10.3 PROPERTIES OF SAMPLING DISTRIBUTION OF $\bar{X}$

We refer again to the sampling distribution of $\bar{X}$ in Table 10.3a, which is based upon simple random sampling of three employees from the population in Table 10.1.

Mean

The mean of the sampling distribution of $\bar{X}$ is calculated in the same way as the mean of any other probability distribution. We utilize (6.29), p. 129, but the variable X is now replaced by $\bar{X}$. Table 10.4 contains the calculation of $\mu_{\bar{X}}$, the mean of the sampling distribution of $\bar{X}$.

Table 10.4 Calculation of Mean and Standard Deviation of Sampling Distribution of $\bar{X}$ for Random Sampling of Three Employees

$\bar{X}$ (*Years*)	$P(\bar{X})$	$\bar{X}P(\bar{X})$	$\bar{X} - \mu_{\bar{X}}$	$(\bar{X} - \mu_{\bar{X}})^2$	$(\bar{X} - \mu_{\bar{X}})^2P(\bar{X})$
31	.1	3.1	−3.8	14.44	1.444
32	.1	3.2	−2.8	7.84	.784
33	.1	3.3	−1.8	3.24	.324
34	.1	3.4	− .8	.64	.064
35	.2	7.0	+ .2	.04	.008
36	.2	7.2	+1.2	1.44	.288
37	.1	3.7	+2.2	4.84	.484
39	.1	3.9	+4.2	17.64	1.764
Total	1.0	34.8			5.160

$$\mu_{\bar{X}} = \Sigma \bar{X}P(\bar{X}) = 34.8 \text{ years} \qquad \sigma^2_{\bar{X}} = \Sigma(\bar{X} - \mu_{\bar{X}})^2P(\bar{X}) = 5.16 \qquad \sigma_{\bar{X}} = \sqrt{\Sigma(\bar{X} - \mu_{\bar{X}})^2P(\bar{X})} = \sqrt{5.16} = 2.3 \text{ years}$$

Note carefully the distinction between $\mu_{\bar{X}}$, the mean of the sampling distribution of $\bar{X}$, and μ_X, the mean of the population being sampled. It happens, however, that as we noted earlier, $\mu_{\bar{X}} = \mu_X = 34.8$ years. In other words, the sampling distribution of $\bar{X}$ is centered around a mean that is equal to the population mean μ_X. This illustrates an important statistical theorem, which applies whether the population sampled is finite or infinite:

(10.2) With simple random sampling, $\mu_{\bar{X}}$, the mean of the sampling distribution of $\bar{X}$, is always equal to the population mean μ_X:

$$\mu_{\bar{X}} = \mu_X$$

Theorem (10.2) indicates that, *on the average*, the sample mean based on a simple random sample neither overestimates nor underestimates the population mean. It is for this reason that $\bar{X}$ is called an unbiased estimator of μ_X. By an unbiased estimator is meant the following:

(10.3) A statistic ($\overline{X}$ in our case) is an ***unbiased estimator*** of the parameter under consideration (μ_X in our case) if the sampling distribution of the statistic has a mean equal to the parameter being estimated.

Note that this type of unbiasedness does not refer to bias due to type of questionnaire, interviewer, and the like. Nor does it refer to any one particular sample result, which usually has a definite positive or negative error due to sampling, as is evident from the sampling distribution of $\overline{X}$ that we have examined. The term unbiasedness, as used here, refers only to the tendency of errors due to sampling to cancel out when one considers all possible sample means that can be obtained.

Standard deviation

The standard deviation of the sampling distribution of $\overline{X}$ is calculated in the same way as the standard deviation of any probability distribution. We utilize (6.34), p. 131, with the variable X now replaced by $\overline{X}$. Table 10.4 contains the calculation of $\sigma_{\overline{X}}$. Remember that $\sigma_{\overline{X}}$ is the standard deviation of the sampling distribution of $\overline{X}$. For conciseness, we shall call $\sigma_{\overline{X}}$ the *standard deviation of the sample mean* or the *standard deviation of* $\overline{X}$. Frequently, $\sigma_{\overline{X}}$ is also called the *standard error of the mean.*

Note that $\sigma_{\overline{X}}$ measures the variability of the possible sample means $\overline{X}$ in the sampling distribution of $\overline{X}$; in contrast σ_X, the population standard deviation, measures the variability of the values X in the population. Note also that the standard deviation of $\overline{X}$ in our example is $\sigma_{\overline{X}} = 2.3$ years, which is smaller than the population standard deviation $\sigma_X = 5.6$ years (see Table 10.1). In other words, the probability distribution of the sample mean is not as variable as the population being sampled. Statistical theory has provided the following important theorem that gives the exact relation between $\sigma_{\overline{X}}$ and σ_X for simple random samples from a finite population:

(10.4) $$\sigma_{\overline{X}} = \sqrt{\frac{N-n}{N-1}}\frac{\sigma_X}{\sqrt{n}} \qquad \text{for finite populations}$$

Here N is the population size and n the sample size.

For our example, where $N = 5$, $n = 3$, and $\sigma_X = \sqrt{30.96}$ (see Table 10.1), substitution into (10.4) gives:

$$\sigma_{\overline{X}} = \sqrt{\frac{5-3}{5-1}}\frac{\sqrt{30.96}}{\sqrt{3}} = \sqrt{5.16} = 2.3 \text{ years}$$

This is exactly the same result as we obtained in Table 10.4 by calculating the standard deviation of the probability distribution of $\overline{X}$ in the usual way.

For any given sample size, $\sqrt{\frac{N-n}{N-1}}$ approaches 1 as the population becomes larger and larger. Therefore, with simple random sampling from an infinite population, (10.4) becomes:

$$\text{(10.4a)} \qquad \sigma_{\overline{X}} = \frac{\sigma_X}{\sqrt{n}} \qquad \text{for infinite populations}$$

The term $\sqrt{\dfrac{N-n}{N-1}}$ in (10.4) frequently is called the *finite correction factor.* Because the finite correction factor is almost 1 if the population size is large relative to the sample size, many statisticians use the working rule that the finite correction factor is taken as 1 if the proportion of the population sampled does not exceed 5 per cent. Hence (10.4a), which is applicable in a strict sense only for infinite populations, frequently is used as well for finite populations as long as the sample size is not greater than 5 per cent of the population size.

Approach to normal distribution

In our example, only ten possible sample combinations could occur, because of the very small population and sample sizes. In general, however, the number of possible sample combinations from a finite population is fantastically large. For instance, if one is selecting a simple random sample of 30 items from a population of 5,000 items, the number of possible sample combinations is so large that it takes 79 digits to write out the number. We may ask, therefore, if any generalizations can be made about the nature of sampling distributions of $\overline{X}$, such as whether they are unimodal or symmetrical.

Central limit theorem. One of the most important theorems in statistics, called the *central limit theorem,* tells us in fact about the specific type of distribution that sampling distributions of $\overline{X}$ follow. This theorem states:

(10.5) For almost all populations, the sampling distribution of $\overline{X}$ is approximately normal if the simple random sample size is sufficiently large.

This theorem is applicable when the population is an infinite one, as well as when the population is finite. In the latter case, the population size must be considerably larger than the sample size for the theorem to apply, but this usually is so in practice.

What is a sufficiently large sample size depends upon the nature of the population sampled and upon the degree of approximation to the normal distribution required. For instance, if the population is highly skewed, larger sample sizes are necessary for the central limit theorem to apply than if the population is fairly symmetrical. We shall show below that for many types of populations, the sample size need not be very large for the sampling distribution of $\overline{X}$ to be approximately normal.

When the population being sampled is a normal probability distribution, the central limit theorem is not needed. In that case, we utilize another theorem that states:

(10.6) If the population sampled is a normal probability distribution, the sampling distribution of $\overline{X}$ is exactly normal for any sample size.

Thus, we see that the sampling distribution of $\overline{X}$ is either exactly normal if the population sampled is normal, or approximately normal if the sample size is reasonably large, regardless of the type of non-normal population sampled. Since we often do not know the type of population being sampled, the central limit theorem is particularly important, because it tells us the nature of the sampling distribution of $\overline{X}$ for a reasonably large sample regardless of the type of distribution the population follows. Inasmuch as the central limit theorem is not intuitively self-evident and a formal proof of it is beyond the scope of this book, we shall present some experimental evidence illustrating its operation.

Illustration. Shewhart, a pioneer in the development of statistical quality control, conducted a series of experiments to study empirically the sampling distribution of $\overline{X}$ (Ref. 10.1). He constructed several populations or universes, two of which are shown in Figure 10.1. Note that the rectangular

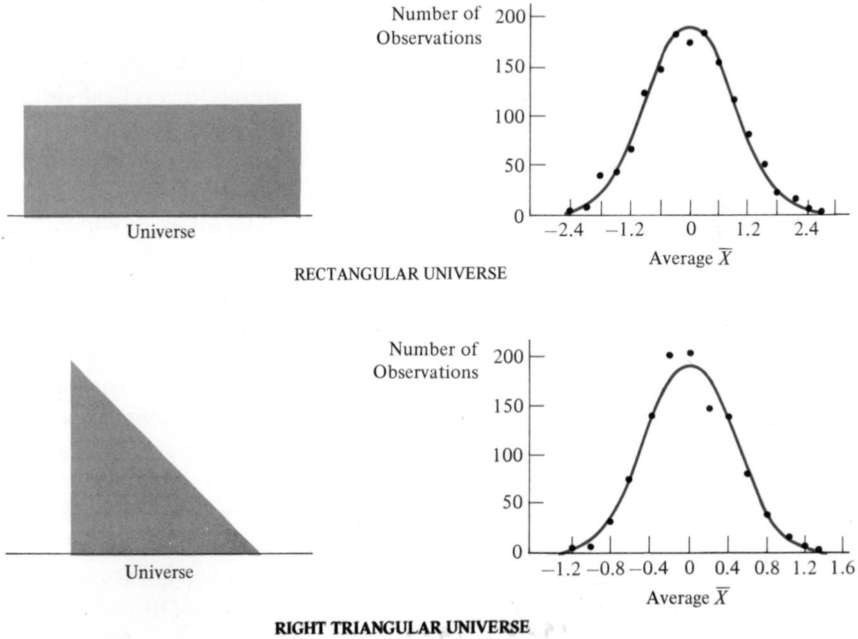

Source: Reprinted by permission from W. A. Shewhart, *Economic Control of Quality of Manufactured Product.* D. Van Nostrand Co., Inc., New York, 1931, p. 182.

Figure 10.1. Shewhart's experimental distributions of $\overline{X}$, based on 1,000 random samples of four observations each from rectangular and right triangular universes

population has no central tendency whatever and the triangular population is skewed. For each population, Shewhart then selected a simple random sample of four observations from the population, calculated $\overline{X}$, replaced the sample into the population, and then selected another simple random sample of four observations. Altogether, he selected 1,000 samples of four observations from each of the populations and calculated $\overline{X}$ for each sample. The distributions of these 1,000 sample means for each population are shown in Figure 10.1 by the dots; corresponding normal distributions also are shown in each graph. Note how close each distribution of $\overline{X}$ is to a normal distribution, although neither population is even slightly similar to a normal one. Note as well that the central limit theorem applies in these instances for sample sizes as small as 4; in other words, samples consisting of only four observations already are large enough here for the sampling distributions of $\overline{X}$ to be approximately normal.

10.4 USE OF THEORY CONCERNING SAMPLING DISTRIBUTIONS OF $\overline{X}$

Example

We now illustrate by example how the various theoretical results concerning sampling distributions of $\overline{X}$ are used together. A company owns a fleet of 2,000 delivery trucks, for each of which it maintains a file containing such information as date of purchase and cost. An estimate of the average age of these 2,000 trucks is needed. The estimate will be obtained by selecting a simple random sample of 100 trucks and using the sample mean age as an estimate of the mean age of the population of 2,000 trucks.

We will assume we know that the population mean age of the trucks is $\mu_X = 3.5$ years and that the standard deviation in this population of 2,000 trucks is $\sigma_X = 1.0$ years. We now are in a position to use statistical theory to describe the sampling distribution of $\overline{X}$ without having to write out all the possible sample combinations, and to calculate the sample means yielded by them.

First, we know that the mean of the sampling distribution of $\overline{X}$ is the same as the mean of the population sampled; hence $\mu_{\overline{X}} = 3.5$ years. Second, since the standard deviation of the population sampled is 1.0 years, statistical theory tells us that the standard deviation of $\overline{X}$ is, by (10.4):

$$\sigma_{\overline{X}} = \sqrt{\frac{2{,}000 - 100}{2{,}000 - 1}}\,\frac{1.0}{\sqrt{100}} = .1 \text{ years}$$

Lastly, we assume that the sample size is large enough in this instance so that the sampling distribution of $\overline{X}$ is approximately normal.

It is essential to distinguish clearly between the population sampled, on the one hand, and, on the other hand, the probability distribution of the sample mean, which indicates the probability that a simple random sample from the population will yield a given sample average. We summarize the distinctions between these two distributions in Table 10.5.

Table 10.5 Characteristics of Population and of Sampling Distribution of $\overline{X}$ for Example

	Population	*Sampling Distribution of* $\overline{X}$
Type of distribution	May be any type of distribution	Approximately normal
Mean	$\mu_X = 3.5$ years	$\mu_{\overline{X}} = 3.5$ years
Standard deviation	$\sigma_X = 1.0$ years	$\sigma_{\overline{X}} = \sqrt{\frac{N-n}{N-1}}\frac{\sigma_X}{\sqrt{n}} = .1$ years

Use of table of normal areas for sampling distribution of $\overline{X}$

We pointed out in Chapter 7 that a normal distribution depends only on its mean and standard deviation. Thus, once we know that the sampling distribution of $\overline{X}$ is normal, that its mean is 3.5 years and its standard deviation is .1 years, we can use the table of normal areas in the usual way. In Chapter 7, the standard normal deviate z was defined for a population whose variable is X, with mean μ_X and standard deviation σ_X, as:

$$z = \frac{X - \mu_X}{\sigma_X}$$

When referring to the sampling distribution of $\overline{X}$, the variable is $\overline{X}$, its mean is $\mu_{\overline{X}}$, and its standard deviation is $\sigma_{\overline{X}}$. Thus, with reference to the sampling distribution of $\overline{X}$, z is:

(10.7) $$z = \frac{\overline{X} - \mu_{\overline{X}}}{\sigma_{\overline{X}}} = \frac{\overline{X} - \mu_X}{\sigma_{\overline{X}}}$$

Note that z is still a standard normal deviate, with a mean of zero and a standard deviation of 1, because $\overline{X}$ (for reasonably large n) is normally distributed, the mean $\mu_{\overline{X}}$ is subtracted from $\overline{X}$, and $\overline{X} - \mu_{\overline{X}}$ is expressed in units of standard deviations of $\overline{X}$.

Thus, the range $\mu_{\overline{X}} \pm \sigma_{\overline{X}}$ will contain about 68.3 per cent of the sample means, the range $\mu_{\overline{X}} \pm 2\sigma_{\overline{X}}$ will contain about 95.4 per cent of the sample means, and so on. For our example, where $\mu_{\overline{X}} = 3.5$ years and $\sigma_{\overline{X}} = .1$ years, we can state that the probability that a simple random sample of 100 trucks will yield a sample mean somewhere between $3.5 \pm .1$ years is about .683. In other words, if we took a great many simple random samples of 100 trucks from this population of 2,000 trucks, about 68.3 per cent of the sample averages would be somewhere between 3.4 and 3.6 years. Similarly, we can state that the probability is about .954 that the sample mean will be between 3.3 and 3.7 years, and that the probability is about .997 that the sample mean will be between 3.2 and 3.8 years.

Let us examine the last probability statement a little more closely. Almost never will a sample mean be less than 3.2 years or more than 3.8 years. Therefore, since the population average age is 3.5 years, almost never will we get a sample average which differs from the population mean by more than about 9 per cent, [(.3/3.5) · 100]. In ordinary practice, of course, we take only one sample, on the basis of which we make an estimate of the population mean. We realize that the particular value of the sample mean $\overline{X}$ which we obtain is but one of many possible values we might have obtained. Since we know, however, that a simple random sample of 100 trucks from the population of 2,000 trucks will nearly always yield an average that is within 9 per cent of the population mean age, we have in this knowledge a measure of the precision of the particular value of $\overline{X}$ actually obtained.

10.5 EFFECT OF SAMPLE SIZE ON SAMPLING DISTRIBUTION OF $\overline{X}$

The variability of the sampling distribution of $\overline{X}$ is affected by the size of the sample and by the variability of the population under study. We consider first the relation between the size of the sample and the variability of the sampling distribution of $\overline{X}$. This relation is illustrated most clearly in the case of an infinite population, for which the standard deviation of $\overline{X}$ is given by:

$$\sigma_{\overline{X}} = \frac{\sigma_X}{\sqrt{n}} \tag{10.4a}$$

Note that the larger the sample size n, the smaller is $\sigma_{\overline{X}}$, so that the probability distribution of the sample mean becomes more concentrated as the sample size is increased.

Consider, for instance, the previous example of the population of 2,000 trucks whose age (number of years since date of purchase) distribution had a mean of 3.5 years and a standard deviation of 1.0 years. Figure 10.2a shows the sampling distribution of $\overline{X}$ for a simple random sample size of 81 trucks; Figure 10.2b shows the distribution for a simple random sample size of 225 trucks. Note that the distribution of $\overline{X}$ is more concentrated for the larger sample size than for the smaller one. This greater concentration means that for the larger sample there is a higher probability that a sample average will be close to the population mean than for the smaller sample. As we shall show in the next chapter, this difference in the probability of a sample average being close to the population mean leads us to say that the sample mean from a large simple random sample gives a more precise

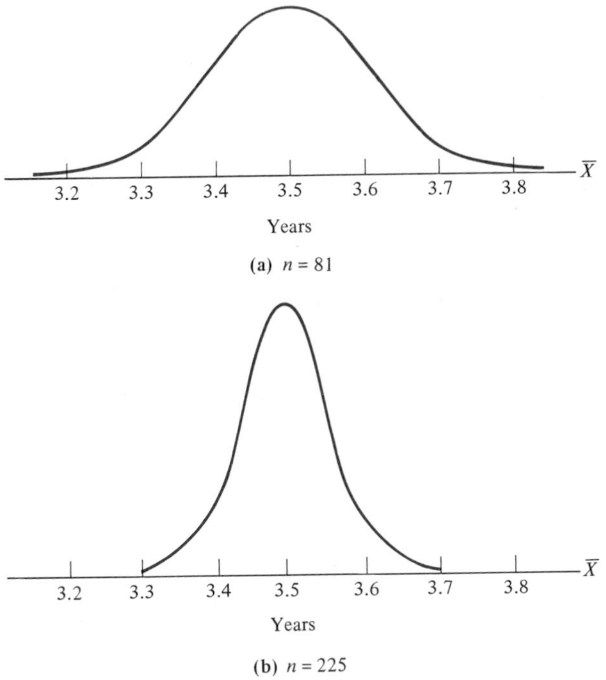

Figure 10.2. Sampling distributions of $\bar{X}$ for simple random samples of 81 and 225 from population with $\mu_X = 3.5$ years and $\sigma_X = 1.0$ years

estimate of the population mean than the sample mean of a small simple random sample.

Equation (10.4a) also indicates the difficulty of reducing the magnitude of $\sigma_{\bar{X}}$ and thereby increasing the probability that a sample mean will be close to the population mean. This difficulty arises because $\sqrt{n}$, not n, is the denominator of $\sigma_{\bar{X}}$. Equation (10.4a) indicates that regarding infinite populations, a quadrupling of sample size is required to reduce the standard deviation of $\bar{X}$ by 50 per cent, and that the sample size must be 16 times as great to reduce the standard deviation by 75 per cent.

10.6 EFFECT OF POPULATION VARIABILITY ON SAMPLING DISTRIBUTION OF $\bar{X}$

An important relationship also exists between the variability of the population and the variability of the sampling distribution of $\bar{X}$. Formulas (10.4) and (10.4a) both indicate that, for any given sample size, the more variable the population—that is, the larger the population standard deviation—the larger is the standard deviation of $\bar{X}$. Therefore, the probability is not as great that a sample mean will be close to the population mean when a sample of given size is selected from a highly variable population as when it is selected from a more uniform population. To put this another way, the less variable the population, the smaller the sample needed to estimate the population mean with given precision.

10.7 NEED FOR SAMPLE INFORMATION ABOUT SAMPLING DISTRIBUTION OF $\overline{X}$

In our previous examples, the population mean and standard deviation were assumed to be known, thus enabling us to derive the mean and standard deviation of the sampling distribution of $\overline{X}$. We made these assumptions to illustrate the meaning of the theorems in a concrete way. In real situations requiring sampling, the population mean and standard deviation are unknown. It then becomes necessary to use the sample from the population first to *estimate* the population mean and standard deviation. Once this is done, one can use the theory explained in this chapter to *estimate* directly the characteristics of the sampling distribution of $\overline{X}$.

Thus, the one sample that is selected will provide information about the distribution of all possible values of the sample mean, a truly remarkable property of simple random sampling. In Chapter 12 we will explain specifically how one can evaluate the precision with which the sample mean estimates the population mean when there is no information about the population other than that provided by the sample.

Cited reference

10.1 Shewhart, W. A., *Economic Control of Quality of Manufactured Product.* New York: D. Van Nostrand Company, Inc., 1931.

QUESTIONS AND PROBLEMS

10.1. Explain briefly each of the following:

a. Unbiasedness
b. Central limit theorem
c. Finite correction factor
d. Standard deviation of $\overline{X}$
e. Sampling distribution

10.2. Distinguish between a population and the sampling distribution of a statistic.

10.3. Distinguish between the sample mean $\overline{X}$, the population mean μ_X, and the mean $\mu_{\overline{X}}$ of the sampling distribution of $\overline{X}$. How do these three means compare in magnitude?

10.4. Distinguish between the sample standard deviation s_X, the population standard deviation σ_X, and the standard deviation $\sigma_{\bar{X}}$ of the sampling distribution of $\bar{X}$. How do these three standard deviations compare in magnitude?

10.5. A student, on studying sampling, asked how there can be a sampling distribution of $\bar{X}$, since only a single sample is selected in practice. Explain to this student the concepts underlying the sampling distributior of $\bar{X}$, and the significance of this distribution.

***10.6.** A population consists of five employees. For this group of employees, the number of days lost from work due to illness during the year was as follows:

Employee	*Number of Days Lost*
A	12
B	5
C	0
D	3
E	0

A simple random sample of three employees is to be selected from this population in order to estimate the mean number of days lost per employee in the population.

a. Calculate the population mean and standard deviation.
b. Obtain the sampling distribution of $\bar{X}$.
c. What is the probability that the sample mean will be: (1) 5? (2) More than 2?
d. What is the probability that the sample mean will differ from the population mean by more than 2 days?
e. Calculate the mean of the sampling distribution of $\bar{X}$. Is it equal to the population mean? Is this always the case?
f. Calculate the standard deviation of the sampling distribution of $\bar{X}$. Does formula (10.4) provide the same result, merely from knowing σ_X?
g. How would the sampling distribution of $\bar{X}$ for a simple random sample of two employees differ from the sampling distribution of $\bar{X}$ in part **b**?

***10.7.** Refer to Problem 10.6.

a. Obtain the sampling distribution of the sample median M_e, given that a simple random sample of three employees is selected.
b. Calculate the mean and standard deviation of this sampling distribution.
c. Is the sample median an unbiased estimator of the population mean here? Explain.
d. How does the variability of the sampling distribution of M_e compare with that of the sampling distribution of $\bar{X}$ in Problem 10.6**f**?
e. Is the sample mean or median the better estimator of the population mean here? Explain the basis of your answer.
f. Calculate the population median. Is the sample median an unbiased estimator of the population median here? Explain.

10.8. A population is composed of five corporations. Last year's dividend yields on the common stocks of these corporations (in per cent) are:

Corporation	*Dividend Yield*
A	0
B	5
C	2
D	4
E	4

A simple random sample of three corporations is to be selected from this population in order that an estimate can be made of the mean dividend yield per corporation in the population.

a. Calculate the population mean and standard deviation.
b. Obtain the sampling distribution of $\bar{X}$.
c. What is the probability that the sample mean will be: (1) 2? (2) Less than 3?
d. What is the probability that the sample mean will differ from the population mean by more than 1 per cent point?
e. Calculate the mean of the sampling distribution of $\bar{X}$. Is it equal to the population mean? Is this always the case?
f. Calculate the standard deviation of the sampling distribution of $\bar{X}$. Does formula (10.4) provide the same result, merely from knowing σ_X?
g. How would the sampling distribution of $\bar{X}$ with a simple random sample of two corporations from the above population differ from the sampling distribution of $\bar{X}$ in part **b**?

10.9. Refer to Problem 10.8.
a. Obtain the sampling distribution of the sample median M_e, given that a simple random sample of three corporations is selected.
b. Calculate the mean and standard deviation of this sampling distribution.
c. Is the sample median an unbiased estimator of the population mean here? Explain.
d. How does the variability of the sampling distribution of M_e compare with that of the sampling distribution of $\bar{X}$ in Problem 10.8**f**?
e. Is the sample mean or median the better estimator of the population mean here? Explain the basis for your answer.
f. Calculate the population median. Is the sample median an unbiased estimator of the population median here? Explain.

***10.10.** In a scrap metal loading process, the weight of metal loaded into freight cars is normally distributed. The process is to be sampled to determine the mean weight of scrap per carload. Suppose that the process mean actually is $\mu_X = 50.0$ tons and the process standard deviation is $\sigma_X = 4.0$ tons.
a. With a simple random sample of 25 carloads, what is the probability that the sample mean will not differ from the process mean by more than 1 ton?
b. With a simple random sample of 25 carloads, the sample mean will fall within what range about 90 per cent of the time? Use symmetrical limits about the process mean.
c. Recalculate the probability in part **a** for each of the following new conditions (in each case, keep other factors at their original values): (1) Quadruple the sample size to 100 carloads. (2) Reduce the process standard deviation to half its previous value, that is, to 2.0 tons. What generalization is suggested by your results?
d. Would the population mean and standard deviation usually be known, as here, in a sampling problem? If not, what are the implications of this?

10.11. A very large population of sales invoices is to be sampled to estimate the mean amount per sale. Suppose that the population mean actually is $\mu_X = \$4,300$ and the population standard deviation is $\sigma_X = \$1,200$.
a. With a simple random sample of 900 sales invoices from this population, what is the probability that the sample mean will be within 2 per cent of the popula-

tion mean? Would you say that a simple random sample of 900 sales invoices from this population is likely to provide a reliable estimate of the population mean? Discuss.

b. With a simple random sample of 900 sales invoices from this population, the sample mean will fall within what range about 99 per cent of the time? Use symmetrical limits around the population mean.

c. Recalculate the probability in part **a** for each of the following new conditions (in each case, keep other factors at their original values): (1) Reduce the sample size to one fourth of its previous value, that is, to 225. (2) Double the population standard deviation to $2,400. What generalization is suggested by your results?

10.12. The Williams Chemical Company fills steel drums with solvent in such a manner that the weight of solvent per drum is normally distributed. The mean weight of solvent in filled drums is to be estimated from a sample. Suppose that the process mean actually is $\mu_X = 363$ pounds and the process standard deviation is $\sigma_X = 1.2$ pounds.

a. What sample size is necessary for the sampling distribution of $\bar{X}$ to be a normal one? Explain.

b. With a simple random sample of 9 drums from the filling process, what is the probability that the sample mean weight of solvent will not be less than 362 pounds?

c. With a simple random sample of 9 drums, the sample mean will fall within what range 95 per cent of the time? Use symmetrical limits around the population mean.

d. What must be the sample size n if the standard deviation of the sampling distribution of $\bar{X}$ is to be $\sigma_{\bar{X}} = .2$ pounds? Show the steps involved in obtaining your answer. Does this suggest that we can control the probability that $\bar{X}$ will be sufficiently close to the process mean by fixing the sample size at an appropriate level? Discuss.

e. Would it usually be the case in a sampling problem that the population is known, as it is here? If not, how can information be obtained about the sampling distribution of $\bar{X}$?

***10.13.** The distribution of small retail establishments in a metropolitan area by number of employees is as follows:

Number of Employees	*Number of Establishments*
0	3,561
1	1,224
2	1,139
3	822
4	536
5	219
Total number of establishments	7,501

A small retail establishment is defined as one with 5 or less employees (exclusive of owners). The mean number of employees per establishment in the population is to be estimated from a simple random sample.

a. What is the probability that the sample mean will not differ from the population mean by more than 10 per cent, with a simple random sample of 100 establishments? (*Hint:* $\mu_X = 1.23$, $\sigma_X = 1.46$) Would you say that a simple random sample of 100 establishments from this population is likely to provide a reliable estimate of the mean number of employees per establishment in the population? Discuss.

b. What would be the probability in part **a** if the sample size were tripled to 300? For such a substantial increase in sample size, has the probability increase been correspondingly large?

c. Ignoring the finite correction factor, what must be the sample size n if the standard deviation of the sampling distribution of $\overline{X}$ is to be $\sigma_{\overline{X}} = .08$ employees? Show the steps involved in obtaining your answer. Does this suggest we can control the probability that $\overline{X}$ will be sufficiently close to the population mean by fixing the sample size at an appropriate level? Discuss. What is the effect of ignoring the finite correction factor here? Explain.

d. The population here is skewed to the right. Are we still justified in using in part **a** the normal probability distribution as an approximation to the true sampling distribution of $\overline{X}$? Explain.

10.14. A simple random sample of 100 items is selected from a process and the sample mean calculated. From the same process, a simple random sample of 1,000 items is also selected and its sample mean calculated.

a. For which of the two cases does the sampling distribution of $\overline{X}$ have smaller variability?

b. Which of the two sample means actually obtained is closer to the population mean? Discuss fully.

10.15. Consider the following three populations:

Population	*Population Size*	*Population Standard Deviation*
I	1,000	\$100
II	10,000	\$100
III	100,000	\$100

A simple random sample of 200 items is to be selected from each of the three populations.

a. Compare the variability in each of the three sampling distributions of $\overline{X}$. Is there much difference in the variability of the sampling distributions of $\overline{X}$ for samples of 200 items from populations I and II? From populations II and III? Discuss your answer.

b. If population III were an infinite one, how much change would this make in the variability of the sampling distribution of $\overline{X}$ for samples of 200 items? What is the significance of your answer?

c. Is the absolute sample size or the relative sample size more important in determining the magnitude of $\sigma_{\overline{X}}$? Explain.

10.16. If a statistic is an unbiased estimator, does this mean that the sample estimate always equals the parameter value to be estimated? That the sample estimate will be less than the parameter value 50 per cent of the time and greater than the parameter value 50 per cent of the time? Discuss.

10.17. Refer to Problem 9.9**a**. Is the sample mean number of children per family for this sample selection of families a biased or an unbiased estimator of the mean number of children per family in the population under study? Explain.

10.18. A simple random sample of inhabitants of a community is selected. The age of the oldest inhabitant in the sample is used as an estimator of the age of the oldest inhabitant in the community. Is this estimator biased or not? Explain.

CLASS PROJECT

10.19. Crandell Motor Freight, Inc., is a small trucking concern located in a medium-size community in a midwestern state. Below, you will find information from 500 freight bills issued during a ten-day period in November 1971 on the amounts of freight charges due Crandell Motor Freight, Inc.:

Bill No.	*Due Crandell*	*Bill No.*	*Due Crandell*	*Bill No.*	*Due Crandell*
000	$1.03	050	$1.14	100	$9.98
001	5.81	051	.53	101	1.21
002	7.28	052	.78	102	1.14
003	3.04	053	3.70	103	.50
004	.86	054	.88	104	1.21
005	1.00	055	5.93	105	2.49
006	.82	056	12.94	106	.74
007	2.02	057	1.32	107	.68
008	3.02	058	2.37	108	.70
009	.87	059	3.97	109	.87
010	1.91	060	.57	110	.63
011	.88	061	10.13	111	.54
012	1.57	062	4.14	112	2.90
013	.89	063	.59	113	1.94
014	2.62	064	.88	114	12.54
015	1.07	065	.68	115	.94
016	.62	066	1.26	116	12.51
017	1.81	067	1.26	117	11.24
018	1.30	068	.58	118	11.24
019	.99	069	.50	119	.70
020	1.15	070	.55	120	7.08
021	5.89	071	.62	121	.87
022	.86	072	.71	122	1.65
023	.59	073	1.53	123	6.52
024	1.65	074	.87	124	1.65
025	.70	075	.70	125	4.44
026	1.02	076	8.06	126	1.15
027	.80	077	.80	127	1.38
028	.77	078	3.11	128	.87
029	.56	079	.64	129	.64
030	2.24	080	.62	130	.79
031	1.63	081	4.81	131	1.23
032	.72	082	1.02	132	2.16
033	.70	083	4.21	133	.82
034	1.57	084	.68	134	.62
035	5.44	085	.54	135	.78
036	.72	086	2.31	136	.72
037	9.86	087	.33	137	3.20
038	1.48	088	.77	138	1.46
039	.70	089	.81	139	1.56
040	.68	090	6.90	140	1.62
041	.62	091	1.83	141	.74
042	4.86	092	5.40	142	.63
043	1.10	093	9.49	143	1.37
044	.63	094	2.26	144	.90
045	11.64	095	4.79	145	.77
046	.64	096	1.40	146	.70
047	1.50	097	.54	147	.70
048	1.66	098	9.42	148	1.08
049	12.86	099	1.18	149	.62

(*Continued*)

Bill No.	*Due Crandell*	*Bill No.*	*Due Crandell*	*Bill No.*	*Due Crandell*
150	$4.00	209	$ .90	268	$ .78
151	1.85	210	7.08	269	1.93
152	.70	211	15.58	270	.52
153	9.47	212	.66	271	.64
154	1.43	213	.66	272	.70
155	3.71	214	.66	273	1.18
156	3.86	215	.66	274	.57
157	1.72	216	.80	275	5.88
158	2.01	217	1.91	276	.70
159	.56	218	.72	277	1.71
160	1.65	219	.50	278	9.67
161	1.65	220	.62	279	.58
162	3.63	221	4.93	280	.91
163	.58	222	4.37	281	1.54
164	.69	223	1.59	282	7.26
165	.69	224	2.46	283	.76
166	.68	225	2.00	284	.74
167	.80	226	1.85	285	.67
168	.84	227	2.42	286	.70
169	3.42	228	1.24	287	1.96
170	4.26	229	.64	288	.72
171	.70	230	.88	289	.88
172	.72	231	.50	290	3.36
173	5.09	232	.50	291	.89
174	.91	233	.50	292	.66
175	1.37	234	.50	293	.78
176	1.23	235	6.60	294	.72
177	1.27	236	.63	295	6.59
178	2.13	237	5.51	296	7.12
179	7.99	238	1.38	297	.65
180	.98	239	4.78	298	12.21
181	.88	240	7.71	299	.80
182	.80	241	.75	300	10.71
183	4.50	242	1.08	301	5.27
184	2.49	243	1.25	302	1.70
185	.85	244	1.78	303	10.62
186	4.06	245	.78	304	.56
187	1.17	246	.78	305	.52
188	.74	247	2.10	306	.47
189	10.99	248	3.45	307	.69
190	4.80	249	1.27	308	.82
191	.67	250	1.12	309	.78
192	.50	251	.80	310	.75
193	.56	252	.82	311	.78
194	2.28	253	.50	312	8.41
195	1.84	254	.87	313	9.08
196	.52	255	5.57	314	.80
197	3.42	256	4.56	315	3.65
198	13.72	257	1.53	316	.80
199	5.12	258	1.57	317	.80
200	.87	259	1.65	318	.64
201	.88	260	.54	319	.80
202	2.57	261	1.09	320	.77
203	.87	262	.81	321	.87
204	13.04	263	.87	322	1.00
205	1.65	264	.95	323	.88
206	1.41	265	1.01	324	.91
207	.88	266	1.75	325	.79
208	.66	267	5.13	326	1.50

Bill No.	*Due Crandell*	*Bill No.*	*Due Crandell*	*Bill No.*	*Due Crandell*
327	$ .64	385	$ .87	443	$ 1.54
328	.93	386	3.21	444	.70
329	.57	387	1.65	445	.77
330	2.45	388	5.76	446	.78
331	.87	389	.68	447	.64
332	.78	390	.62	448	5.63
333	2.34	391	2.16	449	1.01
334	1.87	392	6.88	450	1.10
335	1.75	393	.80	451	1.10
336	1.64	394	2.78	452	1.45
337	.67	395	1.29	453	2.22
338	1.35	396	3.33	454	3.20
339	.64	397	.78	455	.84
340	.76	398	.78	456	3.06
341	.57	399	.68	457	4.74
342	.73	400	.87	458	2.35
343	.70	401	.77	459	1.16
344	.57	402	.68	460	.72
345	.74	403	1.07	461	4.60
346	1.45	404	.58	462	.74
347	.73	405	.74	463	.68
348	1.68	406	.74	464	.70
349	3.61	407	.74	465	.88
350	.73	408	.74	466	.73
351	.70	409	.74	467	.86
352	.70	410	.87	468	.70
353	1.05	411	3.27	469	11.19
354	.76	412	3.07	470	1.77
355	1.00	413	.81	471	.52
356	.57	414	.82	472	.52
357	.80	415	1.75	473	4.30
358	1.35	416	1.34	474	1.39
359	.83	417	2.46	475	9.79
360	.77	418	2.00	476	4.87
361	.78	419	.87	477	1.12
362	3.56	420	6.65	478	1.05
363	6.14	421	1.26	479	1.27
364	.54	422	1.15	480	.78
365	3.07	423	8.52	481	.78
366	3.05	424	1.13	482	.73
367	.70	425	.70	483	3.78
368	.94	426	.72	484	9.58
369	.70	427	.80	485	2.71
370	5.74	428	.55	486	1.78
371	.72	429	1.19	487	3.65
372	4.01	430	.77	488	.78
373	.72	431	5.91	489	5.60
374	4.09	432	1.27	490	.65
375	2.47	433	.77	491	.68
376	2.49	434	.73	492	.96
377	.80	435	.73	493	.95
378	.64	436	.73	494	.63
379	.74	437	.73	495	1.04
380	.58	438	.80	496	.61
381	.80	439	.80	497	11.10
382	3.11	440	.80	498	14.88
383	1.86	441	.80	499	.70
384	.87	442	2.87		

(*Part* **a** *follows*)

a. Construct a frequency distribution of the 500 amounts due Crandell Motor Freight, Inc., in the population under study. Be sure to use an adequately large number of classes.

b. Plot a frequency polygon of the distribution obtained in part **a**.

c. The mean amount of the 500 freight charges is $\mu_X = \$2.23$; their standard deviation is $\sigma_X = \$2.73$. On the basis of this information, what are the mean and standard deviation of the sampling distribution of $\bar{X}$, based on a simple random sample of 50 freight bills from the above population of 500 freight bills?

d. Assuming that the sample size is sufficiently large so that the sampling distribution of $\bar{X}$ is approximately normal, within what range will the sample mean fall 68.3 per cent of the time? 95.4 per cent of the time? 99.7 per cent of the time? Use symmetrical limits around the population mean.

e. Select, by using a table of random digits, 100 independent samples of 50 freight bills each from the population of 500 freight bills.

f. Calculate the sample mean for each sample.

g. Construct a frequency distribution of the 100 sample means, and plot it as a frequency polygon.

h. Does the distribution of the sample means resemble the population pattern of variation? Does it suggest that the sampling distribution of $\bar{X}$ is approximately normal? Discuss.

i. Calculate the mean and standard deviation of the distribution of 100 sample means. Are the results close to those expected from part **c**? Discuss.

j. What per cent of the sample means fell in each of the ranges obtained in part **d**? How do these results compare with the expected percentages? Discuss.

k. Summarize the theoretical aspects of the sampling distribution of $\bar{X}$ that this experiment was intended to illustrate.

Chapter

11

ADDITIONAL TOPICS: SAMPLING DISTRIBUTION OF $\bar{p}$

It often is necessary to make an estimate of, or a decision about, a population proportion, such as the per cent of defective items in a lot or the per cent of consumers holding a given opinion. The sample statistic commonly employed to provide information about a population proportion is the sample proportion. In this chapter, we examine the form and characteristics of the sampling distribution of the sample proportion. *Throughout this chapter, we assume that all sample data result from simple random sampling.*

11.1 EXACT FUNCTIONAL FORM OF SAMPLING DISTRIBUTION OF $\bar{p}$

Let p denote the *population proportion.* On the basis of a simple random sample of size n, the *sample proportion,* denoted by $\bar{p}$, is calculated from:

(11.1) $$\bar{p} = \frac{X}{n}$$

Here X is the number of items in the sample with the given characteristic (number of defective items, number of persons holding a certain opinion, or the like).

In our example in Table 10.1, p. 189, of the previous chapter, the proportion of employees under 35 years old in the population was $p = .4$, and we developed from Table 10.2, p. 190, the sampling distribution of $\bar{p}$ for simple random sampling of three employees from this population. This sampling distribution was shown in Table 10.3c, p. 191. Actually, it was not necessary for us to determine all possible sample combinations in order to derive the sampling distribution of $\bar{p}$. Unlike the sampling distribution of $\overline{X}$, the exact functional form of the sampling distribution of $\bar{p}$ is always known. The sampling distribution of $\bar{p}$ takes two different forms, depending upon whether the population sampled is finite or infinite. We shall now discuss each of these cases in turn.

Hypergeometric probability distribution (finite population sampled)

(11.2) If a simple random sample of n is selected from a finite population of N, in which the population proportion is p, the sampling distribution of $\bar{p}$ is given by the ***hypergeometric probability distribution:***

$$P(\bar{p}) = P\left(\frac{X}{n}\right) = \frac{\binom{Np}{X}\binom{N(1-p)}{n-X}}{\binom{N}{n}}$$

Here X can take on the values 0, 1, 2, up to n or Np, whichever is smaller.[1] The symbol $\binom{x}{y}$ stands for the number of different combinations of y objects that can be formed from x objects, and is defined by:

(11.3) $$\binom{x}{y} = \frac{x!}{y!(x-y)!}$$

where, as was explained previously:

$$x! = (x)(x-1)(x-2)\cdots(2)(1)$$

For instance, the number of different sample combinations of 3 elements that can be formed from a population of 5 elements is:

$$\binom{5}{3} = \frac{5!}{3!(5-3)!} = \frac{5!}{3!2!} = \frac{5\cdot4\cdot3\cdot2\cdot1}{3\cdot2\cdot1\cdot2\cdot1} = 10$$

This is, of course, the same result that we obtained by direct enumeration in Table 10.2, p. 190, of the previous chapter.

We now verify some of the probabilities in Table 10.3c, p. 191. Remember that $N = 5$, $n = 3$, and $p = .4$ for this example. Using (11.2), we obtain:

$$P(\bar{p} = 0) = P\left(\bar{p} = \frac{0}{3}\right) = \frac{\binom{2}{0}\binom{3}{3}}{\binom{5}{3}} = \frac{\frac{2!}{0!2!}\,\frac{3!}{3!0!}}{\frac{5!}{3!2!}} = \frac{1}{10}$$

[1] Actually, the smallest integer X can assume is 0 or $n - N(1-p)$, whichever is larger. Usually, though, 0 is the smallest value that X can take on.

Remember that 0! is defined as being equal to 1. Thus, the numerator is equal to 1, and the denominator is equal to 10, as previously shown.

Similarly, we have:

$$P\left(\bar{p} = \frac{1}{3}\right) = \frac{\binom{2}{1}\binom{3}{2}}{\binom{5}{3}} = \frac{\frac{2!}{1!1!}\,\frac{3!}{2!1!}}{10} = \frac{6}{10}$$

Note that these probabilities are identical to the ones obtained in Table 10.3c from a direct enumeration of all sample combinations.

Formula (11.2) for the hypergeometric probability distribution is easy to interpret. To make the discussion concrete, we shall refer again to the population of Table 10.1, p. 189. The denominator of (11.2) is the number of different sample combinations of n employees that can be formed from the N employees in the population. In this population, there are Np employees under 35, and $N(1-p)$ employees 35 and older. The numerator of (11.2) gives the number of sample combinations that contain X employees under 35. This is obtained as the product of: (1) the number of ways in which X employees under 35 can be selected from the Np employees under 35 in the population, and (2) the number of ways in which $n-X$ employees 35 or older can be selected from the $N(1-p)$ employees 35 or older in the population. Thus, we find that ten sample combinations of 3 employees can be formed from the 5 employees in the population, and that one of these combinations contains no employee under 35, six sample combinations containing 1 employee under 35, and so on.

Binomial probability distribution (infinite population sampled)

When the population is infinite, the exact sampling distribution of $\bar{p}$ can be derived readily from basic probability theorems. We will now show this derivation.

Derivation. Consider a large-scale clerical operation consisting of the calculation of sales invoices in a wholesale supply company. Assume that the probability of an incorrect calculation is equal to $p = .1$ and hence that the probability of a correct calculation is $q = 1 - p = .9$. Further, assume that the outcome on any one calculation is statistically independent of the others. Then, the probability that in a random sample of two calculations, both calculations are incorrect is $p \cdot p = (.1)^2 = .01$. This follows from the fact that the probability of an incorrect calculation is $p = .1$ on each trial, and from the assumed statistical independence of different trials. Remember that with statistical independence, $P(A \text{ and } B) = P(A)P(B)$.

Note that we are sampling here a Bernoulli probability distribution, where $X = 1$ if the calculation is incorrect and $X = 0$ if the calculation is correct.

Further, $P(X = 1) = p = .1$, and $P(X = 0) = q = .9$. Since the two trials are independent, we then have a simple random sample of two observations from this Bernoulli probability distribution.

Similarly, in a random sample of three calculations, the probability that the first two are correct and the last incorrect is:

$$P(0,0,1) = q \cdot q \cdot p = p(q)^2 = (.1)(.9)^2 = .081$$

where $P(0,0,1)$ indicates the probability that the first result is 0 (correct), the second is 0, and the third is 1 (incorrect).

We denote the first sample observation by X_1, the second by X_2, and the third by X_3. Define now:

$$X = X_1 + X_2 + X_3$$

Thus, X is the sum of the three sample observations. Since X_i is equal to zero if the ith sample calculation is correct and equal to 1 if it is incorrect, it can be seen that *X stands for the number of incorrect calculations in the sample.*

Suppose that we are interested in the probability of obtaining one incorrect calculation in a sample of three calculations. In other words, here $n = 3$ and we are interested in the probability that $X = 1$. The probability of .081 just obtained applies only to the case where the one incorrect calculation occurred as the last calculation in the sample. There are two other sample sequences that also contain one incorrect calculation in a sample of three, namely when the one incorrect calculation occurs as the first calculation in the sample and when it occurs as the second. The probabilities of each of these sequences, both containing one incorrect calculation in a sample of three, are respectively:

$$P(1,0,0) = p \cdot q \cdot q = p(q)^2 = (.1)(.9)^2 = .081$$
$$P(0,1,0) = q \cdot p \cdot q = p(q)^2 = (.1)(.9)^2 = .081$$

Thus, we see that the probability of one incorrect calculation in a sample of three for a *specific sample order* is always the same, regardless of the order of the outcomes.

When we wish to determine the probability of getting one incorrect calculation in a sample of three calculations, we do not care about the order of the outcomes, but merely whether one calculation is incorrect in the sample. Since the different orders of outcomes are mutually exclusive—that is, only one order can occur for any given sample—the probability of one incorrect calculation in a sample of three calculations is, by extension of (6.24a), p. 125:

$$\begin{aligned} P(X = 1) &= P(0,0,1 \text{ or } 0,1,0 \text{ or } 1,0,0) \\ &= P(0,0,1) + P(0,1,0) + P(1,0,0) \\ &= .081 + .081 + .081 \\ &= 3(.081) \\ &= .243 \end{aligned}$$

Thus, if the probability of an incorrect calculation is .1, the probability that a random sample of three calculations will contain one incorrect calculation is .243 under the conditions assumed.

In general, the probability of X 1's in a simple random sample of n from a Bernoulli probability distribution *in any specific order* is:

$$p^X q^{n-X}$$

This is simply a generalization of our earlier calculations. There, we had $n = 3$, $p = .1$, $X = 1$.

The number of possible orders or sequences in which X 1's can occur in a sample of n is given by $\binom{n}{X}$, as defined in (11.3). For instance, for $n = 3$, $X = 1$, (11.3) gives:

$$\binom{3}{1} = \frac{3!}{1!2!} = \frac{3 \cdot 2 \cdot 1}{1 \cdot 2 \cdot 1} = 3$$

which is the number of possible orders we obtained by direct enumeration.

We now must combine these two generalizations to obtain the probability of X 1's, denoted by $P(X)$, in a random sample of n from a Bernoulli probability distribution. Since there are $\binom{n}{X}$ different (and mutually exclusive) sequences, each containing X 1's in a sample of size n, and since each of these sequences has a probability of $p^X q^{n-X}$ of occurring, $P(X)$ is simply the sum of $\binom{n}{X}$ probabilities, each with the value $p^X q^{n-X}$, or:

$$P(X) = \binom{n}{X} p^X q^{n-X} \tag{11.4}$$

We now calculate the probabilities that $X = 0$, 1, 2, and 3 for our previous example. The probability of no incorrect calculation in a sample of three calculations is:

$$P(0) = \binom{3}{0}(.1)^0(.9)^3 = \frac{3 \cdot 2 \cdot 1}{1 \cdot 3 \cdot 2 \cdot 1}(.1)^0(.9)^3 = .729$$

The probability of one incorrect calculation in a sample of three calculations is:

$$P(1) = \binom{3}{1}(.1)^1(.9)^2 = \frac{3 \cdot 2 \cdot 1}{1 \cdot 2 \cdot 1}(.1)^1(.9)^2 = .243$$

The probability of two incorrect calculations in a sample of three calculations is:

$$P(2) = \binom{3}{2}(.1)^2(.9)^1 = \frac{3 \cdot 2 \cdot 1}{2 \cdot 1 \cdot 1}(.1)^2(.9)^1 = .027$$

The probability of three incorrect calculations in a sample of three calculations is:

$$P(3) = \binom{3}{3}(.1)^3(.9)^0 = \frac{3 \cdot 2 \cdot 1}{3 \cdot 2 \cdot 1 \cdot 1}(.1)^3(.9)^0 = .001$$

We now need to take only one more step in order to obtain the sampling distribution of $\bar{p}$. Since $\bar{p} = X/3$ for our example, $\bar{p} = 0$ only if $X = 0$, $\bar{p} = 1/3$ only if $X = 1$, and so on. Hence the probabilities for different values of $\bar{p}$ are the same as for the corresponding values of X. Hence, we have:

$$P(\bar{p}) = P\left(\frac{X}{n}\right) = \binom{n}{X}p^X q^{n-X}$$

Thus:

(11.5) If a simple random sample of n is selected from an infinite population, in which the population proportion is p, the sampling distribution of $\bar{p}$ is given by the ***binomial probability distribution:***

$$P(\bar{p}) = P\left(\frac{X}{n}\right) = \binom{n}{X}p^X q^{n-X}$$

Here X can take on the values 0, 1, 2, . . . , n.

The sampling distribution of $\bar{p}$, when $n = 3$, $p = .1$, and the population is infinite, is shown in Table 11.1.

Table 11.1 Binomial Probability Distribution and Calculation of Its Mean and Standard Deviation ($p = .1$, $n = 3$)

Proportion of Incorrect Calculations $\bar{p} = \frac{X}{n}$	$P(\bar{p})$	$\bar{p}P(\bar{p})$	$\bar{p} - \mu_{\bar{p}}$	$(\bar{p} - \mu_{\bar{p}})^2$	$(\bar{p} - \mu_{\bar{p}})^2P(\bar{p})$
0	.729	0	−.1000	.0100	.007290
$\frac{1}{3} = .3333$	.243	.081	.2333	.0544	.013219
$\frac{2}{3} = .6667$	.027	.018	.5667	.3211	.008670
$\frac{3}{3} = 1$	.001	.001	.9000	.8100	.000810
Total	1.000	.100			.03

$\mu_{\bar{p}} = \Sigma\bar{p}P(\bar{p}) = .10$ $\quad\sigma^2_{\bar{p}} = \Sigma(\bar{p} - \mu_{\bar{p}})^2P(\bar{p}) = .03$ $\quad\sigma_{\bar{p}} = \sqrt{\Sigma(\bar{p} - \mu_{\bar{p}})^2P(\bar{p})} = \sqrt{.03} = .17$

Table of binomial probabilities. Tables, such as those in Reference 11.1, are available where binomial probabilities are given, so that one need not go through actual calculations. Table A-4 is an excerpt from such a table.

Note that this table provides binomial probabilities for selected values of p and for small values of n. For instance, if $p = .30$ and $n = 4$, we can determine at once that the probability is .2401 that $\bar{p} = 0$, that the probability is .4116 that $\bar{p} = 1/4$, and so forth.

The tables of binomial probabilities generally provide only probabilities for smaller sample sizes. The reason is that the central limit theorem applies to the sampling distribution of $\bar{p}$, as will be seen, so that one can approximate the binomial probability distribution with the normal distribution for larger n. Hence, one need not go through the tedious, though exact, calculations based on the binomial distribution if n is large.

11.2 CHARACTERISTICS OF SAMPLING DISTRIBUTION OF $\bar{p}$

Skewness

The sampling distribution of $\bar{p}$ is skewed to the right if p is less than .5, and skewed to the left if p is greater than .5, whether the population sampled is finite or infinite.[2] Note the skewness to the right in the sampling distribution of $\bar{p}$ in Table 11.1, where $p = .1$. Only if $p = .5$ is the sampling distribution of $\bar{p}$ exactly symmetrical.

As the sample size becomes larger, however, the sampling distribution of $\bar{p}$ becomes more and more symmetrical, for any given value of the population proportion p. Thus, for reasonably large sample sizes, the sampling distribution of $\bar{p}$ is approximately symmetrical.

Mean

(11.6) Whether the population sampled is finite or infinite, the mean of the sampling distribution of $\bar{p}$ is always equal to the population proportion p, that is:

$$\mu_{\bar{p}} = p$$

The reader should verify this for the sampling distribution of $\bar{p}$ in Table 10.3c, p. 191, where the population was finite. We simply show there the final result that $\mu_{\bar{p}} = p = .4$. In Table 11.1, we show the actual calculation of $\mu_{\bar{p}}$ from the sampling distribution of $\bar{p}$ where the population was infinite, in other words, where a Bernoulli probability distribution was sampled. The calculation of $\mu_{\bar{p}}$ is straightforward. We utilize the definition in (6.29), p. 129, again, but now the variable X is replaced by $\bar{p}$. As expected, we find that $\mu_{\bar{p}} = p = .10$.

---

[2] For the hypergeometric distribution, this comment on skewness applies only if the sample size is less than half the population size, which is the usual case in practice.

Thus, the sample proportion $\bar{p}$ is an unbiased estimator of the population proportion p, since, on the average, $\bar{p}$ neither overestimates nor underestimates p.

We now examine the case of sampling a Bernoulli probability distribution a little further. The ith sample observation can take on the values $X_i = 0$ or 1. We define:

$$X = X_1 + X_2 + \cdots + X_n$$

where X represents the number of 1's in the sample of n. Now $\bar{p} = \frac{X}{n} = \frac{X_1 + X_2 + \cdots + X_n}{n}$. Hence, $\bar{p}$ here is nothing but a sample mean $\overline{X}$, but for the special case where the sample observations can only be 0 or 1. Since we know from (10.2) that $\mu_{\overline{X}} = \mu_X$ always, and since we further know from (7.2) that the mean of the Bernoulli distribution is p, it follows that $\mu_{\bar{p}} = p$ for the case of sampling from a Bernoulli distribution.

Standard deviation

The calculation of the standard deviation of the sampling distribution of $\bar{p}$ is again straightforward. We utilize the definition in (6.34), p. 131, but replace the variable X by $\bar{p}$. In Table 11.1, we present the calculation of $\sigma_{\bar{p}}$ for the case of sampling an infinite population. The reader should also verify the value of $\sigma_{\bar{p}}$ in Table 10.3c, p. 191, for the sampling distribution of $\bar{p}$ where the population sampled was finite.

Fortunately, we need not develop the sampling distribution of $\bar{p}$ in order to determine how variable the sample proportion $\bar{p}$ is from sample to sample. Statistical theory indicates that with simple random sampling, the standard deviation of the sampling distribution of $\bar{p}$ is always equal to:

(11.7) $$\sigma_{\bar{p}} = \sqrt{\frac{N-n}{N-1}}\sqrt{\frac{p(1-p)}{n}}$$ for finite populations

(11.7a) $$\sigma_{\bar{p}} = \sqrt{\frac{p(1-p)}{n}}$$ for infinite populations

We now verify that the results from statistical theory are identical to those we obtained directly from the sampling distribution of $\bar{p}$, for the two cases we considered. In the first case, the population was finite. We had $N = 5$, $n = 3$, $p = .4$. Hence, (11.7) indicates that:

$$\sigma_{\bar{p}} = \sqrt{\frac{N-n}{N-1}}\sqrt{\frac{p(1-p)}{n}} = \sqrt{\frac{5-3}{5-1}}\sqrt{\frac{(.4)(.6)}{3}} = .2$$

This, of course, is the same result as that shown in Table 10.3c based on direct calculation from the sampling distribution.

In our second example, the population was infinite. We had $p = .1$, $n = 3$. Hence (11.7a) indicates that:

$$\sigma_{\bar{p}} = \sqrt{\frac{p(1-p)}{n}} = \sqrt{\frac{(.1)(.9)}{3}} = .17$$

Again, we obtain the same result as that based on a direct calculation from the sampling distribution, shown in Table 11.1.

We conclude this section by further discussing (11.7a) for the case of sampling an infinite population. It will be recalled that $\bar{p}$ in this case is $\bar{X}$, with the sample observations restricted to 0 or 1. We know from (10.4a) that $\sigma_{\bar{X}}^2 = \sigma_X^2/n$, when the population is infinite. We further know from (7.3) that the variance of a Bernoulli probability distribution is $\sigma_X^2 = pq = p(1-p)$. Hence, it follows that $\sigma_{\bar{p}}^2 = p(1-p)/n$, when the population is infinite.

Approach to normal distribution

The central limit theorem is applicable to the sampling distribution of $\bar{p}$. Thus:

(11.8) The sampling distribution of $\bar{p}$ is approximately normal if the simple random sample size is sufficiently large.

For finite populations, the population size must be considerably larger than the sample size if this theorem is to apply, but such would usually be the case in practice.

A working rule frequently used to indicate situations in which the sampling distribution of $\bar{p}$ may be approximated by a normal distribution states that the normal approximation is appropriate if *both* np and $n(1-p)$ are greater than 5. Thus, a sample of only 20 from a population in which $p = .3$ would already be large enough for the sampling distribution of $\bar{p}$ to be approximately normal because $np = (20)(.3) = 6$ and $n(1-p) = (20)(1-.3) = 14$.

Figure 11.1 shows graphically how the sampling distribution of $\bar{p}$ approaches normality as the sample size becomes larger. In this case, an infinite population is being sampled in which $p = .4$. The distributions of $\bar{p}$ for $n = 10$ and $n = 45$ are shown. Note how well the tops of the lines of the distribution of $\bar{p}$ for $n = 45$ outline a normal distribution.

11.3
USE OF THEORY CONCERNING SAMPLING DISTRIBUTION OF $\bar{p}$

By an example we now show how the various theoretical results concerning sampling distributions of $\bar{p}$ are used together. Suppose that we are sampling a population of 100,000 retail establishments, of which 30 per cent are food stores. What is the probability that a simple random sample of 100 stores from this population will give us an estimate of the proportion

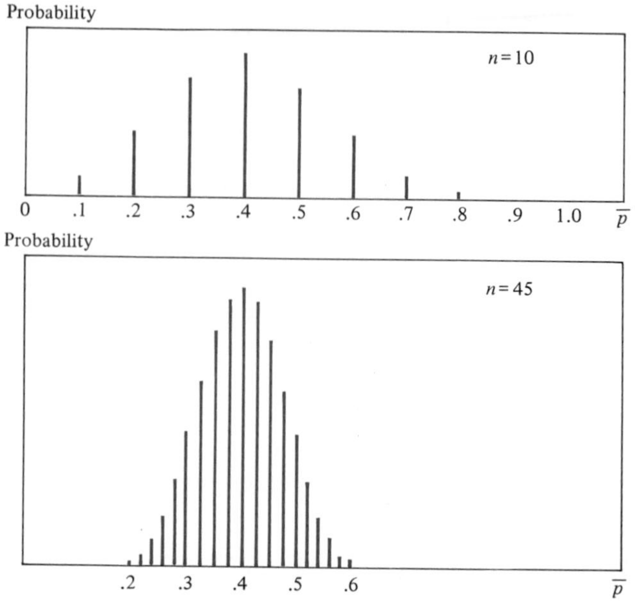

Figure 11.1. Sampling distributions of $\bar{p}$ for simple random samples of 10 and 45 from infinite population with $p = .40$

of food stores in the population within 10 per cent points of the population proportion?

We are told that $N = 100{,}000$, $p = .3$, $n = 100$. Therefore, we know at once that the sampling distribution of $\bar{p}$ is approximately normal [$np = 30$ and $n(1 - p) = 70$], that the mean of the distribution is $\mu_{\bar{p}} = p = .3$, and that the standard deviation of the distribution is:

$$\sigma_{\bar{p}} = \sqrt{\frac{100{,}000 - 100}{100{,}000 - 1}}\sqrt{\frac{(.3)(.7)}{100}} = .046$$

The normal approximation to the sampling distribution of $\bar{p}$ is shown in Figure 11.2; the desired area is also indicated in the chart.

We make use of the table of normal areas as usual, except that the standard normal deviate z now is:

$$z = \frac{\bar{p} - \mu_{\bar{p}}}{\sigma_{\bar{p}}} = \frac{\bar{p} - p}{\sigma_{\bar{p}}} \tag{11.9}$$

Again, z is normally distributed (because $\bar{p}$ is approximately normally distributed for large enough n), with mean zero (because the mean $\mu_{\bar{p}}$ of the distribution of $\bar{p}$ is subtracted) and with standard deviation 1 (because $\bar{p} - \mu_{\bar{p}}$ is expressed in units of the standard deviation of the distribution of $\bar{p}$).

The z value corresponding to $\bar{p} = .4$ is:

$$z = \frac{.4 - .3}{.046} = 2.17$$

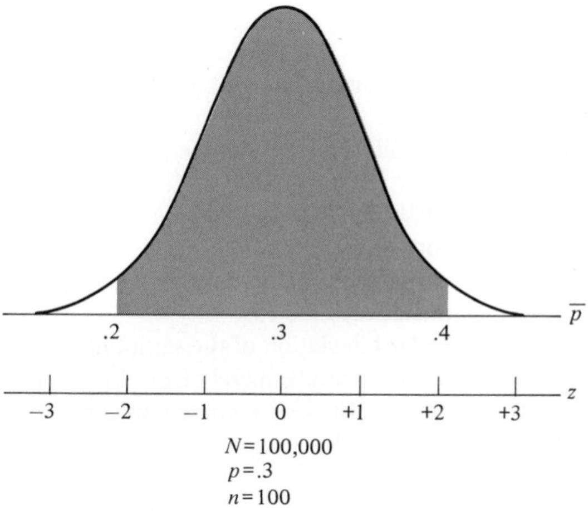

Figure 11.2. Normal approximation to sampling distribution of $\bar{p}$ for example

Hence, the probability that $\bar{p}$ is between .3 and .4 is .485, and by symmetry, the probability that $\bar{p}$ is between .2 and .4 is .97.

Cited reference

11.1 *Tables of the Binomial Probability Distribution,* National Bureau of Standards, Applied Mathematics Series 6. Washington, D.C.: U.S. Government Printing Office, 1949.

QUESTIONS AND PROBLEMS

11.1. Explain briefly each of the following:
a. Population proportion
b. Hypergeometric probability distribution
c. Table of binomial probabilities

11.2. Distinguish briefly between:
a. Population proportion and sample proportion
b. Binomial and hypergeometric probability distributions

***11.3.** A population of five stores is to be sampled to estimate the proportion of stores in the population that carry a certain brand of hair shampoo. Suppose that the population actually is as follows:

Store	*Characteristic*
A	Carries product
B	Does not carry product
C	Does not carry product
D	Carries product
E	Carries product

A simple random sample of two stores is to be selected from this population.

a. What proportion of stores in the population carry the product?

b. Obtain the sampling distribution of $\bar{p}$ by enumeration of all possible sample combinations.

c. What is the probability that the sample proportion will be: (1) 1? (2) Less than .50?

d. What is the probability that the sample proportion will not differ from the population proportion by more than .20?

e. Calculate the mean of the sampling distribution of $\bar{p}$. Is it equal to the population proportion? Is this always the case?

f. Calculate the standard deviation of the sampling distribution of $\bar{p}$. Does formula (11.7) provide the same result, merely from knowing p?

g. Would the population usually be known, as here, in a sampling problem? Discuss the implications of this.

11.4. Refer to Problem 11.3.

a. Obtain the sampling distribution of $\bar{p}$ in Problem 11.3**b** directly from the hypergeometric probability distribution.

b. How would the sampling distribution of $\bar{p}$ with a simple random sample of four stores from the population in Problem 11.3 differ from the sampling distribution of $\bar{p}$ in part **a**?

c. Develop the sampling distribution of X, the number of stores in the sample that carry the product, for a simple random sample size of two. What is the relation of this sampling distribution to the sampling distribution of $\bar{p}$ in part **a**?

11.5. A population of six persons is to be sampled to estimate the proportion of persons in the population who are over 40 years of age. Suppose that the population is actually as follows:

Person	*Age*
A	Over 40
B	Over 40
C	Not over 40
D	Over 40
E	Not over 40
F	Over 40

A simple random sample of three persons is to be selected from this population.

a. What proportion of persons in the population are over 40 years of age?

b. Obtain the sampling distribution of $\bar{p}$ by enumerating all possible sample combinations.

c. What is the probability that the sample proportion will be: (1) 1/3? (2) More than .5?

d. What is the probability that the sample proportion will not differ from the population proportion by more than .3?

e. Calculate the mean of the sampling distribution of $\bar{p}$. Is it equal to the population proportion? Is this always the case?

f. Calculate the standard deviation of the sampling distribution of $\bar{p}$. Does formula (11.7) provide the same result, merely from knowing p?

11.6. Refer to Problem 11.5.

a. Obtain the sampling distribution of $\bar{p}$ in Problem 11.5**b** directly from the hypergeometric probability distribution.

b. How would the sampling distribution of $\bar{p}$ with a simple random sample of two persons from the population in Problem 11.5 differ from the sampling distribution of $\bar{p}$ in part **a**?

c. Develop the sampling distribution of X, the number of persons in the sample who are over 40 years of age, for a simple random sample size of three. What is the relation of this sampling distribution to the sampling distribution of $\bar{p}$ in part **a**?

***11.7.** In a population of five files, the proportion that contains incorrectly filed material is $p = 1/5$. A simple random sample of three files is to be selected.

a. Find the probability that the sample proportion $\bar{p} = 1/3$.

b. Find the probability that X, the number of files in the sample containing incorrectly filed material, is 0.

c. Why would it be inappropriate to use the binomial probability distribution in the above calculations? Discuss.

11.8. In a population of six automobiles, the proportion that will not be operating three years later is $p = 1/3$. A simple random sample of four automobiles is to be selected.

a. Find the probability that the sample proportion $\bar{p} = 1/2$.

b. Find the probability that X, the number of automobiles in the sample that will not be operating three years later, is 1.

c. Why would it be inappropriate to use the binomial probability distribution in the above calculations? Discuss.

11.9. a. Does the sampling distribution of $\bar{p}$ have the same functional form whether the simple random sampling is from an infinite or a finite population? Explain.

b. Describe the conditions when the binomial probability distribution is applicable. Give an example in which these conditions are met, in your opinion, and explain why you think so.

c. Describe the conditions when the hypergeometric probability distribution is applicable. Give an example in which these conditions are met, in your opinion, and explain why you think so.

***11.10.** The probability that a new employee will still be with the firm after one year is .45. Assume that the binomial probability distribution is applicable.

a. Specify the Bernoulli probability distribution being sampled.

b. Obtain the sampling distribution of $\bar{p}$, the proportion of seven new employees who will still be with the firm after one year.

c. What is the probability that the sample proportion will be: (1) 4/7? (2) Less than 3/7?

d. Calculate the mean of the sampling distribution of $\bar{p}$. Is the result the same as expected from formula (11.6)?

e. Calculate the standard deviation of the sampling distribution of $\bar{p}$. Does formula (11.7a) provide the same result, merely from knowing p?

11.11. Refer to Problem 11.10.

a. Graph the sampling distribution of $\bar{p}$ in Problem 11.10**b**.

b. Is the sampling distribution skewed? When is the binomial probability distribution symmetrical?

c. Obtain the sampling distribution of X, the number of new employees in the sample of seven who will still be with the firm after one year. How is this distribution related to the sampling distribution in Problem 11.10**b**?

d. How would the sampling distribution of $\bar{p}$ for 20 new employees differ from that in Problem 11.10**b**?

11.12. The probability that a fire call is a false alarm is .10. Assume that the binomial probability distribution is applicable.

a. Specify the Bernoulli probability distribution being sampled.

b. Obtain the sampling distribution of $\bar{p}$, the proportion of false alarms in four fire calls.

c. What is the probability that the sample proportion will be: (1) .25? (2) More than .50?

d. Calculate the mean of the sampling distribution of $\bar{p}$. Is the result the same as expected from formula (11.6)?

e. Calculate the standard deviation of the sampling distribution of $\bar{p}$. Does formula (11.7a) provide the same result, merely from knowing p?

11.13. Refer to Problem 11.12.

a. Graph the sampling distribution of $\bar{p}$ in Problem 11.12**b**.

b. Is the sampling distribution skewed? When is the binomial probability distribution symmetrical?

c. Obtain the sampling distribution of X, the number of false alarms in the sample of four fire calls. How is this distribution related to the sampling distribution in Problem 11.12**b**?

d. How would the sampling distribution of $\bar{p}$ for 50 fire calls differ from that in Problem 11.12**b**?

***11.14.** The probability that a person will respond to a mail advertisement is .3. Assuming that the binomial probability distribution is applicable, what is the probability that:

a. One out of a group of ten persons will respond?

b. More than four persons out of a group of eight persons will respond?

11.15. The probability of a defective part is .05. Assuming that the binomial probability distribution is applicable, what is the probability that:

a. Two out of ten parts are defective?

b. Not more than one out of six parts are defective?

11.16. An auditor will consider the vouchers of a company satisfactory only if there are no vouchers with errors in a sample of 30 vouchers. Assume that the binomial probability distribution is applicable.

a. What is the probability that the auditor will conclude that the company vouchers are satisfactory if the probability of a voucher with errors is .01? .05?

b. Is the probability of no vouchers with errors in a sample of 30 vouchers very small if the probability of a voucher with errors is .05? Would this probability be smaller with a larger sample size? Discuss.

c. If the auditor were concerned with a group of 100 vouchers and selected 30 vouchers at random from these 100, would the binomial probability distribution be appropriate for calculating the probability that the sample contains no vouchers with errors? Discuss.

11.17. A person is to be tested as to whether he can differentiate between the taste of two brands of cigarettes. If he cannot differentiate, it is assumed that the probability is one-half that he will identify a cigarette correctly. Under which of the following two procedures is there less chance that he will make all correct identifications when he actually cannot differentiate between the two tastes? Use the binomial probability distribution.

a. The subject is given three pairs, each containing both brands of cigarettes (this is known to the subject); he must identify for each pair which cigarette represents each brand.

b. The subject is given six cigarettes and is told that the first three are of one brand and the last three of the other brand.

c. How do you explain the difference in results despite the fact that six cigarettes are tested in each instance?

***11.18.** In repairing a certain type of packaging machine, a complication requiring outside technical assistance arises occasionally. It is desired to estimate the proportion of repair jobs requiring outside assistance on the basis of a simple random sample of 100 repair jobs completed recently. Suppose that outside assistance is actually required in 15 per cent of the repair jobs, that is, the process proportion is $p = .15$.

a. What are the mean and standard deviation of the sampling distribution of $\bar{p}$?

b. Can this sampling distribution of $\bar{p}$ be approximated by a normal distribution? Explain.

c. What is the probability that $\bar{p}$ is within .05 of the process proportion? That $\bar{p}$ is between .12 and .20?

d. Within what range will the sample proportion fall 90 per cent of the time? Use symmetrical limits around the process proportion.

e. What is the range corresponding to part **d** for a simple random sample of 400 jobs? What effect does the increase in sample size have? Discuss.

f. For any given sample size, is the sampling distribution of $\bar{p}$ most variable if p is close to 0, if p is .5, or if p is close to 1?

11.19. A machine is to be observed at random points of time to estimate the proportion of time it is "down," that is, not in a productive state. Suppose that the proportion of down-time for the machine is actually $p = .25$. A simple random sample of 250 observations is to be selected.

a. What are the mean and standard deviation of the sampling distribution of $\bar{p}$?

b. Can this sampling distribution of $\bar{p}$ be approximated by a normal distribution? Explain.

c. What is the probability that $\bar{p}$ is within .05 of the process proportion?

d. What must be the sample size n if the standard deviation of the sampling distribution of $\bar{p}$ is to be $\sigma_{\bar{p}} = .02$? Show the steps involved in obtaining your answer.

e. If the process proportion of down-time were $p = .10$, what would be the probability with a simple random sample of 250 observations that $\bar{p}$ is within .05 of the process proportion? How does this probability compare with the corresponding one in part **c**? Discuss.

f. Would the process proportion usually be known, as here, in a sampling problem? If not, what are the implications of this?

11.20. A shipment of 5,000 parts is to be sampled to determine if it is of acceptable quality. Suppose that the proportion defective in the shipment is actually .10. A simple random sample of 225 parts is to be selected.

a. What are the mean and standard deviation of the sampling distribution of $\bar{p}$?

b. Can this sampling distribution of $\bar{p}$ be approximated by a normal distribution? Explain.

c. What is the probability that $\bar{p}$ is within .03 of the population proportion?

d. Within what range will the sample proportion fall 98 per cent of the time? Use symmetrical limits around the population proportion. *(Continued)*

e. Ignoring the finite correction factor, what must be the sample size n if the standard deviation of the sampling distribution of $\bar{p}$ is to be $\sigma_{\bar{p}} = .01$? Show the steps involved in obtaining your answer. What is the effect of ignoring the finite correction factor here?

f. If the proportion defective in the shipment were .05, what would be the probability with a simple random sample of 225 parts that $\bar{p}$ is within .03 of the population proportion? How does this probability compare with the corresponding one in part **c**? Discuss the implications of this.

g. Would the population proportion usually be known, as here, in a sampling problem? If not, what are the implications?

CLASS PROJECT

11.21. Refer to Problem 10.19. It is desired to estimate the proportion of freight bills in the population for which the amount of freight charges due Crandell Motor Freight, Inc., is \$1.50 or less. A simple random sample of 50 freight bills is to be used.

a. The proportion of freight bills for which the amount of freight charges due Crandell Motor Freight, Inc., is \$1.50 or less is $p = .636$ in the population of 500 freight bills. On the basis of this information, what are the mean and standard deviation of the sampling distribution of $\bar{p}$?

b. Can this sampling distribution of $\bar{p}$ be approximated by a normal distribution? Explain.

c. Within what range will the sample proportion fall 68.3 per cent of the time? 95.4 per cent of the time? 99.7 per cent of the time? Use symmetrical limits around the population proportion.

d. Select, by using a table of random digits, 100 independent samples of 50 freight bills each from the population of 500 freight bills.

e. Calculate the proportion of freight bills with \$1.50 or less in freight charges due Crandell Motor Freight, Inc., for each sample.

f. Construct a frequency distribution of the 100 sample proportions, and plot it as a frequency polygon. Does the frequency polygon suggest that the sampling distribution of $\bar{p}$ is approximately normal?

g. Calculate the mean and standard deviation of the distribution of 100 sample proportions. Are the results close to those expected from part **a**? Discuss.

h. What per cent of the sample proportions fell into each of the ranges obtained in part **c**? How do these results compare with the expected percentages? Discuss.

i. Summarize the theoretical aspects of the sampling distribution of $\bar{p}$ that this experiment was intended to illustrate.

Unit

IV

STATISTICAL ESTIMATION

Chapter

12

ESTIMATION OF POPULATION MEAN

In this chapter, we build on the foundation laid in the previous chapter and explain how population characteristics are estimated from sample data. We then introduce the basic ideas of statistical estimation in terms of estimating a population mean.

12.1 SOME TYPICAL ESTIMATION PROBLEMS

Statistical estimation of population characteristics is needed in a wide variety of circumstances. A class of situations frequently requiring statistical estimation is scientific reporting. Thus an economist wishes to report an estimate of the number of families who are poverty-stricken according to his definition. Again, a market researcher wishes to report the difference in amount of attitude shift induced by two advertisements, one containing direct quotations from a respected source, the other containing indirect references only. In each of these cases, the reporting of the estimate serves primarily to convey new knowledge to other persons, and no direct, immediate action is contemplated on the basis of the estimate. Indeed, the estimate may be used subsequently in different ways by different persons.

Slightly different is the case of an operations analyst who is investigating three alternative inventory policies for a firm. He has constructed an appropriate model and now needs estimates of the average weekly demand for the different items carried in stock. Here, a decision on the best inventory policy is presumably forthcoming, but the estimates of demand may not be the pivotal variables on the basis of which the decision is to be made. For instance, the demand estimates may serve merely as the basis for extrapolating future demands.

In still other cases, statistical estimation provides information for decision-making, but without a formal model being utilized for this purpose. For instance, a sales manager may request an estimate of the number of households with two or more automobiles in a marketing area, but will consider many other factors in his evaluation before deciding on the details of a sales campaign.

It is evident from these examples that statistical estimation is used to furnish information about population characteristics when no immediate decision is to be based directly on this particular information. In later chapters, we shall consider statistical decision-making where decisions follow directly from the sample data, such as when an inspector accepts or rejects a shipment on the basis of the number of defective items that are found in a sample from the shipment.

12.2 POINT ESTIMATION OF POPULATION MEAN

We discuss in this section some basic concepts of statistical estimation. To make the discussion specific, we restrict ourselves at this point to the case where the population characteristic to be estimated is the *population mean* and the method of sampling employed is *simple random sampling.*

The example we shall utilize is a simple one. The Thurston Corporation employs about 2,000 persons. One of its officials had to report on the average length of service of employees in the company. This information could be obtained from the personnel files. Since a census of these files would be too time-consuming, a simple random sample of 50 files—in effect, a sample of 50 employees—was to be selected. The population mean μ_X (average length of service with the company of the 2,000 employees) then was to be estimated on the basis of this simple random sample.

One word of caution is needed before we begin our discussion of statistical estimation. The population mean about which the sample of 50 files will provide information is the average length of service of the 2,000 employees *according to the personnel records.* The population mean μ_X is thus defined in terms of a specific operational procedure for obtaining the length of service of the employees. If there are some serious errors in the personnel records, the population mean μ_X will differ from the "true" mean length of service. A sample of the personnel files in that case would not provide information about this "true" quantity.

One must always remember therefore that the population mean (or other population characteristic) about which the sample will furnish an estimate is the value that would be obtained if a census were taken using the same measurement procedure as that employed in the sample. Thus, in the present example, the sample will furnish an estimate of the mean age that would be obtained for the employees if all 2,000 files were surveyed in the same manner as the 50 in the sample. While we cautioned about this distinction in Chapter 2, it is important to emphasize it here again since it is so easy to consider the population mean μ_X (or any other characteristic) always to be the equivalent of the "true" quantity of interest.

Distinction between estimator and estimate

The most obvious way to estimate the population mean μ_X is to use the sample mean $\overline{X}$. *The sample mean $\overline{X}$ is called an estimator of the population mean μ_X, because it represents a method of estimating the population mean.*

Once the sample has been selected and the sample mean computed, we obtain a specific value of $\overline{X}$. In our example, the personnel office of the Thurston Corporation selected a simple random sample of 50 employees, determined the length of service for each, and found the sample mean to be $\overline{X} = 6.0$ years. (The data from which $\overline{X}$ was computed are not needed here, though they are given in Table 12.1.) *The specific value of the sample mean obtained* (here, 6.0 years) *is called a sample estimate of the population mean.*

Thus, the term *estimator* refers to the *method* of making the estimate, whereas the term *estimate* refers to the actual *result* obtained from the sample.

Definition of point estimation

Because $\overline{X}$ provides a single number as the estimate of the population mean, it is called a *point* estimator:

(12.1) An estimator is a ***point estimator*** of a population characteristic if it provides only a single number as the estimate.

Correspondingly, the estimate $\overline{X} = 6.0$ years is called a *point estimate* of the population mean, because the population mean is estimated by a single number based on the sample.

Point estimation is contrasted with interval estimation, where, say, the population mean is estimated to lie between two limits. We shall take up interval estimation after we complete our discussion of point estimation.

Alternative point estimators

A population characteristic, such as the population mean μ_X, can be estimated by a variety of estimators. The sample mean $\overline{X}$ is certainly an obvious estimator of the population mean to most people, perhaps to the exclusion of other estimators. But there are other possibilities. Consider, for instance:

$$S_1 = \frac{X_S + X_L}{2}$$

the average of the smallest and largest observations in the sample, frequently called the *midrange*. Or we might have used a weighted average:

$$S_2 = \frac{w_1X_1 + w_2X_2 + \cdots + w_nX_n}{w_1 + w_2 + \cdots + w_n}$$

where the w_i's are the weights. Another possibility is the sample median:

$$S_3 = M_e$$

We could enumerate still other possible estimators for estimating the population mean. How then are we to choose between these alternative estimators?

Desired properties of point estimators

A number of properties have been formulated that a "good" point estimator should possess, and we examine several of these properties. Each pertains to the sampling distribution of the estimator, since this probability distribution indicates how far the estimates furnished by the estimator tend to be from the population characteristic to be estimated.

Unbiasedness. The property of unbiasedness was mentioned in Chapter 10:

(12.2) An estimator is ***unbiased*** if the mean of its sampling distribution is equal to the population characteristic to be estimated.

It certainly appears intuitively reasonable that we would like an estimator that furnishes estimates clustered around the population characteristic to be estimated. Consider Figure 12.1, where the mean μ_X for a particular

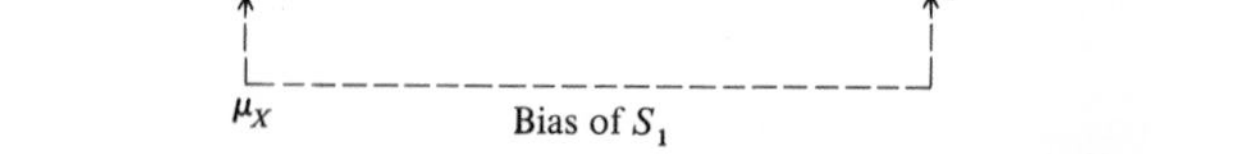

Figure 12.1. Unbiased and biased point estimators of population mean

population is to be estimated. The sampling distribution of $\bar{X}$ is centered around μ_X, while the sampling distribution of the alternative estimator S_1 is located far from μ_X in this particular case. Thus, in this case, $\bar{X}$ tends to furnish estimates that are closer to μ_X than the biased estimator S_1.

In our illustration, the bias of the estimator S_1, $(\mu_{S_1} - \mu_X)$, is so great that $\overline{X}$ is clearly a preferable estimator on this account alone. There are other situations, however, where an estimator may involve only a relatively small bias, and additional criteria must then be examined to determine which estimator is preferable.

At this point, it is appropriate to explain why the sample variance s_X^2 is defined with $n - 1$ in the denominator, as in (4.10) on p. 86. When s_X^2 is so defined it is an unbiased estimator of the population variance σ_X^2 for infinite populations, and is practically an unbiased estimator of σ_X^2 for finite populations as long as the population is not very small. If s_X^2 were defined with n in the denominator, it would be a biased estimator of σ_X^2.

Before concluding this discussion, we wish to emphasize again that the "bias" in connection with unbiased point estimators is not the bias due to errors in the records, leading questions in the questionnaire, or other such factors leading to non-sampling errors. These factors may make the population mean μ_X or other population characteristic "biased," in other words, different from the "true" value of interest. A biased estimator, on the other hand, is one for which the sampling distribution is not centered around μ_X or other population characteristic studied.

Efficiency. If two estimators are each unbiased, or if one involves only a small bias, it appears reasonable to see which estimator is more highly concentrated around the population characteristic to be estimated. That is, given two unbiased estimators, we prefer the estimator with the smaller variability. Thus, we are led to the following definition of relative efficiency:

(12.3) If two estimators are unbiased, the one whose sampling distribution has the smaller variance is ***relatively more efficient*** than the other.

The reason we prefer the more efficient estimator in this case is that it provides a higher probability of getting an estimate within a specified range around the population characteristic. This is illustrated in Figure 12.2, which contains the sampling distributions of $\overline{X}$ and $S_3 = M_e$ for the case where the population sampled is symmetrical. Both estimators are unbiased here, but the variability of the sampling distribution of M_e is greater than that of the sampling distribution of $\overline{X}$. This contrast in variability was noted in Chapter 10, when we examined the sampling distributions of several statistics (see Table 10.3, p. 191). Figure 12.2 makes it clear that the probability is greater that $\overline{X}$ falls in a specific range around the population mean μ_X than that M_e falls in this range.

Consistency. Another property that a good point estimator should have is consistency. Loosely speaking, we define this property as follows:

(12.4) An estimator is ***consistent*** if for large samples the probability is close to 1 that the estimate will be near the population characteristic to be estimated.

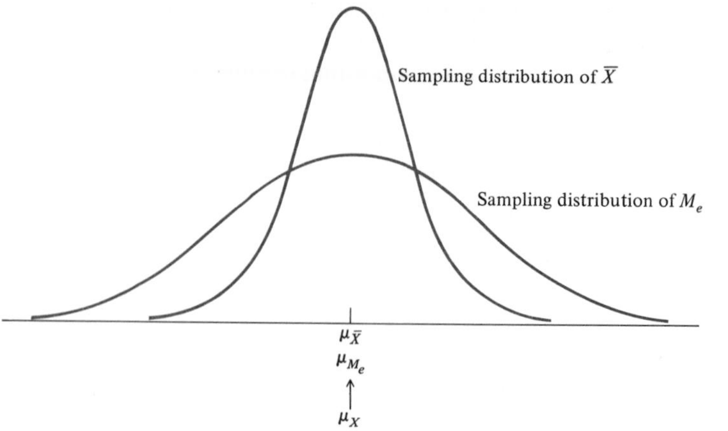

Figure 12.2. Two unbiased point estimators that differ in efficiency

Thus, a consistent estimator provides the assurance that for a large enough sample the probability is very high that the sample estimate will be close to the population characteristic to be estimated. The only difficulty with this criterion is that the sample size might have to be very large before the assurance as to the closeness of the estimate takes effect.

Sample mean as point estimator of population mean

To be able to test whether a particular point estimator meets the criteria of a good point estimator, one needs to know the functional form (e.g., normal, exponential, etc.) of the population sampled, for many of the criteria proposed. Often, however, this functional form is unknown, so that one is then unable to determine which point estimator is best.

It is for this reason that the sample mean $\overline{X}$ is frequently used as an all-purpose estimator of the population mean μ_X, and we shall so use it here. There will be instances where, if we know the functional form of the population sampled, another estimator will be better than $\overline{X}$ to estimate the population mean. On the other hand, $\overline{X}$ always has the property of being an unbiased estimator, almost always is a consistent estimator, and in a number of cases is the most efficient estimator. Further, the central limit theorem enables us to know the approximate form of the sampling distribution of $\overline{X}$ for reasonably large samples, for almost all populations sampled. Thus, the use of $\overline{X}$ as an all-purpose estimator of the population mean μ_X appears to be reasonable in the absence of specific information about the functional form of the population sampled.

Limitation of any point estimate

Any point estimator, even though it has all the desired properties such as unbiasedness, efficiency, and consistency, has the limitation that it provides no information about the *precision* of the estimate furnished—that is, of the *magnitude of the error due to sampling*. Thus, the point estimate of the average length of service of all 2,000 employees of the Thurston Corporation, $\overline{X} = 6.0$ years, gives no indication of the precision of the estimate.

We noted in Chapter 10 that the sample mean based upon a simple random sample can assume many different possible values, and that these are indicated by the sampling distribution of $\overline{X}$. Furthermore, these possible values of $\overline{X}$ are grouped in the sampling distribution of $\overline{X}$ around the true population mean μ_X, with most of the $\overline{X}$'s falling to the right or left of the population mean. Hence, it is a fairly safe bet that any one $\overline{X}$—in other words, any one point estimate—usually will not be correct in the sense that it provides the actual value of the population mean.

Thus, it is quite safe to conclude that 6.0 years is not really the average length of service of all 2,000 employees. Of what value then is a point estimate? Actually, it is of little use unless one has some indication of the precision of the estimate. The precision of the estimate can be evaluated for a simple random sample in the form of an interval estimate, which we discuss in the following section.

12.3 INTERVAL ESTIMATION OF POPULATION MEAN—LARGE SIMPLE RANDOM SAMPLE CASE

Interval estimate

(12.5) An estimate of a population characteristic is an ***interval estimate*** if it consists of an interval (rather than of a single point).

For instance, an interval estimate in our example would indicate that the average length of service of all employees is estimated to be between ________and________ years. *The width of the interval indicates how precisely the population characteristic has been estimated from the sample.* The narrower the interval, the more precise the estimate.

Review of sampling distribution of $\overline{X}$

To construct an interval estimate of the population mean, we again utilize $\overline{X}$ as an all-purpose estimator and consequently make use of the sampling distribution of $\overline{X}$. Let us review the relevant characteristics of the sampling distribution of $\overline{X}$:

1. The mean of the sampling distribution of $\overline{X}$ equals the mean μ_X of the population sampled.
2. $\sigma_{\overline{X}}$, the standard deviation of the sampling distribution of $\overline{X}$, is a multiple of the population standard deviation σ_X, as indicated by (10.4):

$$\sigma_{\bar{X}} = \sqrt{\frac{N-n}{N-1}}\frac{\sigma_X}{\sqrt{n}} \qquad \text{for finite populations}$$

3. The central limit theorem states that the sampling distribution of $\bar{X}$ is approximately normal if the sample is sufficiently large.

Confidence interval: special example

Suppose that we construct an interval estimate of the population mean as follows: Select a simple random sample from the population and calculate the sample mean $\bar{X}$. Then, assert that the population mean is between $\bar{X} - 3\sigma_{\bar{X}}$ and $\bar{X} + 3\sigma_{\bar{X}}$. Thus, $\bar{X} - 3\sigma_{\bar{X}}$ would be the lower limit of the interval estimate, and $\bar{X} + 3\sigma_{\bar{X}}$ the upper limit.

Implications of interval estimate. What are the implications of this interval estimate? To answer this question, we must refer to the sampling distribution of $\bar{X}$, because we are concerned with the behavior of $\bar{X}$. Figure 12.3 presents the sampling distribution of $\bar{X}$ for our example. Note that the distribution is approximately normal, because we assume that our sample size is sufficiently large. Also note that the $\bar{X}$ scale is blank. We only know from statistical theory that the mean of the sampling distribution of $\bar{X}$ must be equal to the unknown population mean μ_X; this fact is shown in Figure 12.3 on the $\bar{X}$ scale. We do not, however, know the value of μ_X.

Below the $\bar{X}$ scale is the z scale. This scale indicates the distance from the mean in units of the standard deviation of $\bar{X}$—in other words, in units of $\sigma_{\bar{X}}$. Remember that z here is:

$$z = \frac{\bar{X} - \mu_{\bar{X}}}{\sigma_{\bar{X}}} = \frac{\bar{X} - \mu_X}{\sigma_{\bar{X}}}$$

The z scale is known because all normal probability distributions are reduced to the standard one when the standard normal deviate z (with mean 0 and standard deviation 1) is used. Thus, $+1$ on the z scale means that this point is $\sigma_{\bar{X}}$ above the mean of the sampling distribution of $\bar{X}$ (equal to the population mean μ_X), $+2$ on the z scale indicates that this point is $2\sigma_{\bar{X}}$ above the population mean, and so on.

If we use the interval estimate $\bar{X} \pm 3\sigma_{\bar{X}}$ to estimate the population mean, the particular interval estimate obtained on the basis of a simple random sample depends on the location of $\bar{X}$ in the distribution of all possible $\bar{X}$'s. Figure 12.3 indicates five possible positions where the sample mean $\bar{X}$ obtained in a particular sample might fall in the sampling distribution of $\bar{X}$. Suppose that the value of the sample mean $\bar{X}$ actually corresponds to position 1 in Figure 12.3. Here, the interval estimate would be indicated by the line centered around $\bar{X}$ at position 1. The limits of the interval are obtained by adding the length representing $3\sigma_{\bar{X}}$, obtained from the z scale, to $\bar{X}$, and by subtracting the length representing $3\sigma_{\bar{X}}$ from $\bar{X}$. The limits obtained in this

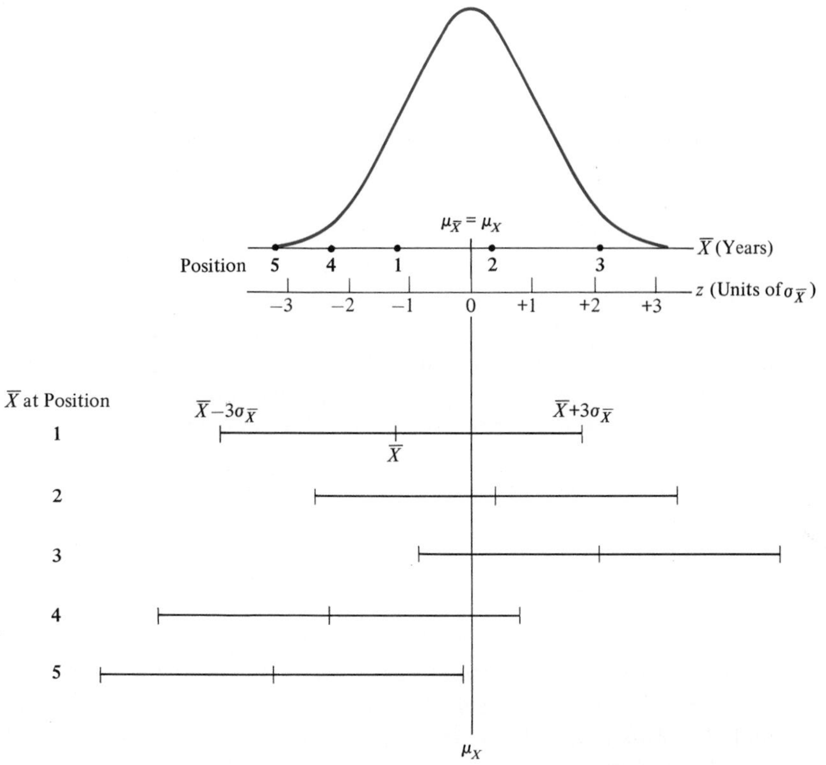

Figure 12.3. Sampling distribution of $\bar{X}$ and various possible confidence intervals

manner then correspond to $\bar{X} + 3\sigma_{\bar{X}}$ and $\bar{X} - 3\sigma_{\bar{X}}$, the desired interval estimate.

Note that this interval covers the population mean. Therefore, if the sample mean falls on position 1, the interval $\bar{X} \pm 3\sigma_{\bar{X}}$ would include the population mean, and the statement that the population mean is within this interval would be correct.

Suppose the sample mean falls on position 2 in Figure 12.3. Again, we construct the limits $\bar{X} + 3\sigma_{\bar{X}}$ and $\bar{X} - 3\sigma_{\bar{X}}$, but this time around the mean $\bar{X}$ located at position 2. The corresponding interval is shown in Figure 12.3. Again, the population mean is covered by the interval. Thus, if the sample mean falls on position 2, the statement that the population mean is within the interval $\bar{X} \pm 3\sigma_{\bar{X}}$ would again be correct.

Similarly, if the sample mean $\bar{X}$ happens to fall on positions 3 or 4, the interval $\bar{X} \pm 3\sigma_{\bar{X}}$ in each case would include the population mean μ_X. Therefore, the statement that the population mean is somewhere between $\bar{X} - 3\sigma_{\bar{X}}$ and $\bar{X} + 3\sigma_{\bar{X}}$ again would be correct in each of these cases.

Will the interval $\bar{X} \pm 3\sigma_{\bar{X}}$ ever fail to include the population mean μ_X? The answer is "yes," and it should be fairly apparent when this will happen.

Since the limits are obtained by adding and subtracting $3\sigma_{\bar{X}}$ to $\bar{X}$, the interval will not include the population mean μ_X whenever $\bar{X}$ falls more than 3 standard deviations ($3\sigma_{\bar{X}}$) from its mean ($\mu_{\bar{X}} = \mu_X$)—that is, whenever $\bar{X}$ falls above $+3$ or below -3 on the z scale. For instance, if the sample mean falls on position 5, the statement that the population mean is within the interval $\bar{X} \pm 3\sigma_{\bar{X}}$ would be incorrect because the interval corresponding to $\bar{X}$ at position 5 does not include the population mean μ_X.

Since the statement, "The value of the population mean is somewhere between $\bar{X} \pm 3\sigma_{\bar{X}}$," will be correct if the sample mean $\bar{X}$ falls within $3\sigma_{\bar{X}}$ of the population mean, what is the probability that $\bar{X}$ will fall within this range? The sampling distribution of $\bar{X}$ is approximately normal, so we know that the probability that $\bar{X}$ falls within $3\sigma_{\bar{X}}$ of the mean of the sampling distribution of $\bar{X}$ (which is equal to the population mean μ_X) is .997. Thus, if we take a great number of sufficiently large simple random samples, calculate the interval $\bar{X} \pm 3\sigma_{\bar{X}}$ for each one, and in each instance state that the population mean is within the interval, about 99.7 per cent of these statements will be correct.

The interval estimate for the population mean μ_X may be written more formally as follows:

$$\bar{X} - 3\sigma_{\bar{X}} \leq \mu_X \leq \bar{X} + 3\sigma_{\bar{X}}$$

which is read: The population mean μ_X is somewhere between $\bar{X} - 3\sigma_{\bar{X}}$ and $\bar{X} + 3\sigma_{\bar{X}}$. This interval is called a *confidence interval for the population mean*, and the probability of a correct statement, in this case .997, is called the *confidence coefficient*.

Alternative approach to confidence interval implications. It will be instructive to arrive at this confidence interval in a somewhat different fashion. For reasonably large samples, we know that $\bar{X}$ is approximately normally distributed. Hence, $(\bar{X} - \mu_{\bar{X}})/\sigma_{\bar{X}}$ is then approximately a standard normal deviate z, so that we know from the relations for a standard normal distribution:

$$P\left(-3 \leq \frac{\bar{X} - \mu_{\bar{X}}}{\sigma_{\bar{X}}} \leq +3\right) = .997$$

Now, we can rearrange the inequalities as follows:

$$P(-3\sigma_{\bar{X}} \leq \bar{X} - \mu_{\bar{X}} \leq +3\sigma_{\bar{X}}) = .997$$

or:

$$P(-3\sigma_{\bar{X}} - \bar{X} \leq -\mu_{\bar{X}} \leq +3\sigma_{\bar{X}} - \bar{X}) = .997$$

or:

$$P(3\sigma_{\bar{X}} + \bar{X} \geq \mu_{\bar{X}} \geq -3\sigma_{\bar{X}} + \bar{X}) = .997$$

Remember that when we multiply both sides of an inequality by -1, the inequality sign is reversed. Hence, we have, by shifting the terms:

$$P(\bar{X} - 3\sigma_{\bar{X}} \leq \mu_{\bar{X}} \leq \bar{X} + 3\sigma_{\bar{X}}) = .997$$

Finally, since we know $\mu_{\overline{X}} = \mu_X$ always, we have:

$$P(\overline{X} - 3\sigma_{\overline{X}} \leq \mu_X \leq \overline{X} + 3\sigma_{\overline{X}}) = .997$$

This probability statement declares that if many random samples of size n are taken from the population, and for each one the assertion is made that:

$$\overline{X} - 3\sigma_{\overline{X}} \leq \mu_X \leq \overline{X} + 3\sigma_{\overline{X}}$$

then 99.7 per cent of such assertions will be correct. Usually, we cannot use this confidence interval estimate, for we do not know the value of $\sigma_{\overline{X}}$, the standard deviation of $\overline{X}$. Instead, we must obtain a point estimate of $\sigma_{\overline{X}}$.

Point estimate of $\sigma_{\overline{X}}$. We obtain a point estimate of $\sigma_{\overline{X}}$ from the sample that actually has been selected. The variability of the lengths of service of the 2,000 employees in the population is measured by the population standard deviation σ_X, which is unknown. However, the sample standard deviation s_X supplies us with a point estimate of σ_X. Table 12.1 contains the results

Table 12.1 Lengths of Service of 50 Thurston Corporation Employees Selected in Simple Random Sample

Length of Service[1] X	X^2	*Length of Service*[1] X	X^2	*Length of Service*[1] X	X^2	*Length of Service*[1] X	X^2
2.0	4.00	22.5	506.25	4.0	16.00	3.0	9.00
3.5	12.25	0	0	13.5	182.25	19.0	361.00
5.5	30.25	7.0	49.00	7.5	56.25	5.0	25.00
6.0	36.00	1.5	2.25	1.0	1.00	5.0	25.00
1.5	2.25	8.5	72.25	4.0	16.00	2.5	6.25
6.0	36.00	7.0	49.00	0	0	7.0	49.00
4.5	20.25	2.0	4.00	4.5	20.25	6.0	36.00
9.0	81.00	12.0	144.00	6.5	42.25	5.0	25.00
4.5	20.25	.5	.25	8.5	72.25	5.5	30.25
7.5	56.25	5.5	30.25	15.5	240.25	9.0	81.00
2.5	6.25	4.5	20.25	2.5	6.25	5.0	25.00
6.5	42.25	13.5	182.25	.5	.25		
3.0	9.00	5.5	30.25	8.0	64.00		
					Total	300.00	2,835.50

$$\overline{X} = \frac{\Sigma X}{n} = \frac{300.0}{50} = 6.0 \text{ years}$$

$$s_X = \sqrt{\frac{\Sigma X^2 - \frac{(\Sigma X)^2}{n}}{n-1}} = \sqrt{\frac{2{,}835.50 - \frac{(300)^2}{50}}{50-1}} = 4.6 \text{ years}$$

[1] To nearest half year.

of the simple random sample of 50 employees actually selected, together with the computations of the sample mean $\overline{X}$ and sample standard deviation s_X. The sample mean of 6.0 years was mentioned earlier in connection with our discussion of a point estimate. The sample standard deviation is $s_X = 4.6$ years, which provides us with a point estimate of σ_X.

We know from statistical theory that the standard deviation of $\overline{X}$ is always a certain multiple of the population standard deviation, namely:

(12.6) $$\sigma_{\overline{X}} = \sqrt{\frac{N-n}{N-1}}\frac{\sigma_X}{\sqrt{n}} \qquad \text{for finite populations}$$

or:

(12.6a) $$\sigma_{\overline{X}} = \frac{\sigma_X}{\sqrt{n}} \qquad \text{for infinite populations}$$

Hence, if we have a point estimate of σ_X, we can get a point estimate of $\sigma_{\overline{X}}$ by using the above relationships that exist between them:

(12.7) $$s_{\overline{X}} = \sqrt{\frac{N-n}{N-1}}\frac{s_X}{\sqrt{n}} \qquad \text{for finite populations}$$

or:

(12.7a) $$s_{\overline{X}} = \frac{s_X}{\sqrt{n}} \qquad \text{for infinite populations}$$

Here $s_{\overline{X}}$ is the symbol for the point estimator of $\sigma_{\overline{X}}$.

Note that $s_{\overline{X}}$ is based on only a single random sample. One sample enables us to estimate $\sigma_{\overline{X}}$ because first, this sample provides us with a point estimate of the population standard deviation, and second, because the standard deviation of $\overline{X}$ is always a certain multiple of the population standard deviation.

For our example, $N = 2{,}000$, $n = 50$, $s_X = 4.6$ years (from Table 12.1); substituting into (12.7), we obtain:

$$s_{\overline{X}} = \sqrt{\frac{2{,}000-50}{2{,}000-1}}\frac{4.6}{\sqrt{50}} = .64 \text{ years}$$

Thus, our point estimate of the standard deviation of $\overline{X}$, based on the one simple random sample of 50 employees selected, is $s_{\overline{X}} = .64$ years.

Completion of interval estimate. We are now ready to complete the interval estimate of the population mean μ_X discussed earlier. The form of this estimate was as follows: "We estimate that the population mean is somewhere between $\overline{X} - 3\sigma_{\overline{X}}$ and $\overline{X} + 3\sigma_{\overline{X}}$." We were unable to use this interval estimate before, because $\sigma_{\overline{X}}$ was unknown. Now, however, we have a point estimate ($s_{\overline{X}} = .64$ years) of the standard deviation of $\overline{X}$, and we shall use this point estimate to replace the unknown $\sigma_{\overline{X}}$. Since $\overline{X} = 6.0$ years for our example, the interval estimate has the lower limit:

$$\overline{X} - 3s_{\overline{X}} = 6.0 - (3)(.64) = 6.0 - 1.92 = 4.08 \text{ years}$$

and the upper limit:

$$\overline{X} + 3s_{\overline{X}} = 6.0 + (3)(.64) = 6.0 + 1.92 = 7.92 \text{ years}$$

Our interval estimate, therefore, indicates that the average length of service of the 2,000 employees of the Thurston Corporation is somewhere between 4.1 and 7.9 years.

Effect of modification on confidence coefficient. Formally, our confidence interval for the population mean just obtained is:

$$\overline{X} - 3s_{\overline{X}} \leq \mu_X \leq \overline{X} + 3s_{\overline{X}}$$

Note that this is of the same basic form as the one discussed earlier, except that the true standard deviation of $\overline{X}$ has been replaced by the point estimate based on the simple random sample. Since the sample standard deviation s_X, which is the basis for our point estimate of $\sigma_{\overline{X}}$, varies from sample to sample, this means that confidence intervals based on repeated samples from the same population will not have the constant widths indicated in Figure 12.3. If s_X is smaller than the population standard deviation σ_X, the modified confidence interval will be narrower than those shown in Figure 12.3; if s_X is larger than σ_X, the modified confidence interval will be wider.

Does this modification affect the confidence coefficient, which we calculated earlier to be 99.7 per cent? The modification does change the confidence coefficient. However, *if the sample size is sufficiently large, replacing $\sigma_{\overline{X}}$ by the point estimator $s_{\overline{X}}$ will have so little effect on the confidence coefficient of 99.7 per cent obtained under the assumption that $\sigma_{\overline{X}}$ is known, that we shall consider the confidence coefficient unchanged.* In other words, with reasonably large samples, the replacing of $\sigma_{\overline{X}}$ by $s_{\overline{X}}$ does not change appreciably the proportion of intervals that include the population mean. It is frequently stated that the sample size should be at least 30 for this treatment to be appropriate.

We may examine the effect of replacing $\sigma_{\overline{X}}$ by $s_{\overline{X}}$ in another fashion. For reasonably large n, we know that $\overline{X}$ is approximately normally distributed. Consider now $(\overline{X} - \mu_{\overline{X}})/s_{\overline{X}}$. Note that the denominator here is a random variable, that is, $s_{\overline{X}}$ will take on different values for different samples. An extension of the central limit theorem is applicable here, and it states:

(12.8) For reasonably large sample sizes, $(\overline{X} - \mu_{\overline{X}})/s_{\overline{X}}$ follows approximately a standard normal distribution (with mean 0 and variance 1).

Hence, for reasonably large n, we know that:

$$P\left(-3 \leq \frac{\overline{X} - \mu_{\overline{X}}}{s_{\overline{X}}} \leq +3\right) = .997$$

Now we can manipulate the inequalities in the same way as before, utilize that $\mu_{\overline{X}} = \mu_X$ always, and obtain:

$$P(\overline{X} - 3s_{\overline{X}} \leq \mu_X \leq \overline{X} + 3s_{\overline{X}}) = .997$$

Hence, the proportion of interval estimates that will include the population mean μ_X is still about 99.7 per cent, even though $\sigma_{\bar{X}}$ is replaced by its point estimator $s_{\bar{X}}$, provided that the sample size is reasonably large.

Meaning of confidence coefficient

In our previous example, the sample of 50 employees leads to the conclusion that the average length of service of the 2,000 employees of the Thurston Corporation is somewhere between 4.1 and 7.9 years, and this statement is made with a 99.7 per cent confidence coefficient. To say that this statement is made with a confidence coefficient of 99.7 per cent does not mean that there is a probability of .997 that the population mean is somewhere between 4.1 and 7.9 years. The average length of service of all employees is some definite, though unknown, number. It either is or is not somewhere between 4.1 and 7.9 years; there is no probability involved. Whether the statement that the average length of service is between 4.1 and 7.9 years is right or wrong depends upon whether the sample mean fell within $3s_{\bar{X}}$ from the population mean; this one does not know. One does know, however, that if one takes a great many simple random samples from this population and constructs a confidence interval with a 99.7 per cent confidence coefficient for each, or if this interval is constructed in a great many different problems, about 99.7 per cent of these statements will be correct.

Thus, any one statement will be right or wrong, and one does not know on the basis of the sample which is the occasional statement that will be wrong. One simply acts as if the statement were correct. This means that once in a while the sample will be misleading. This risk, due to sampling error, cannot be eliminated as long as one relies on incomplete information. However, the success rate of 99.7 per cent inherent in the procedure employed in the example would usually be quite satisfactory.

Usefulness of confidence interval

A high confidence coefficient provides a high degree of assurance of the correctness of the interval estimate; the usefulness of this estimate is another matter, however. To illustrate this point, consider once again the official of the Thurston Corporation who requested information about the average length of service of the employees. Does it help the official if it is reported that the average length of service of the 2,000 employees is somewhere between 4.1 and 7.9 years? The answer to this question depends upon particular circumstances. Suppose the official had ascertained that another company, comparable to the Thurston Corporation, had taken a census of its employees and found their average length of service to be ten years. In this case, the confidence interval would be useful to him in the sense that he could conclude that the average length of service at Thurston differs from that at the other company. On the other hand, if the president of the Thurston Corporation had told this official that he wanted to know the average length of service with a maximum error of only ± 10 per cent for use in an insurance application, the confidence interval would not be useful since its error range is ± 32 per cent, $[\pm(1.9/6.0) \cdot 100]$.

Thus, *statistical methods enable us to measure the magnitude of the sampling error for a simple random sample, but the outside factors that necessitated obtaining the sample information in the first place determine whether or not the sampling error is sufficiently small to make the estimate a useful one.*

Construction of confidence interval for any confidence coefficient

Before we explain how confidence intervals can be constructed for any confidence coefficient, we want to stress that *the procedures for constructing a confidence interval described in this section are only applicable if the simple random sample size is sufficiently large.* Up to this point, we have considered the construction of confidence intervals for the population mean that are associated with a 99.7 per cent confidence coefficient. Actually, we can construct confidence intervals for any magnitude of confidence coefficient; that is, the probability that the procedure will lead to a correct statement can be set at any level. This is done by choosing the appropriate standard deviation multiple in the confidence interval.

In general, the confidence interval for the population mean, based on a sufficiently large simple random sample, is:

$$\overline{X} - zs_{\overline{X}} \leq \mu_X \leq \overline{X} + zs_{\overline{X}} \tag{12.9}$$

Here z, the standard normal deviate, depends upon the value of the confidence coefficient and is obtained from the table of areas for the normal probability distribution. For instance, if we wanted a confidence coefficient of 95.4 per cent, we would use $z = 2$ in (12.9). With reasonably large samples, the sampling distribution of $\overline{X}$ is approximately normal, so that about 95.4 per cent of the sample means fall within 2 standard deviations $(z = \pm 2)$ from the population mean.

Note that (12.9) indicates that the *confidence limits* for μ_X are:

$$\overline{X} \pm zs_{\overline{X}} \tag{12.10}$$

For computational purposes, (12.10) provides the confidence limits most directly. Formula (12.9), on the other hand, shows explicitly that the limits are confidence limits for μ_X.

For our previous example, the confidence limits with a 95.4 per cent confidence coefficient would have been $6.0 \pm (2)(.64)$ years. Thus, we would have made the statement—with a confidence coefficient of 95.4 per cent—that the population mean is somewhere between 4.7 and 7.3 years.

Note that this confidence interval is narrower than the one with a 99.7 per cent confidence coefficient.

Suppose that we had been told to construct a confidence interval with a 90 per cent confidence coefficient. We then have to determine the z value corresponding to this confidence coefficient. In effect, we must answer the question: The central 90 per cent of the sample means fall within how many standard deviations from the population mean? Because of the symmetry of the normal probability distribution, we need concern ourselves only with half of the distribution. We can then enter Table A-1 to see within how many standard deviations from one side of the mean 45 per cent of the area of the distribution lies. Entering the body of the table, we locate .45 and find that it corresponds to 1.64 standard deviations. Hence, the z value for a 90 per cent confidence coefficient is 1.64, and the corresponding confidence limits for our previous example would be $6.0 \pm (1.64)(.64)$ years. We state then, with a confidence coefficient of 90 per cent, that the population mean is somewhere between 5.0 and 7.0 years. Note that this confidence interval is narrower than the ones with 95.4 or 99.7 per cent confidence coefficients. Indeed we can generalize: *In any given situation, the smaller the confidence coefficient, the narrower will be the confidence interval; the larger the confidence coefficient, the wider the confidence interval.*

Choice of confidence coefficient

The generalization just stated indicates that smaller confidence coefficients lead to narrow confidence intervals, which is desirable, but they also signify a higher probability that an interval will be incorrect, which of course is undesirable. Indeed, the case is that a confidence interval based on a given sample size only can be narrowed by increasing the risk of an incorrect estimate.

On the other hand, the risk of an incorrect statement can be made smaller by increasing the confidence coefficient. Such an increase, however, has the effect of widening the confidence interval in any given situation, and thus may make the confidence interval less useful. A statement with a 99.99999 per cent confidence coefficient that the average length of service of employees of the Thurston Corporation is somewhere between zero and 50 years is pretty safe, but also useless for most purposes.

Since the width of the confidence interval is related to the risk that the interval estimate will be incorrect, management or other users of the sample estimates should specify this risk *in advance* on the basis of the problem situation for which the estimates are required. It is the user's responsibility to determine the risk of an incorrect estimate, since this risk falls on him. Confidence coefficients of 90, 95, and 99 per cent have often been used in practice. This does not mean that other values of the confidence coefficient are not also appropriate.

Determination of necessary sample size

Need for planning. Management usually has a general idea about the precision that the estimate to be obtained should possess. For instance, management of a discount store wished to estimate the number of customers who drive more than ten miles to reach the store. It was able to tell the consulting market research firm at once that this number need not be estimated within 1 or 2 per cent, but that a sampling error of 20 per cent or more would be too large.

In this type of situation, a procedure that arbitrarily determines the sample size is not really satisfactory. It may turn out that the confidence interval is too wide, in which case it will not be as useful as desired, or it may be narrower than needed, in which case the estimate is more precise than necessary. If the confidence interval is too wide, the sample was not large enough; remember that $s_{\bar{X}}$ decreases as the sample size increases. If the confidence interval is narrower than necessary, the sample was too large. With too large a sample, money will have been wasted in getting greater precision than necessary. With too small a sample, it may be quite costly—for instance, in market research surveys covering a substantial geographic area—to enlarge the sample subsequently.

A more sensible procedure is to plan the most economical sample design, together with the corresponding type of confidence interval, that meets management's specifications on desired precision and level of confidence. This approach employs statistical theory in an attempt to obtain the required information at minimum cost rather than merely to evaluate the sampling error after the sample has been selected.

Method of determining necessary sample size. We demonstrate by an example how this may be done. The Transportation Corps in the Department of the Army has sampled bills of lading of Army motor truck shipments of gasoline. From such samples, estimates have been made of various population characteristics—for example, the average tonnage of gasoline per truck shipment. Suppose that the average number of tons of gasoline per shipment during the second half of the previous year is to be estimated. In this case, the population to be sampled consists of all bills of lading for Army truck shipments of gasoline during the second half of that year—say 10,000 bills of lading. Further assume that the office making use of this information desires to know the average number of tons per shipment within ± 1 gross ton, and that the confidence coefficient is to be 99 per cent. Given these requirements, how do we determine the appropriate sample size?

First of all, we know that the confidence limits will be of the form $\bar{X} \pm z\sigma_{\bar{X}}$. (In the actual interval estimate based on the sample, $\sigma_{\bar{X}}$ would be replaced by the point estimator $s_{\bar{X}}$.) Let the desired width of the confidence interval be $\pm h$. For our example, $h = 1$ gross ton, since it is desired to estimate the average number of tons per shipment within ± 1 gross ton. Technically, h is called the desired *half-width* of the confidence interval, because the entire width of the confidence interval is $2h$.

The desired limits of the interval estimate are therefore $\overline{X} \pm h$. Since the confidence limits are of the form $\overline{X} \pm z\sigma_{\overline{X}}$, it follows that we want $z\sigma_{\overline{X}}$ to equal h; thus:

$$h = z\sigma_{\overline{X}}$$

If the population is infinite, we know from (12.6a) that $\sigma_{\overline{X}} = \frac{\sigma_X}{\sqrt{n}}$. Hence:

$$h = z\frac{\sigma_X}{\sqrt{n}}$$

Squaring, and solving for n, we obtain:

$$n = \frac{z^2\sigma_X^2}{h^2} \qquad \text{for infinite populations} \tag{12.11}$$

If the population is finite, we know from (12.6) that $\sigma_{\overline{X}} = \sqrt{\frac{N-n}{N-1}}\frac{\sigma_X}{\sqrt{n}}$.

Therefore, $h = z\sigma_{\overline{X}}$ becomes:

$$h = z\sqrt{\frac{N-n}{N-1}}\frac{\sigma_X}{\sqrt{n}}$$

Solving this for n, we obtain after some algebra: [1]

$$n = \frac{\sigma_X^2}{\frac{h^2}{z^2} + \frac{\sigma_X^2}{N}} \qquad \text{for finite populations} \tag{12.11a}$$

Thus, (12.11) and (12.11a) enable us to determine the necessary sample size to estimate a population mean with specified precision for a given confidence coefficient. It should be recognized that *(12.11) and (12.11a) are valid only if the resultant sample size is not too small,* since the derivation of these formulas assumed that the sampling distribution of $\overline{X}$ is approximately normal.

In our example, $h = 1$, as stated earlier, and $N = 10{,}000$. The z value corresponding to a 99 per cent confidence coefficient is 2.58. We are dealing with a finite population, so that (12.11a) is applicable. Note that we still must determine one unknown factor before we can find the necessary sample size, namely the population standard deviation σ_X. We need not know the magnitude of σ_X exactly, but merely in rough terms. This approximate information about the population standard deviation can often be obtained from past experience in the same or in a similar problem, or from a small pilot study.

Here, past experience was available, since the Transportation Corps previously had been sampling this type of population. This experience indicated

[1] In the solution, $N - 1$ in the denominator of the finite correction factor is replaced by N; this change simplifies the result and has negligible effect usually.

that the standard deviation of this type of population would be about 3 gross tons. If we now substitute this value for σ_X, we can solve for n as follows:

$$n = \frac{(3)^2}{\dfrac{(1)^2}{(2.58)^2} + \dfrac{(3)^2}{10{,}000}} = 59.55$$

The calculations above thus indicate that a simple random sample of about 60 bills of lading should be taken. If the advance information about the population standard deviation is at all reliable, the confidence interval with a 99 per cent confidence coefficient, based on a simple random sample of this size, should have a width of about ± 1 gross ton.

Evaluation of precision obtained. Suppose that a simple random sample of 60 bills of lading was selected and the following results were obtained:

$$\bar{X} = 17.1 \text{ gross tons} \qquad s_X = 2.9 \text{ gross tons}$$

We can now construct the confidence interval for the average tonnage of gasoline per shipment in the usual manner. Note carefully that the validity of this interval will depend in no way upon our advance judgment concerning the population standard deviation. That merely was used in arriving at a reasonable sample size. Once the simple random sample has been chosen, it furnishes an objective estimate of the population standard deviation, which we use in constructing the confidence interval.

First, we estimate the standard deviation of the sample mean by (12.7):

$$s_{\bar{X}} = \sqrt{\frac{10{,}000 - 60}{10{,}000 - 1}}\,\frac{2.9}{\sqrt{60}} = .373 \text{ gross tons}$$

Then we substitute into (12.10), with $z = 2.58$ as determined previously, to get the confidence limits with a 99 per cent confidence coefficient:

$$17.1 \pm (2.58)(.373) = 17.1 \pm .96 \text{ gross tons}$$

Hence, the confidence interval for the mean tonnage of gasoline per truck shipment is:

$$17.1 - .96 \leq \mu_X \leq 17.1 + .96$$

or:

$$16.14 \leq \mu_X \leq 18.06$$

Thus, it can be reported with a confidence coefficient of 99 per cent that the average number of gross tons of gasoline per truck shipment during the last half of the year was somewhere between 16.14 and 18.06 gross tons. Note that this estimate is slightly more precise—that is, the interval is narrower—than was specified. That occurred because the advance judgment of the population standard deviation was a little larger than the estimate from the sample. In another instance, of course, the confidence interval might be slightly wider than is desired.

Determining the sample size by advance planning usually will not lead to a confidence interval with a width precisely equal to the desired one. It does, however, permit use of a reasonable advance judgment of the magnitude of the population standard deviation for deciding upon a sample size that roughly will yield the desired precision as economically as possible. Unless this procedure is followed, there is no way of deciding what a reasonable sample size is in any given instance; all that one can do then is to determine the sample size arbitrarily and evaluate the sampling error afterwards, hoping that it will not be too large or too small.

To summarize: *The magnitude of the sampling error can be evaluated by means of the confidence interval, whether the advance planning of the sample size was sound or not. The result of poor planning will be that the confidence interval will have a width other than the desired one. Poor planning will not, however, affect the validity of the confidence interval for evaluating the precision of the estimate actually obtained.*

12.4 INTERVAL ESTIMATION OF POPULATION MEAN—SMALL SIMPLE RANDOM SAMPLE CASE

In the previous section, the construction of a confidence interval for the population mean was explained when the size of the simple random sample is large. In this section we explain the procedure when the sample is a small one.

For this purpose, we shall consider a more limited situation than we did before. Previously, we placed no restriction on the type of population sampled, because the sampling distribution of $\bar{X}$ is approximately normal for almost all populations if the sample size is reasonably large. In discussing the construction of confidence intervals for small samples, however, *we shall confine ourselves to the case in which the population sampled is normally distributed or approximately so.*

Population standard deviation known

If the population sampled is normal, we know from theorem (10.6) on p. 197 that the sampling distribution of $\bar{X}$ is *exactly* normal for *any* sample size. Consequently, $(\bar{X} - \mu_{\bar{X}})/\sigma_{\bar{X}}$ is *exactly* a standard normal deviate z for *any* sample size.

Sometimes, the population standard deviation σ_X is known from past experience; this is the case, for instance, in the control of some production processes. In that event, $\sigma_{\bar{X}}$ is also known exactly, so that $(\bar{X} - \mu_{\bar{X}})/\sigma_{\bar{X}}$ can be used for developing a confidence interval for the population mean. This is exactly what we did initially in the previous section. It was shown there that the resulting confidence interval for the population mean is:

(12.12) $\overline{X} - z\sigma_{\overline{X}} \leq \mu_X \leq \overline{X} + z\sigma_{\overline{X}}$

Thus, when the population is normal and its standard deviation σ_X is known, the confidence interval in (12.12) can be used for *any* sample size.

Effect of unknown population standard deviation

To be sure, the usual case is that the population standard deviation σ_X is unknown and must be estimated from the sample standard deviation s_X. Consequently $\sigma_{\overline{X}}$, the standard deviation of the sampling distribution of $\overline{X}$, is unknown and must be estimated from the point estimator $s_{\overline{X}}$. Hence, in this case we cannot use $(\overline{X} - \mu_{\overline{X}})/\sigma_{\overline{X}}$ for developing the confidence interval, but rather need to work with $(\overline{X} - \mu_{\overline{X}})/s_{\overline{X}}$.

As we stated in theorem (12.8), for reasonably *large* sample sizes, $(\overline{X} - \mu_{\overline{X}})/s_{\overline{X}}$ still follows approximately the standard normal distribution for almost every population sampled, so that the confidence interval for the population mean then is:

(12.9) $\overline{X} - zs_{\overline{X}} \leq \mu_X \leq \overline{X} + zs_{\overline{X}}$

If, however, the sample size is small, $(\overline{X} - \mu_{\overline{X}})/s_{\overline{X}}$ is not approximately a standard normal deviate, and we must determine its distribution in order to set up proper confidence intervals for this case. It turns out that the basic procedure for setting up confidence limits is still the same, even if the sample is small. The confidence limits will be of the form: $\overline{X} \pm$ a certain number of $s_{\overline{X}}$. It is in the determination of the multiple for $s_{\overline{X}}$, corresponding to a given confidence coefficient, that the difference arises. With a large sample, the multiple z was determined from the table of areas for the normal distribution. This cannot be done any more when the sample size is small.

t-Distribution

The distribution of the statistic $(\overline{X} - \mu_{\overline{X}})/s_{\overline{X}}$ has been determined exactly for the case when the population sampled is normal. It is called the *t-distribution*. The functional form of this distribution is quite complicated, and we will not reproduce it here. We will, however, discuss some of the properties of this distribution.

Symmetry. The t-distribution is symmetrical, just as the standard normal distribution is. It ranges from $-\infty$ to $+\infty$, as does the standard normal distribution.

Mean. The mean of the t-distribution is zero. Here again, we have a correspondence to the standard normal distribution, whose mean is also zero.

Variance. The variance of the t-distribution may be expressed for the case considered here as $\dfrac{(n-1)}{(n-1)-2}$ provided that the sample size is 4 or greater. Thus, when $n = 4$, the variance of the t-distribution is 3; when $n = 5$, the variance of the t-distribution is 2; and so on. There are several important points to be noted here:

1. The variance of the t-distribution is greater than 1. Hence, *the t-distribution is more variable or spread out than the standard normal distribution.* Intuitively, this is reasonable; $(\overline{X} - \mu_{\overline{X}})/\sigma_{\overline{X}}$ only involves the random variable $\overline{X}$, but $(\overline{X} - \mu_{\overline{X}})/s_{\overline{X}}$ involves both the random variable $\overline{X}$ and the random variable $s_{\overline{X}}$.
2. *The variance of the t-distribution varies for different sample sizes.* Thus, there is a different t-distribution for each sample size. These t-distributions are all symmetrical and centered around zero, but they differ in variability. In fact, the t-distribution has only one parameter, which for our case may be expressed as $n - 1$. This parameter is called *degrees of freedom.* Note how this parameter appears in the expression for the variance of the t-distribution.
3. *The variance of the t-distribution approaches 1 as n becomes large.* This, together with the earlier points of similarity, may suggest that the t-distribution approaches the standard normal distribution as the sample size increases, and this is indeed correct.

Tabulation of t-distribution

Since there is a different t-distribution for each sample size, it is impractical to give a complete table of areas for all the distributions corresponding to the various sample sizes. Rather a summary of the most essential information about each of these distributions is usually presented in a table such as Table A-5.

Examining this table, one sees that the left column is headed *degrees of freedom,* here $n - 1$. Thus, for the purpose of constructing a confidence interval for the population mean from a simple random sample, the number of degrees of freedom is one less than the sample size. Each line in Table A-5 contains information about the t-distribution corresponding to a given number of degrees of freedom.

In contrast to Table A-1 of the standard normal distribution, where the areas between the mean zero and specified values of z are given, the tabulation of the t-distribution in Table A-5 provides the values of t for specified combined areas in the two tails of the t-distribution. The areas in the two tails are always equal, as the diagram at the top of Table A-5 indicates. Suppose the sample size is 11, so that there are 10 degrees of freedom in our case. The entry in the column "area .05 in two tails" (area .025 in each tail) is 2.228. This entry has the following interpretation: The probability is .05 that $(\overline{X} - \mu_{\overline{X}})/s_{\overline{X}}$ exceeds 2.228 or is less than -2.228. Remember that the t-distribution is symmetrical around zero, so that only the positive values of t are given in the table. Formally, we can write:

$$P\left(\frac{\overline{X} - \mu_{\overline{X}}}{s_{\overline{X}}} < -2.228 \quad \text{or} \quad \frac{\overline{X} - \mu_{\overline{X}}}{s_{\overline{X}}} > 2.228\right) = .05$$

This is equivalent to:

$$P\left(-2.228 \leq \frac{\overline{X} - \mu_{\overline{X}}}{s_{\overline{X}}} \leq 2.228\right) = .95$$

Because of the symmetry of the t-distribution, we also know for instance:

$$P\left(\frac{\overline{X} - \mu_{\overline{X}}}{s_{\overline{X}}} > 2.228\right) = .025$$

Other entries in the table are interpreted in a similar fashion.

Interval estimate of population mean

To develop the confidence interval for a population mean, consider again the following probability statement, for a sample of $n = 11$:

$$P\left(-2.228 \leq \frac{\overline{X} - \mu_{\overline{X}}}{s_{\overline{X}}} \leq 2.228\right) = .95$$

Note that this probability statement corresponds in form to that on p. 241 for the large sample case. By rearranging the inequalities in the same fashion as we did before, we obtain:

$$P(\overline{X} - 2.228s_{\overline{X}} \leq \mu_{\overline{X}} \leq \overline{X} + 2.228s_{\overline{X}}) = .95$$

Since we know that $\mu_{\overline{X}} = \mu_X$ always, we have:

$$P(\overline{X} - 2.228s_{\overline{X}} \leq \mu_X \leq \overline{X} + 2.228s_{\overline{X}}) = .95$$

Hence:

$$\overline{X} - 2.228s_{\overline{X}} \leq \mu_X \leq \overline{X} + 2.228s_{\overline{X}}$$

is a confidence interval for μ_X when $n = 11$, with a confidence coefficient of .95.

In general, we have as a confidence interval for the population mean:

(12.13) $$\overline{X} - t_{n-1}s_{\overline{X}} \leq \mu_X \leq \overline{X} + t_{n-1}s_{\overline{X}}$$

Here t_{n-1} is the value of t obtained from Table A-5 for $n - 1$ degrees of freedom, corresponding to the desired confidence coefficient. The confidence limits can be obtained directly from:

(12.14 $$\overline{X} \pm t_{n-1}s_{\overline{X}}$$

As another illustration, suppose we wish to construct a confidence interval for the population mean with a 90 per cent confidence coefficient, based on a sample of $n = 16$. We are here concerned with the central 90 per cent of the area of the t-distribution. Hence, we must utilize the column that refers to an area of .10 in the two tails (area .05 in each tail). For 15 degrees of freedom, we find the value of t is 1.753. Therefore, the 90 per cent confidence limits when the random sample size is 16 are:

$$\overline{X} \pm 1.753s_{\overline{X}}$$

and the confidence interval is:

$$\overline{X} - 1.753 s_{\overline{X}} \leq \mu_X \leq \overline{X} + 1.753 s_{\overline{X}}$$

Thus, we use the t-distribution in the same way as the standard normal distribution. The only difference in the confidence interval is that we employ a t-multiple rather than a z-multiple.

Illustration

As an illustration of the use of the t-distribution, we consider the following example. A sample of five No. 2½ cans of standard grade tomatoes in purée was taken at random from the production line immediately after the cans were filled and before they were processed (Ref. 12.1, p. 43). The solid content of these cans was weighed, to serve as a basis for estimating the average drained weight per can for the process. It can be assumed on the basis of past experience that the distribution of the drained weight per can is approximately normal.

The drained weights of the cans in the sample are presented in Table 12.2. This table also contains the computations of the sample mean and sample standard deviation; these are 22.9 ounces and .822 ounces respectively. We then can estimate the standard deviation of $\overline{X}$ in the usual manner; we use the formula for an infinite population, because a process was sampled:

$$s_{\overline{X}} = \frac{s_X}{\sqrt{n}} = \frac{.822}{\sqrt{5}} = .37 \text{ ounces}$$

Table 12.2 Results and Calculations for Sample of Five Cans of Tomatoes From Production Line

	Drained Weight (Ounces) X	X^2
	22.0	484.00
	22.5	506.25
	22.5	506.25
	24.0	576.00
	23.5	552.25
Total	114.5	2,624.75

$$\overline{X} = \frac{\Sigma X}{n} = \frac{114.5}{5} = 22.9 \text{ ounces}$$

$$s_X = \sqrt{\frac{\Sigma X^2 - \frac{(\Sigma X)^2}{n}}{n-1}} = \sqrt{\frac{2{,}624.75 - \frac{(114.5)^2}{5}}{5-1}} = .822 \text{ ounces}$$

Assume that a 90 per cent confidence coefficient is desired. For 4 degrees of freedom (5 − 1) and a confidence coefficient of 90 per cent, the value of t is 2.132. Hence the confidence limits for the population mean are:

$$\bar{X} \pm t_{n-1}s_{\bar{X}}$$
$$22.9 \pm 2.132(.37)$$
$$22.9 \pm .79$$

And the confidence interval is:

$$22.9 - .79 \leq \mu_X \leq 22.9 + .79$$

or:

$$22.1 \leq \mu_X \leq 23.7$$

Thus it can be stated, with a 90 per cent confidence coefficient, that the process operating under the given conditions puts an average solid content of somewhere between 22.1 and 23.7 ounces into the cans.

Effect of non-normality of population

We assumed earlier that the population sampled is normal. Suppose, however, that the population is not normal. It can be shown that the confidence interval in (12.13) may be used even with small samples from non-normal populations, provided the population is not highly skewed. The confidence coefficient then will be *approximately* equal to that implied by the t-table. Thus, the confidence interval in (12.13) utilizing the t-distribution has much wider applicability than if it were restricted to samples from normal populations only.

Effect of sample size on t-multiple

Table A-5 makes it clear that for any given level of the confidence coefficient, the value of the t-multiple decreases as the sample size increases. This is simply a reflection of the decrease in variability of the t-distribution as the sample size becomes larger, which we noted earlier. With a confidence coefficient of 90 per cent, for instance, the t-value is 1.812 for 10 degrees of freedom, 1.725 for 20 degrees of freedom, and only 1.697 for 30 degrees of freedom. If the sample size had been large and we had used the normal distribution, the value of z corresponding to a 90 per cent confidence coefficient would have been 1.64. This approach of the t-values to the value of z illustrates that the t-distribution approaches the normal distribution as the sample size becomes larger and larger. Since the z value for a 90 per cent confidence coefficient is 1.64 and the corresponding t-value for 30 degrees of freedom is 1.697, we actually may consider a sample of 31 observations here as a large sample and use the standard normal distribution in constructing the confidence interval for the mean. We also may use the standard normal distribution in constructing confidence intervals for the population mean for other confidence coefficients if the sample size is around 30 or greater, as an examination of Table A-5 will indicate.

Note also that the effect of small sample sizes on the value of t influences the width of the confidence interval. For any given confidence coefficient, the smaller the sample size, the larger is the value of t; this relation, then, is a factor tending to make confidence intervals wider for smaller samples than for larger ones from a given population. Such an effect seems reasonable, since we know that the sample standard deviation will not be as precise an estimate of the population standard deviation if it comes from a small sample as if it comes from a large one.

Cited reference

12.1 Grant, Eugene L., *Statistical Quality Control,* 2d ed. New York: McGraw-Hill Book Company, Inc., 1952.

QUESTIONS AND PROBLEMS

12.1. Explain briefly each of the following:
a. Confidence coefficient
b. Estimator
c. Consistency
d. Half-width of confidence interval
e. t-distribution

12.2. **a.** Distinguish between a point estimate and an interval estimate. Which is more useful? Why?
b. Distinguish between an estimator and an estimate. Which one is a random variable?
c. Distinguish between confidence limits and a confidence interval.

12.3. **a.** Explain why unbiasedness, efficiency and consistency are desirable properties for a point estimator to have.
b. If a point estimator is biased but consistent, does this imply that the bias approaches zero as the sample size gets large? Discuss.
c. Let $\overline{X}_1$ and $\overline{X}_2$ denote the sample means based on random samples of sizes n_1 and n_2 respectively from the same population. If n_1 is larger than n_2, does it follow that $\overline{X}_1$ is a relatively more efficient estimator than $\overline{X}_2$ in estimating the population mean μ_X? Explain.

12.4. The tax commission of a state wishes to estimate the mean reporting error in income tax returns. A sample of returns for the year is to be selected and audited to determine the reporting error in each.
a. Define the population mean μ_X that is being estimated from the sample.
b. Why is this population mean μ_X not necessarily the quantity that the tax commission wishes to estimate? Would an increase in the sample size help to reduce this possible discrepancy? Explain fully.

12.5. Explain fully how we can obtain an estimate of the variability of the sampling distribution of $\overline{X}$ from only a single simple random sample.

12.6. A research report stated that the mean income per person in the population is between \$4,500 and \$6,000, with a confidence coefficient of 95 per cent. A student interpreted this as indicating that 95 per cent of the persons in the population had incomes between \$4,500 and \$6,000. Another student interpreted this in the sense that if many random samples were taken, 95 per cent of them would have sample means between \$4,500 and \$6,000. What basic mistakes did these students make?

12.7. Since one can obtain a confidence interval for the population mean from any large simple random sample, why is it still desirable to control the simple random sample size in advance of taking the sample?

12.8. Discuss each of the following statements:

a. "It is obviously desirable to use a small confidence coefficient, since this reduces the width of the confidence interval for a given sample."

b. "The larger the simple random sample size, the greater is the assurance that the confidence interval includes the parameter being estimated."

***12.9.** An airline researcher studied reservation records for a simple random sample of 60 days in order to estimate the mean number of persons who failed to keep their reservations ("no-shows") on the daily 4 P.M. flight to New York City. The records revealed the following information:

Number of No-shows		*Number of Days*
0		33
1		14
2		6
3		4
4		2
5		1
	Total	60

a. What is the point estimate of the mean number of no-shows per flight for the process? Why is this estimate called a point estimate?

b. Do you have great confidence that your point estimate coincides with the process mean? Explain.

c. Construct an interval estimate of the process mean, with a 98 per cent confidence coefficient.

d. Explain precisely the meaning of your confidence interval. What does the confidence coefficient of 98 per cent signify?

e. If you had constructed the confidence interval corresponding to a 90 per cent confidence coefficient, would it be wider or narrower than the 98 per cent confidence interval constructed in part **c**? Which interval would involve the smaller risk of an incorrect estimate? What generalization does this suggest?

f. Is your interval estimate in part **c** precise enough to be useful? Assume that management wants an interval estimate of the process mean with a maximum half-width of .3, with a 98 per cent confidence coefficient.

12.10. Refer to Problem 12.9.

a. Why is the confidence coefficient for the interval estimate in Problem 12.9**c** only approximately 98 per cent? Explain.

b. In another simple random sample of 60 days from the same process, would the same 98 per cent confidence limits as in Problem 12.9**c** have been obtained? Discuss.

c. Suppose the process mean in the past had been .5 no-shows per flight. Would you conclude from the interval estimate in Problem 12.9**c** that the current process mean is no longer .5 no-shows per flight? Explain the reasoning underlying your answer.

12.11. The planning commission in a city containing 24,900 dwelling places wished to estimate the mean number of inhabitants per dwelling place in the city. It selected a simple random sample of 500 dwelling places, and the sample results were as follows:

X = number of inhabitants in sample dwelling place

$n = 500 \quad \bar{X} = 5.69$ inhabitants $\quad s_X = 4.02$ inhabitants

a. What is the point estimate of the mean number of inhabitants per dwelling place in the city? Why is this estimate called a point estimate?

b. Do you have great confidence that your point estimate coincides with the mean number of inhabitants per dwelling place in the entire city? Explain.

c. Construct an interval estimate, with a 95 per cent confidence coefficient, of the mean number of inhabitants per dwelling place in the city.

d. Explain precisely the meaning of your confidence interval. What does the confidence coefficient of 95 per cent signify?

e. If you had constructed the confidence interval corresponding to a 99 per cent confidence coefficient, would it be wider or narrower than the 95 per cent confidence interval constructed in part **c**? Which interval would involve the greater risk of an incorrect estimate? What generalization does this suggest?

f. Is your interval estimate in part **c** precise enough to be useful? Discuss.

12.12. Refer to Problem 12.11.

a. Why is the confidence coefficient for the interval estimate in Problem 12.11**c** only approximately 95 per cent? Explain.

b. In another simple random sample of 500 dwelling places, would the same 95 per cent confidence limits as in Problem 12.11**c** have been obtained? Discuss.

c. The planning commission also wanted to estimate the total number of inhabitants in the city. What would be the interval estimate of the total number of inhabitants, with a 95 per cent confidence coefficient? (*Hint:* You already have an interval estimate of the mean number of inhabitants per dwelling place in the city from part **c** of Problem 12.11, and you know that there are 24,900 dwelling places in the city.)

d. Define precisely the population mean μ_X that is being estimated from the sample.

e. Why is this population mean μ_X not necessarily the same as the quantity the planning commission wishes to estimate? Does this have any effect on the interpretation of the interval estimate in Problem 12.11**c**? Explain fully.

***12.13.** The Morgan Steel Company wishes to select a simple random sample of steel bars from its production process in order to estimate the mean length of the bars produced by the process. On the basis of past experience, it is estimated that the process standard deviation is about $\sigma_X = .45$ feet.

a. How large a sample is needed to estimate the process mean within $\pm.08$ feet, with a 90 per cent confidence coefficient?

b. Recalculate the required sample size in part **a** under each of the following new conditions (in each case, keep other factors at their original values): (1) Reduce the required half-width to half its previous value, that is, to $h = .04$. (2) Double the process standard deviation to $\sigma_X = .90$. (3) Double the value of the standard normal deviate from $z = 1.645$ to $z = 3.290$. What generalization is suggested by your results?

c. In (3) of part **b**, doubling z from 1.645 to 3.290, in effect, increases the confidence coefficient from 90 to 99.9 per cent. Is the resultant change in the required sample size substantial relative to the increase in the confidence coefficient? What are the implications of this for management?

d. What is the likely effect on the confidence interval obtained from the sample results, if the process standard deviation used in planning the required sample size is an underestimate? Would such a misjudgment affect the validity of the confidence interval based on the sample results? Discuss.

e. Suppose it is known that a calibration error exists in the measuring instrument, so that the length is understated somewhat. Should the sample size therefore be increased? Discuss.

12.14. Refer to Problem 12.4. Suppose there are 1,000,000 returns for the year, and experience in other states indicates that the standard deviation of reporting errors is about $\sigma_X = \$100$.

a. How large a simple random sample is needed to estimate the population mean within $\pm\$20$, with a confidence coefficient of 95 per cent?

b. If the population size had been 10,000,000 tax returns, what sample size would have been needed to estimate the population mean within $\pm\$20$, with a confidence coefficient of 95 per cent? How does this required sample size compare with that in part **a**? What generalization does this suggest?

c. Recalculate the required sample size in part **a** under each of the following new conditions (in each case, keep other factors at their original values and assume the population is sufficiently large that it may be considered infinite): (1) Reduce the required half-width to half its original value, that is, to $h = \$10$. (2) Double the process standard deviation to $\sigma_X = \$200$. (3) Double the value of the standard normal deviate from $z = 1.96$ to $z = 3.92$. What generalization is suggested by your results?

d. In (3) of part **c**, doubling z from 1.96 to 3.92, in effect, increases the confidence coefficient from 95 to 99.99 per cent. Is the resultant change in the required sample size substantial relative to the increase in the confidence coefficient? What are the implications of this for the tax commission?

e. Since the advance judgment about the magnitude of the population standard deviation usually will be somewhat in error, is the validity of the confidence interval based on the sample results affected? Discuss fully. What is the likely effect on the confidence interval if the population standard deviation used for planning the required sample size is an overestimate? Discuss. Why can you not discuss the effect on the confidence interval for any one sample?

12.15. A gas utility company wishes to know how much time is required, on the average, for a company serviceman to handle an appliance service call. A simple random sample of recent service calls is to be selected to obtain the information. On the basis of similar studies in the past, it is estimated that the standard deviation of the population should be between 40 and 80 minutes.

a. In order that the simple random sample will be sufficiently large — that is, rather too large than too small — what value of the population standard deviation should be used for planning the sample size? Explain.

b. If, on the other hand, the simple random sample should not be unnecessarily large — since, if necessary, it can easily be enlarged — what value of the population standard deviation should be used for planning the sample size? Explain.

c. It was decided to use an advance estimate of $\sigma_X = 60$ minutes for planning purposes. What is the necessary simple random sample size in order to estimate the population mean within ± 10 minutes, with a confidence coefficient of

90 per cent?

d. If the population standard deviation actually were $\sigma_X = 70$ minutes, would the sample size needed to estimate the population mean within ± 10 minutes, with a confidence coefficient of 90 per cent, differ substantially in order of magnitude from the needed sample size in part **c**? What generalization does this suggest about the usefulness of only an approximate advance estimate of the population standard deviation?

12.16. In the case described in Problem 12.15, a simple random sample of 150 service calls was actually selected; the results were as follows:

X = number of minutes to handle sample service call

$n = 150 \quad \bar{X} = 62.2 \text{ minutes} \quad s_X = 55.0 \text{ minutes}$

a. Construct a confidence interval for the population mean, with a 90 per cent confidence coefficient.

b. Explain clearly the meaning of the confidence interval obtained in part **a**. What does the confidence coefficient of 90 per cent signify?

c. Is your interval estimate in part **a** precise enough to be useful? Assume that management would like to estimate the population mean with an interval estimate whose half-width does not exceed 10 minutes, with a confidence coefficient of 90 per cent.

d. In the past, the mean time for a service call had been 78 minutes. From your confidence interval in part **a**, would you conclude that the current mean time for a service call differs from that in the past? Explain the reasoning underlying your answer.

12.17. A population of 7,501 small retail establishments (five or fewer employees) in a metropolitan area is to be sampled to estimate the mean number of employees per establishment in the population. Experience in sample surveys indicates that the population standard deviation should be about $\sigma_X = 1.2$ employees.

a. How large a simple random sample is required to estimate the mean number of employees per establishment in the population within $\pm .4$ employees, with a confidence coefficient of 97.5 per cent?

b. How large would the simple random sample size have to be if the population mean is to be estimated within $\pm .2$ employees, with a confidence coefficient of 97.5 per cent?

c. Will a poor advance judgment of the population standard deviation used in planning the required sample size affect the validity of the confidence interval based on the sample results? Will it affect the confidence interval in any way? Discuss.

12.18. In the case described in Problem 12.17, a simple random sample of 75 retail establishments actually was selected. The results were as follows:

Number of Employees in Establishment	*Number of Establishments*
0	33
1	12
2	12
3	9
4	5
5	4
Total	75

a. Construct a confidence interval for the population mean, with a 97.5 per cent confidence coefficient. (*Hint:* $\bar{X} = 1.37$, $s_X = 1.56$)

b. Explain clearly the meaning of your confidence interval. What does the confidence coefficient of 97.5 per cent signify?

c. Is your interval estimate in part **a** precise enough to be useful? Discuss.

d. If employers in the sample establishments made consistent errors in furnishing data on number of employees (for instance, including family helpers as employees), is the validity of the confidence interval affected? To what precisely does the population mean μ_X being estimated refer? Discuss.

12.19. With simple random sampling, what distribution does each of the following statistics follow if: (1) population is normal and n small? (2) population is normal and n large? (3) population is not normal and n small? (4) population is not normal and n large?

a. $\bar{X}$

b. $(\bar{X} - \mu_{\bar{X}})/\sigma_{\bar{X}}$

c. $(\bar{X} - \mu_{\bar{X}})/s_{\bar{X}}$

***12.20.** The time required by a certain mailman to cover his route daily is normally distributed, with unknown mean and standard deviation. For each of the following sample sizes, indicate the appropriate number of degrees of freedom and the t-value for obtaining a confidence interval for the process mean time, with a 98 per cent confidence coefficient: $n = 11, 24, 3, 120$.

***12.21.** The times required by the mailman in Problem 12.20 to cover his route in a simple random sample of five days are 384, 324, 352, 399, and 376 minutes.

a. Estimate the mean time required by the mailman to cover his route; use an interval estimate with a 95 per cent confidence coefficient.

b. Explain clearly the meaning of your confidence interval.

c. What would be the confidence interval if a 99 per cent confidence coefficient had been desired?

d. If a sample of twelve days had been available, what factors would have tended to lead to a more precise interval estimate for a given confidence coefficient? Explain.

e. If the time required to cover the route followed a highly skewed distribution, would your interval estimate in part **a** have a 95 per cent confidence coefficient? What if the distribution were only moderately skewed? Explain.

12.22. In a weaving mill, six observations were taken at random times on a section of 400 looms to determine the number of looms working at a given time. The results on the number of looms working were:

368 looms	376 looms	366 looms
353 looms	361 looms	354 looms

It is known from past experience that the number of looms working at a given time in the battery of 400 looms is approximately normally distributed.

a. Estimate the mean number of looms in the battery that are working at any given time; use an interval estimate with a 90 per cent confidence coefficient.

b. Explain clearly the meaning of your confidence interval.

c. What would be the confidence interval if a 95 per cent confidence coefficient had been desired?

d. Would a 90 per cent confidence interval based on 20 observations have been narrower than the one you obtained in part **a**? Explain.

(Continued)

e. Would the procedures used in constructing your confidence interval in part **a** be appropriate if the number of looms working at a given time followed a distribution highly skewed to the left? Moderately skewed? Discuss.

CLASS PROJECT

12.23. Refer to Problem 10.19.

a. From each sample of 50 freight bills, construct an interval estimate of the mean amount per freight bill due Crandell Motor Freight, Inc., in the population. Use a 95 per cent confidence coefficient.

b. What proportion of the 100 interval estimates do you expect to include the population mean $\mu_X = \$2.23$? Explain.

c. What proportion of the 100 interval estimates actually do include the population mean?

d. What does this experiment illustrate about the meaning of the confidence coefficient of 95 per cent? Discuss.

Chapter

13

SAMPLING PROCEDURES AND APPLICATIONS

In this chapter, we show that a simple random sample is a particular kind of probability sample, and we contrast this type of sample with judgment samples and "chunks." A number of different kinds of probability samples are then explained. Finally, we present several sampling cases to illustrate how the principles discussed in this and the preceding chapters are applied in practice.

13.1 PROBABILITY SAMPLES, JUDGMENT SAMPLES, AND CHUNKS

In our discussion of sampling so far, we have restricted ourselves to simple random sampling, because it is the most basic kind of sample for which we can evaluate the sampling error. There are many other sampling procedures for which we also can evaluate the sampling error; all such sampling procedures fall into the class of *probability samples. Judgment samples* and *chunks,* on the other hand, do not provide direct information on the basis of which the sampling error can be evaluated. In making the distinction between probability samples and judgment samples and chunks, we restrict our discussion to sampling from finite populations. As noted in Chapter 9, it is only when the population is finite that one can engage in a sample selection process. When the population is infinite, sample observations are provided by the process and no actual selection takes place.

Probability samples

(13.1) A ***probability sample*** is a sample where the selection of items from the population for the sample is made according to known probabilities.

More specifically, a probability sample is characterized by three features:

1. A specified statistical design is followed.
2. The selection of the population elements for the sample is determined solely according to known probabilities by means of a random mechanism (usually, a table of random digits).
3. Estimates and sampling error limits are calculated according to predetermined methods (such as those studied in the last chapter).

Note especially that the selection of population elements for the sample with known probabilities allows no discretion as to which particular population items should be included in the sample. Furthermore, once an item has been selected by the probability mechanism, probability sampling requires that it must be included in the sample with no substitute allowed.

It is doubtful that a perfect probability sample is often conducted, except in cases of relatively simple sampling such as in sampling of files. There are usually some departures from the probability model, because of such factors as refusals to participate and failure of interviewers to follow instructions. Nevertheless, the departures from a pure probability sample can usually be made so small in a well-run survey that the sample can be treated as if it were a perfect probability sample.

A chief advantage of a probability sample is that the magnitude of the sampling error can be estimated from a properly designed sample, so that the precision of the sample result can be evaluated. Also, a probability selection of the sample avoids biases that otherwise could enter the sample result if judgment on the part of interviewers or others were used in the selection of the sample items.

Judgment samples

Probability samples may be contrasted with judgment samples.

(13.2) A ***judgment sample*** is a sample where judgment plays a substantial role in the selection of the particular items to be included in the sample and/or in making decisions about parts of the population for which the sample provided no information.

Judgment is also used, of course, in designing probability samples, but the actual selection of the particular items for such samples is made purely by a known probability mechanism. In a judgment sample, on the other hand, judgment may be relied upon to a substantial extent for the selection of "representative" items for the sample.

Consider, for instance, a sales manager who chooses certain communities as typical of communities in the United States, tries out a new type of sales promotion campaign in them, and then draws conclusions about the entire United States from the results in the sample communities. The selected communities constitute a judgment sample of the United States, because the sales manager believes that these communities provide a representative picture of the entire country.

A *quota sample* is a judgment sample. In a quota sample, the interviewer is required to question a certain number of persons with given characteristics; for instance, he may be asked to interview 20 men living in a certain group of blocks, who fall within a certain age class and whose incomes fall within a given range. The quotas are set up so that the entire sample will provide a cross-section, with respect to the characteristics controlled by the quotas, of the population under study. Within the general quotas, however, the actual selection of the persons is up to the interviewer. For this reason, serious biases can enter the survey results. For instance, an interviewer is apt to select persons most readily available; if the interviewing is done during the day only, he will miss persons who are at work; if a person refuses to respond, the interviewer simply can select another person. In these and other ways, biases can enter the survey as a result of the discretion left to the interviewer in selecting the persons to be included in the sample.

Another instance of a judgment sample occurs when a market-research director, who obtained only a 25 per cent response rate to his mail questionnaire, decides according to his judgment that the nonrespondents are similar to the respondents with respect to the characteristics under study. In other words, the returned questionnaires are treated as if they provide a representative picture of the entire population under study. The research director, therefore, makes a judgment about a substantial part of the population for which no information was obtained from the sample. The sample is then a judgment sample, even if the original names on the mailing list were selected by a probability mechanism.

While judgment samples can provide useful results and do so quite often, there are no methods available whereby the sampling error can be estimated from such a sample. Therefore, the precision of the result of a judgment sample depends upon the soundness of the judgment exercised and cannot be evaluated on the basis of the sample itself.

Chunks

Chunks are not samples chosen deliberately either by a probability mechanism or by expert judgment to provide a representative picture about the population under study. Rather:

(13.3) A ***chunk*** is a part of the population that happens to be conveniently at hand.

For instance, suppose that a teacher of marketing wishes to study how consumers choose the particular store from which a given item is to be purchased. If the teacher uses his marketing class in the experiment, he has a chunk—a part of the population that is conveniently available to him. Other examples of chunks are cities chosen for experimental marketing of a new product because the company has regional offices there, or the testing of a new advertising slogan on relatives of employees in the advertising department.

Chunks may be quite useful for limited purposes, but can provide no assurance that the results obtained from them are indicative of characteristics of the entire population under study. In fact, conclusions based on chunks can be far in error.

Choice between probability and judgment samples

We stress probability samples in this book, because statistical sampling theory can be applied to such samples. Our emphasis does not mean that judgment samples should never be used. As stated earlier, such samples have provided useful results, though at other times they have led to biased findings. If the sample must be extremely small due to financial or other reasons, a judgment sample may be preferable to a probability sample. Consider, for instance, a company that owns several hundred retail stores and wishes to experiment with a new method of merchandising (for example, self-service) in one or two of its stores. It probably should select one or two stores that are considered typical in the opinion of the management rather than take a probability sample, since the sampling error for a probability sample of such small size may be extremely great.

In the opinion of Hansen and Hurwitz, two outstanding statisticians in the field of sampling, probability samples should be considered "where results of high precision are needed, or where objective and unbiased results are wanted because important decisions or courses of action will be determined on the basis of the sample results" (Ref. 13.1, p. 364).

13.2 PROBABILITY SAMPLING PROCEDURES

Our discussion in Chapter 12 concerning the evaluation of the magnitude of an estimate's sampling error was based upon the assumption that a simple random sample was taken. We pointed out that a simple random sample is not the only type of probability sample, but that it would be easiest to discuss the basic principles of statistical estimation in terms of this simple kind of probability sample. Now, we discuss some other probability sampling procedures that may be more efficient than simple random sampling.

Efficiency of sampling procedure

Before going any further, we should explain what we mean by more efficient sampling procedures. We mentioned in our previous discussion that an estimate based on a simple random sample of given size from a particular population has a certain sampling error, corresponding to a given confidence coefficient. For example, we estimated in Chapter 12 on the basis of a simple random sample of 50 employees that the average length of service of employees of the Thurston Corporation is between 4.1 and 7.9, (6.0 ± 1.9), years; this estimate was made with a confidence coefficient of 99.7 per cent. The cost of obtaining this precision (±1.9 years with a confidence coefficient of 99.7 per cent) through simple random sampling can be compared with the cost of obtaining the same precision of the estimate through some other probability sampling procedure. *We consider any type of probability sampling procedure that will provide, at a given level of confidence, the same precision of the estimate at less cost or more precision at the same cost, to be a more efficient technique than simple random sampling.*

Stratified random sampling

First, we take up *stratified random sampling,* one of the most basic methods used in practice to obtain greater efficiency than simple random sampling provides.

Nature of stratified random sampling.

(13.4) With ***stratified random sampling,*** the population is divided into a number of mutually exclusive subpopulations, each of which is sampled independently.

The results of these independent samples are then combined to provide the desired estimate for the entire population. For instance, the population of customers of a bank may be divided into commercial and noncommercial customers, each of these subpopulations or strata sampled independently, and the results combined to obtain the desired estimate for the population of customers. Another example of stratified sampling is dividing a company's invoices for a year into, say, five groups according to the amount of the invoice, and then sampling each of the five subpopulations independently.

Why stratified random sampling can be more efficient. To illustrate why stratified random sampling can be more efficient than simple random sampling, we consider again the case discussed in Chapter 12 of estimating the average length of service of the 2,000 employees of the Thurston Corporation. With simple random sampling, the sample of 50 employees is selected at random from all 2,000 employees. Thus, among all the possible different sample combinations are instances in which all employees in the sample come from the plant, or all come from the office, or all are women, and so on. Such samples would, no doubt, be considered "unrepresentative" by most persons. The fact that such "unrepresentative" samples are possible with simple random sampling may increase the sampling error and therefore lessen the precision of the sample estimate.

Why *may* such "unrepresentative" samples increase the sampling error? The significant point to be considered is in what respects these possible sample combinations are unrepresentative. If they are unrepresentative of characteristics not related to the item under study—in this case, the length of service—the sampling error will not be increased. For instance, a possible sample combination in simple random sampling may consist of 50 employees, each of whom smokes. Such a group probably is unrepresentative of all employees insofar as smoking is concerned, but as long as there is no connection between length of service and smoking, this type of unrepresentativeness does not increase the sampling error of the estimate of the average length of service.

On the other hand, unrepresentativeness of samples with respect to place of work in the company would increase the sampling error of the estimate, since there happens to be a definite relationship at the Thurston Corporation between length of service and whether a person works in the plant, in the office, or elsewhere. Thus, if the sample combination consists only of employees from the plant or only of employees from the office, it may yield a sample estimate that differs substantially from the population mean. Such sample combinations, which lead to sample means far from the population mean, tend to make the sampling distribution of $\overline{X}$ more variable, thereby increasing the sampling error.

Stratified random sampling can reduce such causes of increased sampling error, by making it impossible to get some of these "unrepresentative" samples and thus making the sampling distribution of $\overline{X}$ less variable. This is done by subdividing the population and then sampling each part separately. In our example, the population may be divided, for instance, according to the job of the employee. Table 13.1 indicates the sizes of the sub-

Table 13.1 Stratification of Population of Employees of Thurston Corporation by Type of Job

Stratum	*Type of Job of Employees*		*Number of Employees*
1	Plant		1,650
2	Office		300
3	Other		50
		Total	2,000

populations of plant, office, and other employees. Each of these subpopulations is called a *stratum*. The procedure then is to take a simple random sample from the subpopulation (stratum) of plant employees, another simple random sample from the stratum of office employees, and a third simple random sample from the stratum of other employees. Thus, with stratified random sampling, information is sure to be obtained about plant, office, and other employees. With simple random sampling, on the other hand, it is possible to obtain sample combinations that exclude one, or even two, of these groups.

If stratified random sampling is used intelligently, a sample of a given size usually will yield an estimate of the population mean with a smaller sampling error than if a simple random sample of the same size from the entire population had been employed. It is not true, however, that the estimate of the population mean from *any* stratified random sample will have a smaller sampling error than that from a simple random sample of equal size. Note that the division of the population by type of job in our example makes sense only because there is a relationship at the Thurston Corporation between the type of job of an employee and his length of service. If there were no such relationship, this stratification would not reduce the sampling error of the estimate of the population mean.

Sample design and estimation of population mean. Two main problems in designing a stratified random sample are choosing the strata and determining the size of the simple random sample to be selected from each stratum. A discussion of both of these problems, as well as of the procedure for estimating the population mean when stratified random sampling is employed, is given in Section 14.4.

Systematic random sampling

(13.5) In a ***systematic random sample,*** every kth element in the population arranged in some specified order is selected for the sample, with the starting point among the first k elements determined at random.

For instance, suppose that we wish to select a systematic sample of 50 blocks in a community that has 500 city blocks. Here, $k = 10$; in other words, every tenth block will be selected. First, the city blocks are arranged in a specific order such as a geographic one and assigned numbers from 1 to 500. Then a random number between 1 and 10 is selected from a table of random digits. Suppose that it is 3; then the third block is the first one in the sample; the second sample block is block 13; the next is 23; and so on.

Systematic sampling, thus, is a relatively simple and convenient method of sample selection. In addition, systematic sampling may be more efficient than simple random sampling. For example, the arrangement of city blocks in a geographic order will ensure that a systematic sample of city blocks will contain blocks from all parts of the city. Thus, this systematic sample resembles a stratified sample in which the city blocks first are divided into geographic areas to assure that each area is represented in the sample.

If the order in which the population is arranged is a random one, then a systematic sample with a random start is the equivalent of a simple random sample. In this case, systematic selection will not be more efficient than simple random sampling, except for the fact that it still might be a more convenient method of sample selection.

Occasionally, systematic sampling may be less efficient than simple random sampling. This lower efficiency for systematic sampling can occur when the population is arranged in some periodic order. For instance, suppose that all city blocks contain eight houses. Then, a systematic sample of every eighth house might contain only corner houses; since it is known that families living in corner houses generally differ somewhat in a number of respects from other families in the block, a sample of corner houses only could provide results seriously in error. Therefore, systematic sampling should not be used indiscriminately.

Systematic sampling can be modified slightly to avoid the problem of the sampling interval coinciding with a periodic arrangement in the population, and also to facilitate the evaluation of the sampling error. With reference to our previous example of selecting every eighth house, we still would make a listing of all houses in geographic order to achieve the effects of stratification, but then would select a house at random from each consecutive group of eight houses. Thus, one house would be selected at random from houses 1 to 8, another from houses 9 to 16, and so on. By so doing, any periodic arrangement in the population will not affect the different possible samples.

Area sampling

To understand the usefulness of this survey technique, which is being widely employed, consider the problems of selecting and interviewing a sample of the population of the United States. Since no up-to-date list of all the inhabitants exists, such a list would have to be constructed at great cost in order that a simple random sample could be selected. Furthermore, once a simple random sample had been selected, it would be found that the persons in the sample would be scattered all over the country. The cost of sending trained interviewers to these persons, as well as the cost of supervising this operation, again would be extremely high.

In such a situation, area sampling is often used. While interest still centers on characteristics of individual persons or families, the initial sampling unit is taken to be an area. For instance, the area of the United States may be divided by counties. A listing of all counties exists, so that a probability sample of counties can be selected. Similarly, sampling of families in a city may be accomplished by making the city blocks the sampling units. An up-to-date listing of city blocks in a city can be obtained readily, from which one is able to select a probability sample of blocks.

The areas (counties, blocks, or the like) are called *sampling units,* because they are the units being sampled. The units about which information is desired are called *elementary units;* for instance, individuals, families, or houses might be the elementary units in a survey. We therefore may think of the sampling units (areas) as *clusters* of elementary units. Selection of any one area brings a cluster of elementary units into the sample.

Note how area sampling eliminates the problem of listing all elementary units in the population. Area sampling uses a sampling unit (county, block, or the like) for which a complete listing already exists or can be fairly readily obtained. A listing of elementary units (individuals, families, or the like) then is necessary only in those areas selected for the sample. Furthermore, area sampling concentrates the persons or families to be interviewed within certain counties, city blocks, or similar area units. In this way, the cost of interviewing and supervision is reduced, because the persons in the sample are not scattered "all over the map." Cost reduction from this concentration of elementary units is much more important, of course, in a national survey than in a local one.

To obtain the same precision of the estimate, area sampling frequently requires larger samples of elementary units than would be required with simple random sampling. This is because persons living within any one area often tend to be more alike in their characteristics and opinions than persons living in different areas. Thus, interviewing another family in the same house in which one family already has been interviewed may not provide as much additional information as would interviewing another family selected at random from the entire population. Nevertheless, the cost advantage in listing fewer elementary units and having the elementary units clustered in a number of locations often is so great that the area sample is more efficient than a simple random one. This is not always the case, however. For instance, if the population to be sampled consists of the inhabitants of a small community, a simple random sample may furnish the required precision of the estimate at less cost (even including the listing of all the inhabitants, households, or the like) than an area sample.

Sampling with unequal probabilities

In selecting a probability sample of counties or city blocks, each sampling unit need not be given an equal probability of being chosen for the sample. For instance, a block with twice as many inhabitants as another may be given twice as much chance of being included in the sample. While the probabilities of selection need not be equal, they must be known so that the sampling error can be calculated. An important problem here is the choice of probabilities of selection for counties, city blocks, or other such sampling units so that the sampling error of the estimate is reduced as much as possible for a sample of given size. Sampling with *probability proportionate to size* is a widely used method of choosing the probabilities of selection in this type of situation.

Multistage sampling

Once areas, such as counties or city blocks, are selected for the sample, it is not customary practice to interview every individual or family located in these areas. Rather, additional stages of sampling are introduced. Consider, for instance, the following possible procedure of selecting a sample of the inhabitants of a city. In the first stage of sampling, a number of city blocks from the population of all city blocks is chosen. For each selected city block, a list of dwelling units then is prepared, unless an up-to-date list is already available. From the list of dwelling units for each of the chosen blocks, a probability sample of dwelling units then is selected. This is the second stage of sampling. For each of the selected dwelling units, a list of individuals residing in them is constructed. From the list of individuals in each selected dwelling unit, a probability sample of individuals is chosen in the third and final stage of sampling. These chosen individuals then are interviewed. This method of selecting the elementary units for the sample in stages is called *multistage sampling.*

Note that in this type of sampling a listing of dwelling units is necessary only for the blocks selected for the sample, and a listing of individuals is necessary only for the chosen dwelling units. Numerous problems arise in designing multistage samples. How many stages should be used and what should they be? For instance, in our previous example a list of individuals could have been prepared for each selected block; this would have avoided the second stage of selecting dwelling units. Another problem is to determine how many units should be chosen at each stage of sampling so that the desired precision of the sample estimate can be obtained at minimum cost. While the basic approach to the problem of estimation is still the same, the statistical theory for multistage sampling obviously is more complicated than that for simple random sampling.

Multistage sampling is not confined to the case in which areas are chosen in some of the selection stages. Two-stage sampling has been employed, for instance, in determining the percentage of clean wool in lots of domestic wool stored in warehouses (Ref. 13.2, pp. 160–163). In the first stage of sampling, a number of bales were selected from the lot. From these particular bales, a number of cores then were taken in the second stage of sampling. These cores made up the sample and were analyzed for the proportion of clean wool.

Combination of techniques

We have explained briefly some of the sampling techniques that may furnish estimates with the required precision more economically than would simple random sampling. One need not use any one of these techniques to the exclusion of all others. We already have noticed how area sampling and multistage sampling can be employed together. Furthermore, stratification can be used together with area and multistage sampling. For instance, in the sampling of the inhabitants of a city, the city blocks first may be stratified according to relevant economic, social, and other characteristics. From each stratum, a sample of city blocks then would be selected. Further stages of sampling then would follow as described earlier.

13.3 APPLICATIONS OF STATISTICAL ESTIMATION

We now present a number of case studies of applications of statistical estimation have been found useful. Furthermore, these case studies will in business and public administration in which sampling and statistical estimation have been found useful. Furthermore, these case studies will indicate how the various concepts and techniques discussed in this and preceding chapters are applied in different specific situations.

At the same time, the reader should be cautioned that these cases either represent relatively simple sampling applications or that many of the complications have been omitted for the sake of clarity of presentation. Hence, he should not conclude that all actual sampling applications are as simple as these cases may appear.

Sampling of waybills

The Chesapeake and Ohio Railroad has conducted some experiments to determine if a sample of waybills could provide a reliable estimate of the proportion of revenue due the Chesapeake and Ohio on interline, less-than-carload freight shipments (Ref. 13.3). A waybill is a document issued with every shipment of freight, giving details regarding the goods, route, and charges. If a shipment travels over several railroads, the total freight charge is divided among them. The computations necessary to determine the revenue due each railroad are cumbersome and expensive. Hence, the Chesapeake and Ohio Railroad experimented to determine if the allocation of total revenue among several railroads could be made accurately on the basis of a sample and at a substantial saving in clerical expense.

In one of these experiments, the division of revenue for all less-than-carload freight shipments traveling over railroad A and the Pere Marquette district of the Chesapeake and Ohio during a six-month period was studied. The waybills of these shipments constituted the population under examination. The total number of waybills in the population was known, as well as the total freight revenue accounted for by the waybills in the population. The problem was to determine how much of this total revenue belonged to the Chesapeake and Ohio.

The population of waybills for the six-month period under study consisted of nearly 23,000 waybills. Since the amounts of the freight charges on these waybills varied greatly—some freight charges were as low as $2, others as high as $200—and since the total amount of a waybill was related to the amount due the Chesapeake and Ohio on that waybill, it was decided to divide the population into strata according to the amount of the freight charge on each waybill. The strata were set up as follows:

Stratum	*Waybills With Charges Between:*
I	$ 0 –$ 5.00
II	$ 5.01–$10.00
III	$10.01–$20.00
IV	$20.01–$40.00
V	$40.01–over

Note that each stratum contains waybills with freight charges of roughly the same order of magnitude. Because of the existence of a general relationship between total charge on a waybill and the amount due the Chesapeake and Ohio, each stratum is more homogeneous than the total population with respect to the amount of freight charges due the Chesapeake and Ohio on the waybills. At the same time, the strata differ substantially from each other with respect to this characteristic.

Relevant statistical theory then was employed to decide how large the sample from each stratum must be so that the amount of revenue due the Chesapeake and Ohio could be estimated with required precision from as small a sample as possible. This theory led to relatively larger samples in the strata containing waybills with large freight charges. The sampling rates for the strata were as follows:

Stratum	*Proportion to Be Sampled*
I	1 per cent
II	10 per cent
III	20 per cent
IV	50 per cent
V	100 per cent

Once the sample sizes were determined, the next problem concerned the selection of simple random samples from each stratum. It was decided that the sample within each stratum should be selected according to the last two digits in the serial number of the waybill. For instance, 1 per cent of the waybills in stratum I were to be chosen for the sample. The number of possible pairs of digits appearing in the last two places of the serial number (00, 01, 02, . . . , 99) is 100. If one of these pairs is chosen and all waybills with these last two digits in their serial number selected for the sample, it will be found in this type of situation that about 1 per cent of the stratum is included in the sample.

As long as there is no relationship between the amount of the freight charge and its division among the railroads on the one hand and the last two digits in the serial number on the other hand, a random choice of one two-digit number will yield the equivalent of a simple random 1 per cent sample. For stratum I, for instance, a number from 00 to 99 was selected from a table of random digits; it turned out to be 02. Therefore, all waybills with freight charges of $5 or less whose last two digits in the serial number are 02 were selected for the sample. The serial number digits used for the other strata, as well as the sampling rates, were as follows:

Stratum	*Proportion to Be Sampled*	*Waybills With Numbers Ending in:*
I	1 per cent	02
II	10 per cent	2
III	20 per cent	2 or 4
IV	50 per cent	00 to 49
V	100 per cent	00 to 99

Inasmuch as the waybills are serially numbered, this procedure is a simple one for selecting the sample. Furthermore, for reasons already mentioned, it provides essentially the equivalent of a simple random sample from each stratum.

Altogether, 2,072 waybills out of 22,984 in the population (9 per cent) were chosen according to this procedure. For each waybill in the sample, the amount of freight revenue due the Chesapeake and Ohio then was calculated. The results for each stratum were then combined to form an estimate of the total amount of freight revenue due the Chesapeake and Ohio. Since this was an experiment, a complete examination of the population also was made, so that the sample result could be compared with the result obtained from an analysis of all waybills in the population. The findings were:

Total amount due Chesapeake and Ohio on basis of complete examination of population	$64,651
Total amount due Chesapeake and Ohio on basis of sample	64,568
Difference	$ 83

Thus, a sample of only about 9 per cent of the waybills provided an estimate of the total revenue due the Chesapeake and Ohio within $83 of the figure obtained from a complete examination of all waybills. Since it is estimated that the sample cost no more than $1,000, while the complete examination cost about $5,000, the advantage of sampling should be apparent. It just does not make sense to spend $4,000 to catch an error of $83. Furthermore, while the error in this instance was against the Chesapeake and Ohio, the next time it may be against the other railroad, so that in the long run the cumulative error should be relatively small.

Work sampling

This type of sampling, also called ratio-delay sampling, is simply an application of sampling over time. It can best be explained in terms of an example. Consider, for instance, the problem of determining the proportion of time a typist in a typing pool is not engaged in productive work. This proportion could be determined from continuous observation. That procedure, however, is time-consuming, may require skilled personnel, and is liable to influence greatly the operator under study. To avoid these disadvantages, a special type of sampling has been developed that provides an estimate of the proportion of time the operator is in "delay"; hence, the original name ratio-delay sampling. Today, this kind of sampling is called work sampling because of its wide field of applications.

The procedure in using work sampling to estimate the proportion of nonproductive time for the typist mentioned above would be somewhat as follows: First, clear definitions of productive and nonproductive states must be formulated. For instance, the typist may be considered to be in a nonproductive state if she is away from her typewriter for any reason, if she is waiting for work, if she is changing the ribbon on the typewriter, and so on. Then, a series of observations are made at random to determine the typist's state—productive or nonproductive—at these moments. To choose the times of the observations, a number of instantaneous moments are selected at random, usually by means of a table of random digits. For instance, the random numbers selected may indicate that observations be made at 9:01, 9:47, 11:29, and so forth. At the specified moments (unknown to the typist, of course), it is observed whether she is in a productive or in a nonproductive state. For purposes of controlling and improving operations, the cause of a nonproductive state also should be noted.

After a sufficiently large number of random observations have been taken, the proportion of the number of observations when the typist was in a nonproductive state to the total number of observations is computed. For instance, if a total of 225 observations had been taken, of which 50 indicated a nonproductive state, the observed delay-ratio would be 50/225 or 22.2 per cent. As long as the observations are random observations over time, this ratio will be an unbiased estimate of the proportion of nonproductive time for the typist, regardless if the delays are regular or irregular, long or short. Furthermore, we know that the precision of the sample estimate can be evaluated from the sample itself if the observations are taken at random. For the above example, statistical theory to be discussed in Section 14.2 enables us to state that the proportion of time during which the typist is engaged in nonproductive activities is somewhere between 16.8 and 27.6 per cent (95 per cent confidence coefficient). Note that we are sampling a process here, so that the proportion of nonproductive time being estimated refers to the infinite population created if the typist continued her operation indefinitely under the same causal conditions.

We used the example of a typist for simplicity in presentation. Actually, work sampling has been principally employed in the plant to measure the proportion of delay time for machines and operators. Recently, however, the uses of work sampling have been widely expanded. Time studies have been made by the use of this technique, as have material and traffic-flow studies. Work simplification programs also have been based upon studies made with this technique. In fact, it appears that still much more extensive use can be made of work sampling in business and public administration than at present.

People who have applied this sampling technique declare (for example, see Refs. 13.4, 13.5, 13.6) that its advantages over continuous observation of an operation are: (1) It costs much less. (2) It does not require observers with special skill and training. (3) It leads to fewer complaints from operators under study. (4) It does not distort the operator's normal work routine as much. (5) Observations may be taken over a longer period of time. (6) It can be used to analyze the operations of an entire department. (7) It can be used when time study is not feasible.

Two brief examples may indicate the worth of this technique. A work sampling study in a hospital (Ref. 13.6) showed that the head nurses spent 20 per cent of their time charting, which is a job for non-supervisors. The same study also indicated that registered nurses spent a great deal of time running errands and doing menial tasks. A reassignment of duties enabled the same number of nurses to care for more than twice as many patients and to do a better job.

The Wolverine Tube Division of the Calumet and Hecla Consolidated Copper Company made a work sampling study on a group of 16 drawbenches to determine the magnitude and causes of delay time (Ref. 13.6). From the facts learned about the causes of the delays, a work simplification program was instituted. As a result, productivity of this group of drawbenches was increased by 19 per cent.

Cited references

13.1 Hansen, Morris H., and William N. Hurwitz, "Dependable Samples for Market Surveys," *The Journal of Marketing,* October 1949, pp. 363–372.

13.2 Deming, William Edwards, *Some Theory of Sampling.* New York: John Wiley and Sons, Inc., 1950.

13.3 "Can Scientific Sampling Techniques Be Used in Railroad Accounting?" *Railway Age,* June 9, 1952, pp. 61–64.

13.4 Barnes, Ralph M., *Work Sampling,* 2d ed. New York: John Wiley and Sons, Inc., 1957.

13.5 Heiland, Robert E., and Wallace J. Richardson, *Work Sampling.* New York: McGraw-Hill Book Company, Inc., 1957.

13.6 Brisley, C. L., "How You Can Put Work Sampling to Work," *Factory Management and Maintenance,* July 1952, pp. 84–89.

QUESTIONS AND PROBLEMS

13.1. Explain briefly each of the following:

a. Elementary unit
b. Judgment sample
c. Stratified random sample
d. Population stratum

13.2. a. What distinguishes a chunk from a sample? A judgment sample from a probability sample? Explain.

b. Describe several ways in which a sample designed as a probability sample actually can turn out to be a judgment sample, after the execution of the sample survey.

c. In what respects does a quota sample resemble a stratified random sample? How does it differ? Discuss.

13.3. a. Interviewers were instructed to interview persons at random at homes, in the street, and the like, to get a representative sample of individuals. Is the resulting sample a simple random sample? A probability sample? Discuss.

b. During a certain week, employees of a city transit commission distributed questionnaires to passengers on city buses during working hours. Each passenger was requested to complete the questionnaire and return it to the transit commission, so that data could be developed on the adequacy of bus service provided by the transit commission. Did the passengers receiving the questionnaires constitute a probability sample? A judgment sample? A chunk? What about the passengers returning the questionnaires?

c. A simple random sample of 400 U.S. firms was selected in a study of business attitudes toward investment in Latin America. Seventy-five firms completed and returned the mail questionnaire. Are these 75 sample firms a probability sample of the population under study? Why, or why not? Would the fact that many U.S. firms do not engage in foreign trade and therefore may not respond affect your conclusion about whether or not the 75 sample firms are a probability sample? Discuss.

13.4. a. A work sampling study is undertaken in the meat department of a supermarket to establish standards for certain meat-cutting operations. The study supervisor states: "The sample will be a probability sample, provided a sufficiently large number of observations are made of the process." Evaluate this statement, distinguishing clearly between probability samples, judgment samples, and chunks.

b. The joints in the system of pipes in a submarine are to be inspected to determine whether specifications have been met or not. Should a probability sample, judgment sample, or chunk of joints be selected for the inspection? Discuss.

13.5. Officials of a museum wished to determine whether a plan for publishing art portfolios of great paintings would attract and hold enough mail subscriptions to be successful. As an experiment, advertising was placed containing a limited offer of 10,000 copies of a trial portfolio. Subscriptions were cut off as soon as the limit of 10,000 was reached. Of the 10,000 subscribers, 94 per cent decided to continue their subscriptions after seeing the first portfolio.

a. Were the 10,000 subscribers a sample? If not, why not? If so, what was the population sampled, and was the sample a probability or a judgment sample?

b. What limitations are there in using the 94 per cent continuation rate among the 10,000 subscribers as a basis for deciding whether to launch the program on a large scale? Discuss the relative importance of each of these.

13.6. A pollster, replying to criticisms that many of the judgment sampling procedures used in polls are poor and should be replaced by probability sampling, charged that probability sampling is really just another form of judgment sampling. He cited as an example the case of stratified random sampling, in which judgment plays a key role in determining the strata to be used and the sample sizes to be selected from each of the strata. Is the pollster's charge valid? Discuss carefully.

13.7. For each of the following cases in which stratified random sampling is to be employed, describe a basis of stratification likely to be useful and explain why you think it will be useful:

a. A sample of 500 customers of the 500,000 residential customers of an electric utility, to study the proportion that have electric air conditioning in their homes.

b. A sample of 200 school buses from all school buses licensed in Iowa, to determine the state of their maintenance.

c. A sample of 50 manufacturing concerns from all the manufacturing concerns located in a certain river basin, to study their attitudes toward new pollution control measures.

13.8. Refer to Problem 13.7.

a. Explain carefully how you would select a systematic sample for each of the cases cited there.

b. Are any benefits of stratification present in your systematic samples in part **a**? Discuss fully.

c. Are any dangers due to periodic arrangements in the population likely in your systematic samples in part **a**? Discuss.

d. Why can a systematic sample frequently be selected more readily than a simple random one? Explain.

13.9. A population of 5,000 stores is listed in geographic order. A systematic sample of 100 stores is selected with a random start. If the sample results are evaluated as if the sample had been a simple random one, what is likely to be the effect of this on the indicated precision of many sample estimates? Explain.

13.10. "Area sampling frequently is used because up-to-date listings of the elementary units in the population are often unavailable."

a. Discuss the above statement.

b. Why are area sampling units and multistage sampling frequently used together? Explain.

Chapter

14

ADDITIONAL TOPICS IN STATISTICAL ESTIMATION

In Chapter 12, we discussed the basic ideas of statistical estimation, applying the concepts to estimating a population mean. In Chapter 13, we described a variety of probability sampling procedures that may be used to improve estimation efficiency and lower sampling costs. In this chapter, we consider several other important estimation problems that build on concepts introduced in Chapter 12, including estimation of the difference between two population means, estimation of the population proportion, and estimation of the difference between two population proportions. Finally, we discuss two major problems in designing a stratified random sample and how to estimate the population mean from such a sample.

14.1 ESTIMATION OF DIFFERENCE BETWEEN TWO POPULATION MEANS—LARGE SIMPLE RANDOM SAMPLE CASE

Frequently an estimation problem involves not one but two populations. We now take up the estimation of the difference between two population means. This problem arises, for instance, when it is desired to estimate the change in average personal consumption expenditures between two years or the difference in average service life of components made by two different processes.

Point estimate of $\mu_{X_2} - \mu_{X_1}$

We use a specific example to explain the applicable theory for estimating the difference between two population means. The Wilson Metals Corporation wishes to estimate the difference in the average tensile strengths of castings made by two processes. Note that both populations are infinite ones, because each refers to a process of making the metal castings. We call the population corresponding to the first process population 1, and the one corresponding to the second process population 2. Figure 14.1 indicates how these two populations might appear. From each of the two distributions we could determine the probability that a casting made by the corresponding process will have a tensile strength within any particular limits, if we knew the characteristics of the population.

The means and standard deviations of each of the two populations carry the subscripts 1 and 2 respectively as shown in Figure 14.1, so that we can readily identify them. The task then is to estimate $\mu_{X_2} - \mu_{X_1}$, the difference between the two population means. Suppose that we take a random sample

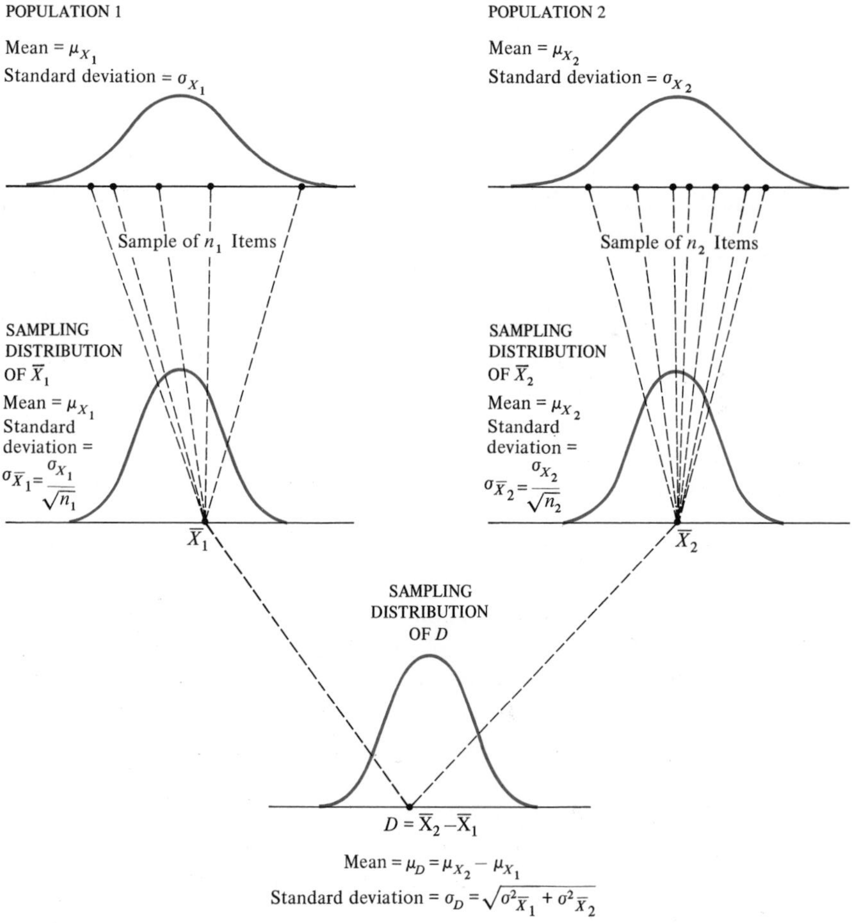

Figure 14.1. Graphic representation of sampling distribution of D and its relation to the two populations sampled

Sheet

of n_1 castings made by process 1 and a random sample of n_2 castings made by process 2, and test the tensile strength of each of these castings. Then, an all-purpose point estimator of $\mu_{X_2} - \mu_{X_1}$ is:

$$D = \overline{X}_2 - \overline{X}_1 \tag{14.1}$$

Here $\overline{X}_1$ is the mean tensile strength of the n_1 sample castings from process 1, $\overline{X}_2$ is the mean tensile strength of the n_2 sample castings from process 2, and D is the difference of the two sample means.

Table 14.1 (p. 282) presents the sample results obtained. It is indicated there that $\overline{X}_1 = 54{,}000$ pounds per square inch (abbreviated psi) and $\overline{X}_2 = 65{,}000$ psi. Therefore, the point estimate of the difference between the two population means is:

$$D = 65{,}000 - 54{,}000 = 11{,}000 \text{ psi}$$

In other words, the point estimate indicates that the mean tensile strength of castings from process 2 is 11,000 psi greater than for process 1.

Sampling distribution of D

To study the properties of the point estimator D, and also to lay the foundation for developing an interval estimate for $\mu_{X_2} - \mu_{X_1}$, we need to study the sampling distribution of D. *Throughout this section, we assume that the two samples are independent and that both are reasonably large.*

Since D is the difference between $\overline{X}_2$ and $\overline{X}_1$, let us review briefly what is known about the sampling distributions of $\overline{X}_1$ and $\overline{X}_2$. We know from earlier discussion that the sampling distribution of $\overline{X}_1$ has mean μ_{X_1} and standard deviation $\sigma_{\overline{X}_1} = \sigma_{X_1}/\sqrt{n_1}$ (remember the population sampled is infinite), and is approximately normal if n_1 is sufficiently large. Similarly, the sampling distribution of $\overline{X}_2$ has mean μ_{X_2} and standard deviation $\sigma_{\overline{X}_2} = \sigma_{X_2}/\sqrt{n_2}$ and is approximately normal if n_2 is sufficiently large. Both of these sampling distributions are shown in Figure 14.1.

Now, the point estimator D has a sampling distribution just as $\overline{X}_1$ and $\overline{X}_2$ do. The sampling distribution of D indicates, first, all the possible values D can assume if pairs of random samples of n_1 from population 1 and n_2 from population 2 are selected and then the difference $D = \overline{X}_2 - \overline{X}_1$ calculated for all pairs of samples, and second, the probabilities that these values of D will occur. Figure 14.1 indicates graphically how the sampling distribution of D is related to the sampling distributions of $\overline{X}_1$ and $\overline{X}_2$ and to the two populations sampled.

We can utilize the probability theory discussed in Chapter 6 to determine the mean and standard deviation of the sampling distribution of D. Formula (14.1) shows that D is defined as the difference between $\overline{X}_1$ and $\overline{X}_2$, and these two are random variables since each will vary from sample to sample. Now, it was noted in (6.41) that for any two random variables X and Y, we have:

$$\mu_{X-Y} = \mu_X - \mu_Y$$

For our case here, $X = \bar{X}_2$, $Y = \bar{X}_1$, and $X - Y = \bar{X}_2 - \bar{X}_1 = D$. Hence, we know that:

$$\mu_D = \mu_{\bar{X}_2} - \mu_{\bar{X}_1}$$

But we also know that $\mu_{\bar{X}_1} = \mu_{X_1}$ and $\mu_{\bar{X}_2} = \mu_{X_2}$ always, so we have:

$$\mu_D = \mu_{X_2} - \mu_{X_1} \tag{14.2}$$

Hence, we see that the sampling distribution of D has a mean equal to the difference between the two population means. It follows at once, therefore, that D is an unbiased point estimator of $\mu_{X_2} - \mu_{X_1}$.

We also noted in (6.42) that for any two *independent* random variables X and Y, we have:

$$\sigma^2_{X-Y} = \sigma^2_X + \sigma^2_Y$$

Hence, in our case, where we assume that the two samples are selected independently, we have:

$$\sigma^2_D = \sigma^2_{\bar{X}_1} + \sigma^2_{\bar{X}_2} \tag{14.3}$$

or:

$$\sigma_D = \sqrt{\sigma^2_{\bar{X}_1} + \sigma^2_{\bar{X}_2}} \tag{14.3a}$$

Thus, the variance of the sampling distribution of D is simply the sum of the variances of $\bar{X}_1$ and $\bar{X}_2$.

Finally, the central limit theorem indicates that $\bar{X}_1$ and $\bar{X}_2$ are approximately normally distributed if n_1 and n_2 are both large, as we assume here. Consequently, theorem (7.10), stating that the sum (or difference) of two independent normal random variables is also normally distributed, applies here, since we assume that the two samples are independently selected. Thus, the sampling distribution of D is approximately normal (given that $\bar{X}_1$ and $\bar{X}_2$ are independent, and that n_1 and n_2 are reasonably large).

Interval estimate of $\mu_{X_2} - \mu_{X_1}$

We now consider how to construct an interval estimate of $\mu_{X_2} - \mu_{X_1}$. Our earlier discussion of interval estimation of a population mean is applicable here. It will be recalled that we obtained confidence limits of the form $\bar{X} \pm z\sigma_{\bar{X}}$, where z is the standard normal deviate and depends on the confidence coefficient to be used. In the development of these confidence limits, the crucial feature was that $\bar{X}$ be approximately normally distributed. Any other unbiased point estimator that is approximately normally distributed could be used instead of $\bar{X}$ in the development, and comparable confidence limits would be obtained. Since D is an unbiased estimator of $\mu_{X_2} - \mu_{X_1}$, and its sampling distribution is approximately normal for the case considered here, it follows at once that the confidence limits for estimating $\mu_{X_2} - \mu_{X_1}$ are of the form:

(14.4) $$D \pm z\sigma_D$$

Usually we do not know σ_D, but can estimate it. Formula (14.3a) indicates that σ_D depends on $\sigma_{\bar{X}_1}$ and $\sigma_{\bar{X}_2}$. We can estimate $\sigma_{\bar{X}_1}$ and $\sigma_{\bar{X}_2}$ by making use of our earlier work; see (12.7) and (12.7a), p. 240. Therefore, we can estimate σ_D by:

(14.5) $$s_D = \sqrt{s_{\bar{X}_1}^2 + s_{\bar{X}_2}^2}$$

Here $s_{\bar{X}_1}$ is the point estimator of $\sigma_{\bar{X}_1}$, and $s_{\bar{X}_2}$ the point estimator of $\sigma_{\bar{X}_2}$. Each of these is calculated in the usual manner.

The confidence limits for $\mu_{X_2} - \mu_{X_1}$ therefore are:

(14.6) $$D \pm zs_D$$

and the confidence interval is:

(14.6a) $$D - zs_D \leq \mu_{X_2} - \mu_{X_1} \leq D + zs_D$$

This confidence interval is interpreted in the usual manner.

We shall illustrate the construction of an interval estimate of the difference of two population means for our earlier example involving two processes for making castings. Table 14.1 contains the sample results obtained for each of the two processes. The calculations of $\bar{X}_1$, s_{X_1} and $s_{\bar{X}_1}$ are the ordinary ones for a sample from a given population; similarly, $\bar{X}_2$, s_{X_2} and $s_{\bar{X}_2}$ are calculated in the usual way.

Table 14.1 Sample Data on Tensile Strengths of Castings Made by Two Different Processes

Process 1	*Process 2*
Sample Results	
$n_1 = 50$	$n_2 = 40$
$\bar{X}_1 = 54{,}000$ psi	$\bar{X}_2 = 65{,}000$ psi
$s_{X_1} = 4{,}000$ psi	$s_{X_2} = 3{,}000$ psi
Standard Deviation of Mean	
Estimate of $\sigma_{\bar{X}_1}$ for Sampling Distribution of $\bar{X}_1$	*Estimate of $\sigma_{\bar{X}_2}$ for Sampling Distribution of $\bar{X}_2$*
$s_{\bar{X}_1} = \dfrac{s_{X_1}}{\sqrt{n_1}} = \dfrac{4{,}000}{\sqrt{50}} = 566$ psi	$s_{\bar{X}_2} = \dfrac{s_{X_2}}{\sqrt{n_2}} = \dfrac{3{,}000}{\sqrt{40}} = 474$ psi
$s_{\bar{X}_1}^2 = 320{,}000$	$s_{\bar{X}_2}^2 = 225{,}000$

Sampling Distribution of D

$$D = \bar{X}_2 - \bar{X}_1 = 65{,}000 - 54{,}000 = 11{,}000 \text{ psi}$$

$$s_D = \sqrt{s_{\bar{X}_1}^2 + s_{\bar{X}_2}^2} = \sqrt{320{,}000 + 225{,}000} = 738 \text{ psi}$$

The standard deviation of D is estimated from (14.5):

$$s_D = \sqrt{320{,}000 + 225{,}000} = 738 \text{ psi}$$

Suppose that the desired confidence coefficient is 99 per cent. The appropriate z value then is 2.58, and the confidence limits for $\mu_{X_2} - \mu_{X_1}$ are:

$$D \pm zs_D$$
$$11{,}000 \pm 2.58(738)$$
$$11{,}000 \pm 1{,}904$$

Thus, the confidence interval is:

$$11{,}000 - 1{,}904 \leq \mu_{X_2} - \mu_{X_1} \leq 11{,}000 + 1{,}904$$

or:

$$9{,}096 \leq \mu_{X_2} - \mu_{X_1} \leq 12{,}904$$

We therefore conclude that castings from process 2 have a mean tensile strength that is somewhere between 9,100 and 12,900 psi greater than that of castings from process 1. This statement is made with a 99 per cent confidence coefficient, which means that a procedure for making interval estimates is being used that will lead to correct interval estimates 99 per cent of the time.

14.2 ESTIMATION OF POPULATION PROPORTION— LARGE SIMPLE RANDOM SAMPLE CASE

In this section, we explain how a population proportion can be estimated by means of point and interval estimates. (Readers who have not read Chapter 11 should do so before proceeding further.)

Point estimate of p

To estimate a population proportion p, we shall use the point estimator $\bar{p}$:

$$\bar{p} = \frac{X}{n} \tag{14.7}$$

where X is the number of elements in the sample with the given characteristic (number of unemployed, number of defective parts, etc.). Thus, if we wish to estimate the proportion of families in a given population who purchased a specified brand of breakfast cereal during the preceding week, and a random sample of 100 families selected from this population contained 10 purchasers, then the point estimate of p is $\bar{p} = 10/100 = .10$.

Review of sampling distribution of $\bar{p}$

To examine the properties of the point estimator $\bar{p}$, and also to prepare for the development of an interval estimate of p, we must review the characteristics of the sampling distribution of $\bar{p}$, discussed in Chapter 11:

1. The mean of the sampling distribution of $\bar{p}$ is always $\mu_{\bar{p}} = p$. Hence, the point estimator $\bar{p}$ is an unbiased estimator of the population proportion p.
2. The standard deviation of the sampling distribution of $\bar{p}$ is:

$$\sigma_{\bar{p}} = \sqrt{\frac{N-n}{N-1}}\sqrt{\frac{p(1-p)}{n}} \qquad \text{for finite populations}$$

$$\sigma_{\bar{p}} = \sqrt{\frac{p(1-p)}{n}} \qquad \text{for infinite populations}$$

3. If the sample size is reasonably large, the sampling distribution of $\bar{p}$ is approximately normal, by the central limit theorem.

Throughout this section, we assume that the random sample size is reasonably large.

Interval estimate of p

Since $\bar{p}$ is an unbiased estimator of the population proportion p, and since the sampling distribution of $\bar{p}$ is approximately normal for large samples, the confidence interval for p will be of the same form as the confidence interval for the population mean discussed earlier. Thus, the confidence limits for p have the form:

(14.8) $$\bar{p} \pm z\sigma_{\bar{p}}$$

We still must estimate $\sigma_{\bar{p}}$ in order to make use of these confidence limits. Note from the formulas above that $\sigma_{\bar{p}}$ depends on the population proportion p, for which we already have the point estimator $\bar{p}$. Therefore, we can obtain a point estimator of $\sigma_{\bar{p}}$ by replacing p with $\bar{p}$:

(14.9) $$s_{\bar{p}} = \sqrt{\frac{N-n}{N-1}}\sqrt{\frac{\bar{p}(1-\bar{p})}{n-1}} \qquad \text{for finite populations}$$

(14.9a) $$s_{\bar{p}} = \sqrt{\frac{\bar{p}(1-\bar{p})}{n-1}} \qquad \text{for infinite populations}$$

Hence, the confidence limits for p are:

(14.10) $$\bar{p} \pm zs_{\bar{p}}$$

and the confidence interval is:

(14.10a) $$\bar{p} - zs_{\bar{p}} \le p \le \bar{p} + zs_{\bar{p}}$$

Here z is the standard normal deviate corresponding to the desired confidence coefficient.

Suppose that we desire an interval estimate of the proportion of time when a typist is in a nonproductive state, and that a confidence coefficient of 95 per cent is to be used. (Recall that this example was used in Chapter 13 to illustrate work sampling.)

A total of 225 observations are made at random, of which 50 indicate that the typist was in a nonproductive state at those times. Thus, we estimate:

$$\bar{p} = \frac{50}{225} = .222$$

We next must calculate $s_{\bar{p}}$. We use (14.9a), because the population sampled is a process—that is, it is an infinite population:

$$s_{\bar{p}} = \sqrt{\frac{(.222)(.778)}{225 - 1}} = .0278$$

Finally, as the value of z corresponding to a 95 per cent confidence coefficient is 1.96, we obtain confidence limits:

$$.222 \pm 1.96(.0278)$$

$$.222 \pm .054$$

so that the confidence interval is:

$$.222 - .054 \leq p \leq .222 + .054$$

or:

$$.168 \leq p \leq .276$$

Thus, we state, with a confidence coefficient of 95 per cent, that the proportion of time when the typist is in a nonproductive state is somewhere between 16.8 per cent and 27.6 per cent.

Determination of necessary sample size

The planning of the necessary simple random sample size to estimate a population proportion corresponds to the planning of the necessary random sample size to estimate a population mean, as discussed in Section 12.3. It is desired to estimate the population proportion within $\pm h$, with a given confidence coefficient. Therefore, $h = z\sigma_{\bar{p}}$, where z is the standard normal deviate corresponding to the specified confidence coefficient. Now, we know that for infinite populations:

$$\sigma_{\bar{p}} = \sqrt{\frac{p(1 - p)}{n}}$$

so that we have:

$$h = z\sqrt{\frac{p(1 - p)}{n}}$$

When we solve for n, we obtain:

$$n = \frac{z^2(p)(1-p)}{h^2} \qquad \text{for infinite populations} \tag{14.11}$$

Similarly, we obtain: [1]

$$n = \frac{p(1-p)}{\dfrac{h^2}{z^2} + \dfrac{p(1-p)}{N}} \qquad \text{for finite populations} \tag{14.11a}$$

Suppose that we wish to estimate the proportion of parts turned out defectively by a machine within ±4 per cent points—in other words, $h = .04$. Suppose also that the confidence coefficient is to be 95.4 per cent, so $z = 2$. To determine the necessary sample size, we shall use (14.11) since the population sampled is an infinite one.

Before we can solve for n, we must be able to substitute an approximate value for p, the population proportion. Note that if various values of p are substituted in (14.11), for given z and h, the nearer p is to 0 or 1, the smaller is the required sample size; the closer p is to .5, the larger is the required sample size. In fact, for given z and h, the maximum sample size in both (14.11) and (14.11a) is reached at $p = .5$. Hence, if absolutely nothing is known about p, we could substitute $p = .5$ and obtain a sample size that will provide the required precision or more than the required precision.

Suppose management states that the proportion of items that are defective certainly will not exceed .2. Use of $p = .2$ therefore will lead to a sample size that is conservatively large, in the sense that the sample size obtained will be adequate if $p = .2$ and more than adequate if p is actually less than .2. We substitute then in (14.11), with $h = .04$, $z = 2$, and $p = .2$:

$$n = \frac{(2)^2(.2)(.8)}{(.04)^2} = 400$$

Therefore, a random sample of 400 parts will provide the necessary precision. If the population proportion p is actually less than .2, the confidence interval based on a random sample of 400 parts will tend to be even narrower than really needed.

Remember that this procedure assumes that the necessary random sample size will not be small. Otherwise, the sampling distribution of $\bar{p}$ will not be approximately normal, as assumed above. Also remember that the confidence interval based on the sample results actually obtained is valid no matter how poor the planning of the necessary sample size. The result of poor planning simply will be that the confidence interval will not have the desired width.

---

[1] We replace $N - 1$ by N in the finite correction factor.

14.3 ESTIMATION OF DIFFERENCE BETWEEN TWO POPULATION PROPORTIONS—LARGE SIMPLE RANDOM SAMPLE CASE

In this section, we discuss how the difference between two population proportions can be estimated by point and interval estimates. (Readers who have not read Sections 14.1 and 14.2 should do so before proceeding further.)

Point estimate of $p_2 - p_1$

Suppose that a simple random sample of 3,000 adult persons in the United States was selected early in 1971 to determine the proportion of persons who expected general business conditions to be good in the coming year. Another random sample of 3,500 adults was independently selected early in 1972 to obtain information on expectations as they existed then. The difference in the proportion of persons expecting business conditions to be good in 1971 and 1972 was to be estimated.

This type of problem is very similar to the problem of estimating the difference between two population means discussed in Section 14.1. Here, we have population 1 with proportion p_1 and population 2 with proportion p_2. It is desired to estimate $p_2 - p_1$, the difference between the two population proportions. A point estimator of $p_2 - p_1$ is:

(14.12) $$d = \bar{p}_2 - \bar{p}_1$$

Here $\bar{p}_1$ is the sample proportion in the sample from population 1, and $\bar{p}_2$ is the sample proportion in the sample from population 2. In other words, d is simply the difference between the two sample proportions.

Sampling distribution of d

Again, we must examine the sampling distribution of the point estimator d in order to determine the properties of this point estimator, and also to pave the way for the development of an interval estimate. *Throughout this section, we assume that the two samples are independent and that both are reasonably large.*

The point estimator $d = \bar{p}_2 - \bar{p}_1$ is the difference between two independent random variables in our case. We know at once from the probability theory utilized in developing the characteristics of the sampling distribution of $D = \bar{X}_2 - \bar{X}_1$ that:

$$\mu_d = \mu_{\bar{p}_2} - \mu_{\bar{p}_1}$$

Since we also know that $\mu_{\bar{p}_2} = p_2$ and $\mu_{\bar{p}_1} = p_1$ always, we have:

(14.13) $$\mu_d = p_2 - p_1$$

Thus, d is an unbiased estimator of $p_2 - p_1$.
Further, we have:

(14.14) $$\sigma_d^2 = \sigma_{\bar{p}_1}^2 + \sigma_{\bar{p}_2}^2$$

or:

(14.14a) $$\sigma_d = \sqrt{\sigma_{\bar{p}_1}^2 + \sigma_{\bar{p}_2}^2}$$

Finally, the sampling distribution of d is approximately normal for the case discussed, for the identical reasons cited in connection with the sampling distribution of D.

Interval estimate of $p_2 - p_1$

Since d is an unbiased estimator of $p_2 - p_1$, and since the sampling distribution of d is approximately normal under the assumed conditions, the confidence limits for $p_2 - p_1$ must be of the same form as those demonstrated previously:

(14.15) $$d \pm z\sigma_d$$

The standard deviation σ_d is estimated using point estimators $s_{\bar{p}_1}$ and $s_{\bar{p}_2}$ for $\sigma_{\bar{p}_1}$ and $\sigma_{\bar{p}_2}$, respectively; these are the usual point estimators for the standard deviation of $\bar{p}$ based on a random sample from a given population as indicated by (14.9) and (14.9a). Hence we have:

(14.16) $$s_d = \sqrt{s_{\bar{p}_1}^2 + s_{\bar{p}_2}^2}$$

Here s_d is the point estimator of σ_d.
The confidence limits for $p_2 - p_1$ then are:

(14.17) $$d \pm zs_d$$

and the confidence interval is:

(14.17a) $$d - zs_d \leq p_2 - p_1 \leq d + zs_d$$

We shall illustrate how to estimate $p_2 - p_1$ by point and interval estimates by referring to our earlier example where the change in expectations is to be estimated. Suppose that 60 per cent of the 3,000 persons in the 1971 sample expected business conditions to be good in the coming year. Then:

$$\bar{p}_1 = .60$$

$$s_{\bar{p}_1} = \sqrt{\frac{(.60)(.40)}{3{,}000 - 1}} = .00894$$

The populations involved here are so large, relative to the sample sizes, that we ignore the finite correction factors. Suppose further that 30 per cent of the 3,500 persons in the 1972 sample expected business conditions to be good in the year ahead. Therefore:

$$\bar{p}_2 = .30$$

$$s_{\bar{p}_2} = \sqrt{\frac{(.30)(.70)}{3{,}500 - 1}} = .00775$$

A point estimate of $p_2 - p_1$ is:

$$d = .30 - .60 = -.30$$

This point estimate indicates that the proportion of persons expecting good business conditions ahead in 1972 was 30 per cent points smaller than in 1971.

To develop an interval estimate of $p_2 - p_1$, we first must calculate s_d. Using (14.16), we obtain:

$$s_d = \sqrt{(.00894)^2 + (.00775)^2} = .0118$$

If a 95 per cent confidence coefficient is desired, the appropriate value of z is 1.96, and the confidence limits for $p_2 - p_1$ are:

$$-.30 \pm (1.96)(.0118)$$
$$-.30 \pm .0231$$

Consequently, the confidence interval is:

$$-.30 - .0231 \leq p_2 - p_1 \leq -.30 + .0231$$

or:

$$-.323 \leq p_2 - p_1 \leq -.277$$

Note that the minus signs in the confidence limits indicate that p_2 is smaller than p_1. Thus, we would state with a confidence coefficient of 95 per cent that the proportion of persons in 1972 expecting business conditions to be good was between 27.7 and 32.3 per cent points smaller than the proportion of persons in 1971 expecting business conditions to be good. The confidence interval, therefore, provides a clear indication of a very substantial change in expectations between 1971 and 1972.

14.4 DESIGN AND EVALUATION OF STRATIFIED RANDOM SAMPLE

In Chapter 13, stratified random sampling was described as one of the most important probability sampling procedures. In this section, we discuss the choice of the strata and the determination of strata sample sizes, as well as the construction of point and interval estimates of the population mean based on stratified random sampling. (Readers who have not read Chapter 13 should do so before proceeding further.)

Setting up strata

As noted, one of the basic problems in designing a stratified random sample is the determination of how many strata to set up and what they should be. We pointed out in Chapter 13 that the criteria of stratification must be related to the characteristics under study; otherwise the stratification of the population does not accomplish anything. To put this in another way, *strata should be set up so that the items in each stratum differ as much as possible, with respect to the characteristic under investigation, from the items in the other strata, while within each stratum the items are as homogeneous as possible.*

To illustrate some of the problems in setting up the strata, we consider the case of a private research organization that was making a study of smaller businesses in a city. The local Chamber of Commerce provided a list of its member firms with less than 100 employees each, which was the frame of the population of interest. The research organization wished to study particularly how much financial support these smaller firms contributed to educational institutions in the previous year.

The ideal basis for stratification in this case would be the amount contributed by each firm. In this way, firms with small contributions could be grouped into one or more strata, while firms with large contributions could be grouped into one or several other strata. This basis of stratification was unavailable, however, as the amount of the contribution by each firm was unknown. The purpose of the survey, indeed, was to obtain information about these contributions.

In this type of situation, a variable related to the characteristic of interest must be used for stratification, which will tend to group firms into separate strata according to the amount of their contributions. The Chamber of Commerce was able to provide some additional information about each firm, such as the type of business it was engaged in, and the number of its employees as of the preceding December. The research organization decided to use the number of employees as the stratifying variable, since past experience suggested this variable to be most highly related to the amount contributed and to the other characteristics of interest among the variables available for stratification. It was decided to use only two strata in this case; specifically, the first stratum consisted of 500 firms with 29 or fewer employees, while the second stratum consisted of 300 firms with 30 to 99 employees.

A simple random sample of 50 firms was taken from the first stratum, and a simple random sample of 30 firms was taken from the second stratum. Table 14.2 shows the sample results in condensed form.

Estimation of population mean

Suppose that the population has been divided into k subpopulations or strata; in the present example, $k = 2$. Denote the number of elements in the jth stratum by N_j, and the total population size by N, where $N = \Sigma_{j=1}^{k} N_j$. Here, $N_1 = 500$, $N_2 = 300$, and $N = 800$.

A simple random sample of size n_j is selected from the jth stratum. We denote the sample mean obtained from this stratum by $\overline{X}_j$, and the sample standard deviation by s_j. For stratum 1 in Table 14.2, for instance, $n_1 = 50$, $\overline{X}_1 = \$75$, and $s_1 = \sqrt{420}$. Similarly, independent samples are selected from the other strata, and the sample means and standard deviations are denoted in the same fashion.

Table 14.2 Sample Results From Stratified Random Sample

Stratum 1 (Firms With 29 or Fewer Employees)	*Stratum 2 (Firms With 30–99 Employees)*
Stratum Size	
$N_1 = 500$ firms	$N_2 = 300$ firms
Sample Results	
$n_1 = 50$ firms $\overline{X}_1 = \$75$ $s_1^2 = 420$	$n_2 = 30$ firms $\overline{X}_2 = \$140$ $s_2^2 = 1{,}400$
Standard Deviation of Mean	
Estimate of $\sigma^2_{\overline{X}_1}$	*Estimate of* $\sigma^2_{\overline{X}_2}$
$s^2_{\overline{X}_1} = \frac{N_1 - n_1}{N_1 - 1} \frac{s_1^2}{n_1} = \frac{500 - 50}{500 - 1} \frac{420}{50} = 7.58$	$s^2_{\overline{X}_2} = \frac{N_2 - n_2}{N_2 - 1} \frac{s_2^2}{n_2} = \frac{300 - 30}{300 - 1} \frac{1{,}400}{30} = 42.14$

An *unbiased* point estimator of the population mean μ_X is:

(14.18)
$$\overline{X}_{st} = \frac{N_1\overline{X}_1 + N_2\overline{X}_2 + \cdots + N_k\overline{X}_k}{N} = \sum_{j=1}^{k} \left(\frac{N_j}{N}\right) \overline{X}_j$$

Note that $\overline{X}_{st}$ is simply a weighted average of the strata sample means, with the stratum weight being the proportion of the total population elements that are in that stratum.

For our example, the estimate of the mean amount contributed per firm in the entire population under study, using the data in Table 14.2, is:

$$\overline{X}_{st} = \frac{500}{800}(75) + \frac{300}{800}(140) = \$99.38$$

Evaluation of precision

We can use the probability theory developed in Chapter 6 to find the variance of the sampling distribution of $\overline{X}_{st}$. Since the $\overline{X}_j$ are independent, we know from an extension of (6.40) that the variances of the terms in $\overline{X}_{st}$ are additive. Further, (6.35) states that the variance of $(N_j/N)\overline{X}_j$ is $(N_j/N)^2\sigma^2_{\overline{X}_j}$. Hence, we have:

$$\sigma^2_{\overline{X}_{st}} = \sum_{j=1}^{k} \left(\frac{N_j}{N}\right)^2 \sigma^2_{\overline{X}_j} \tag{14.19}$$

We know how to obtain a point estimate of $\sigma^2_{\overline{X}_j}$ by means of (12.7) or (12.7a), p. 240. Hence, we have as a point estimator of $\sigma^2_{\overline{X}_{st}}$:

$$s^2_{\overline{X}_{st}} = \sum_{j=1}^{k} \left(\frac{N_j}{N}\right)^2 s^2_{\overline{X}_j} \tag{14.20}$$

From Table 14.2, we obtain:

$$s^2_{\overline{X}_{st}} = \left(\frac{500}{800}\right)^2(7.58) + \left(\frac{300}{800}\right)^2(42.14) = 8.887$$

Hence, we have:

$$s_{\overline{X}_{st}} = \$2.98$$

Interval estimate of μ_X

If the sample sizes in each of the strata are reasonably large, the sampling distribution of $\overline{X}_{st}$ is approximately normal. so that a confidence interval for the population mean is:

$$\overline{X}_{st} - zs_{\overline{X}_{st}} \leq \mu_X \leq \overline{X}_{st} + zs_{\overline{X}_{st}} \tag{14.21}$$

Assuming that the sample sizes in our example are sufficiently large, we obtain for a 95 per cent ($z = 1.96$) confidence interval for the population mean:

$$99.38 - (1.96)(2.98) \leq \mu_X \leq 99.38 + (1.96)(2.98)$$

or:

$$\$94 \leq \mu_X \leq \$105$$

We would therefore assert, with a confidence coefficient of 95 per cent, that the mean amount contributed to educational institutions during the previous year by firms employing under 100 employees in the city was between \$94 and \$105.

Planning sample sizes

It is desirable that the needed sample sizes be planned to minimize cost or maximize precision, rather than be determined arbitrarily. *We shall consider here the case where: (1) the total cost is specified and the precision of the sample estimate is to be maximized, and (2) the unit cost of sampling in each stratum is the same.*

In our illustration, the research organization had a budget of \$800 available to cover the cost of sampling. This budget did not include the cost of planning the sample design and other overhead operations, but rather covered the cost of selecting the sample firms and obtaining the desired information from them, including follow-up calls in case of nonresponse and the like. In many cases of this type, the cost of sampling is about the same in each of the strata, and this was the situation here. It was estimated that it would cost about \$10 per firm to obtain the needed information. Hence, 80 firms could be included in the sample. The only problem left was how to allocate the 80 sample cases to the two strata.

Proportional allocation. A method of allocation frequently employed is proportional allocation.

(14.22) With ***proportional allocation,*** the proportion of items in a stratum selected for the sample is the same for all strata; thus:

$$n_j = \left(\frac{N_j}{N}\right) n$$

Here n is the total available sample size. Notice that the sample sizes actually used (see Table 14.2) were determined by proportional allocation.

Proportional allocation is simple and frequently exploits most of the gain in efficiency that can be achieved with a given stratification. It is an especially desirable allocation when several population characteristics are to be estimated from the same sample design.

Optimal allocation. When it is desired to achieve the maximum gain in efficiency with a given stratification, it can be shown that:

(14.23) The ***optimal allocation*** in each stratum is:

$$n_j = \left(\frac{N_j\sigma_j}{\Sigma N_j\sigma_j}\right) n$$

Here σ_j is the standard deviation of the elements in the jth stratum. The allocation of the total sample size by (14.23) maximizes the precision of the sample estimator in (14.18), given the total cost available for sampling.

Note that (14.23) requires advance judgments about the strata standard deviations. In planning the sample of small firms, the research firm judged that the strata standard deviations for the firm contributions are $\sigma_1 = \$30$ and $\sigma_2 = \$50$ approximately. Hence, we have:

$$\begin{aligned} N_1\sigma_1 &= (500)(30) = 15{,}000 \\ N_2\sigma_2 &= (300)(50) = \underline{15{,}000} \\ \Sigma N_j\sigma_j &= \qquad\qquad\quad 30{,}000 \end{aligned}$$

The optimal allocation then is:

$$n_1 = \left(\frac{15{,}000}{30{,}000}\right) 80 = 40$$

$$n_2 = \left(\frac{15{,}000}{30{,}000}\right) 80 = 40$$

The research firm actually did not use optimal allocation in this case; as noted, it utilized proportional allocation instead. The reason for choosing proportional allocation was that the study was intended to obtain various types of information about the small firms in addition to the amount of their contributions to educational institutions. The optimal allocation would have been substantially different for some of the other characteristics to be estimated. Proportional allocation was considered to be a reasonable compromise to achieve substantial gains in efficiency for estimating each of the characteristics of interest.

QUESTIONS AND PROBLEMS

***14.1.** Early in 1971, a simple random sample of 2,500 spending units was selected to estimate the mean liquid asset holdings per spending unit in the population as of the beginning of 1971. Another simple random sample of 3,000 spending units was selected early in 1972, independently of the first sample, to obtain an estimate of the mean liquid asset holdings per spending unit in the population as of the beginning of 1972. Assume that the population is very large relative to the sample sizes. The sample results were as follows:

1971 Sample	*1972 Sample*
X_1 = Amount of liquid assets held by sample spending unit as of January 1, 1971	X_2 = Amount of liquid assets held by sample spending unit as of January 1, 1972
$n_1 = 2{,}500$	$n_2 = 3{,}000$
$\overline{X}_1 = \$299.6$	$\overline{X}_2 = \$330.4$
$s_{X_1} = \$202$	$s_{X_2} = \$201$

a. Estimate the change in mean liquid asset holdings per spending unit in the population from 1971 to 1972; use an interval estimate with a 95 per cent confidence coefficient.

b. Explain clearly the meaning of your confidence interval. What does the confidence coefficient of 95 per cent signify?

c. Does your confidence interval indicate that spending units, on the average, changed the amount of their liquid asset holdings between 1971 and 1972? Discuss.

d. Would the confidence interval for the change in mean liquid asset holdings per spending unit in part **a** be wider or narrower if a confidence coefficient of 99 per cent had been used? Why?

e. If 1,000 of the persons included in the 1972 survey had been selected from persons included in the 1971 survey, would the statistical techniques described in the text be appropriate to construct an interval estimate of the change in mean liquid asset holdings? Why, or why not?

f. Suppose that the entire same sample as in 1971 had also been used in 1972, the change between 1971 and 1972 liquid asset holdings ascertained for each sample spending unit, and the mean of these changes obtained. To evaluate the precision of this estimate of the population mean change, would you use the same approach as in part **a**? Discuss.

14.2. The Simpson Company operates two large divisions; division A has 8,100 employees and division B has 7,600 employees. The company was evaluating its industrial relations program, and as part of this study, selected a simple random sample of 100 employees from each division; the two samples were selected independently. The selected employees were given a questionnaire to complete. One of the questions asked the employee to rate the company's magazine by giving it a grade between 100 (outstanding) and 0. The questionnaires did not contain any identifying marks so that employees would give frank replies. The sample results on this question were:

Division A Sample	*Division B Sample*
X_1 = Rating given by sample employee	X_2 = Rating given by sample employee
$n_1 = 100$	$n_2 = 100$
$\bar{X}_1 = 72.9$	$\bar{X}_2 = 74.8$
$s_{X_1} = 8.18$	$s_{X_2} = 8.46$

a. Estimate the difference in the mean rating for the company magazine by employees of divisions A and B; use an interval estimate with a 98 per cent confidence coefficient.

b. Explain clearly the meaning of your confidence interval.

c. On the basis of the point estimates $\bar{X}_1$ and $\bar{X}_2$, an administrator in division B concluded that employees of this division rate the company's magazine more highly, on the average, than employees of division A. Does your confidence interval support this conclusion? Explain the reasoning underlying your answer.

***14.3.** Blood contributions from collection clinics are subjected to further testing at the central blood bank. This additional testing results in the rejection of a certain proportion of the blood contributions. It is desired to estimate this proportion currently, on the basis of a simple random sample of 400 contributions. In the sample, 40 blood contributions were rejected.

a. What is the point estimate of the current process proportion? Why is this estimate called a point estimate?

b. Do you have great confidence that your point estimate coincides with the process proportion? Discuss.

c. Construct an interval estimate of the process proportion with a 98 per cent confidence coefficient.

d. Explain precisely the meaning of your confidence interval.

e. If you had constructed the confidence interval corresponding to a 90 per cent confidence coefficient, would it be wider or narrower than the 98 per cent confidence interval constructed in part **c**? Which would involve the smaller risk of an incorrect interval estimate? What generalization does this suggest?

f. Is your interval estimate in part **c** precise enough to be useful? Discuss.

14.4. Refer to Problem 14.3.

a. Why is the confidence coefficient for the interval estimate in Problem 14.3**c** only approximately 98 per cent? Discuss.

b. In another simple random sample of 400 contributions from the process, would the same 98 per cent confidence limits as in Problem 14.3**c** have been obtained? Discuss.

c. In deciding whether or not to reject a blood contribution, the policy is to reject any "doubtful" cases. As a result, a certain number of acceptable contributions are rejected by mistake. Is the validity of the confidence interval in Problem 14.3**c** affected by this fact? To what precisely does the process proportion being estimated refer? Discuss.

14.5. A simple random sample of 400 residents from the 11,500 residents of a section of a city was selected to obtain information on the proportion of residents who would patronize a new supermarket if it were built in this section. Of the sample respondents, 185 indicated they would patronize the new supermarket.

a. Construct an interval estimate of the population proportion, with a 99 per cent confidence coefficient.

b. Explain clearly the meaning of your confidence interval.

c. Does your interval estimate refer to the proportion of persons in the population who would have indicated an intention to patronize the new supermarket if interviewed, or does it refer to the proportion of persons in the population who actually would patronize the new supermarket? What is the distinction between the two? Management, of course, is interested in the latter proportion; if the estimate refers to the first proportion, what are the implications of this? Discuss.

***14.6.** A lathe operator is to be observed at random times to estimate the proportion of time he is in a productive state. It is desired to estimate this proportion within $\pm.05$, with a 97 per cent confidence coefficient.

a. In each of the following cases, what value of p should be used in planning the required sample size to assure that the sample is large enough to provide the desired precision, and what is this required sample size? (1) Nothing is known about the population proportion. (2) It is known that the population proportion is at least .7. (3) It is known that the population proportion is at least .8.

b. Compare the sample sizes in (1), (2), and (3) of part **a.** What generalization does this comparison suggest?

c. If the desired precision were changed to $\pm.025$, what would be the nature of the effect on the required sample size for each of the cases in part **a**? Answer without making actual calculations.

d. If the population proportion used in planning the required sample size is not exactly the correct one, does this affect the validity of the confidence interval obtained from the sample results? Does it have any effect on the confidence interval obtained? Discuss.

14.7. In the case described in Problem 14.6, 250 observations were made on the lathe operator at random times. He was found to be in a productive state at 213 of these observations.

a. Construct an interval estimate, with a 97 per cent confidence coefficient, of the proportion of time when this operator is in a productive state.

b. Explain the meaning of your confidence interval.

c. It is known that other lathe operators in the plant are in a productive state 80 per cent of the time. Does your interval estimate indicate that the operator observed here differs from the others with respect to the proportion of time he is in a productive state? Explain the reasoning underlying your answer.

14.8. A simple random sample survey of 3,000 dwelling units indicated that 64 of these were vacant. Estimate the vacancy rate for the entire community by an interval estimate. Use a 93 per cent confidence coefficient, and assume that the total number of dwelling units in the community is large.

14.9. An estimate of the proportion of serviceable items in a surplus inventory stored under unfavorable conditions is to be obtained within $\pm.05$, with a 94 per cent confidence coefficient. The total inventory consists of 20,000 items, and it is estimated in advance that the proportion of serviceable items is at least .35 but not more than .75.

a. What simple random sample size is necessary to assure an estimate with the desired precision?

b. Can the precision of the sample estimate be evaluated if the advance judgment as to the proportion of serviceable items in the inventory was incorrect? Explain.

14.10. The 15,147 company employees are to be sampled to obtain information on the proportion who live within the city boundary. This proportion is to be estimated within $\pm.10$, with a 98 per cent confidence coefficient.

a. What simple random sample size is needed to provide the desired precision? Past experience indicates that the population proportion is at least .60.

b. What would be the required simple random sample size, if the population proportion were to be estimated within $\pm.01$, with a 98 per cent confidence coefficient?

***14.11.** Bank A selected a simple random sample of 200 persons from its 10,000 customers with thrift checking accounts. At the same time and independently, bank B selected a simple random sample of 150 persons from its 5,000 customers with thrift checking accounts. Bank A found that 59 persons in its sample regularly used other services of the bank, while bank B found 56 persons in its sample who regularly used other services in the bank.

a. Estimate the difference in the proportion of customers having a thrift checking account who regularly use other services of the bank for banks A and B; use an interval estimate with a 92.5 per cent confidence coefficient.

b. Explain clearly the meaning of your confidence interval.

c. Does your interval estimate provide any indication that bank B's thrift checking account customers differ from those of bank A in their regular use of other bank services? Explain fully.

14.12. A simple random sample of 250 shafts selected from the day shift's production contained 19 defective shafts; a simple random sample of 250 shafts, selected at the same time and independently, from the night shift's production contained 34 defective shafts.

a. Estimate the difference in the proportion defective for day shift and night shift production; use an interval estimate with a 99 per cent confidence coefficient.

b. Explain clearly the meaning of your confidence interval.

c. Does your interval estimate provide any indication whether the night shift's production differs from that of the day shift with respect to the proportion defective? Explain fully.

14.13. **a.** Distinguish between proportional and optimal allocation.
b. What information about the population strata is required for optimal allocation but not for proportional allocation?
c. Under what conditions would optimal and proportional allocation lead to identical sample sizes for all strata?

***14.14.** Refer to Table 13.1, p. 266. A stratified random sample of 120 employees is to be selected from the population of 2,000 employees, using the strata indicated in Table 13.1. If proportional sampling is to be used, what are the sample sizes for the different strata? State the sample sizes explicitly, and indicate how you determined them.

14.15. Refer to the case on sampling of waybills on pp. 271–273.
a. Would a stratification of the waybills by the amount due the Chesapeake and Ohio Railroad on the waybill have been more effective than the stratification actually used—namely, by the total amount of the freight charge on the waybill? Explain.
b. Why do you think that the stratification suggested above was not used?

14.16. A stratified random sample of 720 home-owners in a community was selected to estimate the mean property taxes paid during the past year. The strata employed were geographic areas. The sample results were:

Stratum	N_j	n_j	$\overline{X}_j$	s_j
1	12,000	240	$485	$88.00
2	6,000	240	378	46.00
3	10,800	240	506	98.50
Total	28,800	720		

a. Was proportional allocation used in the sample design? Explain.
b. Obtain a point estimate of the mean property taxes paid per household in the population.
c. Develop an interval estimate for the population mean, using a 95 per cent confidence coefficient.
d. Would the calculations employed in part **c** be appropriate if the strata samples were not independent? If the strata sample sizes had been 5 each? Discuss.

***14.17.** A dairy association with 5,000 member producers selected a stratified random sample of 250 of its member producers to estimate the mean herd size per producer for the total membership. The strata were set up according to the size of farm, which was known for each member. The sample results were:

Stratum	N_j	n_j	$\overline{X}_j$	s_j
1	1,800	90	21.4	4.2
2	1,500	75	28.9	5.5
3	1,200	60	36.0	7.1
4	500	25	46.1	10.3
Total	5,000	250		

a. What sample allocation principle was employed in this sample survey?
b. Obtain a point estimate of the mean herd size per producer in the population.
c. Develop an interval estimate for the population mean herd size, using a 98 per cent confidence coefficient.

d. Using the estimates of the strata standard deviations, develop the optimal allocation for a sample of 250 member producers. Do these sample sizes differ substantially from those employed? What are the implications of this? Discuss.

14.18. A company wished to estimate the mean number of days elapsed between the date an invoice is sent to a customer and the date payment is received. The study is to be confined to the 15,000 invoices issued in 1971. Four strata, according to amount of the invoice, are to be employed. One hundred and fifty dollars is available for the study, and it is estimated that the cost of obtaining the information for one sample observation is 50 cents for each of the strata. Strata sizes, and the anticipated strata standard deviations, are as follows:

Stratum	N_j	*Anticipated* σ_j *(Days)*
1	8,000	10
2	4,000	5
3	2,000	3
4	1,000	2
Total	15,000	

a. What is the total sample size that the budget will permit?

b. What are the strata sample sizes if proportional allocation is employed?

c. What is the anticipated standard deviation of the mean with proportional allocation?

d. What are the strata sample sizes if optimal allocation is employed? What is optimized by this allocation?

e. What is the anticipated standard deviation of the mean with optimal allocation?

f. Compare the anticipated precision with proportional and optimal allocation in parts **c** and **e.** Does optimal allocation lead to a substantial gain over proportional allocation in this case? Is this always the case? Discuss.

g. What are the consequences if the anticipated strata standard deviations are substantially in error? Moderately in error? Explain.

h. If the sample survey were also to estimate the mean delivery charges per invoice, would the allocation in part **d** be optimal also for this purpose? Discuss.

CLASS PROJECT

14.19. Refer to Problems 10.19 and 11.21.

a. From each sample of 50 freight bills, construct an interval estimate of the proportion of freight bills with freight charges due Crandell Motor Freight, Inc., of $1.50 or less in the population. Use a 97.5 per cent confidence coefficient.

b. What proportion of the 100 interval estimates do you expect to include the population proportion $p = .636$? Explain.

c. What proportion of the 100 interval estimates actually do include the population proportion?

d. What does this experiment illustrate about the meaning of the confidence coefficient of 97.5 per cent? Discuss.

Unit
V
STATISTICAL DECISION-MAKING (CLASSICAL)

Chapter

15

INTRODUCTION TO DECISION-MAKING

It is no exaggeration to state that administration consists largely of making decisions. Administrators must decide such diverse questions as whether a new plant should be built, what the maintenance policy on a fleet of trucks is to be, whether a particular person should be hired, which is the most appropriate promotional campaign for a new product, what is the most desirable type of financing, and who is the best supplier.

In recent years, decision-making has been subject to intensive study. As a result, some basic types of decision problems have been distinguished and investigated. In this chapter, we consider four of these basic types of decision problems, illustrating each and noting its chief characteristics. The reader will then be able to see the place of *statistical* decision-making, which will be discussed in several of the following chapters, in the larger framework of decision problems in general.

15.1 WHAT IS A DECISION PROBLEM?

Decision problems, whether in business, government, or some other area, have some common basic characteristics. In any decision problem, there are:

(15.1) *Acts.* There must be two or more courses of action or acts available to the decision-maker or decision-making unit.

(15.2) *Consequences.* Each act entails some results or consequences, which in general differ from act to act.

(15.3) *Criterion.* The decision-maker must select the act which is best in the light of some criterion, or basis of choice, applied to the consequences of the acts.

To illustrate these concepts, consider a decision problem on plant layout. The acts available to the decision-maker were the possible alternative layouts of machines in the plant. The consequences of interest were the total distances over which the material would have to move as it was being worked on, for each layout. The criterion employed for selecting the optimal layout was: minimize the total distance the material has to move.

15.2 DECISION-MAKING UNDER CONDITIONS OF CERTAINTY

One important class of decision problems includes those problems in which each act available to the decision-maker has a consequence that can be known in advance with certainty. Such decision problems are frequently said to involve *decision-making under conditions of certainty.*

For instance, consider a municipality that must decide with which investment firm to place its bonds. Each firm has made a bid in writing, guaranteeing a specified net interest rate. Then the consequence of choosing a particular investment firm, in terms of the net rate of interest to be paid, is certain.

This illustration should not be taken as implying that decision-making under certainty is necessarily simple. Each of the tasks facing a decision-maker under certainty—to identify the available acts, to measure the consequences, and to select an act that is "best"—may involve substantial difficulties. We now illustrate a problem involving decision-making under certainty where the number of available acts is very large. In fact, until the development of linear programming theory, it was often not feasible to evaluate the consequence of each available act.

Linear programming case illustration

A certain textile mill finishes cotton cloth obtained from weaving mills. This mill turns out two styles of cloth, a lightly printed style and a heavily printed one. It is uneconomical for this mill to store finished goods in inventory; thus at the end of each week, the mill ships out the week's production to customers.

The mill's output during a week is limited only by the capacity of its equipment for two of the finishing operations—printing and bleaching—and not by demand considerations. The maximum weekly output of the printing machinery is 800 thousand yards of cloth if the light pattern is printed exclusively, or 400 thousand yards if the heavy pattern is printed exclusively. If the printing equipment is allocated to the light pattern for, say, 50 per cent of the time and to the heavy pattern for the remaining 50 per cent, the maximum weekly output would be 400 thousand and 200 thousand yards, respectively. In general, the maximum weekly output for each type of cloth is given by the printing line in Figure 15.1, which indicates the various possible maximum outputs for the light and heavy patterns, depending upon the portion of time that is allocated on the printing equipment to each type of pattern. This line may be represented by:

$$L + \left(\frac{800}{400}\right) H = 800$$

where L is the amount of the light pattern printed, and H the amount of the heavy pattern printed. Thus, any combination of L and H that falls in the area between the two axes and the printing line in Figure 15.1 can be printed during a week.

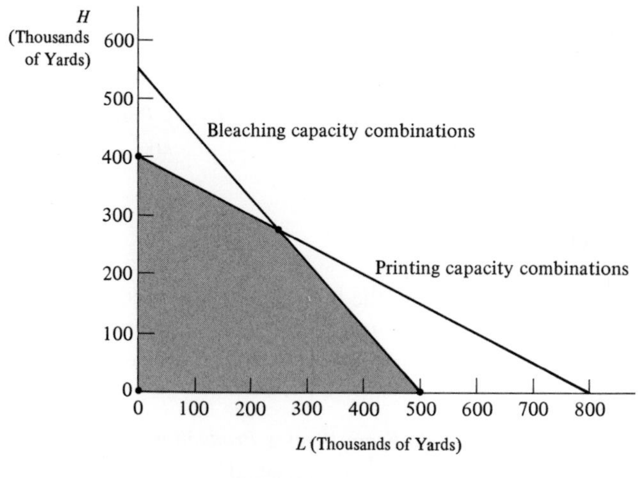

Figure 15.1. Possible combinations of output

However, some of these combinations are not actually attainable by the overall production process. As noted, the other limiting factor on output is the bleaching capacity. Cloth to be given the light pattern requires somewhat more bleaching than does cloth destined to receive the heavy pattern. In a week, the maximum the bleaching equipment can handle is 500 thousand yards of the light-patterned cloth exclusively, 550 thousand yards of the heavy-patterned cloth exclusively, or any combination on the bleaching line in Figure 15.1. This line may be represented by:

$$\left(\frac{550}{500}\right) L + H = 550$$

Again, any combination of L and H that falls in the area between the two axes and the bleaching line can be bleached in a week.

Hence, it must follow that all combinations of outputs of light and heavy patterns in the shaded area of Figure 15.1 are feasible in terms of *both* the printing and bleaching capacity restrictions. Note that there are indefinitely many output mixes that are attainable under the joint capacity restrictions. Each of these different mixes must then be evaluated in terms of dollar gains (contributions to overhead and profit) arising from that mix in a week's production.

The task facing the manager, to identify and produce the mix that would yield the highest gain at prevailing prices, seems overwhelming in view of the indefinitely large number of acts available to him. A consultant called in by the manager used linear programming theory to identify those attainable output mixes that could yield the greatest gains. We simply state here that linear programming theory shows that only the corners of the shaded area in Figure 15.1 (shown as heavy dots) need be considered by the manager, since the greatest gain will always be attained at one of these corner combinations:

	Output (Thousands of Yards)	
Mix	*Light Pattern*	*Heavy Pattern*
A	0	400
B	250	275
C	500	0
D	0	0

At the time of the study, the mill gained \$300 and \$290 per thousand yards of the light- and heavy-patterned cloths, respectively. The manager then calculated the total gain arising from each of the four attainable mixes worth considering:

Mix	*Gain From Week's Production*
A	\$116 thousand
B	\$155 thousand
C	\$150 thousand
D	\$0

The dollar gain for each production mix is called the payoff.

(15.4) A ***payoff*** is the consequence of an act measured on a quantitative scale.

Given that the manager wishes to obtain the highest possible gain from the week's operations, he should select mix B. This is to say, *the selection of mix B is the optimal act under the criterion of maximization of payoff.*

Note that in this illustration, the manager knew with certainty the amount of gain realized from any possible mix. Hence the case cited was one of decision-making under certainty. Of course, whenever the gain from either style of cloth changes, the manager would have to rework his calculations to ascertain which mix is now best. Should limitations in output capacity be changed, linear programming theory again would have to be employed to ascertain the new attainable mixes that are worth considering.

To summarize the general structure of this decision problem:

1. The group of possible acts here consisted of the output mixes that could be attained under existing capacity restrictions.
2. The payoff for each act was the dollar gain for the particular production mix. In some other problem, the payoff might not be measured in dollars but in share of the market, or number of units sold, or by some other quantitative measure.
3. The criterion according to which an act was identified as being best was simply: maximize the payoff. As we shall see, the choice of criterion is not always so elementary.

15.3 DECISION–MAKING UNDER COMPETITIVE CONDITIONS

In our previous illustration, the payoff was affected only by the mix of light- and heavy-patterned cloth, since the existing production capacity and the gain from each style of cloth were given. The production mix was under the full control of the manager, within the restraints imposed by capacities. In many problems, however, variables that are not controlled by the decision-maker also affect the payoff. For instance, when a store manager reduces the price of an item for a special sale, the increase in sales volume is affected not only by this price change but also by many uncontrollable variables, such as weather conditions.

When uncontrollable variables affect the payoffs, the decision-maker exercises only partial control over payoffs and cannot be certain in advance of the payoff he actually will receive from an act. All of the remaining classes of decision problems we shall take up fall into this category, where uncontrollable variables affect the payoff.

The first of these is *decision-making under competitive conditions,* where the uncontrollable variables are actually controlled by adversaries, each seeking his own objectives, possibly at the expense of the decision-maker. For instance, in the illustration of the store manager who reduces the price of an item, the payoff (increase in sales volume) will be affected by whether the competitor also lowers prices.

This type of problem has been analyzed extensively by economists and decision theorists. We shall take up an example that illustrates the approach involved in *game theory.*

Game theory case illustration

One type of game-theory model categorizes situations of pure competition or conflict between two individuals or decision units, in which the payoff received by one side is directly at the expense of that received by the other. We can consider in this connection a proxy fight between an established management group in a corporation and an opposition group striving to obtain control. Several individual stockholders who control large blocks of voting stock are still undecided about which group they will assign their votes to. Each group is attempting to obtain the greatest possible share of these uncommitted votes for itself. Every vote gained by one side is lost to the other.

Suppose that the established group has three alternative courses of action that it may follow in the campaign to obtain the uncommitted votes. These might involve, for example, alternative promises about the emphasis to be placed on capital growth rather than short-term dividend yield. However, it will suffice for our purposes simply to call these acts *A*, *B*, and *C*. Suppose also that the opposition group has three courses of action open to it, which we shall call acts *a*, *b*, and *c*. Each group recognizes the courses of action open to the other, and each seeks to ascertain the course of action that would be wisest for itself to follow.

The established management group has carefully studied the desires and leanings of the uncommitted large stockholders and has estimated the per cents of the uncommitted votes it will receive if each side selects particular courses of action. These per cents are shown in Table 15.1. For example, if act *A* is chosen by the established group and *a* by the opposition group, the former group will receive 75 per cent of the uncommitted votes. On the other hand, if acts *B* and *a* are chosen by the two groups respectively, the established group will receive only 40 per cent of the uncommitted votes. The established group knows that the opposition has the same information about the feelings of the uncommitted stockholders and that it has arrived at the same figures as those in Table 15.1 as to the per cent of votes the established group will receive under various conditions.

Table 15.1 Acts Available to Established and Opposition Groups, and Payoffs to Established Group (Payoffs Show Per Cent of Uncommitted Vote Obtained by Established Group)

		Act Available to Opposition Group			
		a	*b*	*c*	*Row Guarantee*
Act Available to Established Group	*A*	75%	75%	60%	60%
	B	40%	80%	45%	40%
	C	85%	40%	45%	40%
Column Guarantee		85%	80%	60%	

Criterion for selecting act

Which act—*A*, *B*, or *C*—should the decision-maker for the established group choose? He wishes to attain the greatest per cent of the votes possible, keeping in mind that his counterpart in the opposition group will strive to limit him to as small a per cent as possible. The decision-maker cannot predict with certainty the payoff (per cent of the votes) he will attain in selecting any given act, since this payoff also depends upon the action of the opposition and he cannot control this action. If he attempts to achieve the greatest payoff possible to him, namely 85 per cent of the votes by selecting *C* in the hope that the opposition will select *a*, he may end up with the worst possible payoff—40 per cent—because the opposition may have anticipated his strategy and selected *b* as its own counterstrategy. Thus, the choice of a criterion, or basis for selecting an act as optimal, is a more complex issue than in the case of decision-making under certainty, where each act has a single known payoff.

Minimax or maximin criterion. The choice of criterion would be obvious enough if the decision-maker had to commit himself first, after which the opposition would be free to select its best counterstrategy. In this case, it generally would make sense for the decision-maker to select the act that best limited the opposition's ability to hurt his group once it was committed. Table 15.1 shows that if *A* is selected, the worst the opposition can do is to limit the established group to 60 per cent of the votes by selecting *c*. If *B* or *C* were selected, the worst possible payoffs would be 40 per cent and 40 per cent, respectively. These figures represent for the decision-maker the floors or guarantees in the rows of the payoff table and are shown in the right-most column. In selecting an act, the decision-maker cannot attain less than the guarantee in that row, though he will attain more if the opposition fails to select its most effective counterstrategy. Assuming the opposition will retaliate as effectively as possible, the decision-maker would be wise to follow course *A* if he had to commit himself first, since this act gives the highest floor or guarantee attainable in the three available acts. In other words, *A* maximizes the minimum payoff to which the opposition can restrict the decision-maker's group.

(15.5) The criterion that prescribes the act that maximizes the minimum payoff to which one can be restricted is called the ***maximin criterion.***

The same considerations would apply to the opposition group if it had to commit itself first, and the established group then could select the most effective counterstrategy. If the opposition group selected *a*, it would be guaranteed only that the established group would not obtain more than 85 per cent of the votes. If it selected *b* or *c*, the guarantees would be 80 per cent and 60 per cent, respectively. These column guarantees are shown in the bottom row in Table 15.1. Since the opposition group wishes to limit the established group to as small a per cent as possible, it should select *c* if it has to commit itself first. In selecting *c*, the opposition group would be applying a *minimax* criterion. That is, it would be minimizing the maximum payoff that the opposition can possibly attain. Obviously the *maximin* and *minimax* criteria involve the same basis for selecting an act, but from the point of view of opposite payoffs.

In many situations of conflict or competition, the groups have to commit themselves more or less simultaneously. Suppose this were the case in the present example. What criterion for selecting an act then would be wisest? Some decision theorists suggest that the wisest approach for each group still would be to use the maximin (minimax) criterion, thus following the course of action that gives the best available guarantee, regardless of the strategy employed by the opposing side. For example, the established group can assure itself of 60 per cent of the available votes by selecting *A*; it will receive more than this if the other side happens to select *a* or *b* instead of *c*, but it cannot receive less. Similarly, the opposition group, by choosing *c*, can make sure that the other side will obtain no more than 60 per cent and may obtain less.

Difficulties in choice of criterion. The maximin (minimax) criterion seems reasonable if the opposition can be expected to use this criterion. In fact, the established management group would then have to use the maximin strategy in order to get the highest payoff (see Table 15.1). The opposition, however, does not have to use the minimax criterion. The opposition decision-maker may not be clever or knowledgeable, or he may be willing to take risks in order to get a higher payoff. In that case, a maximin strategy may be a poor countermove. If, for instance, the opposition group chose *b*, the established management group would do better to choose *B* than *A*.

Thus, the maximin (minimax) criterion has weaknesses. Indeed, difficulties in choosing a criterion will be encountered also in other classes of decision problems.

Additional comments

The example just discussed concerns a situation in which there are two opposing groups in direct conflict, the gain to one side represents an equivalent loss to the other, each side knows the courses of action open to the other, and the payoffs are known to both sides. This type of case is called a *two-person, zero-sum game*. We have examined a special case of such a "game," in which the maximin and minimax payoffs are the same—in this case, 60 per cent at the intersection of row *A* and column *c*. In the vocabulary of game theory, this payoff is called the *equilibrium point* or *saddle point* for the conflict situation categorized in Table 15.1.

All two-person, zero-sum conflict situations do not contain saddle points in the payoff table. If they do not, *mixed* or *randomized* strategies must be considered in order to find the equilibrium point. In a mixed or randomized strategy, the decision-maker selects the act he will use according to probabilities determined from relevant aspects of game theory.

Game theory goes beyond the model of the two-person, zero-sum situation to consider cases where there are several competing groups, or where the gain to one group does not involve an equivalent loss to the other or others. There are, indeed, important connections between game theory and statistical decision theory. Here, however, we utilize game theory only as an illustration of decision-making under competitive conditions.

15.4 DECISION–MAKING UNDER CONDITIONS OF UNCERTAINTY

Reasons for uncertainty

In the proxy-fight example just analyzed, the payoff was affected by a variable that was uncontrollable by the established management group, namely the act chosen by the rival group. This rival group was presumed to be rational and was expected to select the act that it considered wisest in the light of its own objective. Hence, the established management group could anticipate the behavior of the rival group.

In many decision problems, however, uncontrollable variables are present that are not under the command of a rational competitor, and about which the decision-maker has little or no information on the basis of which to assess the future state of affairs. For instance, a large manufacturing company has a plant located in a small midwestern town. Across the street is a restaurant, the owner of which is considering whether or not to renovate and expand the facilities. One of the variables affecting the owner's payoff (future profits) is whether the plant will be moved to another location in the near future. As far as the restaurant owner is concerned, this variable is uncontrollable. In addition, he has no information about the intentions of the manufacturing company. He is unlike the management in the game theory situation in that he cannot anticipate what the manufacturing company will do by analyzing the effect of the move on his profits, since the manufacturing company will not take the restaurant's profits into account when it makes a decision about moving. Decision-making under these conditions is designated as being made *under uncertainty*.

In general, decision-making under uncertainty arises when the future cannot be forecast readily on the basis of past experience. Often, many uncontrollable variables are present. Sometimes, it is possible to consolidate the effects of these uncontrollable variables in terms of a probability distribution, and we shall discuss this case later. Here, we consider the case where little or no information is available for constructing such a distribution. For instance, many factors influence a household decision as to whether to purchase a new appliance during its first year on the market. For the population of potential purchasers, one may conceive of a probability distribution indicating the likelihood of different sales volumes during the first year. At the time the marketing decisions on the new product must be made, however, no relevant information about this probability distribution may be at hand, and management may be unwilling or unable to assign subjective probabilities. Here, then, is another case of decision-making under uncertainty.

Case illustration

To illustrate decision-making under uncertainty in more detail, we consider the case of a pharmaceutical house that has developed a new drug and plans to submit it to the U.S. Food and Drug Administration for marketing approval. The outcome of the application to market the drug is uncertain. In the past, about half the drugs submitted have been approved, but management believes this information is not relevant for the new drug, which is of an unusual type. The basic issue facing the decision-making group is whether to invest in production capacity and planning for product promotion now or to await the outcome of the application.

For the type of drug considered here, the first firm to capture the market retains most of the business even after rival firms bring out their own version of the product. Consequently, to exploit fully the profit potential in the new drug, the innovating firm must be prepared to attract and to satisfy most of the prospective customers quickly once the drug is sanctioned for marketing. Otherwise, it may find that a rival firm has seized the dominant position by acting quickly in developing, producing, and promoting its own version of the product. On the other hand, it is possible that investment in production capacity and product promotion prior to action on the application will be wasted because the drug will not be approved.

Suppose the decision-making unit is considering four alternative courses of action, as shown at the left in Table 15.2. Suppose also that the deci-

Table 15.2 Acts, Outcome States, and Payoffs—Drug Firm Case (Payoffs Show Present Value of Estimated Earnings in Millions of Dollars)

		Outcome State		
		a	*b*	*c*
Act		*Early Approval*	*Approval After Delay*	*Disapproval*
A	Build capacity, promote	55	40	−4
B	Build capacity, delay promotion	52	43	−2
C	Delay capacity, promote	40	43	−2
D	Delay capacity, delay promotion	10	30	0

sion unit has grouped the possible outcomes of the marketing application into three payoff-affecting classes, as shown in the column labels at the right. From the point of view of the decision unit, these outcomes represent *all* possible states of the uncontrollable variable that could arise.

(15.6) The possible states of the uncontrollable variable or variables are called ***states of nature*** or ***outcome states.***

In decision-making under uncertainty, there are at least two outcome states. In decision-making under certainty, on the other hand, there is only *one* possible outcome state for any act. In Table 15.2, the available acts are indicated by A, B, C, and D, and the different outcome states by a, b, and c.

For reasons just described, the payoff that will be obtained by the firm depends not only upon the course of action chosen by the decision unit, but also on the outcome state that ultimately prevails. Taking these considerations into account, the decision unit developed the payoff estimates shown in Table 15.2 on the basis of estimated market potential for the item and extensive industry experience with new drugs. The figure represents the present value of estimated future earnings over the lifetime of the product in millions of dollars. In other problems, of course, a different payoff measure might be more relevant, such as share of the market, number of units sold, or return on investment.

Admissible acts

If the decision unit knew in advance which outcome state would prevail —that is, which column in Table 15.2 would be the relevant one—the problem would be that of decision-making under certainty. The decision unit could then examine only the relevant outcome state column and identify the act that is best in the light of the criterion.

In decision-making under uncertainty, however, the eventual outcome state is unknown at the time the decision must be made. Before we consider how the decision should be made under these circumstances, it should be noted that management need not consider act C any further. The reason is that act B yields a payoff at least as good as or better than C *under every possible outcome state*. For instance, Table 15.2 indicates that if state a prevails, B's payoff is higher than C's, namely \$52 million versus \$40 million. If b or c prevails, both acts have the same payoff, \$43 million under b or −\$2 million under c. In the vocabulary of decision theory:

(15.7) One act ***dominates*** another if for each possible outcome state the first act yields a payoff at least as good as that of the second and yields a higher payoff under at least one outcome state. An act is ***admissible*** if it is not dominated.

In the drug firm case, acts A, B, and D are all admissible. Act C, on the other hand, is said to be *inadmissible* because it is dominated by B.

In a decision problem, it is but common sense to choose only from among the admissible acts. This principle applies to decision problems in general. Note that in Table 15.1, p. 308, which pertains to the proxy-fight example discussed in the previous section, each of the acts available to either side was admissible.

Possible criteria for selecting act

On what basis should the decision unit select its course of action from among the admissible acts *A*, *B*, and *D*? We now examine briefly a number of criteria that have been proposed.

Maximin criterion. A decision unit might take the approach of expecting the worst and therefore consider the lowest payoff possible with any act. This would be the same as the unit's committing itself against a still uncommitted rational adversary in a situation of pure conflict or competition, such as that in the proxy-fight case. If the decision unit does feel this way, it would seem reasonable for it to apply the maximin criterion as the basis for selecting its course of action. The worst payoffs that could be received with *A*, *B*, and *D* are, respectively, −$4 million, −$2 million, and $0. Act *D* maximizes the minimum possible payoff, hence satisfies the maximin criterion. Of course, it does not follow that the firm would necessarily receive a payoff of $0 in choosing *D*. This contingency would occur only if the firm's application to market the drug were turned down by the government agency. Better payoffs would be received under states *a* or *b*. At the least, however, the maximin criterion guarantees that the firm cannot receive a payoff lower than $0; that is, it cannot incur any losses from wasted investment in production capacity or promotion for the drug.

Maximax criterion. An optimistic and venturesome firm might take the approach that it should consider the maximum payoff possible with each act and select the act that maximizes the maximum payoff. The basis of choice in this approach is the *maximax* criterion. Table 15.2 shows that act *A* meets this criterion: It can yield a payoff as high as $55 million (if *a* prevails), and no other available act has a maximum payoff this high.

Minimax regret criterion. A decision-maker may feel that there is no basis for the degree of pessimism implicit in using the maximin criterion in decision problems involving uncertainty. Yet he also would be reluctant to embark on a course of action that could have a seriously adverse effect should an undesirable outcome state prevail, as might happen with the maximax criterion. In our case illustration, the decision-maker might reason somewhat as follows: "We must decide right now whether to go ahead or wait in building production capacity and promoting this product. We won't know the outcome of our marketing application for quite a while.

Table 15.3 Payoffs in Earnings and in Regret—Drug Firm Case (Million Dollars)

(a) *Payoffs in Earnings*

	Outcome State		
Act	*a*	*b*	*c*
A	55 *	40	−4
B	52	43 *	−2
D	10	30	0 *

(b) *Payoffs in Opportunity Loss, or Regret*

	Outcome State			
Act	*a*	*b*	*c*	*Maximum Regret in Row*
A	0	3	4	4
B	3	0	2	3
D	45	13	0	45

But later the results of our decision are liable to be judged against the best results we could have obtained with a perfect crystal ball. We ought to be sure we don't fall too short!"

For a decision-maker who feels this way, it is convenient to convert the payoff measures in Table 15.2 to *opportunity losses*. Table 15.3a repeats the payoffs of Table 15.2. Note that if state *a* ultimately prevails, the best payoff that could be obtained would be $55 million, with act *A*. This payoff has been starred. If under these circumstances, *B* had been chosen, the payoff would be only $52 million, which is $3 million less than the best obtainable under state *a*. Thus act *B* entails an opportunity loss of $3 million if state *a* prevails, relative to the best act for this outcome state. Similarly, act *D* entails an opportunity loss of $45 million, (55 − 10), if state *a* prevails. The opportunity losses if state *a* prevails are shown in Table 15.3b in the column pertaining to outcome state *a*.

Frequently, the opportunity losses are called regrets.

(15.8) A payoff measured in terms of ***regret*** indicates for a given act the difference between the best payoff that could be obtained under a given outcome state and the actual payoff of that act under this state.

If outcome state *b* prevails, act *B* yields the highest payoff, namely $43 million. This payoff also has been starred in Table 15.3a. Under state *b*, then, act *A* would involve an opportunity loss of $3 million, (43 − 40), and act *D* an opportunity loss of $13 million, (43 − 30). The regrets for outcome state *c* in Table 15.3b are calculated in a similar manner.

For the decision-maker whose objective is to avoid falling too short at all costs, it may be wise to employ the minimax regret criterion:

(15.9) The ***minimax regret criterion*** prescribes that act which minimizes the maximum possible regret.

Note that this criterion is the equivalent of the maximin criterion, but applied to payoffs measured in opportunity losses.

The maximum regrets that could arise in selecting *A, B,* and *D* are 4, 3, and 45, respectively. Consequently, *B* minimizes the maximum possible regret and is the course of action that would be chosen on a minimax regret basis. In choosing this course, the decision-maker is assured that *at the worst,* the dollar payoff actually obtained would not fall short by more than $3 million of the best result that could have been obtained with a perfect prediction of the outcome state.

Choice of criterion

We have considered three criteria that have been proposed for decision-making under uncertainty. Still others have been suggested.

Unlike decision-making under certainty, where the criterion for choosing the optimal act for our textile mill case was no problem, decision-making under uncertainty involves difficult problems in choosing the criterion according to which the optimal act is determined. The criteria proposed differ so substantially that they can designate different acts as optimal. In our illustration, for instance, the maximin criterion led to act *D*, the maximax criterion to act *A*, and the minimax regret criterion to act *B*.

None of the criteria that have been proposed for decision-making under uncertainty have been generally accepted by decision theorists as being demonstrably superior to the others. Indeed, for any criterion that has been advocated by some writers as being generally applicable under uncertainty, other writers have devised uncertainty situations for which *they* believe this criterion would be unwise. At the present stage of decision theory, one can say only that the choice of a criterion under conditions of uncertainty must depend upon the decision-maker's attitude toward uncertainty itself in the context of the particular decision problem. In this connection, company policy plays an important role in guiding its executives' attitudes toward uncertainty.

15.5 DECISION-MAKING UNDER CONDITIONS OF RISK

Decision-making under uncertainty involves not knowing the likelihood that one or another of the outcome states will prevail. Frequently, however, decision-makers do have information about the probability that each outcome state will occur, even though they are uncertain as to the actual outcome state. For instance, the controller of a firm may be uncertain as to how many machines will break down during the year and need to be replaced, yet he will have reliable information from past experience as to the probabilities that no machines need be replaced, that one machine needs to be replaced, and so on. Again, the actuary of an insurance company may be uncertain about the number of deaths of insured persons during the next year, but he does have good information about the probability distribution of the number of deaths occurring in a year.

Decision-making when there are a number of possible outcome states, for which the probability distribution is known, is called *decision-making under risk*. Many decision problems fall into this category, and we shall illustrate this type of problem in some detail with a simple case.

Case illustration

A newsboy must decide how many copies of a certain out-of-town paper to stock on Sundays in addition to the regular stock of local Sunday papers. He can handle up to eight copies of this out-of-town paper in addition to the local papers he carries, but cannot handle more. Thus, the acts available to him with respect to the out-of-town Sunday paper are to stock zero copies, stock one copy, and so on, up to eight copies. A copy costs the newsboy 30 cents and he sells it for 50 cents, making a profit of 20 cents on each copy sold. Unsold copies may not be returned. Thus, there is a loss of 30 cents on each unsold copy. The newsboy does not have regular Sunday customers for this out-of-town paper, and the exact number of copies that he could sell on a given Sunday cannot be known with certainty in advance.

The situation as described up to this point is summarized in Table 15.4. Note that this table has all the structural components previously encountered:

1. A set of available acts involving the controllable variables, in this case the variable "number of copies stocked."
2. A set of outcome states involving the uncontrollable variables, in this case the variable "number of copies demanded."
3. A payoff for each combination of act and outcome state.

To illustrate how the payoffs are determined, suppose the newsboy stocks eight copies (bottom row of table) at an outlay of $2.40. If zero copies are demanded, he loses the entire outlay; if one copy is demanded, he loses $1.90. On the other hand, if, say, eight copies are demanded, he receives a gross return of $4.00, netting $1.60. If more than eight copies are demanded, he still nets only $1.60 because he has stocked only eight copies and cannot satisfy the additional demand.

The newsboy must place a standing order for the number of copies that he wishes to stock. Which course of action—stock zero copies, stock one copy, and so on—should be recommended to him as best? If there were no information available on the likelihood of occurrence of the various outcome states (number of copies demanded), the decision problem would be one under uncertainty.

However, in the present problem it could be determined from past experience that the number of copies the newsboy can sell each Sunday follows a Poisson probability distribution with mean $\mu_X = 5$ copies. Consequently, the probabilities of each outcome state can be determined readily from a table of Poisson probabilities (Table A-2). These probabilities are shown in Table 15.4. On the basis of this information, we can develop

Table 15.4 Acts, Outcome States and Probabilities, and Payoffs—Newsboy Case (Payoffs Stated in Dollars)

Act (No. Stocked)	*Outcome State and Probability*								
	Number Demanded								
	0	*1*	*2*	*3*	*4*	*5*	*6*	*7*	*8+*
	Probability								
	.0067	*.0337*	*.0842*	*.1404*	*.1755*	*.1755*	*.1462*	*.1044*	*.1334*
0	0	0	0	0	0	0	0	0	0
1	−.30	.20	.20	.20	.20	.20	.20	.20	.20
2	−.60	−.10	.40	.40	.40	.40	.40	.40	.40
3	−.90	−.40	.10	.60	.60	.60	.60	.60	.60
4	−1.20	−.70	−.20	.30	.80	.80	.80	.80	.80
5	−1.50	−1.00	−.50	0	.50	1.00	1.00	1.00	1.00
6	−1.80	−1.30	−.80	−.30	.20	.70	1.20	1.20	1.20
7	−2.10	−1.60	−1.10	−.60	−.10	.40	.90	1.40	1.40
8	−2.40	−1.90	−1.40	−.90	−.40	.10	.60	1.10	1.60

a probability distribution of payoffs for each available course of action.

(15.10) A ***probability distribution of payoffs*** is associated with a given course of action, and shows the different payoffs that could be received from that act, together with their respective probabilities of being received.

For example, the payoffs for the act "stock eight copies" are as shown in the bottom row of Table 15.4, and the probabilities of each of the payoffs are given at the top of the table. Note that if the act "stock eight copies" is taken, then the payoff is −\$2.40 if no papers are demanded. Since the probability that no papers are demanded is .0067, the probability of a payoff of −\$2.40 when eight copies are stocked is .0067. In the same way, the probabilities are associated with any other payoff. The probability distribution of payoffs for the act "stock eight copies" is assembled in columns 1 and 2 of Table 15.5. Of course, for other acts such as "stock seven copies," there is a different probability distribution of payoffs.

Expected payoff criterion

Since the newsboy is in the business of selling papers day after day, it would appear reasonable to seek the act that will maximize his long-run profit in carrying the Sunday editions of this out-of-town paper. This is equivalent to maximizing the mean profit per Sunday over a long series of Sundays. In other words, we seek the act for which the associated probability distribution of payoffs has the highest mean.

To put this in another way, the payoff is a random variable, since the actual payoff on any Sunday is a function of the number of newspapers demanded, which is a random variable. Thus, we wish to find the act for which the *expected value of the payoff* is the highest.

(15.11) The criterion that prescribes the act that maximizes the expected value of the payoff, or briefly the expected payoff, is called the ***expected payoff criterion.***

The expected value of a random variable was defined in (6.29), p. 129. This value is simply the weighted average of the possible outcomes (here payoff amounts), where the probabilities of these outcomes serve as weights. Table 15.5 illustrates the calculation of the expected payoff for the act "stock eight copies." We see that the expected payoff with a stock level of eight copies is \$0.039, or about 4 cents per Sunday.

Table 15.5 Calculation of Expected Payoff for Stock Level of Eight Copies

No. Demanded	(1) *Payoff* *X*	(2) *Probability* *P(X)*	(3) *Col. 1 × Col. 2* *XP(X)*
0	−\$2.40	.0067	−\$0.01608
1	− 1.90	.0337	− .06403
2	− 1.40	.0842	− .11788
3	− .90	.1404	− .12636
4	− .40	.1755	− .07020
5	+ .10	.1755	+ .01755
6	+ .60	.1462	+ .08772
7	+ 1.10	.1044	+ .11484
8 or more	+ 1.60	.1334	+ .21344
		1.0000	+\$0.03900

The expected payoff for each of the available acts is shown in Table 15.6, but the detailed calculations are not presented. The method of calcu-

Table 15.6 Expected Payoffs for Stock Levels of Zero to Eight Copies

Stock Level	*Expected Payoff*	*Stock Level*	*Expected Payoff*
0	\$0.	5	\$0.5614
1	.1966	6	.4534
2	.3764	7	.2723
3	.5142	8	.0390
4	.5816		

lation for each of the other acts is exactly the same as that shown in Table 15.5 for the act "stock eight copies." Note that the expected payoff becomes larger with higher stock levels up to four, but then begins to decline. The reason for this is that with higher stock levels, the occasional large earnings are more than balanced by frequent losses when all the copies are not sold. Thus, to maximize his profit over the long run, the newsboy should stock four copies.

Incidentally, a "common-sense" recommendation to the newsboy might be to stock five copies, since this is the average number demanded on Sunday. However, this approach neglects to consider the probability distribution of payoffs and does not maximize long-run profits.

The expected payoff criterion is appealing in the type of problem illustrated by the newsboy case. Decision-makers who maximize expected payoff in this type of situation would obtain better results in the long run than their counterparts who chose courses of action on some other basis.

Need for payoff measure in utilities

There are many cases in which it is reasonable to select the act that maximizes the expected payoff measured in dollar terms or in other conventional units such as share of the market, quantity sold, or rate of return on investment. Sometimes, however, this approach is not appropriate. Consider the following situation confronting the owner of a small business:

	Outcome State:	*a*	*b*
Act	*Probability:*	(.6)	(.4)
A		−$ 1,000	$ 10,000
B		− 50,000	100,000

Act *A* has an expected payoff of $3,400, while act *B* has an expected payoff of $10,000. Yet this businessman without hesitation chooses act *A*. He reasons that act *B* might entail a loss of $50,000, which would bankrupt him. The difficulty here is that a loss of $50,000 is *more than* 50 times as serious for this owner of a small business as a loss of $1,000, but this effect is not shown in the dollar figures and therefore is not reflected in the expected dollar payoffs. A measure has been developed that does reflect the relative desirability to the decision-maker of the payoffs in monetary or other conventional units. Such a measure has the name *utility*. While maximization of expected payoff measured in dollars or other conventional units is not always a reasonable criterion, as was just shown, maximization of expected payoff measured in utilities is always a reasonable criterion. We shall not go further into this subject, but do wish to point out that much recent work in decision theory has been concerned with utility measures.

Payoffs measured in utilities are needed chiefly when some of the possible payoffs measured in dollars are large relative to the total resources of the company or individual. This was the case in the illustration above. Frequently, however, the magnitudes of the possible dollar payoffs are not large relative to total resources. In such cases, many decision-makers feel that the relative desirability of the possible payoffs is properly reflected in the dollar figures, so that maximization of expected dollar payoff is then a reasonable criterion. In our discussions in Chapters 20 and 21 involving expected payoffs, we shall assume that the maximization of expected payoff expressed in conventional units, such as dollars, is an appropriate criterion.

Use of subjective probabilities

It has been suggested by a number of decision theorists that decision-making under risk should be utilized even when the probability distribution of the different outcome states is unknown, or when objective probabilities are inapplicable. Subjective probabilities would be utilized instead. Thus, the decision-maker would be asked to assess the likelihood of each of the outcome states and to provide subjective probabilities of each outcome occurring. Once these subjective probabilities are at hand, the mechanics of determining the act that maximizes the expected payoff are the same as already described.

15.6 SUMMARY

We have described four different decision models. Each of these has the following structural elements in common:

1. A set of available acts, relating to the controllable variables in the problem
2. A set of outcome states, determined by the uncontrollable variables
3. A payoff for each particular combination of act and outcome state
4. A criterion for selecting the best or optimal act

In decision-making under certainty, there is only one outcome state; all the other models involve more than one outcome state. In decision-making under competitive conditions, the outcome state is chosen by a rational competitor, while in decision-making under risk, the outcome state is determined by a known probability mechanism. In decision-making under uncertainty, the decision-maker is largely ignorant about which outcome state will prevail. In this latter case, the choice of a criterion for selecting an act as "optimal" is particularly difficult.

15.7 STATISTICAL DECISION-MAKING

The reader will have noted that in each of the cases discussed, the decision-maker could not obtain predictive information about the prevailing outcome state as an aid in selecting a course of action. In the problems involving uncertainty (the drug firm case) and risk (the newsboy case), the outcome state was a contingency about which the decision-maker at worst was completely in the dark and about which at best he had probability information. But in any case he had no way of obtaining information in advance about the particular state that would eventually prevail.

Often, it is possible to obtain specific information about the outcome state. Consider a cannery that has received a shipment of produce. A decision must be made to accept the shipment or send it back. Suppose that the relevant payoff-affecting variable is the spoilage rate in the shipment. If about 10 per cent of the shipment is spoiled, it does not matter financially whether the shipment is accepted or sent back, since there is about the same inconvenience and economic loss with either act. To the extent that the spoilage rate is less than 10 per cent, it is increasingly profitable to accept the shipment, and to the extent that the rate is greater than 10 per cent, it is better to send the shipment back. The per cent of the shipment spoiled is some *existing* but *unknown* figure. Thus, one is concerned here with an existing state, not with an eventual outcome state. Before committing himself, the decision-maker has an informational option that was not present in the problems previously discussed. He may obtain complete information about the shipment state (per cent spoiled) by examining the entire shipment, or obtain incomplete information by sampling the shipment, or decide to commit himself with no advance information.

The ability to obtain information so as to increase the likelihood of selecting the best act broadens the decision problem into that of ascertaining the best strategy for sampling and acting on the sample data. This problem, which is fundamental in management, involves statistical inference and falls into the purview of *statistical decision-making*. We concentrate on this aspect of decision theory in several chapters that follow.

QUESTIONS AND PROBLEMS

15.1. Explain briefly each of the following:

a. Equilibrium point
b. Inadmissible act
c. Expected payoff
d. Regret
e. Criterion

15.2. Contrast decision-making under certainty and decision-making under uncertainty. Give an example of each.

15.3. Discuss contrasts and similarities in decision-making under uncertainty and decision-making under competitive conditions. Use examples to illustrate your points.

15.4. Smith, who operates a gas station near a residential neighborhood, tries to make some extra money each year by selling Christmas trees. He must order the trees in advance, and his problem is to determine how many trees to order. In determining the best order size, does Smith face a problem in decision-making under certainty, uncertainty, or risk? Explain, indicating any assumptions you made.

***15.5.** In the textile mill example on pp. 304–307, suppose that prices have shifted so that the mill now gains $330 and $300 per thousand yards of the light- and heavy-patterned cloths, respectively. Limitations in output capacity are the same as in the text discussion, hence Figure 15.1 still applies.

a. For each of the output mixes that need to be considered, calculate the gain from a week's production at the new prices.

b. Is the criterion used by the manager in the text discussion still meaningful, now that two output mixes yield the same gain? Discuss.

15.6. The Elmer Food Company cans vegetables in cylindrical 20-ounce cans. The cost of a can is directly proportional to its surface area since this determines the amount of metal required for its manufacture. It is desired to choose the dimensions of the can so surface area is minimized subject to the requirement that the can have a volume of 20 fluid ounces (about 36 cubic inches).

a. Is this a problem of decision-making under certainty, uncertainty, or risk? Explain.

b. What are the available acts in this decision problem? Is it obvious which act is best? Discuss.

***15.7.** Joe Sparrow, a habitual horse player, sets up the following dollar payoff table relating to a $2 bet on the horse Stableboy in the fifth race:

	Stableboy's Outcome			
Act	*Win*	*Place*	*Show*	*Lose*
Bet on win	10	−2	−2	−2
Bet on place	2	4	−2	−2
Bet on show	1	3	3	−2
Don't bet	0	0	0	0

a. Do you believe that the maximin criterion will appeal to Sparrow as a basis for choosing his course of action? Discuss.

b. Convert the payoff data to regrets and present these in a table. Might the minimax regret criterion appeal to Sparrow? Discuss.

15.8. The Precision Casting Company has received an order for four large lenses, which must be specially cast. Any flaws in a lens do not become apparent until several weeks after casting, when the lens has cooled somewhat. Flawed lenses must be scrapped. Past experience indicates that the probability is about .8 that a lens will be free from flaws, that this probability is constant from lens to lens, and that the outcome for each lens is independent of the outcomes for the other lenses. There is a fixed cost of $400 for setting up the process to cast a batch of these lenses, plus a direct cost of $250 for each lens cast in the batch. The production manager would like to determine the best arrangement for producing four unflawed lenses to fill the order. Unflawed lenses in excess of the number needed to fill the order have only salvage value ($115 each) since there is no regular demand for this type of lens and it does not pay to store excess lenses to await an eventual order.

a. Is this a decision problem under certainty, uncertainty, or risk? Explain.

b. It is suggested to the manager that he cast lenses in batches of one until he has four acceptable lenses. Why is this not a good suggestion? Outline two alternative approaches that might be worth consideration by the manager.

15.9. A retired manager said: "Jargon changes with time but the actions remain the same. We used to allocate capital funds on the basis of the most probable return. Now they use 'expected' return. The words differ but the approach is exactly the same." Comment.

***15.10.** The following table shows dollar payoffs for several combinations of stock level and demand, for a new fashion item that will be sold in a certain clothing store:

	Outcome State (Level of Demand)		
Act (Stock Level)	*Low*	*Medium*	*High*
Low	150	150	150
Medium	125	250	250
High	100	200	300

a. Are all three acts admissible? Explain.

b. It has been suggested that the manager of the store faces a problem involving decision-making under uncertainty, in deciding the level of stockage for this item. Do you agree? Indicate any assumptions implicit in your point of view.

c. Assume that the manager does treat the problem as one of decision-making under uncertainty. For each of the following criteria, indicate which act would be selected and explain why the store management might be attracted by this criterion: (1) maximin; (2) minimax regret; (3) maximax.

15.11. Suppose someone has given *you* a ticket in a sweepstakes conducted abroad, and you now find that your ticket has drawn a horse. There are ten horses in the sweepstakes. If your horse comes in first, you will win $200,000; if he comes in second, you will win $75,000; and if he comes in third, you will win $25,000. If your horse comes in fourth or worse, you get $2,000 in consolation money. On the basis of the best available expert opinion, you decide that the probability is .10 that your horse will come in first, .18 that he will come in second, .27 that he will come in third, and .45 that he will come in fourth or worse.

a. Calculate your expected payoff on the basis of these probabilities.

b. Before the race, a syndicate offers you $25,000 for your ticket. This is the only offer you will receive. Would you take the offer, or hold the ticket and take your chances on the race? Explain. Are the dollar payoffs an appropriate measure for your decision problem? Discuss.

***15.12.** A $40,000 shipment of glassware by a small export firm to a dealer in a foreign country may be stolen, damaged, or lost in transit, resulting in a loss with the following probability distribution:

Loss as a Per Cent of Shipment Value	*Probability*
0	.94
10	.03
50	.02
100	.01

a. What is the expected dollar loss for the shipment?

b. By paying a single premium of $1,500, the shipment can be insured totally against loss. If you were the owner of the small export firm, would you decide that the export firm purchase the insurance or bear the loss itself (i.e. self-insure)? Explain. Are the dollar losses an appropriate measure for the decision problem? Discuss.

15.13. The executive committee of a steel corporation is considering whether to replace certain obsolescent equipment with modern equipment. The alternative courses of action are to modernize now, or to delay modernization for another six years, at which time the present equipment will be worn out and will have to be replaced in any case. If replacement is delayed, it is possible that a new technological breakthrough will be made that will result in better equipment than can be purchased now. A committee staff member has set up a table, shown in simplified form here, indicating the present value of future payoffs in millions of dollars for different act and outcome state combinations:

	Outcome State			
	Breakthrough and:		*No Breakthrough and:*	
Act	*High Demand for Steel*	*Moderate Demand for Steel*	*High Demand for Steel*	*Moderate Demand for Steel*
Modernize now	1,500	1,200	1,500	1,300
Delay modernization	2,000	1,600	1,100	900

a. Are both acts admissible? Explain.

b. For each of the following criteria, indicate which act would be selected and explain why management might be attracted by this criterion: (1) maximin; (2) minimax regret; (3) maximax.

15.14. Refer to Problem 15.13.

a. Suppose that subjective probabilities are to be assigned to the outcome states. In your opinion, would it be a good idea in the absence of any information about the likelihood of the different outcome states to assign each outcome state equal probability of occurrence? Discuss.

b. Assume that the outcome states in Problem 15.13 are in fact assigned equal probabilities of occurrence. Calculate the expected payoff for each act and indicate which act maximizes expected payoff.

15.15. Two razor blade manufacturers, A and B, compete in foreign market X. The two manufacturers share 100 per cent of market X between them, and there is no prospect that any other manufacturer will try to enter this market in the foreseeable future. Firms A and B have each developed a stainless steel blade for the domestic market, and are studying whether to introduce the new blade into foreign market X.

Firm A's objective is to retain as large a share of market X as possible, since this market has great growth potential. As of now, firm A has 85 per cent of market X. The market manager of firm A believes that he will retain this share of market X if he does not introduce his stainless steel blade and if firm B continues in turn to ship only its regular blades to this market. On the other hand, the market manager of firm A estimates that his share of market X will drop to 50 per cent if firm B introduces its new blade and he does not introduce his new blade. But if both firms introduce their new blades, the manager estimates that his share will drop to 70 per cent because some brand switching will occur. Finally, the manager feels that if he introduces the new blade and firm B does not introduce its new blade, firm A will retain 80 per cent of the market (it will lose 5 per cent) because the new blade will cause some brand switching, including switching by persons who continue to use regular blades. The market manager of firm B has made the same assessment of the share of the market that firm A will receive under the different possible situations just covered. Further, each manager knows that his counterpart in the other firm has made these same assessments, and will try to obtain the largest possible share of the market.

a. Which conditions of decision-making are illustrated by this problem? Discuss.

b. Would the market manager of firm A be well-advised to use the maximax criterion in selecting his course of action? Why, or why not?

c. If you were the manager of firm A, which course of action would you select? Why? Which would you select if you were the market manager of firm B? Why?

d. Suppose the two managers follow the courses of action recommended by you in part **c**. Does this lead to the equilibrium solution? Discuss.

***15.16.** The firm of Officepower, Inc., supplies various types of substitute office clerks on a full-day basis to meet emergency requirements of clients. Past experience indicates that the number of posting-machine operators requested by clients on a given day follows a Poisson distribution with a mean of 1.0 operators. It costs Officepower, Inc. $25 a day in salary, fringe benefits, and other direct costs for each posting-machine operator that it has on its staff. The firm charges $45 a day for the services of a posting-machine operator. However, if any posting-machine operator's services are not required by some client on a given day, the firm assigns that operator to stand-by work at a local university for which it has contracted to charge only $15 a day. The firm would like to determine the best number of posting-machine operators to have available each morning for assignments.

a. Set up a table showing the acts, outcome states, and payoffs in the firm's decision problem. Consider only acts 0, 1, 2, and 3 operators on the staff. Assume, in calculating payoffs, that no cost arises to the firm from loss of goodwill if the number of operators requested by clients on a given day exceeds the firm's supply so that one or more requests cannot be filled.

b. For the acts being considered, determine the best number of posting-machine operators for the firm to have available for assignments. Explain in what sense this number is best. Treat the probabilities of outcomes for which there are no entries in Table A-2 as zero.

c. Do you think it would be necessary to consider also acts 4, 5, 6, and so on, operators in order to find the best staffing level? Discuss.

15.17. Refer to Problem 15.16. Suppose the firm imputes a cost of $30 to loss of goodwill for each occasion on which the firm cannot supply an operator to a client because the available operators are already assigned for that day. Set up a new payoff table, for the acts 1, 2, 3, and 4 operators on the staff. What would now be the best number of operators for the firm to have available on its staff each morning, among the acts being considered?

15.18. Refer to Problem 15.16. Answer parts **a** through **c** of this problem, but assume that daily demand for posting-machine operators follows a Poisson distribution with a mean of 2.0 operators.

15.19. The public accounting firm of Wisdom & Lore has been invited by a large supermarket chain to make a "presentation" for the chain's auditing account. This chain rotates its auditors fairly often. Two other accounting firms are also being invited to make presentations. One of the three firms will win the account. The senior partners in Wisdom & Lore are now considering the size of the fee to include in the bid. A "loss-leader" bid is under consideration, which will assure the firm of getting the account. In obtaining the account with the loss-leader bid, the firm anticipates that it would lose $30,000 in the first year, since the auditing work load is heaviest in the first year of a new account. In the second year, the accounting firm would gain $20,000 for that year. During the third year, and any following years, the firm would gain $40,000 for each year.

You are asked by the partners of Wisdom & Lore to draw up a brief statement as to whether the proposed loss-leader bid would be a "good gamble" if the only alternative act to be considered is not to bid. You decide to structure the problem in terms of decision-making under risk and ask the partners for their assessment of the chances of retaining the account for the first year only, for the first two years, and so on. After some reflection, the partners state that they feel there are two chances in ten of keeping the account for one year only, four chances in ten of keeping the account for two years, and four chances in ten of keeping the account for three years. There is no chance of keeping the account for more than three years because the chain's auditor-rotation policy is very firm. Is the loss-leader bid a good gamble? Why, or why not? Show calculations to support your answer. Assume the firm can easily stand any dollar losses that might be incurred.

15.20. Refer to Problem 15.19. The partners are also considering a bid with a higher fee than that of the loss-leader bid. With this alternative bid, the firm will lose $10,000 in the first year if it wins the account. In the second year the firm will gain $40,000 in that year, and in the third year will gain $60,000 in that year. If the firm wins the account the chances of retaining it for one, two, or three years respectively are the same as those cited in Problem 15.19; however, the partners estimate that there is only one chance in five that the firm would win the account in the first place if it made the alternative bid instead of the loss-leader bid.

a. Calculate the expected payoff for this alternative bidding strategy; show all steps in your calculations.

b. Which of the following three strategies is optimal: "don't bid," "submit loss-leader bid" (Problem 15.19), "submit higher-fee bid"? Why?

c. Suppose that the partners' assessment of one chance in five of winning the account with the higher-fee strategy is only a rough guess. Would the optimal strategy in **b** change if the probability of winning the account with the higher-fee bid was .1? .3? In general, what is the range of the probability of winning the account with the higher-fee bid, for which the optimal strategy remains unchanged? Discuss the implications of this.

15.21. A small chemical company is purchasing a special machine. The manufacturer is prepared to provide replacement units for a certain major component of the machine at a price of $200 per unit if the replacement units are purchased with the machine. On the other hand, any future order for replacement units would be filled, but at a price of $800 per unit. Unused replacement units are worthless because of the specialized nature of the component. Staff engineers of the company estimate that the requirement for replacement units for this component, during the life of the machine, has the following probability distribution:

Replacement Units Required	*Probability*
0	.65
1	.20
2	.10
3	.05

The company must decide what number of replacement units it will purchase with the machine.

a. Ignoring the time-value of money, set up a table showing the acts available to the company, the outcome states, and the payoffs (costs, in this case). What act maximizes the expected payoff (minimizes the expected cost)?

b. Are dollar payoffs an appropriate measure for this decision problem? Discuss.

15.22. Refer to Problem 15.21. Answer part **a** of this problem, but assume that any future order for replacement units would be filled at a price of $1,000 per unit instead of $800.

Chapter

16

STATISTICAL DECISION-MAKING

In Chapter 15, we examined the general features of decision-making and considered four basic types of decision problems. In this chapter, we present the basic ideas of *statistical* decision-making. Several important types of statistical decision problems will then be taken up in the following three chapters.

16.1
NATURE OF STATISTICAL DECISION PROBLEM

Example

The Harold Aircraft Company received an order for a large job lot of replacement parts. A special welding operation was performed by one employee in the course of filling this order. Management had trained a welder for this operation, and he had been working on the order for one week. Past experience in the company indicated that the learning curve would reach a plateau after about one week, so that no further improvements in productivity could be expected without additional training. Management had decided to measure the time required for this operation for a sample of 36 parts and then to make a decision on the basis of the sample observations as to whether to retrain the welder or to let him continue without retraining.

Note the correspondence of the structural elements of this decision problem and the ones considered in the previous chapter:

1. *Acts.* There are two acts being considered by the decision-maker in our example, to be denoted C_1 and C_2:

C_1 Do not retrain
C_2 Retrain

2. *Consequences.* Each of the two acts, C_1 and C_2, entails consequences in the form of dollar payoffs. Figure 16.1 shows the payoff functions for the two acts, as derived from data provided by the accounting staff of the company. Note that the payoff for each act is a function of the welder's mean required time μ_X. Figure 16.1 shows, for instance, that if management decides to retrain the welder when his mean required time

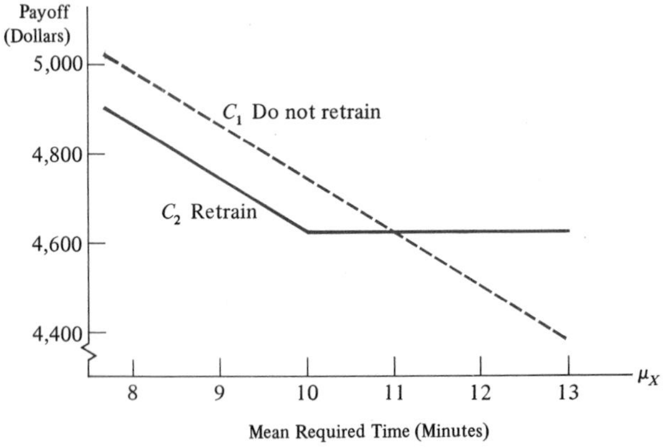

Figure 16.1. Payoff functions for two acts

μ_X is 10 minutes, the payoff of this act to the company is \$4,630. If the company decides not to retrain the welder when the welder's mean required time is 10 minutes, the payoff to the company is \$4,750.
3. *Outcome States.* The different possible values of the welder's mean required time μ_X are the outcome states for our problem.

Essential feature of statistical decision problems

The new element which arises in the foregoing example of a decision problem which was not encountered in earlier ones is that the outcome state μ_X is some *existing* value, not some *eventual* value. Though the mean required time μ_X for the employee is unknown, management can obtain sample information about the outcome state and then make the decision whether or not to retrain the employee on the basis of this information about the outcome state. Thus, *the essential feature distinguishing statistical decision-making from the types of decision problems discussed earlier is the use of information about the outcome state from a random sample in making the decision.*

Additional comments

In our example, the payoff is a function of the employee's mean required time μ_X. There happen to be infinitely many possible mean required times—infinitely many outcome states—in the present example, but in some other problems involving statistical decision-making the number of outcome states is finite. Furthermore, in other problems the payoff-affecting outcome states may involve a population proportion, population standard deviation, or still other population characteristics. We consider some of these other types of problems in later chapters.

Also note that our example involves a sample size of $n = 36$, which for this situation may be considered large. In a later chapter, we shall consider statistical decision-making when the sample size is small.

Finally, it should be noted that while our discussion will concentrate on statistical decision-making when there are two alternative courses of action, problems involving three or more courses of action can also be handled by statistical decision theory though the theory then becomes more complicated.

16.2 STATISTICAL DECISION RULES

We noted that the two courses of action considered by management in our example are:

C_1 Do not retrain

C_2 Retrain

and that the decision is to be based on sample information about the mean length of time μ_X required to perform the welding operation. For the same reasons that the sample mean $\overline{X}$ is a desirable all-purpose *estimator* of the population mean μ_X, this sample statistic will also be used as the basis for making the decision in our example.

The rule used to indicate the appropriate act for any given sample information is called a statistical decision rule.

(16.1) A ***statistical decision rule*** specifies, for each possible outcome in the sample space, the course of action to be taken.

Thus, a statistical decision rule may be thought of as a partition, or division, of the sample space such that a specified course of action is to be followed in each of the parts.

The concept of a decision rule is illustrated in Figure 16.2 for our example. At the top is the sample space containing the possible outcomes of $\overline{X}$. It is simply a line starting at zero; remember that $\overline{X}$ cannot be negative

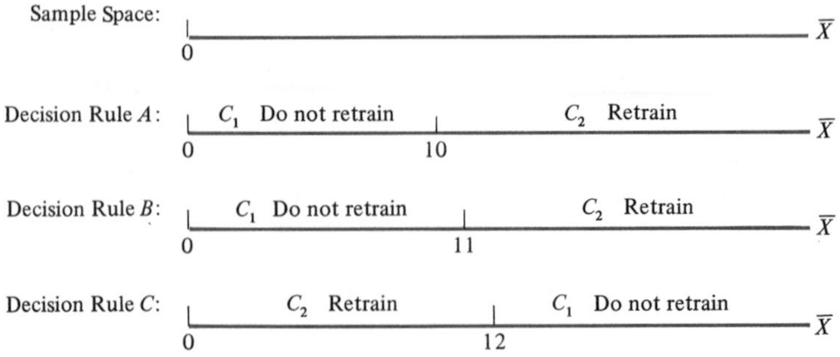

Figure 16.2. Sample space and three decision rules

since we are measuring elapsed time, but can take on any non-negative value. Decision rule A in Figure 16.2 represents a simple partition of this sample space. This rule states:

If $\overline{X} \leq 10$ minutes, do not retrain
If $\overline{X} > 10$ minutes, retrain

where $\leq$ signifies "less than or equal to" and $>$ signifies "greater than."

Similarly, decision rules B and C in Figure 16.2 are simple partitions. Decision rule B is:

If $\overline{X} \leq 11$ minutes, do not retrain
If $\overline{X} > 11$ minutes, retrain

while rule C is:

If $\overline{X} \geq 12$ minutes, do not retrain
If $\overline{X} < 12$ minutes, retrain

Note that each of these decision rules states explicitly the action to be followed for *every* possible sample result that may be obtained.

Many other ways of partitioning the sample space are possible. For the present, however, it will be enough to consider the three decision rules shown in Figure 16.2.

16.3 CLASSICAL STATISTICAL DECISION–MAKING

Reasons for modification

Two basic problems exist in using statistical decision rules:

1. How does one *evaluate* a statistical decision rule to determine how good it is?
2. How does one obtain the *best* statistical decision rule for a particular application?

Unfortunately, solving these two problems generally involves a number of difficulties. First, the number of decision rules that may need to be considered can be very large, and finding the best decision rule according to a particular criterion of choice may be highly complex. Second, there are great difficulties in selecting a decision criterion. These same difficulties, it will be recalled, are encountered in decision-making under uncertainty. Finally, it often is difficult to determine the payoffs of an act for all possible outcome states. For instance, if a manufacturer is deciding whether or not to ship a lot of consumer appliances to retailers without 100 per cent screening, the payoff function would need to reflect the loss of consumer goodwill if a defective appliance is purchased by the consumer. It is not easy to evaluate an intangible such as loss of customer goodwill. Similarly, in a decision problem on whether or not to continue an employee newspaper, there may be obstacles to assessing the consequences of each of the possible acts. Again, in experimental research on consumer behavior, it may be difficult to assess the payoffs of various eventualities, since the research may have no immediate bearing on the company's actions.

In view of these difficulties in evaluating statistical decision rules and choosing the best rule for a particular application, a modified approach to statistical decision-making is frequently used in practice. This modified approach is often called *classical statistical decision-making.* It focuses on the parameter affecting the payoff (μ_X in our example), and is concerned with the probabilities of error in making decisions. We illustrate this classical approach for our Harold Aircraft Company example.

Statement of alternatives based on μ_X

On the basis of the payoff functions developed in Figure 16.1, it is apparent that management would like to retrain the welder if his mean required time μ_X at the end of the first week is greater than 11 minutes and not to retrain him if μ_X is less than 11 minutes. At $\mu_X = 11$ minutes, the payoffs of the two acts are equal. Nevertheless, a discussion with management indicated that they would prefer not to retrain if $\mu_X = 11$ minutes, since retraining of an employee may involve some consequences (e.g., the employee's attitude may be affected) that are not fully reflected in the payoff function. Thus, the decision problem:

C_1 Do not retrain
C_2 Retrain

can be stated equivalently as:

C_1 $\mu_X \leq 11$ minutes
C_2 $\mu_X > 11$ minutes

Note that the reason for the equivalence of the two sets of alternatives is that the value of μ_X immediately determines which action is desired. Thus, we shall use C_1 and C_2 here either to denote respectively the *acts* "do not retrain," and "retrain," or to denote *conclusions* about the magnitude of the population characteristic, namely $\mu_X \leq 11$ and $\mu_X > 11$, respectively.

We have now restated the decision problem to involve alternatives based on the parameter of interest, i.e., the parameter affecting the payoff of the acts. Frequently, the statistical decision-making approach based on these alternatives is called *testing hypotheses,* since the two alternative conclusions C_1 and C_2 can be thought of as hypotheses about the true value of the parameter. Concluding C_1 is often called *accepting the null hypothesis,* and concluding C_2, *rejecting the null hypothesis.*

By convention, *we shall always label the alternative conclusion containing the equality sign as* C_1.

Setting up the alternative conclusions in terms of the parameter of interest can be done, as in our example, by explicit consideration of the payoff functions. If these cannot be developed explicitly, management would need to assess subjectively at what level of the parameter of interest the two acts have approximately equal consequences, and then set up the decision-problem alternatives accordingly.

Types of errors

As noted, the classical approach to statistical decision-making focuses on the errors in making decisions for purposes of controlling the risks of making such errors. We now consider the types of errors that can be made in a decision problem where a choice between two alternative courses of action or conclusions must be made. Again we refer to the Harold Aircraft Company example. Two types of errors can be made in the decision problem under consideration:

1. Being led by the decision rule to conclude that the mean time μ_X is greater than 11 minutes when actually the mean time μ_X is 11 minutes or less—this is called a *Type I error.*
2. Being led by the decision rule to conclude that the mean time μ_X is 11 minutes or less when actually μ_X is greater than 11 minutes—this is called a *Type II error.*

These two types of errors are illustrated in Table 16.1, which shows for each of the two possible sets of outcome states whether the conclusion reached is correct or incorrect.

Table 16.1 Illustration of Two Types of Errors

	Outcome State	
Conclusion Reached	$\mu_X \leq 11$	$\mu_X > 11$
C_1 $(\mu_X \leq 11)$	Correct conclusion	Type II error
C_2 $(\mu_X > 11)$	Type I error	Correct conclusion

In general, with the convention that alternative C_1 contains the equality sign (e.g., $C_1 : \mu_X \leq 11$ minutes):

(16.2) A ***Type I error*** is made when the decision rule leads to conclusion C_2 when the correct conclusion is C_1.

(16.3) A ***Type II error*** is made when the decision rule leads to conclusion C_1 when the correct conclusion is C_2.

Thus, in our illustration, the Type I error consists of retraining the employee when this is not necessary, and the Type II error consists of failing to retrain him when retraining is needed.

To determine the risks of making these two types of errors with a statistical decision rule, we first need to obtain the act probabilities for the decision rule.

16.4 ACT PROBABILITIES

We shall concentrate on decision rule A for our earlier example for purposes of explaining how to determine the act probabilities associated with a statistical decision rule. Recall that decision rule A, based on a simple random sample of 36 observations on the welding operation, is:

If $\overline{X} \leq 10$ minutes, do not retrain
If $\overline{X} > 10$ minutes, retrain

or equivalently:

If $\overline{X} \leq 10$ minutes, conclude C_1 $(\mu_X \leq 11)$
If $\overline{X} > 10$ minutes, conclude C_2 $(\mu_X > 11)$

Thus, the probability that $\overline{X}$ is 10 or less is the same as the probability that rule A leads to the act "do not retrain," or equivalently, to the conclusion that $\mu_X \leq 11$. The probability that $\overline{X}$ exceeds 10 is the same as the probability that rule A leads to the act "retrain," or equivalently, to the conclusion that $\mu_X > 11$. These probabilities depend upon the parameter of interest, the welder's mean required time μ_X in our example, and are called act probabilities.

(16.4) ***Act probabilities*** are the probabilities that a statistical decision rule leads to each of the two different acts, for the possible values of the parameter of interest.

These act probabilities are obtained from the sampling distribution of $\overline{X}$. We shall first review briefly the key theorems about the sampling distribution of $\overline{X}$ that we need to utilize.

Review of sampling distribution of $\overline{X}$

1. The central limit theorem states that the sampling distribution of $\overline{X}$ is approximately normal for reasonably large simple random samples. We assume here that the sample size of 36 observations required by decision rule A is sufficiently large for this approximation to apply, since the distribution of required times for the type of production operation considered here is usually not highly skewed.
2. It is also known that the standard deviation of the sampling distribution of $\overline{X}$ is a certain multiple of the population standard deviation, namely, $\sigma_{\overline{X}} = \sigma_X/\sqrt{n}$, when sampling a process, as we are doing here. We assume now that the standard deviation of the required times is known from past experience to be about $\sigma_X = 3$ minutes, and that it is fairly stable at this level over time. Hence, the standard deviation of the sampling distribution of $\overline{X}$ for our example, where $n = 36$, is $\sigma_{\overline{X}} = 3/\sqrt{36} = .5$ minutes.
3. We know that the mean of the sampling distribution of $\overline{X}$ is equal to the population mean μ_X, but μ_X is the unknown population characteristic involved in our decision problem.

Calculation of act probabilities

Act probabilities when $\mu_X = 8$ *minutes.* Figure 16.3 shows decision rule A in graphic form. Note that the act C_2 (to retrain, or equivalently, to conclude that $\mu_X > 11$) is to be followed whenever $\overline{X}$ exceeds 10 minutes, while the act C_1 (not to retrain, or equivalently, to conclude that $\mu_X \leq 11$) is to be followed whenever $\overline{X}$ is 10 minutes or less. Suppose now that the welder's mean required time at the end of the first week is $\mu_X = 8$ minutes; what then are the probabilities that rule A will lead to acts C_1 and C_2 respectively? Thus, we wish to obtain:

$$P(C_2;\ \mu_X = 8) = P(\overline{X} > 10;\ \mu_X = 8)$$

and:

$$P(C_1;\ \mu_X = 8) = P(\overline{X} \leq 10;\ \mu_X = 8)$$

Note that we write these probabilities in a manner that shows explicitly that they depend on the assumed value of μ_X. The semicolon is read as "given." Thus, $P(C_2;\ \mu_X = 8)$ is the probability that the rule leads to retraining, given that $\mu_X = 8$.

If $\mu_X = 8$ minutes, we know that the mean of the sampling distribution of $\overline{X}$ also would be 8 minutes; we already know that the standard deviation of the mean is $\sigma_{\overline{X}} = .5$ minutes and that the sampling distribution is approximately normal. This sampling distribution of $\overline{X}$ is shown at the top of Figure 16.3. Since we are led to C_1 whenever $\overline{X}$ is 10 minutes or less, the unshaded area in the distribution corresponds to the probability of being led by the rule to the act C_1, and the shaded area corresponds to the probability of being led to the act C_2. We can evaluate these probabilities in the usual manner.

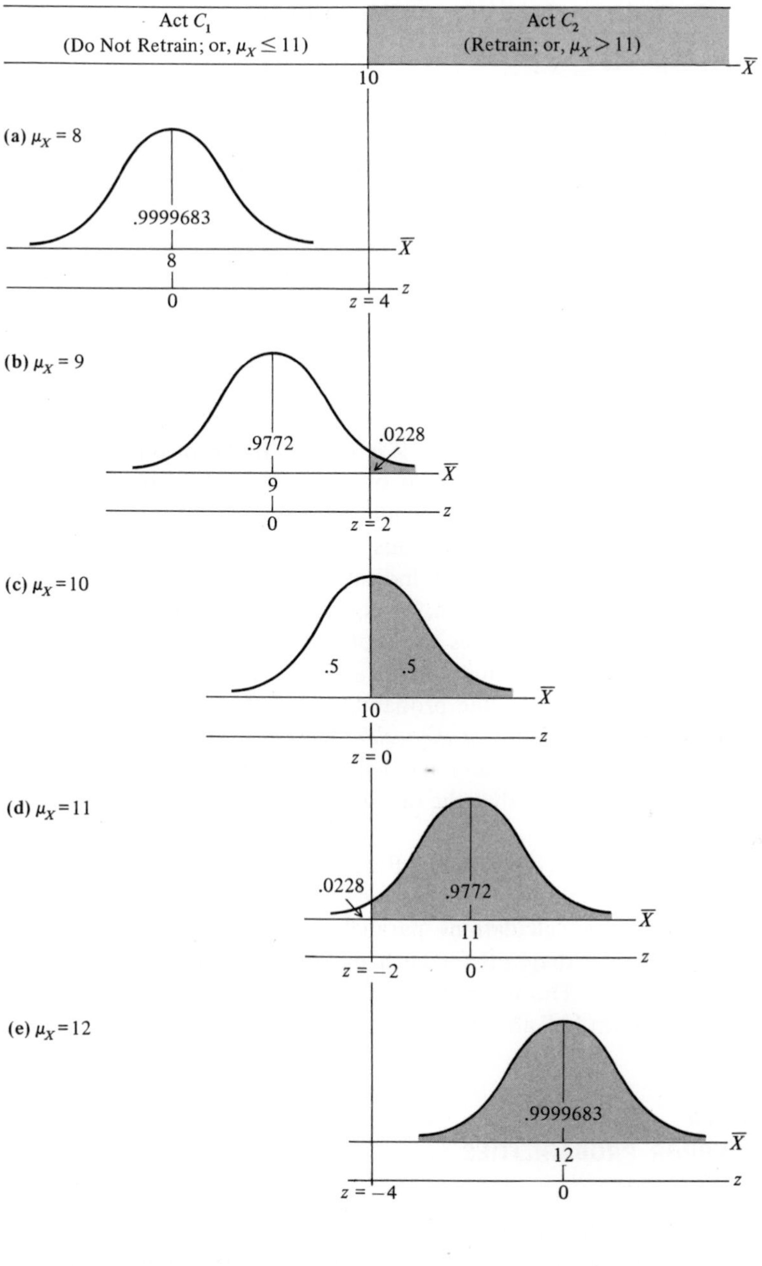

Figure 16.3. Illustrations of act probability calculations for decision rule A ($n = 36$; $\sigma_{\overline{X}} = 3/\sqrt{36} = .5$ minutes)

First, the z value corresponding to 10 minutes is:

$$z = \frac{\overline{X} - \mu_{\overline{X}}}{\sigma_{\overline{X}}} = \frac{\overline{X} - \mu_X}{\sigma_{\overline{X}}} = \frac{10 - 8}{.5} = 4$$

Table A-1 then indicates that the probability that $\overline{X}$ is 10 minutes or less is $.5 + .4999683 = .9999683$, *if the welder's mean time is 8 minutes*. Thus, the probability that decision rule A leads to C_1 is .9999683 when μ_X actually is 8 minutes. Consequently, the probability that $\overline{X}$ exceeds 10 minutes, or that the rule leads to C_2, is $1 - .9999683 = .0000317$, when $\mu_X = 8$ minutes.

Hence, we have:

$$P(C_1; \mu_X = 8) = .9999683$$
$$P(C_2; \mu_X = 8) = .0000317$$

Act probabilities when $\mu_X = 9$ minutes. If the mean required time for the welding operation at the end of the first week were $\mu_X = 9$ minutes, the sampling distribution of $\overline{X}$ would have a mean of 9 minutes, and $\sigma_{\overline{X}}$ is still assumed to be .5 minutes. This distribution also is shown in Figure 16.3. Again, the unshaded area indicates the probability that decision rule A leads to C_1 (do not retrain, or equivalently, conclude that $\mu_X \leq 11$), while the shaded area indicates the probability that the rule leads to C_2 (retrain, or equivalently, conclude that $\mu_X > 11$). The z value corresponding to 10 minutes is 2, so that the probability of $\overline{X}$ being 10 minutes or less is $.5 + .4772 = .9772$. Hence, *if the welder's mean time is 9 minutes*, the probability is .9772 that the decision rule leads to C_1. Consequently, the probability is $1 - .9772 = .0228$ that the decision rule leads to C_2 when $\mu_X = 9$ minutes.

Additional act probabilities. Figure 16.3 contains some additional illustrations of obtaining act probabilities, for the cases when $\mu_X = 10$, 11, and 12 minutes. The calculations parallel those described above. Note how the drawing of a diagram for each outcome state facilitates obtaining the act probabilities. The act probabilities obtained in Figure 16.3 are shown in tabular form in Table 16.2, columns (1) and (2).

16.5 ERROR PROBABILITIES

As noted, the evaluation of a decision rule in the classical approach to statistical decision-making is based on the probabilities that the decision rule will lead to the wrong conclusion in a given decision problem. These probabilities depend upon the parameter of interest (μ_X in our case).

(16.5) The probabilities of making incorrect decisions with a statistical decision rule, for different possible values of the parameter of interest, are called ***error probabilities*** or risks of making incorrect decisions.

Determination of error probabilities

Let us determine the error probabilities for decision rule A. As noted before, this rule, based on a sample of 36 observations, states:

If $\overline{X} \leq 10$ minutes, do not retrain
If $\overline{X} > 10$ minutes, retrain

or equivalently:

If $\overline{X} \leq 10$ minutes, conclude C_1 ($\mu_X \leq 11$)
If $\overline{X} > 10$ minutes, conclude C_2 ($\mu_X > 11$)

For this example, we saw earlier that the two types of error are:

1. Being led by the decision rule to conclude C_2, that the mean time μ_X is greater than 11 minutes, when actually C_1 holds, i.e., μ_X is 11 minutes or less—a Type I error.
2. Being led by the decision rule to conclude C_1, that the mean time μ_X is 11 minutes or less, when actually C_2 holds, i.e., μ_X is greater than 11 minutes—a Type II error.

The error probabilities for decision rule A can be determined readily from our earlier calculations of the act probabilities for this rule. Columns (1) and (2) of Table 16.2 contain the act probabilities for decision rule A. Consider the case where $\mu_X = 9$ minutes. We know from the payoff functions that when $\mu_X = 9$ minutes the correct act is C_1. Thus the error probability with rule A when $\mu_X = 9$ minutes is the probability that conclusion C_2 will be reached. This probability is seen to be .0228. As another example, when $\mu_X = 12$ minutes the correct conclusion is C_2. The probability of an error when $\mu_X = 12$ minutes is the probability of conclusion C_1—namely .0000317. Column (3) of Table 16.2 contains these and other error probabilities for decision rule A for selected values of μ_X.

Table 16.2 Act Probabilities and Error Probabilities for Decision Rule A

Outcome State	(1)	(2)	(3)
	Act Probability		*Error Probability*
μ_X	$P(C_1)$	$P(C_2)$	
8	.9999683	.0000317	.0000317
9	.9772	.0228	.0228
10	.5	.5	.5
11	.0228	.9772	.9772
12	.0000317	.9999683	.0000317

Note that the error probabilities are simply one or the other of the act probabilities, depending upon the value of μ_X. Also note that the sum of the two act probabilities is always 1, since one of the two acts must be selected with the decision rule. Thus, any one of the columns of Table 16.2 contains the essential information for evaluating decision rule A in terms of the risks of making errors inherent in following this rule. Either of the act probability columns provides this information indirectly, while the error probability column provides the information directly. In practice, each of the three columns is used at different times to describe graphically the error probability characteristics of a statistical decision rule, and we shall now discuss each of these three graphic presentations.

Power curve

Figure 16.4a presents the act probabilities for act C_2 (retrain) in the form of a graph, based on column (2) of Table 16.2. Remember that the act "retrain" is the equivalent of concluding that $\mu_X > 11$. On the X axis are the different possible values of the mean required time μ_X; the Y axis indicates the probability that the decision rule will lead to C_2. This curve is called the power curve of the decision rule and is frequently used as the vehicle for portraying the error probabilities.

(16.6) The ***power curve*** for a given decision rule shows the probability of choosing the conclusion or act designated as C_2, for different possible values of the parameter of interest.

The error probabilities for making Type I errors are shown directly by the power curve. For instance, if $\mu_X = 9.5$ minutes, we would like the decision rule to lead to C_1. The power curve indicates that decision rule A will lead to C_2 when $\mu_X = 9.5$ with probability .16. Thus, there is a risk of .16 of being led by the decision rule to retrain the employee when his mean required time μ_X for the operation is only 9.5 minutes. In the same way, the power curve indicates the probability of making a Type I error for other values of μ_X in the range $\mu_X \leq 11$ minutes—that is, in the range where C_1 should be chosen.

The probability of making a Type II error is indicated indirectly by the power curve. For instance, if $\mu_X = 11.2$ minutes, we would like the decision rule to lead to C_2. Figure 16.4a indicates that decision rule A in this case leads to C_2 with probability .992. Hence, the probability of concluding C_1 when μ_X is 11.2 minutes and hence C_2 is correct is .008. Thus, the risk with decision rule A of making a Type II error when $\mu_X = 11.2$ minutes is .008. Note from Figure 16.4a that the error probabilities for making Type II errors are shown by the power curve as the difference between 1 and the probability of C_2, when μ_X exceeds 11 minutes.

The power curve of decision rule A indicates that generally this rule will lead to the act "do not retrain" when μ_X is low, and to the act "retrain" when μ_X is high. Thus, decision rule A has generally desirable characteristics, though one may not be satisfied with the particular error probabilities that are inherent in this decision rule.

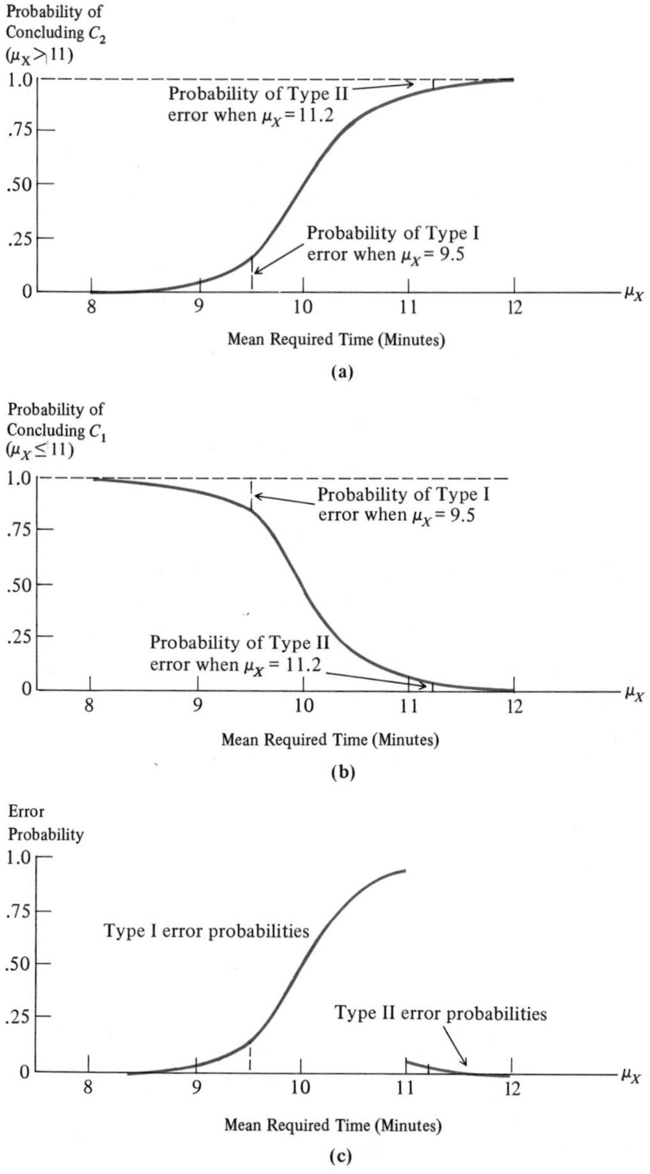

Figure 16.4. Power curve, operating-characteristic curve, and error curve for decision rule A

Operating-characteristic curve

Figure 16.4b contains the act probabilities for act C_1 (do not retrain) with decision rule A, based on column (1) of Table 16.2. Remember that the act "do not retrain" is the equivalent of concluding that $\mu_X \leq 11$. This curve is called the operating-characteristic curve of the decision rule.

(16.7) The ***operating-characteristic curve*** for a given decision rule shows the probability of choosing the conclusion or act designated as C_1, for different possible values of the parameter of interest.

Note that the operating-characteristic curve shows the Type II error probabilities directly and the Type I error probabilities indirectly. Note also that both the power curve and the operating-characteristic curve present the same information about the decision rule. Since only two acts are involved in the type of decision problem being considered, the act probabilities for one of the acts must be the complement of the act probabilities for the other act.

Error curve

Figure 16.4c shows the error probabilities for decision rule A directly, based on column (3) of Table 16.2. The Y axis indicates the error probability, and the X axis the different possible values of μ_X. To the left of $\mu_X = 11$ minutes are the probabilities of retraining the employee when retraining is not warranted. To the right are the probabilities of failing to retrain when retraining should be given. Note that the error probability curve is not affected by which act is designated as C_1. Only the labels as to type of error are affected. Given our designation that C_1 stands for the conclusion that $\mu_X \leq 11$ minutes, the portion of the curve to the left of $\mu_X = 11$ minutes shows the Type I error probabilities and the portion to the right of $\mu_X = 11$ minutes shows the Type II error probabilities. Of course, the error probabilities indicated in Figure 16.4c correspond to those indicated in Figures 16.4a and b. Note again from Figure 16.4c that the smaller μ_X is, the lower is the probability of making a Type I error with decision rule A; similarly, the larger μ_X is, the lower is the probability of making a Type II error with this decision rule.

16.6 APPROPRIATE TYPE OF DECISION RULE

We noted earlier that there are many ways to partition the sample space involving $\overline{X}$ such that for one part we conclude C_1 and for the other part we conclude C_2. Decision rule A is one such partition, and it has the reasonable property, as noted earlier, of tending to lead to retraining when μ_X is high and to no retraining when μ_X is low. Intuition tells us that for small values of $\overline{X}$ we should conclude C_1 and for large values of $\overline{X}$ we should conclude C_2. The reasonableness of this may be demonstrated by considering a reverse decision rule. Suppose we examine decision rule C, also based on 36 random observations:

If $\overline{X} \geq 12$ minutes, conclude C_1 ($\mu_X \leq 11$ minutes)
If $\overline{X} < 12$ minutes, conclude C_2 ($\mu_X > 11$ minutes)

Figure 16.5 contains the power curves for decision rules A and C. The power curve for decision rule C was obtained in the manner described earlier for decision rule A, but the detailed calculations are not shown. Figure 16.5 shows that the two power curves are equal at $\mu_X = 11$ minutes. For smaller values of μ_X, decision rule A involves smaller risks of Type I errors than does decision rule C. Similarly, for values of μ_X above 11 minutes, decision

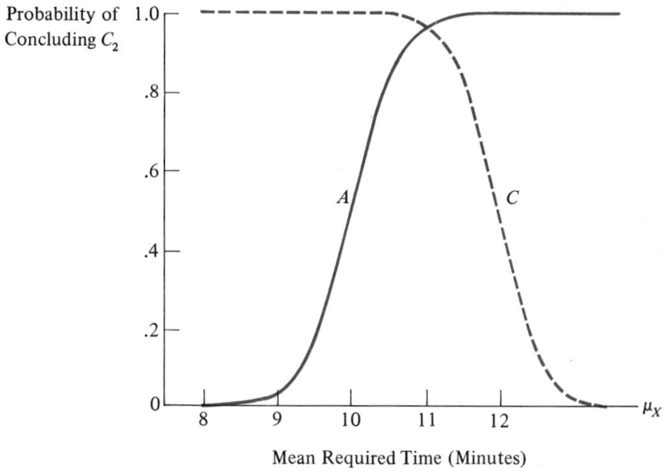

Figure 16.5. Power curves for decision rules A and C

rule A involves smaller risks of Type II errors. Thus, for $\mu_X = 11$ minutes, rule C performs as well as rule A, but for all other possible outcome states (for all other μ_X) it performs worse in terms of the magnitude of the error probabilities.

In Chapter 15, we developed the concept of inadmissibility of an act when its payoffs were compared with those of another act. Correspondingly:

16.8) A decision rule based on a given simple random sample size is ***inadmissible*** in terms of error probabilities if there exists another decision rule based on the same simple random sample size for which both the Type I and Type II error probabilities are never greater and for at least one outcome state are smaller.

By this definition, decision rule C is inadmissible because decision rule A has smaller error probabilities for all outcome states other than $\mu_X = 11$, for which the two decision rules perform equally well.

Indeed, it can be shown that for the decision problem:

C_1 $\quad \mu_X \leq 11$ minutes

C_2 $\quad \mu_X > 11$ minutes

a decision rule of the type:

If $\overline{X} \leq A$, conclude C_1
If $\overline{X} > A$, conclude C_2

has certain optimal properties. The term A in the decision rule is called the action limit.

(16.9) The ***action limit*** is the dividing point in the sample space between the values of the sample statistic ($\overline{X}$ in our example) leading to C_1 and the values leading to C_2.

In decision rule A, for instance, the action limit was 10 minutes.

16.7 EFFECT OF CHANGE IN ACTION LIMIT ON POWER CURVE OF RULE

Given that for our decision problem, the decision rule should be of the type where large values of $\overline{X}$ lead to conclusion C_2 and small values to conclusion C_1, what is the effect of the position of the action limit A on the error probabilities? To answer this question, we shall compare decision rules A and B:

Rule A	*Rule B*
If $\overline{X} \leq 10$, conclude C_1	If $\overline{X} \leq 11$, conclude C_1
If $\overline{X} > 10$, conclude C_2	If $\overline{X} > 11$, conclude C_2

Both these rules are based on a sample of 36 observations and differ only in that the action limit is 10 minutes in one instance and 11 minutes in the other.

Figure 16.6a contains the power curves for decision rules A and B. The power curve for decision rule B is derived in the same manner as that explained for decision rule A, but detailed calculations are not shown. Note that rule B is less likely than rule A to lead to C_2 (retrain) when the mean required time μ_X exceeds 11 minutes and retraining is warranted. However, rule B is also less likely than rule A to lead to C_2 when μ_X is less than 11 minutes and retraining is not warranted. Thus, decision rule B involves smaller risks of making Type I errors than rule A, but larger risks of making Type II errors. These same error probabilities are shown directly in Figure 16.6b.

This example illustrates the general principle that:

(16.10) With a given sample size, one type of risk can be reduced only at the expense of increasing the other type.

Intuitively, it seems reasonable that a sample of given size provides only a certain amount of information, and that the more one protects oneself

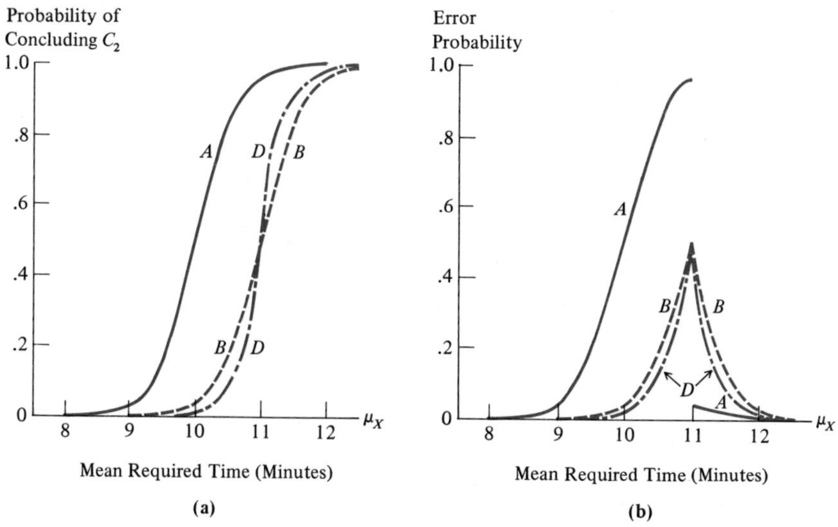

Figure 16.6. Power curves and error curves for decision procedures A, B, and D

against one type of risk of making an incorrect decision, the less protection is left against the other type of risk.

If we had moved the action limit below 10, incidentally, the risks of making Type II errors would have become smaller and the risks of making Type I errors larger.

16.8 EFFECT OF CHANGE IN SAMPLE SIZE ON POWER CURVE OF RULE

The only way in which one can reduce both types of risks simultaneously in this case is by increasing the sample size. As an illustration, consider decision-making procedure D:

> Select 81 random observations.
> If $\overline{X} \leq 11$, conclude C_1 $(\mu_X \leq 11)$
> If $\overline{X} > 11$, conclude C_2 $(\mu_X > 11)$

Note that this decision procedure has the same action limit as decision rule B but involves a sample size of 81 instead of 36.

Again, we shall compute the power curve of this decision-making procedure. Since the sample size is larger than in the earlier cases, we must recalculate the standard deviation of the mean $\sigma_{\overline{X}}$. We still assume that the standard deviation of the required times is about $\sigma_X = 3$ minutes; hence, the standard deviation of the sample mean for a simple random sample of size 81 is $\sigma_{\overline{X}} = \sigma_X/\sqrt{n} = 3/\sqrt{81} = .33$.

Now we proceed as before. Figure 16.7 indicates how to obtain the probabilities of concluding C_2 by following the decision procedure D, for various possible values of the mean required time μ_X. Note that the sampling dis-

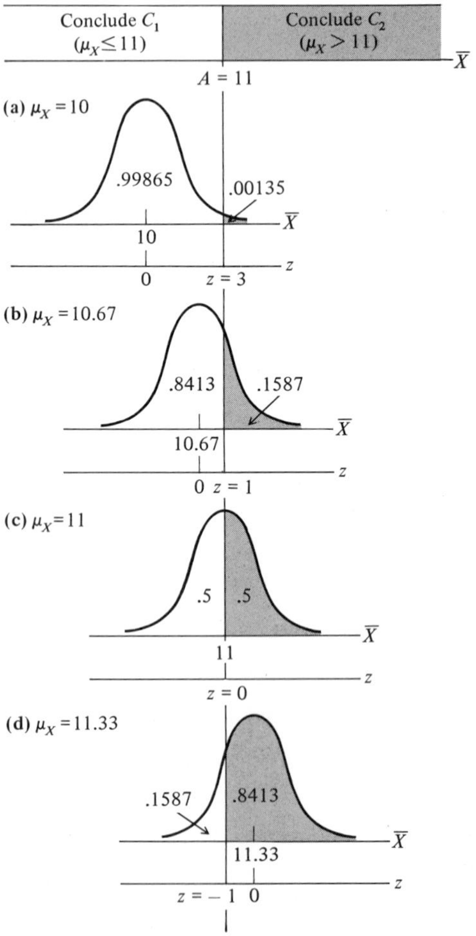

Figure 16.7. Illustrations of power probability calculations for decision procedure D ($n = 81$; $\sigma_{\overline{X}} = 3/\sqrt{81} = .33$ minutes)

tribution of $\overline{X}$ is more concentrated than in Figure 16.3 because of the larger sample size.

The power calculations are the same as described earlier. For instance, if $\mu_X = 10$ minutes, the z value of the action limit $A = 11$ minutes is $z = (11 - 10)/.33 = 3$. Hence, the probability that the sample mean $\overline{X}$ exceeds 11 minutes is $.5 - .49865 = .00135$. It therefore follows that the probability is .00135 that decision procedure D leads to C_2 when actually $\mu_X = 10$ minutes.

The power curve and error probabilities for decision-making procedure D are plotted in Figure 16.6. Compare now decision procedure B, based on a sample of 36 observations, with decision procedure D, based on a sample of 81 observations. Note that both procedures perform equally well when $\mu_X = 11$ minutes. If the mean required time μ_X is less than 11 minutes, however, decision procedure D embodies smaller risks of leading to C_2 (retrain) than decision procedure B. Again, if μ_X exceeds 11 minutes, decision procedure D involves smaller risks of leading to conclusion C_1 (do not retrain) than decision procedure B.

Here, then, is a clear illustration that:

(16.11) A simultaneous reduction in both types of risks of making incorrect decisions from a simple random sample can only be achieved by increasing the sample size (which is usually the equivalent of increasing the cost of making the decision).

16.9 CONTROL OF ERROR PROBABILITIES

Up to this point, we have considered statistical decision procedures that were arbitrarily arrived at, and examined the effect of changes in the action limit and sample size on the error probabilities inherent in the statistical decision rule. Our basic interest, however, is in the construction of statistical decision rules that embody error probabilities at reasonably low levels. The construction of statistical decision rules will be discussed in the next chapter. Here, however, we should note two important implications of the previous discussion on the construction of statistical decision rules with controlled error probabilities:

1. If the sample size is predetermined, the error probabilities for making *one* of the two types of incorrect decisions can be controlled at specified levels, but the error probabilities for making the other type of incorrect decision cannot be controlled.
2. If the risks of making *both* types of incorrect decisions are to be controlled, the sample size must not be fixed in advance but must be determined from the specifications on control of the error probabilities.

QUESTIONS AND PROBLEMS

16.1. Explain briefly each of the following:

a. Power curve
b. Type I error
c. Act probabilities
d. Statistical decision rule
e. Action limit

16.2. Distinguish briefly between:
a. Type I error and Type II error
b. Power curve, operating-characteristic curve, and error curve
c. Admissible and inadmissible decision rules
d. Statistical decision-making and decision-making under certainty (considered in Chapter 15)

16.3. For each of the following statistical decision problems: (1) specify the population parameter of interest, (2) state the alternative conclusions, C_1 and C_2, and (3) describe the Type I and Type II errors that are possible.
a. Because of inherent variability in filling 20-ounce cans with mixed vegetables, it is necessary for the process mean to be at least 20.5 ounces so that the proportion of underweight cans is kept reasonably small. A simple random sample of cans is to be selected from the process to decide whether the filling process is operating at the appropriate level.
b. A market study for a new industrial product with special installation problems indicates that annual sales per customer must average at least 2.3 units for it to be profitable. Advance orders for the new product are to be obtained from a simple random sample of customers to determine the product's sales potential.
c. The mean donation per contributor to the Community Appeal was \$8.59 prior to the initiation of a new public relations program aimed at making the community more aware of the social services sponsored by the Appeal. A simple random sample of donations received while the new public relations program was in effect is to be used to decide whether the new program was worthwhile or not.

***16.4.** Refer to Figure 16.6 (p. 345). Consider decision rules A, B, and D as the set of decision rules of interest.
a. Are all three decision rules admissible in terms of error probabilities? Explain fully.
b. Which decision rule minimizes the maximum error probability?
c. Which decision rule minimizes the maximum Type II error probability?

16.5. The traffic department of a city converted several major avenues to one-way traffic. Vehicle accident statistics for the first year after conversion showed that accidents on these one-way streets had fallen by 3 per cent, as compared with the last year when two-way traffic operated on these streets. This drop occurred despite the fact that overall volume, speed, and composition of traffic on these streets had remained the same during the two-year period. Can it be concluded with assurance, therefore, that one-way operations on these streets lead to fewer accidents than two-way operations under the traffic conditions prevailing during this two-year period? Discuss.

16.6. A business statistician stated that statistical estimation frequently is more useful than statistical decision-making, that the practical significance of a conclusion reached from a statistical decision rule often must be evaluated by statistical estimation, and that business problems frequently cannot be forced into the framework required for statistical decision-making.
a. Discuss each of the points made by the business statistician. How valid is each?
b. Describe three business situations in which statistical estimation is appropriate.
c. Describe three business situations in which statistical decision-making is appropriate.

***16.7.** The Morgan Steel Company wishes to control the production of cold rolled steel bars with respect to the length of the bars. The payoff is affected by the process mean length. If this is too low, many bars are short and must be scrapped. If the mean length is too high, many bars are long and must be cut. The production process can be stopped and adjusted, but this involves considerable cost because of lost production. The company plans to select a simple random sample of 36 bars every two hours, on the basis of which it wishes to decide whether to leave the process alone for the next two hours (C_1), or to stop and adjust the process (C_2). The payoffs for the two acts (net of sampling costs) are as follows for a number of outcome states:

μ_X	*Act* C_1	*Act* C_2
30.6 feet	\$ 600	\$800
30.7	650	800
30.8	800	800
30.9	900	800
31.0	1,000	800
31.1	920	800
31.2	870	800
31.3	870	800

The process standard deviation of the lengths of the steel bars is inherent in the production process, and is known from past experience to be $\sigma_X = .6$ feet. Assume that the dollar payoffs reflect properly the relative desirability to the company of the different outcomes.

a. At what value of μ_X do the two acts have equal payoffs?

b. State the acts C_1 and C_2 in the form of alternative conclusions about μ_X.

c. Suppose the company is adopting the following decision rule, based on a simple random sample of 36 bars:

If $\bar{X} \geq 30.8$ feet, leave the process alone (C_1)

If $\bar{X} < 30.8$ feet, stop and adjust the process (C_2)

Determine the act probabilities and error probabilities for this decision rule for each of the outcome states given above.

d. Suppose the decision rule, based on a sample of 36 bars, were:

If $\bar{X} \geq 31.1$ feet, select act C_1

If $\bar{X} < 31.1$ feet, select act C_2

Determine the act probabilities and error probabilities for this decision rule for each of the outcome states given above.

e. For the decision rules in parts **c** and **d**, and for the set of outcome states given:

(1) Is either decision rule inadmissible? Explain.

(2) Which decision rule gives the greater protection against a Type I error? Against a Type II error? Explain.

16.8. A firm periodically receives large shipments of rough shafts that require machining to fine tolerances. The firm is faced with the decision problem as to whether to do the machining in the house (C_1), or to subcontract it out at a fixed price (C_2). The payoff to the firm is affected by the mean weight of the rough shafts in the shipment, since this largely determines the amount of metal to be removed. The payoffs for the two acts (net of sampling costs) are as follows for a number of outcome states:

μ_X	*Act* C_1	*Act* C_2
26.1 pounds	\$5,200	\$4,800
26.2	5,100	4,800
26.3	5,000	4,800
26.4	4,900	4,800
26.5	4,800	4,800
26.6	4,700	4,800
26.7	4,500	4,800
26.8	4,200	4,800

The standard deviation of shaft weights is known from past experience to be $\sigma_X = .63$ pounds. Assume that the dollar payoffs reflect properly the relative desirability to the firm of the different outcomes.

a. At what value of μ_X do the two acts have equal payoffs?

b. State the acts C_1 and C_2 in the form of alternative conclusions about μ_X.

c. Suppose the firm plans to select a simple random sample of 49 shafts, and to use the following decision rule:

If $\bar{X} \leq 26.6$ pounds, do the machining in the house (C_1)

If $\bar{X} > 26.6$ pounds, subcontract the machining out (C_2)

Determine the act probabilities and error probabilities for this decision rule for each of the outcome states given above.

d. Suppose the decision rule, based on a sample of 49 shafts, were:

If $\bar{X} \leq 26.4$ pounds, select act C_1

If $\bar{X} > 26.4$ pounds, select act C_2

Determine the act probabilities and error probabilities for this decision rule for each of the outcome states given above.

e. For the decision rules in parts **c** and **d**, and for the set of outcome states given:

(1) Is either decision rule inadmissible? Explain.

(2) Which decision rule gives the greater protection against a Type I error? Against a Type II error? Explain.

***16.9.** A police department is concerned with the waiting time from the moment a person telephones until he is connected with a staff officer. In the past, the mean waiting time has been $\mu_X = 19$ seconds. A new switchboard arrangement has been set up with the intent of reducing the mean waiting time. The department wishes to sample calls under the new conditions to decide whether the new arrangement is effective or not. Thus, the alternatives in the decision problem are:

C_1 $\quad \mu_X \geq 19$ seconds

C_2 $\quad \mu_X < 19$ seconds

A sample of 64 calls is to be checked, and the following decision rule employed:

If $\bar{X} \geq 18$ seconds, conclude C_1

If $\bar{X} < 18$ seconds, conclude C_2

The process standard deviation of waiting times is known to be $\sigma_X = 8$ seconds.

a. Calculate the ordinates of the power curve for this decision-making procedure for the following possible values of the process mean waiting time: 14, 15, 16, 17, 18, 19, 20, 21 seconds.

b. What is the maximum risk of making a Type II error for this decision-making procedure, assuming that the department wants assurance of being notified if a decrease has occurred in the process mean waiting time of 2 seconds or more? Is this risk an acceptable one? Discuss.

c. What is a Type I error in this case? Does the decision-making procedure provide adequate protection against making this type of error? Explain.

d. Suppose that the action limit in the decision rule were changed to 17 seconds, with no change in sample size. Calculate the ordinates of the power curve for this new decision-making procedure for the same possible values of the process mean waiting time as in part **a**.

e. Plot the power curves in parts **a** and **d** on the same graph. On another graph, plot the error curves for the decision rules being compared. What effect did the change in the action limit have? Explain fully. What generalization does this suggest?

f. If you had also obtained the operating-characteristic curves for the two decision rules, would these have provided any more information about the effectiveness of the decision rules than the power curves? Discuss.

16.10. Refer to Problem 16.9.

a. Suppose that the sample size were increased to 144 observations, with the action limit still at 17, as it is in Problem 16.9**d**. Calculate the ordinates of the power curve for this new decision-making procedure for the same possible values of the process mean waiting time as in Problem 16.9**a**.

b. Plot the power curves in part **d** of Problem 16.9 and part **a** of this problem on the same graph. What effect did the increase in sample size have on the power curve? What generalization is suggested by this effect?

c. What effect does a change in the population standard deviation have on the power curve of a decision-making procedure, for given action limit and sample size? Does this effect resemble that of either a change in the action limit or a change in the sample size? Explain.

16.11. A purchasing agent for a cafeteria chain purchases broiling chickens in very large shipments from a vendor. He specified that the mean weight of broilers in a shipment should be at least 32.0 ounces. From past experience, it is known that the standard deviation of the weight of broilers supplied by this vendor is 1.5 ounces. It is suggested to the purchasing agent that he adopt the following decision-making procedure: Select a simple random sample of 196 broilers from each shipment. If the mean weight of the broilers in the sample is 31.7 ounces or more, accept the shipment; if the mean weight is less than 31.7 ounces, reject the shipment—that is, seek a price reduction or take other appropriate action.

a. Calculate the ordinates of the power curve for this decision-making procedure for the following possible mean weights in the shipment: 31.4, 31.6, 31.7, 31.8, 32.0, 32.1, 32.2 ounces.

b. Plot this power curve on a graph.

c. Plot the error curve for this decision rule on another graph. Does this curve provide any information additional to that given by the power curve in part **b**? Explain.

d. On each of the charts in parts **b** and **c**:

(1) Show the maximum risk of making a Type I error. What is the magnitude of this risk?

(2) Show the risk of making a Type II error when the population mean is 31.5 ounces. What is the magnitude of this risk?

e. What is a Type I error in this decision problem? A Type II error? Does the suggested decision-making procedure provide adequate protection against making these errors? Explain.

16.12. Refer to Problem 16.11.

a. Suppose that the action limit in the decision rule were changed to 32.0 ounces, with no change in the sample size. Calculate the ordinates of the power curve for this new decision-making procedure for the same possible values of the shipment mean as in Problem 16.11**a**.

b. Plot the power curve in part **a** on the same graph as the one in Problem 16.11**b**. What effect did the change in the action limit have on the power curve? What generalization does this suggest?

c. Suppose that the sample size was only 90 broilers, with the action limit remaining at 31.7 ounces, as in the original decision rule. Calculate the ordinates of the power curve for this new decision-making procedure for the same possible values of the shipment mean as in Problem 16.11**a**.

d. Plot the power curve in part **c** on the same graph as the one in Problem 16.11**b**. What effect did the reduction in sample size have on the power curve? What generalization is suggested by this effect?

Chapter

17

STATISTICAL DECISION-MAKING CONCERNING POPULATION MEAN

In Chapter 16, we introduced the basic ideas of statistical decision-making, and explained the concept of a statistical decision rule and how to determine the risks of making incorrect decisions inherent in the rule. In the present chapter, we show how to construct decision rules in statistical decision problems involving an unknown population mean such that the error probabilities are controlled at specified levels.

17.1 CONSTRUCTION OF DECISION RULE TO CONTROL TYPE I ERRORS

In this section, we take up the case where:

1. The sample is a large simple random one.
2. The sample size has been predetermined.
3. The risks of making Type I errors are to be controlled, and the risks of making Type II errors are to remain uncontrolled.

We shall continue to use the example of the Harold Aircraft Company, dealing with the retraining of an employee after one week's work on a job lot. The steps involved in constructing an appropriate statistical decision rule are examined below.

Step 1—statement of alternatives

As explained in the previous chapter (p. 333), management wishes to consider the following two alternatives:

C_1 $\mu_X \leq 11$ minutes (do not retrain)
C_2 $\mu_X > 11$ minutes (retrain)

Step 2—desired type of power curve

For this set of alternatives, the desired type of power curve is that shown in Figure 17.1a. If the employee's mean required time μ_X at the end of the first week is low, management wishes to have a small probability of concluding C_2; if the mean time is high, management would like a high probability of concluding C_2.

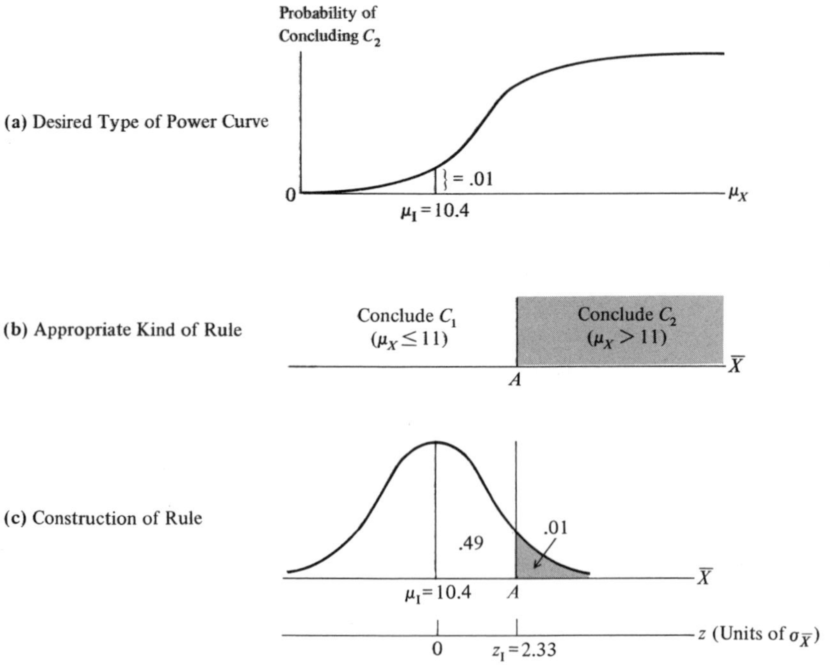

Figure 17.1. Steps in the construction of decision rule when Type I error controlled

Step 3—choice of appropriate kind of decision rule

From our earlier work, it is known that the appropriate kind of decision rule for this decision problem, yielding the desired type of power curve, is that shown in Figure 17.1b. There is no need, however, to memorize the appropriate kind of decision rule, because common sense will indicate the right approach here. As long as the sample mean $\bar{X}$ is small, we shall conclude C_1 ($\mu_X \leq 11$). If, however, the value of $\bar{X}$ is high, we shall conclude C_2 ($\mu_X > 11$).

Step 4—specification of risk of making Type I error

The Harold Aircraft Company determined in advance that 36 random observations were to be made on the welding operation at the end of the first week. Since the sample size was predetermined, the risks of only one of the two types of incorrect decisions can be controlled in the construction of the decision rule. To decide which of the two types is to be controlled, management should, whenever possible, make at least some rough evaluation of the payoff functions for each of the two acts, as was done explicitly in Figure 16.1, p. 330. On the basis of this evaluation, management is in a better position to choose which type of incorrect decision to control than it is without this evaluation. The choice is essentially a judgmental one, however. Management may consider the differences in payoffs, the levels of each of the payoff functions, or other characteristics of the payoff functions. Management also may use some judgment as to the range in which it would expect μ_X to fall, as well as other relevant information it has available.

Suppose that management has decided it wishes to control the risks of retraining when there is no need to retrain. In other words, management wants to control the risks of concluding C_2 when C_1 is the correct conclusion, that is, the risks of a Type I error. Specifically, management has indicated that if the mean required time μ_X is 10.4 minutes or less, it is willing to accept a maximum error probability of .01 of concluding C_2 (retrain). Since the power curve continuously decreases as μ_X becomes smaller, this risk specification is equivalent to: If $\mu_X = 10.4$ minutes, the probability of concluding C_2 is to be .01. This specified risk of an incorrect decision is indicated on the desired power curve in Figure 17.1a. Note that in effect management specified a point on the power curve.

(17.1) The specified risk of making a Type I error is frequently called the *level of significance.*

Why would management wish to control the risk of making a Type I error at $\mu_X = 10.4$ minutes instead of at some value of μ_X closer to the indifference point in payoffs, namely $\mu_X = 11$ minutes? The reason lies in management's assessment of the payoff functions shown in Figure 16.1 and of other factors entering the decision problem. For instance, at $\mu_X = 10.8$ minutes, the payoff for act C_1 (do not retrain), though higher than that for act C_2 (retrain), was not sufficiently higher in management's judgment to make management concerned if conclusion C_2 were reached. If, however, the mean time μ_X were as low as 10.4 minutes or less, management would wish to control at a specified low level the error probabilities of concluding C_2 (retrain) since here conclusion C_1 leading to no retraining is strongly preferable in their judgment.

Step 5—determination of action limit

Since the sample size has been fixed in advance at $n = 36$, the only remaining parameter of the statistical decision rule is the action limit A. We wish to determine the value of A so as to meet management's specification on controlling the risks of Type I errors. Since management's specification pertained to the situation when $\mu_X = 10.4$ minutes, we must consider the sampling distribution of $\overline{X}$ in that case.

If $\mu_X = 10.4$ minutes, the sampling distribution of $\overline{X}$ is centered around $\mu_{\overline{X}} = 10.4$ minutes, as shown in Figure 17.1c. Since the sample size is reasonably large, the sampling distribution of $\overline{X}$ is approximately normal. The shaded area in Figure 17.1c indicates the probability of concluding C_2 by following the decision rule when $\mu_X = 10.4$ minutes. This probability was specified by management to be .01.

Note the correspondence and difference from the calculations of the power curve of a given decision rule made in the last chapter. Then, the action limit was given, and we had to find the probability that $\overline{X}$ would fall above the action limit. Now, this probability is provided by the management specification, and we must determine the appropriate value of the action limit so that the shaded area will equal .01.

From Table A-1, we must determine the z value such that the area between the mean and the action limit is .49. This z value is 2.33. Therefore, the action limit is 2.33 standard deviations ($\sigma_{\overline{X}}$, because we are referring to the sampling distribution of $\overline{X}$) above 10.4 minutes; in other words, $A = 10.4 + 2.33\ \sigma_{\overline{X}}$.

Usually, $\sigma_{\overline{X}}$ is unknown so that the determination of the action limit cannot be completed until a sample estimate of $\sigma_{\overline{X}}$ is obtained.

Step 6—completion of statistical decision rule

At this point, we must await the sample results before the statistical decision rule can be completed. Suppose that the 36 random observations were made, and the sample mean and sample standard deviation were as follows:

$$\overline{X} = 9.63 \text{ minutes}$$
$$s_X = 2.22 \text{ minutes}$$

($\overline{X}$ and s_X were calculated in the usual manner from the original 36 observations, not presented here.)

We can therefore estimate $\sigma_{\overline{X}}$ as usual: $s_{\overline{X}} = s_X/\sqrt{n} = 2.22/\sqrt{36} = .37$ minutes. Remember that a process is being sampled, so that a finite correction factor is not involved.

Hence, we obtain the action limit A:

$$A = 10.4 + 2.33\ s_{\overline{X}} = 10.4 + 2.33(.37) = 11.26 \text{ minutes}$$

Our decision rule, based on the 36 observations, then is as follows:

If $\overline{X} \leq 11.26$, conclude C_1 ($\mu_X \leq 11$ minutes)
If $\overline{X} > 11.26$, conclude C_2 ($\mu_X > 11$ minutes)

Step 7—application of decision rule

Since the sample mean of the 36 observations was $\overline{X} = 9.63$ minutes, the above decision rule leads us to the conclusion C_1, that the welder's mean time is 11 minutes or less. Hence, management should not retrain the welder.

Properties of constructed decision rule

Type I error probabilities. The decision rule just utilized was so constructed that the probability of concluding C_2 when $\mu_X = 10.4$ minutes is about .01. To put this another way, the maximum risk of being led by the decision rule to conclude C_2 when the mean time μ_X is actually 10.4 minutes or less is about .01.

It should be noted that this maximum risk of making a Type I error is only approximate. The reason is that the use of the normal distribution in constructing the decision rule is only an approximation. Recall that theorem (12.8) indicates that $(\overline{X} - \mu_{\overline{X}})/s_{\overline{X}}$ is *approximately* normal for large sample sizes. Usually, however, the approximation is close for large sample sizes.

Type II error probabilities. A major limitation of a statistical decision rule constructed for an arbitrarily determined sample size is the lack of control over both types of risks of making incorrect decisions. In our example, the decision rule had a specified maximum risk of concluding that retraining was needed when actually the mean required time μ_X was 10.4 minutes or less; the maximum risk of this Type I error was set at .01. However, there was no control over the risks of Type II errors, namely failing to retrain when retraining is needed. With an arbitrary sample size, these latter risks might be satisfactorily small, or they might not; one simply cannot control both types of risks when the sample size is arbitrarily predetermined.

We can estimate the probability that the decision rule constructed will lead to conclusion C_2 $(\mu_X > 11)$ when μ_X does exceed 11 minutes. Note that only estimates of these power probabilities are possible since the population standard deviation σ_X is unknown. Suppose the mean required time μ_X actually were 11.5 minutes. In that case, the probability that $\overline{X}$ exceeds the action limit of 11.26 minutes (so that the decision rule leads to conclusion C_2) is about .74, using the sample estimate $s_{\overline{X}} = .37$ in place of $\sigma_{\overline{X}}$. Thus, if $\mu_X = 11.5$ minutes, there is a probability of about .26 that our decision rule based on a random sample of 36 observations will not lead to conclusion C_2 and thus will fail to lead to retraining. This probability might be intolerably high or tolerable, depending upon the circumstances.

Suppose that such a risk is much too high. Then the decision rule is not a satisfactory one, even though the risks of making Type I errors were controlled at a satisfactory level. For a fixed simple random sample size, we know that the risks of a Type II error can be *reduced* only by *increasing* the risks of a Type I error. Hence, it is apparent that it generally is not desirable to determine the sample size arbitrarily because then only one of the two types of risks of incorrect decisions can be controlled. Rather, one first should specify the permissible risks of making both types of incorrect decisions and then determine the sample size necessary to achieve these requirements. This approach is discussed below.

Recapitulation

We now summarize the procedure in constructing the statistical decision rule for the type of decision problem considered above. The alternative conclusions are of the type:

$$\begin{array}{ll} C_1 & \mu_X \leq \mu_0 \\ C_2 & \mu_X > \mu_0 \end{array} \tag{17.2}$$

Here μ_0 is the indifference level, level of past experience, standard, or the like. In our example, μ_0 was 11 minutes, the indifference level between no retraining and retraining. A decision problem of the type in (17.2) is called a *one-sided alternative* problem; specifically it is called an *upper-tail* problem because the decision rule will require large values of $\overline{X}$ (the upper end of the $\overline{X}$ scale) to lead to conclusion C_2.

The appropriate type of decision rule for this kind of problem is:

$$\begin{array}{l} \text{If } \overline{X} \leq A, \text{ conclude } C_1 \\ \text{If } \overline{X} > A, \text{ conclude } C_2 \end{array}$$

where A is the action limit.

To determine the value of the action limit, we utilize the specification on risks of making incorrect decisions. For the case considered, the risks being controlled pertain to making Type I errors. For a given level of μ_X, denoted by μ_I, the risk of concluding C_2 is specified. In our example, μ_I was 10.4 minutes, and the probability of concluding C_2 in that case was to be controlled at the level .01. The value of μ_I is determined according to where in the scale of possible outcome states (μ_X) it becomes important to control Type I errors. In some problems, the Type I error may be controlled at the level μ_0, so that in these cases $\mu_I = \mu_0$.

The action limit is then obtained by considering the sampling distribution of $\overline{X}$ when $\mu_X = \mu_I$. The action limit is a certain number of standard deviations ($\sigma_{\overline{X}}$) above μ_I, as determined by the z value corresponding to the specified risk of an incorrect decision; we denote this z value by z_I. The standard deviation of $\overline{X}$ ($\sigma_{\overline{X}}$) is estimated from $s_{\overline{X}}$, and the action limit therefore is: $A = \mu_I + z_I s_{\overline{X}}$.

Formally, we can write the decision rule as:

$$\begin{array}{l} \text{If } \overline{X} \leq \mu_I + z_I s_{\overline{X}}, \text{ conclude } C_1\ (\mu_X \leq \mu_0) \\ \text{If } \overline{X} > \mu_I + z_I s_{\overline{X}}, \text{ conclude } C_2\ (\mu_X > \mu_0) \end{array} \tag{17.3}$$

Here z_I is the standard normal deviate associated with the specified risk of concluding C_2 when $\mu_X = \mu_I$.

In our previous case, the decision rule was:

If $\overline{X} \leq 10.4 + 2.33(.37)$, conclude C_1 ($\mu_X \leq 11$)
If $\overline{X} > 10.4 + 2.33(.37)$, conclude C_2 ($\mu_X > 11$)

where 2.33 is the z_{I} value associated with the specified risk of .01 of concluding C_2 when $\mu_X = 10.4$ minutes.

The reader need not rely on (17.3) mechanically. If he understands the basic steps involved in constructing a statistical decision rule, he will have no trouble in reasoning through to the actual rule to be employed. This will prevent a number of mistakes that can occur from a mechanical reliance on formulas.

17.2 CONSTRUCTION OF DECISION RULE TO CONTROL TYPE II ERRORS

We now consider the case where:

1. The sample is a large simple random one.
2. The sample size has been predetermined.
3. The risks of making Type II errors are to be controlled, and the risks of Type I errors are to remain uncontrolled.

Again, we use the example of the Harold Aircraft Company. Steps 1, 2, and 3, dealing with the statement of alternatives, desired type of power curve, and choice of appropriate kind of decision rule, are unchanged. Figure 17.2a indicates again the desired type of power curve, and Figure 17.2b the appropriate kind of decision rule.

Step 4—specification of risk of making Type II error

Suppose now that management felt it more important to control the risks of failing to retrain the welder when retraining is needed—that is, the risks of making Type II errors. In particular, suppose that management assessed the payoff functions and other aspects of the decision problem, and concluded that it is important to have a maximum error probability of .05 of concluding C_1 (do not retrain) if the welder's mean time μ_X is 11.5 minutes or higher. Thus, management specifies that for a point on the power curve, namely $\mu_X = 11.5$, the probability of concluding C_2 should be $1 - .05 = .95$. The specified risk is indicated in Figure 17.2a.

Step 5—determination of action limit

Now, in the same manner as before, we determine the action limit A. We consider the sampling distribution of $\overline{X}$ when $\mu_X = 11.5$. In that case, the

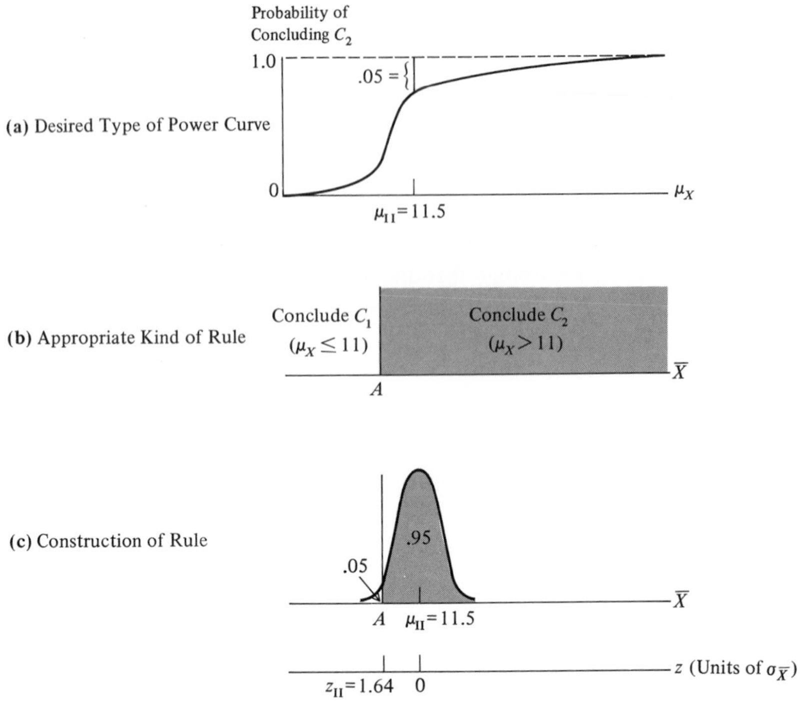

Figure 17.2. Steps in the construction of decision rule when Type II error controlled

sampling distribution of $\overline{X}$ is centered around $\mu_{\overline{X}} = 11.5$, as shown in Figure 17.2c. Since the sample size is reasonably large, the sampling distribution is approximately normal. The unshaded area in Figure 17.2c indicates the probability of concluding C_1 by following the decision rule when $\mu_X = 11.5$ minutes. This probability was specified by management to be controlled at the level .05.

From Table A-1, we determine the z value such that the area below the action limit is .05. This z value is 1.64. Therefore, the action limit A is 1.64 standard deviations ($\sigma_{\overline{X}}$) below 11.5; in other words, $A = 11.5 - 1.64\sigma_{\overline{X}}$.

Step 6—completion of statistical decision rule

Again, one usually must await the sample results in order to obtain an estimate of $\sigma_{\overline{X}}$. Utilizing the estimate $s_{\overline{X}} = .37$ minutes as before, we have:

$$A = 11.5 - 1.64s_{\overline{X}} = 11.5 - 1.64(.37) = 10.89 \text{ minutes}$$

Thus, our decision rule based on 36 observations is:

If $\overline{X} \leq 10.89$, conclude C_1 ($\mu_X \leq 11$ minutes)
If $\overline{X} > 10.89$, conclude C_2 ($\mu_X > 11$ minutes)

Step 7—application of decision rule

Since $\overline{X} = 9.63$ minutes (see p. 356), the above decision rule would again lead to conclusion C_1, that the welder's mean time is 11 minutes or less and that therefore he should not be retrained.

Recapitulation

The alternative conclusions and the appropriate type of decision rule are the same whether the risks of Type I or Type II incorrect decisions are being controlled.

If the risks of Type II errors are being controlled, a level of μ_X, denoted by μ_{II}, is specified for which the probability of concluding C_1 is to be controlled. In our example, $\mu_{II} = 11.5$ minutes, and the probability of concluding C_1 in that case was to be controlled at .05. The value of μ_{II} again must be determined according to where it is important to control Type II errors.

The action limit then is obtained by considering the sampling distribution of $\overline{X}$ when $\mu_X = \mu_{II}$. The action limit is a certain number of standard deviations ($\sigma_{\overline{X}}$) below μ_{II}, as determined by the z value corresponding to the specified risk of an incorrect decision; we denote this z value by z_{II}. The standard deviation of $\overline{X}$ ($\sigma_{\overline{X}}$) is estimated from $s_{\overline{X}}$, and the decision rule therefore is:

$$\begin{aligned} &\text{If } \overline{X} \leq \mu_{II} - z_{II}s_{\overline{X}}, \text{ conclude } C_1\ (\mu_X \leq \mu_0) \\ &\text{If } \overline{X} > \mu_{II} - z_{II}s_{\overline{X}}, \text{ conclude } C_2\ (\mu_X > \mu_0) \end{aligned} \tag{17.4}$$

Here z_{II} is the standard normal deviate associated with the specified risk of concluding C_1 when $\mu_X = \mu_{II}$.

In our example, the decision rule was:

$$\begin{aligned} &\text{If } \overline{X} \leq 11.5 - 1.64(.37), \text{ conclude } C_1\ (\mu_X \leq 11) \\ &\text{If } \overline{X} > 11.5 - 1.64(.37), \text{ conclude } C_2\ (\mu_X > 11) \end{aligned}$$

where 1.64 is the z_{II} value associated with the risk of .05 of concluding C_1 when $\mu_X = 11.5$ minutes.

17.3 CONTROL OF BOTH TYPES OF RISKS THROUGH SAMPLE SIZE DETERMINATION

If the sample size is not predetermined, one can specify permissible risks of making *both* types of incorrect decisions and determine the sample size needed to achieve these requirements. *The procedure to be presented in this section is applicable if the necessary sample size turns out to be reasonably large.*

Again, we use the Harold Aircraft Company example to explain the procedure for controlling both types of risks of incorrect decisions. Steps 1 through 3, relating to statement of alternatives, desired type of power curve, and choice of appropriate kind of decision rule, are unchanged.

Step 4—specification of risks of making Type I and Type II errors

Suppose now that management of the Harold Aircraft Company had not decided in advance on the number of observations to be taken on the welding operation, and that it wished to control both types of risks of making incorrect decisions. Specifically, assume that management wants to control the risks of Type I errors by specifying that if $\mu_X = 10.4$ minutes, the probability of concluding C_2 ($\mu_X > 11$) should be .01. Also, it wants to control the risks of Type II errors by specifying that if $\mu_X = 11.5$ minutes, the probability of concluding C_1 ($\mu_X \leq 11$) should be .05. These requirements on the power curve are shown in Figure 17.3a. Figure 17.3b shows the appropriate kind of decision rule for this problem.

Step 5—determination of sample size

Figure 17.3c contains the sampling distribution of $\overline{X}$ when $\mu_X = \mu_{\text{I}} =$ 10.4 minutes, and when $\mu_X = \mu_{\text{II}} = 11.5$ minutes. The shaded area of the upper tail of the distribution when $\mu_X = \mu_{\text{I}} = 10.4$ minutes corresponds to the risk of concluding C_2; this shaded area is to be .01. The shaded part of the lower tail in the distribution when $\mu_X = \mu_{\text{II}} = 11.5$ minutes corresponds to the risk of concluding C_1; this shaded area is to be .05. The z value for the action limit A when $\mu_X = \mu_{\text{I}}$, denoted by z_{I}, is 2.33 (area .01 in the tail). The z value for the action limit A when $\mu_X = \mu_{\text{II}}$, denoted by z_{II}, is 1.64 (area .05 in the tail). *Note that both z_{I} and z_{II} are taken to be positive.*

We can write the following two simultaneous equations for A:

$$A = \mu_{\text{I}} + z_{\text{I}}\sigma_{\overline{X}}$$
$$A = \mu_{\text{II}} - z_{\text{II}}\sigma_{\overline{X}}$$

where $\sigma_{\overline{X}}$ is the standard deviation of $\overline{X}$. If we are sampling an infinite population or a very large finite one (as is assumed in this section), $\sigma_{\overline{X}} = \sigma_X/\sqrt{n}$, so we have:

$$A = \mu_{\text{I}} + z_{\text{I}}\frac{\sigma_X}{\sqrt{n}}$$

$$A = \mu_{\text{II}} - z_{\text{II}}\frac{\sigma_X}{\sqrt{n}}$$

Solving for n by subtracting the second equation from the first, we obtain:

$$0 = (\mu_{\text{I}} - \mu_{\text{II}}) + \frac{\sigma_X}{\sqrt{n}}(z_{\text{I}} + z_{\text{II}})$$

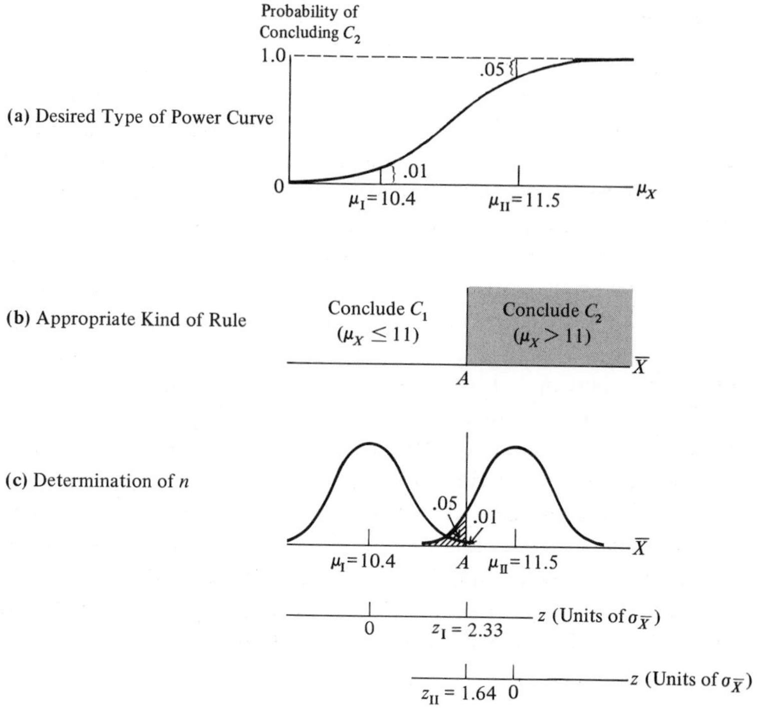

Figure 17.3. Steps in the determination of necessary sample size to control both types of risks of incorrect decisions

or:

$$n = \frac{(z_I + z_{II})^2 \sigma_X^2}{(\mu_I - \mu_{II})^2} \tag{17.5}$$

We still need an advance estimate of the population standard deviation σ_X, as we also did in planning the necessary sample size for estimating a population mean with specified precision. Suppose that the population standard deviation is judged to be about $\sigma_X = 2.5$ minutes. Then we have:

$$\mu_I = 10.4 \qquad z_I = 2.33 \qquad \sigma_X = 2.5$$
$$\mu_{II} = 11.5 \qquad z_{II} = 1.64$$

and:

$$n = \frac{(2.33 + 1.64)^2(2.5)^2}{(10.4 - 11.5)^2} = 81$$

Hence, a simple random sample of about 81 observations would be needed to provide the protection desired by management against reaching an incorrect decision of either type.

Step 6—completion of statistical decision rule

In general, the value of the population standard deviation is unknown, and an advance judgment of σ_X is used in planning the needed sample size to control both types of risks of incorrect decisions. This advance judgment may not be correct, however, and therefore one does not want it to affect the actual decision rule employed. Consequently, one usually proceeds at this point by treating the sample size obtained in the previous step as fixed, and employing the procedures explained earlier when only one of the two types of incorrect decisions can be controlled. Thus, the sample size now is considered an arbitrary one, the decision rule is set up from the specification on one type of risk of making incorrect decisions, and the standard deviation of $\overline{X}$ ($\sigma_{\overline{X}}$) is estimated from the sample results actually obtained.

This procedure assures us that at least one of the two types of risks of an incorrect decision is at the desired level, namely at the one specified for the actual construction of the decision rule. If the advance judgment of the population standard deviation was sound, the risk of making the other type of incorrect decision will be close to the desired level used in determining the necessary sample size. If the advance judgment was not sound, however, this second risk will not be close to the desired level, though the first risk is still controlled at the specified level.

17.4 LOWER-TAIL DECISION PROBLEMS

Up to this point, we have considered upper-tail decision problems, which call for large values of $\overline{X}$ to lead to conclusion C_2. Now we discuss briefly *lower-tail decision problems,* where the decision rule will require that small values of $\overline{X}$ lead to C_2. We need not go into too many details, since the basic approach to setting up statistical decision rules is the same as that described previously for upper-tail problems. *Again, we assume that the statistical decision rule is based on a reasonably large simple random sample,* so that the sampling distribution of $\overline{X}$ can be assumed to be approximately normal.

Alternative conclusions

Consider a steel company producing steel bars of specified length. If the production process turns out bars that are too long, the excess length can be cut off and the scrap utilized again. If the bars are short, however, the entire bar must be scrapped. Clearly, producing short bars leads to lower payoffs than producing bars that are slightly long. In a case of this type, the company may wish to control the process so that the mean length of the bars does not fall below a specified level μ_0. This level μ_0 would be determined from an assessment of the costs of scrapping short bars and trimming long bars, and the relative number of such bars produced at different levels of the mean length μ_X of the production process. Thus, the alternatives would be:

$$(17.6)\qquad \begin{array}{ll} C_1 & \mu_X \geq \mu_0 \\ C_2 & \mu_X < \mu_0 \end{array}$$

Desired type of power curve

The desired type of power curve is shown in Figure 17.4a. If μ_X is large, we want a small probability of concluding C_2 ($\mu_X < \mu_0$), whereas if μ_X is small, we want a high probability of concluding C_2.

Appropriate kind of decision rule

The appropriate kind of decision rule yielding the desired type of power curve is shown in Figure 17.4b. As one would expect, small values of $\overline{X}$ lead to conclusion C_2 ($\mu_X < \mu_0$) while large values of $\overline{X}$ lead to conclusion C_1.

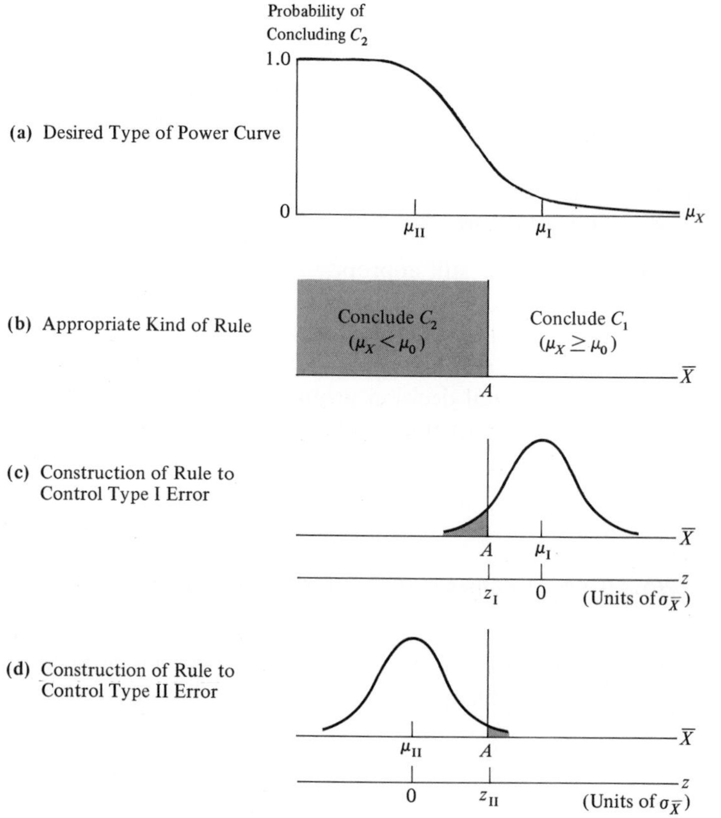

Figure 17.4. Steps in the construction of decision rule for lower-tail decision problems

Construction of decision rule to control Type I errors

When the sample size has been predetermined and it is desired to control the risks of making Type I errors, the construction of the decision rule proceeds according to the illustration in Figure 17.4c. For a given level $\mu_X = \mu_I$, the risk of concluding C_2 is specified. The decision rule then is:

$$\text{(17.7)} \quad \begin{aligned} &\text{If } \overline{X} \geq \mu_I - z_I s_{\overline{X}}, \text{ conclude } C_1\ (\mu_X \geq \mu_0) \\ &\text{If } \overline{X} < \mu_I - z_I s_{\overline{X}}, \text{ conclude } C_2\ (\mu_X < \mu_0) \end{aligned}$$

Here z_I is the standard normal deviate associated with the specified risk of concluding C_2 when $\mu_X = \mu_I$, and $s_{\overline{X}}$ is the sample estimator of $\sigma_{\overline{X}}$.

Construction of decision rule to control Type II errors

Figure 17.4d illustrates the construction of the decision rule when the sample size has been predetermined and it is desired to control the risks of Type II errors. For a given level $\mu_X = \mu_{II}$, the risk of concluding C_1 is specified. The decision rule then is:

$$\text{(17.8)} \quad \begin{aligned} &\text{If } \overline{X} \geq \mu_{II} + z_{II} s_{\overline{X}}, \text{ conclude } C_1\ (\mu_X \geq \mu_0) \\ &\text{If } \overline{X} < \mu_{II} + z_{II} s_{\overline{X}}, \text{ conclude } C_2\ (\mu_X < \mu_0) \end{aligned}$$

Here z_{II} is the standard normal deviate associated with the specified risk of concluding C_1 when $\mu_X = \mu_{II}$, and $s_{\overline{X}}$ is the sample estimator of $\sigma_{\overline{X}}$.

Determination of sample size to control both kinds of errors

Formula (17.5) is still appropriate here. Simply remember that z_I and z_{II} are always taken to be positive for (17.5). Also recall that (17.5) is applicable whenever the resultant sample size is reasonably large.

Once the sample size has been determined, we would proceed as in the case of an upper-tail decision problem. That is, using the sample estimator s_X of σ_X, the decision rule would be set up to control one of the two types of risks of incorrect decisions.

17.5 TWO-SIDED ALTERNATIVE DECISION PROBLEMS

Having considered upper- and lower-tail decision problems, we now take up a decision problem involving the population mean where the alternative is two-sided.

Example

The Superior Canning Company processes a variety of vegetables, including whole kernel corn. A particular filling machine has been set to fill cans with 20 ounces of corn on the average, and management wishes to decide on the basis of a sample of cans whether the setting is appropriate or whether the machine should be reset. If the filling machine is actually filling the cans with less than 20 ounces of corn on the average, the process may turn out a substantial portion of underweight cans. On the other hand, if the filling machine is placing more than 20 ounces of corn, on the average, into the cans, a large portion of cans may be substantially overweight. Thus, the payoff to the company is reduced if the mean weight of the fill deviates from 20 ounces in either direction—in one direction because of possible damage claims and legal difficulties if underweight cans are sold, in the other direction because excess corn is placed into the cans while the selling price is based on a lower weight. Consequently, management wants to be sure that the filling machine is set so that the mean fill per can does not deviate either above or below 20 ounces per can.

Statement of alternatives

The management of the Superior Canning Company wishes to choose one of the following two courses of action:

C_1 Do not reset the filling machine

C_2 Reset the filling machine

Alternatively, the problem may be formulated as follows:

C_1 $\mu_X = 20$ ounces

C_2 $\mu_X \neq 20$ ounces

where $\neq$ signifies "not equal." Note the equivalence of the two formulations, since $C_1\!:\mu_X = 20$ implies that the machine should not be reset, while $C_2\!:\mu_X \neq 20$ implies that the filling machine should be reset.

Since conclusion C_2 involves alternatives on either side of $\mu_X = 20$ ounces, this type of problem is called a *two-sided alternative* decision problem.

Types of incorrect decisions

As we have noted already, there are two types of incorrect decisions that can be made when two alternative courses of action are being considered. A Type I error is made when C_1 is correct but C_2 is selected. Thus in our example, a Type I error is made if it is concluded that the mean weight of the fill is not 20 ounces ($C_2\!:\mu_X \neq 20$) when in fact $\mu_X = 20$ ounces. In other words, a Type I error involves a resetting of the machine when the resetting is not necessary. A Type II error, on the other hand, is committed when C_2 is correct but C_1 is selected—in the present problem, if it is concluded that the mean weight of the fill is 20 ounces ($C_1\!:\mu_X = 20$) when in fact the mean weight deviates from 20 ounces in either direction. Thus, a Type II error involves a failure to reset the filling machine when it should be reset, either because of underfill or overfill.

Appropriate type of statistical decision rule

Intuitively, it appears reasonable that we conclude C_1 ($\mu_X = 20$) when $\overline{X}$ is near 20 ounces, and that we conclude C_2 ($\mu_X \neq 20$) when $\overline{X}$ deviates substantially from 20 ounces in either direction. As we shall show below, such a statistical decision rule has desirable properties.

Suppose that the management had decided in advance to select a sample of 64 cans, weigh the contents of each, and then employ the following decision rule:

If $19.8 \leq \overline{X} \leq 20.2$, conclude C_1 ($\mu_X = 20$)
Otherwise, conclude C_2 ($\mu_X \neq 20$)

Thus, the filling machine would be left alone (C_1) as long as the sample mean $\overline{X}$, based on the 64 sample cans, falls between 19.8 and 20.2 ounces, and it would be reset (C_2) if $\overline{X}$ falls below 19.8 ounces or above 20.2 ounces.

We shall evaluate this decision rule by obtaining its power curve.

Evaluation of statistical decision rule

The evaluation of a statistical decision rule for a two-sided alternative decision problem is similar to that for the one-sided alternative case. We calculate the probability that the decision rule leads to conclusion C_2 for different possible values of the process mean μ_X and plot these probabilities in the form of a power curve.

We again need to utilize the sampling distribution of $\overline{X}$ to obtain the desired probabilities, since the decision rule is based on the value of the sample mean $\overline{X}$. We assume that the sample size of 64 cans is large enough so that the sampling distribution of $\overline{X}$ is approximately normal. Suppose that it is known from past experience that the standard deviation of the weights of the fills is about .8 ounces, and that the standard deviation has been fairly stable at this level over time. Hence, the standard deviation of the sampling distribution of $\overline{X}$ is:

$$\sigma_{\overline{X}} = \frac{\sigma_X}{\sqrt{n}} = \frac{.8}{\sqrt{64}} = .1 \text{ ounce}$$

(Remember that we are sampling a process here, so that a finite correction factor is not involved.) Finally, we know that the mean of the sampling distribution of $\overline{X}$ is equal to the population mean μ_X, which is the unknown population characteristic involved in our decision problem.

Probability of concluding C_2 when $\mu_X = 19.7$. Figure 17.5 shows at the top in graphic form the decision rule to be evaluated. Note that there are two action limits, at 19.8 and 20.2 ounces, respectively. Conclusion C_1 ($\mu_X = 20$) is to be reached as long as $\overline{X}$ falls between 19.8 and 20.2 ounces, and conclusion C_2 ($\mu_X \neq 20$) is to be reached if $\overline{X}$ is below 19.8 or above 20.2 ounces.

Suppose now that the process mean fill is $\mu_X = 19.7$ ounces. What then is the probability that the decision rule leads to conclusion C_2? If $\mu_X = 19.7$ ounces, we know that the mean of $\overline{X}$ is $\mu_{\overline{X}} = \mu_X = 19.7$; we already know that the standard deviation of $\overline{X}$ is $\sigma_{\overline{X}} = .1$ ounce, and that the sampling distribution is approximately normal. The sampling distribution of $\overline{X}$ centered around $\mu_{\overline{X}} = 19.7$ is shown in Figure 17.5a. The shaded area in the

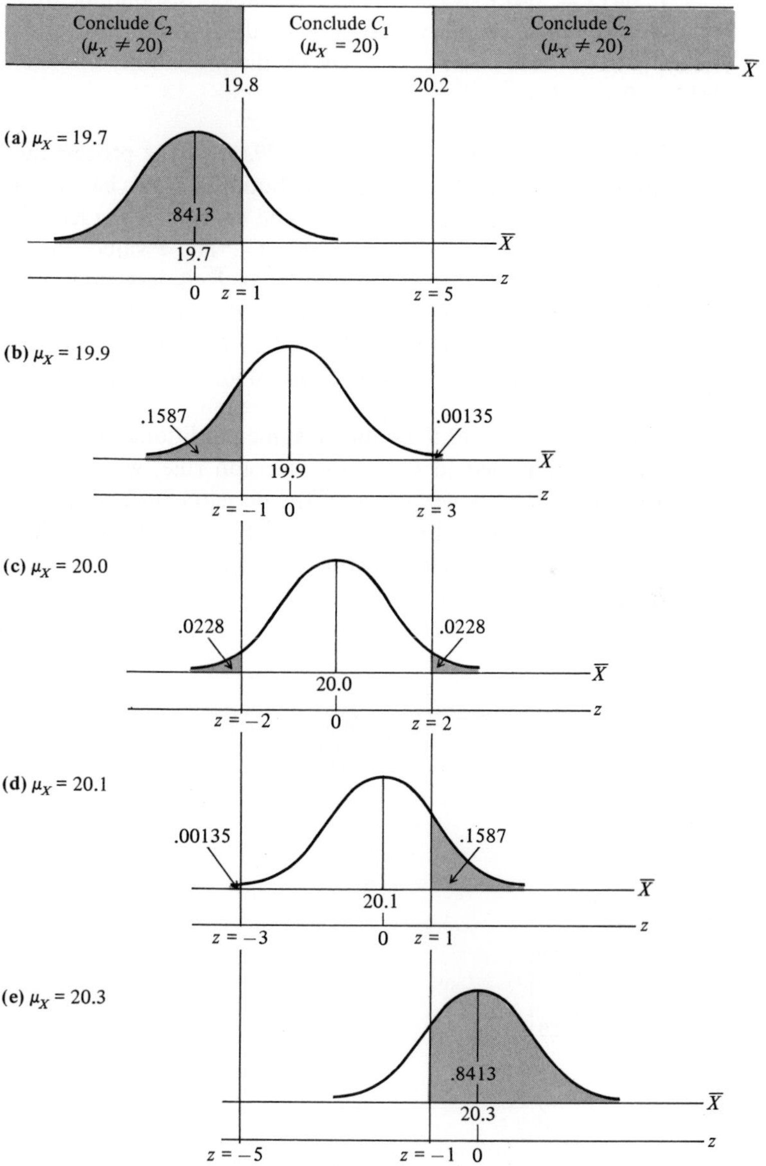

Figure 17.5. Illustrations of power probability calculations for two-sided decision rule ($n = 64$; $\sigma_{\overline{X}} = .8/\sqrt{64} = .1$ ounce)

distribution corresponds to the probability of being led to conclude C_2 by the decision rule. We can evaluate this probability in the usual manner.

First, the z value corresponding to 19.8 ounces is:

$$z = \frac{\overline{X} - \mu_{\overline{X}}}{\sigma_{\overline{X}}} = \frac{19.8 - 19.7}{.1} = 1$$

Table A-1 then indicates that the probability that $\overline{X}$ is less than 19.8 ounces is $.5 + .3413 = .8413$. Second, the z value corresponding to 20.2 ounces is 5, so that the probability that $\overline{X}$ exceeds 20.2 ounces is practically nil. Hence, *if the process mean is 19.7 ounces*, the probability of concluding C_2 is $.8413 + 0 = .8413$.

Probability of concluding C_2 when $\mu_X = 20.0$. If the process mean fill were $\mu_X = 20.0$ ounces, the sampling distribution would be centered around $\mu_{\overline{X}} = 20.0$, as shown in Figure 17.5c. The combined shaded area indicates the probability of being led to conclude C_2. The z value corresponding to 19.8 ounces is -2, so the probability that $\overline{X}$ is less than 19.8 ounces is $.5 - .4772 = .0228$. Because of symmetry, the probability that the sample mean $\overline{X}$ exceeds 20.2 ounces is also .0228, so that the probability of the decision rule leading to conclusion C_2 is .0456 *when $\mu_X = 20.0$ ounces.*

Power curve. Figure 17.5 contains some additional evaluations of the probability of being led to C_2 by the decision rule, when $\mu_X = 19.9$, 20.1, and 20.3 ounces. The power curve of the decision rule, based on the probabilities obtained in Figure 17.5, is shown in Figure 17.6. Note that this power curve indicates that the decision rule has generally desirable properties. It will lead to conclusion C_2 ($\mu_X \neq 20$) generally when the process mean μ_X has deviated substantially from the desired mean fill of 20 ounces, and it will lead

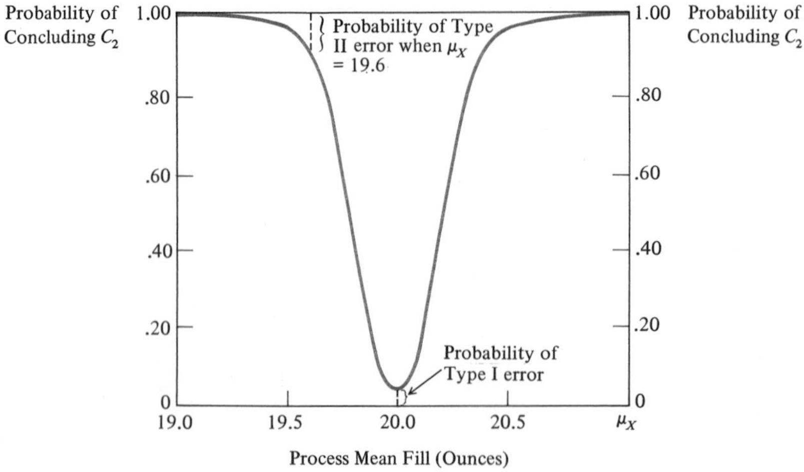

to conclusion C_1 ($\mu_X = 20$) generally if the process mean fill is at the desired level of 20 ounces. The risk of making a Type I error, when $\mu_X = 20$ ounces, is shown directly by the power curve, as indicated in Figure 17.6. The risk of making a Type II error with this decision rule is shown indirectly by the power curve; Figure 17.6 indicates this risk for the case when $\mu_X = 19.6$ ounces.

While the particular magnitudes of risks of incorrect decisions inherent in the decision rule may not be at desirable levels, the shape of the power curve in Figure 17.6 does indicate that the type of statistical decision rule utilized has reasonable properties.

Control of error probabilities

The effects of changes in the action limits and sample size on the power curve are similar to those in the one-sided alternative case. We therefore only summarize these effects. It is helpful to refer again to Figure 17.5:

1. With a given simple random sample size, widening the action limits increases the probability of concluding C_1, hence reduces the risk of making a Type I error but increases the risks of making Type II errors.
2. With a given sample size, narrowing the action limits reduces the probability of concluding C_1, hence reduces the risks of making Type II errors but increases the risk of making a Type I error.
3. A simultaneous reduction in both types of risks of making incorrect decisions from a simple random sample can only be achieved by reducing the variability of the sampling distribution through increasing the sample size.

Consequently, in the construction of a decision rule for a two-sided alternative decision problem, one can control at a specified level only one of the two types of risks of making incorrect decisions when the sample size is predetermined. If one wishes to control both types of risks at specified levels, the sample size will have to be determined from the specifications on the control of risks of incorrect decisions.

Construction of decision rule to control Type I error

We now explain how to construct a statistical decision rule for a two-sided alternative decision problem when:

1. The sample is a large simple random one.
2. The sample size has been predetermined.
3. The risk of making a Type I error is to be controlled, and the risks of Type II errors are to remain uncontrolled.

We continue to use the example of the Superior Canning Company, dealing with the problem of whether or not to reset the filling machine.

Step 1—statement of alternatives. The Superior Canning Company is considering the alternatives:

C_1 $\mu_X = 20$ (do not reset)
C_2 $\mu_X \neq 20$ (reset)

Step 2—desired type of power curve. For this set of alternatives, the desired type of power curve is that shown in Figure 17.7a. If the process mean fill μ_X is 20 ounces, we wish to have a small probability of concluding C_2 ($\mu_X \neq 20$), leading to resetting the filling machine. If the process mean fill has deviated from 20 ounces in either direction, on the other hand, we wish to have a high probability of concluding C_2, leading to resetting the machine.

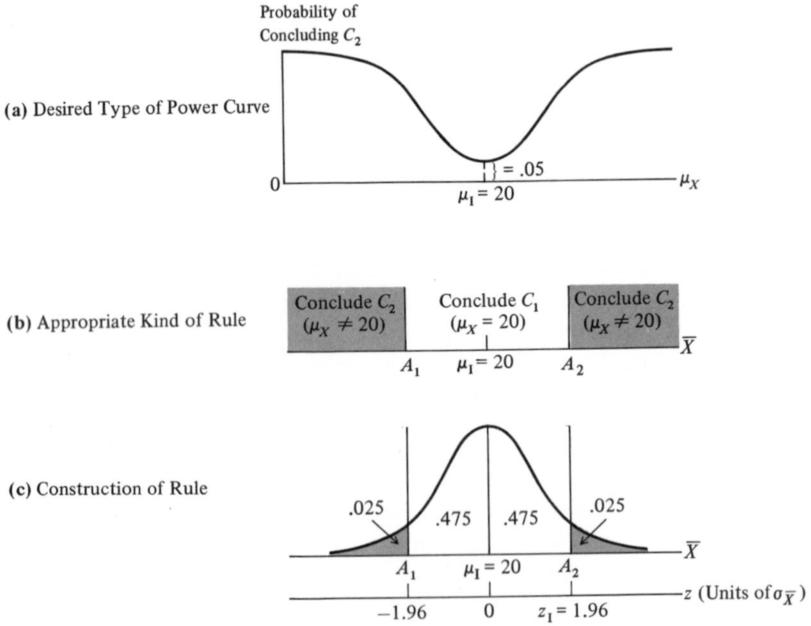

Figure 17.7. Steps in the construction of two-sided decision rule when Type I error controlled

Step 3—choice of appropriate kind of decision rule. It is clear that the desired type of power curve is obtained by the kind of decision rule shown in Figure 17.7b. As long as $\bar{X}$ is close to 20 ounces, the rule leads to conclusion C_1 ($\mu_X = 20$), while a substantial deviation of $\bar{X}$ from 20 ounces in either direction will lead to conclusion C_2 ($\mu_X \neq 20$).

Step 4—specification of risk of making Type I error. Since the Superior Canning Company determined arbitrarily in advance to select a sample of 64 cans, it can control only one of the two types of risks of making incorrect decisions. Suppose that management, after assessing the payoff functions and other aspects of the decision problem, felt it most important to control the risk of making a Type I error. Specifically, it wants to control at the level .05 the risk of concluding C_2 ($\mu_X \neq 20$) when in fact the process mean fill is $\mu_X = 20$ ounces. This specified risk of an incorrect decision is indicated on the desired power curve shown in Figure 17.7a.

Step 5—determination of action limit. If the process mean fill is $\mu_X = 20$ ounces, the sampling distribution of $\overline{X}$ is centered around $\mu_{\overline{X}} = 20$ ounces, as shown in Figure 17.7c. This sampling distribution is approximately normal because the sample size $n = 64$ is reasonably large. The combined shaded area indicates the probability of concluding C_2 ($\mu_X \neq 20$) by following the decision rule, when the process mean fill is $\mu_X = 20$. This probability was specified by management to be controlled at the level .05.

To obtain the desired type of power curve shown in Figure 17.7a, the action limits need to be symmetrical around 20 ounces. This means that each of the two tails is to have area .025. We begin with the upper action limit. From Table A-1, we must determine the z value such that the area in the upper tail is .025. This z value is 1.96. Therefore, the upper action limit is 1.96 standard deviations ($\sigma_{\overline{X}}$, because we are referring to the sampling distribution of $\overline{X}$) above 20 ounces; in other words, it is $A_2 = 20 + 1.96\sigma_{\overline{X}}$. By symmetry of the action limits around 20 ounces, the lower action limit is $A_1 = 20 - 1.96\sigma_{\overline{X}}$. Since $\sigma_{\overline{X}}$ is usually unknown, we must await the sample results to obtain an estimate of $\sigma_{\overline{X}}$ and complete the action limits.

Step 6—completion of statistical decision rule. Suppose now that 64 cans have been selected from the filling process, the corn in each weighed, and the following results obtained:

$$\overline{X} = 20.82 \text{ ounces}$$

$$s_X = .96 \text{ ounces}$$

(The 64 sample observations are not recorded here.) We can then estimate $\sigma_{\overline{X}}$ by $s_{\overline{X}} = s_X/\sqrt{n} = .96/\sqrt{64} = .12$.

Hence, the upper action limit is:

$$A_2 = 20 + 1.96s_{\overline{X}} = 20 + 1.96(.12) = 20.24 \text{ ounces}$$

and the lower action limit is:

$$A_1 = 20 - 1.96s_{\overline{X}} = 20 - 1.96(.12) = 19.76 \text{ ounces}$$

The decision rule is therefore as follows:

If $19.76 \leq \overline{X} \leq 20.24$, conclude C_1 ($\mu_X = 20$)
Otherwise, conclude C_2 ($\mu_X \neq 20$)

This decision rule is so constructed that if the process mean fill is at the desired level of 20 ounces, the probability is only about .05 that the rule will lead to C_2.

Step 7—application of decision rule. We can now apply this decision rule. Since $\bar{X} = 20.82$ ounces, the decision rule leads to conclusion C_2 ($\mu_X \neq 20$), which calls for a resetting of the filling machine.

Recapitulation. For a two-sided alternative decision problem concerning the population mean μ_X, the alternatives are:

(17.9)
$$C_1 \qquad \mu_X = \mu_0$$
$$C_2 \qquad \mu_X \neq \mu_0$$

Here μ_0 is the level of past experience, the standard, or the like. In our example, μ_0 was 20 ounces.

When the sample size is predetermined and the risk of making a Type I error is to be controlled, one must select a level of μ_X, denoted by μ_I, for which the probability of concluding C_2 is to be controlled. In problems of this type, μ_I usually is set at the level of past experience, the standard, or the like. In other words, in these cases $\mu_I = \mu_0$. Decision rules can also be constructed when μ_I is set at some distance above and below μ_0, but *here we consider only the case when* $\mu_I = \mu_0$.

In our present example, management wished to control the risk of making a Type I error when $\mu_X = \mu_0 = 20$ ounces. Thus, here we have $\mu_I = \mu_0 = 20$ ounces. In that case, we find the values of the action limits by using the sampling distribution of $\bar{X}$ when $\mu_X = \mu_I = 20$ ounces. The action limits are a certain number of standard deviations ($\sigma_{\bar{X}}$) above and below μ_I, as determined by the z value corresponding to the specified risk of an incorrect decision, denoted by z_I. The standard deviation $\sigma_{\bar{X}}$ is estimated by $s_{\bar{X}}$, and the upper action limit therefore is: $A_2 = \mu_I + z_I s_{\bar{X}}$ and the lower action limit is $A_1 = \mu_I - z_I s_{\bar{X}}$. Formally, when μ_I is set at the level μ_0, the statistical decision rule is:

(17.10)
$$\text{If } \mu_I - z_I s_{\bar{X}} \leq \bar{X} \leq \mu_I + z_I s_{\bar{X}}, \text{ conclude } C_1\ (\mu_X = \mu_0)$$
$$\text{Otherwise, conclude } C_2\ (\mu_X \neq \mu_0)$$

Here z_I is the standard normal deviate associated with the specified risk of concluding C_2 ($\mu_X \neq \mu_0$) at $\mu_I = \mu_0$.

Relation to confidence intervals. Suppose that in our previous example, we had simply wished to *estimate* the process mean fill. Given $\bar{X} = 20.82$, $s_X = .96$, and $s_{\bar{X}} = .12$, the confidence limits for the process mean μ_X with a 95 per cent confidence coefficient ($z = 1.96$) would be $20.82 \pm 1.96(.12)$. Hence, the confidence interval for the process mean would be:

$$20.82 - 1.96(.12) \leq \mu_X \leq 20.82 + 1.96(.12)$$
$$20.58 \leq \mu_X \leq 21.06$$

We would therefore have concluded, with a 95 per cent confidence coefficient, that the process mean fill is between 20.58 and 21.06 ounces.

Note first of all the correspondence between the 95 per cent confidence coefficient and the risk of Type I error of .05. Both lead to $z = 1.96$. Second, note that the confidence interval does not include the desired mean fill level of 20 ounces. This corresponds to the conclusion from the decision rule that $\mu_X \neq 20$ ounces (C_2).

We can generalize for a two-sided alternative decision problem involving the population mean μ_X that if the decision rule based on a specified risk of a Type I error of α at $\mu_I = \mu_0$ (in our example, $\alpha = .05$) leads to conclusion C_1 ($\mu_X = \mu_0$), then the confidence interval with a confidence coefficient of $1 - \alpha$ will include μ_0, and vice versa. If μ_0 is not included in the confidence interval, then the corresponding decision rule will lead to conclusion C_2 ($\mu_X \neq \mu_0$), and vice versa.

Thus, the confidence interval furnishes the same information about the population mean as does the decision rule when the decision problem is a two-sided alternative one and the risk of making a Type I error is being controlled. In addition, however, the confidence interval indicates more directly whether a deviation in the population mean μ_X from the level μ_0, if it has occurred, is a major one or not, and how precisely this can be known. In our example, for instance, the confidence interval indicates that the process mean fill is at least at the level 20.58 ounces and may be as high as 21.06 ounces. This indication is a very important contribution of confidence intervals in some problems, because a conclusion from a decision rule that $\mu_X \neq \mu_0$ does not provide any information about the magnitude by which μ_X differs from μ_0.

Control of both types of risks through sample size determination

We consider now the case where the sample size has not been predetermined, and both types of risks of making incorrect decisions are to be controlled. *The procedure to be described assumes that the resultant sample size will be sufficiently large so that the sampling distribution of $\overline{X}$ is approximately normal.*

Steps 1 through 3, dealing with the statement of alternatives, desired type of power curve, and appropriate kind of decision rule, are unchanged.

Step 4—specification of risks of making Type I and Type II errors. Suppose that the management of the Superior Canning Company wishes to control both types of risks of making incorrect decisions and makes the following two specifications after an analysis of the decision problem:

1. If the process mean fill μ_X is 20 ounces, denoted by μ_I, the risk of concluding C_2 ($\mu_X \neq 20$) is to be .01.
2. If the process mean fill μ_X is .5 ounces above or below the desired level of 20 ounces, the risk of concluding C_1 ($\mu_X = 20$) is to be .01. We denote these levels where it is important to conclude C_2 by μ_{II}; thus, $\mu_{II} = 19.5$ or 20.5 ounces here.

These requirements on the power curve are shown in Figure 17.8a.

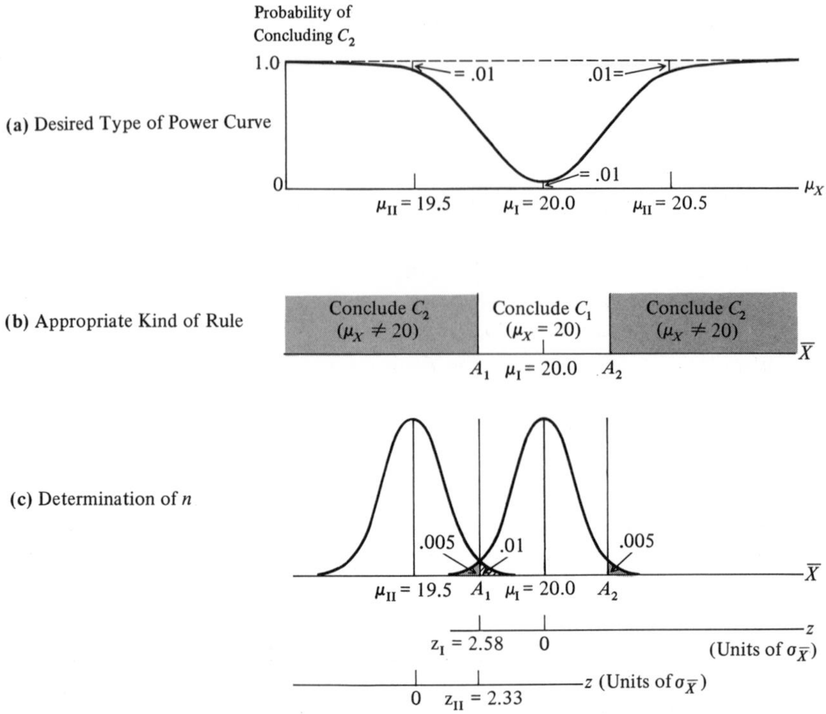

Figure 17.8. Steps in the determination of necessary sample size for two-sided alternative

Step 5—determination of sample size. Figure 17.8b contains the appropriate kind of decision rule that provides the desired type of power curve. Figure 17.8c shows the sampling distribution of $\bar{X}$ when $\mu_X = \mu_I = 20$ ounces, and also that for $\mu_X = \mu_{II} = 19.5$ ounces. Because of the symmetry of the action limits around 20 ounces, it does not matter whether we work with $\mu_{II} = 19.5$ ounces or $\mu_{II} = 20.5$ ounces.

Since the probability of concluding C_2 when $\mu_X = \mu_I = 20$ ounces is to be .01 and we are using symmetrical action limits, the area in the *left* tail of the sampling distribution of $\bar{X}$ when $\mu_{\bar{X}} = 20$ ounces should be .005. Thus, the z value, denoted by z_I, is 2.58. When $\mu_X = \mu_{II} = 19.5$ ounces, the probability of concluding C_1 is to be .01, so the *right* tail of the sampling distribution of $\bar{X}$ when $\mu_{\bar{X}} = 19.5$ ounces should be .01. Hence, the z value, denoted by z_{II}, is 2.33. *Note that both* z_I and z_{II} *are taken to be positive.*

We can then write the following two simultaneous equations for A_1:

$$A_1 = 20 - 2.58\sigma_{\bar{X}}$$
$$A_1 = 19.5 + 2.33\sigma_{\bar{X}}$$

or, in general, when $\mu_I = \mu_0$:

$$A_1 = \mu_I - z_I\sigma_{\bar{X}}$$
$$A_1 = \mu_{II} + z_{II}\sigma_{\bar{X}}$$

If we solve these two equations for n (remember $\sigma_{\bar{X}} = \sigma_X/\sqrt{n}$) as we did in Section 17.3, we obtain:

$$n = \frac{(z_{\text{I}} + z_{\text{II}})^2\sigma_X^2}{(\mu_{\text{I}} - \mu_{\text{II}})^2} \tag{17.11}$$

In our example, we have:

$$\mu_{\text{I}} = 20 \qquad z_{\text{I}} = 2.58$$
$$\mu_{\text{II}} = 19.5 \qquad z_{\text{II}} = 2.33$$

We still need an advance estimate of the process standard deviation; suppose it is judged to be about $\sigma_X = .9$ ounces. We then obtain for n:

$$n = \frac{(2.58 + 2.33)^2(.9)^2}{(20 - 19.5)^2} = 78$$

Hence, a simple random sample of 78 cans would be needed to provide the protection specified by management against reaching an incorrect decision of either type.

Step 6—completion of statistical decision rule. Again, we usually proceed at this point by treating the sample size as fixed, setting up the decision rule using the sample estimator s_X of σ_X, and controlling one of the two types of risks of incorrect decisions. In this way, it is certain that at least one of the two types of risks is controlled at the specified level, regardless of how poor the planning was. Of course, if the advance planning was good, both types of incorrect decisions will be controlled at the levels specified.

17.6 SPECIFICATION OF ACCEPTABLE RISK LEVELS

The classical approach to statistical decision-making that we have discussed does not consider explicitly the payoff functions for each of the two acts. As we explained earlier, management still needs to assess the structure of these payoff functions with the classical approach to statistical decision-making, even though it may not be able to evaluate these functions explicitly. This assessment is needed to formulate the decision problem properly, and to aid in specifying the levels at which the risks of incorrect decisions are to be controlled.

Essentially, the specifications of the levels at which the risks are to be controlled and from which the needed sample size is to be determined are based, in the absence of explicit payoff functions, on a subjective evaluation of the order of magnitude of the consequences of the two different types of incorrect decisions and the cost of sampling. Risks of incorrect decisions need to be balanced against costs of sampling. In general, the larger the simple random sample size, the lower will be the risks of one or both types of errors but the greater will be the cost of sampling. If sampling is cheap and incorrect decisions are costly, it will pay to enlarge the sample size so as to keep risks of errors very low. In contrast, if sampling is expensive relative to costs of errors, it will not pay to set risks of errors so low that an excessively large sample is required.

If the sample size has been predetermined, the risk of one type of error can be reduced only by increasing the risk of the other type. The more serious the consequences of one type of error relative to the other, the smaller should be the tolerable risk of the former type of error relative to that of the latter. For instance, suppose that an incoming shipment is to be inspected by sampling to see if it is of acceptable quality. An erroneous conclusion that the shipment is of unacceptable quality leads to a 100 per cent screening of the entire shipment, which costs a certain amount of inspection time. On the other hand, an erroneous conclusion that the shipment is of acceptable quality when it is not can lead to difficulties in the production process much more costly than the needless 100 per cent inspection of an acceptable shipment. In this case, the risk of a Type II error (concluding shipment is of acceptable quality when it is not) usually would be set lower than the risk of a Type I error (concluding shipment is of unacceptable quality when it is actually of acceptable quality).

QUESTIONS AND PROBLEMS

17.1. Distinguish briefly between:

a. One-sided and two-sided alternative decision problems

b. Upper-tail and lower-tail decision problems

c. μ_0, μ_I, and μ_{II}

d. Statistical decision rule and confidence interval

17.2. Briefly explain the term *level of significance*. In a statistical decision problem with a predetermined sample size, does one achieve any control over the risks of a Type II error by specifying the level of significance to be used?

***17.3.** Refer to Problem 16.9. Suppose that the waiting time was measured for a random sample of 64 calls, and the following results obtained:

$X =$ Length of waiting time, in seconds

$n = 64 \qquad \overline{X} = 15.98 \text{ seconds} \qquad s_X = 7.94 \text{ seconds}$

a. Construct the appropriate decision rule to be used in notifying the department whether or not the mean waiting time has been reduced below 19 seconds. Assume that the department will accept a maximum risk of .05 of concluding that the mean waiting time has been reduced, when it has not. What conclusion should be reached?

b. Does your decision rule control the specified risk at the exact level .05? Explain.

c. Estimate the risk of failing to be notified of a reduction in the mean waiting time by your decision rule when the new mean waiting time actually is 17 seconds. Why is this only an estimate of the risk? What additional information would you need to decide whether this risk is acceptable? Explain.

d. In what sense does the construction of the decision rule in part **a** follow a modified approach to the decision problem? Discuss.

e. Suppose that the department had wished to control the risk of making a Type II error—specifically, if the mean waiting time is 17 seconds, the risk of concluding C_1 is to be .05. Construct the appropriate decision rule for this case. What conclusion would be reached?

17.4. In a certain city, the maximum permissible level of sulphur dioxide in the air is .10 parts per million. The levels of sulphur dioxide were observed at 36 random times; the results were as follows:

X = Level of sulphur dioxide, in parts per million, for sample time

$n = 36$ $\quad \overline{X} = .114$ parts per million $\quad s_X = .042$ parts per million

The city's pollution control officer wants to know if the actual mean level of sulphur dioxide exceeds the permissible level. If it does, action is to be taken to control the primary sources of air pollution in the city.

a. Construct the appropriate decision rule, assuming that the pollution control officer wishes to take a maximum risk of only .01 of concluding the permissible level has not been exceeded when it has been exceeded by .02 parts per million or more. What conclusion should be reached?

b. Why does your decision rule not provide exactly the risk specified in part **a**? Explain.

c. Estimate the risk of concluding the permissible level has been exceeded, when the actual mean level equals the permissible level. Why is this only an estimate of the risk? Is this risk at an acceptable level? Discuss.

d. In what sense does the construction of the decision rule in part **a** follow a modified approach to the decision problem? Explain.

e. Suppose that the officer had wished to control the risk of making a Type I error—specifically, if the actual mean level is .10 parts per million, the risk of concluding that the permissible level has been exceeded is to be .075. Construct the appropriate decision rule for this case. What conclusion should be reached?

***17.5.** Refer to Problem 16.9. Suppose that the department called you before the sample was selected and asked you to recommend the appropriate sample size. The department wants to control the risk of concluding C_2 when the mean waiting time is 19 seconds at .02, and the risk of concluding C_1 when the mean waiting time is 17 seconds at .05. Past experience indicates that the process standard deviation is about $\sigma_X = 8$ seconds.

a. What is the required sample size?

b. Recalculate the required sample size in part **a** under each of the following new conditions (in each case, keep other factors at their original values): (1) Reduce the process standard deviation to half its previous value, that is, to $\sigma_X = 4$ seconds. (2) Double the difference $\mu_{\text{I}} - \mu_{\text{II}}$ by shifting μ_{II} to 15 seconds from 17 seconds. What generalization is suggested by your results?

c. If the process standard deviation used in planning the required sample size is an overestimate, what is the likely effect of this overestimate on the protection offered by the decision rule? Assume that this rule is constructed by using the sample standard deviation, with the risk of making a Type I error controlled.

(Continued)

d. How would the department's choice of the desired levels for controlling risks of making Type I and Type II errors be changed if the social cost of keeping a person waiting more than 19 seconds is greater than previously thought? If the cost of sampling calls is less than previously thought? Explain.

***17.6.** Refer to Problem 17.5.

a. Suppose the department wishes to control the risks of making a Type I error at $\mu_{\mathrm{I}} = 19$ and a Type II error at $\mu_{\mathrm{II}} = 17$ at the same level, namely .05. Assuming the process standard deviation is $\sigma_X = 8$ seconds, find the necessary sample size.

b. It is possible to determine the action limit of the decision rule in this case without knowing the sample estimate of the population standard deviation. Explain why this is so and set up the appropriate decision rule.

17.7. The standard time for a polishing operation is 45 seconds. A simple random sample of cycles of this work operation by employee Jackson is to be observed. Management wants to know if Jackson's mean time exceeds the standard. If it exceeds the standard by a sufficient amount, he is to be retrained.

Suppose management calls you before the sample is selected and asks you to recommend the appropriate sample size. Management wishes to have a maximum risk of only .10 of failing to retrain Jackson if his mean time is 46 seconds or more. At the same time, the maximum risk of retraining Jackson when his mean time actually is 45 seconds or less should be only .01. Similar studies in the past indicate that the standard deviation of the distribution of time required for the operation is about $\sigma_X = 2.5$ seconds.

a. What are the points on the power curve specified by the above requirements?

b. What is the required sample size?

c. If the population standard deviation were $\sigma_X = 2.0$ seconds, what would be the necessary sample size? How does this sample size compare with that in part **b**? What generalization does this suggest?

d. Suppose that the maximum risk of failing to retrain Jackson when his mean time is 46 seconds or more is lowered to .05, the other risk specification remaining the same. Given these conditions, what is the necessary sample size? Assume that the population standard deviation is $\sigma_X = 2.5$ seconds. How does the needed sample size compare with that in part **b**? What generalization is suggested by this?

e. How would the desired levels for controlling Type I and II errors be affected if good operators were scarce? If they were plentiful?

f. If the process standard deviation used in planning the required sample size is actually somewhat of an underestimate, what is the likely effect of this on the risks inherent in the decision rule, assuming that this rule is constructed by using the sample standard deviation with the risk of making a Type II error controlled? Explain.

17.8. Refer to Problem 17.7.

a. Suppose that management wishes to control the risks of making a Type I error at $\mu_{\mathrm{I}} = 45$ and a Type II error at $\mu_{\mathrm{II}} = 46$ at the same level, namely .05. Assuming the population standard deviation is $\sigma_X = 2.5$ seconds, find the necessary sample size.

b. It is possible to determine the action limit of the decision rule in this case without knowing the sample estimate of the population standard deviation. Explain why this is so and set up the appropriate decision rule.

***17.9.** A governmental agency is studying whether a proposed questionnaire wording on library usage during the past month leads to unbiased responses. A simple random sample of 225 households is to be selected, and information on the number of books borrowed from the public library during the past month is to be obtained from the sample households. Then these responses are to be compared against library records. The error in the reported number of books borrowed is the variable of interest (X). Thus, the alternatives are:

$C_1 \quad \mu_X = 0$

$C_2 \quad \mu_X \neq 0$

The decision rule to be employed is:

If $-.3 \leq \overline{X} \leq .3$, conclude C_1

Otherwise, conclude C_2

Assume that the standard deviation of the response errors is $\sigma_X = 4.5$ books.

a. State C_1 and C_2 in words. If conclusion C_1 is reached, does this signify that there are no errors in household reports on number of books borrowed?

b. Evaluate this decision procedure by calculating the ordinates of the power curve for the following possible values of the mean response error: -1.0, $-.6$, $-.4$, $-.2$, 0, $+.2$, $+.4$, $+.6$, $+1.0$ books.

c. What constitute Type I and Type II errors in this case? What is the magnitude of the risk of making a Type I error with the proposed decision rule?

d. Is this an effective decision procedure? Discuss.

e. Suppose the action limits in the previous decision rule were changed to $-.5$ and $+.5$, respectively, with the sample size unchanged. Calculate the ordinates of the power curve for this new decision-making procedure for the same possible values of the mean response error as in part **b**.

f. Plot the power curves in parts **b** and **e** on the same graph. What effect did widening the action limits have on the power curve? What generalization does this suggest?

g. If the sample size were increased and the decision rule in part **e** employed, what effect would this have on the power curve? Discuss.

17.10. In the past, the mean number of manhours required by the Worth Construction Company to assemble and finish one of its Model S prefabricated homes was $\mu_X = 400$ manhours. To determine whether the current mean assembling and finishing time for this model is the same as in the past, management adopted the following decision-making procedure: Select a simple random sample of 36 of the recent contracts for Model S homes and obtain the number of manhours required to assemble and finish each of them. If the sample mean is between 390 and 410 manhours, conclude that the process mean is still 400. Otherwise, conclude that there has been a change in the process mean.

a. Evaluate this decision-making procedure by calculating the ordinates of the power curve for the following possible values of the process mean: 380, 390, 395, 400, 405, 410, 420 manhours. Assume in these calculations and the ones to follow that the process standard deviation is $\sigma_X = 42$ manhours.

b. Is this an effective decision-making procedure for detecting shifts in the process mean of 20 manhours or more? Discuss.

c. What constitute the Type I and Type II errors in this case?

d. Suppose that the action limits in the previous decision rule were 395 manhours and 405 manhours, respectively, with the sample size unchanged. Calculate the ordinates of the power curve for this new decision-making procedure for the same possible values of the process mean as in part **a**.

e. Plot the power curves in parts **a** and **d** on the same graph. What effect did narrowing the action limits have on the power curve? What generalization does this suggest?

f. Suppose that the decision-making procedure was modified to lead to the conclusion of no change in the process mean if the sample mean, based on a simple random sample of 144 homes, is between 395 and 405 manhours. Calculate the ordinates of the power curve for this decision-making procedure for the same possible values of the process mean as in part **a**.

g. Plot the power curves in parts **d** and **f** on the same graph. What effect did the increase in sample size have on the power curve? What generalization does this suggest?

h. Given the same action limits and sample size as in part **f**, what changes in the power curve would occur if the population standard deviation were larger than $\sigma_X = 42$ manhours? What generalization does this suggest?

17.11. The Metropolitan Supply Company laboriously determined from a study of all sales invoices for the year 1971 that the mean gross profit per sales invoice in 1971 was \$12.41. In 1972, management decided to obtain this information from a sample of sales invoices. A simple random sample of 900 sales invoices was selected from the 185,541 sales invoices for the year 1972, and the gross profit for each invoice in the sample determined. The results were as follows:

X = Gross profit on sample sales invoice

$n = 900 \qquad \bar{X} = \$13.12 \qquad s_X = \$18.04$

Management wants to know if there has been a change in the mean gross profit per sales invoice from 1971 to 1972.

a. Construct the appropriate decision rule, assuming that management wants to take a risk of only .01 of concluding that a change has taken place when no change actually took place. What conclusion should be reached?

b. Why is the risk of making a Type I error with your decision rule not exactly .01? Explain.

c. How could the same conclusion as in part **a** have been reached from a confidence interval for the mean gross profit per sales invoice in 1972? Explain. What would be the confidence coefficient corresponding to the specified risk in part **a**?

d. Construct the corresponding confidence interval. What information does it provide in addition to indicating the conclusion to be reached in the decision problem? Explain.

e. Estimate the power of your decision rule in part **a** if $\mu_X = \$14.00$. Why is this only an estimate of the power? Is the power at an acceptable level? Discuss.

***17.12.** Refer to Problem 12.9. Suppose that the researcher wants to determine if the current mean number of no-shows per flight has changed from the past process mean of .5. The sample results obtained from the current process are given in Problem 12.9. For this sample, $n = 60$, $\bar{X} = .85$, and $s_X = 1.22$.

a. Set up the appropriate decision rule, assuming that the researcher wants to take a risk of only .05 of concluding that a change has taken place when no change actually took place. What conclusion should be reached?

b. Does your decision rule provide exactly the specified risk of .05 of making a Type I error? Explain.

c. How could the same conclusion as in part **a** have been reached from a confidence interval for the current process mean? Explain. What would be the confidence coefficient corresponding to the specified risk in part **a**?

d. Construct the corresponding confidence interval. What information does it provide in addition to indicating the conclusion to be reached in the decision problem? Explain.

e. Estimate the power of your decision rule in part **a** if $\mu_X = 1.0$. Why is this only an estimate of the power? What additional information would you need to decide if this risk is at an acceptable level? Explain.

17.13. Refer to Problem 12.15. Suppose that in the past the mean time required by a company serviceman to handle an appliance service call was 78 minutes. You have been asked to obtain the sample size needed to determine whether the current mean time is the same as in the past or not. The risk of concluding that the mean time differs from that in the past, when it does not, is to be .05. Also, if the mean time differs by 15 minutes from that in the past, the risk of concluding that there is no difference in the mean times is to be .10. Past experience indicates that the standard deviation of the time required for a service call is about $\sigma_X = 60$ minutes.

a. What is the required sample size?

b. If the population standard deviation was $\sigma_X = 50$ minutes, what would be the necessary sample size? How does this sample size compare with that in part **a**? What generalization does this suggest?

c. Suppose that management would accept a risk of .10 of concluding that the mean time does not differ from that in the past when it actually differs by 20 minutes; the other risk specification is to remain the same. Given these specifications, what is the needed sample size? Assume that the population standard deviation is $\sigma_X = 60$ minutes. How does this sample size compare witn that in part **a**? What generalization is suggested by this comparison?

d. Could management in this decision problem protect itself completely against making Type I and II errors? Discuss.

e. Since the population standard deviation used in planning the necessary sample size usually is only an approximation, what effect does this use of an approximation have on the protection against incorrect decisions actually furnished by the decision rule? Why should the sample standard deviation, rather than the value for the population standard deviation used in planning the necessary sample size, be used in constructing the decision rule? Discuss.

***17.14.** Refer to Problem 17.9. Suppose you had been called in before the sample was selected to recommend the appropriate sample size. You are informed that the risk of concluding that the question wording leads to bias in the responses when it does not should be controlled at the level .05, and the risk of concluding that the question wording does not lead to bias when actually the mean response error is 1.2 books is to be controlled at the level .05. Past experience indicates that the standard deviation of response errors is $\sigma_X = 4.5$ books.

a. What is the required sample size?

b. What would be the required sample size if $\sigma_X = 3$ books? How does this sample size compare with that in part **a**? What generalization does this suggest?

c. If $\mu_{II} = 1.5$ books instead of 1.2 books, all other risk specifications remaining the same, what is the required sample size? Assume that $\sigma_X = 4.5$ books. How does this sample size compare with that in part **a**? What generalization does this suggest?

CLASS PROJECT

17.15. Refer to Problem 10.19. In the past, the mean amount due Crandell Motor Freight, Inc., per freight bill has been $\mu_X = \$2.23$. Management wishes to determine if the mean in the current population of 500 freight bills is now higher than \$2.23.

a. From each sample of 50 freight bills, construct the appropriate decision rule; assume that the risk of concluding that the current population mean is higher than \$2.23, when it actually still is equal to \$2.23, is to be .025. What conclusion should be reached from each of the 100 samples?

b. Since we know that the mean of the 500 freight bills in the population is still \$2.23, what proportion of incorrect conclusions do you expect among the 100 conclusions? Explain.

c. What proportion of the conclusions from the 100 samples actually are incorrect?

d. What does this experiment illustrate about the construction of statistical decision rules from large simple random samples? Discuss.

Chapter

18

ADDITIONAL TOPICS I: POPULATION MEANS AND PROPORTIONS

In this chapter, we expand our previous discussion of statistical decision-making to cover a variety of decision problems. First, we take up a decision problem involving the population mean when the decision rule is based on a small sample size. Then we discuss a decision problem involving the difference between two population means. Next, we consider decision problems involving the population proportion and the difference between two population proportions. Finally, we discuss some applications of statistical decision rules and present several case studies to illustrate these applications.

18.1 DECISION–MAKING CONCERNING POPULATION MEAN—SMALL SIMPLE RANDOM SAMPLE CASE

In this section, we explain the construction of statistical decision rules involving the population mean when these are based on small simple random samples. Again, as in Section 12.4 of the chapter on statistical estimation, *we confine ourselves to the case in which the population sampled is normally distributed or not highly skewed.*

The construction of a statistical decision rule in this case needs little explanation. Assuming that the population standard deviation σ_X is unknown and must be estimated by the sample standard deviation s_X, which is usually the situation, one must use the t-distribution instead of the normal distribution. With this one difference, the procedures discussed in the previous chapter for setting up decision rules involving the population mean are still applicable.

Consider again the sample of five cans of tomatoes, described in Section 12.4 (p. 252). Suppose that the average drained weight content for the process had been 22.0 ounces and that the management wants to know if there has been any change in the process average. Thus, the alternatives being considered are:

$C_1 \quad \mu_X = 22.0$ ounces
$C_2 \quad \mu_X \neq 22.0$ ounces

Suppose further that management specifies that the risk of concluding C_2 ($\mu_X \neq 22.0$) at $\mu_I = 22.0$ is to be controlled at .05. Figure 17.7 (p. 372) provides an analogous picture of the problem for the large sample case. We now must determine the value of t (rather than of z as before), so that the area in the two tails of the distribution is .05. From Table A-5, we determine for 4 degrees of freedom (sample size is 5) that the appropriate t value is 2.776. Remember that we use the column headed .05, since the captions in the table refer to the total area in the two tails. Thus, we shall conclude that the process average has remained the same whenever the sample average falls within $2.776s_{\bar{X}}$ from 22.0 ounces; otherwise, we shall conclude that the process average has changed. That is, the lower action limit is $A_1 = 22.0 - 2.776s_{\bar{X}}$, and the upper action limit is $A_2 = 22.0 + 2.776s_{\bar{X}}$.

From the sample of five cans, we estimate that the standard deviation of the sample mean is $s_{\bar{X}} = .37$ ounces (see p. 252). Hence, the decision-making rule is as follows:

If $22.0 - 2.776(.37) \leq \bar{X} \leq 22.0 + 2.776(.37)$, conclude C_1 ($\mu_X = 22.0$)
Otherwise, conclude C_2 ($\mu_X \neq 22.0$)

That is, the decision rule leads to conclusion C_1, that the process mean has not changed, as long as the sample mean $\bar{X}$ falls between 20.97 and 23.03 ounces. Otherwise, the decision rule leads to conclusion C_2, that the process mean has changed. Since the average drained weight of the five sample cans was $\bar{X} = 22.9$ ounces (see Table 12.2), the decision rule leads to conclusion C_1, that the process mean has not changed.

Note that the above decision rule was constructed so as to provide the assurance that the risk of concluding C_2 (that the process mean has changed), when in fact the process mean is at the past level of 22.0 ounces, is only .05. Also note that the construction of the decision rule followed (17.10), p. 374, with the exception that z was replaced by t.

The construction of a decision rule for a one-sided alternative when the sample size is small also follows the procedure described earlier, except that the t-distribution instead of the normal distribution would be used. In this case one must be careful in entering Table A-5, since the captions in that table refer to the area in *both* tails of the distribution, whereas the area in *one* tail is required here. Thus, to obtain the t value corresponding to an area of .05 in one tail, one must look in the column headed .10. Formulas

(17.3) and (17.7) are applicable to the small sample case, under the conditions previously stated, except that the z-multiple must be replaced by the t-multiple.

18.2 DECISION–MAKING CONCERNING DIFFERENCE BETWEEN TWO POPULATION MEANS—LARGE SIMPLE RANDOM SAMPLE CASE

Frequently, a statistical decision problem deals with two population means. For instance, one may wish to know whether average personal income this year exceeds that of last year, or whether the mean tensile strength of metal castings made by a new process is greater than the mean tensile strength with the existing process. *In this section, we consider the construction of decision rules when each of the two samples is a large simple random one, with the sample sizes predetermined and the two samples selected independently.* (Readers who have not read Section 14.1 should do so before proceeding further.)

Review of sampling distribution of D

From Section 14.1, it will be recalled that we denote the two populations under consideration as populations 1 and 2, and that these have means μ_{X_1} and μ_{X_2} and standard deviations σ_{X_1} and σ_{X_2}, respectively. Simple random samples of sizes n_1 and n_2 are selected from the respective populations. The sample means and standard deviations are $\bar{X}_1$ and s_{X_1} and $\bar{X}_2$ and s_{X_2}, respectively, for the two samples.

The decision rule involves $D = \bar{X}_2 - \bar{X}_1$. We know that the sampling distribution of D has mean and standard deviation:

$$\mu_D = \mu_{X_2} - \mu_{X_1} \qquad \sigma_D = \sqrt{\sigma_{\bar{X}_1}^2 + \sigma_{\bar{X}_2}^2}$$

if the two samples are independent. Finally, if *both* samples are reasonably large, the sampling distribution of D is approximately normal. Since the sampling distribution of D is approximately normal for large samples, the construction of decision rules involving D corresponds to the previous procedures for only one population.

Construction of decision rule

We continue our example from Section 14.1 concerning the two processes for making metal castings (see p. 278). Let population 1 be the present process and population 2 the proposed process. Management of the Wilson Metals Corporation wishes to switch to the new process if the mean tensile strength of castings with the new process is *greater* than the mean tensile strength with the existing process. If the two processes provide equal mean tensile strengths of castings, management prefers to keep the existing process because of the conversion costs required to install the new process. In other words, the alternatives are:

C_1 $\mu_{X_2} \leq \mu_{X_1}$ (retain existing process)
C_2 $\mu_{X_2} > \mu_{X_1}$ (switch to new process)

The desired power curve is shown in Figure 18.1a. Note that if $\mu_{X_2} \leq \mu_{X_1}$, management wants to retain the old process; hence the probability of being led to switch processes (C_2) should be low in that case. If μ_{X_2} is greater than

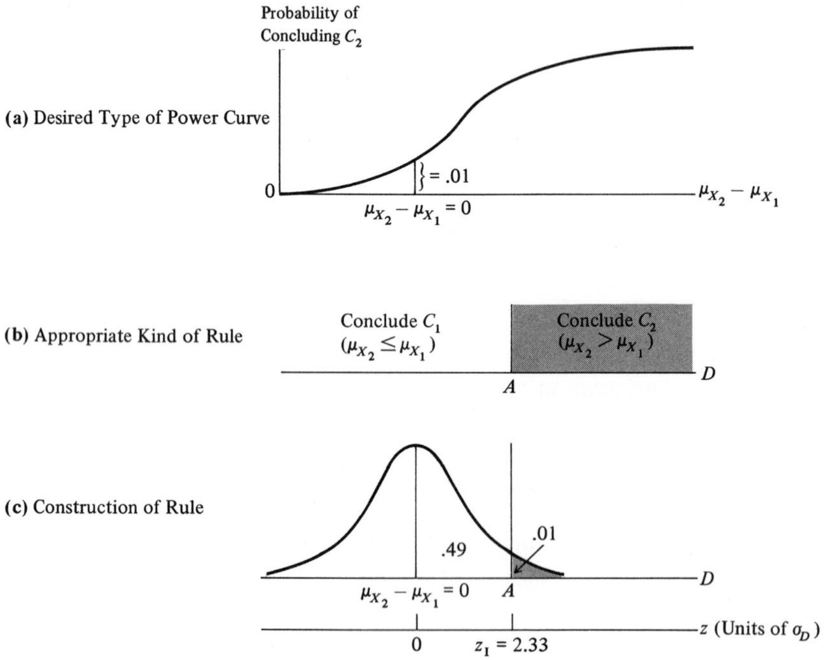

Figure 18.1. Steps in the construction of one-sided decision rule involving two population means

μ_{X_1}, on the other hand, the probability of being led to C_2 should be high. The type of decision rule that has this desired type of power curve is shown in Figure 18.1b. Suppose management wishes to control at the level .01 the risk of being led by the decision rule to conclusion C_2 ($\mu_{X_2} > \mu_{X_1}$), when actually $\mu_{X_1} = \mu_{X_2}$.

If $\mu_{X_1} = \mu_{X_2}$, then $\mu_D = 0$. Figure 18.1c contains the sampling distribution of D for the case $\mu_D = \mu_{X_2} - \mu_{X_1} = 0$. The shaded area in the upper tail represents the probability of concluding C_2 (switch to new process) if the new process has the same mean tensile strength as the old one. This shaded area is to be .01, which means that the z value of the action limit is 2.33. Hence, the action limit is $2.33\sigma_D$ above the mean zero. The standard deviation σ_D, as before, must be estimated from the samples. Using the sample results from Table 14.1 (p. 282), we find that $s_D = 738$ psi and the action limit therefore is:

$$A = 0 + 2.33s_D = 0 + 2.33(738) = 1{,}719.54 \text{ psi}$$

Hence, the decision rule is:

If $D \leq 1{,}719.5$, conclude C_1 $(\mu_{X_2} \leq \mu_{X_1})$
If $D > 1{,}719.5$, conclude C_2 $(\mu_{X_2} > \mu_{X_1})$

Since the sample means were $\bar{X}_1 = 54{,}000$ psi, $\bar{X}_2 = 65{,}000$ psi, so that $D = 11{,}000$ psi, conclusion C_2 would be drawn, that the mean tensile strength of castings for process 2 is greater than that for process 1. Hence, management would wish to switch to the new process.

Recapitulation. We can summarize this problem in a more formal fashion. The alternatives are:

(18.1)
C_1 $\mu_{X_2} \leq \mu_{X_1}$
C_2 $\mu_{X_2} > \mu_{X_1}$

The controlled risk is the risk of concluding C_2 at $\mu_I = \mu_{X_2} - \mu_{X_1} = 0$ — that is, the risk of a Type I error is controlled. The decision rule is:

(18.2)
If $D \leq z_I s_D$, conclude C_1 $(\mu_{X_2} \leq \mu_{X_1})$
Otherwise, conclude C_2 $(\mu_{X_2} > \mu_{X_1})$

Here z_I is the standard normal deviate associated with the specified risk of concluding C_2 $(\mu_{X_2} > \mu_{X_1})$ at $\mu_I = \mu_{X_2} - \mu_{X_1} = 0$.

In view of the correspondence of problems involving two population means with those involving only one population mean, we need not discuss in detail the construction of decision rules for other types of alternatives involving two population means. Simply note that the sampling distribution of D is utilized in the same way as that of $\bar{X}$ in setting up decision rules.

18.3 DECISION-MAKING CONCERNING POPULATION PROPORTION—LARGE SIMPLE RANDOM SAMPLE CASE

In this section, we deal with decisions concerning the population proportion. As will be evident, the procedures for making decisions concerning the population proportion correspond to the procedures already explained for making decisions concerning the population mean. *In this section, again we consider only the case in which the sample is a large simple random one.* (Readers who have not read Chapter 11 should do so before proceeding further.)

Review of sampling distribution of $\bar{p}$

The sample proportion $\bar{p}$, based on a simple random sample of size n, has a probability distribution whose mean $\mu_{\bar{p}}$ is equal to p, the population proportion. The standard deviation of the sampling distribution of $\bar{p}$ is $\sigma_{\bar{p}} = \sqrt{p(1-p)/n}$ if the population is infinite. Finally, it is known that the sampling distribution of $\bar{p}$ is approximately normal if the sample size is reasonably large.

Power curve of decision rule

Suppose that a shipment of 50,000 items is to be sampled to determine if its quality is acceptable. The purchasing contract specifies that the shipment is to contain no more than 3 per cent defective items. If the lot is of acceptable quality, it will be released immediately to production; otherwise, the lot will be rejected, which means in the present case that each of the items in the lot will be inspected at the vendor's expense before being turned over to production.

Hence, the two alternatives are:

$C_1 \quad p \leq .03$ (accept)

$C_2 \quad p > .03$ (reject)

Suppose management intends to select a simple random sample of 400 items from the lot and employ the following *arbitrary* decision rule:

If $\bar{p} \leq .035$, conclude C_1 $(p \leq .03)$

If $\bar{p} > .035$, conclude C_2 $(p > .03)$

where $\bar{p}$ is the proportion of defective items in the sample.

In constructing the power curve for this decision rule, we proceed in the usual manner. We determine for all possible values of the population proportion p the probability that the decision rule leads to conclusion C_2 $(p > .03)$. Figure 18.2 illustrates some of these calculations, and Figure 18.3 contains the power curve of the decision rule. Note that the finite correction factor is ignored in calculating $\sigma_{\bar{p}}$, because the shipment size is large relative to the sample size. Also note that *the standard deviation of* $\bar{p}$ *must be re-calculated for each value of* p *since it depends on the population proportion.* Aside from these re-calculations, everything pointed out earlier regarding the relations between decision rules and power curves still applies here.

Construction of decision rule to control Type I error

We continue with the decision problem concerning the acceptance of the shipment. Suppose that management has arbitrarily decided to use a simple

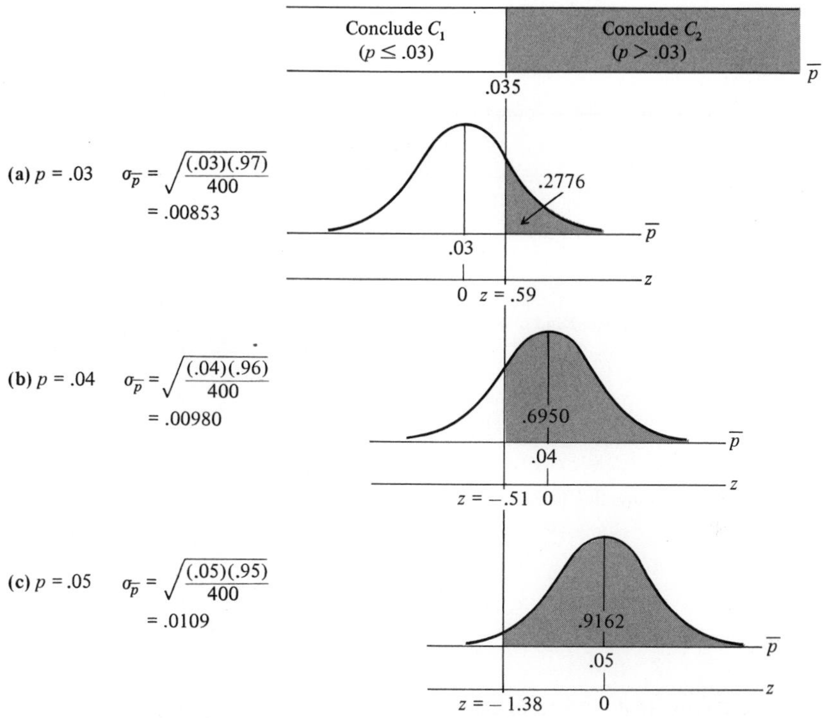

Figure 18.2. Illustrations of power probability calculations for one-sided decision rule involving population proportion (n = 400)

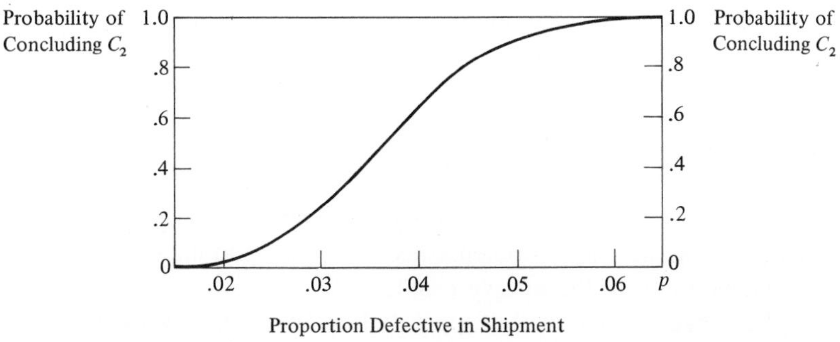

Figure 18.3. Power curve for one-sided decision rule involving population proportion

random sample of 300 items and wishes to control at the level .10 the risk of concluding C_2 (rejecting the shipment) at $p_I = p_0 = .03$. Note that in this instance, the Type I error is controlled at the level $p_I = p_0$. In other cases, the level p_I will differ from p_0, depending upon the structure of the payoff functions.

Figure 18.4a indicates the desired power curve, and Figure 18.4b the ap-

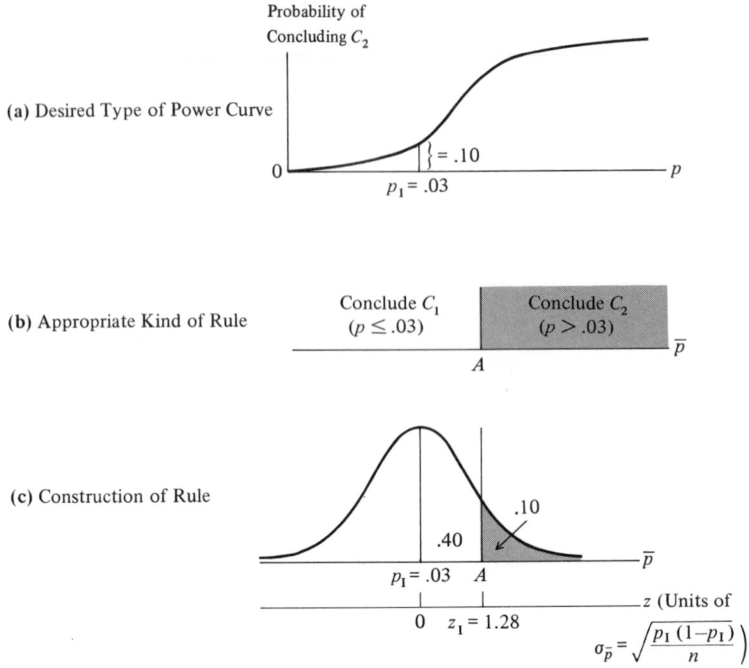

Figure 18.4. Steps in the construction of one-sided decision rule involving population proportion

propriate kind of decision rule that should be used to yield the desired type of power curve. The sampling distribution of $\bar{p}$ when $p = p_I = .03$ is shown in Figure 18.4c, centered around its mean $\mu_{\bar{p}} = p_I = .03$, with standard deviation:

$$\sigma_{\bar{p}} = \sqrt{\frac{(.03)(.97)}{300}} = .00985$$

Note that we know $\sigma_{\bar{p}}$ for the sampling distribution of $\bar{p}$ when $p = p_I = .03$. In previous decision problems involving the population mean, we had to estimate $\sigma_{\bar{X}}$ from the sample results.

The shaded area in the upper tail of the sampling distribution of $\bar{p}$ in Figure 18.4c represents the probability of being led by the rule to conclude C_2 (reject the shipment) when $p = .03$, and this probability is to be .10. Hence, the z value of the action limit is 1.28, and the action limit must be $1.28\sigma_{\bar{p}}$ above .03, or:

$$A = .03 + 1.28\sigma_{\bar{p}} = .03 + 1.28(.00985) = .0426$$

The final rule then is:

If $\bar{p} \le .0426$, conclude C_1 ($p \le .03$)
If $\bar{p} > .0426$, conclude C_2 ($p > .03$)

Suppose that $\bar{p}$ for the sample selected was actually .039. In that case, the rule would lead to conclusion C_1 ($p \leq .03$), which implies that the shipment should be accepted and released directly to production.

Recapitulation. Note how the construction of this decision rule is similar to the procedures discussed earlier. Here, the alternatives are:

$$\begin{array}{ll} C_1 & p \leq p_0 \\ C_2 & p > p_0 \end{array} \tag{18.3}$$

In our example, p_0 was .03. The controlled risk is the risk of concluding C_2 ($p > p_0$) when $p = p_{\text{I}}$ (in our example, $p_{\text{I}} = .03$), and the decision rule for a large simple random sample then is:

$$\begin{array}{l} \text{If } \bar{p} \leq p_{\text{I}} + z_{\text{I}}\sqrt{\dfrac{p_{\text{I}}(1-p_{\text{I}})}{n}}, \text{ conclude } C_1\ (p \leq p_0) \\ \text{Otherwise, conclude } C_2\ (p > p_0) \end{array} \tag{18.4}$$

Here z_{I} is the standard normal deviate associated with the specified risk of concluding $C_2(p > p_0)$ when $p = p_{\text{I}}$. Decision rules involving other alternatives are constructed in a similar manner.

Determination of necessary sample size to control both types of errors

If the sample size is predetermined arbitrarily, the risks of making both types of incorrect decisions cannot be controlled in problems involving population proportions. (This was also the case in problems involving population means.) We now explain how to determine the sample size necessary to control both types of risks of incorrect decisions at specified levels. *The procedure to be presented is applicable if the necessary sample size turns out to be reasonably large.*

Suppose that management in our previous example, where the alternatives were:

$$\begin{array}{ll} C_1 & p \leq p_0 = .03 \\ C_2 & p > p_0 = .03 \end{array}$$

wants to control both types of risks of incorrect decisions. As before, management wants to control the risk of a Type I error (concluding C_2 and rejecting the lot when $p = p_{\text{I}} = .03$) at the level .10. In addition, it has determined that if the proportion defective in the lot is as high as .06 or even higher, the payoff for the act "reject the lot" is much preferable to that for the act "accept the lot." Hence, management wishes to control the risk of a Type II error (concluding C_1 and accepting the lot when $p = p_{\text{II}} = .06$) at the level .05. Figure 18.5a indicates the desired power curve; Figure 18.5b contains the appropriate kind of decision rule to yield this type of power curve. Finally, Figure 18.5c contains the sampling distribu-

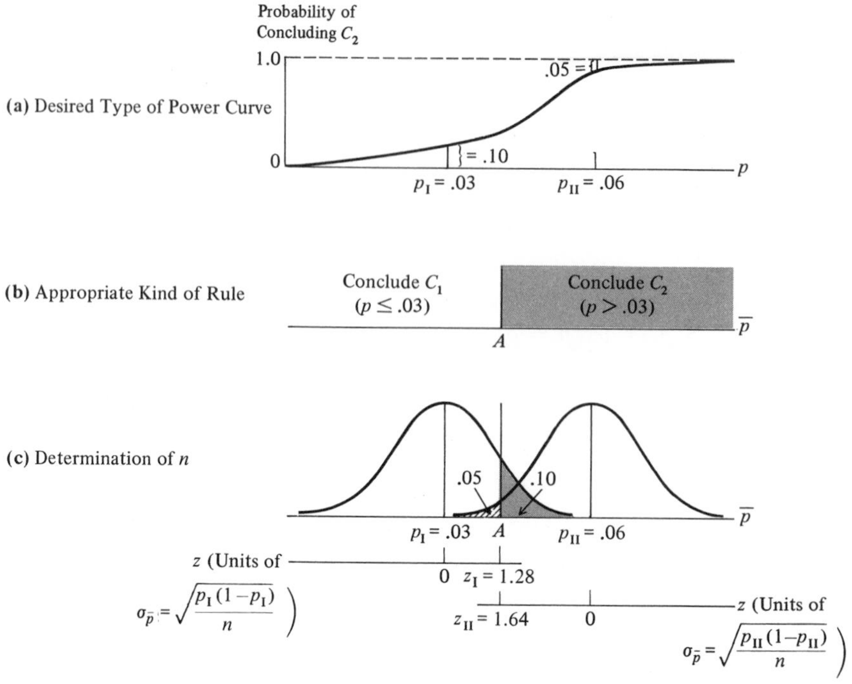

Figure 18.5. Steps in the determination of necessary sample size for one-sided alternative involving population proportion

tion of $\bar{p}$ when $p = p_I = .03$ and also when $p = p_{II} = .06$. The z value for the action limit when $p = p_I = .03$ is $z_I = 1.28$ and when $p = p_{II} = .06$ is $z_{II} = 1.64$. *Note that the z values are always taken to be positive.*

As in earlier examples, we write two simultaneous equations for the action limit A:

$$A = p_I + z_I \sqrt{\frac{p_I(1 - p_I)}{n}}$$

$$A = p_{II} - z_{II} \sqrt{\frac{p_{II}(1 - p_{II})}{n}}$$

Note again that $\sigma_{\bar{p}}$ depends on the value of p. Also note that the omission of the finite correction factor in $\sigma_{\bar{p}}$ assumes that the resulting sample size will not be large relative to the population size. Solving for n, we obtain after some algebraic manipulations:

(18.5) $$n = \frac{\left[z_I\sqrt{p_I(1 - p_I)} + z_{II}\sqrt{p_{II}(1 - p_{II})}\right]^2}{(p_I - p_{II})^2}$$

For our example, n is:

$$n = \frac{\left[1.28\sqrt{(.03)(.97)} + 1.64\sqrt{(.06)(.94)}\right]^2}{(.03 - .06)^2} = 410.6$$

The action limit A is obtained by substituting into either of the two simultaneous equations—for example:

$$A = .03 + 1.28\sqrt{\frac{(.03)(.97)}{411}} = .041$$

Hence, the decision procedure is to select a simple random sample of 411 items from the shipment, and to use the rule:

If $\bar{p} \leq .041$, conclude C_1 $(p \leq .03)$
If $\bar{p} > .041$, conclude C_2 $(p > .03)$

This decision-making procedure then controls the risks of making both types of incorrect decisions at the levels specified by management.

Note that the entire decision-making procedure in this case can be formulated in advance. On the other hand, when the decision problem involves a population mean and we must estimate $\sigma_{\bar{X}}$ from the sample, we must wait until the sample is selected to complete the construction of the rule.

If the alternative conclusions are two-sided or one-sided involving a lower-tail test, (18.5) still may be used. Just remember that the appropriate values of z always are taken to be positive in this formula. Also remember that the use of (18.5) is only appropriate if the resulting sample size is large, though not a large fraction of the population.

18.4

DECISION-MAKING CONCERNING DIFFERENCE BETWEEN TWO POPULATION PROPORTIONS—LARGE SIMPLE RANDOM SAMPLE CASE

In this section, we deal with decisions concerning the difference between two population proportions. *We consider the case in which each of the two samples is a large simple random one, with the sample sizes predetermined and the two samples selected independently.* (Readers who have not read Section 14.3 should do so before proceeding further.)

To illustrate this type of problem, we use our earlier example in Section 14.3, in which surveys were undertaken in 1971 and 1972 to study expectations regarding future business conditions (see p. 287). Here p_1 represents the proportion of persons in 1971 expecting business conditions to be good, and p_2 the proportion with these expectations in 1972. Suppose that the following alternatives are considered in the decision problem:

C_1 $\quad p_1 = p_2$
C_2 $\quad p_1 \neq p_2$

and that the Type I risk (concluding that a change in expectations has taken place (C_2), when actually none has) is to be controlled at the level .02.

The construction of the appropriate decision rule presents no new problems. Figure 18.6a indicates the desired power curve, and Figure 18.6b the appropriate kind of decision rule. The sampling distribution of $d = \bar{p}_2 - \bar{p}_1$ is shown in Figure 18.6c for the case $\mu_d = p_2 - p_1 = 0$, since the specified risk relates to this situation. The shaded areas in the two tails represent the probability of concluding that a change in expectations has taken place (C_2), when none did. These areas are to total .02, so that each area is to be .01.

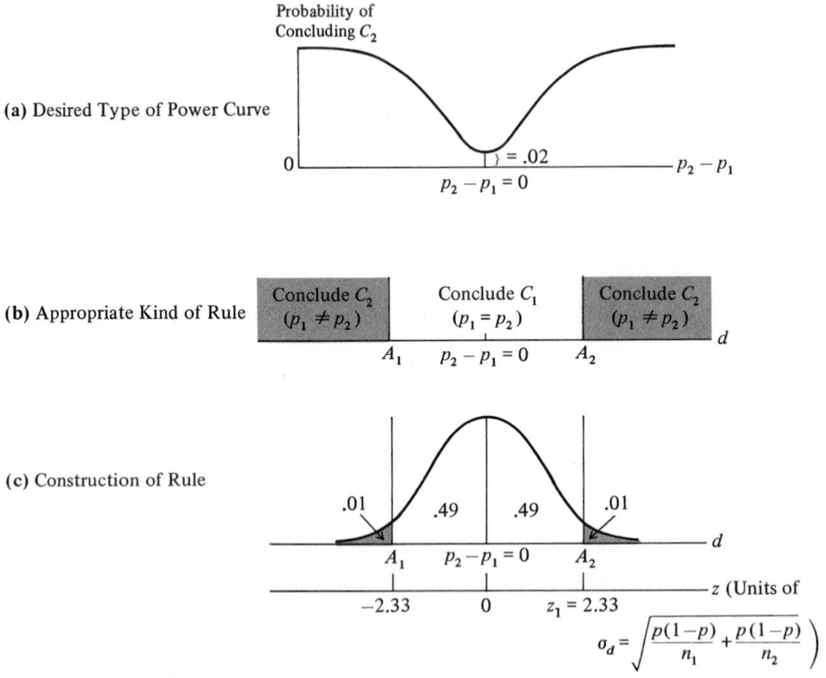

Figure 18.6. Steps in the construction of two-sided decision rule involving two population proportions

Hence, the appropriate z value for the action limits is 2.33, and the two action limits are $2.33\sigma_d$ above and below the mean of zero, respectively.

We still must estimate σ_d from the samples. If the two samples are independent, as is the case here, we have from (14.14a):

$$\sigma_d = \sqrt{\frac{p_1(1 - p_1)}{n_1} + \frac{p_2(1 - p_2)}{n_2}}$$

The finite correction factors are not included, because the population sizes are very large relative to the sample sizes. We are concerned with the sampling distribution of d when $p_1 = p_2$. In that case, we have:

$$\sigma_d = \sqrt{\frac{p(1 - p)}{n_1} + \frac{p(1 - p)}{n_2}}$$

Here p *is the common value of* p_1 *and* p_2. We take as our estimate of this common proportion:

(18.6) $$\bar{p} = \frac{n_1\bar{p}_1 + n_2\bar{p}_2}{n_1 + n_2}$$

In other words, $\bar{p}$ is the weighted average of the two sample proportions. Then, we estimate σ_d when $p_1 = p_2$ from:

(18.7) $$s_d = \sqrt{\frac{\bar{p}(1-\bar{p})}{n_1 - 1} + \frac{\bar{p}(1-\bar{p})}{n_2 - 1}}$$

For our example we have (p. 288):

$$n_1 = 3{,}000 \qquad \bar{p}_1 = .60$$
$$n_2 = 3{,}500 \qquad \bar{p}_2 = .30$$

so:

$$\bar{p} = \frac{3{,}000(.60) + 3{,}500(.30)}{3{,}000 + 3{,}500} = .438$$

and:

$$s_d = \sqrt{\frac{(.438)(.562)}{3{,}000 - 1} + \frac{(.438)(.562)}{3{,}500 - 1}} = .0123$$

Hence, the two action limits are:

$$A_1 = 0 - 2.33s_d = -2.33(.0123) = -.0287$$
$$A_2 = 0 + 2.33s_d = 2.33(.0123) = .0287$$

The decision rule then is:

If $-.0287 \leq d \leq .0287$, conclude C_1 $(p_1 = p_2)$
Otherwise, conclude C_2 $(p_1 \neq p_2)$

In our example, $d = .30 - .60 = -.30$. We would conclude C_2, therefore, that the proportion of persons expecting good business conditions in the year ahead did not remain the same between 1971 and 1972.

Recapitulation

Our decision problem concerns two random samples, each being large and selected independently of the other. The alternatives are:

(18.8)
C_1 $\quad p_1 = p_2$
C_2 $\quad p_1 \neq p_2$

The controlled risk is the risk of concluding C_2 $(p_1 \neq p_2)$ at $\mu_I = p_2 - p_1 = 0$, and the appropriate decision rule then is:

(18.9)
If $-z_I s_d \leq d \leq z_I s_d$, conclude C_1 $(p_1 = p_2)$
Otherwise, conclude C_2 $(p_1 \neq p_2)$

Here $\bar{p}$ is defined by (18.6), s_d is defined by (18.7), and z_I is the standard normal deviate associated with the specified risk of concluding C_2 ($p_1 \neq p_2$) at $\mu_I = p_2 - p_1 = 0$.

18.5
STATISTICAL CONTROL CHARTS AND ACCEPTANCE SAMPLING

We now discuss two applications of statistical decision rules, namely statistical control charts and acceptance sampling. In each case, we describe several applications of these procedures to illustrate their usefulness.

Statistical control charts

Statistical control charts have become a widely used tool for controlling the quality of a process. Essentially, they represent a continuous application of the statistical decision rules discussed previously. The setting up and use of a control chart can best be explained in terms of an example. We therefore consider again the production of drug tablets mentioned in earlier chapters. It will be recalled that the thickness of the tablets is an important quality characteristic to be controlled. Management wishes to know when a change in the process average takes place, so that it can search for the causes and take appropriate remedial action.

Setting up a control chart. To set up a control chart for the quality characteristic under consideration, one must first obtain information about the average and standard deviation of the thickness of tablets turned out by the production process. Many important problems are involved in getting this information; these are discussed in specialized texts on statistical quality control. We simply assume here that past information indicates that the mean thickness of tablets turned out by the process is $\mu_X = .241$ inches and that the standard deviation of the thickness of tablets is $\sigma_X = .001$ inches.

Suppose that a sample of five tablets is to be taken periodically, on the basis of which decisions are to be made about whether any changes have occurred in the average thickness of tablets turned out by the process. What are the characteristics of the sampling distribution of $\bar{X}$? In a situation of this nature, the sampling distribution of $\bar{X}$ often will be approximately normal, even though the sample size is quite small. Furthermore, we know on the basis of the past information given above that the mean of the sampling distribution of $\bar{X}$ is $\mu_{\bar{X}} = \mu_X = .241$ inches and that its standard deviation is $\sigma_{\bar{X}} = \sigma_X/\sqrt{n} = .001/\sqrt{5} = .000447$ inches.

It is then customary practice in the United States to construct action limits of 3 standard deviations above and below the process average:

$$\mu_X \pm 3\sigma_{\bar{X}} \tag{18.10}$$

For our example, these limits are .241 ± 3(.000447) = .241 ± .0013 inches.

These action limits are then used to choose between the following two courses of action:

(18.11)
C_1 Let process alone
C_2 Look for assignable cause and take appropriate action

The following decision-making procedure is employed:

If the average thickness of the five sample tablets is between .2397 inches and .2423 inches, conclude C_1—that the process average has not changed, and therefore, *let the process alone.*

If the sample average is less than .2397 inches or greater than .2423 inches, conclude C_2—that the process average has changed, and therefore, *look for the assignable cause of change.*

Note the correspondence to the decision rule in (17.10), p. 374. Assuming that the samples are simple random ones, that the sampling distribution of $\overline{X}$ is normal or approximately so, and that the information obtained from past experience is fairly reliable, we know from previous work that the probability that the above rule will lead one to look for an assignable cause of change, when in fact the process average has remained the same, is negligibly small.

To facilitate the use of this decision rule by plant personnel, as well as for some other reasons to be discussed shortly, the rule is usually presented graphically. The graph of the decision rule is called a *control chart.* Figure 18.7 presents the control chart for our example. Note that the process average and the upper and lower action limits of the decision rule are plotted as horizontal lines. The Y axis denotes thickness of tablets; the X axis represents time over which samples are taken periodically. The upper limit

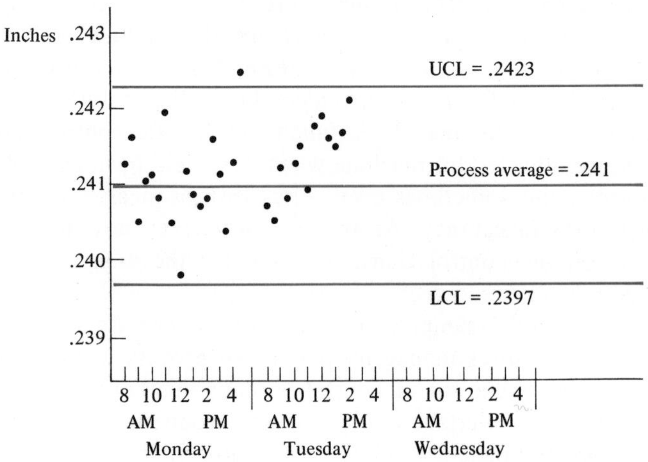

Figure 18.7. Control chart for process average thickness of drug tablets

is called *upper control limit* (UCL) and the lower limit *lower control limit* (LCL).

Using the control chart. Periodic samples—in this instance, of five tablets—are taken from the process, and a point representing the average thickness $\overline{X}$ for each sample is plotted on the control chart. As long as the points stay within the control limits, it is concluded that any variation in the average thickness of tablets found in the various samples is simply a result of chance, and therefore, that there has been no change in the underlying factors influencing the average performance of the process. In terms of actions to be taken, this means that the process is to be let alone. If a point falls outside the control limits, however, it is concluded that the process average has changed as a result of an assignable cause that was not present previously. Hence, a point outside the control limits indicates that a search for the assignable cause should be undertaken, on the basis of which appropriate remedial action can be initiated. Points inside the control limits indicate that the process is *in control;* points outside show that the process is *out of control*. For instance, Figure 18.7 indicates that the process went out of control on Monday between 4 and 4:30 P.M.

Information provided by control chart. A key characteristic of the control chart is that it furnishes the approximate time when a process goes out of control. This knowledge often provides a valuable clue to the assignable cause. For instance, a process may have gone out of control at about the same time that raw material from a new supplier was put into the process. Hence, the improvement or worsening of the quality of the product may have been due to this factor. If investigation discloses that this, indeed, was the reason for the change in the process and if the change represents a worsening of quality, management should take action to prevent receiving such poor raw material in the future. If, however, the change represents an improvement in quality, management should take action to obtain raw material of this quality in the future. Note how the out-of-control point can lead to a future improvement in quality in either event. In another instance, a point may have fallen outside the control limits because an operator adjusted his machine when he should have let it alone. An out-of-control point sometimes even arises from a measuring instrument's or an inspector's inaccuracy. At any rate, whenever an out-of-control point appears on the control chart, a search for the assignable cause should be undertaken.

The periodic sampling of the process, necessary in the control-chart approach, assures management that the process will not operate too long after it has gone out of control without this condition being detected. If inspection is undertaken only after the production of a large batch of units has been completed, a process may turn out many defective items before the condition is discovered.

The control chart furnishes other valuable clues in addition to indicating when a process is out of control. Through the plotting of sample results over a period of time, one can study trends or other changes in the quality of performance. For instance, Figure 18.7 indicates that there has been an upward trend in the average thickness of the tablets in the Tuesday samples. Should that continue, the process soon would go out of control. In such a case, remedial action can sometimes be undertaken even before the process actually goes out of control. Statistical theory must be used, however, to decide whether the upward tendency in the sample averages is due to a real trend in the process average or whether the process average has not, in fact, changed and what appears to be a trend is merely a result of chance.

When an assignable cause has been discovered and appropriate remedial action taken, changes in the process average, the process variability, or both, frequently result. For instance, it may be found after a particular remedial action has been taken that the next ten sample averages are all below the process average (the center line on the control chart). Statistical theory then can be used to decide whether this indicates that there has been a lowering of the process average or whether it has remained the same and the result is merely due to chance. If there has been a change in the process average, or in the variability of the process, the quality control chart should be revised to reflect the new process conditions.

Additional comments. We now examine further the construction of the control limits in the previous example. Why should past experience have been used in calculating the control limits when the quality performance in the past may not even have been satisfactory? Its use illuminates the philosophy underlying the control-chart approach. Quality cannot be produced by edict. For instance, the engineering department may set standards that are to be adhered to. If, however, the machines and operators are not capable of meeting these standards, the desired quality requirements cannot be satisfied.

In order to discover the capabilities of machines and operators, assignable causes that are present must first be eliminated. Control charts lead to the detection of such causes by depicting a process as it is, not as someone says it should be. This use of statistical control charts has led to substantial improvements in the quality of products in one application after another, because control charts furnish valuable clues in the search for assignable causes by indicating when a process goes out of control.

The fact that a process is in control does not mean it is operating satisfactorily. For instance, the thickness of drug tablets turned out by the production process may be in control but at an undesirable level of average thickness. When a control chart is first applied to a process, however, the process usually is not in control. The search for and elimination of assignable causes of process variation frequently leads not only to control of the process but also to production at a satisfactory level of quality.

The quality of a product depends not only upon the average performance of the process but also upon the process variability. Should there be an increase in the population standard deviation, for instance, the product would be more variable. This increased variability might signify that a larger proportion of items will not meet specifications. Hence, it is important to control also the process variability, and this is done by another control chart similar to the one described earlier for the process average. Control charts also can be constructed for controlling the population proportion in cases in which the quality of the process is measured in terms of the proportion of defective items, errors, and the like. Still other control charts can be constructed; the basic philosophy explained above applies to all of these.

The discussion of control charts so far has been principally in terms of production processes in a plant. However, clerical work also represents a type of repetitive production process and hence has been controlled successfully by this statistical approach. Indeed, control-chart techniques have been applied to all kinds of processes, ranging from accident rates to sales performance.

Several cases in which statistical control charts have been applied are now described to illustrate the nature of these applications and to indicate the substantial benefits that usually accompany the introduction of these techniques.

Federal Products Corporation. The Federal Products Corporation has applied the control-chart approach to the operation of turning the diameter of a cylindrical hub located in the center of a brass forging (Ref. 18.1). Initially, samples of five pieces were selected from each machine every 20 minutes. If the sample result indicated that the process was out of control, the operator interrupted the production to correct for the dimensional trend indicated by the sample, or took some other appropriate corrective action. If the sample indicated that the process was in control, production was let alone. Control charts were maintained at each machine.

As the operators gained practice and experience with the statistical control-chart approach, it became feasible to reduce sampling in most instances to once every half hour. This application of control-chart techniques led to some remarkable results:

1. The quality of the work improved. In the past, about 14 per cent of total production had to be either scrapped or re-worked. Within a short time after the introduction of the statistical control program, this proportion declined to 1.6 per cent.
2. With the improved quality of the product, it was possible to reduce final inspection, which formerly had been undertaken as a matter of routine, to not more than four patrol visits per shift, and then only to make a

visual check of the control charts. In this way, 90 per cent of the previous inspection time and cost was eliminated.

3. The number of units produced per hour increased.
4. Operators obtained a renewed interest in the quality of their output.

Alden's, Inc.[1] Alden's, a mail-order house, was one of the earliest companies to apply statistical control-chart techniques to clerical work. This technique was used, among other instances, for controlling the filling of customers' orders in merchandise departments. In this application, 100 work units (orders) are selected at random several times a day and inspected. A work unit is considered to have been incorrectly handled if any error, such as in size, color, and quantity, has been made. Error rates are posted on the control charts as quickly as possible and remedial action is undertaken when out-of-control points appear.

Before control charts were used in one merchandise department, about 3 out of each 100 work units were handled incorrectly. Within a few weeks after the introduction of the control charts, the error rate dropped to 1.65 per cent and still later to .7 per cent. The error rate for all merchandise departments combined decreased 58 per cent during the first four years of operation of statistical control techniques.

Acceptance sampling

Acceptance sampling is another application of the types of decision rules discussed earlier. The choice of alternatives in this case is between accepting or rejecting a lot of material, that is:

(18.12)

C_1 Accept lot

C_2 Reject lot

This application of statistical decision rules has been used for testing the quality of incoming material from a vendor and for testing the quality of a particular lot of items after these have been produced. Acceptance sampling also has been used to test the quality of clerical work.

In each of these instances, a decision is to be made about the quality of a particular group of items, such as a lot of incoming material. Since the population under study is finite, every item could be examined, checked, or inspected. Such 100 per cent inspection is often prohibitively expensive, however, and in any case does not usually detect all of the defective units, errors, and the like. Hence, sampling often is used to decide whether the quality of the lot is satisfactory enough so that the lot should be accepted (C_1), or whether the quality is so unsatisfactory that the lot should be re-

[1] The discussion of this case, and the Standard Register Company case below, has been adapted, by permission of the American Statistical Association, from Reference 18.2, pp. 8–13.

jected (C_2). The latter decision may lead to 100 per cent inspection of the items, a return of the lot to the vendor, or some other action of this nature. If rejection of a lot also leads to a search for the causes of the poor quality, the approach is quite similar to that of the control-chart philosophy. Usually, however, acceptance sampling is used simply to decide whether to accept the particular lot of material that was sampled or whether to reject it.

In acceptance sampling, the quality of an item is often expressed simply by classifying the item as being either satisfactory or defective. A decision rule with specified risks of making incorrect decisions can then be constructed to fit this method of quality specification (see Section 18.3). For instance, the rule might be:

> Select at random 100 items from the lot.
> If more than 2 items in the sample are defective, reject the lot.
> If 2 or fewer items in the sample are defective, accept the lot.

There are two types of possible incorrect decisions in a case of this nature—namely, accepting a lot that should have been rejected (Type II error), and rejecting a lot that should have been accepted (Type I error). Risks of making these incorrect decisions can be specified at reasonably low levels and the necessary sample size determined from these requirements; often this sample size is relatively small. Tables are available that provide ready-made decision rules with known risks of the two types of possible incorrect decisions. The cost advantage in making a decision from a relatively small sample, with low risks of an incorrect decision, over one based upon 100 per cent inspection that probably is not perfectly accurate anyway, should be readily apparent. Several cases below describe the magnitude of savings that companies have been able to achieve by replacing 100 per cent inspection with acceptance sampling while still maintaining or even improving the quality of performance.

Stewart-Warner Corporation. The Alemite Division of Stewart-Warner Corporation produces hydraulic fittings in astronomical quantities (Ref. 18.3). At one time, each of these fittings was inspected after manufacture, but it was subsequently concluded that this practice was economically unsound. A statistical acceptance sampling plan was introduced whereby it could be decided on the basis of a sample whether to accept or reject a lot of hydraulic fittings. If a lot is rejected, the adopted procedure specified that each of the fittings in the lot be inspected to sort the acceptable ones from the defective ones. The statistical sampling plan, together with the provision of 100 per cent inspection of rejected lots, was so designed that the manufacturer could be assured that in the long run he would ship out no more than a specified proportion of defective pieces, no matter what the state of quality of the production process. During the first two and one-half years of operation of this plan, the savings in inspection costs alone amounted to about \$100,000. This saving was accompanied by better product quality, together with an assurance to the manufacturer about the quality of shipments leaving the plant.

The Standard Register Company. The Standard Register Company applies an acceptance sampling plan to control the accuracy of its sales invoices. Previously, these had been inspected 100 per cent, but that procedure did not detect all erroneous invoices anyway. With the use of the statistical sampling technique, the time spent on verifying invoices has been reduced by 47 per cent while simultaneously a satisfactory accuracy level has been maintained. If the sample indicates that the quality of a group of invoices is unsatisfactory, the entire lot is verified. In addition, a control chart is also maintained. Out-of-control points have brought to light such conditions as improper or nonuniform training and improper placement of personnel.

Cited references

18.1 Kennedy, Clifford W., "Statistical Control Cuts Scrap Cost 88 Percent," *Factory Management and Maintenance,* November 1946, pp. 102–105.

18.2 Neter, John, "Some Applications of Statistics for Auditing," *Journal of the American Statistical Association,* March 1952, pp. 6–24.

18.3 Peterson, David C., "Statistical Quality Control Cuts Inspection Costs $100,000," *Steel,* January 29, 1951, pp. 58–62, 80–82.

QUESTIONS AND PROBLEMS

18.1. Explain briefly each of the following:

a. Assignable cause

b. Sampling distribution of D

c. Acceptance sampling

d. Control chart

18.2. Distinguish briefly between:

a. p_0, p_{I}, and p_{II}

b. Process control and acceptance sampling

18.3. Refer to Problem 12.22. In the past, the mean number of looms working at a given time in the section was 353 looms. Management wants to know if the process currently is still operating at the same level. The sample results obtained from the current process are given in Problem 12.22. For this sample, $n = 6$, $\overline{X} = 363$, $s_X = 8.81$.

a. Set up the appropriate decision rule, assuming that management wants to take a risk of only .02 of concluding that a change has taken place in the mean number of looms working at a given time, when no change actually occurred. What conclusion should be reached?

b. By using a larger sample size, would the power of the decision rule be improved? Discuss.

(Continued)

c. How could the same conclusion as in part **a** have been reached from a confidence interval for the current process mean? Explain. What would be the confidence coefficient corresponding to the specified risk in part **a**?

d. Construct the corresponding confidence interval. What information does it provide besides indicating the conclusion to be reached in the decision problem? Explain.

***18.4.** Refer to Problem 12.21. An analysis of the postal delivery system suggests that no more than 350 minutes, on the average, should be required by this mailman to cover his route. It is desired to determine whether or not this mailman's mean delivery time exceeds 350 minutes. The sample results are given in Problem 12.21. For this sample, $n = 5$, $\overline{X} = 367$, $s_X = 29.4$.

a. Set up the appropriate decision rule, assuming that the maximum risk of concluding that the mailman's mean delivery time exceeds 350 minutes, when it actually does not, is to be .05. What conclusion should be reached?

b. Does your decision rule provide exactly the risk specified in part **a**? Explain.

c. With a larger sample size, would the power of the decision rule be improved? Discuss.

***18.5.** Two appraisers of homes were tested as to the comparability of their appraisals. Two simple random samples of 100 homes each were selected independently in the community; each appraiser was then assigned one of these samples and asked to appraise the value of each of the homes in the sample. The sample results were as follows:

Appraiser A	*Appraiser B*
X_1 = Appraised value of sample home by A	X_2 = Appraised value of sample home by B
$n_1 = 100$	$n_2 = 100$
$\overline{X}_1 = \$21,420$	$\overline{X}_2 = \$19,610$
$s_{X_1} = \$2,500$	$s_{X_2} = \$2,520$

a. What are the two populations being sampled? Explain.

b. Construct the appropriate decision rule for deciding whether appraiser A, on the average, values homes at a higher level than appraiser B; assume that the risk of concluding that appraiser A values homes higher, on the average, than appraiser B, when actually they value homes at the same average level, should be .025. What conclusion should be reached?

c. Does your decision rule provide exactly the risk specified in part **b**? Explain.

d. Estimate the risk of concluding from your decision rule that appraiser A does not value homes higher than appraiser B when he actually values them higher, on the average, by \$500. Why is this only an estimate of the risk? Is this risk at an acceptable level? Discuss.

e. If the two appraisers were assigned the same sample of 100 homes to appraise independently, would the statistical techniques employed in the previous parts of this problem be appropriate to construct the decision rule? Why, or why not?

18.6. Refer to Problem 14.2. Suppose that management wants to determine if the mean rating given by employees for the company magazine differs for the two divisions. The sample results are shown in Problem 14.2.

a. Set up the appropriate decision rule, assuming that management wants to take a risk of only .05 of concluding that the mean rating differs for employees in the two divisions, when it actually is the same for both divisions. What conclusion should be reached?

b. Does your decision rule provide exactly the specified risk of .05 of making a Type I error? Explain.

c. How could the same conclusion as in part **a** have been reached from a confidence interval for the difference between the two mean grades? Explain. What would be the confidence coefficient corresponding to the specified risk in part **a**?

d. Construct the corresponding confidence interval. What additional information does it provide besides indicating the conclusion to be reached in the decision problem? Explain.

18.7. A shipment of material is acceptable if it contains 4 per cent or less defective items. The following decision-making procedure is employed: From the lot of 20,000 items, select at random 300 items and examine them. If no more than 4.6 per cent of the sample items are defective, accept the shipment. Otherwise, reject the shipment.

a. Calculate the ordinates of the power curve for this decision-making procedure for the following possible values of the proportion defective in the lot: .02, .03, .04, .05, .06, .07.

b. Plot this power curve on a graph.

c. How effective is the decision-making procedure if it is important to reject lots containing 5 per cent or more defective items? Discuss.

d. What would be the effect on the power curve if the action limit were lowered to 4.3 per cent in the above decision-making procedure, with no change in sample size? Calculate the ordinates of the new power curve for 4 per cent and 5 per cent defective items in the lot. What generalization does this suggest?

e. What would be the effect on the power curve if the sample size were increased to 500 items, with the action limit remaining at 4.3 per cent as in part **d**? Calculate the ordinates of the new power curve for 4 per cent and 5 per cent defective items in the lot. What generalization does this suggest?

***18.8.** Refer to Problem 14.3. In the past, 5 per cent of all blood contributions were rejected when subjected to additional testing at the central blood bank. To test if the current process proportion has changed from the prior value, the following decision-making procedure is used: Select a simple random sample of 400 contributions from the process. If the sample proportion of contributions rejected is between .03 and .07, conclude that no change has taken place in the process proportion. Otherwise, conclude that a change in the process proportion has occurred.

a. Calculate the ordinates of the power curve for this decision-making procedure for the following possible values of the process proportion: .01, .02, .03, .05, .07, .08, .09.

b. Plot this power curve on a graph.

c. What constitute the Type I and II errors in this case?

d. How effective is this decision-making procedure?

e. What would be the effect on the power curve if the action limits were narrowed to .04 and .06 in the above decision-making procedure, with no change in sample size? Calculate the ordinates of the new power curve for the following possible values of the process proportion: .02, .05, .09. What generalization does this suggest?

f. What would be the effect on the power curve if the sample size were decreased to 225 contributions, with the action limits remaining at .04 and .06 as in part **e**? Calculate the ordinates of the new power curve for the following possible values of the process proportion: .02, .05, .09. What generalization does this suggest?

***18.9.** In the past, 70 per cent of the persons entering a store made no purchases. A recent simple random sample of 750 persons showed that 580 of them made no purchases. Management wishes to know if a change has occurred in the proportion of persons not making any purchase.

a. Construct the appropriate decision rule, assuming that the risk of concluding that a change has taken place, when no change actually took place, is to be .025. What conclusion should be reached?

b. Why was it unnecessary to estimate $\sigma_{\bar{p}}$ from the sample in constructing your rule, although it is necessary to estimate $\sigma_{\bar{X}}$ from the sample in constructing a decision rule concerning the population mean? Explain.

c. Could the conclusion reached in part **a** have been deduced from a confidence interval for the current population proportion of persons not making any purchases? Explain. What would be the confidence coefficient corresponding to the specified risk in part **a**?

d. Construct the corresponding confidence interval. What additional information does it provide besides indicating the conclusion to be reached in the decision problem? Explain.

e. What is the power of your decision rule in part **a** if $p = .6$? Is this power at a satisfactory level? Discuss.

18.10. A simple random sample of 400 items from all of the items filed by a clerk during a week contained 10 incorrectly filed items. Assuming that a 2 per cent error rate or less is satisfactory, would you conclude that his work is not satisfactory? You are to take only a maximum risk of .05 of concluding that his work is not satisfactory when it actually is satisfactory.

18.11. The Allison Company purchased a shipment of 25,000 units. The contract specified that no more than 5 per cent of the units in the shipment could be defective. A simple random sample of 200 units was selected by the Allison Company from the shipment, and 12 of these were found defective.

a. Construct the appropriate decision rule for deciding if the shipment is of acceptable quality, assuming that the risk of concluding that the shipment is of acceptable quality when it actually contains 7 per cent defective units is to be only .02. What conclusion should be reached?

b. Why do you think that the risk of making a Type II error was specified here? Explain.

c. Why was it unnecessary to estimate $\sigma_{\bar{p}}$ from the sample in constructing the decision rule, although it is necessary to estimate $\sigma_{\bar{X}}$ from the sample in constructing decision rules concerning the population mean? Explain.

d. What is the maximum risk of rejecting an acceptable shipment with your decision rule? What additional information would you need to decide whether this risk is at an acceptable level? Explain.

***18.12.** A machine is to be observed at random times to determine if the proportion of time it is "down," that is, not in a productive state, does not exceed the standard $p = .15$. The maximum risk of concluding that the proportion of down-time for the machine exceeds the standard, when it does not, should be .06. At the same time, if the proportion of down-time for the machine is .22, the risk of failing to detect this should be .03.

a. What is the required sample size?

b. What is the appropriate decision rule?

c. Suppose the risk of failing to detect that the proportion of down-time for the machine exceeds the standard, when the proportion actually is .22, must be controlled at .01; the other risk specification is to be unchanged. Given these specifications, what is the necessary sample size? How does this sample size compare with that in part **a**? What generalization does this suggest?

18.13. Union and management representatives have tentatively agreed to contract terms. Ultimately, the contract must be ratified by at least 50 per cent of the 50,000 union members. Before seeking this ratification, the union leaders decided to select a simple random sample of union members to determine if they find the contract acceptable or not. If 50 per cent or more of the union members would accept the contract, the union representatives wish to take a maximum risk of .01 of concluding it would be rejected by the membership. At the same time, if only 40 per cent or less of the union members would accept the contract, the union representatives wish to take a maximum risk of .01 of concluding it would be accepted by the membership.

a. What are the points on the power curve specified by the above requirements? How do these points correspond to the specified maximum risks?

b. How large should the simple random sample size be to determine the members' preferences, on the basis of which the union representatives would make their decision to seek membership ratification or not?

c. What is the appropriate decision rule?

d. Suppose that the union representatives would be willing to take a maximum risk of .05 of concluding that the contract would be rejected by the membership when actually 50 per cent or more of the members would accept the contract; the other risk specification is to remain unchanged. Given these specifications, what is the necessary simple random sample size? How does this sample size compare with that in part **b**? What generalization does this comparison suggest?

18.14. Refer to Problem 14.12. Suppose that the production manager wishes to determine if the night shift's production contains the same proportion of defective gears as the day shift's production. The sample results are given in Problem 14.12. Set up the appropriate decision rule, assuming that the risk of concluding that the night shift's production differs in quality from that of the day shift, when the two actually contain the same proportion defective, is to be .04. What conclusion should be reached?

***18.15.** A market-research organization conducted two surveys at about the same time. Both pertained to the population of persons 16 years of age or older in the United States, though the two samples were selected independently. One survey, which we shall call the income survey, sought to obtain information on changes in consumption expenditures as a result of changes in income. The other survey, which we shall call the brand preference survey, sought to obtain information on brand preferences for various types of packaged foods.

In the income survey, which contained 1,000 persons, 149 refusals were encountered. In the brand preference survey, which contained 1,500 persons, 93 refusals were encountered. Assume that both samples were simple random ones, and that they were carried out in the same manner, and with the same care and supervision.

a. Do these results indicate that the subject matter of the survey affects the refusal rate? Set up the appropriate decision rule, assuming that the risk of concluding that the subject matter has an effect, when it actually has no effect, is to be .02. What conclusion should be reached?

(Continued)

b. Could the same conclusion have been reached from a confidence interval for the difference between the refusal rates for the two survey subjects? Explain. What would be the confidence coefficient corresponding to the specified risk in part **a**?

c. Construct the corresponding confidence interval. What information does it provide besides indicating the conclusion to be reached in the decision problem? Explain.

18.16. Samples of eight incandescent lamps are taken weekly from the production process and subjected to forced-life tests. On the basis of extensive past experience, it has been found that the lifetimes of the lamps produced by the manufacturing process are approximately normally distributed, with mean $\mu_X = 1{,}044$ hours and standard deviation $\sigma_X = 128$ hours.

a. Calculate the appropriate control limits of 3 standard deviations to decide whether any change in the process mean has taken place.

b. Plot the control limits on a chart. Then, plot the following sample results on the same chart:

Week of	*Sample Mean*	*Week of*	*Sample Mean*
1/8	1,035 hours	2/12	1,158 hours
1/15	984 hours	2/19	1,117 hours
1/22	1,045 hours	2/26	1,054 hours
1/29	1,013 hours	3/5	895 hours
2/5	1,148 hours	3/12	863 hours

c. Was the process in control during this period with respect to the mean life? Explain.

d. What other process characteristic, besides the mean, would you be interested in controlling with respect to the lifetimes of the lamps? Why?

e. Do any advantages result from using an accelerated life test if a high degree of relationship exists between these results and the ones under the normal testing procedures? Explain.

f. When must the control limits calculated in part **a** be changed? Explain.

g. Would your procedure in part **a** have to be modified if the process standard deviation had been estimated from a sample of eight lamps? Explain.

18.17. Samples of 200 invoices are taken daily from the sales invoices prepared during the day and are checked for computational accuracy. Past experience has indicated that the proportion of incorrect sales invoices is $p = 2.4$ per cent.

a. Calculate the appropriate control limits of 3 standard deviations to decide whether any change in the process error rate has taken place.

b. Plot the control limits on a chart. Then plot the following sample results on the same chart:

Date	*Number of Incorrect Invoices in Sample*	*Date*	*Number of Incorrect Invoices in Sample*
7/2	1	7/12	0
7/3	9	7/13	2
7/4	2	7/16	3
7/5	7	7/17	1
7/6	4	7/18	2
7/9	3	7/19	2
7/10	2	7/20	1
7/11	1		

c. Was the process in control during this period with respect to the computational error rate? Explain.

d. Does your control chart for the three-week period indicate anything else besides the fact that the process was or was not in control? Discuss.

e. How do you explain that the lower control limit in part **a** was less than zero, even though $\bar{p}$ cannot be negative? (*Hint:* Is the sampling distribution of $\bar{p}$ exactly normal?) What is the effective lower control limit in a case like this?

***18.18.** The D. S. Bender Corporation receives raw material in lots of 5,000 units. A sample of 50 units is selected from each lot, on the basis of which a decision is made whether to accept or reject the lot. A rejected lot is inspected 100 per cent, all defective units are replaced with acceptable ones, and the vendor is charged for the work and defective materials.

Suppose that the inspectors use a decision-making procedure which has the following properties:

If lot has per cent defectives amounting to:	*Probability of accepting the lot is:*	*Probability of rejecting the lot is:*
1%	.91	.09
3%	.56	.44
10%	.03	.97

a. If the submitted lots contain 1 per cent defectives, what is the average quality of the lots after inspection? (Ignore defective units found in samples from accepted lots.) If the submitted lots contain 3 per cent defectives? 10 per cent defectives?

b. How do you explain that the average quality of the lots after inspection is better if the incoming rate of defectives is 10 per cent than if it is 3 per cent? Is it, therefore, desirable that the supplier submit material of poor quality? Explain.

c. What is the average number of units inspected per lot if the incoming rate of defectives is 1 per cent? 3 per cent? 10 per cent?

CLASS PROJECT

18.19. Refer to Problems 10.19 and 11.21. In the past, the proportion of freight bills with freight charges due Crandell Motor Freight, Inc., of \$1.50 or less has been $p = .636$. Management wants to determine if this proportion in the current population of 500 freight bills is now lower.

a. Construct the appropriate decision rule for a sample of 50 freight bills; assume that the risk of concluding that the current population proportion is less than .636, when it actually still is equal to .636, is to be .02.

b. What conclusion should be reached from each of the 100 samples?

c. Since we know that the proportion of the 500 freight bills in the population that have freight charges due Crandell Motor Freight, Inc., of \$1.50 or less is still .636, what proportion of incorrect conclusions do you expect among the 100 conclusions? Explain.

d. What proportion of the conclusions from the 100 samples actually are incorrect?

e. What does this experiment illustrate about the construction of statistical decision rules from large simple random samples? Discuss.

Chapter

19

ADDITIONAL TOPICS II: CHI-SQUARE TESTS AND ANALYSIS OF VARIANCE

In this chapter, we extend our discussion of the classical approach to statistical decision-making to three additional types of decision problems that are important in business and economics: tests of goodness of fit, contingency tables, and analysis of variance.

19.1 TESTS OF GOODNESS OF FIT

Our initial topic deals with procedures for making a decision about the nature of the probability distribution that one faces in a given problem. These procedures are frequently called *tests of goodness of fit.*

Some typical problems

Consider an operations-research analyst who is developing a model of replacement demand for a spare part stocked in a depot. He knows that in many situations involving spare parts, demand follows a Poisson distribution. The analyst now wishes to decide whether the number of units demanded per week for this particular part also follows a Poisson distribution. If so, the analyst can utilize Poisson probabilities to ascertain the optimal inventory level at which another batch of parts should be ordered from the manufacturer.

Note then that the decision problem in this example involves the following two alternatives:

C_1 The probability distribution is Poisson

C_2 The probability distribution is not Poisson

Another typical case in which one needs to decide about the nature of the probability distribution concerns the diameter of a part that is produced by an automatic process. Experience in producing similar items suggests that the diameters of the parts may be normally distributed. The production engineer would like to know whether this is in fact the case. If the diameters are normally distributed, he can use a table of areas for the normal distribution to determine what proportion of the parts produced will meet tolerance specifications if the process mean shifts from the optimal setting by a certain amount.

Here, the two alternatives in the decision problem are:

C_1 The probability distribution is normal

C_2 The probability distribution is not normal

Note that these alternatives are similar to the ones cited above, except that a different probability distribution is specified.

For a final example, consider a study of length of service time at tellers' windows in a bank. The analyst making the study believes from past experience that the distribution of service times in this bank should be exponential with a mean service time μ_X equal to the standard of 2.0 minutes. The question to be answered is whether the distribution in this particular bank does actually follow an exponential distribution with $\mu_X = 2.0$ minutes. If it does, the analyst will utilize this particular exponential distribution in simulating servicing at the tellers' windows to determine how changes in the number of windows open at different times of the day will affect the waiting time of customers for service.

The two alternatives here are:

C_1 The probability distribution is exponential with $\mu_X = 2.0$ minutes

C_2 The probability distribution is not exponential with $\mu_X = 2.0$ minutes

Note that C_1 for the third example, unlike the earlier two examples, specifies not only the functional form of the distribution but also the value of the parameter. Correspondingly, C_2 here includes exponential distributions that have mean times other than 2.0 minutes as well as distributions that are not exponential.

Appropriate test statistic

We now discuss the construction and use of a decision rule concerning the nature of the probability distribution. Specifically, we return to the spare-part example and construct a rule for deciding whether weekly demand for this item does follow a Poisson distribution. Recall that the alternatives in this problem are:

C_1 The probability distribution is Poisson

C_2 The probability distribution is not Poisson

Table 19.1 contains data on the number of units of the spare part demanded per week for a sample of 52 weeks. The demand for this part, incidentally, is not affected to any extent by seasonal or other such factors. The table shows that no units were demanded during 2 of the 52 weeks, 1 unit was demanded during 2 of the weeks, and so on. All in all, 208 units were demanded during the 52 weeks. Thus, the mean number of units demanded weekly in the sample was $\bar{X} = 208/52 = 4.0$ units.

Table 19.1 Distribution of Weekly Demand in Sample, Calculation of Sample Mean, and Calculation of Expected Weekly Demand

(1)	(2)	(3)	(4)	(5)
	Sample		*Expected*	
Number of Units Demanded in Week X	*Number of Weeks* f	fX (*Col. 1* × *Col. 2*)	*Estimated Probability*	*Estimated Expected Frequency* (*Col. 4* × *52*)
0	2	0	.0183	.95
1	2	2	.0733	3.81
2	9	18	.1465	7.62
3	11	33	.1954	10.16
4	7	28	.1954	10.16
5	9	45	.1563	8.13
6	7	42	.1042	5.42
7	2	14	.0595	3.09
8	2	16	.0298	1.55
9	0	0	.0132	.69
10	1	10	.0053	.27
11	0	0	.0019	.10
12	0	0	.0006	.03
13	0	0	.0002	.01
14	0	0	.0001	.01
Total	52	208	1.0	52.0

$$\bar{X} = \frac{208}{52} = 4.0$$

Estimation of expected frequencies if C_1 holds. To determine whether the distribution is Poisson, we compare the distribution of weekly demand actually obtained in the sample with the distribution that we would expect to obtain if C_1 is correct and demand does indeed follow a Poisson distribution. To obtain this expected distribution, we utilize the Poisson probabilities in

Table A-2. On the basis of the sample data, we estimate that the mean of the distribution of weekly demand is 4.0 units. Entering Table A-2 to obtain Poisson probabilities for $\mu_X = 4.0$, we find the probability that X equals zero is .0183, the probability that X equals 1 is .0733, and so on. These probabilities are shown in Table 19.1, column 4. Since we have 52 observations in the sample, we estimate that the expected number of sample observations for which X equals zero is 52 multiplied by .0183, or .95, the expected number of sample observations for which X equals 1 is 52 multiplied by .0733, or 3.81, and so on. These estimated expected frequencies are shown in Table 19.1, column 5. Note that we obtained *estimated* expected frequencies because we initially estimated the mean of the distribution.

Table 19.2 repeats from Table 19.1 the sample results and the estimated expected frequencies if the functional form of the probability distribution is in fact Poisson, but with some of the classes in Table 19.1 combined. The reason for combining certain classes will be discussed later.

Table 19.2 Calculation of Test Statistic for Decision Problem Concerning Poisson Distribution

Number Demanded X	(1) Sample Frequency f_s	(2) Estimated Expected Frequency if C_1 Holds f_e	(3) Deviation $f_s - f_e$	(4) Squared Deviation $(f_s - f_e)^2$	(5) Relative Squared Deviation $(f_s - f_e)^2/f_e$
0–2	13	12.38	.62	.3844	.0311
3	11	10.16	.84	.7056	.0694
4	7	10.16	−3.16	9.9856	.9828
5	9	8.13	.87	.7569	.0931
6	7	5.42	1.58	2.4964	.4606
7 or more	5	5.75	− .75	.5625	.0978
Total	52	52.0	0		1.7348

$$V_1 = \sum \frac{(f_s - f_e)^2}{f_e} = 1.735$$

Calculation of test statistic. The test statistic that we shall use to determine whether demand follows a Poisson distribution is based on the deviations between the *expected frequencies* of the different levels of demand if C_1 holds, and the corresponding *observed frequencies* in the sample of 52 observations. We calculate this test statistic as follows:

1. We obtain the deviations of the observed sample frequencies around the expected frequencies. These deviations are shown in column 3 of Table 19.2. The sum of these deviations always equals zero.
2. We square these deviations; the results are shown in column 4.

3. We express each squared deviation relative to the frequency that is expected if C_1 holds—that is, we divide the numbers in column 4 by those in column 2. The relative squared deviations are shown in column 5 of Table 19.2.
4. We obtain the value of the test statistic by summing the relative squared deviations in column 5. We will denote the test statistic by V_1. Thus:

(19.1) $$V_1 = \sum \frac{(f_s - f_e)^2}{f_e}$$

Here f_s is an observed sample frequency and f_e is the corresponding expected frequency. We see from Table 19.2 that in the present example, $V_1 = 1.735$.

Distribution of test statistic if C_1 holds

The test statistic V_1 is a random variable, since its value will vary from sample to sample. The sampling distribution of V_1 depends on the probability distribution being sampled. We are interested in particular in the distribution of V_1 if C_1 holds. The reason is that the classical approach to statistical decision-making that we utilize here will enable us to control only one type of error at a specified level, since the sample size was determined in advance. The statistical technique most commonly used in making a decision about the nature of the probability distribution lends itself well to controlling the Type I error, and we illustrate this technique here. Remember that a Type I error is made if C_1 is correct but is rejected in favor of C_2. Thus, we would like to know the distribution of the test statistic V_1 if C_1 holds, so that we can control the risk of a Type I error at a specified level.

(19.2) Statistical theory indicates that if the simple random sample size is large, the distribution of the test statistic V_1 is approximately a χ^2 (read: chi-square) distribution when C_1 holds.

Properties of chi-square distributions. Chi-square probability distributions are a family of distributions that are continuous, unimodal, and skewed to the right. A chi-square random variable can take on any value between 0 and $+\infty$. The chi-square distribution has one parameter, called *degrees of freedom,* which we will denote by δ (Greek delta). The mean of any chi-square distribution is equal to the degrees of freedom δ. Figure 19.1a shows chi-square distributions corresponding to several values of δ. Note that as δ increases, the distributions move to the right, and the skewness becomes less marked.

As with other continuous probability distributions, the area under a chi-square distribution indicates probability. Since there is a different chi-square distribution for each value of δ, it is impractical to give complete tables of

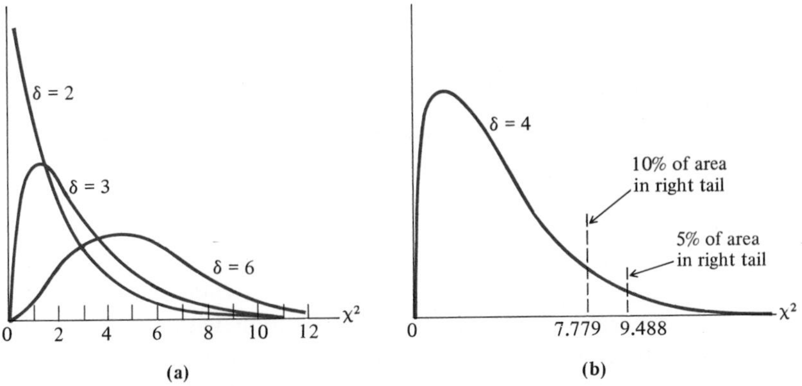

Figure 19.1. Chi-square distributions

areas. Instead, a summary of the most essential information about the distributions usually is presented in a table such as Table A-6.

Note that in Table A-6 the left-hand column is headed degrees of freedom. Each row in the table contains information on the chi-square distribution corresponding to the indicated degrees of freedom, δ. Specifically, the table gives values on the chi-square scale corresponding to areas in the right tail of the distribution.

Table A-6 shows, for example, that in the distribution with 4 degrees of freedom, the value 7.779 on the chi-square scale corresponds to an area of .10 in the right tail, and the value 9.488 corresponds to an area of .05 in the right tail. Thus, the probability that a random variable following the χ^2 distribution with 4 degrees of freedom exceeds 7.779 is .10, and the probability that it is larger than 9.488 is .05. Figure 19.1b shows the chi-square distribution with 4 degrees of freedom and illustrates the relationships just mentioned.

Appropriate decision rule

Intuitively we would expect in our example that if C_1 is correct, the actual sample frequencies f_s would be close to the corresponding expected frequencies f_e based on the Poisson distribution. On the other hand, if the distribution is not Poisson, we would expect the sample frequencies f_s to diverge from the expected frequencies f_e since the latter are based on a Poisson probability distribution. Consequently if C_2 holds, we would expect the deviations $(f_s - f_e)$ to be larger, and also the squared deviations, the relative squared deviations, and the value of the test statistic V_1. Therefore intuition suggests that large values of the test statistic should lead to conclusion C_2 while small values should lead to conclusion C_1.

Intuition is correct here, because statistical theory indicates that a one-sided decision rule is appropriate for this case, with large values of the test statistic leading to conclusion C_2. Let us examine the situation more closely.

We already noted that if C_1 holds and the sample size is large, the test statistic V_1 is distributed approximately according to the chi-square distribution. Now we must add that the relevant chi-square distribution for our example is that with $k-2$ degrees of freedom, where k is the number of classes in which f_s and f_e are compared, or to put this in a more general way, k is the number of individual squared deviations that are summed to give the value of the test statistic V_1. In Table 19.2, $k=6$. Thus, we can say that if C_1 holds, the test statistic in our example is distributed approximately according to a chi-square distribution with $6-2=4$ degrees of freedom. Since we know that the mean of a chi-square distribution is equal to the degrees of freedom δ, we can also say that if C_1 holds, the distribution of the test statistic in the present problem is centered around a mean of 4.

Statistical theory shows further that if C_1 does not hold—that is, if C_2 holds—the distribution of the test statistic V_1 falls to the *right* of the distribution of the test statistic for the case when C_1 holds, and consequently has a higher mean. Thus, for our example if the value of the test statistic is substantially above 4 (the mean of the distribution of the test statistic if C_1 holds), conclusion C_2 should be drawn; otherwise, C_1 is the appropriate conclusion. In general, then, the statistical decision rule should be one-sided, with large values of the test statistic leading to C_2 and small values of the test statistic leading to C_1.

Construction and use of decision rule. Consequently the appropriate kind of decision rule is the one-sided rule shown in Figure 19.2a. Before we can

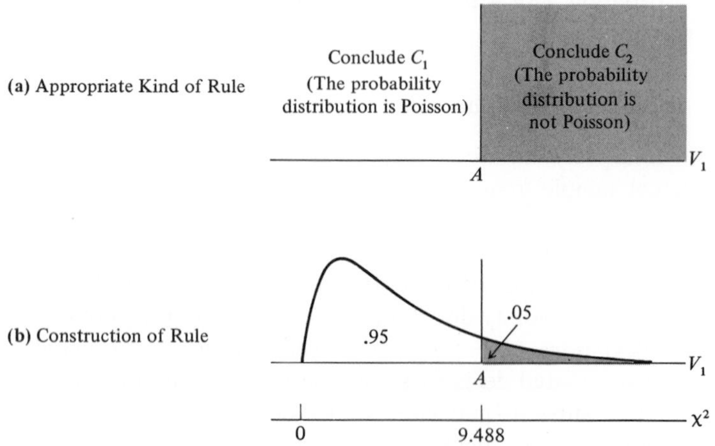

Figure 19.2. Steps in construction of decision rule for test about Poisson distribution

construct the rule, we must specify the level at which we wish to control the risk of a Type I error. Suppose we specify this level to be .05. Since large values of V_1 are to lead to C_2 and since the Type I error is to be controlled at the level .05, we must find the value on the chi-square scale associated with an area of .05 in the right tail of the distribution with 4 degrees of freedom. We have already noted that this value is 9.488 (see Figure 19.1b). The value 9.488 is the action limit in the decision rule, as shown graphically in Figure 19.2b. The decision rule then is:

If $V_1 \leq 9.488$, conclude C_1 (the distribution is Poisson)
If $V_1 > 9.488$, conclude C_2 (the distribution is not Poisson)

Note that this rule is so constructed that if the probability distribution is Poisson (C_1), the decision rule will lead to conclusion C_2 only 5 per cent of the time.

For our example, we calculated that $V_1 = 1.735$ (from Table 19.2). Consequently the decision rule leads us to conclude C_1. On the basis of the sample data, it is reasonable to assert that the pattern of demand for this particular spare part does follow a Poisson distribution.

Recapitulation. In general, if:

1. The alternatives are:

(19.3)
C_1 Probability distribution is Poisson (normal, etc.)
C_2 Probability distribution is not Poisson (normal, etc.)

2. The simple random sample size is large,
3. The risk of a Type I error is to be controlled,

then, the appropriate decision rule is:

(19.4)
If $V_1 \leq A$, conclude C_1
If $V_1 > A$, conclude C_2

Here the action limit A is determined from the relevant chi-square distribution according to the specified risk of a Type I error.

Additional comments

Sample size. We indicated earlier that the distribution of V_1 is approximately a chi-square distribution if C_1 holds and if the sample size is large. The question naturally arises as to when the sample size is large. One commonly used rule is that the sample size can be considered large if each expected frequency f_e is 5 or greater. In Table 19.2, we had to combine some classes at each end of the distribution so that this condition would be met. Thus, we combined the outcomes $X = 0$, $X = 1$, and $X = 2$ into the single class "0–2" because the expected frequencies for $X = 0$ and $X = 1$ did not each or together equal 5 or more. For the same reason, outcomes in the right tail of the distribution were combined into the single class "7 or more."

Specification of parameter values in C_1. In the example just discussed, the functional form of the probability distribution was specified in C_1, but the value of the parameter was not specified. Consequently, in order to estimate the expected frequencies, we first needed to estimate the value of the parameter from the observed sample data.

At times, however, one wishes to test whether the probability distribution follows a particular functional form with a specified value of each parameter. This case was encountered in one of our illustrations, where the alternatives were:

C_1 The probability distribution is exponential with $\mu_X = 2.0$ minutes

C_2 The probability distribution is not exponential with $\mu_X = 2.0$ minutes

In cases of this type, the expected frequencies f_e are determined by using the probability distribution and parameter values specified in C_1. Otherwise, the calculation of the test statistic parallels the procedure for the case where only the functional form of the distribution is specified in C_1. There is one other difference between the two cases, namely in connection with the degrees of freedom. When the probability distribution is completely specified by C_1 so that no parameters need to be estimated from the sample observations, the degrees of freedom for the test statistic are $k - 1$, where k is defined as above.

Rule for determining degrees of freedom. We can generalize as follows:

(19.5) If C_1 specifies the probability distribution completely including the parameter value or values, the degrees of freedom are $k - 1$, where k is the number of classes used in the calculation of the test statistic. For each parameter value that needs to be estimated from the sample, an additional degree of freedom is lost.

Thus in our spare-part example, where the mean μ_X of the Poisson distribution had to be estimated from the sample, there are $k - 2$ degrees of freedom. In the illustration cited earlier in which C_1 specified that the functional form of the distribution is normal but did not specify the values of the mean and standard deviation (these being the parameters of a normal distribution), the degrees of freedom would be $k - 3$, since the values of two parameters would have to be estimated from the sample.

Use of per cent data. Note that absolute data, not per cents, were used in comparing observed and expected frequencies. If the observed sample data happen to be tabulated as a per cent distribution, these data should either be converted back to absolute magnitudes before the test statistic V_1 is calculated by (19.1), or (19.1) should be modified accordingly.

19.2 CONTINGENCY TABLES

In Chapter 6 we discussed bivariate probability distributions and defined statistical independence of two variables in such a population. Now we take up the problem of deciding whether two variables are statistically independent, when only *sample* information is available on which to base this decision.

Some typical problems

For an example involving the need to decide whether two variables are statistically independent, consider a market-research analyst who has selected a random sample of 100 buyers of a certain make of pleasure boat and has classified these buyers by income bracket ("upper" or "other" income bracket) and by the medium by which the buyer's attention was first drawn to this make of boat (magazine, television, word of mouth). The analyst believes that income bracket and the medium by which attention was first drawn are unrelated in the purchasing of this make of boat and wishes to test this belief.

The two alternative conclusions here are:

C_1 Income and medium are statistically independent
C_2 Income and medium are not statistically independent

Another example involving the need to test for statistical independence comes from product research and development. An engineer has obtained data for a certain type of vacuum tube on type of failure and location in the circuit. The engineer now needs to determine whether or not type of failure and location in the circuit are statistically independent. The alternatives are:

C_1 Type of failure and location are statistically independent
C_2 Type of failure and location are not statistically independent

Appropriate test statistic

We will use our example involving income and medium to demonstrate the construction and use of statistical decision rules for determining whether or not two variables are statistically independent.

First, we must develop the appropriate test statistic. Table 19.3 contains the data on the 100 buyers in the sample, cross-classified by income and medium. For convenience, the income classes have been denoted by A_1 and A_2, and the media classes by B_1, B_2, and B_3. For example, of the 100 buyers, 40 came from the upper income bracket, and of these, 13 had their attention first drawn to this make of boat by magazine advertising. Table 19.3, containing the bivariate classification of the sample of 100 buyers, is frequently called a *contingency table.*

Table 19.3 Sample of 100 Buyers
Cross-Classified by Income Bracket and Medium

		Medium		
	B_1	B_2	B_3	
Income Bracket	*Magazines*	*Television*	*Word of Mouth*	*Total*
A_1 Upper	13	13	14	40
A_2 Other	37	7	16	60
Total	50	20	30	100

Estimation of expected frequencies if C_1 holds. As in the type of problem discussed in the previous section, we need to obtain the estimated expected frequencies if C_1 holds—here, if the two variables are statistically independent. We know from Chapter 6 that if the two variables are independent, any joint probability is the product of the two marginal probabilities. Thus, for example, $P(A_1 \text{ and } B_1) = P(A_1)P(B_1)$ with statistical independence.

We estimate the marginal probabilities directly from the data in Table 19.3:

$$\bar{P}(A_1) = \frac{40}{100} = .40 \qquad \bar{P}(B_1) = \frac{50}{100} = .50$$

$$\bar{P}(A_2) = \frac{60}{100} = .60 \qquad \bar{P}(B_2) = \frac{20}{100} = .20$$

$$\bar{P}(B_3) = \frac{30}{100} = .30$$

where $\bar{P}$ denotes the estimated probability.

We then estimate the joint probabilities if independence holds, as follows:

$$\begin{aligned}
\bar{P}(A_1 \text{ and } B_1) &= \bar{P}(A_1)\,\bar{P}(B_1) = (.40)(.50) = .20\\
\bar{P}(A_2 \text{ and } B_1) &= \bar{P}(A_2)\,\bar{P}(B_1) = (.60)(.50) = .30\\
\bar{P}(A_1 \text{ and } B_2) &= \bar{P}(A_1)\,\bar{P}(B_2) = (.40)(.20) = .08\\
\bar{P}(A_2 \text{ and } B_2) &= \bar{P}(A_2)\,\bar{P}(B_2) = (.60)(.20) = .12\\
\bar{P}(A_1 \text{ and } B_3) &= \bar{P}(A_1)\,\bar{P}(B_3) = (.40)(.30) = .12\\
\bar{P}(A_2 \text{ and } B_3) &= \bar{P}(A_2)\,\bar{P}(B_3) = (.60)(.30) = \underline{.18}\\
& \qquad\qquad\qquad\qquad\qquad\qquad\quad 1.0
\end{aligned}$$

These probabilities are shown in Table 19.4, column 2.

Finally, we estimate the expected frequencies if C_1 holds by multiplying each estimated joint probability by 100. For example, the estimated probability that a person will belong to A_1 and B_1 jointly if the two variables are independent is .20. Consequently we would expect that (100)(.20) = 20 persons in the sample will fall into classes A_1 and B_1 jointly if C_1 holds. The estimated expected frequencies for each cell are shown in Table 19.4, column 3.

Table 19.4 Calculation of Test Statistic for Example Involving Statistical Independence

Joint Classification	(1) *Sample Frequency* f_s	(2) *Estimated Joint Probability if C_1 Holds*	(3) *Estimated Expected Frequency* f_e	(4) *Deviation* $(f_s - f_e)$	(5) *Squared Deviation* $(f_s - f_e)^2$	(6) *Relative Squared Deviation* $(f_s - f_e)^2/f_e$
A_1 and B_1	13	.20	20	−7	49	2.4500
A_2 and B_1	37	.30	30	+7	49	1.6333
A_1 and B_2	13	.08	8	+5	25	3.1250
A_2 and B_2	7	.12	12	−5	25	2.0833
A_1 and B_3	14	.12	12	+2	4	.3333
A_2 and B_3	16	.18	18	−2	4	.2222
Total	100	1.0	100			9.8471

$$V_1 = \sum \frac{(f_s - f_e)^2}{f_e} = 9.8471$$

Calculation of test statistic. The test statistic that we now employ is identical to that used in the previous example. Thus, we calculate the deviations of the sample frequencies f_s around the estimated expected frequencies f_e, square the deviations, and express the squared deviations relative to the estimated expected frequencies. The calculations are shown in Table 19.4. The value of the test statistic V_1 is obtained as before by summing the relative squared deviations. In Table 19.4, $V_1 = 9.8471$.

Distribution of test statistic if C_1 holds

As in the previous example, we are interested in the distribution of the test statistic if C_1 holds—in the present case, if the two variables are statistically independent. The reason is the same as before. The sample size was determined in advance, and the technique that is commonly used in tests for statistical independence lends itself to controlling the risk of making a Type I error—that is, the risk of concluding C_2 when in fact C_1 is correct.

(19.6) Statistical theory shows that for tests of statistical independence in contingency tables, if the simple random sample size is large, the distribution of the test statistic when C_1 holds is approximately a chi-square distribution with $(R - 1)(C - 1)$ degrees of freedom.

Here R is the number of classes into which one of the variables is classified and C is the number of classes of the other variable. To put this another way, R is the number of rows (excluding the "Total" row) in a table such as Table 19.3, while C is the number of columns (excluding the "Total" column) in the table. Thus in the present example, if C_1 holds, the test statistic is distributed approximately as a chi-square distribution with $(2 - 1)(3 - 1) = 2$ degrees of freedom.

Appropriate decision rule

As before, we would expect large values of the test statistic to lead to conclusion C_2, because the deviations, squared deviations, relative squared deviations, and test statistic would tend to be larger if C_2 holds than if C_1 holds. This expectation is correct, since statistical theory shows that the distribution of the test statistic if C_2 holds falls to the right of the distribution that applies if C_1 holds, and consequently has a higher mean.

Thus the appropriate kind of decision rule is a one-sided rule, with large values of the test statistic leading to conclusion C_2, as in the previous case illustrated in Figure 19.2.

Suppose in the present example that the risk of a Type I error is to be .01. Table A-6 is then entered for 2 degrees of freedom, and it is found that the value on the chi-square scale corresponding to an area of .01 in the right tail is 9.210. Consequently the decision rule is:

If $V_1 \leq 9.210$, conclude C_1 (income and medium are statistically independent)

If $V_1 > 9.210$, conclude C_2 (income and medium are not statistically independent)

In the present example $V_1 = 9.8471$, as shown in Table 19.4. Hence the consultant would conclude C_2, that income and medium are not independent.

Recapitulation. In general, if:

1. The alternatives are:

(19.7)

C_1	The two variables are statistically independent
C_2	The two variables are not statistically independent

2. The simple random sample size is large,
3. The risk of a Type I error is to be controlled,

then, the appropriate decision rule is:

(19.8) If $V_1 \leq A$, conclude C_1
If $V_1 > A$, conclude C_2

Here A is the action limit obtained from the chi-square distribution with $(R-1)(C-1)$ degrees of freedom according to the specified risk of Type I error.

Additional comments

Sample size. Again, the sample size needs to be large so that the chi-square approximation will apply for the distribution of V_1 when C_1 holds. The rule for determining when the sample is large is the same as before—that is, each expected frequency should be 5 or greater.

Correction for continuity. When each of the variables has only two classes so that the degrees of freedom are $(R-1)(C-1) = 1$, the test statistic V_1 may be modified slightly so that the chi-square approximation is improved. The modified test statistic V_1' is:

(19.9) $$V_1' = \sum \frac{(|f_s - f_e| - .5)^2}{f_e}$$

V_1' incorporates a *correction for continuity*, which amounts to subtracting .5 from each *absolute* deviation (the plus or minus sign is disregarded) before squaring.

19.3 ONE-WAY ANALYSIS OF VARIANCE

In Chapters 14 and 18, we compared *two* population means. Frequently, however, one is interested in a simultaneous comparison of *more than two* population means. *One-way analysis of variance* is a statistical method for making such a comparison.

Some typical problems

Consider an experiment on the effectiveness of three different counter displays for a new item on sale in drugstores. Suppose that this experiment is conducted over a period of time in 15 similar drugstores. Each type of display is assigned to five of the drugstores by means of a table of random digits, to obtain randomization in the assignment of displays to stores. The marketing analyst conducting the test wishes to decide as a first step in his analysis whether or not the three counter displays are equally effective in selling the item. In other words, he wishes to know whether or not the mean number of units of the item sold by each type of display over a given period is the same for the three displays. Thus the two alternative conclusions are:

$C_1 \quad \mu_1 = \mu_2 = \mu_3$

$C_2 \quad \mu_1, \mu_2,$ and μ_3 are not all equal

where μ_1 is the mean number of units sold over the specified time period by display 1, and so on.

For another example that involves a comparison of several means, consider a company that uses a preliminary screening test in its hiring procedures. Four different versions of this test have been developed, to be administered on alternate days. The personnel director wants to know whether applicants, on the average, do equally well on all four versions of the test. The two alternatives are:

$C_1 \quad \mu_1 = \mu_2 = \mu_3 = \mu_4$

$C_2 \quad \mu_1, \mu_2, \mu_3,$ and μ_4 are not all equal

where μ_1 is the average score made by applicants on the first version of the test, and so on.

Total variation and its components

We will return to the first example. As the first step in determining whether or not the population means μ_j are the same for the three treatments (displays) studied in the experiment, we wish to measure the total variation in the experimental data as a whole. Table 19.5 shows, for each type of display, the sales (in dozens of units) in each of the five drugstores containing that display. Note that the sales in a given drugstore constitute one sample observation.

Table 19.5 Sales (Dozens of Units) From Three Displays in Five Stores Each

		Display	
Sample Observation	*1*	*2*	*3*
1	6.3	8.5	6.0
2	8.5	8.0	5.7
3	5.5	8.3	6.3
4	7.0	7.7	6.0
5	6.7	8.5	6.0
Total	34.0	41.0	30.0
Mean	6.8	8.2	6.0

$$\bar{X}_1 = 6.8 \qquad \bar{X}_2 = 8.2 \qquad \bar{X}_3 = 6.0$$

$$\bar{\bar{X}} = \frac{6.8 + 8.2 + 6.0}{3} = \frac{21.0}{3} = 7.0$$

In Table 19.5, the columns pertain to the three treatments, and the rows pertain to the different sample stores in the experiment for each of the treatments. We will denote the sales in a given drugstore by X_{ij}, where i refers to a row or sample observation ($i = 1, 2, 3, 4, 5$) and j refers to a column or treatment ($j = 1, 2, 3$). Thus X_{12} is the sales of the first sample store using display 2. Table 19.5 shows that $X_{12} = 8.5$ dozen units.

The mean sales for each display are given at the bottom of the columns in Table 19.5. We denote these means by $\overline{X}_1$, $\overline{X}_2$, and $\overline{X}_3$ respectively. Thus $\overline{X}_1$ denotes the mean sales in the sample stores for display 1, and so on. The overall mean sales in all 15 sample stores is denoted by $\overline{\overline{X}}$. In Table 19.5, $\overline{\overline{X}}$ is simply the average of the three column means, since equal sample sizes were used for the three displays.

Total variation. We now calculate the total variation in the experimental data. We do this in the usual way, by taking the deviation of each sample observation X_{ij} from the overall mean $\overline{\overline{X}}$, squaring this deviation $(X_{ij} - \overline{\overline{X}})$, and then summing the squared deviations $(X_{ij} - \overline{\overline{X}})^2$ over all observations in the experiment to obtain:

$$Q = \sum_j \sum_i (X_{ij} - \overline{\overline{X}})^2 \tag{19.10}$$

Here Q denotes the total variation, and $\Sigma_j \Sigma_i$ symbolizes that all combinations of i and j (that is, all cells in Table 19.5) are included in the sum. Thus, for our example, where $\overline{\overline{X}} = 7.0$, we obtain as the total variation:

$$Q = (6.3 - 7.0)^2 + (8.5 - 7.0)^2 + \cdots + (6.0 - 7.0)^2 = 17.94$$

The total variation Q is called the *total sum of squares*. Theory shows that the total variation Q can be broken down into parts:

1. The inherent variation in the sample observations for each of the treatments (displays)—i.e., the variation *within* the columns in Table 19.5.
2. The variation between treatments—that is, the variation *between* the columns in Table 19.5.

Within-treatments variation. This component measures the inherent variation in store sales that exists even though each store utilizes the same display. The within-treatments variation is calculated by working with each treatment sample separately. For each treatment, say treatment j, we take the deviation of each sample observation X_{ij} from the treatment mean $\overline{X}_j$, square the deviation $(X_{ij} - \overline{X}_j)$, and sum these squared deviations $(X_{ij} - \overline{X}_j)^2$ over all sample observations for that treatment. Then we sum these totals $\Sigma_i (X_{ij} - \overline{X}_j)^2$ over all treatments to obtain:

$$Q_1 = \sum_j \sum_i (X_{ij} - \overline{X}_j)^2 \tag{19.11}$$

Here Q_1 denotes the within-treatments component of the total variation.

The steps to calculate Q_1 are shown in Table 19.6. The procedure for treatment 1 is shown in detail, but only the squared deviations are shown for treatments 2 and 3. Just remember that the same basic procedure is used with each treatment, but that the deviations are calculated around the mean for that treatment. Thus, in treatment 2, the deviations are calculated around $\overline{X}_2 = 8.2$, while in treatment 3, they are calculated around $\overline{X}_3 = 6.0$. The within-treatments variation Q_1 is also called the *within-treatments sum of squares*. We see in Table 19.6 that $Q_1 = 5.54$.

Between-treatments variation. The second component of variation, that between the treatments, measures the variability of the treatment sample means. We take the deviation of each treatment mean $\overline{X}_j$ from the overall mean $\overline{\overline{X}}$, square these deviations $(\overline{X}_j - \overline{\overline{X}})$, and weight each by the sample size (denoted by n), since these squared deviations refer to deviations of sample means. Then we sum these terms over all treatments and obtain:

$$Q_2 = \sum_j n(\overline{X}_j - \overline{\overline{X}})^2 \tag{19.12}$$

Here Q_2 denotes the between-treatments variation. The quantity Q_2 is also called the *between-treatments sum of squares.*

Table 19.6 summarizes the calculation of Q_2. Note that $n = 5$ for our example, since each display was assigned to five stores. The term n then

Table 19.6 Calculation of Within- and Between-Treatments Sums of Squares

(a) Within-Treatments Sum of Squares $Q_1 = \sum_j \sum_i (X_{ij} - \overline{X}_j)^2$

Treatment 1		*Treatment 2*	*Treatment 3*
$X_{i1} - \overline{X}_1$	$(X_{i1} - \overline{X}_1)^2$	$(X_{i2} - \overline{X}_2)^2$	$(X_{i3} - \overline{X}_3)^2$
6.3 − 6.8 = − .5	.25	.09	0
8.5 − 6.8 = +1.7	2.89	.04	.09
5.5 − 6.8 = −1.3	1.69	.01	.09
7.0 − 6.8 = + .2	.04	.25	0
6.7 − 6.8 = − .1	.01	.09	0
Total	4.88	.48	.18

$$Q_1 = 4.88 + .48 + .18 = 5.54$$

(b) Between-Treatments Sum of Squares $Q_2 = \sum_j n(\overline{X}_j - \overline{\overline{X}})^2$

$$Q_2 = 5(6.8 - 7.0)^2 + 5(8.2 - 7.0)^2 + 5(6.0 - 7.0)^2 = 12.40$$

stands for the sample size for any one treatment, not for the total number of observations in the experiment. For our example, $Q_2 = 12.40$, as shown in Table 19.6.

The formal identity between the sums of squares is:

$$Q = Q_1 + Q_2 \tag{19.13}$$

This simply states that the total sum of squares is equal to the within-treatments sum of squares plus the between-treatments sum of squares. The magnitudes of the three sums of squares in the present problem are $17.94 = 5.54 + 12.40$. We place these values in an analysis of variance table—Table 19.7—for further use.

Computation formulas. The formulas that we have used for Q, Q_1, and Q_2 are best for showing the kind of variation measured by each of the terms. Shortcut formulas are available that involve algebraic variations of the definitional formulas we have given, as follows:

$$Q = \sum_j \sum_i X_{ij}^2 - \frac{\left(\sum_j \sum_i X_{ij}\right)^2}{mn} \tag{19.14}$$

$$Q_1 = \sum_j \sum_i X_{ij}^2 - \sum_j \frac{\left(\sum_i X_{ij}\right)^2}{n} \tag{19.15}$$

$$Q_2 = \sum_j \frac{\left(\sum_i X_{ij}\right)^2}{n} - \frac{\left(\sum_j \sum_i X_{ij}\right)^2}{mn} \tag{19.16}$$

where m is number of treatments and the other terms are defined as above.

Degrees of freedom. We must now consider the degrees of freedom that are associated with each sum of squares. The total sum of squares, Q, is based on 15 observations. We draw a correspondence with an ordinary sample standard deviation based on 15 observations and find that there are $15 - 1 = 14$ degrees of freedom associated with the total sum of squares.

Correspondingly, since there are five sample observations for any one treatment (display), and the deviations within a treatment are calculated around the mean of that treatment, there are $5 - 1 = 4$ degrees of freedom associated with the squared deviations within a treatment. There are three displays or treatments, hence altogether there are $(4)(3) = 12$ degrees of freedom associated with Q_1, the within-treatments sum of squares.

The between-treatments sum of squares, Q_2, is based on three treatment means, hence there are $3 - 1 = 2$ degrees of freedom associated with Q_2.

The degrees of freedom are also shown in Table 19.7. Notice that the degrees of freedom of the two components are additive, just as are the respective sums of squares.

Mean square. When we divide a sum of squares by its degrees of freedom, we obtain a *mean square*. Thus, the ordinary sample variance s_X^2 is a mean square. Here, we denote the within-treatments mean square by MS_1, and

Table 19.7 Analysis of Variance Table for Text Example

Component of Variation	*Sum of Squares*	*Degrees of Freedom*	*Mean Square*
Between treatments	12.40	2	6.20
Within treatments	5.54	12	.46
Total	17.94	14	

$$V_2 = \frac{6.20}{.46} = 13.5$$

the between-treatments mean square by MS_2. For our example, $MS_1 = 5.54/12 = .46$, and $MS_2 = 12.40/2 = 6.20$. These mean squares are shown in Table 19.7.

Development of test statistic

We know that there is variability from event to event even under a constant cause system. If the 15 drugstores all had the same display, we would still expect some variability in sales from store to store. This inherent variability in the sample data is estimated by MS_1, the within-treatments mean square. It can be shown that MS_1 *estimates the inherent variability in the sample data whether or not the treatment means* μ_j *are equal, that is, whether or not* C_1 *holds.*

This, however, is not the situation for MS_2, the between-treatments mean square. Statistical theory shows that if C_1 holds ($\mu_1 = \mu_2 = \mu_3$), then MS_2 is also an estimate of the *same* inherent variability as that estimated by MS_1. On the other hand, if C_2 holds, so that the means μ_j are not all equal, then MS_2 estimates the sum of two components: (1) the same inherent variation that is estimated by MS_1, and (2) an additional component of variation in the data due to the differences between the treatment means μ_j. If C_2 holds, in other words, MS_2 will tend to be greater than MS_1 because it reflects the variability between the treatment means as well as the inherent sampling variability.

Consequently, we decide whether to conclude C_1 or C_2 by comparing MS_2 and MS_1. Specifically, we use the ratio of the two as our test statistic and will denote it by V_2:

(19.17) $$V_2 = \frac{MS_2}{MS_1}$$

If the treatment means are equal, then MS_1 and MS_2 estimate the same inherent sampling variability and the two terms should be of about equal magnitude. Hence, the test statistic V_2 should be near 1. On the other hand, if the treatment means are unequal, MS_2 reflects the variation in treatment means as well as the inherent sampling variation, while MS_1 still reflects only the inherent sampling variation. Hence, MS_2 would then tend to be larger than MS_1 and the test statistic would tend to be substantially greater than 1.

Thus, our argument suggests (and statistical theory provides the rigorous foundation) that the decision rule should be one-sided, with large values of the test statistic V_2 leading to conclusion C_2 (not all μ_j are equal).

Distribution of test statistic if C_1 holds

We are interested in the distribution of the test statistic V_2 if C_1 holds. The reason is the same as that encountered in previous sections. The classical approach to decision-making that we utilize here enables us to control only one type of error at a specified level since the sample sizes were determined in advance for the three displays. The statistical technique most commonly used in making a decision about the means of several populations lends itself to controlling the Type I error—the error of concluding C_2 when in fact C_1 is the correct conclusion. We therefore need to know the distribution of the test statistic V_2 if C_1 holds, so that we can control the risk of a Type I error.

(19.18) Statistical theory shows that if C_1 holds and certain other conditions (discussed below) prevail, the test statistic V_2 is distributed according to an F-distribution.

Properties of F-distributions. F-distributions are a family of distributions that are continuous, unimodal, and skewed to the right. A typical F-distribution is shown in Figure 19.3. The F-distribution scale ranges from 0 to $+\infty$. Since the F-distribution is a continuous probability distribution, area under this distribution indicates probability.

The F-distribution has two parameters, which we will denote by δ_2 and δ_1. δ_2 is the degrees of freedom in the mean square MS_2, which appears in the numerator of the test statistic V_2, and δ_1 is the degrees of freedom in the mean square MS_1, which appears in the denominator. Thus in our example, $\delta_2 = 2$ and $\delta_1 = 12$ (see Table 19.7).

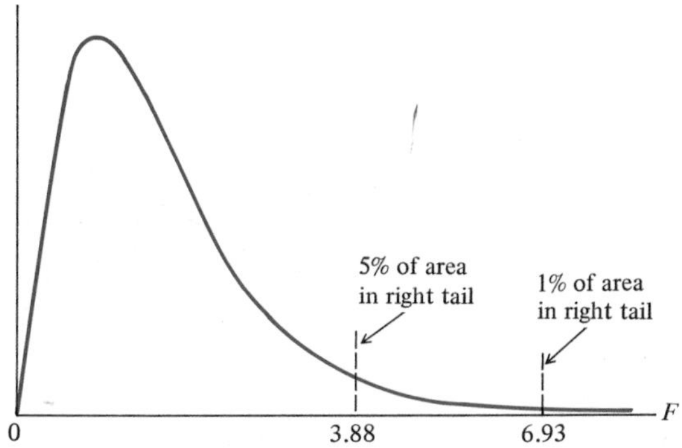

Figure 19.3. F-distribution ($\delta_2 = 2$, $\delta_1 = 12$)

There is a separate F-distribution for each pair of parameter values δ_2 and δ_1. Hence it is only feasible to present summaries of essential information about the distributions. Table A-7 shows values on the F-distribution scale corresponding to areas of .05 and .01 in the right tail of the distribution. Note that each cell in Table A-7 relates to a different F-distribution, identified by δ_2 and δ_1, respectively. For our example, we are interested in the cell corresponding to $\delta_2 = 2$ and $\delta_1 = 12$. The cell values are 3.88 and 6.93. This tells us that in the F-distribution with $\delta_2 = 2$ and $\delta_1 = 12$, the F-scale value 3.88 corresponds to an area of .05 in the right tail and the value 6.93 corresponds to an area of .01 in the right tail. Thus, the probability that a random variable following the F-distribution with $\delta_2 = 2$ and $\delta_1 = 12$ degrees of freedom will exceed 3.88 is .05, and the probability that it will exceed 6.93 is .01. These relations are shown in Figure 19.3.

Now we can be more specific for our example and state that in the present problem, if C_1 holds, the test statistic V_2 is distributed according to the F-distribution with parameters $\delta_2 = 2$ and $\delta_1 = 12$.

Construction of appropriate decision rule

For reasons mentioned earlier, large values of the test statistic lead to C_2. Thus the appropriate type of decision rule is as shown in Figure 19.4a.

Suppose the analyst in the display example specifies that the risk of a Type I error is to be .05. We therefore need to find the value on the F-scale associated with an area of .05 in the right tail of the relevant distribution.

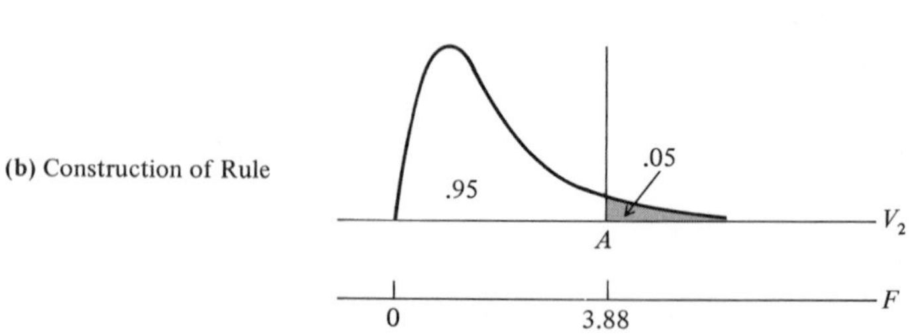

Figure 19.4. Steps in construction of decision rule for test concerning means of several populations

We noted earlier that this value is 3.88 (Figure 19.3). This value therefore serves as the action limit in the decision rule. The rule then is:

If $V_2 \leq 3.88$, conclude C_1 ($\mu_1 = \mu_2 = \mu_3$)
If $V_2 > 3.88$, conclude C_2 (μ_1, μ_2, and μ_3 are not all equal)

The construction of this decision rule is shown graphically in Figure 19.4b.

In the present example, $V_2 = 6.20/.46 = 13.5$ (see Table 19.7). Thus the analyst would conclude C_2, that the displays are not equally effective. It would be natural for him to investigate next how the displays differ in effectiveness. This kind of approach may involve a whole series of comparisons, requiring statistical techniques that are beyond the scope of this text. If, however, only a single comparison were to be made between two displays of particular interest and if this comparison had been anticipated before the experiment began, then the procedures of comparing two population means discussed in this text would be appropriate.

Recapitulation. In general, if:

1. The alternatives are:

(19.19)
$$\begin{array}{ll} C_1 & \mu_1 = \mu_2 = \cdots = \mu_m \\ C_2 & \mu_1, \mu_2, \ldots, \mu_m \text{ are not all equal} \end{array}$$

2. The conditions in (19.21) below are satisfied,
3. The risk of a Type I error is to be controlled,

then, the appropriate decision rule is:

(19.20)
$$\begin{array}{l} \text{If } V_2 \leq A\text{, conclude } C_1\ (\mu_1 = \mu_2 = \cdots = \mu_m) \\ \text{If } V_2 > A\text{, conclude } C_2\ (\mu_1, \mu_2, \ldots, \mu_m \text{ are not all equal}) \end{array}$$

Here the action limit A is determined from the relevant F-distribution according to the specified risk of a Type I error.

Additional comments

Further remarks on distribution of test statistic. Earlier we discussed the distribution of the test statistic when C_1 holds and pointed out that this follows the F-distribution if certain conditions are met. Specifically:

(19.21) $V_2 = MS_2/MS_1$ follows the F-distribution when C_1 holds if:

1. The populations associated with the several treatments are distributed normally,
2. These populations all have the same standard deviation,
3. All sample observations are independent.

The last requirement means, for example, that sales in one store in our earlier illustration must not influence sales in another store.

What is the consequence if the conditions of normality and equal standard deviations are not fully met in practice? Investigations have shown that departures from normality in the populations are not serious as long as the populations are not highly skewed. Also, lack of equality of standard deviations is not serious if the sample sizes are equal, as in our display experiment. Under these modified conditions, the risk of Type I error is not exactly at the level specified, but is close to it. Thus, the distribution of the test statistic V_2 when C_1 holds can be considered to be approximately an F-distribution for a wide variety of situations.

Experimental design. The ability of the statistical decision rule to detect differences in the population means when these exist, depends in large part upon the magnitude of the inherent sampling variability, or experimental error, as this is frequently called. This inherent variability reflects the effects of factors that are not controlled in the experiment. Specifically, in the display experiment, the inherent or within-treatments variation reflects effects of such factors as differences in neighborhoods in which the stores are located and differences in sales volumes among the stores. To minimize the within-treatments variability, the analyst confined the experiment to stores that were as alike as possible with respect to identifiable key factors, such as sales volume and type of clientele. In addition, a randomization process was employed in assigning displays to stores so that any major uncontrolled effects would tend to be distributed equally over the three displays.

Had he wished, the analyst could have employed a more refined experimental design, in which key factors such as type of neighborhood and sales volume would be controlled explicitly. In this way, the inherent variation would be reduced, which in turn would reduce the risks of Type II errors for given sample sizes and specified risk of Type I error. The basic procedure explained in this section can be expanded readily to accommodate more refined experimental designs.

Sample size. The example discussed here illustrated the type of approach to decision-making in which the sample sizes and risk of Type I error were specified in advance. This approach is the one frequently followed in tests concerning means of several populations. In particular cases, however, one might wish to control risks of both types of errors at specified levels. Procedures are available whereby one can specify the risks of both Type I and Type II errors, and then determine the necessary sample sizes.

Note also that in our example, the sample sizes for each treatment were the same. At times, these sample sizes will differ. The formulas given in this section would then need to be modified.

QUESTIONS AND PROBLEMS

19.1. Briefly explain each of the following:

a. Contingency table
b. Within-treatments variation
c. Correction for continuity
d. Mean square

19.2. Distinguish briefly between:

a. Expected frequencies, estimated expected frequencies, and observed frequencies

b. Total, within-treatments, and between-treatments sums of squares

***19.3.** In a test of the nature of the probability distribution faced in a reliability engineering problem, the alternative conclusions were: C_1: The probability distribution is exponential; C_2: The probability distribution is not exponential. There were 14 degrees of freedom associated with the test statistic.

a. What can be said about the distribution of V_1 here, if C_1 holds?

b. How is the location of the distribution of the test statistic affected here if C_2 holds instead? What does this imply as to the type of decision rule that is appropriate? Discuss.

c. What is the value of the action limit in the decision rule if the risk of a Type I error is to be controlled at .10? At .01?

d. If C_1 holds, what approximately is the area of the sampling distribution of the test statistic to the right of the value 23.7 on the chi-square scale? To the right of the value 26.9?

e. State the appropriate decision rule if the risk of a Type I error is to be controlled at .01.

f. Are the risks of Type II errors affected by the level at which the risk of a Type I error is controlled? Discuss.

g. Suppose C_1 had been: The probability distribution is exponential with mean 500 hours; and C_2 had been modified accordingly. How many degrees of freedom would now be associated with the test statistic? Why?

h. State the alternative C_2 in part **g** explicitly. Does it include exponential probability distributions? Explain.

19.4. It is known from extensive past experience that the probability distribution of breaking strengths of hardwood charcoal briquettes made with a certain binder is normal with mean and standard deviation equal to 48.5 and .5 psi (pounds per square inch), respectively. In a sample of 100 briquettes made by using a new shipment of this binder, the breaking strength of each was measured. The decision concerning the new shipment of binder was formulated as follows: C_1: The probability distribution of breaking strengths using the new binder shipment is normal with mean and standard deviation equal to 48.5 and .5 psi, respectively; C_2: The probability distribution is not normal with mean and standard deviation equal to 48.5 and .5 psi, respectively. The sample data were grouped into eight classes, and the expected frequencies obtained.

a. How many degrees of freedom are associated with the distribution of the test statistic V_1 here? Explain.

b. What can be said about the distribution of V_1 here, if C_1 holds?

c. How is the location of the distribution of the test statistic affected if C_2 holds instead? What does this imply as to the type of decision rule that is appropriate here? Discuss.

d. If the risk of a Type I error is to be controlled at .02, what is the value of the action limit in the decision rule? State the appropriate decision rule.

e. The observed and expected frequencies are not shown here, but the analyst who conducted the test concluded C_2. Should he now report that the breaking strengths of briquets made with the new binder shipment are not normally distributed? Explain.

f. How would your answers to parts **a** and **b** change if the alternative conclusions were: C_1: The probability distribution is normal; C_2: The probability distribution is not normal?

***19.5.** To test whether the number of calls per hour received at an emergency switchboard are Poisson-distributed, a police department consultant took a sample of 100 randomly selected hours and obtained the following results:

No. of Calls in Hour		*No. of Hours*
0		11
1		26
2		31
3		19
4		10
5		3
	Total	100

a. Specify the alternative conclusions in the decision problem posed by the consultant.

b. Obtain the appropriate expected frequencies. Explain what these represent. Treat the probabilities of outcomes for which there are no entries in Table A-2 as zero.

c. Calculate the test statistic. How many degrees of freedom are associated with the test statistic? Explain.

d. Develop the appropriate decision rule; assume the risk of a Type I error is to be controlled at .10. What conclusion should the consultant reach?

19.6. Refer to Problem 19.5. Answer all parts, but assume the consultant wants to test whether the number of calls per hour received at the switchboard are Poisson-distributed with mean equal to 2.5 calls. In part **d**, control the risk of a Type I error at .05.

19.7. An extensive regional research study of the number of hospital admissions resulting from outpatient treatments of mental-health patients with a certain type of illness during a two-year period indicated that the distribution of number of hospital admissions per patient in the two-year period was Poisson with a mean equal to .6 admissions. A mental-health researcher at a certain clinic has collected admissions data for 200 outpatients with this type of illness treated at his clinic and wants to know whether the number of admissions per patient over the two-year period in his clinic follows a Poisson distribution with a mean of .6 admissions. His data are shown below:

Number of Admissions per Patient in Two-year Period	*Number of Outpatients*	*Number of Admissions per Patient in Two-year Period*	*Number of Outpatients*
0	120	5	1
1	43	6	0
2	25	7	0
3	6	8	1
4	4	*Total*	200

a. Specify the alternative conclusions in the decision problem posed by the researcher.

b. Obtain the appropriate expected frequencies. Explain what these represent. Treat the probabilities of outcomes for which there are no entries in Table A-2 as zero.

c. Calculate the test statistic. How many degrees of freedom are associated with the test statistic? Explain.

d. Develop the appropriate decision rule; assume the risk of a Type I error is to be controlled at .05. What conclusion should be reached?

e. If C_1 were the appropriate conclusion in part **d**, would this imply that the number of admissions is Poisson-distributed? If C_2 were the appropriate conclusion, would this imply that the number of admissions is not Poisson-distributed? Discuss.

19.8. Refer to Problem 19.7. Answer parts **a** through **d**, but assume the researcher wants to know only whether the number of admissions follows a Poisson distribution. In part **d**, control the risk of a Type I error at .10.

19.9. The marketing-research department of a soft drink company selected a random sample of 120 teenagers and asked each to indicate independently which of three new drink flavors he preferred. The results were as follows:

Flavor Preferred	*Number of Teenagers*
A	25
B	53
C	42
Total	120

The manager of the marketing-research department wants to conduct a test on the basis of the sample data to determine whether or not the proportions of teenagers preferring each of the three flavors are the same.

a. Specify the alternative conclusions.

b. Obtain the appropriate expected frequencies. Explain what these represent.

c. Calculate the test statistic. How many degrees of freedom are associated with the test statistic?

d. Develop the appropriate decision rule. Assume that the manager wants to control the risk of a Type I error at .10. What conclusion should be reached?

e. If C_2 were the appropriate conclusion in part **d**, what do you think would be the next question about preferences for flavors that the manager of the marketing-research department would wish to investigate? Discuss.

***19.10.** A savings bank surveyed a random sample of 200 heads-of-household to determine whether such persons knew about a recent increase in interest rates paid by the bank on savings accounts. The following results were obtained when the survey data were cross-classified by occupational category and type of response:

Occupational Category	*Did Know*	*Did Not Know*
Wage earner or clerical worker	58	52
Managerial or professional worker	26	14
Other	16	34

The vice-president in charge of public relations for the bank would like to know whether type of response and occupational category are statistically independent in the population sampled.

a. Specify C_1 and C_2.

b. Obtain the appropriate expected frequencies. What do these represent?

(Continued)

c. Calculate the test statistic. How many degrees of freedom are associated with the test statistic?

d. How does the location of the distribution of the test statistic if the variables are statistically independent differ from that if they are not statistically independent? What does this imply as to the type of decision rule that is appropriate here? Discuss.

e. Develop the appropriate decision rule; assume the risk of a Type I error is to be controlled at .02. What conclusion should be reached?

f. What are the implications for the bank of the conclusion reached in part **e**? Discuss.

g. Would your conclusion in part **e** change if the risk of a Type I error had been controlled at .10? Discuss.

19.11. Refer to Problem 19.10. Answer the questions, but assume the data are as follows:

Occupational Category	*Did Know*	*Did Not Know*
Wage earner or clerical worker	43	57
Managerial or professional worker	19	31
Other	18	32

19.12. An investment analyst is studying the relationship between stock price movements in two consecutive weekly time periods in March. A simple random sample of 100 stocks is selected and the price movements of each stock during the two consecutive weeks in March are cross-tabulated as follows:

		Movement in Second Week		
		Increase	*No Change*	*Decrease*
Movement in First Week	*Increase*	10	12	8
	No Change	15	20	5
	Decrease	15	8	7

The analyst wishes to determine if price movements in the two periods are statistically independent.

a. Specify C_1 and C_2.

b. Obtain the appropriate expected frequencies. What do these represent?

c. Calculate the test statistic. How many degrees of freedom are associated with the test statistic?

d. Develop the appropriate decision rule; assume the risk of a Type I error is to be controlled at .05. What conclusion should be reached?

e. What are the implications of the conclusion reached in part **d**? Discuss.

f. Would your conclusion in part **d** change if the risk of a Type I error had been controlled at .02? Explain.

g. Do the given data indicate that knowledge of the price movement in the first week would be useful in predicting the price movement in the second week? Discuss.

19.13. Refer to Problem 19.12. Answer the questions, but assume the data are as follows:

		Movement in Second Week		
		Increase	*No Change*	*Decrease*
Movement in First Week	*Increase*	14	9	7
	No Change	20	10	10
	Decrease	16	11	3

***19.14.** In an experiment, four observations were obtained for each of the five treatments studied.

a. What is δ_1 here? δ_2?

b. What is the value on the F-scale appropriate here corresponding to an area .05 in the right tail? An area .01 in the right tail?

c. Answer parts **a** and **b** if five observations were obtained for each of four treatments studied.

***19.15.** A trucking firm tested capacities in samples of five batteries from each of three brands. All the batteries were of the same type. The following results were obtained:

Sample	*Capacity of Battery (Hundred Ampere Hours)*		
Observation	*Brand A*	*Brand B*	*Brand C*
1	1.0	1.8	1.1
2	.8	1.6	1.6
3	1.2	1.8	1.5
4	1.1	1.1	1.0
5	.9	1.7	1.3

It must now be decided whether the mean capacity is the same for the three brands.

a. Specify the alternative conclusions.

b. How many degrees of freedom are associated with the total sum of squares in these data? With the within-treatments sum of squares? With the between-treatments sum of squares? Discuss.

c. Calculate the respective sums of squares, set up an analysis of variance table, and obtain the value of the test statistic.

d. What is estimated by MS_1 and MS_2, respectively, if the mean capacities for the three brands are the same? If they differ? What are the implications of your answers as to the appropriate type of decision rule?

e. What is the distribution of your test statistic if the mean capacities for the three brands are the same? Under what conditions is the test statistic distributed exactly in this manner? What are the implications if the test statistic is distributed only approximately in the indicated manner?

f. State the appropriate decision rule if the risk of a Type I error is to be controlled at .05.

g. What conclusion should be reached? What are the implications of this conclusion? Discuss.

h. Estimate the inherent sampling variability in this experiment. Would there be any advantage in reducing this variability if it were possible to do so? Discuss.

19.16. Refer to Problem 19.15. Answer all the questions, but assume that six batteries from each of the three brands were tested and that the results were as follows:

Sample	*Capacity of Battery (Hundred Ampere Hours)*		
Observation	*Brand A*	*Brand B*	*Brand C*
1	1.4	1.7	1.9
2	1.8	1.6	1.8
3	1.5	2.0	1.9
4	1.6	1.5	2.0
5	1.4	1.8	1.8
6	1.3	1.6	2.0

19.17. An accountant wishes to determine whether four different accounting procedures have different effects on reported net earnings of railroads as determined originally according to I.C.C. accounting rules. Sixteen railroads are selected and randomly divided into four groups of four each. Last year's reported net earnings of each railroad are recalculated using the accounting procedure for the group to which the railroad is assigned. The data for the 16 railroads are shown below. The value shown for each railroad is the per cent change in last year's reported net earnings which is produced by the accounting procedure.

	Accounting Procedure			
Sample Railroad	A_1	A_2	A_3	A_4
1	−11	+ 4	−14	+ 2
2	+ 1	+20	− 2	+12
3	− 5	− 2	0	+ 7
4	− 3	+10	− 4	+ 3

The accountant now wants to decide whether the mean per cent change in reported net earnings is the same for all four accounting procedures.

a. Specify the alternative conclusions.

b. How many degrees of freedom are associated with the total sum of squares in these data? With the within-treatments sum of squares? With the between-treatments sum of squares? Discuss.

c. Calculate the respective sums of squares, set up an analysis of variance table, and obtain the value of the test statistic.

d. What is the action limit in the decision rule if the risk of a Type I error is to be controlled at .01?

e. What conclusion is appropriate? What are the implications of this conclusion? Discuss.

f. Estimate the inherent sampling variability in this experiment. How might this variability be reduced by designing the experiment differently? Would there be any advantage in reducing the inherent variability? Discuss.

19.18. Refer to Problem 19.17. Answer all the questions, but assume that three accounting procedures and fifteen railroads were used in the experiment and that the per cent changes in reported net earnings were as follows:

	Accounting Procedure		
Sample Railroad	A_1	A_2	A_3
1	0	+8	+5
2	−3	0	0
3	+2	+9	−7
4	0	−1	+4
5	+1	+4	+8

Unit

VI

STATISTICAL DECISION-MAKING (BAYESIAN)

Chapter

20

INTRODUCTION TO BAYESIAN DECISION-MAKING

In this chapter, we discuss an important probability theorem called Bayes' Theorem. We then introduce Bayesian decision-making, a topic which is receiving intensive study from decision theorists and is likely to grow in importance as statistical theory continues to develop.

20.1 BAYES' THEOREM

Bayes' Theorem represents an application of conditional probabilities. Recall that we discussed conditional probability in Chapter 6 (p. 122). To illustrate Bayes' Theorem, consider a population in which 30 per cent of the people own one or more savings accounts. If B_1 denotes owning one or more savings accounts and B_2 denotes not owning a savings account, we have $P(B_1) = .3$ and $P(B_2) = .7$, where $P(B_1)$ is the probability that a person selected at random has one or more savings accounts, and $P(B_2)$ is defined correspondingly.

Suppose now that a person is selected at random and asked if he owns one or more savings accounts. He may not give the correct response, for a variety of reasons. Let A_1 denote the answer "owns one or more accounts," and A_2 "does not own any accounts." We shall assume that the probabilities of correct response are known, given the savings status of the respondent. Suppose these are:

$$P(A_1|B_1) = .80 \qquad P(A_1|B_2) = .30$$
$$P(A_2|B_1) = .20 \qquad P(A_2|B_2) = .70$$

Here $P(A_1|B_1)$ denotes the conditional probability that a person picked at random answers that he owns one or more accounts, given that he does own one or more accounts, and so on.

If a person selected at random now responds that he does not own a savings account, what is the probability that in fact he does own one? In other words, we wish to find $P(B_1|A_2)$. We can obtain this probability by first calculating the joint probabilities, as shown in Table 20.1. The given information is enclosed in boxes; from this all joint probabilities can be obtained. For instance, from the multiplication theorem (6.25), p. 125, we have:

$$P(A_1 \text{ and } B_1) = P(B_1)P(A_1|B_1) = (.3)(.8) = .24$$

Table 20.1 Computation of Joint Probabilities

Account Status	Response: Owns 1 or More Accounts A_1	Response: Owns No Account A_2	Total
B_1 Owns one or more accounts	.24	.06	.30
B_2 Owns no account	.21	.49	.70
Total	.45	.55	1.00

$P(A_1\|B_1) = .80$	$P(A_1\|B_2) = .30$
$P(A_2\|B_1) = .20$	$P(A_2\|B_2) = .70$

From Table 20.1, we then obtain the desired conditional probability, using definition (6.23), p. 123:

$$P(B_1|A_2) = \frac{P(A_2 \text{ and } B_1)}{P(A_2)} = \frac{.06}{.55} = .11$$

We *interpret* $P(B_1|A_2)$ as follows: If a large number of random selections were made from the population and each person asked whether he owned any savings accounts, about 11 per cent of those who reply that they do not own such accounts would in fact own one or more savings accounts.

Bayes' Theorem expresses the relation between the desired conditional probability $P(B_1|A_2)$ and the given probabilities:

(20.1) $$P(B_1|A_2) = \frac{P(B_1)P(A_2|B_1)}{P(B_1)P(A_2|B_1) + P(B_2)P(A_2|B_2)}$$

In fact, (20.1) is equivalent to definition (6.23) for conditional probability. We know from the multiplication theorem that the numerator of (20.1) is:

$$P(B_1)P(A_2|B_1) = P(A_2 \text{ and } B_1)$$

Further, the denominator of (20.1) can be written as follows, using the multiplication theorem:

$$P(B_1)P(A_2|B_1) + P(B_2)P(A_2|B_2) = P(A_2 \text{ and } B_1) + P(A_2 \text{ and } B_2)$$

But we have:

$$P(A_2 \text{ and } B_1) + P(A_2 \text{ and } B_2) = P(A_2)$$

since A_2 can happen either with B_1 or B_2, but not with both simultaneously. Hence, (20.1) simply reduces to:

$$P(B_1|A_2) = \frac{P(A_2 \text{ and } B_1)}{P(A_2)}$$

Substituting into (20.1), we obtain:

$$P(B_1|A_2) = \frac{(.3)(.2)}{(.3)(.2) + (.7)(.7)} = \frac{.06}{.55} = .11$$

which, of course, is the same result obtained by using the definition of conditional probability.

Formula (20.1) can be adapted to other desired probabilities, such as $P(B_2|A_2)$ or $P(B_1|A_1)$. The general form of Bayes' Theorem is:

(20.2) $$P(B_i|A_j) = \frac{P(A_j \text{ and } B_i)}{P(A_j)} = \frac{P(B_i)P(A_j|B_i)}{\sum_i P(B_i)P(A_j|B_i)}$$

Probabilities of the type $P(B_i)$ are called *prior probabilities* in the terminology of Bayes' Theorem; that is, they are the probabilities attached to outcomes B_i prior to obtaining further information. Probabilities of the type $P(B_i|A_j)$ are called *posterior probabilities,* since they are probabilities of outcomes B_i conditional on the observance of a particular outcome A_j.

Returning to our example, we can summarize the prior probabilities and the posterior probabilities, given the response that no account is owned, as follows:

Account Status	*Prior Probability* $P(B_i)$	*Posterior Probability, Given Response That No Account Owned* (A_2) $P(B_i\|A_2)$
B_1 Owns one or more accounts	.3	.11
B_2 Owns no account	.7	.89

Note that if a person replies he owns no savings account, the probability that he does not own an account (.89) is higher than the prior probability, with no further information, that a person does not own an account (.7). In another instance, of course, the prior and posterior probabilities may have a different relation to each other.

20.2

BAYESIAN DECISION-MAKING WITH PRIOR PROBABILITIES ONLY

Thus far in our discussion of statistical decision problems, the population parameter was considered to have some specific, though unknown, value. For instance, in the problem in Section 18.3 involving a decision to accept or reject a particular shipment, the proportion of defective items in the shipment was considered to be some specific, though unknown, number in the analysis.

In some decision problems, however, formal probability distributions can be attached to the parameters of interest. For example, a quality-control engineer wishes to obtain information about a process mean at the present point in time. He knows that this mean is affected by random factors that cause it to change over time, and he has data available on the relative frequency distribution of the process mean over time. Thus, the engineer may think of the process mean at any one point in time as being a random variable, and may attach probabilities to the different possible values that this variable can take.

(20.3) Probabilities that are attached to a population parameter prior to any current sampling of the population form the ***prior probability distribution*** of the parameter.

Case example

A second example of the treatment of population parameters as random variables is presented here in some detail, since it will be utilized as the basis of discussion throughout this chapter. A manufacturer's agent has agreed to receive, periodically, flatcar-load shipments of four large machines from one of the firms he represents. The machines must be moved from the railroad yard upon arrival and installed in good working order in the customers' plants.

Each time a shipment arrives, the representative faces a decision problem involving the following two alternative acts:

C_1 Accept responsibility for the shipment
C_2 Reject responsibility for the shipment

Payoffs. If the agent accepts responsibility, he receives a flat fee of \$400 from the manufacturer but must reset, at his own cost, any machines that have been jarred out of alignment while being shipped on the flatcar. The cost of resetting a machine is about \$150. If the representative rejects the responsibility for a given shipment, he receives no fee but is reimbursed by the manufacturer for any direct costs incurred in resetting of damaged machines in that shipment. The costs of moving machines from the yard to customers' plants are paid by the buyers, hence do not enter into the agent's decision problem.

Thus, the population parameter that determines the agent's payoff from a given act is the *number of machines damaged in the shipment.* (The *proportion* of machines in the shipment that are damaged is an equivalent parameter, but it will be easier to work with the *number* of damaged machines.) We can easily develop the payoff functions for the two acts:

	Payoff of Act	
No. Damaged	C_1 *(Accept)*	C_2 *(Reject)*
0	\$400	\$0
1	250	0
2	100	0
3	−50	0
4	−200	0

For instance, if the agent accepts responsibility and no machine requires resetting, he clears \$400; if one machine is damaged, he clears \$400 − \$150 = \$250; and so on. If he rejects responsibility, his payoff is \$0 regardless of the number of machines damaged, since he receives no fee and must not pay for any of the resetting costs.

Prior probabilities. The agent has collected extensive data on the number of machines per flatcar that have had to be reset in relevant past shipments. The relative frequency distribution is as follows:

No. of Damaged Machines	*Relative Frequency*
0	.4
1	.2
2	.1
3	.1
4	.2
Total	1.0

Thus, in 40 per cent of shipments no machine needed resetting, in 20 per cent of shipments one machine needed resetting, and so on.

The agent will treat these relative frequencies as prior probabilities, since they are based on a substantial body of relevant data. Thus, he considers the prior probability that a shipment contains no defective machine to be .4, and so on.

We will utilize this case for our discussion of decision-making with prior probabilities.

Decision-making when only prior probabilities are available

Suppose that the agent must decide whether to accept or to reject responsibility for the next shipment before he has time to examine the shipment or any part of it. Thus, the only information he has available for his decision is the prior probability distribution and the payoff functions.

This problem, as will be recognized from our discussion in Chapter 15, is one of decision-making under risk:

1. The set of available acts consists of:

   C_1 Accept responsibility for shipment

   C_2 Reject responsibility for shipment

2. The set of outcome states consists of the possible number of damaged machines in the shipment—namely 0, 1, 2, 3, or 4.
3. The payoff for each act and outcome state combination was developed earlier.
4. The probability distribution of the outcome states is the prior probability distribution shown earlier.

Assuming that the relative desirability of the possible payoffs is properly reflected in the dollar figures, the conventional criterion in decision-making under risk is to choose the act that maximizes the expected payoff. Table 20.2 contains the prior probability distribution of the outcome states, and

Table 20.2 Calculation of Expected Payoff for Each of Two Acts ($n = 0$)

(1)	(2)	(3)	(4)	(5)	(6)
		Act C_1		*Act C_2*	
Number of Damaged Machines in Shipment	*Prior Probability*	*Payoff*	*Weighted Payoff (Col. 2 × Col. 3)*	*Payoff*	*Weighted Payoff (Col. 2 × Col. 5)*
0	.4	$400	$160	$0	$0
1	.2	250	50	0	0
2	.1	100	10	0	0
3	.1	−50	−5	0	0
4	.2	−200	−40	0	0
	1.0		$175		$0

the payoffs for each of the two acts. The calculation of the expected payoff for each act is straightforward—each payoff is multiplied by the probability that this payoff will be received, and the products are summed. Since the expected payoff for act C_1 is greater, the agent should accept responsibility for the next shipment, assuming that no sample information can be had.

(20.4) The procedure that calls for choosing the act that maximizes the expected payoff is often called a ***Bayes procedure.*** The optimal act (in our example, "accept responsibility for shipment") is then called the ***Bayes act.***

Note that the term *Bayes procedure* is merely an alternative expression for the criterion of "maximization of expected payoff" in situations under risk where, in the terminology here, prior probabilities are applicable to the different outcome states. Thus, there is nothing new beyond our discussion of Chapter 15 up to this point. It is when prior probabilities and sample data are available that a new situation exists; this is discussed next.

20.3 BAYESIAN DECISION-MAKING WITH PRIOR PROBABILITIES AND SAMPLE INFORMATION

For convenience, we call the previous case, when only prior probabilities and no sample data are available, the *no-sample case* ($n = 0$). Now we want to consider the case when both prior probabilities and sample data are available for decision-making. In our example, for instance, the agent may be able to inspect a sample of the machines on the flatcar before committing himself as to acceptance or rejection of the shipment.

Note that the agent still must decide whether to accept or reject responsibility, but now his decision can be based not only on the prior probabilities but also on the sample results from the shipment under consideration. The decision procedure is still to be a Bayes procedure, that is, selecting the act that maximizes the expected payoff. The finding of this Bayes act can be simplified by breaking up the problem into two parts:

1. Combine the prior probabilities and the sample data in a suitable fashion to obtain revised prior probabilities (that is, revised in the light of the sample data).
2. Use these revised prior probabilities as in the no-sample case to find the Bayes act.

Combining prior probabilities and sample data

So that we can explain specifically how to combine prior probabilities and sample data, we assume that the agent decided to sample $n = 2$ machines, and that he found one damaged machine in the sample.

The outcome state—number of damaged machines in the *shipment*—is denoted by B_i. Thus, B_0 denotes no machine damaged in shipment, B_1 one machine damaged, and so on.

Correspondingly, let A_j denote the sample result—number of machines damaged in the *sample of two machines*. Thus, A_0 stands for no damaged machine in the sample, A_1 for one damaged machine in the sample, and A_2 for both machines in the sample damaged.

The prior probabilities of the outcome states will be denoted by $P(B_i)$. Thus, we know $P(B_0) = .4$, and so on.

The method whereby the prior probabilities are revised on the basis of the sample data is quite simple conceptually. Each prior probability $P(B_i)$ is revised on the basis of the sample result A_j by finding the corresponding conditional probability $P(B_i|A_j)$ by means of Bayes' Theorem (20.2). In our case, $A_j = A_1$ since one machine in the sample was damaged. Therefore, $P(B_i)$ is revised by finding $P(B_i|A_1)$—that is, the conditional probability of i machines damaged in the shipment, given that one damaged machine was found in the sample of two.

For $P(B_1|A_1)$, for instance, Bayes' Theorem takes the form:

(20.5) $$P(B_1|A_1) = \frac{P(A_1 \text{ and } B_1)}{P(A_1)} =$$

$$\frac{P(B_1)P(A_1|B_1)}{P(B_0)P(A_1|B_0)+P(B_1)P(A_1|B_1)+P(B_2)P(A_1|B_2)+P(B_3)P(A_1|B_3)+P(B_4)P(A_1|B_4)}$$

Let us find the numerator first. We know that $P(B_1) = .2$. $P(A_1|B_1)$ is the probability that one machine in the sample of two is damaged, given that the shipment contains one damaged machine. This probability is given by the hypergeometric probability distribution, as shown by (11.2), p. 212, since simple random sampling without replacement is being employed here in the selection of the sample machines. Note that while (11.2) gives the probability of a sample *proportion,* the same probabilities are applicable for the *number* of damaged machines in the sample, since there is a one-to-one correspondence between the two.

In terms of the notation of Chapter 11, the population size here is $N = 4$, the number of damaged machines in the population is $Np = 1$, and the number of damaged machines in the sample of $n = 2$ is $X = 1$. Hence, we have: [1]

$$P(A_1|B_1) = P(X = 1|Np = 1) = \frac{\binom{Np}{X}\binom{N(1-p)}{n-X}}{\binom{N}{n}} = \frac{\binom{1}{1}\binom{3}{1}}{\binom{4}{2}} = \frac{1}{2}$$

Combining this result with the known prior probability $P(B_1) = .2$, we obtain:

$$P(A_1 \text{ and } B_1) = P(B_1)\,P(A_1|B_1) = (.2)(.5) = .10$$

Thus, the probability is .10 that the shipment contains one damaged machine *and* that one of the two machines sampled from the shipment is damaged.

Next, we find the denominator of (20.5), which equals $P(A_1)$. Since the terms in the sum are of the same type as the joint probability that we just obtained for the numerator, we must repeat the same type of calculation to

[1] See (11.3), p. 212, for an explanation of the notation $\binom{x}{y}$.

find these other joint probabilities. We do this systematically in Table 20.3. Thus, we obtain in column 4:

$$P(A_1) = 0 + .1000 + .0667 + .0500 + 0 = .2167$$

Note, incidentally, that by definition:

$$\binom{0}{1} = 0$$

Hence $P(A_1 \text{ and } B_0) = 0$. Clearly, one cannot find a damaged machine in the sample if there is none in the shipment. For corresponding reasons, $P(A_1 \text{ and } B_4) = 0$, since both sample machines must be damaged if all machines in the shipment are damaged.

Now, we can find the revised prior probability in (20.5) by substituting for the numerator and denominator as follows:

$$P(B_1|A_1) = \frac{.1000}{.2167} = .4615$$

The interpretation of this revised prior probability is similar to any other conditional probability: $P(B_1|A_1) = .4615$ simply means that among all shipments for which the sample of two machines contains one damaged machine, about 46 per cent of these shipments have one damaged machine. Note how this interpretation follows from the definition of the conditional probability. $P(A_1) = .2167$ indicates that among all shipments, 21.67 per cent yield one damaged machine in the sample of two machines. $P(A_1$ and $B_1) = .10$ indicates that among all shipments, 10 per cent contain one damaged machine and also yield one damaged machine in the sample of two. Thus among all those shipments that yield a sample result of one damaged machine, .10/.2167 = .4615 or 46.15 per cent of these have one

Table 20.3 Calculation of Posterior Probabilities ($n = 2$, $A_j = A_1$)

(1) *Outcome State* B_i	(2) *Prior Probability* $P(B_i)$	(3) $P(A_1 \vert B_i)$	(4) $P(A_1 \text{ and } B_i) =$ $P(B_i) \times P(A_1 \vert B_i)$ (*Col. 2 × Col. 3*)	(5) $P(B_i \vert A_1) =$ $P(A_1 \text{ and } B_i)/P(A_1)$ (*Col. 4 ÷ .2167*)
B_0	.4	$\binom{0}{1}\binom{4}{1} \div \binom{4}{2} = 0$	0	0
B_1	.2	$\binom{1}{1}\binom{3}{1} \div \binom{4}{2} = .50$	.1000	.4615
B_2	.1	$\binom{2}{1}\binom{2}{1} \div \binom{4}{2} = .67$	.0667	.3077
B_3	.1	$\binom{3}{1}\binom{1}{1} \div \binom{4}{2} = .50$	.0500	.2308
B_4	.2	$\binom{4}{1}\binom{0}{1} \div \binom{4}{2} = 0$	0	0
	1.0		$P(A_1) = .2167$	1.0

damaged machine in the shipment. Hence, the revised prior probability that the shipment contains one damaged machine, given the sample result of one damaged machine, is .4615.

In similar fashion, we find the other revised probabilities. Mechanically, we simply express each entry in column 4 of Table 20.3 relative to the total of that column. Thus, no further extensive calculations are necessary to find the other revised probabilities.

The revised prior probabilities in column 5 of Table 20.3 are posterior probabilities.

(20.6) Probabilities attached to a population parameter which are derived by combining the prior probabilities and the sample data through Bayes' Theorem form a ***posterior probability distribution*** of the parameter.

Note from Table 20.3 that the posterior probabilities in column 5, given one damaged machine in the sample, indicate a greater likelihood that the shipment contains one, two, or three damaged machines than the prior probabilities. This is a reflection of the fact that one of the two sample machines was damaged.

Bayes act

Now that we have the posterior probabilities, given that one damaged machine was found in the sample of two machines, it is a simple matter to find the Bayes act, that is, the act that maximizes the expected payoff. As stated earlier, the posterior probabilities are now used as in the no-sample case. Thus, we determine the expected payoff for each of the acts C_1 and C_2 in the manner of the no-sample case, but use the posterior probabilities. These calculations are shown in Table 20.4. Note that the payoffs in Table 20.4 are the same as those for the no-sample case in Table 20.2. Since the sample size is fixed at $n = 2$ no matter which act is chosen, we can ignore the sampling cost for determining the optimal act.

Table 20.4 Calculation of Expected Payoff for Each of Two Acts ($n = 2$, $A_j = A_1$)

(1)	(2)	(3)	(4)	(5)	(6)
		Act C_1		*Act C_2*	
Number of Damaged Machines in Shipment	*Posterior Probability*	*Payoff*	*Weighted Payoff (Col. 2 × Col. 3)*	*Payoff*	*Weighted Payoff (Col. 2 × Col. 5)*
0	0	\$400	\$ 0	\$0	\$0
1	.4615	250	115.38	0	0
2	.3077	100	30.77	0	0
3	.2308	−50	−11.54	0	0
4	0	−200	0	0	0
	1.0		\$134.61		\$0

We see from Table 20.4 that C_1 maximizes the expected payoff, and hence the agent should accept responsibility for the shipment.

Bayes decision rule

If the only concern is to find the *optimal act, given the particular sample result,* the previous discussion has shown that this can be found directly without working out a complete strategy or decision rule indicating the optimal act for each possible sample outcome.

There are times, however, when it is necessary to develop a complete Bayes decision rule or Bayes strategy.

(20.7) A ***Bayes decision rule*** or ***Bayes strategy*** indicates the Bayes act for each possible sample outcome for a given sample size.

To develop this decision rule in our example, we need to repeat the earlier calculations for the cases when the sample of two machines contains no damaged machine and two damaged machines. Since no new problems are encountered in these calculations, we merely summarize the pertinent results for all possible sample outcomes, based on $n = 2$, in Table 20.5.

A glance at the expected payoffs in Table 20.5 (which do not reflect the cost of sampling) indicates that the Bayes acts are as follows:

Number of Defective Machines in Sample	*Bayes Act*
0	C_1
1	C_1
2	C_2

The Bayes decision rule now can be readily formulated, since it simply indicates the Bayes act for each possible sample outcome. It is for our example:

If $X \leq 1$, select act C_1 (accept responsibility)
If $X = 2$, select act C_2 (reject responsibility)

where X is the number of damaged machines in the sample of two machines.

Expected payoff of Bayes decision rule

The Bayes decision rule indicates which act to select for each possible sample outcome. The expected payoffs for each of these optimal acts are underlined in boldface in Table 20.5. The probabilities of obtaining each of the sample outcomes are also shown in Table 20.5. It will be recalled that we calculated the probability $P(A_1)$ in Table 20.3. The others are obtained in similar fashion. It is then a simple matter to calculate the ex-

Table 20.5 Bayes Acts for All Possible Sample Outcomes ($n = 2$)

(1) Sample Outcome	(2)	(3) Expected Payoff of Act	(4)
A_j	$P(A_j)$	C_1	C_2
A_0	.5167	$361.29	$0
A_1	.2167	134.61	0
A_2	.2667	−153.12	0
	1.0		

pected payoff with the Bayes decision rule, based on $n = 2$, from the data in Table 20.5. Using the ordinary expected payoff calculations, we obtain:

$$\text{Expected Payoff of Bayes Decision Rule } (n = 2) = (361.29)(.5167) + (134.61)(.2167) + (0)(.2667) = \$215.84$$

It is a property of the Bayes decision rule that this rule maximizes the expected payoff for the given sample size and the given prior probabilities. Thus, while other possible decision rules based on $n = 2$ exist (e.g., select act C_1 only if no damaged machines are found in the sample; otherwise, select act C_2), none of these would lead to any higher expected payoff than the Bayes decision rule for the given prior probabilities.

Note that the Bayes decision rule that we obtained is optimal for the prior probabilities that exist in this case. If the prior probabilities had been different, a different Bayes decision rule might have been obtained.

20.4 DETERMINATION OF OPTIMAL SAMPLE SIZE

We have determined above the Bayes decision rule based on a sample of two machines and found that the expected payoff of this strategy is $215.84. However, the agent does not necessarily have to sample two machines. It may be that the expected payoff of the Bayes decision rule for some other sample size is still greater. Thus, one must examine the expected payoffs of the Bayes decision rules for all sample sizes in order to determine the sample size that will lead to the greatest expected payoff.

For this purpose, the cost of sampling must be considered, since one wishes to maximize expected payoff after the cost of sampling. Up to this point, we have not considered the cost of sampling, since we were concerned only with a particular sample size. Suppose that it costs the agent $16 each to inspect machines in the freight yard. The procedure then is to determine the Bayes decision rule for each sample size, evaluate the expected payoff net of sampling costs, and then determine the sample size that leads to the greatest net expected payoff. We have already determined the expected payoffs of the Bayes decision rules when $n = 0$ and when $n = 2$. Table 20.6 summarizes these decision rules and gives the expected payoffs, sampling costs, and net expected payoffs for each. Table 20.6 also contains the corresponding results for the sample size $n = 1$. We do not show the calculations for $n = 1$, but they parallel those for $n = 2$. There is no need to consider sample sizes beyond $n = 2$ in this case, for a reason we shall explain shortly.

Table 20.6 shows quickly that the optimal sample size for the case discussed is $n = 1$, since the Bayes decision rule for $n = 1$ has a higher net expected payoff than the Bayes decision rules for the other sample sizes that need to be considered. Hence the agent would be well-advised to sample one machine in the shipment, and follow the Bayes decision rule for that sample size shown in Table 20.6.

Table 20.6 Bayes Decision Rules and Payoffs for Different Sample Sizes

(1) *Sample Size*	(2) *Bayes Decision Rule*		(3)	(4)	(5)
n	*Choose* C_1	*Choose* C_2	*Expected Payoff of Decision Rule*	*Sampling Cost*	*Net Expected Payoff of Decision Rule*
0	Always	Never	\$175.00	\$ 0	\$175.00
1	If $X = 0$	If $X = 1$	201.25	16.00	185.25
2	If $X \leq 1$	If $X = 2$	215.84	32.00	183.84

Two comments should be made concerning the determination of the optimal sample size. First, different prior probabilities might lead to a different optimal sample size and decision rule in our example. Second, we have assumed that the sample size is fixed. This rules out sample information being built up sequentially by examining one machine at a time and deciding after each whether to make a decision to accept or reject or continue sampling. Sequential sampling can be very useful, but involves greater complexities than sampling with a fixed sample size.

20.5 EXPECTED PAYOFF WITH PERFECT INFORMATION

We explain now how we knew in our example that samples beyond $n = 2$ did not need to be considered in this instance when we were searching for the optimal sample size. One way of establishing this is by utilizing the concept of the expected payoff with perfect information.

(20.8) The ***expected payoff with perfect information*** is the expected payoff based on perfect and free information about the outcomes B_i.

Note that this concept considers the situation where we have, at no cost, perfect information about B_i. For our example, this means that we know, at no cost, the number of damaged machines in the shipment. Then a glance at the payoffs (see, for instance, Table 20.4, columns 3 and 5) indicates that the optimal strategy is to select act C_1 if there are zero, one, or two damaged machines in the shipment, and to select C_2 if there are three or four damaged machines in the shipment. Thus, with *perfect information* our payoffs would be as follows for the different possible numbers of damaged machines in the shipment:

B_i	*Payoff*
0	$400
1	250
2	100
3	0
4	0

The probabilities of the number of damaged machines B_i are given by the prior probabilities $P(B_i)$ in Table 20.2. Hence, we can calculate the expected payoff with perfect information in the usual manner:

$$\text{Expected Payoff with Perfect Information} = (400)(.4) + (250)(.2) + (100)(.1) + (0)(.1) + (0)(.2) = \$220$$

The significance of the expected payoff with perfect information can be seen from the following theorem:

(20.9) Decision rules based on sample information cannot have expected payoffs that are higher than the expected payoff with perfect information in a given decision problem.

Thus, in our example, for no possible sample size can the expected payoff be greater than $220 before deducting sampling costs.

Since it costs $16 to inspect a machine, a sample of three machines would have a sampling cost of $48. The expected payoff net of sampling costs for the Bayes strategy based on $n = 3$ could therefore not exceed $220 − $48 = $172. In like manner the expected payoff net of sampling costs for the Bayes strategy based on $n = 4$ could not exceed $220 − $64 = $156. Since both of these upper limits are less than any of the expected payoffs net of sampling costs shown in Table 20.6, sample sizes of three and four in this instance cannot be optimal.

Note, incidentally, that a sample of four machines represents 100 per cent inspection in our example, and hence would provide exact information about B_i, the number of machines damaged in the shipment. That $n = 4$ is not an optimal sample size implies that the cost of sampling four machines is greater than the value of the information provided by the sample.

20.6 EXPECTED VALUE OF PERFECT INFORMATION

The exclusion of samples beyond $n = 2$ in our example can also be established by considering the concept of the expected value of perfect information.

(20.10) The ***expected value of perfect information*** is the difference between the expected payoff with perfect information and the expected payoff of the Bayes decision rule based only on the prior probabilities of the decision problem (i.e., the no-sample case).

For our illustration, the expected payoff with perfect information is \$220. From Table 20.6, it is seen that the expected payoff of the Bayes decision rule based only on the prior probabilities (the no-sample case) is \$175. Thus, the expected value of perfect information in this decision problem is:

$$\text{Expected Value of Perfect Information} = 220 - 175 = \$45$$

Any type of information about the number of damaged machines in the shipment, whether perfect or imperfect, is not worth more than \$45 to the agent since otherwise he would do better relying on the no-sample Bayes rule.

It is now readily apparent why sample sizes beyond $n = 2$ should be excluded from consideration in our example. Sampling costs \$16 per machine; hence the cost of sampling more than two machines exceeds \$45, the expected value of perfect information. To put this another way, the expected payoff, net of sampling costs, for any sample size beyond $n = 2$ would be less than the expected payoff for the no-sample case in our example, and hence cannot be optimal.

It should be noted that different prior probabilities could lead to a different expected value of perfect information and, possibly, to a different upper limit on the optimal sample size.

20.7 OBJECTIVE AND SUBJECTIVE APPROACHES TO PRIOR PROBABILITIES

In considering the use of prior probabilities up to this point, we illustrated several cases that involved repeatable events, and in which the prior probabilities were based objectively on past observations. Decision theorists of the subjective probability school will employ the prior probability approach not only in these instances but also when the event is nonrepeatable or when no firm information on prior probabilities is available. Essentially, this school views *any* population parameter as a random variable, for which the prior probabilities may be determined either from past data or by subjective assessment. Whether prior probabilities are determined from past data or by subjective assessment, the mechanics of determining Bayes acts and optimal sample sizes and decision rules are the same.

QUESTIONS AND PROBLEMS

20.1. Explain briefly each of the following:
- **a.** Bayes act
- **b.** No-sample case
- **c.** Bayes decision rule

20.2. Distinguish briefly between:
- **a.** Prior and posterior probabilities
- **b.** Expected value of perfect information and expected payoff with perfect information

***20.3.** The women's clothing department of a large store has found from past experience that the probability that a customer will return a purchase is .10. It also has found that 70 per cent of all purchases returned by the customer are charged, and that 50 per cent of all purchases not returned are charged.
- **a.** Use Bayes' Theorem to find the probability that if a purchase is charged it will be returned. Interpret this probability.
- **b.** Develop the prior probability distribution of a purchase return. Develop the posterior probability distribution of a purchase return, given that the purchase is charged.
- **c.** What is the probability that a cash purchase will not be returned?
- **d.** Suppose that 60 per cent of the returned purchases are for \$15 or more and are charged, and that 45 per cent of all purchases are for \$15 or more and are charged. Find the probability that if a purchase is for \$15 or more and is charged, it will be returned.

20.4. The personnel director of a steel company has learned from past experience that the probability is .80 that a management trainee successfully completes the two-year program. The proportion of trainees with previous business experience at another company is .10 among the trainees successfully completing the program, and .20 among those who do not successfully complete the program.
- **a.** Use Bayes' Theorem to find the probability that if a trainee has previous business experience, he will successfully complete the training program. Interpret this probability.
- **b.** Develop both the prior probability distribution of training success and the posterior probability distribution, given that the trainee has previous business experience.
- **c.** Do either the prior or posterior probabilities take account of the trainee's academic record? Discuss.
- **d.** Are the differences between the prior and posterior probability distributions necessarily due to the effect of previous business experience? Would information about persons *not* hired for the management training program be relevant for answering this question? Discuss.

*20.5. A chemical plant has two major fractionating columns which require occasional internal cleaning and maintenance. During the mid-year maintenance period, the plant manager must decide to either strip both columns for cleaning and maintenance (C_1) or leave the columns untouched until the end of the year (C_2) when cleaning and maintenance of both columns will be undertaken in either case. The condition of the two columns—that is, whether or not they require extensive cleaning and maintenance—is the key determinant of the payoffs in this decision problem. The payoffs (in thousands of dollars) for the two acts and the different possible outcome states are shown below. It is impossible to accurately assess the condition of the columns by external inspection alone. However, on the basis of personal judgment and experience, the plant manager is able to assign the prior probabilities shown below to the different outcome states:

Number of Columns Requiring Cleaning and Maintenance	*Prior Probability*	*Payoff of Act*	
		C_1	C_2
0	.6	30	40
1	.1	20	20
2	.3	10	0

a. Suppose the plant manager must choose between C_1 and C_2 without obtaining further information on the condition of the two columns. Which act is the Bayes act? Explain how you identified the Bayes act here.

b. Suppose, on the other hand, that the plant manager has the option of having one or both columns opened and inspected before he makes his decision. He arbitrarily decides to have one of the two columns inspected, and picks one column at random. The inspection shows that this column requires cleaning and maintenance. Revise the plant manager's prior probabilities on the basis of this sample information by means of Bayes' Theorem.

c. Identify the Bayes act for the sample result in part **b**. Explain how you determined the Bayes act.

d. Determine the Bayes decision rule when one column is inspected ($n = 1$). Show the steps by which you obtained this rule. What properties does this decision rule have? Explain.

e. Suppose that the cost of having a column opened and inspected is $1,000 per column. What is the expected payoff net of sampling costs (the cost of opening and inspecting the column) for the Bayes decision rule when $n = 1$?

f. Determine the expected payoff net of sampling costs for the Bayes decision rule based on $n = 2$. Compare this expected net payoff with those of the Bayes decision rules for $n = 0$ in part **a** and for $n = 1$ in part **e**. What is the optimal sample size here?

g. If the plant manager's prior probabilities had been different, might the optimal sample size in part **f** be changed? Discuss.

*20.6. Refer to Problem 20.5.

a. Prior to opening and inspecting any columns, what is the plant manager's expected payoff with perfect information?

b. Compare the expected payoff in part **a** with the expected payoff net of sampling costs for the Bayes decision rule based on $n = 2$ in part **f** of Problem 20.5. What accounts for the difference in these two values?

c. What is the expected value of perfect information to the plant manager? How can perfect information be obtained in this problem?

20.7. Refer to Problems 20.5 and 20.6. Answer all the questions, but assume that the plant manager's prior probabilities are as follows:

Number of Columns Requiring Cleaning and Maintenance	*Prior Probability*
0	.2
1	.1
2	.7

20.8. The Roberts Excavation Company is offered a contract to excavate sites for three experimental radar towers to be erected by a local university. If Mr. Roberts accepts the contract, his firm will be paid $9,000 for the job. Roberts estimates that it will cost his firm $2,500 to excavate each site where no rock layer is encountered in the work and $3,500 to excavate each site where a rock layer is encountered. The payoff if Roberts rejects the offer is simply zero. Roberts knows that he must take the offer (C_1) or leave it (C_2), because an out-of-town firm has already offered to do the job for $9,000 and will get the contract if Roberts turns the offer down.

Roberts cannot predict with certainty whether a rock layer will be encountered in any of the three sites, but is able to assign the following prior probabilities on the basis of extensive experience in the general region of the excavation sites:

Number of Sites Containing Rock Layer	*Prior Probability*
0	.3
1	.4
2	.2
3	.1

a. Develop the payoff functions for Roberts' two acts.

b. Suppose Roberts must decide whether to accept the contract or to reject it before he can drill experimentally at any of the sites to determine whether rock layers will be encountered. Which act is the Bayes act? Explain how you identified the Bayes act here.

c. Suppose, on the other hand, that Roberts has time to drill at one site. He picks a site at random from among the three, and encounters a rock layer in his experimental drilling. Revise Roberts' prior probabilities on the basis of this sample information by means of Bayes' Theorem.

d. Identify the Bayes act, given the sample outcome in part **c**. Explain how you determined the Bayes act.

e. Determine the Bayes decision rule when experimental drilling is conducted at one site ($n = 1$). Show the steps by which you obtained this rule. What properties does this decision rule have? Explain.

f. Suppose the cost of drilling experimentally at a site is $50 for each site drilled, and that this cost must be paid by Roberts. What is the expected payoff net of sampling costs (costs of experimental drilling) for the Bayes decision rule when $n = 1$?

g. Determine the expected payoffs net of sampling costs for the Bayes decision rules based on $n = 2$ and $n = 3$. Assume as above that the cost of experimental drilling is $50 per site.

h. What sample size is optimal in Roberts' decision problem? Explain how you determined this.

20.9. Refer to Problem 20.8.

a. Prior to drilling at any of the sites, what is Roberts' expected payoff with perfect information?

b. Compare the expected payoff in part **a** with the expected payoff net of sampling costs for the Bayes decision rule based on $n = 3$ in part **g** of Problem 20.8. What accounts for the difference in these two values?

c. What is the expected value of perfect information to Roberts? How can perfect information be obtained in this problem?

20.10. Refer to Problems 20.8 and 20.9. Answer all the questions asked, but assume that the cost of experimental drilling is $120 per site and that Roberts' prior probabilities are as follows:

Number of Sites Containing Rock Layer	*Prior Probability*
0	.4
1	.1
2	.1
3	.4

***20.11.** Refer to Problem 15.13. Suppose that each of the outcome states in this decision problem is assigned probability .25.

a. Which act has the maximum expected payoff (i.e., which is the Bayes act)?

b. In the context of this decision problem, what is meant by *perfect information* about the outcome state that will prevail? Is it likely that the executive committee has access to perfect information here?

c. In this decision problem, what is the expected payoff with perfect information? What is the expected value of perfect information?

d. The steel corporation's economic research department could devote its resources to forecasting the demand for steel in the future and technological breakthroughs in steel production. What is the maximum expected value of such a forecast in this decision problem, no matter how accurate it is? Would you expect the research department to be able to prepare a forecast sufficiently accurate so that it has an expected value close to this maximum? Discuss.

e. Could the maximum expected value in part **d** change if the prior probabilities given earlier were changed? What is the implication of this for a decision whether or not to direct the economic research department to prepare the forecast?

20.12. Refer to the decision problem displayed in Table 15.2 and described on pp. 312–313. Suppose the decision-making group assigns the prior probabilities $P(a) = .5$, $P(b) = .4$, and $P(c) = .1$ to the three possible outcome states.

a. Which act has the maximum expected payoff (i.e., which is the Bayes act)?

b. In the context of this decision problem, what is meant by *perfect information* about the outcome state that will prevail? Is it likely that the decision-making group has access to perfect information here?

c. In this decision problem, what is the expected payoff with perfect information? What is the expected value of perfect information?

d. A certain law firm, which specializes in U.S. Food and Drug Administration decisions on drug applications, is known for its outstanding investigations in this field. This law firm has offered to study the decision-making group's application, the nature of the drug, and so on, and to forecast the outcome of the application. What is the maximum expected value of the law firm's forecast, no matter how accurate it is?

e. Could the maximum expected value in part **d** change if the prior probabilities given above were changed? What is the implication of this for a decision on whether to accept or reject the law firm's offer?

Chapter

21

ADDITIONAL TOPIC: BAYESIAN DECISION-MAKING WITH NORMAL PRIOR AND SAMPLING DISTRIBUTIONS

In this chapter, we again discuss Bayesian decision-making. Specifically, we deal with decision problems concerning the population mean μ_X when the prior probability distribution for μ_X is normal. We first consider decision-making when only the prior distribution for μ_X is available. Following this, we consider the case where information about μ_X is obtained by sampling and a decision made on the basis of the prior probabilities and the sample data. Finally, we take up the determination of the optimal sample size.

21.1 DECISION-MAKING WITH PRIOR PROBABILITIES ONLY

Case example

A company has a process for removing impurities from a certain chemical which is produced exclusively for a special customer. After a batch of chemical passes through the process, the level of impurities remaining in the batch is some unknown value μ_X, which varies from one batch to another. The customer's contract with the company contains a penalty clause for impurities; the higher the level of impurities, the lower the price paid by the customer for the chemical. Upon receiving each batch from the company, the customer undertakes extensive testing to establish the exact value of μ_X in order to determine the penalty amount. Two acts are available to the company after a batch of chemical has passed through the process:

C_1 Send the batch directly to the customer
C_2 Recycle the batch to remove additional impurities

Payoff functions

If the batch is sent directly to the customer, the company incurs the penalty costs associated with the level of impurities remaining in the chemical. On the other hand, if the batch is recycled (i.e., put through the process again), most of the impurities are removed so a very small penalty cost results, but the company incurs the cost of recycling the batch. Based on the recycling characteristics of the process and the terms of the penalty clause, the company has constructed payoff functions showing the effect on annual profits of acts C_1 and C_2 for various possible levels of impurities, μ_X. These payoff functions are shown in Figure 21.1 and are described by the following linear equations:

(21.1a) $P_1 = 200 - 30\mu_X$ for act C_1

(21.1b) $P_2 = 125 - 5\mu_X$ for act C_2

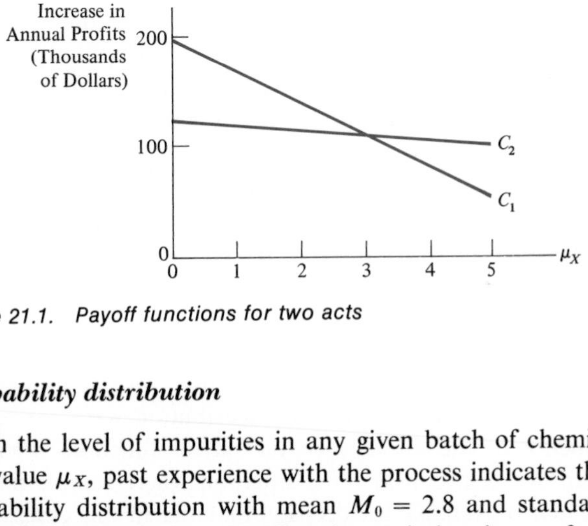

Figure 21.1. Payoff functions for two acts

Prior probability distribution

Although the level of impurities in any given batch of chemicals is some unknown value μ_X, past experience with the process indicates that a normal prior probability distribution with mean $M_0 = 2.8$ and standard deviation $S_0 = .4$ would appropriately describe the variation in μ_X from batch to batch. Note that although μ_X is a parameter for a given batch, it is regarded as a random variable which takes on different values in different batches. The normal prior distribution with parameters M_0 and S_0 is the probability distribution of μ_X considered as a random variable. The normal prior distribution for our example is shown in Figure 21.2.

Bayes act

Suppose the firm must make a decision without any sample information and decides to employ a Bayes procedure to choose between C_1 and C_2. Recall from the previous chapter that a Bayes procedure calls for choosing the act that maximizes the expected payoff, i.e., choosing the Bayes act. To

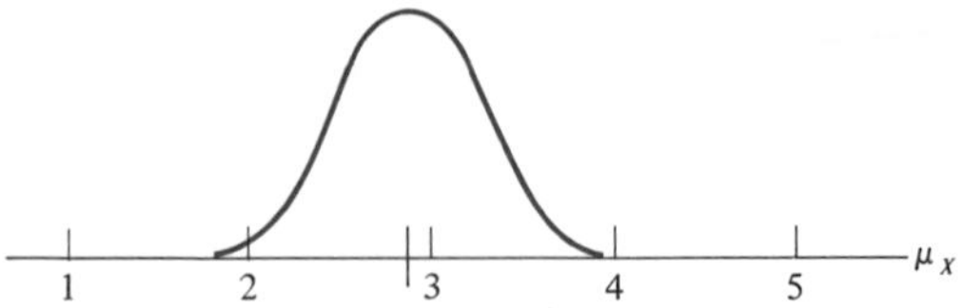

Figure 21.2. Normal prior distribution for text example ($M_0 = 2.8$, $S_0 = .4$)

determine the Bayes act in our example, we must obtain the expected payoffs of acts C_1 and C_2 using the payoff functions in (21.1a) and (21.1b) and the normal prior distribution in Figure 21.2. In taking the expected values of the payoff functions, we utilize theorem (6.32) on properties of the expected value and obtain:

(21.2a) $$E(P_1) = 200 - 30E(\mu_X) \qquad \text{for act } C_1$$

(21.2b) $$E(P_2) = 125 - 5E(\mu_X) \qquad \text{for act } C_2$$

Now, by definition, we know that the expected value of a random variable is identical to the mean of its probability distribution. Hence, $E(\mu_X) = M_0$, the mean of the prior distribution. Since $M_0 = 2.8$ in our case, we may substitute $E(\mu_X) = 2.8$ in the foregoing equations to obtain:

$$E(P_1) = 200 - 30(2.8) = 116 \text{ or \$116 thousand for act } C_1$$
$$E(P_2) = 125 - 5(2.8) = 111 \text{ or \$111 thousand for act } C_2$$

Since the expected payoff for C_1 is the higher, it is the Bayes act. Thus, in the absence of any information about μ_X for the given batch, the company should send the batch to the customer without recycling.

Note that we only required knowledge of the prior mean M_0 to choose the Bayes act in this case. The assumption of normality and the value of the standard deviation S_0 of the prior distribution were not required. This is a consequence of the linearity of the payoff functions where only $E(\mu_X)$ is required. We next consider the situation where sample information on the given batch is available for decision-making. In this case, the assumption of normality and the value of S_0 are important.

21.2 DECISION-MAKING WITH PRIOR PROBABILITIES AND SAMPLE INFORMATION

Frequently it is possible to obtain sample information about μ_X before making a decision. This is the case in our example, where the company is able to obtain sample information about the level of impurities remaining in the batch (μ_X) before deciding whether to send the batch directly to the customer (C_1) or recycle it to remove additional impurities (C_2). The company can obtain the additional information by selecting a random sample of briquettes into which the chemical is pressed. Analysis of each briquette provides a sample observation, and the sample mean $\overline{X}$ of these observations provides an estimate of μ_X, the level of impurities in the batch.

The statistical procedure to be employed with the sample information requires that:

1. The sampling distribution of $\overline{X}$ be normal or approximately so.
2. The population standard deviation σ_X must be known or approximated well.

As we know from earlier work, with random sampling from a normal population, the distribution of $\overline{X}$ is exactly normal. Further, the distribution of $\overline{X}$ is approximately normal for almost any population if the sample is sufficiently large. Also, if σ_X is unknown, the sample standard deviation s_X is a good approximation of σ_X when n is large. Thus, sampling a normal population with known standard deviation, or almost any population when n is large, meets the above requirements.

In our present example, it is known that the distribution of impurities in the briquettes is approximately normal, with a standard deviation known from extensive past experience to be $\sigma_X = 1.0$. Thus the distribution of $\overline{X}$ here is normal with mean $\mu_{\overline{X}} = \mu_X$ and standard deviation $\sigma_{\overline{X}} = \sigma_X/\sqrt{n} = 1.0/\sqrt{n}$.

To find the Bayes act when both prior probabilities and sample information are available, we use the two-part approach described in the previous chapter:

1. We combine the prior probabilities and sample data by means of Bayes' Theorem to obtain a posterior probability distribution.
2. We use the posterior probability distribution as in the no-sample case to determine the Bayes act.

Determining the posterior probability distribution

Bayes' Theorem may be used to show that, given:

1. A normal prior probability distribution for μ_X with mean M_0 and standard deviation S_0;
2. A normal sampling distribution of $\overline{X}$ with standard deviation $\sigma_{\overline{X}} = \sigma_X/\sqrt{n}$, where n is the simple random sample size;

the posterior probability distribution of μ_X is normal, with mean M_1 and standard deviation S_1, where M_1 and S_1 are given by:

$$M_1 = \frac{\dfrac{M_0}{S_0^2} + \dfrac{\overline{X}}{\sigma_{\overline{X}}^2}}{\dfrac{1}{S_0^2} + \dfrac{1}{\sigma_{\overline{X}}^2}} \tag{21.3}$$

$$\frac{1}{S_1^2} = \frac{1}{S_0^2} + \frac{1}{\sigma_{\overline{X}}^2} \tag{21.4}$$

Suppose, in our example, that the company has decided to select a simple random sample of $n = 16$ briquettes from the batch and obtains $\overline{X} = 3.5$. Since $\sigma_{\overline{X}} = \sigma_X/\sqrt{n} = 1.0/\sqrt{16} = .25$ and we know $M_0 = 2.8$ and $S_0 = .4$, it follows that the posterior probability distribution for μ_X is normal with mean and standard deviation given by:

$$M_1 = \frac{\dfrac{2.8}{(.4)^2} + \dfrac{3.5}{(.25)^2}}{\dfrac{1}{(.4)^2} + \dfrac{1}{(.25)^2}} = 3.30$$

and:

$$\frac{1}{S_1^2} = \frac{1}{(.4)^2} + \frac{1}{(.25)^2} = 22.25 \quad \text{or} \quad S_1 = .212$$

The normal prior distribution of μ_X, the normal sampling distribution of $\overline{X}$, and the normal posterior distribution of μ_X for our example are shown in Figure 21.3.

Bayes act

As we stated already, we find the Bayes act by using the posterior probability distribution in the same manner as the prior probability distribution in the no-sample case; namely, we obtain the expected payoff for each act and we select the act with the larger expected payoff.

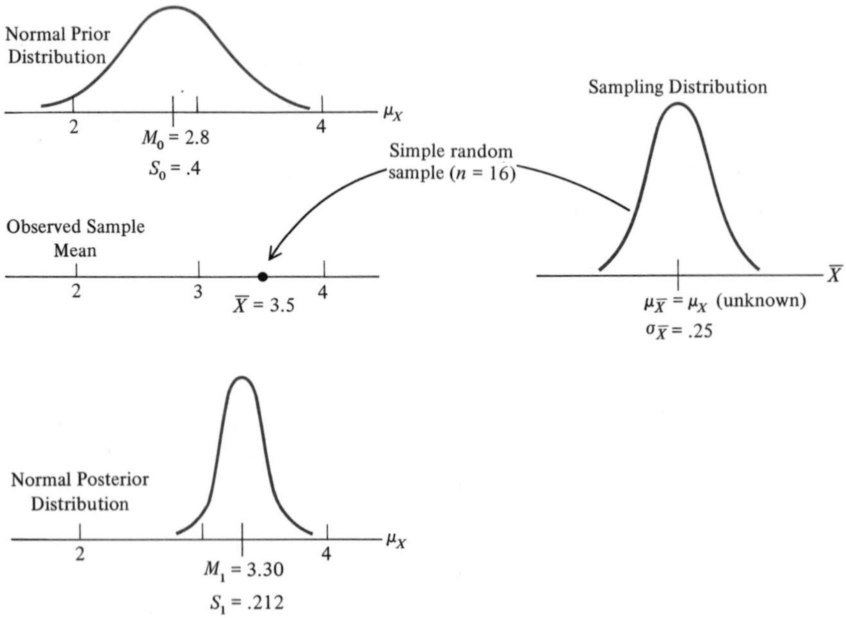

Figure 21.3. Prior distribution, sampling distribution, and posterior distribution for text example

We found earlier, in (21.2a) and (21.2b), the expected value of the payoff functions in (21.1a) and (21.1b):

$$E(P_1) = 200 - 30E(\mu_X) \quad \text{for act } C_1$$
$$E(P_2) = 125 - 5E(\mu_X) \quad \text{for act } C_2$$

In contrast to the no-sample case, the expected value of the random variable μ_X for the sample case is obtained from the posterior distribution. In particular, $E(\mu_X) = M_1 = 3.30$. Substituting, we obtain:

$$E(P_1) = 200 - 30(3.30) = 101 \text{ or \$101 thousand for act } C_1$$
$$E(P_2) = 125 - 5(3.30) = 108.5 \text{ or \$108.5 thousand for act } C_2$$

Since act C_2 has the higher expected payoff, it is the Bayes act. Thus, the company should recycle the batch to remove additional impurities.

Bayes decision rule

If the only concern is to find the Bayes act for a particular sample result, the procedure described above is adequate. At times, however, we require the complete Bayes decision rule, indicating the Bayes act for each possible sample outcome. It is easy to see that the Bayes rule has the following form in the case considered in this chapter:

(21.5) If $M_1 \leq K$, select the act which is best for μ_X values below the indifference point K;
If $M_1 > K$, select the act which is best for μ_X values above the indifference point.

The indifference point K is the point where the two linear payoff functions intersect, i.e., where both acts have the same payoff. We can see from Figure 21.1 that for our example $K = 3$.

To see why K is the action limit of decision rule (21.5), observe that substitution of $K = 3.0$ for $E(\mu_X)$ in (21.2a) and (21.2b) gives $E(P_1) = E(P_2) = 110$, that is, both acts have the same expected payoff when $E(\mu_X) = M_1 = K$. For values of M_1 below $K = 3.0$, $E(P_1) > E(P_2)$; the reverse holds when M_1 is above $K = 3.0$.

In our example, $M_1 = 3.30$ and $K = 3.0$. Figure 21.1 then indicates that the best act is C_2, to recycle the batch, since C_2 has the higher payoff at $M_1 = 3.30$. This is, of course, the same best act as we obtained by explicitly calculating the expected payoft for each act.

21.3 EXPECTED VALUE OF PERFECT INFORMATION

In the two previous sections, we considered how to obtain the Bayes act when only prior information is available and when both prior information and sample information based on a given sample size are available.

Now we shall consider how to determine the optimal sample size. First, we take up the expected value of perfect information. As we demonstrated in the previous chapter, the expected value of perfect information is helpful when determining the optimal sample size, by indicating the maximum sample size which need be considered. More generally, the expected value of perfect information provides an upper bound to the expected value of any type of additional information about the unknown outcome state, such as the batch level of impurities μ_X in our example.

Opportunity loss functions

To find the expected value of perfect information (henceforth denoted EVPI) in the case considered here, it is convenient to convert the linear payoff functions in (21.1a) and (21.1b) into linear opportunity loss functions.

(21.6) The ***opportunity loss*** of an act at a particular value of μ_X is the difference between the maximum payoff which may be realized from the best act at that value of μ_X and the payoff received from the act under consideration. The opportunity losses, computed for all values of μ_X, define the ***opportunity loss function*** for that act.

For instance, at $\mu_X = 4.0$, it is clear from Figure 21.1 that act C_2 yields the maximum payoff, specifically, $P_2 = 125 - 5(4.0) = 105$. Act C_1 has a payoff of $P_1 = 200 - 30(4.0) = 80$ at $\mu_X = 4.0$. Hence, at $\mu_X = 4.0$, the opportunity loss of act C_2 is zero, while the opportunity loss of act C_1 is $105 - 80 = 25$. Opportunity losses at other values of μ_X are calculated in a similar fashion. The opportunity loss functions for both acts are shown in Figure 21.4. The opportunity loss function for act C_1 is denoted by OL_1 and is described by the following equation:

$$OL_1 = \begin{cases} 0 & \text{for } \mu_X \leq 3.0 \\ -75 + 25\mu_X & \text{for } \mu_X > 3.0 \end{cases}$$

The opportunity loss function for act C_2 is denoted by OL_2 and is given by:

$$OL_2 = \begin{cases} 75 - 25\mu_X & \text{for } \mu_X \leq 3.0 \\ 0 & \text{for } \mu_X > 3.0 \end{cases}$$

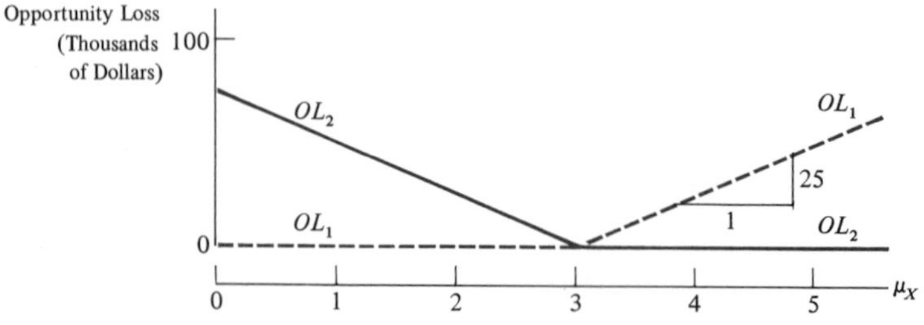

Figure 21.4. Opportunity loss functions for two acts

Note that C_1 is the better act for all μ_X values below 3.0 and therefore has an opportunity loss of zero for these μ_X values. Similarly, C_2 is the better act for all μ_X values above 3.0 and therefore has an opportunity loss of zero for these μ_X values. At one value of μ_X, both acts have opportunity losses of zero.

(21.7) The value of μ_X for which the opportunity loss is zero for both acts is called the ***indifference*** or ***break-even*** point and is denoted by K.

In our example, both acts have zero opportunity losses at $\mu_X = 3.0$; therefore, $K = 3.0$. Note that this is the same point as the one where the two acts have equal payoffs. Indeed, this is always the case.

Observe in Figure 21.4 that both opportunity loss functions have slopes with the same *absolute* value. We will denote this common absolute value by t. From the graphs in Figure 21.4 or the above equations for the opportunity loss functions, we see that $t = 25$ thousand dollars per unit of μ_X.

The value of t also can be obtained directly from the payoff functions of the decision problem. Writing the payoff functions in the following form:

$$P_1 = k_1 + m_1\mu_X$$
$$P_2 = k_2 + m_2\mu_X$$

it is easily shown that:

(21.8) $$t = |m_1 - m_2|$$

where the absolute sign $|\ |$ indicates that any minus sign of the quantity $m_1 - m_2$ should be disregarded.

In our example, we see from (21.1a) and (21.1b) that $m_1 = -30$ and $m_2 = -5$; therefore, $t = |(-30) - (-5)| = 25$, as we found before.

EVPI

We are now ready to obtain the expected value of perfect information for our example.

(21.9) When the prior probability distribution of μ_X is normal and the payoff functions for the two acts are linear (as they are in our example), the expected value of perfect information (EVPI) is given by:

$$\text{EVPI} = tS_0L(D) \qquad \text{where} \quad D = |(K - M_0)/S_0|$$

$L(D)$ is the value of the *unit normal loss function* at D. Note that D is the *absolute* value of the deviation of the indifference point K from the prior mean M_0, relative to the prior standard deviation S_0.

The unit normal loss function is a special function derived from the standard normal distribution. Values of $L(D)$ have been tabulated, as in Table A-8. To illustrate the use of Table A-8, note that if $D = 1.18$, for instance, then $L(D) = L(1.18) = .05844$.

For our example, we have $M_0 = 2.8$, $S_0 = .4$, $K = 3.0$, and $t = 25$.

Therefore, $D = |(3.0 - 2.8)/.4| = .50$ and, from Table A-8, $L(D) = L(.50) = .1978$. Substituting in (21.9) gives:

$$\text{EVPI} = 25(.4)(.1978) = 1.978 \text{ or } \$1{,}978$$

The value of EVPI here provides an upper bound on the expected value of any type of additional information that might be obtained about μ_X, the unknown level of impurities in the batch. Since EVPI = \$1,978 in our example, any type of incomplete or sample information about the unknown level of impurities in the batch is not worth more than \$1,978.

21.4 EXPECTED VALUE OF SAMPLE INFORMATION

In the foregoing discussion of Bayes decision-making with sampling, the sample size was arbitrarily fixed at $n = 16$. Often it is desired to calculate the *expected value of sample information* (EVSI) prior to its collection in order to assess the feasibility of sampling in the first place.

(21.10) When the prior distribution of μ_X is normal, the sampling distribution of $\overline{X}$ is normal with known standard deviation, and the payoff functions are linear, the expected value of sample information (ignoring sampling costs) is given by:

$$\text{EVSI} = tS_*L(D_*) \text{ where } D_* = |(K - M_0)/S_*| \text{ and } S_* = \sqrt{S_0^2 - S_1^2}$$

For our example, suppose that the company had not yet decided on a sample size, but was considering a sample of $n = 16$ briquettes as a possibility. To find EVSI for that sample size, recall that $M_0 = 2.8$, $S_0 = .4$, $K = 3.0$, $S_1 = .212$ and $t = 25$. Thus, $S_* = \sqrt{(.4)^2 - (.212)^2} = .339$, $D_* = |(3.0 - 2.8)/.339| = .59$, and, from Table A-8, $L(D_*) = L(.59) = .1714$. Therefore:

$$\text{EVSI} = 25(.339)(.1714) = 1.453 \text{ or } \$1{,}453$$

Ignoring sampling costs, the result indicates that selecting a sample of $n = 16$ increases the expected payoff to the company by \$1,453. After the sample has been selected, of course, the actual increase in payoff will vary from \$1,453.

The result on EVSI can be stated in the following equivalent manner. Since the expected payoff of the Bayes act based on prior probabilities only (i.e., the no-sample case) is 116 (see p. 464) and the increase in expected payoff from employing a sample of $n = 16$ is 1.453, it follows that:

$$\text{Expected Payoff of Bayes Decision Rule } (n = 16) = 116 + 1.453 = 117.453 \text{ or } \$117{,}453$$

Keep in mind however that the above expected payoff does not consider the cost of obtaining the sample.

21.5 DETERMINATION OF OPTIMAL SAMPLE SIZE

When one wishes to determine the optimal sample size, the cost of sampling must be considered, since one would like to maximize the expected payoff after sampling costs. If c is the cost of obtaining each sample observation, then cn is the total cost of obtaining a sample of size n. Letting ENGS denote the *expected net gain from sampling*, then:

(21.11) $$\text{ENGS} = \text{EVSI} - cn$$

Here EVSI is the expected value of sample information for the given sample size n.

For our case example, suppose the cost of selecting and analyzing each sample briquette is \$40 or \$.04 thousand, that is, $c = .04$. We can then compute the expected net gain from sampling for the two situations considered thus far.

For the no-sample case ($n = 0$), EVSI $= 0$ by definition. Since no sampling cost is incurred in this case, it follows that ENGS$(n = 0) = 0$.

For the case when $n = 16$, we obtained EVSI $= 1.453$ and the sampling cost in this case is $cn = .04(16) = .64$. Therefore, ENGS$(n = 16) = 1.453 - .64 = .813$ or \$813.

Following the same procedure as we did for $n = 16$, we can obtain EVSI, cn, and then ENGS for other sample sizes. The results are given in Figure 21.5 (calculations not shown). Figure 21.5a shows the expected value of sample information and the cost of sampling for various sample sizes. Figure 21.5b shows the expected net gain from sampling as a function of sample size. Note that the ENGS curve in Figure 21.5b is obtained directly from Figure 21.5a by considering the difference between the EVSI and cn curves for different sample sizes. From Figure 21.5b we see that the expected net gain from sampling is a maximum at $n = 12$ where ENGS $= .851$,

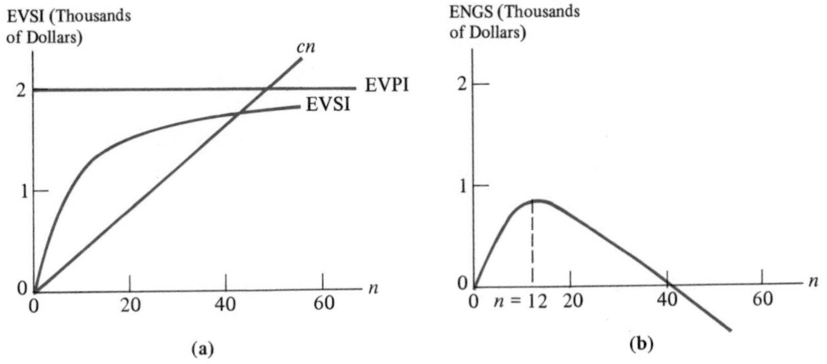

EVSI = 1.331, and $cn = .48$. Thus, the optimal procedure for the company in the case at hand is as follows:

1. Obtain $n = 12$ sample observations from the batch of chemicals and compute the sample mean $\overline{X}$.
2. Substitute $\overline{X}$ and the other known values in (21.3) to obtain the posterior mean M_1.
3. Apply the Bayes decision rule in (21.5) to M_1 to determine the Bayes act.

Of course, if any of the factors entering ENGS change—for instance, the prior distribution is modified in the light of recent experience—the optimal sampling procedure would have to be obtained anew.

Figure 21.5a illustrates that the expected value of perfect information is an upper bound on the expected value of sample information for any sample size. Indeed, EVPI may be thought of as the value of EVSI for an indefinitely large sample. Obviously, the sample size selected for a particular decision problem should not be so large that sampling costs exceed EVPI. Hence, an upper bound on the sample size which should be considered is given by $cn \leq$ EVPI, or $n \leq$ EVPI$/c$. In our example, $c = .04$ and EVPI = 1.978. Therefore, EVPI$/c = 1.978/.04 = 49$ and hence the optimal sample size certainly will be less than 49. In fact, it is 12 as we saw.

21.6 ADDITIONAL COMMENTS

The manner in which Bayes' Theorem revises the normal prior distribution on the basis of the sample data to give the normal posterior distribution may not be directly obvious from formulas (21.3) and (21.4), p. 465, so let's examine them more closely. Observe in (21.3) that the posterior mean M_1 is actually a weighted average of the prior mean M_0 and the observed sample mean $\overline{X}$. The weights are the reciprocals of S_0^2 and $\sigma_{\overline{X}}^2$. Thus, in the weighted average, the prior and sample means are given weights which reflect their relative reliability. That is, the smaller the variance of a mean, the greater is the weight given to that mean by the reciprocal of its variance. Also, observe in (21.4) that the reciprocal of the posterior variance is equal to the sum of the reciprocals of both the prior variance and the variance of $\overline{X}$. Thus, regardless of the sample size, the posterior variance S_1^2 will always be smaller than either the prior variance, S_0^2, or the variance of $\overline{X}$, $\sigma_{\overline{X}}^2$.

A special case arises when prior knowledge of μ_X is vague relative to information about μ_X provided by the sample, that is, when S_0^2 is large relative to $\sigma_{\overline{X}}^2$. In this case, we note from (21.3) that the posterior mean M_1 is approximately equal to the sample mean $\overline{X}$. Further, we note from (21.4) that the posterior variance S_1^2 is then approximately equal to $\sigma_{\overline{X}}^2$. These two points indicate that when prior information is vague relative to the sample information, the characteristics of the posterior distribution are determined almost entirely by the sample information, that is, M_1 and S_1 will be approximately equal to $\overline{X}$ and $\sigma_{\bar{X}}$ respectively in this case.

Formulas (21.3) and (21.4) also show very clearly the effect of sample size on the posterior distribution. Since $\sigma_{\bar{X}}^2 = \sigma_X^2/n$, it follows that the larger the sample size, the smaller is $\sigma_{\bar{X}}^2$. Of course, the smaller is $\sigma_{\bar{X}}^2$, as we have just seen, the greater is the influence of the sample information in determining the mean and variance of the posterior distribution.

QUESTIONS AND PROBLEMS

21.1. Explain briefly each of the following:

a. Indifference point

b. Opportunity loss function

c. M_0 and S_0

21.2. Distinguish briefly between:

a. Normal prior distribution, normal sampling distribution, and normal posterior distribution

b. EVSI, EVPI, and ENGS

21.3. In each of the following situations, indicate whether your prior probability distribution for the parameter of interest might be approximately normal or not, and explain why.

a. The mean number of empty seats aboard flight 643, the daily flight to New York City.

b. The proportion of defective items in a shipment of 100 items.

c. The average yield of wheat per acre in the U.S. in the coming year.

d. The mean expenditure per customer in a restaurant.

***21.4.** For a government study of health care, an analyst must estimate μ_X, the mean personal health care expenditures per family in the U.S. for the coming year. After some reflection and study, he states that his subjective probabilities for μ_X are as follows: (1) 5 chances in 10 that it will be less than \$530 per family, and (2) 1 chance in 10 that it will be more than \$580.

a. Does the analyst's statement that there is only 1 chance in 10 that mean personal health care expenditures per family will be more than \$580 imply that he believes only one U.S. family in ten on the average will expend more than \$580 on personal health care in the coming year? What does the statement imply?

b. On the basis of the analyst's subjective probability assessments and assuming a normal prior distribution for μ_X is appropriate, obtain M_0 and S_0 for his prior distribution.

c. After providing the two probability assessments given above, the analyst states that there is 1 chance in 10 that mean personal health care expenditures per family will be less than \$500. Why is this last probability assessment inconsistent with the normal prior distribution for μ_X derived in part **b**? Explain why inconsistencies might arise in detailed questioning of individuals about their subjective probabilities. What are the implications of this?

***21.5.** A firm periodically receives large shipments of rough shafts that require machining to fine tolerances. The firm is faced with deciding for the next shipment whether to do the machining in the house (C_1), or to subcontract it out at a fixed price (C_2). The payoff to the firm is affected by the mean weight of the rough shafts in the shipment, since this largely determines the amount of metal to be removed. The payoff functions for the two acts (in dollars) are:

$$P_1 = 31{,}300 - 1{,}000\mu_X \quad \text{for act } C_1$$
$$P_2 = 4{,}800 \quad \text{for act } C_2$$

Based on past experience, the firm believes that a normal prior probability distribution with mean $M_0 = 26.7$ pounds and standard deviation $S_0 = .5$ pounds appropriately describes the variation in μ_X from shipment to shipment.

a. Graph the payoff functions of this decision problem. What is the break-even point at which the two payoff functions intersect?

b. Suppose that no sample information is obtained from the shipment. What is the expected payoff for each of the acts C_1 and C_2? Which is the Bayes act?

c. Suppose that the firm selects a simple random sample of 50 shafts from the shipment and obtains $\overline{X} = 26.4$ pounds and $s_X = .63$ pounds. Assume that $s_X = .63$ is a good approximation of the population standard deviation σ_X, and that the population of shaft weights is normally distributed. What are the mean and standard deviation of the posterior distribution of μ_X for this shipment? Is the posterior distribution normal in this case? Why or why not?

d. For the posterior distribution in part **c**, what is the expected payoff for each of the acts C_1 and C_2 for the sampled shipment? Which is the Bayes act?

e. Does the Bayes decision rule (21.5) on p. 467 yield the same decision as in part **d**, simply by knowing M_1 and K? Explain.

21.6. Refer to Problem 21.5.

a. Following the pattern of Figure 21.3, sketch graphs of the normal prior distribution of μ_X, the sampling distribution of $\overline{X}$, and the normal posterior distribution of μ_X for a sample of size 50 in the decision problem under consideration.

b. Is the mean of the sampling distribution of $\overline{X}$ known here? Explain.

c. Which has greater variability, the prior or posterior distribution of μ_X? Why is this so?

***21.7.** Refer to Problem 21.5. Suppose that the sample size has not yet been determined.

a. Graph the opportunity loss functions for this decision problem. Does the absolute value of the slopes of these functions correspond to the value of t obtained directly from formula (21.8)?

b. What is the EVPI for this decision problem?

c. Suppose that the firm is considering selecting a simple random sample of 50 shafts from the shipment. Further, suppose that it is known from past experience that the weights of shafts in the shipment are normally distributed with standard deviation $\sigma_X = .60$ pounds. What is the EVSI for this sample size? What is the expected payoff of the Bayes decision rule for this sample size (ignoring the cost of sampling)?

d. Does the EVSI in part **c** represent a substantial portion of the EVPI for this decision problem? What are the implications of this for the sample size to be used?

e. If the cost of sampling each shaft is \$1.00, what is the maximum number of shafts that the firm should consider sampling from each shipment? Explain the reasoning behind your answer.

f. For each of the following sample sizes, calculate EVSI, cn, and ENGS: $n = 0, 25, 50, 100$.

g. For which of the sample sizes in part **f** is ENGS a maximum? Interpret the meaning of this ENGS value within the context of this decision problem.

h. Following the pattern of Figure 21.5, sketch graphs of EVSI, cn, and ENGS. Show the EVPI line (calculated in part **b**). Calculate EVSI, cn, and ENGS values for sample sizes other than those in part **f** if necessary to obtain a reasonably accurate sketch of the curves.

21.8. The Wilson Textile Company is being acquired by another company. Two acquisition arrangements, C_1 and C_2, have been proposed. The financial impact of either arrangement depends on the length of time employees choose to remain with the company before retirement under the guaranteed employment plan in effect. Employees under existing rules may retire at age 60 or at any age thereafter until age 69 at which time they must retire. Arrangement C_1 would be attractive to Wilson Textile if the employees choose to retire early, and arrangement C_2 would be attractive if the employees choose to retire late. The finance department has calculated the following payoffs (in million dollars) as a function of μ_X, the mean age at which employees retire:

$$P_1 = 153 - .9\mu_X$$

$$P_2 = 121 - .4\mu_X$$

No information is presently available about the expected retirement ages of the employees. However, the finance department feels that a normal prior distribution with mean $M_0 = 65.0$ years and standard deviation $S_0 = 1.0$ year represents a reasonable subjective probability assessment of μ_X.

a. Graph the payoff functions for this decision problem. What is the break-even point at which the two payoff functions intersect?

b. Suppose the company decides to choose one of the acquisition arrangements without obtaining any sample information about the expected retirement ages of the employees. What is the expected payoff for each of the acts C_1 and C_2? Which is the Bayes act?

c. Suppose that the company selects a random sample of 100 employees, and obtains the sample results $\overline{X} = 63.1$ years and $s_X = 1.4$ years. Assuming that $s_X = 1.4$ years is a satisfactory approximation of σ_X in this case, and that the distribution of expected retirement ages is approximately normal, what are the mean and standard deviation of the posterior distribution of μ_X? What is the functional form of the posterior distribution?

d. For the posterior distribution in part **c**, what is the expected payoff for each of the acts C_1 and C_2? Which is the Bayes act?

e. Does the Bayes decision rule (21.5) on p. 467 yield the same decision as in part **d**, simply by knowing M_1 and K? Explain.

21.9. Refer to Problem 21.8.

a. Following the pattern of Figure 21.3, sketch graphs of the normal prior distribution of μ_X, the sampling distribution of $\overline{X}$, and the normal posterior distribution of μ_X for a sample of size 100 in the decision problem under consideration.

b. Is the mean of the sampling distribution of $\overline{X}$ known here? Explain.

c. Which has greater variability, the prior or posterior distribution of μ_X? Why is this so?

21.10. Refer to Problem 21.8. Suppose that the sample size has not yet been determined.

a. Graph the opportunity loss functions for this decision problem. Does the absolute value of the slopes of these functions correspond to the value of t obtained directly from formula (21.8)?

b. What is the EVPI for this decision problem?

c. Suppose that the company is considering selecting a simple random sample of 100 employees to determine their expected retirement ages. Further, suppose the company is willing to assume that the expected retirement ages of employees are normally distributed with standard deviation $\sigma_X = 1.5$ years. What is the EVSI for this sample size? What is the expected payoff of the Bayes decision rule for this sample size (ignoring the cost of sampling)?

d. Does the EVSI in part **c** represent a substantial portion of the EVPI for this decision problem? What are the implications of this for the sample size to be used?

e. What is the effect on the EVSI in part **c** if σ_X is actually greater than 1.5 years? Less than 1.5 years? What generalization does this suggest?

f. If the cost of sampling each employee to determine his expected retirement age is \$20, that is, $c =$ \$.00002 million, calculate for each of the following sample sizes, EVSI, cn, and ENGS: $n = 0, 25, 50, 100, 400$.

g. For which of the sample sizes in part **f** is ENGS a maximum? Interpret the meaning of this ENGS value within the context of this decision problem.

h. Following the pattern of Figure 21.5, sketch graphs of EVSI, cn, and ENGS. Show the EVPI line (calculated in part **b**). Calculate EVSI, cn, and ENGS values for sample sizes other than those in part **f** if necessary to obtain a reasonably accurate sketch of the curves.

Unit

VII

REGRESSION AND CORRELATION

Chapter

22

INTRODUCTION TO REGRESSION AND CORRELATION

22.1 INTRODUCTION

Many problems in administration involve predictions. For instance, setting sales quotas for salesmen involves predictions of total company sales and of sales for the various sales territories. The determination of next year's budget necessitates predictions of the level of operations, capital equipment and personnel needed to carry out the operations, and many other factors. Selection of employees requires predictions of the aptitudes of specific individuals for given jobs. These are but a few examples of the many cases in which predictions are needed in administration.

In this and the next two chapters, we consider one method of making predictions, that of regression and correlation analysis. It has proven to be an extremely useful management tool for studying the statistical relation between two or more variables so that one variable can be predicted on the basis of the other, or others. For example, if one knows the relation between the hardness and the tensile strength of a certain type of steel, one can estimate the tensile strength of a piece of this steel once its hardness is ascertained.

In this chapter, we explain the basic concepts underlying regression and correlation analysis. Chapter 23 contains a discussion of how regression analysis can be used for making predictions and other types of inferences. In Chapter 24, we present a number of additional topics, including case studies of regression and correlation applications, the use of several independent variables for making predictions through multiple regression analysis, and curvilinear regression analysis.

22.2
RELATION BETWEEN TWO VARIABLES

The concept of a relation between two quantitative variables, such as the relation between price of a product and quantity sold or the relation between height and weight of persons, is a familiar one. It is useful to distinguish between *functional* and *statistical* relations, and we shall explain each in turn.

Functional relation between two variables

A functional relation is an exact relation expressed by a mathematical formula. For instance, let Y stand for sales revenue, X for number of units sold, and b for the price per unit. We can then express the functional relation between number of units sold (X) and sales revenue (Y) as follows:

$$Y = bX$$

Figure 22.1a presents this functional relation for the case where the unit price is $b = \$5$.

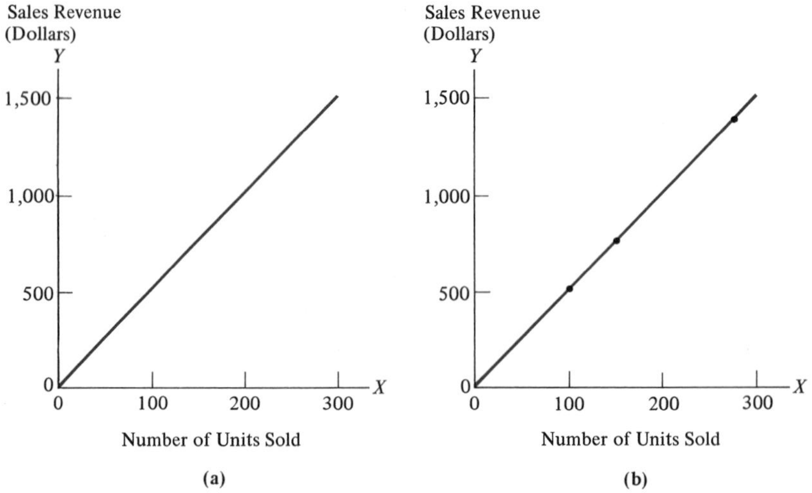

Figure 22.1. Example of functional relation

Suppose that 100 units were sold in period 1, 150 in period 2, and 280 in period 3, and that no price changes occurred. The sales revenues then must have been:

Period	X *Number of Units Sold*	Y *Sales Revenue*
1	100	\$ 500
2	150	750
3	280	1,400

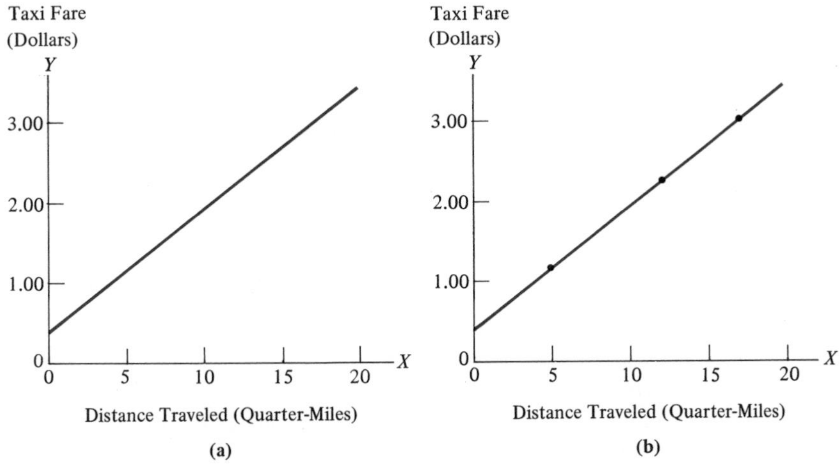

Figure 22.2. Example of functional relation

These three observations are plotted in Figure 22.1b. Note that all three points fall on the line of relationship. This is typical of all functional relations.

A second example of a functional relation is that between mileage of a trip and taxi fare. Suppose this functional relation is given by:

$$Y = .40 + .15X$$

where: Y is the taxi fare, in dollars
.40 is the service charge, in dollars
.15 is the fare per quarter-mile, in dollars
X is the number of quarter-miles for the trip

Figure 22.2a presents this functional relation. Assume that the taxi driver's most recent three trips had the following characteristics:

Trip Number	X *Distance (in quarter-miles)*	Y *Fare (in dollars)*
1	17	2.95
2	5	1.15
3	12	2.20

These three observations are plotted in Figure 22.2b. Again, all points fall on the line of relationship.

Statistical relation between two variables

A statistical relation between two variables differs from a functional one in that it is not exact; that is, not all observations fall directly on the line of relationship.

Table 22.1 Population and Amount of Federal Grants for North Central States, 1969

State	*Population (Millions)*	*Federal Grants (Millions of Dollars)*
Ohio	10.7	784
Indiana	5.1	319
Illinois	11.0	896
Michigan	8.8	672
Wisconsin	4.2	312
Minnesota	3.7	365
Iowa	2.8	222
Missouri	4.7	442
North Dakota	.6	74
South Dakota	.7	90
Nebraska	1.4	124
Kansas	2.3	183

Source of data: Statistical Abstract of the United States: 1970, pp. 12, 279.

Consider, for instance, Figure 22.3a, which presents data on 1969 population size (X) and amount of federal grants to the state and local governments (Y) of 12 North Central States. The actual data are shown in Table 22.1. The plotting of the data in Figure 22.3a is done as for the previous graphs. For instance, the observation for Ohio is plotted as a point at $X = 10.7$, $Y = 784$.

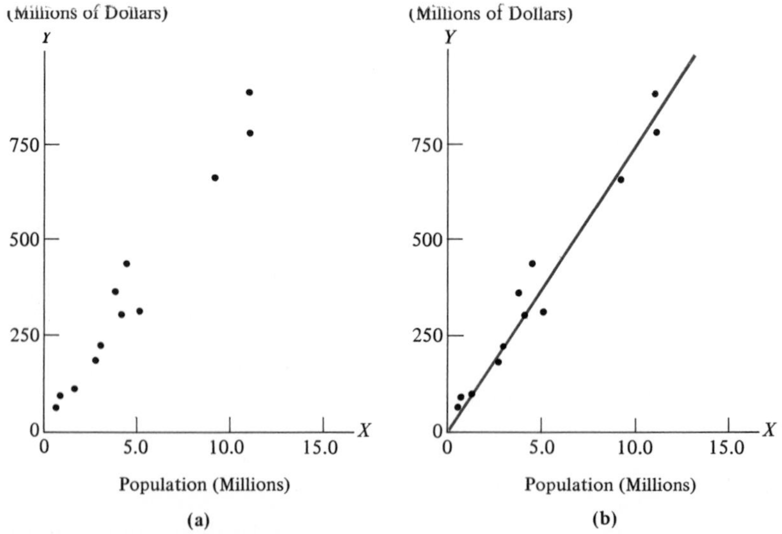

Source of data: Table 22.1.

Figure 22.3. Example of statistical relation

Figure 22.3a suggests clearly that there is a relation between population size and amount of federal grants, namely, the greater the population size, the larger the amount of federal grants. However, the relation is not a functional one where all points fall on the line of relationship. Instead, there is a scattering of points suggesting variation in amounts of federal grants which is not completely accounted for by population size. Figure 22.3a indeed is called a *scatter plot* or *scatter diagram,* and illustrates that a statistical relation between two variables indicates only a general tendency, not an exact relation.

In Figure 22.3b, we have plotted a line of relationship that indicates the general tendency of the statistical relation between population size and amount of federal grants. Note that most points do not fall exactly on the line of statistical relationship but are scattered around it. Usually, this variation of points around the line of statistical relationship is ascribed to random effects. Statistical relations between two variables can be highly useful, but they should not be considered as having the exactitude of functional relations.

Statistical relations, like functional relations, need not be linear. Figure 22.4 contains data on gross national product and volume of merchandise imports for selected years during the period 1960–1969. The data suggest

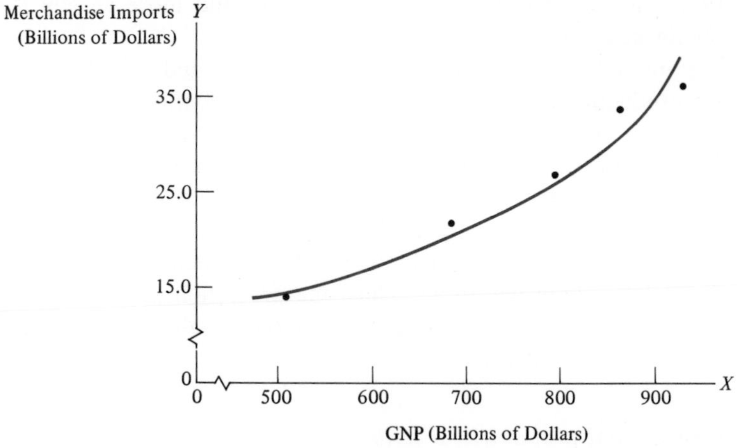

Source of data: Statistical Abstract of the United States: 1970, pp. xviii, xxiv.

Figure 22.4. Example of statistical relation

a *curvilinear* (not linear) relation between the two variables, and this curve of statistical relationship has been drawn in Figure 22.4. Note that the curve of statistical relationship in Figure 22.4 implies that the volume of imports tends to be higher as GNP increases and that the increase in imports tends to accelerate with higher GNP. Again, we note the scattering of points around the curve of statistical relationship, typical of any statistical relation.

22.3
BASIC CONCEPTS IN REGRESSION ANALYSIS

Regression analysis deals with statistical relations between quantitative variables. It embodies in a formal model the basic notions just explained, namely the idea of a line or curve of statistical relationship between two (or more) quantitative variables, and a scattering of the observations around the line or curve. To explain the formal model, we first describe a typical situation in which regression analysis can be applied.

Description of case

The Hi-Ace Company manufactures a variety of valves, including a particular type used by oil refineries. During the years 1965–1969, the company obtained a number of contracts to produce this valve. Competition increased, however, during this period and the Hi-Ace Company found that it would have to estimate costs more and more closely if it were to obtain contracts in the future.

Late in 1969, the Hi-Ace Company was invited to bid on a contract for the production of 10,000 valves. In order to submit a realistic bid, company officials were anxious to get a fairly precise prediction of their direct labor cost for this contract. Since wage rates were fixed under union agreement, the problem was to predict the number of direct labor hours which would be expended by the company in the production of 10,000 valves. In turn, the number of direct labor hours can be obtained from a prediction of the direct labor time per valve. Thus, the prediction problem for the Hi-Ace Company involved predicting the unit direct labor time for a production run of 10,000 valves.

Conditional probability distributions

As stated already, in regression analysis we use one or more variables to predict another variable. To make predictions with this approach in the Hi-Ace case, we shall have to select one or more variables related to unit direct labor time that are known in advance for any particular contract. For purposes of this discussion, we shall use the number of valves in the production run as the variable to be employed in making predictions.

To illustrate how the size of the production run can be used in predicting unit direct labor time, we consider the case in which the size of the production run is 10,000 valves. We do not, of course, expect that the unit direct labor time will be the same for each production run of 10,000 valves; such a degree of uniformity is found very rarely in economic and business situations. Rather, we expect to find variability in the unit direct labor time.

The distribution describing the pattern of this variability is called a *conditional probability distribution.* It is a probability distribution just like any other discussed so far, but it is a "conditional" one because it relates only to those production runs when the number of valves produced is 10,000. This conditional probability distribution can be considered to describe the pattern of variability in the unit direct labor time for an indefinitely large number of production runs of 10,000 valves each, assuming that the underlying causal conditions affecting the process remain the same throughout.

We discussed conditional probability distributions in Chapter 6. There, we obtained the conditional probability distribution of age for male workers; this was a case in which the condition (male worker) referred to a qualitative characteristic. Here we are concerned with the conditional probability distribution of unit direct labor time for a given size of production run, where the condition (size of production run) is a quantitative characteristic.

Figure 22.5 shows what the conditional probability distribution of unit direct labor time might look like when 10,000 valves are produced in the production run. This figure also contains conditional probability distributions of unit direct labor time for production runs of 8,000 and 14,000 valves. Each of the conditional probability distributions in Figure 22.5 indicates the pattern of variability in the unit direct labor time for indefinitely many production runs where the specified number of valves are produced, with the basic conditions affecting the process remaining the same.

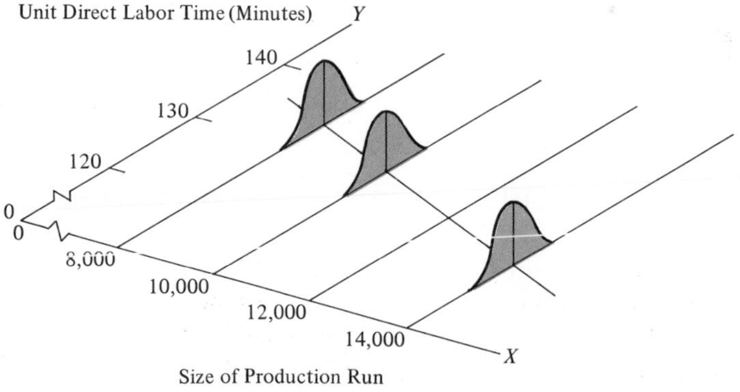

Figure 22.5. Conditional probability distributions of unit direct labor times for selected sizes of production runs

Properties of conditional probability distributions

A conditional probability distribution involving a quantitative characteristic (e.g., unit direct labor time) has a mean, called a *conditional mean.* We denote this by $\mu_{Y.X}$ to indicate that it measures the mean of the Y characteristic (unit direct labor time) for a given value of X (size of production run). Thus, $\mu_{Y.10,000} = 130$ minutes denotes that the *average* or *mean* unit direct labor time when 10,000 valves are produced in the production run is 130 minutes. A conditional probability distribution involving a quantitative characteristic also has a standard deviation, called a *conditional standard deviation.* We denote this by $\sigma_{Y.X}$ to indicate that it measures the variability in Y (unit direct labor time) for a given X (size of production run). Note again the use of the Greek symbols for the mean and standard deviation to denote that these are the population values, but this time for conditional probability distributions.

The conditional probability distributions shown in Figure 22.5 are normal distributions, and all have the same amount of variability—that is, the conditional standard deviations $\sigma_{Y.X}$ are equal. While these conditions do not always exist, they are met approximately in many actual circumstances. In order to simplify the discussion of regression and correlation analysis, *we consider in these chapters only the case in which the conditional probability distributions are all approximately normal and have the same conditional standard deviation.* This restriction will simplify the discussion and still provide an understanding of the basic principles and uses of regression and correlation analysis. Even if the conditions just stated are not met, regression and correlation analysis would still be applicable, but the formulas to be used would have to be modified.

A conditional probability distribution is used in the same way as any other probability distribution. Suppose that the conditional probability distribution for $X = 10,000$ valves is normal, with a conditional mean of $\mu_{Y.10,000} = 130$ minutes and a conditional standard deviation of $\sigma_{Y.X} = 2$ minutes. The actual unit direct labor time when 10,000 valves are produced in the production run is taken as being the result of a random selection from this conditional probability distribution. Making use of the properties of a normal distribution, we can state, for instance, that the unit direct labor time will be between 126 and 134 minutes [$130 \pm 2(2)$] for about 95.4 per cent of production runs of 10,000 valves each.

Regression curve

In addition to showing that each conditional probability distribution has: (1) its own mean, and (2) the same standard deviation, Figure 22.5 discloses another property linking the various conditional probability distributions. Note from this figure that the means of the conditional probability distributions follow a definite relationship, called a regression curve, which is represented by the straight line in Figure 22.5.

(22.1) The ***regression curve*** describes the relation between any given value of X and the mean $\mu_{Y.X}$ of the corresponding conditional probability distribution of Y.

Thus, in our example, the regression curve relates the means of the conditional probability distributions of unit direct labor time and size of the production run.

The regression curve is the formal counterpart in the regression model to the curve of statistical relationship that we discussed earlier as being descriptive of the statistical relation between two quantitative variables. Knowledge of the regression curve aids in making predictions of the unit direct labor time for any given size of production run. The use of the regression curve for this purpose will be discussed shortly.

The shape of the regression curve varies from problem to problem. In Figure 22.5, the regression curve happens to be a straight line. In other instances, it will be curvilinear. For example, we would expect the regression curve relating amount of advertising expenditures (X) to sales volume (Y) to be curvilinear, since a point is ordinarily reached where further increases in advertising bring about smaller and smaller increases in sales volume.

In Section 24.4, we consider curvilinear regression models. Elsewhere in these chapters, however, to simplify the discussion, *we shall restrict ourselves to the case in which the regression curve is linear.*

Properties of linear regression curve. If the regression curve is a straight line, then the mean $\mu_{Y.X}$ of any conditional probability distribution is related to X by:

(22.2) $$\mu_{Y.X} = \alpha + \beta X$$

In this equation, α and β are *parameters*—that is, they are constants for any particular problem.

Example 1. Suppose that $\alpha = 25$, $\beta = .7$. Then, we would have $\mu_{Y.X} = 25 + .7X$. This equation is plotted in Figure 22.6. Note that α is the value of $\mu_{Y.X}$ when $X = 0$. Also, β is the slope of the straight line; thus, $\beta = .7$ states that the value of $\mu_{Y.X}$ increases by .7 for each additional unit of X. The slope β may be positive or negative depending upon whether $\mu_{Y.X}$ increases or decreases with increasing values of X.

Example 2. Suppose that for our valve production example, the regression equation has parameter values $\alpha = 150$ and $\beta = -.002$. Thus, the regression equation would be $\mu_{Y.X} = 150 - .002X$. If the size of the production run is $X = 8{,}000$ valves, we would have $\mu_{Y.8,000} = 150 - .002(8{,}000) = 134$ minutes. Thus, the conditional distribution of Y (unit direct labor time) when $X = 8{,}000$ valves has a *mean* of 134 minutes; that is, over many production runs of 8,000 valves, the unit direct labor time on the average is

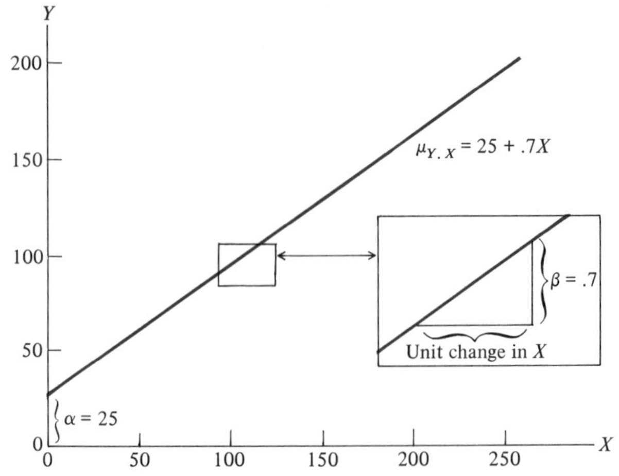

Figure 22.6. Properties of a straight-line regression curve

134 minutes. The parameter $\beta = -.002$ has the meaning that each increase of one valve in the size of the production run leads to a decrease of .002 minutes in the *mean* unit direct labor time.

Given that the regression function is linear, we need only know the values of α and β to be able to determine the mean of any conditional probability distribution. The problem generally is that α and β, the population values, are unknown and must be estimated.

Major uses of regression analysis

Three major uses of regression analysis will be discussed in these chapters.

Estimation of parameters of regression model. There is often intrinsic interest in the values of some or all of the parameters of the regression model. Since these are generally unknown, they must be estimated on the basis of sample information. In a linear regression model, for instance, particular interest may exist in the slope of the regression function, since the slope indicates the mean change that is expected in Y with a unit increase in X. Thus, if X is advertising expenditure and Y is sales, the slope indicates the mean change in sales volume that is expected with a unit increase in advertising expenditure. Interest in the parameters of the regression model either leads to point or interval estimates of these parameters, or to statistical decision-making concerning the values of the parameters.

Estimation of conditional means. A second important use of regression models is the estimation of the conditional mean for specified levels of the X variable. Thus, in our earlier illustration, management may be interested in estimating the mean unit direct labor time when there are 8,000 or 10,000 or 14,000 valves produced in a production run. As another example, a sales manager may be interested in estimating the mean number of units sold when the price is \$5.00. Since the parameters of the regression model are usually unknown, statistical estimation is required for this use.

Prediction of next observation of Y for given X. A third major use of regression models is for predicting the next observation of the Y variable for some known level of the X variable. For instance, in our illustration, management may wish to predict the unit direct labor time for the next contract of 10,000 valves. Again, the sales manager may wish to predict the number of units sold next period when the price is \$5.00. Statistical estimation is usually required for this use of regression models, since the parameters of the regression model are generally unknown.

22.4 POINT ESTIMATION OF PARAMETERS OF REGRESSION MODEL

Obtaining sample information

To estimate the parameters of a regression model, we need sample information. Table 22.2 contains, for our valve example, data on: (1) the number of valves in the production run, and (2) the unit direct labor time, for 12 contracts completed between 1965 and 1969. Note that our sample consists of 12 observations; that is, for 12 production runs we have infor-

Table 22.2 Size of Production Run and Unit Direct Labor Time for 12 Contracts, Hi-Ace Company

Contract Date	(1) *Unit Direct Labor Time* Y	(2) *Contract Size* X
April 1965	145	5,000
August 1965	145	4,800
December 1965	135	9,000
April 1966	146	3,000
December 1966	141	6,000
March 1967	149	3,000
July 1967	131	9,300
August 1967	126	11,500
February 1968	134	8,000
June 1968	137	8,000
December 1968	128	11,500
March 1969	144	4,000

mation on the unit direct labor time and the size of production run. Thus, for each sample observation, we have *both* an observed X value and an observed Y value. We assume that any Y observation (unit direct labor time) is the result of a random selection from a conditional probability distribution for the corresponding X (size of production run). For instance, $Y = 145$ in the April 1965 contract would be considered a random observation of unit direct labor time from the conditional probability distribution corresponding to $X = 5{,}000$ valves.

The years 1965–1969 were used in this study because the basic conditions affecting the unit direct labor time—such as the manufacturing equipment available—had remained about the same during this period and were approximately the same as those in effect during the period for which predictions were to be made.

Scatter diagram

Before performing any calculations, it is usually advisable to present the sample information in graphic form. This gives a rough indication of the relationships involved and the kind of model that is appropriate. Figure 22.7 presents the information concerning the 12 contracts in the sample in the form of a scatter diagram. On the Y axis is plotted the unit direct labor time, and on the X axis the size of the production run. This arrangement follows a convention of placing on the Y axis the variable to be predicted (unit direct labor time) and placing on the X axis the variable to be used for making a prediction (size of production run). The variable to be predicted, following mathematical convention, also is called the *dependent variable,* and the variable used for making the prediction the *independent variable.* We want to repeat what was stated in Chapter 2, however: these terms have no causal significance.

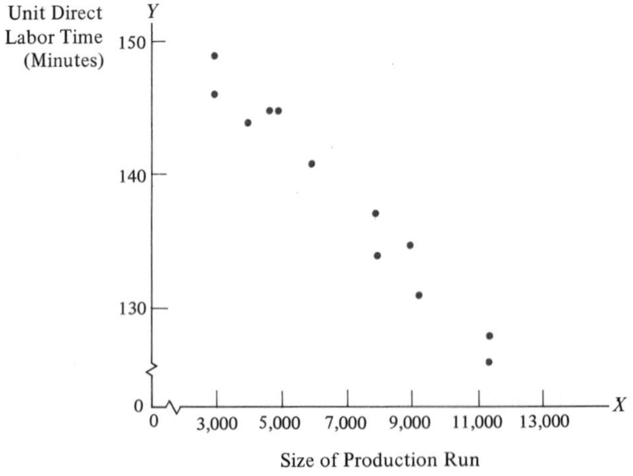

Figure 22.7. Scatter diagram for valve production example

The procedure for constructing the scatter diagram was explained earlier: we plot for each production run a point corresponding on the Y axis to the unit direct labor time and on the X axis to the size of the production run. For instance, the data for the April 1965 contract are plotted as a point corresponding to $Y = 145$ and $X = 5{,}000$.

Figure 22.7 clearly indicates a general tendency for the unit direct labor time to be smaller for those contracts for which a large number of valves were produced. In fact, it appears from the scatter of the points that the regression function is linear, because a straight line plotted on the scatter diagram through the center of the scatter would follow approximately the shape of the scatter. This interpretation of a scatter diagram is, of course, a subjective matter and has important limitations. Statistical tests are available to aid in determining from the sample information whether the regression relationship is, for instance, a straight-line one; these are discussed in advanced statistics books. For our purposes, we shall assume that the regression function is linear.

As we noted earlier, however, many situations exist in which the regression function is not a straight line. Figure 22.8 presents two scatter diagrams showing regression relationships that evidently are not linear. The

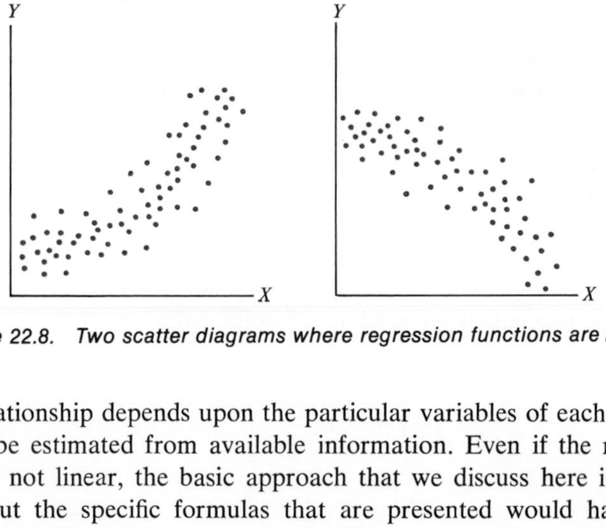

Figure 22.8. Two scatter diagrams where regression functions are not linear

type of relationship depends upon the particular variables of each problem, and must be estimated from available information. Even if the regression function is not linear, the basic approach that we discuss here is still applicable, but the specific formulas that are presented would have to be modified. We discuss one type of curvilinear regression model in Section 24.4.

Point estimation of parameters of regression equation

Sight-judgment method. The simplest method of estimating a linear regression curve is to plot a scatter diagram and then to draw by sight a straight line that describes the relationship. The values of the Y intercept and of the slope of the line can then be read from the graph. When the scatter of points forms a well-defined pattern, this approach may be fairly satisfactory if only crude estimates are desired. There are, however, two major disadvantages in estimating regression curves by judgment or free-hand methods. In the first place, different people probably will not draw identical regression curves for the same data. Secondly, it will not be possible to evaluate from the sample data the precision of any prediction based on this judgment regression curve; that is, one will not be able to set confidence limits on such predictions.

Method of least squares. The disadvantages of the sight-judgment method can be avoided by using statistical methods. The most common statistical method employed to estimate regression curves is that of *least squares*. This method can be used to estimate both linear and curvilinear regression equations.

For the model we are now considering, the method of least squares has some very desirable properties. The estimators furnished by the method of least squares are unbiased estimators of the regression parameters and are more precise (subject to smaller sampling errors) than any other possible unbiased estimators. The least-squares estimators are also frequently used in cases where the conditions of the model discussed here are not met, because of mathematical convenience. We shall describe some of the important properties of the method of least squares in a following subsection.

The method of least squares leads to two *normal equations*, which must be solved simultaneously for a and b, the point estimators, respectively, of α and β:

(22.3)
$$\begin{aligned} \Sigma Y &= na + b\Sigma X \\ \Sigma XY &= a\Sigma X + b\Sigma X^2 \end{aligned}$$

These two equations yield as the point estimator of β:

(22.3a)
$$b = \frac{\Sigma XY - \dfrac{\Sigma X \Sigma Y}{n}}{\Sigma X^2 - \dfrac{(\Sigma X)^2}{n}}$$

which can be expressed equivalently as:

(22.3b)
$$b = \frac{\Sigma(X - \overline{X})(Y - \overline{Y})}{\Sigma(X - \overline{X})^2}$$

and as the point estimator of α:

(22.3c)
$$a = \frac{1}{n}(\Sigma Y - b\Sigma X)$$

The derivation of these least-squares estimators is shown in Section 24.2.

The basic calculations can be performed systematically in a table such as Table 22.3. Substituting into (22.3a) and (22.3c), we obtain:

$$b = \frac{11{,}250{,}300 - \dfrac{(83{,}100)(1{,}661)}{12}}{678{,}030{,}000 - \dfrac{(83{,}100)^2}{12}} = \frac{-252{,}125}{102{,}562{,}500} = -.0024583$$

$$a = \frac{1}{12}[1{,}661 - (-.0024583)(83{,}100)] = 155.440$$

Table 22.3 Computations for Linear Regression Analysis, Hi-Ace Company

Contract Date	*Unit Direct Labor Time* Y	*Contract Size* X	XY	Y^2	X^2
April 1965	145	5,000	725,000	21,025	25,000,000
August 1965	145	4,800	696,000	21,025	23,040,000
December 1965	135	9,000	1,215,000	18,225	81,000,000
April 1966	146	3,000	438,000	21,316	9,000,000
December 1966	141	6,000	846,000	19,881	36,000,000
March 1967	149	3,000	447,000	22,201	9,000,000
July 1967	131	9,300	1,218,300	17,161	86,490,000
August 1967	126	11,500	1,449,000	15,876	132,250,000
February 1968	134	8,000	1,072,000	17,956	64,000,000
June 1968	137	8,000	1,096,000	18,769	64,000,000
December 1968	128	11,500	1,472,000	16,384	132,250,000
March 1969	144	4,000	576,000	20,736	16,000,000
Total	1,661	83,100	11,250,300	230,555	678,030,000
Mean	$\bar{Y} = 138.417$	$\bar{X} = 6{,}925$			

Point estimate of conditional mean $\mu_{Y.X}$. Once we have estimators a and b of the corresponding parameters α and β in the regression line, we can write the estimated linear regression equation:

$$\bar{Y}_X = a + bX \qquad (22.4)$$

Here $\bar{Y}_X$ denotes the estimated mean of the conditional probability distribution of Y corresponding to a given X; in other words, $\bar{Y}_X$ is a point estimator of $\mu_{Y.X}$. For our example, the estimated regression equation is:

$$\bar{Y}_X = 155.440 - .002458X$$

From this equation, we can estimate the mean of the conditional probability distribution corresponding to any size production run. For instance, for production runs of $X = 10{,}000$ valves, we would estimate that the mean of the conditional probability distribution is:

$$\bar{Y}_{10{,}000} = 155.440 - (.002458)(10{,}000) = 130.9 \text{ minutes}$$

Thus, while the unit direct labor time varies for different production runs of 10,000 valves, we would estimate that the *mean* unit direct labor time for this size production run is 130.9 minutes. Of course, this estimate is only a point estimate, and we require information about its precision. We shall discuss in Chapter 23 how we can set up an appropriate confidence interval estimate.

Properties of least-squares line. We consider now some of the properties of the least-squares regression line. The estimated linear regression equation for our valve production example has been plotted in Figure 22.9, together with the unit direct labor time and size of production run for each of the

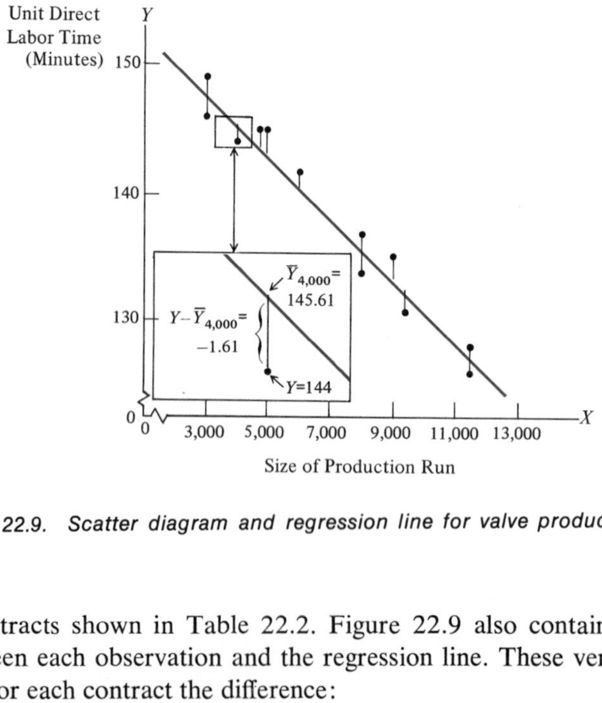

Figure 22.9. Scatter diagram and regression line for valve production example

twelve contracts shown in Table 22.2. Figure 22.9 also contains vertical lines between each observation and the regression line. These vertical lines represent for each contract the difference:

$$Y - \bar{Y}_X$$

that is, by how much the actual unit direct labor time differed from the estimated mean of the conditional probability distribution corresponding to the given size production run. For instance, the March 1969 contract was for 4,000 valves. The estimated mean, corresponding to a production run of 4,000 valves, is:

$$\bar{Y}_{4,000} = 155.440 - (.002458)(4,000) = 145.61 \text{ minutes}$$

The actual unit direct labor time was 144 minutes. Thus, the vertical line for that contract indicates the difference between the actual unit direct labor time of 144 minutes and the estimated mean unit direct labor time corresponding to a production run of 4,000 valves, which is 145.61 minutes:

$$Y - \bar{Y}_{4,000} = 144 - 145.61 = -1.61 \text{ minutes}$$

The deviations from the estimated conditional means for the other contracts are derived in Table 22.4. Column 3 contains the estimated conditional mean for the corresponding contract size, and column 4 contains the deviations $Y - \bar{Y}_X$, obtained by subtracting column 3 from column 1.

It is a property of the estimated regression equation calculated by the method of least squares that the positive deviations (where the actual unit direct labor time is greater than the respective estimated mean) cancel out the negative deviations (where the actual unit direct labor time is less than the respective estimated mean). One may think therefore of the least-squares regression line as going through the center of the scatter of the points. This property is evident from column 4 in Table 22.4, which sums to zero (except for minor rounding errors). Note that this property corresponds to the situation for the arithmetic mean in which the sum of the deviations of the individual observations around the mean is always zero.

Another property of a least-squares regression line is that the sum of the *squares* of the deviations around it is less than the sum of the squared deviations around any other straight line through the scatter of the points; hence, the name "least squares" is used. Under certain conditions, such as

Table 22.4 Computations of Deviations and Squared Deviations, Hi-Ace Company

Contract Date	(1) *Unit Direct Labor Time* Y	(2) *Contract Size* X	(3) $\bar{Y}_X$	(4) $Y - \bar{Y}_X$	(5) $(Y - \bar{Y}_X)^2$
April 1965	145	5,000	143.15	1.85	3.4225
August 1965	145	4,800	143.64	1.36	1.8496
December 1965	135	9,000	133.32	1.68	2.8224
April 1966	146	3,000	148.07	−2.07	4.2849
December 1966	141	6,000	140.69	.31	.0961
March 1967	149	3,000	148.07	.93	.8649
July 1967	131	9,300	132.58	−1.58	2.4964
August 1967	126	11,500	127.17	−1.17	1.3689
February 1968	134	8,000	135.78	−1.78	3.1684
June 1968	137	8,000	135.78	1.22	1.4884
December 1968	128	11,500	127.17	.83	.6889
March 1969	144	4,000	145.61	−1.61	2.5921
Total	1,661	83,100	1,661.0	0	25.1435

$$\bar{Y}_X = 155.440 - .002458X$$

the model considered here, the estimators calculated by the method of least squares may be said to be the "best" estimators of the population regression function. At other times, as we have pointed out, the method of least squares is used principally because of mathematical convenience.

Point estimate of conditional standard deviation $\sigma_{Y.X}$

A conditional standard deviation is just an ordinary standard deviation, measuring the variability in Y (unit direct labor time, in our example); the only difference is that the Y's in any conditional probability distribution refer to a given condition such as a certain size production run. We would estimate the ordinary population standard deviation σ_Y (we now use Y to denote the variable, rather than X as in earlier chapters) by:

$$s_Y = \sqrt{\frac{\Sigma(Y - \bar{Y})^2}{n - 1}}$$

We use the same approach when estimating the conditional standard deviation $\sigma_{Y.X}$. Remember, however, that the different Y observations (unit direct labor time, in our example) come from different conditional distributions. Hence, the deviation of any Y is taken around its own estimated conditional mean $\bar{Y}_X$, so that the deviations are of the form $Y - \bar{Y}_X$. Despite the fact that the different Y observations come from different conditional distributions, we still can combine the deviations around the respective estimated conditional means, because we are working with the model in which all conditional probability distributions have the same conditional standard deviation.

We have already explained how the deviations $Y - \bar{Y}_X$ are obtained. The estimated conditional standard deviation then is computed by squaring these deviations, calculating the mean of the squared deviations (but dividing by $n - 2$), and finally by taking the square root of this number. In symbols, these calculations are represented as follows:

$$s_{Y.X} = \sqrt{\frac{\Sigma(Y - \bar{Y}_X)^2}{n - 2}} \qquad (22.5)$$

The reason for dividing by $n - 2$ is that both α and β in the regression equation had to be estimated from the sample to obtain the estimated conditional means. Defined in this way, $s^2_{Y.X}$ will be an unbiased estimator of the population conditional variance $\sigma^2_{Y.X}$.

Table 22.4 shows the calculations necessary to estimate the conditional standard deviation. Substituting into (22.5), we obtain, in our example:

$$s_{Y.X} = \sqrt{\frac{25.14}{12 - 2}} = 1.586 \text{ minutes}$$

While (22.5) shows the meaning of the conditional standard deviation, it usually is too cumbersome to work with. For instance, in our example, it was necessary to calculate estimated conditional means ($\overline{Y}_X$ values) for each of 12 contracts. If the sample had been much larger, these calculations would have been far too tedious. A simpler method of calculating the estimated conditional standard deviation is as follows:

$$s_{Y.X} = \sqrt{\frac{1}{n-2}\left\{\left[\Sigma Y^2 - \frac{(\Sigma Y)^2}{n}\right] - \frac{\left(\Sigma XY - \frac{\Sigma X \Sigma Y}{n}\right)^2}{\Sigma X^2 - \frac{(\Sigma X)^2}{n}}\right\}} \qquad (22.6)$$

which can also be expressed as:

$$s_{Y.X} = \sqrt{\frac{1}{n-2}\left\{\Sigma(Y-\overline{Y})^2 - \frac{[\Sigma(X-\overline{X})(Y-\overline{Y})]^2}{\Sigma(X-\overline{X})^2}\right\}} \qquad (22.6a)$$

Formulas (22.5), (22.6), and (22.6a) are algebraically identical. Formula (22.6) looks most complicated, but usually is the easiest to work with. We recommend that it be used ordinarily in preference to the other formulas.

Formula (22.6) is preferable for two reasons. First, errors due to rounding at intermediate stages of the calculations are least serious when it is used. Second, most of the calculations needed for (22.6) already have been made in calculating b for the regression equation. With reference to our example, we already calculated:

$$\Sigma XY - \frac{\Sigma X \Sigma Y}{n} = -252{,}125$$

$$\Sigma X^2 - \frac{(\Sigma X)^2}{n} = 102{,}562{,}500$$

when we obtained b (see p. 493). Hence, the only new calculation needed is to find ΣY^2, which is done in Table 22.3. Then, we obtain:

$$\Sigma Y^2 - \frac{(\Sigma Y)^2}{n} = 230{,}555 - \frac{(1{,}661)^2}{12} = 644.92$$

Now, we can substitute into (22.6):

$$s_{Y.X} = \sqrt{\frac{1}{12-2}\left[644.92 - \frac{(-252{,}125)^2}{102{,}562{,}500}\right]} = \sqrt{2.513} = 1.585 \text{ minutes}$$

This, of course, is the same result as that obtained with (22.5), except for slight differences due to rounding.

Additional comments

A great many algebraic variants of the above formulas may be found in various statistics books. They all lead to the same least-squares estimates but by varying computational procedures.

The reader may have observed that more digits were carried in the calculations than indicated in the usual rules of rounding. This practice ensures that no errors are introduced due to rounding in the various calculational steps. However, one should use appropriate rounding when the final results, such as a confidence interval, are presented.

22.5 COEFFICIENTS OF CORRELATION AND DETERMINATION

Frequently, it is useful to express the degree of statistical relationship between the independent variable X and the dependent variable Y by a descriptive measure. The *coefficient of correlation* and the *coefficient of determination* are two such descriptive measures. We now explain the motivation underlying these measures.

Coefficient of determination

Suppose that in our valve production example we wish to predict the unit direct labor time. Suppose further that we only possess information on the unit direct labor times for the past twelve production runs, and do not have any knowledge of the independent variable X, size of production run. Thus, the only data available to us would be those contained in column 1 of Table 22.2. Uncertainty in making predictions arises because of the variability of the Y's. If, for instance, all of the Y observations in Table 22.2 were near 135 minutes, we would be much less uncertain about making a prediction than we are for the situation represented in Table 22.2, where the Y observations range from 126 to 149 minutes.

The variability of the Y observations is conventionally measured either by the standard deviation or the variance. We shall employ the variance. Using the computations in Table 22.3, we obtain:

$$s_Y^2 = \frac{\Sigma Y^2 - \dfrac{(\Sigma Y)^2}{n}}{n-1} = \frac{230{,}555 - \dfrac{(1{,}661)^2}{12}}{12-1} = \frac{644.917}{11} = 58.629$$

The larger s_Y^2 is, the more uncertainty there is in predicting Y; the smaller s_Y^2, the less uncertainty there is.

If an independent variable X is available for predicting Y, the uncertainty surrounding a prediction of Y arises from the variability of the Y's around the regression line. The greater the deviations around the regression line, such as those shown in Figure 22.9, the more uncertainty there is in predicting Y; the smaller the deviations around the regression line, the less uncertainty there is. The variability of the Y observations around the regression line is measured by the estimated conditional standard deviation $s_{Y.X}$, or by the estimated conditional variance $s_{Y.X}^2$. For the valve production example, we obtained earlier:

$$s_{Y.X}^2 = (1.585)^2 = 2.513$$

Note that the variability of the Y's around the regression line is substantially smaller than the variability of the Y's around their mean $\bar{Y}$:

$$s_{Y.X}^2 = 2.513; \quad s_Y^2 = 58.629$$

The degree of relationship between X and Y can thus be measured by comparing $s_{Y.X}^2$ with s_Y^2. Consider the measure:

$$\frac{s_{Y.X}^2}{s_Y^2}$$

This measure indicates the fraction which the variability of the Y's around the regression line is of the variability of the Y's when X is not considered for making predictions. A modified measure:

$$1 - \frac{s_{Y.X}^2}{s_Y^2} = \frac{s_Y^2 - s_{Y.X}^2}{s_Y^2}$$

indicates how much less is the variability of the Y's around the regression line relative to the variability of the Y's when X is not considered.

The *coefficient of determination,* denoted by r^2, is a minor variant of this second measure:

(22.7) $$r^2 = 1 - \left(\frac{n-2}{n-1}\right)\frac{s_{Y.X}^2}{s_Y^2}$$

It includes an adjustment factor $(n-2)/(n-1)$ which, for all but very small sample sizes, is practically equal to 1. Thus, we can effectively interpret r^2 as before, namely, r^2 measures how much less is the variability of the Y's around the regression line, relative to the variability of the Y's when X is not considered. More loosely speaking, r^2 measures how much less uncertainty there is in making predictions of Y when X is considered than when X is not considered.

For our valve production example, the coefficient of determination is:

$$r^2 = 1 - \left(\frac{12-2}{12-1}\right)\frac{2.513}{58.629} = .961$$

Thus, there is about 96 percent less uncertainty in making predictions of the unit direct labor time when the size of the production run is considered than when this independent variable is not employed.

Coefficient of correlation

The *coefficient of correlation,* denoted by r, is the square root of the coefficient of determination:

(22.8) $$r = \sqrt{r^2}$$

A plus or minus sign is usually attached to r, depending on whether the regression line has a positive or negative slope.

For our example, the coefficient of correlation is:

$$r = -\sqrt{.961} = -.980$$

One cannot assign to the coefficient of correlation as clear a meaning as to the coefficient of determination; therefore, the coefficient of determination is considered to be the more meaningful measure of the two.

An algebraically equivalent formula for r, which automatically provides the proper plus or minus sign, is:

(22.8a) $$r = \frac{\Sigma XY - \dfrac{\Sigma X \Sigma Y}{n}}{\left[\Sigma X^2 - \dfrac{(\Sigma X)^2}{n}\right]^{\frac{1}{2}}\left[\Sigma Y^2 - \dfrac{(\Sigma Y)^2}{n}\right]^{\frac{1}{2}}}$$

For our example, this formula yields (using earlier calculations):

$$r = \frac{-252{,}125}{(102{,}562{,}500)^{\frac{1}{2}}(644.917)^{\frac{1}{2}}} = -.980$$

which is the same result obtained with (22.8).

Properties of the two coefficients

The coefficient of determination, as well as the absolute value of the coefficient of correlation, ranges between 0 and 1. Let us consider each of these two extreme cases.

1. If perfect predictions can be made from the independent variable X, all observations would fall directly on the regression line, as shown in Figure 22.10a. In that case, all deviations $Y - \overline{Y}_X$ would be zero, the variability of the Y's around the regression line would be $s^2_{Y.X} = 0$, and we would obtain:

$$r^2 = 1 - \left(\frac{n-2}{n-1}\right)\frac{0}{s^2_Y} = 1$$

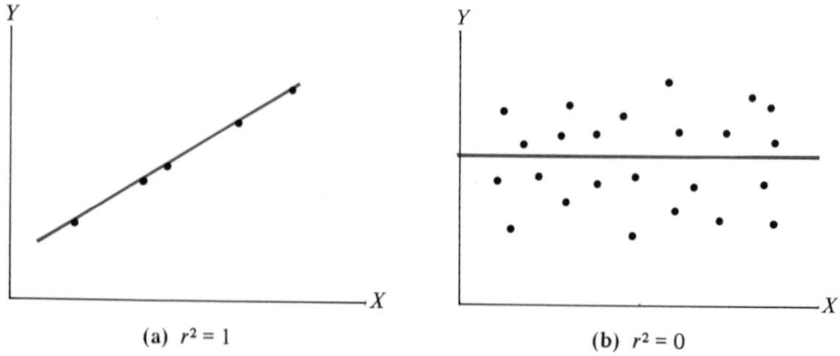

Figure 22.10. Scatter diagrams when $r^2 = 1$ and $r^2 = 0$

Thus $r^2 = 1$ or $r = \pm 1$ indicates an exact, or functional, relation between X and Y in the sample.

2. If X is of no help in predicting Y whatsoever, the uncertainty remaining after X is considered would be exactly the same as when X is not considered. This implies that $\Sigma(Y - \bar{Y}_X)^2 = \Sigma(Y - \bar{Y})^2$, which in turn implies that $(n - 2)s^2_{Y.X} = (n - 1)s^2_Y$, so that we would obtain:

$$r^2 = 1 - 1 = 0$$

Hence, $r^2 = 0$ or $r = 0$ indicates that X is of no help in predicting Y in the sample. Figure 22.10b illustrates this case. Note that the regression line is a horizontal straight line, implying for our model that there is no relation between X and Y.

Usefulness of the two coefficients

Neither of these two extreme cases is usually found in practice. Rather, the coefficient of determination or the absolute value of the correlation coefficient may be fairly close to zero, fairly close to 1, or between these two points. For these cases, one needs to be careful in interpreting the coefficients. A coefficient of determination or a coefficient of correlation close to zero indicates that X is of little help in predicting Y. On the other hand, coefficients not near zero only indicate that the independent variable X is of help in reducing the uncertainty in predicting Y. Even if the coefficient of determination (or the absolute value of the correlation coefficient) is near 1, we cannot infer that useful predictions of Y necessarily can be made when considering X. The reason is that r and r^2 measure only the *relative* reduction in uncertainty, and hence do not indicate anything about the actual precision with which predictions of Y can be made. There could be two cases, each with $r^2 = .98$, for one of which useful predictions of Y can be made from X while for the other the predictions of Y from X would not be precise enough to be useful. We shall expand upon these ideas in the next chapter.

Correlation and causality

It has been stated that the coefficient of determination and the coefficient of correlation measure the "degree of relationship" between X and Y. The closer these two coefficients are to 1 absolutely, the greater is the degree of relationship. In no case, however, do these coefficients provide any information about *causal* relations between X and Y. The reason is that an existing statistical relation may or may not be a causal one, as will be discussed in Chapter 23.

QUESTIONS AND PROBLEMS

22.1. Describe briefly each of the following:

a. Scatter diagram
b. Conditional standard deviation
c. Regression curve
d. Coefficient of correlation
e. Method of least squares

22.2. Contrast briefly each of the following:

a. Functional relation and statistical relation
b. Dependent and independent variable

22.3. For each of the following cases, indicate whether a functional relation or a statistical relation is involved. Explain the reason for your answer.

a. Relation between family income and entertainment expenditures of families in a community.
b. Relation between speed of a falling body and time.
c. Relation between department store sales and number of employees in a chain of department stores.

22.4. Plot each of the following sets of data as a scatter diagram. What is the nature of the regression curve that seems to be indicated by each of the scatter diagrams?

I		II		III	
Lot Size X	*Average Unit Cost* Y	*Book Value of Inventory Item* X	*Audited Value of Inventory Item* Y	*Daily Average Temperature* X	*Error Rate* Y
12,500	$2.39	$ 7.93	$ 7.93	79.3	.034
5,600	3.12	12.42	12.12	68.4	.021
7,900	2.64	51.64	51.64	82.1	.041
6,300	3.02	17.93	18.93	84.7	.048
9,800	2.51	5.02	5.02	81.3	.040
11,200	2.42	29.17	29.17	78.8	.032
4,700	3.73	30.04	30.52	75.4	.028
8,900	2.59	14.72	14.91	72.7	.025
9,200	2.61	8.39	8.09	79.6	.033

22.5. Below are data on motorcycle registrations (in thousands) and on life insurance in force (in billions of dollars) in the United States in selected years during the period 1960–1969:

Year	*Motorcycle Registrations*	*Life Insurance in Force*
1960	570	586
1965	1,382	901
1966	1,753	985
1967	1,953	1,080
1968	2,101	1,183
1969	2,255	1,285

Source: U.S. Bureau of the Census, *Statistical Abstract of the United States: 1970.* Washington, D.C., 1970, pp. 457, 544.

a. Plot the above data as a scatter diagram.
b. Does there appear to be a statistical relation between motorcycle registrations and amount of life insurance in force during the period 1960–1969? Explain.

c. Does your scatter diagram indicate anything about the effect of motorcycle registrations on the amount of life insurance in force? Is any causal relation evident? Discuss.

22.6. An analyst in a gas utility studied the relation between daily mean outdoor temperature (X) and daily residential gas consumption in the utility's service area (Y) during a recent 90-day period. As the relation appeared to be linear on the scatter diagram, he calculated the estimated regression line by the method of least squares, then calculated the estimated conditional standard deviation, and ascertained that 62 of the 90 points on which the regression analysis was based fell within ± 2 standard deviations from the regression line. What is the significance of this finding? Discuss.

22.7. Solve the two simultaneous equations in formula (22.3) for a and b, and verify the expressions in formulas (22.3a) and (22.3c).

22.8. For each of the following cases, explain precisely the meaning of the slope β of the regression line:

a. Y = Sales in territory, in millions of dollars
X = Mean disposable income per spending unit in territory, in dollars

b. Y = 1972 sales of retail establishment, in thousands of dollars
X = 1971 sales of retail establishment, in thousands of dollars

c. Y = Sales by salesman, in thousands of dollars
X = Number of calls on prospects made by salesman

***22.9.** The A.C. Brown Company wished to know if disposable personal income is a reliable indicator for predicting company sales. Some relevant data were as follows:

Year	*Disposable Personal Income (Billions of Dollars)*	*Company Sales (Thousands of Dollars)*
1959	337	404
1960	350	412
1961	364	425
1962	385	429
1963	405	436
1964	438	440
1965	473	447
1966	512	458
1967	546	469
1968	591	477

a. Plot a scatter diagram of these data. Which variable did you treat as the independent variable? Why?

b. Estimate the linear regression equation, using the method of least squares.

c. What relationship is described by the regression equation?

d. What is the exact meaning of β in the regression equation?

e. Is α in the regression equation a meaningful parameter from an economic point of view? Discuss.

f. Obtain a point estimate of the mean of the conditional distribution of company sales when disposable personal income is 500 billion dollars.

g. Estimate the conditional standard deviation of the distributions of company sales. Does the standard deviation appear to be relatively large or small?

h. Calculate the coefficients of determination and correlation. What is the meaning of the coefficient of determination here?

22.10. The administration of a college was disturbed because recent forecasts of enrollments were substantially in error. This caused serious problems in budgeting. The Registrar was asked to study various methods of forecasting to see if they would be helpful. One of these involved the relation between the number of applications received by January 1 and the number of new students entering the college the following fall. Some relevant data were as follows:

Year	*Number of Applications Received by Jan. 1*	*Number of New Students Entering in Fall*
1965	2,350	1,500
1966	2,190	1,420
1967	2,380	1,520
1968	2,570	1,640
1969	2,810	1,890
1970	2,590	1,680

a. Plot a scatter diagram of these data. Which variable did you treat as the independent variable? Why?
b. Estimate the linear regression equation, using the method of least squares.
c. What relationship is described by the regression equation?
d. What is the exact meaning of β in the regression equation?
e. Is α in the regression equation a parameter that has meaning for administrative purposes? What would be the significance if $\alpha = 0$? Discuss.
f. Obtain a point estimate of the mean of the conditional distribution of number of entering students when the number of applications by January 1 is 2,600.
g. Estimate the conditional standard deviation of the distributions of number of entering students. Does it appear to be small?
h. Calculate the coefficients of determination and correlation. What is the meaning of the coefficient of determination here?

***22.11.** An automobile dealer, attempting to improve his ability to predict sales, collected data for the past three years on the number of inquiries about cars received during a week and on the number of cars sold during the following week. He wished to study whether the number of inquiries about cars received during any given week would be a reliable guide for predicting sales of cars for the following week. The data collected can be summarized as follows:

X = number of inquiries received during given week
Y = number of cars sold during following week

$n = 156$ weeks $\qquad \Sigma X = 54{,}649$ inquiries
$\Sigma Y = 11{,}492$ cars sold $\qquad \Sigma X^2 = 19{,}207{,}423$
$\Sigma Y^2 = 855{,}766$ $\qquad \Sigma XY = 4{,}047{,}975$

a. Estimate the linear regression equation, using the method of least squares.
b. What relationship is described by the regression equation?
c. On the average, how many cars does the dealer sell during a week when he had 300 inquiries during the preceding week? Use a point estimate. Do you have great confidence that your point estimate is correct? Explain.
d. Is it reasonable that α in the regression equation is negative, as the point estimate a seems to indicate? Discuss. What does this indicate about the validity of the regression model? Explain.
e. Estimate the conditional standard deviation of the distributions of car sales. In what units is it expressed?

f. Calculate the coefficient of determination. In what units is it expressed? What is its meaning here?

g. Calculate the coefficient of correlation.

22.12. The Zeus supermarket chain has collected data on sales and manhours expended for the major departments of its stores as a basis for developing staffing guides. For the last week of October, sales and manhours were as follows for the meat departments in the stores in the chain:

X = meat department sales of store, in thousands of dollars
Y = number of manhours expended in meat department of store

$n = 144$ stores	$\Sigma X = 558.6$ thousand dollars
$\Sigma Y = 26{,}281$ manhours	$\Sigma X^2 = 2{,}475.81$
$\Sigma Y^2 = 5{,}122{,}074$	$\Sigma XY = 111{,}679.6$

a. Estimate the linear regression equation, using the method of least squares.

b. What relationship is described by the regression equation?

c. Since the Zeus chain operates 144 supermarkets, each with a meat department, are the above data on the 144 meat departments sample data, or are they based upon a full enumeration? Explain, keeping in mind the purpose for which management has collected the data.

d. On the average, what number of manhours are expended in a meat department when weekly sales of the department are $4.6 thousand? Use a point estimate. Do you have great confidence that your point estimate is correct? Explain.

e. Is it reasonable that α in the regression equation is positive, as the point estimate a seems to indicate? Discuss.

f. Calculate the estimated conditional standard deviation of the distributions of manhours expended in meat departments. In what units is the standard deviation expressed?

g. Calculate the coefficient of determination. What is its meaning here?

h. Calculate the coefficient of correlation.

22.13. **a.** What is the essential difference between a situation where $r = +1$ and one where $r = -1$? Is the regression line a better fit in one case than the other?

b. Why is the coefficient of determination frequently a more meaningful measure than the coefficient of correlation? What do both coefficients seek to measure?

c. If $r^2 = .984$, what does this imply about the presence of a direct causal relationship between the two variables? Discuss.

22.14. In each of the following cases, indicate whether you expect the correlation coefficient to be positive, zero, or negative, and give the reason for your opinion:

a. X = Income of family
Y = Per cent of income spent by family for food

b. X = Sales of retail store
Y = Average inventory carried by retail store

c. X = Traffic density of cars approaching a toll bridge
Y = Average delay time for cars at toll bridge

d. X = Size of family
Y = Expenditures for new clothing, per person, by family

22.15. An advertising agency selected a simple random sample of 250 families to study the age differences between husband and wife in families as a factor in designing a special type of advertisement. The correlation coefficient between the husband's age and the wife's age in the 250 sample families was .974. *(Continued)*

a. Since the correlation coefficient is so close to 1, does this mean that in most families the husband and wife are of the same age? To help answer this question, calculate the correlation coefficient by formula (22.8a) for each of the following two cases:

Case I		*Case II*	
Husband's Age	*Wife's Age*	*Husband's Age*	*Wife's Age*
40	40	40	35
26	26	26	21
55	54	55	49
29	28	29	23
44	44	44	39

How do the two cases differ? What is the difference in r for these two cases? What generalization does this suggest?

b. Does the correlation coefficient provide the kind of information about the age differences between husbands and wives in the families in the population that the advertising agency needs to design the advertisement? Discuss.

22.16. Refer to Problem 14.2. The personnel department of the Simpson Company was interested, among other things, in the correlation between an employee's length of service and his rating of the company magazine. The correlation coefficient between these two variables was computed for the 100 employees of division A included in the sample, and it turned out to be .73. In division B of the Simpson Company, the correlation coefficient between an employee's length of service and his rating of the company magazine was .59, based on the sample of 100 employees from division B. Does this imply that employees of division A rated the company's magazine more highly than those of division B? If so, why? If not, what does the higher correlation coefficient indicate?

Chapter

23

INFERENCES IN REGRESSION ANALYSIS

In the previous chapter, we considered the fundamental concepts of regression analysis. We discussed the notions of a statistical relation and of a curve describing the statistical relation. We saw that the regression model formalizes these basic ideas by postulating that there is a conditional probability distribution of the Y's for each level of the independent variable X. The curve relating the means of the conditional probability distributions to the independent variable X is the regression curve. Thus, the regression curve corresponds to the intuitive notion of a curve of statistical relationship, while the conditional probability distributions are the counterpart in the model to the observed scattering of observations around the curve of statistical relationship.

The particular model considered in Chapter 22 had the following characteristics:

(23.1) 1. All conditional probability distributions are normal.
2. All conditional probability distributions have the same variability, i.e., $\sigma_{Y.X}$ is constant for all X.
3. The means of the conditional probability distributions, $\mu_{Y.X}$, are related to X by a linear relation:

$$\mu_{Y.X} = \alpha + \beta X$$

Thus, according to this model, any Y observation is viewed as a random selection from a normal distribution which has mean $\mu_{Y.X}$, depending on the level of X, and standard deviation $\sigma_{Y.X}$.

Model (23.1) continues to be the model assumed. In this chapter, we extend the developments of Chapter 22 by considering how to estimate a conditional mean $\mu_{Y.X}$ with an interval estimate, how to predict a new observation on Y, and how to estimate the regression slope β with an interval estimate. These inferences concerning regression model (23.1) will require the use of the t-distribution rather than the standard normal distribution. (The reader who has not yet studied the t-distribution should refer to Section 12.4 before proceeding further.)

23.1
INTERVAL ESTIMATE OF CONDITIONAL MEAN $\mu_{Y.X}$

Many problems in business and economics require the estimation of a conditional mean. For instance, in our valve production example, management may be concerned with its policy of bidding on contracts involving small production runs, and therefore wishes to know the *mean* unit direct labor time expected for various sizes of production runs. Again, a sales manager may wish to know the *mean* sales volume of a product which is expected when the unit price is set at a particular level. Note in each of these examples that interest centers on the *mean* of a conditional probability distribution and not on the prediction for the *next* event, such as the prediction of the unit direct labor time for the *next* contract or the sales volume during the *next* period.

Development of interval estimate

An interval estimate of a conditional mean is constructed similarly to an interval estimate of an ordinary population mean. It will be recalled that the confidence limits for the population mean, based on a simple random sample from a normal population (using Y to denote the variable instead of X as in earlier chapters), are:

$$\overline{Y} \pm t_{n-1}s_{\overline{Y}}$$

where t_{n-1} is the t-multiple based on $n - 1$ degrees of freedom corresponding to the desired confidence coefficient.

For the regression model (23.1), the confidence limits for the conditional mean $\mu_{Y.X}$ are similar:

$$\overline{Y}_X \pm t_{n-2}s_{\overline{Y}_X} \tag{23.2}$$

Here t_{n-2} is the t-multiple based on $n - 2$ degrees of freedom corresponding to the desired confidence coefficient, and $s_{\overline{Y}_X}$ is the estimated standard deviation of the sampling distribution of $\overline{Y}_X$. Note that the t-multiple here is associated with $n - 2$ degrees of freedom, since both the α and β coefficients in the regression equation have to be estimated from the sample. The value of t_{n-2} depends, as before, upon the confidence coefficient that is to be associated with the interval estimate.

The estimated standard deviation of the sampling distribution of $\bar{Y}_X$ is:

(23.3) $$s_{\bar{Y}_X} = \frac{s_{Y.X}}{\sqrt{n}} + s_{Y.X}\sqrt{\frac{(X - \bar{X})^2}{\Sigma X^2 - \frac{(\Sigma X)^2}{n}}}$$

which can be written in equivalent form as:

(23.3a) $$s_{\bar{Y}_X} = s_{Y.X}\sqrt{\frac{1}{n} + \frac{(X - \bar{X})^2}{\Sigma X^2 - \frac{(\Sigma X)^2}{n}}}$$

Note from the expression in (23.3) that the first term on the right corresponds to the usual estimated standard deviation of the sample mean except that the standard deviation s_Y is replaced by the *conditional* standard deviation $s_{Y.X}$. The second term on the right of (23.3) involves the value of X for which the conditional mean $\mu_{Y.X}$ is to be estimated. The implications of this second term will be discussed shortly.

The confidence interval for the conditional mean $\mu_{Y.X}$ therefore is:

(23.4) $$\bar{Y}_X - t_{n-2}s_{\bar{Y}_X} \leq \mu_{Y.X} \leq \bar{Y}_X + t_{n-2}s_{\bar{Y}_X}$$

Here $s_{\bar{Y}_X}$ is defined by (23.3) or (23.3a). When the sample size is large, t_{n-2} is as usual replaced by z.

Illustration

We shall use again our valve production example discussed in the previous chapter. For convenience, we repeat here some of the earlier results:

$$a = 155.440 \qquad b = -.002458$$
$$\bar{Y}_X = 155.440 - .002458X$$
$$s_{Y.X} = 1.585 \text{ minutes}$$
$$\bar{X} = 6{,}925 \text{ valves}$$
$$\Sigma(X - \bar{X})^2 = \Sigma X^2 - \frac{(\Sigma X)^2}{n} = 102{,}562{,}500$$
$$n = 12$$

Suppose that management wishes to estimate with a 95 per cent confidence interval the mean unit direct labor time for production runs of 10,000 valves. In other words, we are to estimate the mean of the conditional probability distribution of unit direct labor time when $X = 10{,}000$. The point estimate of the mean direct labor time expended per valve for production runs of 10,000 valves was obtained in the last chapter:

$$\bar{Y}_{10,000} = 155.440 - (.002458)(10{,}000) = 130.9 \text{ minutes}$$

From Table A-5, we find that the value of t for $12 - 2 = 10$ degrees of freedom and for a 95 per cent confidence coefficient (5 per cent area in both tails) is 2.228. The estimated standard deviation of the sampling distribution of $\bar{Y}_X$, using (23.3a), is:

$$s_{\bar{Y}_{10,000}} = 1.585\sqrt{\frac{1}{12} + \frac{(10{,}000 - 6{,}925)^2}{102{,}562{,}500}} = .6640$$

Hence, the appropriate 95 per cent confidence interval for the mean direct labor time per valve for contracts of 10,000 valves is:

$$\bar{Y}_{10,000} - t_{n-2}s_{\bar{Y}_{10,000}} \leq \mu_{Y.10,000} \leq \bar{Y}_{10,000} + t_{n-2}s_{\bar{Y}_{10,000}}$$
$$130.9 - 2.228(.6640) \leq \mu_{Y.10,000} \leq 130.9 + 2.228(.6640)$$
$$129 \leq \mu_{Y.10,000} \leq 132$$

One therefore can state that the mean direct labor time per valve for contracts of 10,000 valves is between 129 and 132 minutes. This statement is made with a 95 per cent confidence coefficient. We have confidence that the statement is correct because a procedure has been used that will lead to correct interval estimates 95 per cent of the time.

Whether this particular confidence interval is a useful one depends on the requirements of the specific problem. Everything that was said about confidence intervals in general in Chapter 12 applies here as well.

In the same manner in which a confidence interval for the average direct labor time per valve for contracts of 10,000 valves has been constructed, confidence intervals for the average unit direct labor time corresponding to other contract sizes can be computed. Figure 23.1 shows the estimated

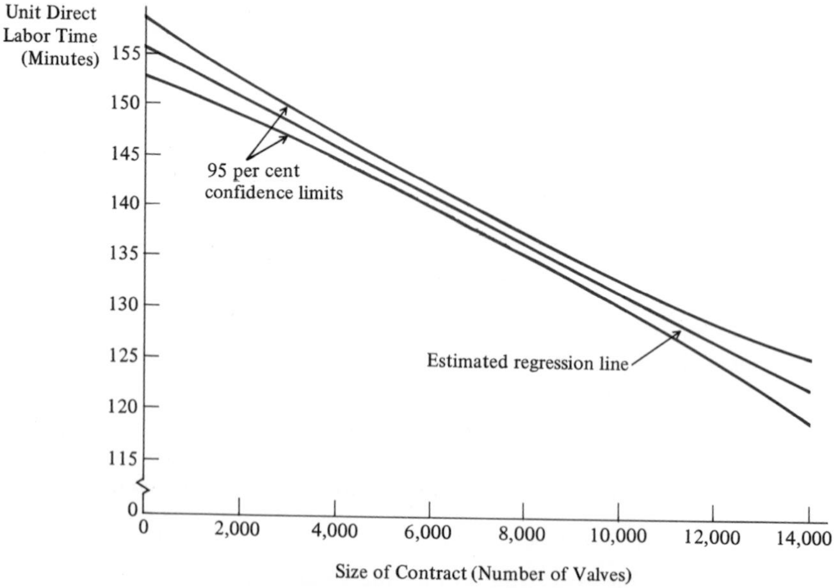

Figure 23.1. Estimated regression line and 95 per cent confidence limits for estimating average unit direct labor time for given size of contract

regression line and the 95 per cent confidence limits for the average unit direct labor time corresponding to various contract sizes. Note that the width of the confidence interval is slightly larger for small and large contract sizes than for contract sizes that are nearer the average. The reason for this difference in the width of the confidence interval will be explained in the section that immediately follows.

Factors affecting width of confidence interval

Let us now take a closer look at the factors affecting the *width* of the confidence interval for a conditional mean:

$$\pm t_{n-2}s_{\bar{Y}_X} = \pm t_{n-2}s_{Y.X}\sqrt{\frac{1}{n} + \frac{(X - \bar{X})^2}{\Sigma X^2 - \frac{(\Sigma X)^2}{n}}} \tag{23.5}$$

The sample size, conditional standard deviation, deviation of X from $\bar{X}$, and variability of the observed X's affect the width of this interval:

1. *Sample size:* The larger the sample size n, the smaller will be the value of the square root in (23.5), and consequently, the smaller will be the width of the interval. The value of t in the interval is also affected by the sample size. The larger the sample, the smaller the value of t, and therefore, the narrower the interval. Remember, though, that the value of t approaches a limit for large n. For instance, the t values associated with a confidence coefficient of 95 per cent approach 1.96 as n becomes larger and larger. If the degrees of freedom exceed, say, 30, there is only a relatively small decrease in the value of t for larger samples, so that the confidence interval will not be much narrower for larger samples on account of this factor.
2. *Conditional standard deviation:* The smaller the conditional standard deviation, the narrower the interval generally will be. The magnitude of the conditional standard deviation is inherent in the particular problem and does not depend upon the sample size.
3. *Deviation of X from $\bar{X}$:* The farther X is from $\bar{X}$, the larger will be $(X - \bar{X})^2$, the larger the square root, and therefore, the wider the interval at that X. This relationship indicates that, in our example, the confidence interval for the mean unit direct labor time will be wider for a very large or a very small contract than for a contract of average size, as is shown in Figure 23.1.
4. *Variability of observed X's:* The greater the variability of the observed X's (in the example of the Hi-Ace Company, the greater the variability in the size of the contracts), the greater will be $\Sigma(X - \bar{X})^2 = \Sigma X^2 - \frac{(\Sigma X)^2}{n}$, the smaller the square root, and consequently, the narrower the width of the confidence interval.

23.2 PREDICTION OF NEXT VALUE OF Y FOR GIVEN X

Construction of prediction interval when parameters known

Frequently, problems in business and economics require predictions for the *next* event—i.e., for a *specific* coming event. Thus, management may wish to know what will be the direct labor time per valve for the *next* contract of 10,000 valves, or a sales manager would like a prediction of company sales of a product for *next* month when the unit price is \$5.

To illustrate the basic elements of how we predict the next observation by means of a *prediction interval,* we shall assume first that the relevant parameters are known. Later we will discard this assumption. Suppose we wish to predict the unit direct labor time for the next contract of 10,000 valves, and the parameters of the relevant conditional probability distribution are as follows:

$$\mu_{Y.10,000} = 130 \text{ minutes}; \quad \sigma_{Y.X} = 2 \text{ minutes}$$

Since the conditional probability distribution is assumed to be normal, we know that, say, 99.7 per cent of the observations fall within $130 \pm 3(2)$, or between 124 and 136 minutes. If we were to assert, therefore, that the unit direct labor time for the next contract of 10,000 valves will be somewhere between 124 and 136 minutes, we would have a probability of .997 of being correct.

In general, then, we shall employ the following prediction limits when the parameters of model (23.1) are known:

$$\mu_{Y.X} \pm z\sigma_{Y.X} \tag{23.6}$$

where z is the standard normal deviate corresponding to the desired confidence coefficient. Thus, the prediction interval would be:

$$\mu_{Y.X} - z\sigma_{Y.X} \leq Y_{\text{next}} \leq \mu_{Y.X} + z\sigma_{Y.X} \tag{23.7}$$

where Y_{next} denotes the next value of Y at a specified level of X (unit direct labor time for the next contract for X valves, in our example).

If a confidence coefficient of 99.7 per cent is desired, $z = 3$ and the prediction interval for our example would be:

$$130 - 3(2) \leq Y_{\text{next}} \leq 130 + 3(2)$$
$$124 \leq Y_{\text{next}} \leq 136$$

We then would state that the unit direct labor time for the next contract of 10,000 valves will be somewhere between 124 and 136 minutes. This prediction interval is like a confidence interval. Any specific statement will be right or wrong, but we treat the statement as correct because a procedure has been used that leads to correct statements 99.7 per cent of the time. Remember that we assume the conditional distributions are normal, so that

99.7 per cent of the time the unit direct labor time will fall within three conditional standard deviations from the conditional mean. We also assume that the basic causal factors affecting the process of producing valves remain about the same.

Distinction between conditional mean and specific event

It is very important to observe the distinction between estimating a conditional mean and predicting a specific event. A confidence interval for a conditional mean is constructed when interest centers on the *average* value of Y for a given X. A confidence interval for the conditional mean then indicates a range within which one concludes that the conditional mean lies. Note that the range in the confidence interval for the conditional mean reflects the precision with which one estimates this mean and has nothing to do with the range of individual values.

When the next observation must be predicted, one is not interested in the conditional mean, because the individual observations will seldom, if ever, coincide with the mean of the distribution. Rather, one is concerned with the spread of the distribution within which the individual values of Y will fall. The prediction interval (23.7) indicates, for any confidence coefficient, the range within which the next value of Y selected at random from the distribution can be expected to fall.

Construction of prediction interval from sample estimates

When the population characteristics $\mu_{Y.X}$ and $\sigma_{Y.X}$ are not known, as is usually the case, the prediction interval (23.7) cannot be used. Instead, the population characteristics must be estimated from sample information.

When the population parameters are unknown and one wishes to predict a *specific* event—that is, the next value of Y for a given X—the appropriate prediction interval for the regression model (23.1) is:

$$\overline{Y}_X - t_{n-2}s_{Y_{\text{next}}} \leq Y_{\text{next}} \leq \overline{Y}_X + t_{n-2}s_{Y_{\text{next}}} \tag{23.8}$$

where:

$$s_{Y_{\text{next}}} = \sqrt{s^2_{\overline{Y}_X} + s^2_{Y.X}} \tag{23.9}$$

Note that $s_{Y_{\text{next}}}$ is made up of two components:

1. $s^2_{\overline{Y}_X}$—the sampling error in using $\overline{Y}_X$ for estimating $\mu_{Y.X}$
2. $s^2_{Y.X}$—the inherent variation in the conditional probability distribution

These two components are independent, hence the variances are additive. An equivalent expression for $s_{Y_{\text{next}}}$ is:

$$s_{Y_{\text{next}}} = s_{Y.X}\sqrt{1 + \frac{1}{n} + \frac{(X - \overline{X})^2}{\Sigma X^2 - \frac{(\Sigma X)^2}{n}}} \tag{23.9a}$$

Illustration

Suppose that management wants to predict the unit direct labor time for the *next* contract of 10,000 valves; in other words, an individual event is to be predicted for $X = 10{,}000$. If a 95 per cent confidence coefficient is desired, t_{n-2} is again 2.228; remember that there are 10 degrees of freedom for our example. Using our earlier results, we obtain:

$$s_{Y_{\text{next}}} = 1.585\sqrt{1 + \frac{1}{12} + \frac{(10{,}000 - 6{,}925)^2}{102{,}562{,}500}} = 1.719$$

We found earlier that $\bar{Y}_{10,000} = 130.9$ minutes. Hence, the desired prediction interval is:

$$\bar{Y}_{10,000} - t_{n-2}s_{Y_{\text{next}}} \leq Y_{\text{next}} \leq \bar{Y}_{10,000} + t_{n-2}s_{Y_{\text{next}}}$$
$$130.9 - 2.228(1.719) \leq Y_{\text{next}} \leq 130.9 + 2.228(1.719)$$
$$127 \leq Y_{\text{next}} \leq 135$$

One can then state that the direct labor time per valve for the *next* contract of 10,000 valves will be somewhere between 127 and 135 minutes. This prediction is either correct or incorrect, but management would treat it as correct, because a statistical procedure has been used that leads to correct statements 95 per cent of the time, in accord with the confidence coefficient management had specified initially. In making such a prediction, we assume, of course, that the basic causal factors affecting the production of valves for the next contract are similar to those on which the regression analysis is based.

In a similar manner, a prediction could have been made of the unit direct labor time for other contract sizes. Figure 23.2 contains a graph showing the estimated regression line and the prediction limits for unit direct labor times corresponding to a 95 per cent confidence coefficient for various sizes of production runs. With a 95 per cent assurance of being correct, we can state that the unit direct labor time for any given contract of specified size will fall within the prediction limits indicated on the graph.

Note that the *prediction* intervals in Figure 23.2 are wider than the confidence intervals for estimating the *mean* performance for contracts of given size (Figure 23.1). This is because the prediction interval for an individual event must consider the variability inherent in the conditional probability distribution, in addition to the sampling error in the estimate of the conditional mean.

Note also from Figure 23.2 that the width of the prediction interval is larger for very small or very large contracts than for average size contracts. The factors affecting the width of the prediction interval are exactly the same as those already discussed for the confidence interval for a conditional mean (see the discussion under "Factors affecting width of confidence interval," on page 511).

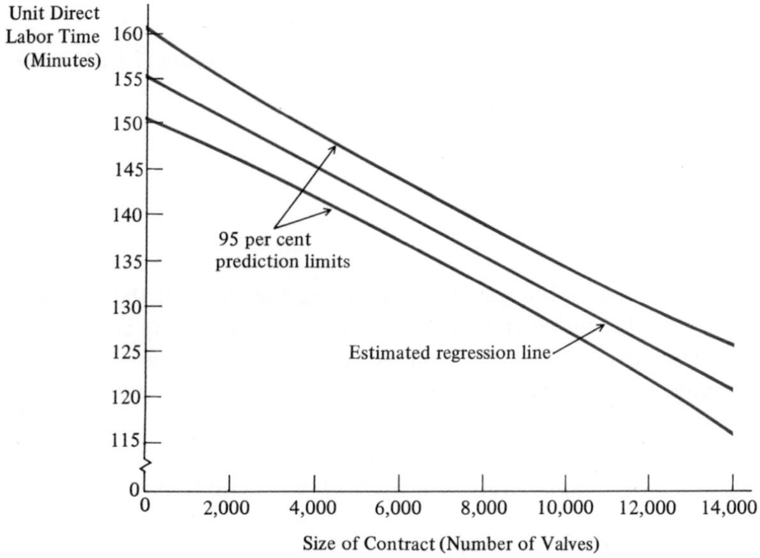

Figure 23.2. Estimated regression line and 95 per cent prediction limits for predicting unit direct labor time for specific contract from size of contract

Usefulness of prediction interval

The usefulness of a prediction interval, as that of any confidence interval, depends upon the width of the interval and management's needs for precision with reference to the particular circumstances of the problem. In the case of predicting the unit direct labor time for a contract of 10,000 valves, management felt that it was useful to state with a 95 per cent confidence coefficient that the unit direct labor time for a contract of 10,000 valves would be 130.9 ± 3.8 minutes. The interval here was narrow enough to permit management to bid realistically and competitively. A prediction interval with a width of ± 10 minutes for the same degree of assurance would not have been considered as useful, because it would not have helped as much in bidding competitively. In another type of problem, however, a prediction with that wide an error margin might have been useful.

Large-sample prediction interval

When the sample size is large, the t-multiple in the prediction interval (23.8) is replaced by z, since the t-distribution approaches the standard normal distribution. Furthermore, the last two terms under the radical in formula (23.9a) for $s_{Y_{\text{next}}}$ are small relative to 1 when n is large and the value of X is within the range of past experience or not too far outside it. Hence, an approximate prediction interval for large n is:

(23.10) $$\bar{Y}_X - z s_{Y.X} \leq Y_{\text{next}} \leq \bar{Y}_X + z s_{Y.X}$$

It has been suggested that n should exceed 100 before (23.10) is used in place of (23.8).

23.3 INTERVAL ESTIMATE OF β

At times, one is interested in estimating the slope of the regression line for its own sake, rather than merely as a step in estimating conditional averages. In our valve production example, the slope β indicates by how much the average unit direct labor time changes with each additional valve in the production run. As another example, if Y were individual consumption expenditures and X personal income, β would indicate by how much average consumption expenditures change with each additional dollar of income.

Sampling distribution of b

We already have noted that the point estimator of β by the method of least squares is b, as given by (22.3a). With different samples, the value of b will vary, of course, and we must know something about the sampling distribution of b if we are to construct an interval estimate of β. For the model we are considering in this chapter, the mean of the sampling distribution of b is β; thus b is an unbiased estimator of β. Furthermore, the standard deviation of the sampling distribution of b, denoted by σ_b, is:

(23.11) $$\sigma_b = \frac{\sigma_{Y.X}}{\sqrt{\Sigma X^2 - \dfrac{(\Sigma X)^2}{n}}} = \frac{\sigma_{Y.X}}{\sqrt{\Sigma(X - \bar{X})^2}}$$

Finally, the sampling distribution of b is normal for the model considered in this chapter.

Confidence interval for β

In order to construct a confidence interval for β, we first need to estimate σ_b, the standard deviation of the sampling distribution of b. This can be done as follows, using $s_{Y.X}$ as an estimator of $\sigma_{Y.X}$:

(23.12) $$s_b = \frac{s_{Y.X}}{\sqrt{\Sigma X^2 - \dfrac{(\Sigma X)^2}{n}}}$$

Here s_b denotes the point estimator of σ_b.

It can be shown that the confidence interval for β, for the conditions of model (23.1), then is:

(23.13) $$b - t_{n-2} s_b \leq \beta \leq b + t_{n-2} s_b$$

Here s_b is the estimated standard deviation of the sampling distribution of b as given by (23.12). Note the similarity of this confidence interval to that for the conditional mean in (23.4). If n is large, the t-multiple in (23.13) would simply be replaced by z, since the t-distribution approaches the standard normal distribution as n increases.

Illustration

Suppose that we are to estimate the slope β of the regression line in the Hi-Ace case, using a 99 per cent confidence coefficient. From previous calculations, we have:

$$b = -.0024583$$
$$s_{Y.X} = 1.585$$
$$\Sigma X^2 - \frac{(\Sigma X)^2}{n} = 102{,}562{,}500$$

so that:

$$s_b = \frac{s_{Y.X}}{\sqrt{\Sigma X^2 - \frac{(\Sigma X)^2}{n}}} = \frac{1.585}{\sqrt{102{,}562{,}500}} = .0001565$$

For 10 degrees of freedom and a 99 per cent confidence coefficient (area .01 in the two tails), the value of t is 3.169, and the confidence interval for β is:

$$b - t_{n-2}s_b \leq \beta \leq b + t_{n-2}s_b$$
$$-.0024583 - 3.169(.0001565) \leq \beta \leq -.0024583 + 3.169(.0001565)$$
$$-.002 \leq \beta \leq -.003$$

Hence, we would conclude that the mean direct labor time per valve decreases between .002 and .003 minutes for each additional valve in the production run. This interval estimate, like the others for the Hi-Ace case, must be used cautiously, since the regression curve is likely to be nonlinear if the contract size departs substantially from the range of past experience.

Significance of case when $\beta = 0$

With our model, where it is assumed that all conditional probability distributions are normal with the same conditional standard deviation and that the regression curve is a straight line, the case when $\beta = 0$ is an important one. In that event, all conditional probability distributions have the same mean and, in fact, are then identical. This situation is portrayed in Figure 23.3. We say in situations of this type that there is no statistical relation between X and Y because all conditional distributions of Y are the same no matter what the value of X is.

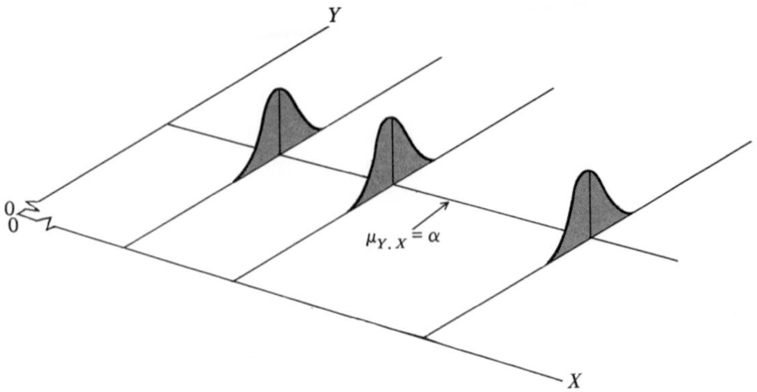

Figure 23.3. Regression model when $\beta = 0$

Because $\beta = 0$ implies no statistical relation between X and Y for our model, the following decision problem frequently is formulated:

$C_1 \quad \beta = 0$

$C_2 \quad \beta \neq 0$

We could set up a formal statistical decision rule, given the specified risk of concluding $\beta \neq 0$ when actually $\beta = 0$, and the reader should be able to do this.[1] However, we can get the same information from the confidence interval for β. If the confidence interval includes zero, we would have concluded from the corresponding statistical decision rule that $\beta = 0$. If the confidence interval does not include zero, we would have concluded that $\beta \neq 0$.

In our example, the confidence interval for β covered $-.002$ to $-.003$. Hence, we would conclude that β is not equal to zero, or that a statistical relation does exist between size of production run and unit direct labor time. Remember that the interpretation of no statistical relation when $\beta = 0$ depends on the model used in this chapter and may not be valid for some other models.

23.4
ADDITIONAL CONSIDERATIONS IN THE USE OF REGRESSION ANALYSIS

In the previous sections, some inferences with regression analysis were explained. To employ this type of analysis meaningfully, a number of additional considerations must be kept in mind.

[1] The decision rule is:

Conclude $\beta = 0$ if $-t_{n-2}s_b \leq b \leq t_{n-2}s_b$
Otherwise, conclude $\beta \neq 0$

where t_{n-2} is the t-multiple for $n - 2$ degrees of freedom associated with the specified risk of concluding $\beta \neq 0$ when actually $\beta = 0$.

Relevancy of past data

Whenever past experience is used to predict events in the future, one must ascertain that the past data are relevant, i.e., that the same fundamental conditions of operation existing in the past will prevail at the time for which predictions are being made. In our Hi-Ace example, basic changes in the type of manufacturing equipment available might alter radically the relationship between the size of the production run and the unit direct labor time. One may still utilize past experience if such changes have taken place, but must then make adjustments to reflect the changes in conditions. Such adjustments usually are subjective—sometimes they are just "educated guesses"–and are based on judgment and experience. Even so, the use of past data provides a valuable point of departure for applying subjective adjustments.

If the past experience is to serve as a direct guide for the future, only that portion of past experience can be utilized that reflects similar operating conditions to those expected during the period for which predictions are being made. In our valve production illustration, for instance, only the experience of 1965 to 1969 was utilized. These years were chosen because the Hi-Ace Company in earlier years had substantially different manufacturing equipment, causing the earlier experience to be no longer relevant. All too often, inexperienced persons tend to utilize all past data, whether or not the data reflect current and anticipated conditions. Highly misleading results may follow from this practice.

Extrapolation beyond range of past data

In our Hi-Ace example, there were no contracts between 1965 and 1969 in which the production run was below 3,000 or above 11,500. Extreme caution would have to be exercised if one wanted to predict the unit direct labor time for a production run whose size falls considerably outside these limits, because the shape of the regression curve becomes more and more doubtful as the size of the production run departs from the limits of past experience.

We concluded from Figure 22.7 that the regression function for the Hi-Ace Company is linear. Properly, we should have stated that it appears linear within the range of past experience, since we have no assurance that the regression curve will be approximately linear beyond that range. Indeed, there are obvious reasons for expecting that the regression curve will not be linear as the size of the production run becomes smaller or larger. If the regression curve in Figure 22.9 were extrapolated to the right, for instance, the questionable result would be obtained that the mean unit direct labor time is zero for production runs of 63,238 valves. This uncertainty regarding the shape of the regression function beyond the range of past data is also found in many other cases.

Regression analysis and causality

Regression analysis utilizes any existing relation between the independent (X) and dependent (Y) variables, as described by the regression function, to enable one to make predictions about the dependent variable. A statistical relation exists between X and Y when the averages $\mu_{Y.X}$ for the conditional probability distributions of Y for given values of X are not all equal—that is, when the regression function is not a horizontal straight line (i.e., when $\beta \neq 0$).

If a statistical relation between X and Y does exist, it may be the result of a causal connection between the two variables, or it may simply be due to coincidence. If the relation is the result of a causal connection, it may be either that X and Y are linked in a causal relation, or that X and Y are simultaneously reacting to a third variable with which both are connected.

It is important to remember, therefore, that regression analysis reveals only statistical relations, and that statistical relations by themselves are not a proof of causal relations. Additional analytical work is necessary if one is to learn about the pattern of cause and effect operating in a given situation. In Chapter 26, we shall demonstrate the use of cross-classification for exploring the cause-and-effect relations between two or more variables.

Alternative regression models

Another important consideration in the use of regression analysis is the appropriateness of the regression model. Our discussion has been restricted to the case where all conditional probability distributions are normal and have the same standard deviation, and the regression function is linear. This model is not always appropriate, to be sure. In many cases, the regression function is not linear but curvilinear. Again, it is not infrequent that the standard deviations of the conditional probability distributions are not equal, but vary with the level of X.

While we have discussed only one type of regression model to avoid excessive detail, many other types of models have been developed. The selection of the appropriate model is an important, though often a difficult, problem. Relevant theory, such as that derived from managerial economics, and empirical analysis of sample data can be of great help in selecting the appropriate model.

QUESTIONS AND PROBLEMS

Note: *Where calculations are required in the following problems, consider that the relevant assumptions stated in the text are met.*

23.1. Contrast briefly the estimation of a conditional mean and the prediction of a next value of Y. Which of these involves greater uncertainties?

23.2. For each of the following cases, indicate whether a conditional mean is to be estimated or a specific event is to be predicted. Explain the reason for your answer.

a. What will sales be next year, given the expected level of gross national product for that year?

b. Is it more efficient to produce in lots of 1,000 or 2,000 items?

c. What is the tensile strength of this piece of steel, given its hardness?

d. How much do persons with an income of $5,000 per year tend to spend for food?

23.3. Explain why a prediction interval for a specific event is wider than a confidence interval for the corresponding conditional mean, with the same confidence coefficient used in both cases. Does this mean that one should be more interested in estimating conditional means than in predicting specific events? Discuss.

23.4. The Supreme Life Insurance Company selected a sample of 150 of its salesmen and gave each a psychological test designed to measure the person's selling ability. A regression analysis of the salesmen's test scores and sales in the preceding year was then made. The company wished to be able to estimate the mean sales to be expected for any test-score level within ±$20,000, with a 95 per cent confidence coefficient. The actual error margin, for that confidence level, turned out to be ±$40,000.

a. If the company had used 300 salesmen in its study, would you expect the confidence limits to have been narrower? Explain fully.

b. If cost considerations dictated that a sample of only 150 salesmen could be included in the study, would it have helped to reduce the confidence coefficient to obtain narrower error margins? Discuss.

c. In the absence of increasing the sample size or reducing the confidence coefficient, could the company have done anything else to reduce the width of the confidence interval for mean sales expected at a given test-score level? Discuss.

23.5. Why are statisticians frequently interested in the question, Is $\beta = 0$? Does the magnitude of β indicate how well predictions can be made? Discuss.

***23.6.** Refer to Problem 22.9. Some preliminary results obtained there were:

$$a = 323.05 \qquad b = .26505 \qquad s_{Y.X} = 4.6552$$

$$\bar{X} = 440.1 \qquad \Sigma X^2 - \frac{(\Sigma X)^2}{n} = 69{,}048.9$$

a. On the average, what are company sales when disposable personal income is $525 billion? Use an interval estimate, with a 95 per cent confidence coefficient.

b. Would the 95 per cent confidence interval for mean company sales, when disposable personal income is $600 billion, have the same width or a different width than the confidence interval in part **a**? Explain.

c. 1969 disposable personal income was expected to be $630 billion. What would have been the prediction of the company's 1969 sales? Use a prediction interval with a 95 per cent confidence coefficient. Is the prediction interval precise enough to be useful? Management wishes to have a prediction interval with a width of ±2.5 per cent, with a 95 per cent confidence coefficient.

d. What assumptions were made in predicting the company's 1969 sales? Would these assumptions be reasonable for making a prediction of the company's 1976 sales in 1969? Discuss.

e. The regression model discussed in the text involves various restrictions. Which of these is least likely to be met in the type of study made by the A.C. Brown Company?

(Continued)

f. Estimate β with an interval estimate; use a confidence coefficient of 95 per cent.

g. Does your confidence interval provide any indication of whether or not there exists a relationship between disposable personal income and company sales? Explain.

23.7. Refer to Problem 22.10. Some preliminary results obtained there were:

$$a = -264.85 \qquad b = .75481 \qquad s_{Y.X} = 30.412$$

$$\overline{X} = 2{,}481.7 \qquad \Sigma X^2 - \frac{(\Sigma X)^2}{n} = 240{,}083.3$$

a. On the average, how many new students enter in the fall when there are 2,500 applications by January 1? Use an interval estimate, with a 99 per cent confidence coefficient.

b. By January 1, 1971, 2,750 applications had been received. What would have been the prediction of the number of new students entering in the fall? Use a prediction interval with a 99 per cent confidence coefficient.

c. If the number of applications received by January 1, 1971 had been 2,500, would the width of the 99 per cent prediction interval differ from that in part **b**? Why?

d. Is the prediction interval in part **b** precise enough to be useful? The administration would be well satisfied with a prediction interval whose half-width does not exceed 5 per cent, with a 99 per cent confidence coefficient.

e. Would it be reasonable to use the regression analysis above, based on 1965–1970 experience, to make predictions for 1975? Discuss.

f. Estimate β with an interval estimate; use a confidence coefficient of 90 per cent.

g. Does your confidence interval provide any indication whether or not there is a relationship between the number of applications received by January 1 and the number of new students entering that fall? Explain.

***23.8.** Refer to Problem 22.11. Some preliminary results obtained there were:

$$a = -49.374 \qquad b = .35123 \qquad s_{Y.X} = 3.0189$$

a. Estimate the mean number of car sales when 300 inquiries are made during the preceding week, using an interval estimate with a 98 per cent confidence coefficient.

b. Explain precisely the meaning of your confidence interval.

c. During the week just ended, 420 inquiries were received. What would you predict sales to be next week? Use a prediction interval with a 99 per cent confidence coefficient. Is the prediction interval precise enough to be useful? Discuss.

d. What assumption is made when the regression analysis based on data for the past two years is used for making predictions of future sales?

e. On Friday of the week just ended, 92 inquiries were received. Can the regression analysis above be used to predict sales for Friday of next week? Discuss.

f. Estimate the slope of the regression line with an interval estimate; use a 94 per cent confidence coefficient.

g. Explain precisely the meaning of your confidence interval.

h. Does your confidence interval provide any indication of whether or not there is a relationship between the number of inquiries during a week and the number of cars sold during the following week? Explain.

23.9. Refer to Problem 22.12. Some preliminary results obtained there were:

$$a = 60.305 \qquad b = 31.502 \qquad s_{Y.X} = 11.584$$

a. Estimate the mean number of manhours expended in a meat department when department sales are \$4.6 thousand, using an interval estimate with a 95 per cent confidence coefficient.

b. Explain precisely the meaning of your confidence interval.

c. Predict the required manhours in a specific meat department for a given week when sales are \$5.8 thousand; use a prediction interval with a 97.5 per cent confidence coefficient. Is the prediction interval precise enough to be useful? Discuss.

d. The data used in the regression analysis were collected by the Zeus chain during the last week of October as a basis for setting up manhour standards for the following year. What assumptions are made by management in this utilization of the data?

e. Estimate the slope of the regression line with an interval estimate; use a 94 per cent confidence coefficient.

f. Explain precisely the meaning of your confidence interval.

g. Does your confidence interval provide any indication of whether or not there is a relationship between dollar sales of meat departments and manhours expended in the departments? Explain.

h. An efficiency expert has stated that each additional thousand dollars of meat department sales should require no more than 25 additional manhours in meat departments of the kind operated by the Zeus chain. Set up the appropriate decision rule to see if the meat departments in the Zeus chain meet this standard; assume a maximum risk of .01 of concluding that the standard is not met when it actually is met. What conclusion should be reached?

Chapter

24

ADDITIONAL TOPICS IN REGRESSION AND CORRELATION

24.1 CASES OF REGRESSION AND CORRELATION APPLICATIONS

We present here two cases to illustrate typical applications of regression analysis to business and economic problems.

Use of regression analysis to improve quality control

The first case illustrates a frequent use of regression analysis, namely, to obtain indirectly data that cannot economically be obtained directly. The Nestlé's Company, for example, uses regression techniques in this way to improve quality control over a product (Ref. 24.1). Many of the quality control tests that this company performs periodically on its products are made during the operations of the manufacturing processes so that remedial action can be taken promptly when trouble develops.

One such test is the determination of the fat content of material. This test had been performed by a standard extraction procedure that required from 4 to 5 hours to run. In many instances, this lapse of time before the availability of test results led to excessive delays before remedial action could be taken. Therefore, it was desired that a new test be developed to provide for a more rapid determination of fat content.

Previous experience had indicated that a relation might be found between the fat content of the material and the refractive index of a solvent fat mixture taken from the material. Since a refractive index reading could be obtained in 5 to 7 minutes, it was felt that this relation was worth investigating further.

Samples of material were collected as part of the regular control procedure, and the per cent of fat in each sample was determined by the conventional, time-consuming, extraction method. An additional test on each sample of material was made to determine the refractive index of a solvent fat mixture derived from the sample. Eighty-four samples of material were measured. The fat content of these samples ranged from less than 1 per cent to almost 15 per cent.

The 84 observations were then plotted as a scatter diagram. The refractive index was treated as the independent variable, since it was to be used for predicting the fat content. This, incidentally, illustrates why the terms *independent variable* and *dependent variable* should not be interpreted literally. The refractive index is the independent variable here, even though the refractive index reading actually depends upon the fat content.

From the scatter diagram, it appeared that the relation between the fat content as determined by the extraction process and the refractive index is linear. A straight-line regression equation was estimated by the method of least squares, and it turned out to be: $\overline{Y}_X = 10.575 - .10315X$. The estimate of the conditional standard deviation was also computed; it was $s_{Y.X} = .43$ per cent fat content.

Since the problem was to determine the fat content of a *particular* batch of material, a prediction interval for the specific event was needed. It was assumed that the large sample prediction interval (23.10) was appropriate. A confidence coefficient of 95.4 per cent was desired; this meant that $z = 2$. To illustrate the construction of the prediction interval, suppose that the coded refractive index were 50. Using the previous sample data, it would be concluded with a confidence coefficient of 95.4 per cent that the fat content reading that would have been obtained for the sample by the extraction method would be somewhere within the interval:

$$\overline{Y}_{50} - 2s_{Y.X} \leq Y_{\text{next}} \leq \overline{Y}_{50} + 2s_{Y.X}$$

$$[10.575 - (.10315)(50)] - 2(.43) \leq Y_{\text{next}} \leq [10.575 - (.10315)(50)] + 2(.43)$$

$$4.6 \text{ per cent} \leq Y_{\text{next}} \leq 6.3 \text{ per cent}$$

A degree of approximation probably exists in this statement because the basic assumptions underlying this prediction interval may not be met completely. Nevertheless, it was considered useful to know that the reading of fat content of the sample with the extraction method could be estimated from the refractive index within about 1 per cent point. Such an error range, it was felt, was satisfactory for purposes of a continuing control over the quality of the material. The fact that this refractive test takes only a few minutes, as compared to a number of hours for the extraction method, enables major shifts in quality to be discovered more quickly and remedial action to be undertaken more promptly.

Reduction in staffs of Army civilian personnel offices [1]

The second case describes an instance in which only a partial use of regression analysis was of utmost benefit in handling a difficult management problem. A number of years ago the Department of the Army established a goal of no more than one civilian personnel office employee for each 88 civilian employees in Army establishments within the continental United States. There were some 300 establishments in this category. They included arsenals, depots, military camps, ports of embarkation, hospitals, and other installations. These establishments were divided into groups that were homogeneous with respect to the pattern of functions performed by the civilian personnel offices. One of these groups consisted of 15 manufacturing arsenals. It is with this group that we will be concerned in our present example.

An index of the work load of each establishment's civilian personnel office was developed. The work load index for each office reflected the number of personnel actions that occurred (accessions, changes, and separations), number of positions analyzed and evaluated, number of hours of off-the-job training sessions, and number of civilian employees in the establishment. The index was calculated in such a manner that the larger the work load of an office, the greater the index would be. Data on work load and number of employees in civilian personnel offices were collected for a three-month period for the 15 manufacturing arsenals. These data were plotted as a scatter diagram, as shown in Figure 24.1. The regression curve appears to be linear; therefore, a straight-line regression equation was calculated by the method of least squares. This line, whose equation is $\overline{Y}_X = 13.95 + .221X$, also is plotted in Figure 24.1.

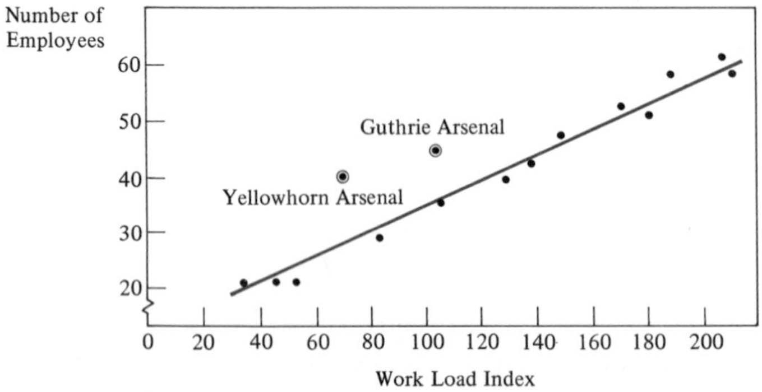

Figure 24.1. Scatter diagram and regression line—Department of the Army civilian personnel offices in manufacturing arsenals

[1] Background information for this case was kindly furnished by the Office of the Director of Civilian Personnel, Department of the Army. All data, including numbers and names of arsenals, are disguised.

Figure 24.1 indicates that the number of employees in most of the 15 civilian personnel offices is close to the respective "yardstick" or regression value. Two offices, on the basis of their respective work loads, do appear to have substantially more employees than is indicated by the flexible "yardstick" developed from the group experience. One of these is the office of the Yellowhorn Arsenal; the other is the office of the Guthrie Arsenal.

The proper action that followed this analysis was a management appraisal of those civilian personnel offices whose number of employees appeared excessive. When this was done, it was found that the Yellowhorn Arsenal, located in an area of relative isolation from civilian communities, had to spend an unusually large amount of time in direct labor recruitment outside the local area and consequently required extra civilian personnel office employees. In the case of the Guthrie Arsenal, however, it was determined that operating efficiency had lagged and could be improved, and that some cuts in personnel could be made there with little detriment to operating efficiency.

24.2 DERIVATION OF LEAST SQUARES ESTIMATORS (Calculus Needed)

The least squares method of obtaining estimators of the parameters α and β in the regression equation (22.2) calls for consideration of the deviations:

$$Y - \mu_{Y.X} = Y - \alpha - \beta X$$

Specifically, we need to consider the sum of the squared deviations for the sample of n observations, to be denoted by Q:

$$Q = \Sigma(Y - \alpha - \beta X)^2 \tag{24.1}$$

Given the pairs of X and Y values in the sample, Q may be viewed as a function of α and β. The method of least squares requires that we find those values of α and β, as functions of the X's and Y's, which minimize Q. We proceed by finding the partial derivatives of Q with respect to α and β:

$$\begin{aligned} \frac{\partial Q}{\partial \alpha} &= \Sigma \frac{\partial}{\partial \alpha}(Y - \alpha - \beta X)^2 = \Sigma[-2(Y - \alpha - \beta X)] \\ \frac{\partial Q}{\partial \beta} &= \Sigma \frac{\partial}{\partial \beta}(Y - \alpha - \beta X)^2 = \Sigma[-2X(Y - \alpha - \beta X)] \end{aligned} \tag{24.2}$$

We then set these partial derivatives equal to 0, showing the specific values of α and β which minimize Q as a and b:

$$\Sigma[-2(Y - a - bX)] = 0 \tag{24.3a}$$

$$\Sigma[-2X(Y - a - bX)] = 0 \tag{24.3b}$$

Equation (24.3a) can be rewritten as follows:

$$-2[\Sigma Y - na - b\Sigma X] = 0$$

or as:

$$\Sigma Y = na + b\Sigma X \tag{24.4a}$$

Similarly, we can rewrite (24.3b) as follows:

$$-2[\Sigma XY - a\Sigma X - b\Sigma X^2] = 0$$

or as:

$$\Sigma XY = a\Sigma X + b\Sigma X^2 \tag{24.4b}$$

Equations (24.4a) and (24.4b) are the *normal equations,* given earlier in (22.3). Solving these two equations for a and b, we obtain the least squares estimators of (22.3a) and (22.3c):

$$b = \frac{\Sigma XY - \dfrac{\Sigma X \Sigma Y}{n}}{\Sigma X^2 - \dfrac{(\Sigma X)^2}{n}} \tag{24.5}$$

$$a = \frac{1}{n}[\Sigma Y - b\Sigma X]$$

24.3
MULTIPLE REGRESSION ANALYSIS

The precision of a prediction can usually be improved by considering more than one variable as the predictor. In our earlier valve production case, for instance, the Hi-Ace Company might have used size of production run *and* length of time since the previous production run as the independent variables to predict the unit direct labor time for the next contract. When more than one predicting variable is used, the problem is one of *multiple regression* analysis. The basic concepts still remain the same; we simply use two or more variables in order to predict Y.

Multiple regression analysis is a logical and, indeed, a most useful extension of simple regression analysis. In the field of marketing, for instance, sales for a given territory are often predicted on the basis of a number of factors; such factors as population, income, and volume of retail sales in the territory are frequently used. In investment studies, as another example, one organization employs multiple regression analysis in order to make predictions of average annual stock market prices; such factors as last year's average price and company earnings are used as predicting variables.

Model

We consider here the case of the Andover Corporation, which wants to predict territory sales on the basis of the population in the territory and budgeted advertising expenditures for the territory. Let X_1 denote the population size and X_2 the amount of advertising expenditure. The multiple regression model that we now consider has the following features:

(24.6) 1. For given X_1 and X_2, the conditional distribution of sales (Y) is normal.
2. All conditional distributions of sales have the same standard deviation $\sigma_{Y.X_1X_2}$.
3. The conditional mean $\mu_{Y.X_1X_2}$ is given by:

$$\mu_{Y.X_1X_2} = \alpha + \beta_1 X_1 + \beta_2 X_2$$

where α, β_1, and β_2 are the parameters of the linear multiple regression equation.

Estimation of regression parameters

For this model, the method of least squares again provides "best" estimators of the regression parameters. For our example, there will be three normal equations. These are:

$$\begin{aligned} \Sigma Y &= na + b_1\Sigma X_1 + b_2\Sigma X_2 \\ \Sigma X_1 Y &= a\Sigma X_1 + b_1\Sigma X_1^2 + b_2\Sigma X_1 X_2 \\ \Sigma X_2 Y &= a\Sigma X_2 + b_1\Sigma X_1 X_2 + b_2\Sigma X_2^2 \end{aligned} \tag{24.7}$$

Here, a, b_1, and b_2 are the point estimators of α, β_1, and β_2, respectively. These three normal equations must be solved simultaneously for the values of the three estimators.

Example

Table 24.1 contains data on sales, population, and advertising expenditure in six sales territories of the Andover Corporation for a recent period. All necessary computations are carried out in Table 24.1, leading to the following three normal equations:

$$\begin{aligned} &(1) \qquad 180 = 6a + 24b_1 + 30b_2 \\ &(2) \qquad 835.2 = 24a + 131.5b_1 + 154.3b_2 \\ &(3) \qquad 1{,}016.5 = 30a + 154.3b_1 + 185.5b_2 \end{aligned}$$

Multiplying equation (1) by 4 leads to:

$$(4) \qquad 720 = 24a + 96b_1 + 120b_2$$

Subtracting (4) from (2) yields:

$$(5) \qquad 115.2 = 35.5b_1 + 34.3b_2$$

Multiplying equation (1) by 5 leads to:

$$(6) \qquad 900 = 30a + 120b_1 + 150b_2$$

Table 24.1 Computations for Linear Multiple Regression Analysis, Andover Corporation

Territory	*Sales (Million \$)* Y	*Population (Millions)* X_1	*Advertising Expenditure (Ten Thousand \$)* X_2	X_1Y	X_2Y	X_1^2	X_2^2	X_1X_2
1	34	5.0	5.0	170.0	170.0	25.00	25.00	25.0
2	29	4.2	4.5	121.8	130.5	17.64	20.25	18.9
3	43	8.5	10.0	365.5	430.0	72.25	100.00	85.0
4	12	1.4	2.5	16.8	30.0	1.96	6.25	3.5
5	35	3.6	5.0	126.0	175.0	12.96	25.00	18.0
6	27	1.3	3.0	35.1	81.0	1.69	9.00	3.9
Total	180	24.0	30.0	835.2	1,016.5	131.50	185.50	154.3

Subtracting (6) from (3) yields:

$$(7) \qquad 116.5 = 34.3b_1 + 35.5b_2$$

When we multiply (5) by $35.5/34.3 = 1.035$, we obtain:

$$(8) \qquad 119.230 = 36.742b_1 + 35.5b_2$$

Subtracting (7) from (8) and solving for b_1, we find:

$$b_1 = 1.12$$

We can now solve for b_2 in, say, (8), obtaining:

$$b_2 = 2.20$$

Finally, we can substitute in, say, (1) to obtain:

$$a = 14.52$$

Hence, the estimated multiple regression equation is:

$$\bar{Y}_{X_1X_2} = 14.52 + 1.12X_1 + 2.20X_2$$

If, for example, the population in a territory is four million and the budgeted advertising expenditure is \$50,000, then:

$$\bar{Y}_{X_1X_2} = 14.52 + 1.12(4) + 2.20(5) = 30$$

Consequently, our point estimate of the mean sales volume of a territory with a population of four million and advertising expenditure of \$50,000 is \$30 million.

Estimation of conditional standard deviation

The conditional standard deviation $\sigma_{Y.X_1X_2}$ in a multiple regression model with two independent variables is estimated in a fashion analogous to that for simple regression:

(24.8) $$s_{Y.X_1X_2} = \sqrt{\frac{\Sigma(Y - \bar{Y}_{X_1X_2})^2}{n - 3}}$$

Note that the denominator is $n - 3$, since three parameters (α, β_1, β_2) of the regression equation need to be estimated.

Table 24.2 contains the needed data for calculating $s_{Y.X_1X_2}$ for the Andover Corporation example. We obtain:

$$s_{Y.X_1X_2} = \sqrt{\frac{158.734}{3}} = \sqrt{52.911} = \$7.27 \text{ million}$$

Table 24.2 Additional Computations, Andover Corporation

Territory	*Sales (Million \$)* Y	*Population (Millions)* X_1	*Advertising (Ten Thousand \$)* X_2	$\bar{Y}_{X_1X_2}$	$(Y - \bar{Y}_{X_1X_2})$	$(Y - \bar{Y}_{X_1X_2})^2$	Y^2
1	34	5.0	5.0	31.120	2.880	8.294	1,156
2	29	4.2	4.5	29.124	−.124	.015	841
3	43	8.5	10.0	46.040	−3.040	9.242	1,849
4	12	1.4	2.5	21.588	−9.588	91.930	144
5	35	3.6	5.0	29.552	5.448	29.681	1,225
6	27	1.3	3.0	22.576	4.424	19.572	729
Total	180	24.0	30.0	180.0	0.0	158.734	5,944

$$\bar{Y}_{X_1X_2} = 14.52 + 1.12X_1 + 2.20X_2$$

Multiple correlation and determination coefficients

The *coefficient of multiple determination,* denoted by R^2, is a descriptive measure of the degree of relationship between the dependent variable and all the independent variables in the regression model. It is defined as follows when there are two independent variables in the multiple regression model:

(24.9) $$R^2 = 1 - \left(\frac{n - 3}{n - 1}\right)\frac{s^2_{Y.X_1X_2}}{s^2_Y}$$

Like the coefficient of determination for simple regression, it essentially measures how much less is the variability of the Y's around the regression function, relative to the variability of the Y's when X_1 and X_2 are not considered. To put this more loosely, R^2 measures how much less uncertainty there is in making predictions of Y when X_1 and X_2 are considered than when they are not considered. The bounds on R^2, like those on r^2, are:

(24.10) $$0 \leq R^2 \leq 1$$

The *coefficient of multiple correlation* is the positive square root of the coefficient of multiple determination:

$$R = \sqrt{R^2} \tag{24.11}$$

To calculate R and R^2 for the Andover Corporation example, we need to obtain s_Y^2 first, making use of the calculations in Table 24.2:

$$s_Y^2 = \frac{1}{n-1}\left[\Sigma Y^2 - \frac{(\Sigma Y)^2}{n}\right] = \frac{1}{5}\left[5{,}944 - \frac{(180)^2}{6}\right] = 108.8$$

We then find:

$$R^2 = 1 - \left(\frac{3}{5}\right)\frac{52.911}{108.8} = .708$$

Thus, territory sales variability around the regression function utilizing X_1 and X_2 is about 71 per cent less than territory sales variability when X_1 and X_2 are not considered.

The coefficient of multiple correlation is:

$$R = \sqrt{.708} = .84$$

Other inferences

One can also obtain interval estimates of the conditional mean or prediction intervals for a specific event with multiple regression analysis, but the computations are much more cumbersome than for a simple regression model. The development of electronic computers makes it possible now to utilize elaborate multiple regression models that could not have been employed earlier because of the complexity of the calculations.

24.4
CURVILINEAR REGRESSION ANALYSIS

In many applications, a linear regression model may not be appropriate because the regression function is really curvilinear. For instance, if the Hi-Ace Company had produced valves in lot sizes that extended over a wider range, a curvilinear regression model probably would have been more appropriate than the linear regression model that was utilized. A linear regression function implies that for sufficiently large contracts the average unit direct labor time could be reduced to zero—clearly an unreasonable condition. Generally, a point is reached in production runs beyond which only small improvements in efficiency are possible.

Instead of the linear regression function, $\mu_{Y.X} = \alpha + \beta X$, where Y is the direct labor time per valve and X the contract size, the Hi-Ace Company might have used a second-degree polynomial regression function:

$$\mu_{Y.X} = \alpha + \beta_1 X + \beta_2 X^2 \tag{24.12}$$

Note that the lot size appears here twice, once in squared form. This is one means of recognizing diminishing returns in production efficiency with larger contract sizes.

A second-degree polynomial regression function involves three parameters, α (the value of $\mu_{Y.X}$ when $X = 0$), β_1 (the linear effect coefficient), and β_2 (the curvature effect coefficient). The method of least squares again can be employed to obtain point estimators for the parameters of the regression equation. Indeed, note that the regression equation (24.12) is of the same form as that of the linear multiple regression equation (24.6). There, the first independent variable X_1 corresponds to X, the contract size, and the second independent variable X_2 corresponds to X^2, the contract size squared. Hence, the normal equations (24.7) are still applicable, with X_1 replaced by X and X_2 replaced by X^2:

$$\begin{aligned} \Sigma Y &= na + b_1\Sigma X + b_2\Sigma X^2 \\ \Sigma XY &= a\Sigma X + b_1\Sigma X^2 + b_2\Sigma X^3 \\ \Sigma X^2Y &= a\Sigma X^2 + b_1\Sigma X^3 + b_2\Sigma X^4 \end{aligned} \tag{24.13}$$

These three simultaneous equations have to be solved for a, b_1, and b_2 in the same way as in the multiple regression case.

Example

Table 24.3 contains the needed calculations for estimating a second-degree polynomial regression function for the Hi-Ace case. Note that contract size is expressed in units of 1,000 valves. We obtain the following normal equations:

Table 24.3 Calculations for Second-Degree Polynomial Regression, Hi-Ace Company

Contract Date	*Unit Direct Labor Time* Y	*Contract Size (Thousands)* X	XY	X^2	X^2Y	X^3	X^4
April 1965	145	5.0	725.0	25.00	3,625.00	125.00	625.00
August 1965	145	4.8	696.0	23.04	3,340.80	110.59	530.84
December 1965	135	9.0	1,215.0	81.00	10,935.00	729.00	6,561.00
April 1966	146	3.0	438.0	9.00	1,314.00	27.00	81.00
December 1966	141	6.0	846.0	36.00	5,076.00	216.00	1,296.00
March 1967	149	3.0	447.0	9.00	1,341.00	27.00	81.00
July 1967	131	9.3	1,218.3	86.49	11,330.19	804.36	7,480.52
August 1967	126	11.5	1,449.0	132.25	16,663.50	1,520.88	17,490.06
February 1968	134	8.0	1,072.0	64.00	8,576.00	512.00	4,096.00
June 1968	137	8.0	1,096.0	64.00	8,768.00	512.00	4,096.00
December 1968	128	11.5	1,472.0	132.25	16,928.00	1,520.88	17,490.06
March 1969	144	4.0	576.0	16.00	2,304.00	64.00	256.00
Total	1,661	83.1	11,250.3	678.03	90,201.49	6,168.71	60,083.48

$$1{,}661 = 12a + 83.1b_1 + 678.03b_2$$
$$11{,}250.3 = 83.1a + 678.03b_1 + 6{,}168.71b_2$$
$$90{,}201.49 = 678.03a + 6{,}168.71b_1 + 60{,}083.48b_2$$

Solving these three equations simultaneously yields the following estimates:

$$a = 153.510$$
$$b_1 = -1.8131$$
$$b_2 = -.04491$$

Hence, our estimated regression equation is:

$$\bar{Y}_X = 153.510 - 1.8131X - .04491X^2$$

Thus, for a production run of size 8,000 ($X = 8$), for instance, we would estimate that the mean direct labor time per valve is:

$$\bar{Y}_X = 153.510 - 1.8131(8) - .04491(8)^2 = 136.1 \text{ minutes}$$

Cited reference

24.1 Donohue, Francis J. X., "Nestlé's Chocolate Company, Inc.," in *Quality Control in Central New York Industry.* Syracuse: Syracuse Section of American Society for Quality Control, 1952, pp. 132–135.

QUESTIONS AND PROBLEMS

24.1. Contrast briefly each of the following:

a. Simple and multiple regression analysis

b. Linear and curvilinear regression analysis

c. Coefficients of simple and multiple determination

24.2. (Calculus needed) Suppose the regression line goes through the origin; then $\alpha = 0$ and the simple linear regression function is:

$$\mu_{Y.X} = \beta X$$

Derive the estimator of β by the method of least squares.

24.3. (Calculus needed) Using the method of least squares, derive the normal equations (24.7) for estimating the parameters of the multiple linear regression function:

$$\mu_{Y.X_1X_2} = \alpha + \beta_1 X_1 + \beta_2 X_2$$

***24.4.** Refer to Problem 22.9. Suppose that the A.C. Brown Company also wished to utilize data on industry sales for predicting company sales. The relevant data are:

Year	*Industry Sales (Millions of Dollars)*	*Year*	*Industry Sales (Millions of Dollars)*
1959	4.9	1964	5.8
1960	5.4	1965	6.0
1961	5.6	1966	6.1
1962	5.7	1967	6.1
1963	5.8	1968	6.3

a. Estimate the linear multiple regression equation, using the method of least squares with disposable personal income and industry sales as the independent variables.
b. What relationship is described by the regression equation?
c. On the average, what are company sales when disposable personal income for the year is $600 billion, and industry sales are $6.5 million? Use a point estimate.
d. Estimate the conditional standard deviation of the distributions of company sales. In what units is the standard deviation expressed?
e. Calculate the coefficient of multiple determination. What is its meaning here?
f. Calculate the coefficient of multiple correlation.

24.5. The Niles Company placed eight college graduates in its one-year management training program. At the beginning, each trainee was given two different aptitude tests. At the end of the training program, each trainee was rated by a committee of three executives. The relevant data are:

Trainee	*Test A Score*	*Test B Score*	*Final Rating*
Smith	569	78	84
Wilkins	490	83	72
Sherman	719	91	95
Charles	660	85	90
Monroe	623	82	88
Jones	778	94	98
Adams	594	75	78
Green	588	73	75

a. Estimate the linear multiple regression equation, using the method of least squares.
b. What relationship is described by the regression equation?
c. On the average, what is the mean rating of trainees who receive scores of 600 and 80 on aptitude tests A and B, respectively? Use a point estimate.
d. Estimate the conditional standard deviation of the distributions of final ratings. Is it relatively small or large?
e. Calculate the coefficient of multiple determination. What is its meaning here?
f. Calculate the coefficient of multiple correlation.

***24.6.** Refer to Problem 22.9. Suppose that economic and business analysis suggests that the relationship between disposable personal income and company sales should be a second-degree polynomial one.
a. Estimate the second-degree polynomial regression function, using the method of least squares.
b. On the average, what are company sales when disposable personal income is $600 billion for the year? Use a point estimate.

24.7. Refer to Problem 22.10. Suppose that an analyst suggested that a second-degree polynomial function should be used for the regression of number of entering students on number of applications received by January 1.
a. Estimate the second-degree polynomial regression function, using the method of least squares.
b. On the average, what is the number of entering students when 2,600 applications have been received by January 1? Use a point estimate.

Unit

VIII

DATA ANALYSIS AND PRESENTATION

Chapter

25

RATIOS

In previous chapters, we discussed the use of regression analysis for describing and examining statistical relationships between quantitative variables. In this chapter, we take up the use of ratio analysis to examine the relations between quantitative variables. Ratio analysis has greater limitations than regression analysis, but is extremely simple and hence widely used.

In Chapter 26, we consider the analysis of relationships, by means of cross-classification, between variables which are qualitative or, though quantitative, are treated qualitatively for ease of analysis.

Finally, in Chapter 27, we take up tabular and graphic methods of presenting statistical data.

25.1 RATIOS AS AN AID TO ANALYSIS

Ratios, in all their various forms, are the most widely used statistical measure in the analysis of business and economic data. Examples of ratios are income per capita, gross profit as a per cent of sales, number of accidents per thousand manhours, ratio of current assets to current liabilities, this year's sales as a per cent of last year's sales.

In each instance, the statistical ratio expresses the magnitude of the variable in the numerator in relation to a given number of units of the variable in the denominator. For instance, consider a governmental agency which had 37,422 requests for information during a month and was able to send replies within a week for 28,952 of these requests. Therefore, the number of replies dispatched within a week per hundred requests for information was $(28{,}952/37{,}422) \cdot 100 = 77.4$. One other illustration: A company had 173 accidents during the month of March, when 74,564 manhours were worked. The number of accidents per thousand manhours consequently was $(173/74{,}564) \cdot 1{,}000 = 2.3$.

Note that in each of these cases the fraction represents the magnitude of the variable in the numerator per one unit of the variable in the denominator. Thus, in the first example the fraction 28,952/37,422 represents the number of replies per one request for information; this quantity is then multiplied by 100 to calculate the number of replies per hundred requests. If the reader has difficulty in setting up the ratio at a glance, it may help to study the formal proportion involved:

$$28{,}952:37{,}422 = X:100$$

This proportion is read as follows: 28,952 is to 37,422 as X is to 100. The letter X represents the numerator of the desired ratio, and 100 (requests received) is the specified denominator of the ratio. From this proportion, we obtain:

$$\frac{28{,}952}{37{,}422} = \frac{X}{100}$$

$$X = \frac{28{,}952}{37{,}422} \cdot 100 = 77.4$$

Functional relationship appropriate for ratio analysis

A ratio is strictly appropriate for describing the relationship between two variables only when this relationship is a straight line through the origin. To show the type of error that can arise in overlooking this point, consider a hypothetical analyst who intends to develop a standard for controlling warehousing costs in four distribution points set up by a manufacturing firm. As part of his analysis, he obtains the following data on work units performed and manhours expended at the four warehouses for a representative period:

Warehouse	*No. of Work Units Performed*	*No. of Manhours Expended*
A	150	525
B	400	900
C	270	705
D	350	825

The analyst considers warehouse B to be operating efficiently, requiring for each work unit $(900/400) \cdot 1 = 2.25$ manhours. He therefore reasons that the standard should be:

$$\text{Manhours} = 2.25 \cdot \text{Work units}$$

This standard indicates that warehouse A should have expended only $2.25 \cdot 150 = 337.5$ manhours; warehouse C, 607.5 manhours; and warehouse D, 787.5 manhours.

Note that the use of 2.25 manhours per work unit as standard implies that the functional relationship between work load and number of required manhours is:

$$Y = 2.25X$$

where Y is the standard number of manhours and X is the number of work units performed. This is a straight line through the origin, as shown by the solid line in Figure 25.1. This line through the origin simply states that each work unit should require 2.25 manhours, irrespective of the level of operations.

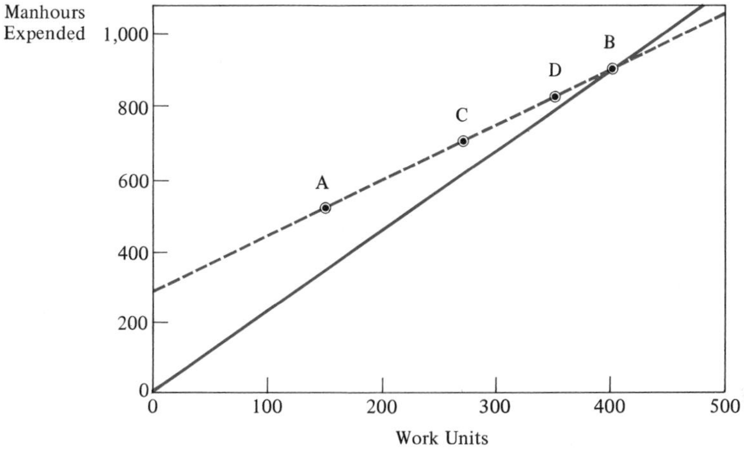

Figure 25.1. Assumed and actual relationship between manhours and work units, warehouse example

By this standard, the analyst concluded that all other warehouses were being operated inefficiently. Note from Figure 25.1 that the actual number of manhours expended in warehouses A, C, and D were well in excess of their respective standards. Then it was pointed out to the analyst that all warehouses were actually operating at the same level of efficiency, but that there is a certain amount of manhour expenditure in each warehouse that is fixed, regardless of the work load. The functional form of the actual relationship, shown by the dotted line in Figure 25.1, is:

$$Y = 300 + 1.5X$$

where Y and X have the same meaning as before. According to this relationship, the manhour requirements in each warehouse begin from a fixed level of 300; then each work unit adds 1.5 manhours to the total requirement.

If the analyst had calculated the ratio of manhours expended per work unit for warehouses A, C, and D, he would have found these ratios to be greater than 2.25 manhours per work unit. Larger ratios for these warehouses resulted because the overhead component is spread over a smaller work load than that for warehouse B. Thus, the ratio of 2.25 manhours per work unit describes the relationship between total required manhours and work load *only* at the level of 400 work units. The ratio between these two variables will not be the same at other work-load levels, due to the fixed component in manhour requirements. This means that the ratio of total required manhours to work load for any particular work-load level cannot be used as a standard for other work-load levels. In general:

(25.1) When ratios are used as standards for all magnitudes of the variable X in the denominator of the ratio, the assumption is that the relationship between the variable Y in the numerator of the ratio and the variable X in the denominator is a straight line through the origin, of the form: $Y = bX$, where b is the specified standard.

If the actual relationship between the two variables does not go through the origin (because of the presence of a fixed component, for instance) and/or if it is not linear (because of diminishing returns, for instance), then any one particular ratio cannot be used to describe the relationship between the two variables at all levels of the variable in the denominator. Instead, the appropriate functional relationship must be used.

25.2 TYPICAL USES OF RATIOS IN ADMINISTRATION AND ECONOMIC ANALYSIS

The use of ratios in business and public administration and in economic analysis is so widespread that the few illustrative examples to be cited here constitute only a small sampling of the whole field. Nevertheless, these examples should provide some understanding of the way in which ratios can be of aid in administration and analysis.

Use of ratios in study of interrelationships between several variables

Components of rate of return on investment. A series of interrelated ratios can be used to study corresponding interrelationships between variables. This helps management to keep various aspects of an operation in balance and to locate trouble spots. A good example of this use of ratios is found in analysis of rate of return on investment, a measure which has been used increasingly by management to evaluate a business operation as a single system. In evaluating a business operation, the net operating profit plays a key role. Consider, for example, the R. L. Smith Company, a manufacturer of industrial machinery, which earned the following net operating profits from 1969 to 1971:

Year	*Net Profits From Operations*
1969	\$47,932
1970	52,841
1971	61,903

Clearly, net profits from operations increased from 1969 to 1971. However, this does not necessarily mean that the effectiveness with which company operations have been conducted has similarly improved. The effectiveness of operations depends upon the skill with which the capital and labor at the company's disposal have been employed. One method of measuring the effectiveness of operations relates the net operating profit to the total capital invested. The total investments available to the R. L. Smith Company to carry on its operations were:

Year	*Total Investment*
1969	\$665,722
1970	775,812
1971	982,587

Note that the total investment also increased from 1969 to 1971, so that it would be reasonable to expect on this account alone that total operating profits should have increased. By relating net operating profits to total investment through the ratio "net operating profit per \$100 of investment" —usually called *rate of return on investment*—we find that the rate of return in 1969 was $(47{,}932/665{,}722) \cdot 100 = 7.20$ per cent. The rates of return for the other years are calculated in a similar manner; they are:

Year	*Rate of Return on Investment* (%)
1969	7.20
1970	6.81
1971	6.30

These ratios reveal that the effectiveness of operations, as measured by the relation between net operating profit and investment available for earning this profit, has declined during the period. To study the reasons for this decline, changes in company sales, among other factors, should be considered. Company sales from 1969 to 1971 were:

Year	*Company Sales*
1969	\$ 998,583
1970	1,182,244
1971	1,469,880

It is apparent that sales increased substantially during the years 1969 to 1971. This information is not very meaningful by itself; rather, sales must be related to net operating profits and investments, so that the interrelationships between these factors can be studied. Two ratios that perform this task are: (1) net operating profit per $100 of sales, usually called *net operating profit as a per cent of sales;* (2) number of sales dollars generated by one dollar of investment, sometimes called the ***turnover rate.*** In 1969, for instance, the net operating profit as a per cent of sales was $(47{,}932/998{,}583) \cdot 100 = 4.80$ per cent, and the turnover rate was $(998{,}583/665{,}722) \cdot 1 = 1.50$. These ratios for the three years are:

Year	*Net Operating Profit as a Per Cent of Sales*	*Turnover Rate*
1969	4.80	1.50
1970	4.47	1.52
1971	4.21	1.50

Note that the number of dollars of sales generated by each investment dollar remained about the same during the period, but that the proportion of each sales dollar constituting net operating profit declined. This information has special significance in view of the following relationship between the three ratios studied:

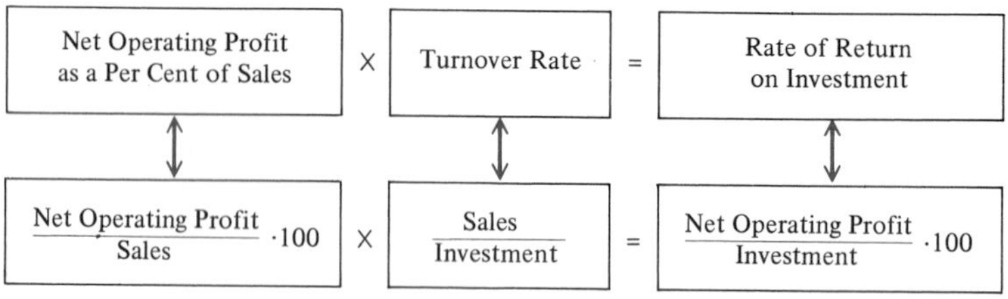

Therefore, since the turnover rate has remained about constant, the decline in the rate of return on investment is accounted for by the decrease in the proportion of net operating profit earned on each sales dollar.

Note how the use of ratios has made possible study of changes in the relationships between sales, profits, and investments—changes that would not be readily apparent otherwise. The analysis shown here is not complete, of course. Studies of competing companies would have to be made to see, for instance, whether their net operating profits per sales dollar also decreased during this period. Further, a thorough tracing of costs through the company's accounting records would have to be made to find those areas where cost ratios have gotten out of line either on the basis of company experience in previous years, or on the basis of the experience of other companies. The reasons for these departures also would have to be studied.

Per cent distributions. Another use of interrelated ratios to keep operations in balance and to locate causes of trouble involves per cent distributions. One of the main uses of per cent distributions in business is in the analysis of financial data, and we shall now take up an example from this area.

Table 25.1 shows the comparative profit and loss statements of a certain owner-managed florist shop for the fiscal years 1972 and 1971. Net profit

Table 25.1 Comparative Profit and Loss Statements, Main Street Florist Shop, Fiscal Years 1972 and 1971, and Standard Per Cent Distribution

	Thousand Dollars		*Per Cent of Sales*		*Standard Distribution*
	1972	*1971*	*1972*	*1971*	
Net sales	66.00	57.30	100.0	100.0	100.0
Cost of goods sold	35.24	30.58	53.4	53.4	53.2
Gross margin	30.76	26.72	46.6	46.6	46.8
Expenses					
Owner's compensation	6.73	6.76	10.2	11.8	12.2
Employees' wages	8.71	6.88	13.2	12.0	11.5
Rental expense	4.29	3.89	6.5	6.8	6.7
Advertising	.73	.63	1.1	1.1	1.5
Bad-debt losses	.60	.40	.9	.7	.1
Supplies	1.51	.97	2.3	1.7	1.7
Delivery expense	2.64	1.78	4.0	3.1	2.8
All other	4.36	3.78	6.6	6.6	6.6
Total expenses	29.57	25.09	44.8	43.8	43.1
Net profit before income taxes	1.19	1.63	1.8	2.8	3.7

before income taxes declined during these two years, despite an increase in sales from $57.30 thousand in 1971 to $66.00 thousand in 1972. A more detailed look at the dollar columns shows that gross margin increased in line with sales and that expenses also increased. It is not too clear from the dollar columns whether profits declined because the gross margin increase was not great enough or because the increase in expenses was out of line.

Ratio analysis will help find the answer. A relevant relation to be studied is the distribution of each sales dollar—that is, the per cent distribution of sales. These per cent distributions are shown to the right of the dollar columns in Table 25.1. For example, costs of goods sold accounted for $(35.24/66.00) \cdot 100 = 53.4$ per cent of each sales dollar in 1972. The other percentages for the fiscal year 1972 are calculated in the same manner, by expressing each item as a per cent of $66.00 thousand. The percentages for fiscal year 1971 are calculated by expressing each item as a per cent of $57.30 thousand, the net sales in 1971.

Note how revealing the per cent distributions are. While the relative gross margin remained the same, expenses took a substantially larger share of each sales dollar, especially supplies and delivery expense. The net effect of the changes in the distribution of each sales dollar from 1971 to 1972 was that only 1.8 cents was left for profits out of each sales dollar in 1972 as compared with 2.8 cents in 1971.

Often per cent distributions of company sales are compared with a "standard" distribution that may be based on industry data or on data obtained from a sample of comparable firms. This comparison reveals places where company experience is out of line with the standard. Such comparisons must be used cautiously, since average experience in an industry or group of firms may not be a relevant standard for any one company, but they can point out areas where investigation may be warranted.

A standard distribution for the florist shop is shown in the right-most column of Table 25.1. This distribution was developed by Dun and Bradstreet, Inc., from a sample of over 200 florists. Here again, the comparison is revealing. We see, for example, that some of the florist's expenses are appreciably higher than in the standard—bad-debt losses are the outstanding example—and it may be that an analysis of these expenses will quickly identify areas where money could be saved without an adverse effect on operations.

Use of ratios to study relative changes from base periods

Per cent relatives. Ratios can be used to study relative growth from a base period by relating the magnitude of a variable in a given period to the base period magnitude. A comparison of relative growth in two or more related activities is especially useful in assessing the future comparative importance of the activities.

Suppose, for example, that an analyst wishes to report on changes in the value of ordinary and group life insurance in force in the United States between 1964 and 1969 inclusive. Table 25.2 shows data on the dollar

Table 25.2 Value of Ordinary and Group Life Insurance in Force in the United States, 1964–1969

	Billions of Dollars		*Per Cent Relatives (1964 = 100)*		*Link Relatives*	
Year	*Ordinary*	*Group*	*Ordinary*	*Group*	*Ordinary*	*Group*
1964	455.9	252.2	100	100	—	—
1965	497.6	306.1	109	121	109	121
1966	539.0	343.4	118	136	108	112
1967	582.6	391.1	128	155	108	114
1968	630.4	438.2	138	174	108	112
1969	678.9	483.2	149	192	108	110

Source of basic data: Life Insurance Fact Book, 1970, pp. 26, 29. New York: Institute of Life Insurance, 1970.

value for each of the two types of insurance during this period. It is apparent that both types of plans showed substantial increases in the dollar value of life insurance in force. But were the two types growing at the same rate since 1964? This question can be answered by taking 1964 as the base period for each plan and expressing the value of life insurance in force in any given year as a per cent of the 1964 value. The per cents so obtained are called per cent relatives. In general:

(25.2) A ***per cent relative*** expresses the magnitude of a variable in a given period as a per cent of the magnitude of the variable in the base period.

The calculation of per cent relatives is quite simple. For ordinary life insurance plans, as an example, the per cent relative for the *base year* 1964 is, by definition, 100; the per cent relative for 1965 is $(497.6/455.9) \cdot 100 = 109$, and so on. Similarly, the per cent relatives for group insurance are calculated by expressing each year's value of insurance in force as a per cent of the base year (1964) value of $252.2 billion.

The per cent relatives for both types of life insurance plans are presented in Table 25.2. Thus the relative of 149 for ordinary life insurance in 1969 means that the value of ordinary life insurance policies in force in the United States in 1969 was 149 per cent as great as the value of policies of this type in 1964. It is evident from Table 25.2 that the value of group life insurance policies in force increased at a faster rate from 1964 to 1969 than the value of ordinary life insurance policies in force. There was an increase of 92 per cent in the value of group policies during this period compared with an increase of 49 per cent in the value of ordinary policies.

Link relatives. Sometimes it is desirable to analyze a variable by making comparisons between adjacent time periods, instead of between each period and a fixed base period. For example, one may wish to learn whether the period-to-period rates of change in the magnitude of the variable follow any regular pattern. Such comparisons are facilitated by calculating link relatives.

(25.3) A ***link relative*** expresses the magnitude of the variable in a given period as a per cent of the magnitude of the variable in the immediately preceding period.

Link relatives for the life insurance data are shown in the last two columns of Table 25.2. The link relative of 109 for ordinary life insurance in 1965, for instance, means that the value of such insurance in force in 1965 was 109 per cent as great as the value in 1964; the link relative of 108 for 1966 means that the value in 1966 was 108 per cent as great as the value in 1965, and so on.

The link relatives show that the two types of insurance plans maintained uninterrupted year-to-year growth in the value of insurance in force during

1964–1969 inclusive, but the annual growth rate in group life insurance was greater than in ordinary life insurance. The annual growth rate in ordinary life insurance tended to be around 8 per cent per year, while in group life insurance it varied from 10 to 14 per cent except for a spurt of 21 per cent from 1964 to 1965.

Per cent changes. Another method of comparing magnitudes of a variable in two periods is to calculate per cent changes. A per cent relative or link relative can be converted directly to the corresponding per cent change. However, per cent changes are so commonly used in analysis that a short separate discussion of this type of ratio is warranted.

In the preceding example, the value of ordinary life insurance in force in 1965 was $(497.6/455.9) \cdot 100 = 109$ per cent as great as the value in force in 1964. From this it is apparent that the 1965 value was 9 per cent greater than the 1964 value. Formally, this per cent change is obtained as follows: $[(497.6/455.9) \cdot 100] - 100 = +9$ per cent.

In general, we calculate a per cent change as follows:

$$\text{(25.4)} \qquad \text{Per cent change} = \left(\frac{X_L}{X_E} \cdot 100\right) - 100$$

Here X_E denotes the magnitude in the *earlier* period and X_L denotes the magnitude in the *later* period. Note that the term in parentheses is the per cent relative, so that the per cent change is obtained simply by subtracting 100 from the per cent relative.

Alternatively, formula (25.4) can be written:

$$\text{(25.4a)} \qquad \text{Per cent change} = \frac{X_L - X_E}{X_E} \cdot 100$$

In general, we restrict the concept of a per cent change to cases where the variable can take on only positive values, which is the usual situation in business and economic problems. Incidentally, analogous restrictions were implied in our discussion of per cent and link relatives. Note, though, that the per cent *change* may be negative, namely when X_L is smaller than X_E. Thus, if the number of paid employees was 150 last year and 100 this year, the per cent change is, by (25.4):

$$\left(\frac{100}{150} \cdot 100\right) - 100 = 67 - 100 = -33 \text{ per cent}$$

Per cent decreases of more than 100 per cent are not possible. Occasionally, one reads statements such as, "Prices Slashed 200 Per Cent." A 100 per cent reduction in price would mean that the item is being given away free; how then can there have been a 200 per cent decrease? The difficulty in this type of case is usually that the more recent figure is used as the base. Thus, if the price of an item is slashed from \$3 to \$1, and the price decrease of \$2 is expressed relative to the *new* price of \$1, there would indeed be a price decrease of 200 per cent, *relative to the new price.* This latter "per cent change" reverses the sequence of time and is ordinarily an improper expression.

Interpretation of relative changes. Referring again to Table 25.2, recall that the per cent relative for 1969 is 149 for ordinary life insurance and 192 for group life insurance. Of course, one cannot conclude from these per cent relatives that the value of group life insurance in force in 1969 was greater than the value of ordinary life insurance in force during that same year; nor can one necessarily conclude that the actual dollar increase in the value of group life insurance in force between the years 1964 and 1969 was greater than the dollar increase in the value of ordinary life insurance between the same years. In fact, the dollar figures in Table 25.2 make it clear that the first of these conclusions would be incorrect. The 1969 per cent relatives simply indicate that the *relative* growth between 1964 and 1969 has been greater for group than for ordinary life insurance plans. This precaution in interpreting per cent changes applies to all ratios, of which per cents are one particular type. Any ratio only indicates the magnitude of the numerator relative to that of the denominator. Hence *no conclusion can be drawn from a ratio alone about the absolute magnitude of the variable in the numerator.*

The base of a ratio is therefore crucial in the interpretation of that ratio. A casual reading might suggest that the following statement cannot be correct: "Unemployment in this city increased 100 per cent during the quarter while employment declined only .3 per cent." Each per cent, however, is computed on a different base. For instance, unemployment might have increased from 3,000 to 6,000—an increase of 100 per cent—while employment might have declined from 1,000,000 to 997,000—a decline of .3 per cent. In view of the fact that the significance of per cent changes depends so much on the level of the base, it is considered good practice when presenting ratios in analysis to show also the absolute magnitudes on which the ratios are based. An increase of 100 per cent in unemployment, considered alone, might appear to have much more drastic implications than when it is also known that the increase involved 3,000 persons out of a total of 1,000,000 employed persons.

The interpretation of large per cent changes is rather difficult; hence, percentages should not be used in these cases. For instance, the statement that the work load of an office increased 8,000 per cent during the last ten years is harder to comprehend than the statement that the work load increased eighty-fold.

Distinction between per cent points of change and per cent changes. A difficulty that often arises in the interpretation of per cent data is failure to distinguish between *per cent points of change* and *per cent changes.* Suppose that a production line is turning out radios and that two radios per

100 on the average do not pass final inspection. We would say that the defective rate is 2 per cent. Suppose that for some reason the proportion of defective radios increases to three per 100; that is, the defective rate increases to 3 per cent. The defective rate has increased by *one per cent point*. This does not mean, of course, that the defective rate increased by one per cent. Actually, the defective rate increased by $[(3 - 2)/2] \cdot 100 =$ 50 per cent.

Averaging of ratios

When ratios are averaged, "weights" must usually be employed to obtain meaningful results. Consider, for instance, an economic research group in a firm that was assigned the task of screening possible locations for a new plant. Three factors were felt by management to be of prime importance in assessing locations, namely new labor supply, truck and railroad transportation facilities, and higher-education opportunities for technical and managerial employees. It was decided that in order to facilitate the screening process, each location would be rated for these three factors and the three ratings would be averaged. These average ratings would then be compared to narrow down the number of locations to be given more intensive study by the research group.

Each factor rating was in the form of an index or ratio. An index is a ratio usually expressed on a base of 100. For example, the index of new labor supply in a location was determined by expressing the average number of high-school graduates in commuting range of that location during the past five years as a per cent of the average for all locations being considered. Indexes for the other two factors were derived similarly, by obtaining quantitative measures for each location and expressing these as a per cent of the average for all locations. Suppose that location A is rated as follows with respect to the three factors:

Factor	*Index*
Labor	120
Transportation	110
Education	90

The indexes now must be averaged for this location. If the factors were equally important, a simple average could be taken by summing the index values and dividing by 3. However, assume management believes that labor supply is the most important factor, that transportation is about half as important as labor supply, and that education is about one-fourth as important as labor supply. Consequently weights of 4, 2, 1, respectively, can be assigned to the ratings of these factors in calculating the weighted average of the three indexes.

In calculating a weighted average, the ratios to be averaged are first multiplied by their respective weights, the products are then totaled, and finally the total is divided by the sum of the weights. The weighted average rating for location A is:

Factor	(1) *Ratio (Index)*	(2) *Weight*	(3) *Ratio × Weight*
Labor	120	4	480
Transportation	110	2	220
Education	90	1	90
		7	790

$$\text{Weighted Average} = \frac{790}{7} = 113$$

Incidentally, any other weights in the proportions 4, 2, and 1 will give this same result.

25.3 CONSIDERATIONS IN THE COMPILATION AND USE OF RATIOS

Here, we will briefly survey some points that must be resolved before ratios can be compiled and used effectively in given situations.

Compilation of ratios

Variables to be related. Ratios are calculated to aid in the study of relationships between two or more variables. Each given problem governs the particular relationships to be studied. For instance, suppose a company wishes to study the accident record in its plant during a recent period. The number of accidents in the plant per 1,000 *company* employees is certainly a ratio from a technical point of view, but it will not be as meaningful to the problem as the number of accidents in the plant per 1,000 *production* employees. The latter ratio relates *plant* accidents to *plant* employees, while the former relates *plant* accidents to *all* employees, including, for instance, office and sales personnel, whose accidents are not included in the numerator and for whom the conditions affecting the incidence of accidents are substantially different from those in the plant.

Similarly, in studying transportation accidents, the question arises as to what comparisons are most meaningful. Insurance actuaries are interested in the risk to all occupants in buses, trains, or airplanes, and hence have developed accident ratios based on passenger miles traveled. From the viewpoint of manufacturers and operators of the equipment, however, such ratios may not be meaningful, because accidents are generally attributable to such factors as the person at the controls or condition of the vehicle, and the chance factor of number of passengers is usually irrelevant. Hence, interest would center on comparisons of ratios based on vehicle miles or vehicle hours.

Choice of denominator. The denominator of a ratio serves as the base of comparison. The circumstances of each problem determine which of the two variables is to be taken as the base of comparison. Nevertheless, certain generalizations can be made:

1. *If the magnitude of a part relative to the corresponding total is to be determined, the total is generally taken as the base.* For instance, in relating the number of unemployed to the total labor force, the number of persons in the labor force would be the denominator of the ratio.
2. *If the relative change from an earlier period to a later period is to be determined, the earlier period is generally used as the denominator.* For example, in calculating the per cent change in sales *from* 1971 *to* 1972, the sales in 1971 would be taken as the base.
3. *If a relation is to be studied between two variables, where the first variable depends in a causal sense on the second, the second variable is generally used as the base of comparisons.* Thus, in relating the number of accidents to total passenger miles, the latter would generally be taken as the base.
4. Sometimes, custom governs which variable is to be taken as the base.

Choice of units in denominator. The reader will have noted that different units are employed in the denominators of various ratios. Income per capita uses a denominator of one unit; any per cent has 100 units in the denominator; accidents per 1,000 manhours employs a denominator of 1,000 units; and so on. As a general guide, it may be stated that *the number of units in the denominator of a statistical ratio should be such that the numerator, if possible, is a number that is neither too large nor too small;* otherwise, it becomes difficult to interpret the relative magnitudes involved. Furthermore, *the denominator generally should be expressed in powers of 10 to facilitate the understanding of the ratio.*

To illustrate these ideas, consider the case of a company that had 147 plant accidents during a recent month when 42,178 manhours were worked in the plant. Each of the following ratios expresses the same relationship between these two variables:

.0035 accidents per manhour
.035 accidents per 10 manhours
.35 accidents per 100 manhours
3.5 accidents per 1,000 manhours
3,500 accidents per 1,000,000 manhours

Note that it is difficult to comprehend .0035 accidents per manhour. At the other extreme, it is difficult to comprehend the relative magnitudes involved from the ratio 3,500 accidents per 1,000,000 manhours; furthermore, this base is much larger than the actual number of manhours worked and would tend to give an erroneous impression. Among the above expressions, the ratio with a base of 1,000 manhours is the best choice, because the numerator is then a number that is neither too small nor too large. One can readily grasp from this ratio the quantitative relationship between number of accidents and manhours.

Use of ratios

One difficulty with the use of ratios—though this difficulty applies to the use of all quantitative data—is the ease with which they can be misinterpreted. For instance, *The New Yorker* reprinted the following statement from a newspaper: "Each year Reno has 128 visitors per resident. Such statistics prove that if you visit Reno you probably don't live there." Although this analysis is merely a gross blunder, it is still easy to make more subtle misinterpretations. A number of points about ratios are worth special mention because misinterpretations can arise when they are overlooked:

1. *A ratio is always affected by both the variable in the numerator and that in the denominator; hence, both variables should be included in the interpretation of the ratio.* Consider, for instance, the inventory turnover ratio for a department store. This ratio is often calculated as the number of dollars of sales per one dollar of inventory. The interpretation often is made that a large inventory turnover ratio implies that the sales force is doing an effective job, and that a small inventory turnover ratio indicates that the sales force is not doing an effective job. To be sure, sales are made by the selling force, but inventory is obtained as the result of a buying function. Thus, a low inventory turnover ratio may indicate an inefficient selling job, but it also may indicate an inefficient buying job resulting in failure to move unsalable or obsolete merchandise, or the carrying of inappropriate levels of inventory.
2. *Any one ratio reveals only a partial picture in most administrative and analytical situations.* Suppose that one is interested in the employment turnover in a company. The ratio of separations per 100 employees can be calculated. The larger this ratio, the more employees relatively are leaving the company. This one ratio surely does not, however, provide all significant information about employee turnover in the company. Even with respect to employee separations, this ratio does not tell, for instance, whether the separated employees had been in the organization for a short time or for a long time. Again, in another instance, the per cent of persons in the labor force who are unemployed is a ratio that describes the relative severity of unemployment in terms of the portion of the labor force affected. This ratio does not, however, indicate over a period of time whether the same persons are still unemployed or whether there has been a turnover in those persons who are unemployed—a distinction that is most important to economists and public administrators who have to decide on action to be taken in any given situation.

Because most problems in business and public administration and in economic analysis are complex, one should be very skeptical of any attempt to answer such problems from an analysis of a single ratio. Any one ratio relates only two variables and consequently will provide only a part of the total picture.

3. *Comparisons between ratios are necessary, but they will be meaningless unless the basic data relate to comparable activities and are collected according to similar standards.* Thus, crime rates in different cities may not be comparable because of differences in definitions and in accuracy of reporting, accident rates in different industries may not be comparable for the same reasons, and so on. The requirement that data to be analyzed must be comparable before one can draw significant conclusions from comparisons is especially important in the case of ratio analysis, where it is easy to lose sight of the original data on which the ratios are based.
4. Finally, we reiterate that *the use of a ratio to relate two variables assumes that the functional form of the relationship is a straight line through the origin.*

QUESTIONS AND PROBLEMS

25.1. Explain briefly each of the following:

a. Per cent distribution **c.** Base of a ratio **e.** Base period
b. Standard distribution **d.** Turnover rate **f.** Weighted average of ratios

25.2. Distinguish briefly between:

a. Per cent relative and link relative
b. Per cent points of change and per cent change
c. $Y = a + bX$ and $Y = bX$

25.3. A participant in a conference on uses of statistical methods in control made the following statement:

> In the cement manufacturing industry a firm may operate five or six different plants, each in a different marketing area. Ratio analysis is a key to a common approach to cost control in the different plants. The key control statistic can be either the ratio of total variable cost to total output in each plant, or the ratio of total fixed plus variable cost to total output. Since fixed costs do not change with changes in level of output, either ratio will give the same result and the choice can be based on personal preference.

Do you agree with the statement that either ratio will give the same result? Discuss.

***25.4.** Data on net operating profit, investments, and sales for Database, Inc., are presented below for the period 1970–1972 inclusive (data in thousands of dollars):

Year	*Net Operating Profit*	*Total Investment*	*Sales*
1970	28.2	404.8	761.0
1971	28.2	457.6	784.2
1972	28.6	482.0	834.6

a. Utilizing the ratio "rate of return on investment," analyze the effectiveness of operations during this period.
b. How has the effectiveness of operations changed during this period?
c. Calculate the ratios "net operating profit as a per cent of sales" and "turnover rate." What additional information do these ratios provide?

25.5. Net operating income, average operating investment, and sales of Global Plastics, Inc. for the period 1966–1969 inclusive were (in millions of dollars):

Year	*Net Operating Income*	*Average Operating Investment*	*Sales*
1966	292.4	2,112.4	1,909.2
1967	258.4	2,251.7	1,888.4
1968	265.7	2,421.0	1,964.6
1969	212.5	2,581.0	1,829.2

a. Calculate the rate of return on investment for each year and describe your findings.
b. Calculate net operating income as a per cent of sales, and the turnover rate, for each of the years. What insights do you obtain relevant to your findings in part **a**?
c. In the years 1966 through 1969 inclusive, domestic scheduled trunk airlines in the United States earned rates of return on investment of, respectively, 9.7, 7.7, 5.3, and 4.8 per cent. From a comparison of these rates with those obtained in part **a**, can you determine whether Global Plastics, Inc. or the airlines were more effectively managed during these years? Discuss.

***25.6.** The condensed consolidated income statements (in millions of dollars) of a manufacturing corporation for the years 1970 and 1971 were:

	1971	*1970*
Net sales and other income	642.4	782.1
Cost of goods sold and operating expenses	425.3	511.3
Selling, general administrative, and other expenses	57.4	71.9
Amortization, depletion and depreciation	37.4	64.0
Interest expense	11.4	11.4
Taxes, excluding income taxes	9.5	8.8
	541.0	667.4
Income before income taxes	101.4	114.7
Income taxes	58.7	60.9
Net income	42.7	53.8

a. Compute the per cent distribution of sales for each year.
b. What major differences do you find between the two per cent distributions? Do these help to explain the decrease in profits?

25.7. On page 556 are data on sales and costs of the Jones Office Supply Company for 1971 and 1972. A "standard" per cent distribution of sales for office supply and equipment dealers is also shown. This standard distribution was developed by the National Stationery and Office Equipment Association from a survey of operating ratios in business operations similar to those of the Jones firm.
a. Calculate the per cent distribution of sales for each year.
b. Analyze the two per cent distributions of sales. Did any significant changes occur between 1971 and 1972?

c. Compare the per cent distributions for the Jones Office Supply Company with the standard distribution. Does this comparison bring out any important facts not already uncovered in part **b**? Discuss.

d. What precautions must be particularly kept in mind in making the comparison called for in part **b**? In part **c**? Explain.

	1972	*1971*	*Standard Distribution (%)*
Net sales	$308,000	$295,000	100.0
Cost of goods sold	200,816	191,450	64.8
Gross margin	$107,184	$103,550	35.2
Expenses			
Owner's compensation	$ 12,000	$ 12,000	4.6
Employees' wages	56,500	53,675	16.8
Occupancy cost	13,300	12,900	4.0
Advertising	4,200	4,000	1.3
Bad-debt losses	4,545	1,360	.3
Other expenses	15,400	15,100	5.3
Total expenses	$105,945	$ 99,035	32.3
Net profit before income taxes	$ 1,239	$ 4,515	2.9

***25.8.** Data are presented below on population and disposable personal income corrected for price-level changes in the United States for the period 1965–1969 inclusive:

Year	*Disposable Personal Income (Billions of 1969 Dollars)*	*Population (Millions of Persons)*
1965	537.6	194.6
1966	567.2	196.9
1967	590.4	199.1
1968	615.0	201.2
1969	629.7	203.2

Source: U.S. Department of Commerce.

a. Calculate disposable personal income per capita (per person) for each year.

b. For the series on disposable personal income and per capita disposable personal income, calculate per cent relatives using 1965 as the base. Compare the two sets of relatives and briefly state your findings.

c. Calculate link relatives for the series on disposable personal income and per capita disposable personal income. Do the link relatives provide information equivalent to that of the per cent relatives in part **b**? Discuss fully.

25.9. Annual sales (in millions of dollars) of the three major product lines of a diversified manufacturing corporation are shown below for alternate years during the period 1962–1972 inclusive:

Year	*Motor Vehicle Components*	*Aircraft Components*	*Electronic Systems*
1962	135	101	124
1964	160	125	143
1966	176	140	146
1968	194	162	184
1970	214	169	205
1972	238	194	220

a. Which product line showed the greatest absolute increase in sales from 1962 to 1972?

b. For each year shown, calculate per cent relatives of sales for each product line, using 1962 as the base year. Which product line showed the greatest relative increase in sales between 1962 and 1972?

c. Explain why the product line showing the greatest absolute increase between 1962 and 1972 will not necessarily show also the greatest relative increase.

d. For each product line, calculate link relatives. Do the link relatives provide information equivalent to that of the per cent relatives in part **b**? Discuss fully.

e. Since 1962 the company encountered increasingly heavy competition in domestic sales of electronic systems, and in 1965 began a campaign to expand European sales of this line. Calculate new per cent relatives of sales of each product line for each year shown, but use 1966 as the base year.

f. Compare your results in parts **b** and **e**. Did the choice of a new base period affect the rankings of the product lines, as to relative increases in sales between the base period and 1972? Discuss.

g. Which set of per cent relatives—those on a 1962 base or those on a 1966 base—would be more useful for studying the expected relative sales growth of the product lines in the decade after 1972? Discuss.

***25.10.** Annual expenditures of the Seymour Smelting Company to control air pollution were $12.5 thousand in 1967 and $35.0 thousand in 1972. Using these expenditures data, complete the following blanks to make the appropriate ratio.

a. For each dollar spent in 1967, there were ________ dollars spent in 1972.

b. The annual expenditures increased by ________ per cent between 1967 and 1972.

c. The amount expended in 1967 was ________ per cent as great as the amount expended in 1972.

d. The ratio of the number of dollars spent in 1972 to the number of dollars spent in 1967 was ________ to 10.

e. The number of dollars spent in 1972 was ________ per cent as great as the number spent in 1967.

f. For every 100 dollars spent in 1972, there were only ________ dollars spent in 1967.

25.11. Funds obligated under federal anti-poverty direct programs were as follows in millions of dollars for the fiscal years ending June 30, 1965 and June 30, 1969:

Program	*1965*	*1969*
Community Action Programs	236.2	1,011.1
Job Corps	195.8	278.4
Vista	2.7	32.8
Other direct programs	6.3	15.9
Total	441.0	1,338.2

Source: Executive Office of the President.

a. Funds for Community Action Programs represented what per cent of the total for direct programs each year?

b. Funds for Job Corps increased by what per cent from 1965 to 1969?

c. For every ten dollars obligated for Job Corps in 1969, how many dollars were obligated for Community Action Programs in the same year?

d. Funds obligated for "other" direct programs increased by what per cent between 1965 and 1969?

25.12. A state tollroad authority reported that 6 per cent more vehicles of all types used the road in 1972 than in 1971 but that toll revenues increased by only 4 per cent from 1971 to 1972. What factors could bring about the greater relative increase in number of vehicles using the road than in toll revenues?

25.13. A union in a public announcement declared that management in a certain company could grant wage increases without raising prices of its products. To support this argument, the union cited data that labor costs accounted for 37 cents of each sales dollar of the firm in 1971 and for 35 cents of each sales dollar in 1972, while net profits of the company had doubled during this period from $100 million to $200 million.

a. While you cannot analyze the merits of the argument because of insufficient data, do the data cited provide a meaningful comparison? Discuss.

b. What generalization does your answer in part **a** suggest about presenting actual data and ratios based on these data in an analysis?

25.14. U.S. Public Health Service statistics indicate that the number of bed disability days in the United States was 6.0 per person per year in 1960 and 5.7 per person per year in 1967. A student stated that according to these figures there was a decline in the need for hospital beds during this period and therefore no additional hospital-bed capacity need have been constructed. Discuss fully.

25.15. Last year the Department of Sanitation of a large city had a truck accident record that ranged from 1,903 vehicle-miles per one accident in the downtown business district to 14,830 vehicle-miles per one accident in the purely residential districts.

a. Restate each of the ratios so that the base of each is an appropriate number of vehicle-miles.

b. How did you decide upon the appropriate number of vehicle-miles to be used in the denominator?

c. Which is preferable to use in the denominator, accidents or vehicle-miles? Why?

25.16. The per cent relatives shown below pertain to dollar charges for two types of medical cases in a private clinic operated by a consortium of physicians. A commentator offered the following analysis of these data: "In 1968 a father sending his wife to this clinic to have a baby had to pay the same amount as if he sent one of his children to have his tonsils and adenoids removed. But by 1973 the father had to pay more for the obstetrical case than for the tonsillectomy and adenoidectomy." Do the data demonstrate this? Discuss.

Per Cent Relatives of Medical Charges, 1968 = 100

Year	*Obstetrical Case*	*Tonsillectomy and Adenoidectomy*
1968	100	100
1973	143	137

25.17. **a.** If the net assets of a mutual fund had increased by 7 per cent between December 31, 1968 and December 31, 1969, and then had fallen by 7 per cent between December 31, 1969 and December 31, 1970, would the assets as of December 31, 1968 and December 31, 1970 have been equal? Why or why not?

b. Suppose, for the dates given, the net assets had first fallen by 7 per cent and then had increased by 7 per cent. Would the net assets as of December 31, 1968 and December 31, 1970 have been equal? Why or why not?

c. Do the contrasting situations in parts **a** and **b** lead to opposite results? Explain why or why not.

***25.18.** A tobacco company reported that sales of its mentholated filter tip cigarettes during 1971 were 500 per cent as great as sales during 1965. Sales during 1972 were 525 per cent as great as 1965 sales.

a. Calculate the per cent increase in sales between 1971 and 1972.

b. Calculate, from the above per cent relatives on the 1965 base, by how many per cent points sales increased between 1971 and 1972.

c. How do you explain the different answers to parts **a** and **b**?

***25.19.** The following data on actual and anticipated operating revenues were presented in a planning report of the Middlesex Electric and Power Corporation:

Actual and Anticipated Operating Revenues, 1970 & 1980

Department	*Actual Operating Revenues (Millions of Dollars)* 1970	*Anticipated Operating Revenues (Millions of Dollars)* 1980
Electric	57.3	120.0
Gas	8.7	13.5
Total	66.0	133.5

a. It is anticipated that annual operating revenues in the Electric Department will increase by what per cent between 1970 and 1980? What is the corresponding per cent increase in the Gas Department?

b. Calculate the anticipated per cent increase between 1970 and 1980 in revenues for the combined departments from the totals for each year. Then calculate the same per cent increase by taking a weighted average of the per cent increases obtained in part **a**, using the 1970 revenue data as weights. Do you obtain the same anticipated per cent increase with both methods? Why, or why not?

Chapter

26

CROSS-CLASSIFICATION

The use of cross-classification is most helpful in studying relationships between variables which are qualitative or which are treated for convenience as qualitative though they are inherently quantitative. We encountered cross-classification in earlier chapters: bivariate probability distributions and contingency tables are cases in point. In the present chapter, we discuss the use of cross-classification for studying relations between qualitative variables in its own right. Further, we shall explore ways of using cross-classification to obtain clues about the nature of the causal relationships between variables.

We shall dwell on the descriptive aspects of the analysis in this chapter, and not on problems of statistical inference connected with sample data. We discussed earlier, in Chapter 19, the use of the chi-square test for testing whether two qualitative variables are independent. This, and other statistical methods, would play an important role in firming up the analysis based on cross-classification.

26.1 CLASSIFICATION AND CROSS-CLASSIFICATION

Classification was initially discussed in Chapter 2. Recall from there that classification entails the setting up of groupings or classes for the alternative outcomes of a variable in such a manner that certain formal requirements are observed:

1. There is a class or grouping for every possible outcome.
2. These classes are mutually exclusive.

3. Any one class should not mix together outcomes that have different implications for analysis. For instance, the class "defective" would be too coarse if it is important to distinguish between defects caused by faulty material and those caused by poor workmanship.

In order to analyze relationships between variables in classified data, one must classify observations jointly by two or more systems of classification. To illustrate, suppose that a supermarket has sponsored a survey of 1,324 households in a given area to study the factors affecting the saving of trading stamps by households. Saving of trading stamps thus is the dependent variable. The independent variables include household income. As an initial step in the analysis, the effect of household income on the saving of trading stamps is to be evaluated. The survey indicates that trading stamps are saved regularly in 85 per cent of the households and not saved in 15 per cent; also that 57 per cent of the households have weekly incomes under $100 and 43 per cent have weekly incomes of $100 or more.

Can one determine from these data whether a greater proportion of households save stamps in one income class than in the other? Clearly not. In order to do this, it is necessary to know what per cent of the sample households in *each* income class save stamps, whereas the given data only show that 85 per cent of *all* households save stamps. Thus, tabulations are required in which the two systems of classification are used jointly, that is, the data must be cross-classified. Cross-classified data may be presented in a statistical table, such as Table 26.1a. This table presents data on the 1,324 households cross-classified jointly as to stamp-saving and income. Note, for example, that 674 households save stamps *and* have weekly incomes under $100, 87 households do not save stamps *and* have weekly incomes under $100, and so on.

Table 26.1 Relationship Between Trading-Stamp Saving and Household Income (Data From Survey of 1,324 Households; Absolute Data in Parentheses)

(a)

		Weekly Income (Dollars)	
Save Trading Stamps	*Under 100*	*100 or Over*	*Total, All Incomes*
Yes	(674)	(446)	(1,120)
No	(87)	(117)	(204)
Total households	(761)	(563)	(1,324)

(b)

	Weekly Income (Dollars)	
Save Trading Stamps	*Under 100*	*100 or Over*
Yes	89%	79%
No	11	21
Total per cent	100%	100%
Total households	(761)	(563)

26.2
STUDY OF STATISTICAL RELATIONSHIPS BETWEEN TWO VARIABLES

The simplest procedure in the analysis of cross-classified data, and one that is often a preliminary to more refined analysis, is to study the nature of the relationship between the dependent variable and individual independent variables one at a time. We now turn to such a study.

Identification of statistical relationships in cross-classified data

In general, a statistical relationship is suggested between two variables if the outcomes taken by one variable tend to shift or change when the outcome of the other variable changes. Thus, in Table 26.1a, a statistical relationship is suggested between stamp-saving and income if there is a difference in the proportion of households that save stamps as one goes from the lower to the higher income group. On the other hand, if the proportion of households that save stamps is about the same in the two income groups, one would say that there does not appear to be a statistical relationship between these variables.

Use of per cent distributions

It is difficult to study the relationship between household income and stamp-saving from Table 26.1a because there are different numbers of households in each income group, and this difference affects the comparison. The data must be converted to relative terms, such as percentages, to facilitate comparison. There are various bases for converting the data in Table 26.1a to relative terms. For purposes of analyzing the effect of income (the independent variable) on saving of trading stamps (the dependent variable), the most appropriate form is that shown in Table 26.1b. Here the frequencies within each income class are converted to per cent distributions, to facilitate comparisons between the two income classes. For example, there are 761 households in the income class "under $100." Of these, 674 households save stamps. Thus the per cent of households in this income class that save stamps is $(674/761) \cdot 100 = 89$ per cent. The per cent of households in this income class that do not save stamps is $(87/761) \cdot 100 = 11$ per cent. These per cents are shown in the left-hand column of Table 26.1b and constitute the per cent distribution of the 761 households in the lower income class. The right-hand column shows the per cent distribution of the 563 households in the higher income class. Note that the bases of the per cent distributions are shown in parentheses in Table 26.1b, as are all the absolute data in Table 26.1a. Throughout this chapter, we adopt the convention of presenting all absolute data in parentheses and percentages without parentheses.

By comparing the two per cent distributions in Table 26.1b one can readily ascertain that relatively more of the households in the lower income class save trading stamps than in the higher income class.

Note in Table 26.1b that the dependent variable is located in the leftmost part of the table, which is called the *stub* of the table. In this way, each per cent distribution ranges down over all the classes of the dependent variable. In cross-classifications involving more than one independent variable (to be discussed in the next section) this arrangement greatly facilitates analysis of the relation between the dependent variable and each independent variable in turn. Therefore, throughout this chapter, we will adopt the convention of always placing the dependent variable in the stub of the table and calculating per cent distributions down the columns.

Effect of number of classes

The number of classes employed in a system of classification sometimes can affect the study of relationships between variables. Consider Table 26.2, for example, which was constructed with hypothetical data to make this point. There is evidence in Table 26.2 of a statistical relation between household income and stamp-saving, with the per cent of households saving stamps first increasing with higher income and then decreasing with still higher income. Yet, if only two income classes had been used for the same data, "under $100" and "$100 and over," we would have found identical percentages of households saving trading stamps in the two income classes, namely 85 per cent in each class. This would imply, contrary to Table 26.2 with five income classes, that there is no statistical relation between household income and stamp-saving. Thus, the number of classes used in the cross-classification can affect the conclusion as to the nature of the statistical relation between the variables.

Table 26.2 Relationship Between Trading-Stamp Saving and Household Income, Using Five Income Classes (Hypothetical Data; Absolute Data in Parentheses)

	Weekly Income (Dollars)				
Save Trading Stamps	*Under 75*	*75–99*	*100–124*	*125–149*	*150 or Over*
Yes	79%	92%	94%	84%	64%
No	21	8	6	16	36
Total households	(410)	(351)	(326)	(105)	(132)

This illustrates a problem in classification mentioned before in Chapter 2. A proper balance must be achieved in the number of classes in a classification so that one neither: (1) overlooks a relationship because the data are broken down into only a few large classes, nor (2) obscures a relationship (or causes the appearance of one when there is none) by including so many classes that extraneous factors and chance effects unduly influence the analysis.

26.3
NEED TO CONSIDER SEVERAL VARIABLES SIMULTANEOUSLY

The procedures just discussed enable us to observe whether there is an apparent statistical relationship or lack of one between the dependent variable and the independent variable. In many cases, several independent variables must be studied simultaneously to determine how they are jointly related to the dependent variable. We will therefore expand our discussion of cross-classification to cover the three-variable case. The procedure to be shown, however, applies to any number of variables.

Procedure

A third variable—that is, a second independent variable—will be incorporated into the cross-classification of the data shown in Table 26.1a. It is useful to recall how the data in this table were developed. We began with a breakdown in terms of one variable. Of the 1,324 households covered in the survey, 1,120 saved stamps and 204 did not. We then stratified these results, in effect, by household income to obtain the data in Table 26.1a cross-classified by the two variables simultaneously.

The same process is repeated in adding a third variable. The data in each cell of Table 26.1a are stratified by a third system of classification to obtain a simultaneous cross-classification in terms of three variables. In practice, of course, the classifications would not have to be introduced piecemeal, one system at a time, but could be made simultaneously for all three systems.

Table 26.3a shows how data tabulated by three classifications simultaneously can be presented in a table. Here the third classification or variable is type of household—*R*, *S*, or *T*. The *R* class includes recently founded households with no children and with head aged under 40, and households with one or more children under 10 years of age. The *S* class includes households with children all aged 10 years or older. The *T* class includes households with head aged 40 years or older and no children residing in the household.

We see, for example, that of the 761 cases in the lower income class, 320 households are of type *R*, 290 of type *S*, and 151 of type *T*. Similarly, every other figure in Table 26.1a is now distributed over the three classes of households.

Calculation of per cent distributions

Again, we wish to convert the absolute data in Table 26.3a to per cents to facilitate analysis. In order to calculate per cent distributions over the

Table 26.3 Relationship Between Trading-Stamp Saving, Household Income, and Type of Household (Data from Survey of 1,324 Households; Absolute Data in Parentheses)

(a)

	Weekly Income and Type of Household					
	Under $100			*$100 or Over*		
Save Trading Stamps	*R*	*S*	*T*	*R*	*S*	*T*
Yes	(307)	(258)	(109)	(79)	(177)	(190)
No	(13)	(32)	(42)	(5)	(27)	(85)
Total households	(320)	(290)	(151)	(84)	(204)	(275)

(b)

	Weekly Income and Type of Household					
	Under $100			*$100 or Over*		
Save Trading Stamps	*R*	*S*	*T*	*R*	*S*	*T*
Yes	96%	89%	72%	94%	87%	69%
No	4	11	28	6	13	31
Total per cent	100%	100%	100%	100%	100%	100%
Total households	(320)	(290)	(151)	(84)	(204)	(275)

(c)

	Weekly Income and Type of Household					
	Under $100			*$100 or Over*		
Save Trading Stamps	*R*	*S*	*T*	*R*	*S*	*T*
Yes	96%	89%	72%	94%	87%	69%
Total households	(320)	(290)	(151)	(84)	(204)	(275)

classes of the dependent variable, we work within each column and take the column total as the base of each per cent in that column. For example, of the 320 cases in the leftmost column, 307 are in the top cell and 13 are in the lower cell. The per cents in the distribution are, respectively, $(307/320) \cdot 100 = 96$ per cent and $(13/320) \cdot 100 = 4$ per cent. This per cent distribution is shown in the leftmost column of Table 26.3b. The other per cent distributions in this table are obtained in the same manner.

Simplification for analysis

Here, we will pause to introduce a simplification that is frequently useful, especially in tables that are more complex than those employed here. The full per cent distributions in Table 26.3b are not really needed, because a household can fall into only one of two classes with respect to stamp-saving. Thus, if 96 per cent of the *R*-type households with incomes under $100 save stamps, we know automatically that 4 per cent of these households do not save stamps. Therefore, the rows labeled "No" and "Total per cent" in Table 26.3b can be eliminated without losing any information required in the analysis. This has been done in Table 26.3c. Note that the data in parentheses still indicate the total number of cases in the base of each per cent.

Analysis of data in three-way cross-classification

Given data that are cross-classified three ways as in Table 26.3b or 26.3c, one can control each independent variable in turn in order to study the relationship between the dependent variable and the other independent variable. Specifically, to study the relationship between stamp-saving and type of household *with income controlled,* one compares the per cent of households of different types that save stamps *within each income class.* Table 26.3c shows that for households in the lower income class, 96 per cent of *R*-type households save stamps versus 89 per cent of *S*-type households and 72 per cent of *T*-type. The differences between these per cents cannot be due to income, since all these households are in the same income grouping. For the data within the higher income class, we note again that the propensity to save stamps declines significantly as we consider *R*, *S*, and *T*-type households in turn. Thus, within each income class—or in other words, with the income variable controlled—a similar statistical relationship exists between stamp-saving and type of household.

A somewhat different finding emerges when we study the relationship between stamp-saving and income, *with type of household controlled.* Now the per cent of households that save stamps in the different income classes are compared *within each type of household.* Thus, the per cent of *R*-type households that save trading stamps are compared in the two different income classes. These per cents differ but slightly—96 per cent versus 94 per cent, respectively. Similar comparisons are made for the *S*-type and *T*-type households. Again, small but consistent differences appear in the per cents, namely 89 versus 87, and 72 versus 69.

These differences are small but consistent in direction. Assuming that they are not due to chance, we can conclude that income shows a statistical relationship with stamp-saving, but this relationship is secondary to that between type of household and stamp-saving.

It will be recalled that Table 26.1b showed a pronounced statistical relationship between stamp-saving and income. Now it appears that this relationship is secondary to that between stamp-saving and type of household. How, then, did the appearance of a strong relationship between the original variables (stamp-saving and income) arise? Table 26.3a gives the answer. The relative frequencies of *R*, *S*, and *T*-type households differ in the two income groups, and the proportion of stamp-savers differs sharply between the different types of households. Stamps are saved in a large proportion of *R*-type households and relatively more of these households are in the under-$100 income group. In contrast, relatively more *T*-type households, where the proportion saving stamps is relatively low, are in the $100-or-over income class.

26.4 STUDY OF CAUSES AND EFFECTS BY CROSS–CLASSIFICATION

Thus far we have explained how cross-classification can be utilized to study statistical relationships between a dependent variable and one or more independent variables. Frequently statistical relationships are studied to obtain insights into possible cause-and-effect patterns which may underlie the relationships. We shall now take up, in a series of case studies, representative cause-and-effect patterns that underlie revealed statistical relationships. Examples involving three-way cross-classifications will be used, but the discussion could be broadened to cover cross-classified data involving more than three variables.

Antecedent independent variable affects other two variables jointly

Case 1. We continue our discussion concerning the relationship among stamp-saving, income, and type of household as shown in Table 26.3c. What is the cause-and-effect relationship between the three variables? The three are related, but the data suggest that the primary causal factor is type of household, not income. To a substantial extent, income is related to type of household. The heads of *R*-type households are relatively young and generally are at the early stages of their careers; hence they tend to have lower incomes. In contrast, heads of *S* and *T*-type households are older and tend to have higher incomes. The type of household also affects stamp-saving. Persons saving trading stamps typically tend to redeem them for housewares and appliances. Younger households still in the process of accumulating these items especially might be expected to favor trading stamps. Again, the data seem to bear this out.

The third variable (type of household) appears to be antecedent in order of time to each of the original variables (stamp-saving and household income). Consequently, the relationships between the three variables could be presented as in Figure 26.1. Here, the solid arrows indicate the direction of the cause-and-effect relationship, and the broken arrow indicates that income may have some effect on stamp-saving but that this effect is of secondary importance.

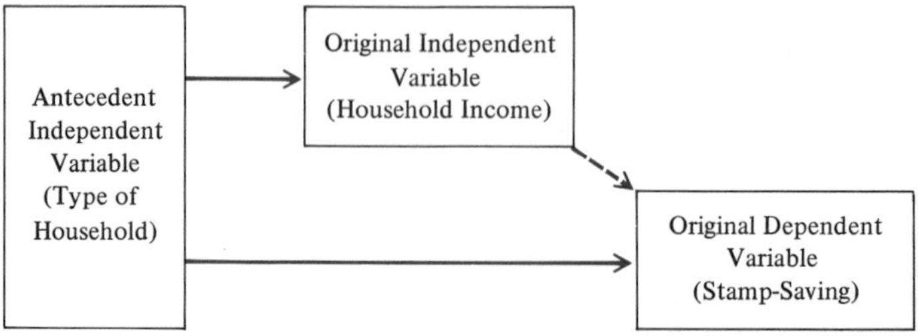

Figure 26.1. Antecedent independent variable affects other two variables jointly: Case 1

Case 2. Another type of case is similar statistically to the one just described, but the nature of the cause-and-effect relationship differs, as shown in Figure 26.2. Here, the influence of a third variable having a direct cause-and-effect relationship with the original two variables leads to a *spurious* statistical relationship between the first two variables.

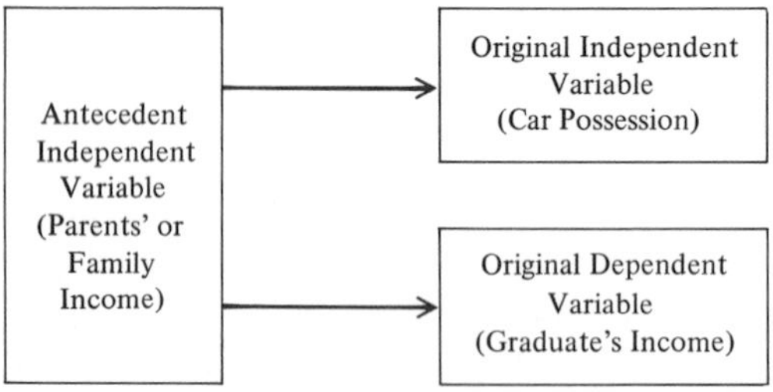

Figure 26.2. Antecedent independent variable affects other two variables jointly: Case 2

For an example of this type of case, see the data in Table 26.4. A study was made of the 1972 earnings of a class that had graduated in 1970 from a large liberal arts men's college. Among the independent variables included in the study was undergraduate car possession—that is, whether the student possessed his own car at any time during his undergraduate career. As Table 26.4a shows, there is a statistical relationship between earnings in 1972 and possession of a car as an undergraduate, when no other variables are controlled. Specifically, only 50 per cent of those with cars as undergraduates were in the lower earnings group in 1972, as compared with 63 per cent of those without cars as undergraduates.

Table 26.4 Relationship Between Earnings in 1972, Undergraduate Car Possession, and Parents' or Family Income, for Class of 1970 of Large Liberal Arts College (Absolute Data in Parentheses)

(a)

1972 Earnings of Graduate (Thousands of Dollars)	*Possessed Car as Undergraduate* Yes	No
Under 10	50%	63%
10 or over	50	37
Total per cent	100%	100%
Total cases	(330)	(702)

(b)

1972 Earnings of Graduate (Thousands of Dollars)	*Car Possession and Parents' or Family Income (Thousands of Dollars) in Graduating Year*					
	Yes			*No*		
	Under 12	*12–20*	*Over 20*	*Under 12*	*12–20*	*Over 20*
Under 10	74%	64%	45%	74%	62%	46%
10 or over	26	36	55	26	38	54
Total per cent	100%	100%	100%	100%	100%	100%
Total cases	(31)	(48)	(251)	(235)	(332)	(135)

Table 26.4b suggests the reasons for this apparent statistical relationship. A second independent variable, parents' or family income in the year of graduation, has been added in this table. When the data are stratified by parents' or family income, there is no real difference in per cent of graduates in each earnings group, whether or not they possessed cars as undergraduates. For instance, among the graduates from families in the under $12,000 income group, 74 per cent of those who had cars earned under $10,000 in 1972 and 74 per cent of those who did not have cars earned under $10,000. There are comparable similarities in the other classes of parents' or family income. Thus it is reasonable to conclude that there is no statistical relationship between earnings after graduation and undergraduate car possession.

On the other hand, there is a pronounced statistical relationship between parents' or family income and earnings after graduation. Table 26.4b indicates that the higher the income group of the parents or family, the greater the proportion of the graduates in the upper earnings group regardless of car possession.

A comparison of the total number of cases in each column in Table 26.4b explains the original relationship in Table 26.4a between 1972 earnings and car possession. We see that car ownership is related to family income. The higher the family income group, the greater the tendency for the undergraduate to have possessed a car. Thus, each of the two original variables is directly affected by parents' or family income. The wealthier the undergraduate's parents or family, the more likely it was that he both possessed a car as an undergraduate and had higher earnings several years after graduation. The relationship shown in Table 26.4a between earnings after graduation and undergraduate car possession can be called a *spurious relationship*.

Comparison of cases 1 and 2. An examination of Figures 26.1 and 26.2 indicates that the corresponding cases have elements in common, yet differ in important ways. In both cases, the third variable is *antecedent in time* to the original two variables, and thus could only be a cause, never an effect, in relation to these.

In the case schematically shown in Figure 26.2, we designated the relationship between the original two variables as spurious, yet did not do this in the first case. The distinction results from an analysis of the nature of the variables, and not from the behavior of the data. In Figure 26.1 all three variables (type of family, income, and stamp-saving) were special aspects of a transcending variable, namely, the socioeconomic status and behavior of the responding families. In the second case, undergraduate car possession and earnings in 1972 tended to be effects of a common cause, parents' or family income, but otherwise were unrelated to one another.

Cases 1 and 2 indicate clearly that an analyst cannot assume a cause-and-effect relationship between two variables simply because a statistical relationship has been found in survey data. He must control the possible effects of other independent variables by incorporating these into the cross-classification and thence into his analysis.

Second independent variable links other two variables

Case 3. When a statistical relationship between two variables has stood the test of adding antecedent variables, the analyst's attention ordinarily shifts to the next stage of the problem. Here, he tests if other possible variables are *links* in the chain of cause and effect connecting the dependent variable and the original independent variable. The action of a linking variable is shown schematically in Figure 26.3. Note particularly that a linking variable affects the dependent variable and is in turn affected by the first independent variable. An antecedent variable, on the other hand, affects the dependent variable and the first independent variable jointly.

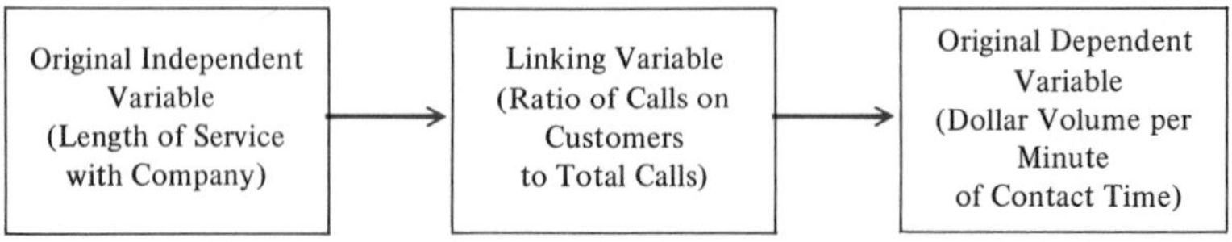

Figure 26.3. Second independent variable links other two variables: Case 3

The linking effect of a third variable can be studied by the same procedure that was used in cases 1 and 2. Cases 1, 2, and 3 differ only in the temporal sequence of the variables and in the nature of the cause-and-effect relationships between the three variables, but not in the behavior of the data.

For a specific example of a third variable linking the original two variables in a study, consider the case of a precision tool firm that analyzed the performance of its salesmen. It was found that a statistical relationship existed between the number of years salesmen had been with the firm and dollar volume of orders written per minute of contact time in the field. The longer the time the salesman had been with the firm, the greater tended to be the dollar volume per minute of contact time. However, when the data were stratified by a second independent variable, ratio of contact time expended on customer calls to contact time on all calls, it was revealed that there was little difference between new and old salesmen in the volume of orders written per minute of contact time spent *with customers.* The original relationship was explained largely by the fact that the older salesmen tended to spend their time predominantly on customer calls and spent little or no time on calls on new prospects. In this case, then, the new variable is revealed to be a link in the chain of cause and effect connecting the original variables. Had no linking variable been found, its absence would have suggested that experience per se led to a higher dollar volume of orders written per minute of contact time.

The analysis need not stop when a linking variable is uncovered. The data can be stratified still further by adding other possible linking variables, though the cross-classifications then become rather complicated and difficult to use. A fruitful alternative approach would be to treat the linking variable as a new independent variable, and to look for new linking variables between this and the original dependent variable. In proceeding further, the linking variable can be taken as a new dependent variable, and new links sought between this and the original independent variable. In this way a series of new links can be inserted between the boxes in Figure 26.3 until the underlying cause-and-effect relationships are clarified adequately for purposes of making decisions and taking actions.

Case 4. Sometimes the direction of the relationship between the dependent variable and the first independent variable differs at different levels of a linking variable. Here, we will consider a special case where a relationship between the first two variables was not apparent until the linking variable was added to the analysis. The case is illustrated in Table 26.5, which shows some results of a survey of library-card possession in a community.

Table 26.5a indicates no statistical relationship between library-card possession and educational level; in each educational class slightly less than half the respondents had library cards. When the second independent variable (age) is added, however, as in Table 26.5b, a relationship between educational level and library-card possession becomes apparent. This relationship takes opposite directions within the two age groups, and it just happened to cancel out in the aggregate data. Specifically, among the respondents who did not complete high school, proportionately more in the younger age group had cards than in the older age group. The reverse was true, however, for respondents who had completed high school. Here, then, the third variable both links the original two variables and uncovers a relationship between these variables that happened to be canceled out in Table 26.5a, where the third variable was not controlled.

Table 26.5 Relationship Between Library-Card Possession, Educational Level, and Age (Absolute Data in Parentheses)

(a)

Library-Card Possession	*Educational Level:* *Did Not Complete High School*	*Completed High School*
Have	47%	48%
Do not have	53	52
Total per cent	100%	100%
Total cases	(180)	(350)

(b)

	Educational Level and Age			
	Did Not Complete High School		*Completed High School*	
Library-Card Possession	*Under 35*	*35 or Over*	*Under 35*	*35 or Over*
Have	72%	24%	34%	62%
Do not have	28	76	66	38
Total per cent	100%	100%	100%	100%
Total cases	(85)	(95)	(172)	(178)

Recapitulation of basic patterns in cross-classified data

We will recapitulate our discussion by comparing basic patterns that can appear in data cross-classified three ways. Consider the following blank table, to be used for presenting results of an in-plant survey on employee attitudes. The dependent variable is job-satisfaction; the two classes are "satisfied" and "dissatisfied." Two independent variables are shown, namely sex of employee (male, female) and skill level of job (skilled, unskilled):

	Sex and Skill Level			
	Male		*Female*	
Attitude	*Skilled*	*Unskilled*	*Skilled*	*Unskilled*
Satisfied				
Dissatisfied				
Total cases	(350)	(150)	(100)	(200)

Note that among the males, relatively more employees have skilled jobs, whereas the reverse is true for the females.

Now consider four alternative situations:

1. *Neither of the independent variables exhibits a statistical relationship with the dependent variable.* Let us assume that among all employees as a group, about two-thirds are satisfied. The per cent distributions for this case would then be more or less as follows:

	Male		*Female*	
	Skilled	*Unskilled*	*Skilled*	*Unskilled*
Satisfied	67%	67%	67%	67%
Dissatisfied	33%	33%	33%	33%
	(350)	(150)	(100)	(200)

Note that there are no differences in the per cent distributions as we compare males and females within each skill group and as we compare skilled and unskilled employees within each sex group.

2. *Sex is related statistically to attitude, but skill level is unrelated.* Suppose that 70 per cent of the males are satisfied but only 45 per cent of the females feel this way. The per cents then would be about as follows:

	Male		*Female*	
	Skilled	*Unskilled*	*Skilled*	*Unskilled*
Satisfied	70%	70%	45%	45%
Dissatisfied	30%	30%	55%	55%
	(350)	(150)	(100)	(200)

Here, the differences in job-satisfaction between males and females cannot be explained statistically by skill level, since the same per cent of males are satisfied in each skill level, and the same per cent of females are satisfied in each skill level. On the other hand, we observe a sharp decline in the per cent satisfied, as males and females are compared within each skill level.

3. *Skill level is related statistically to attitude, but sex is unrelated.* Suppose that 80 per cent of the skilled employees are satisfied as compared with only 40 per cent of the unskilled employees. The per cents then would be about as follows:

	Male		*Female*	
	Skilled	*Unskilled*	*Skilled*	*Unskilled*
Satisfied	80%	40%	80%	40%
Dissatisfied	20%	60%	20%	60%
	(350)	(150)	(100)	(200)

Here, 80 per cent of the male skilled employees are satisfied and 80 per cent of the female skilled employees are satisfied, as compared with 40 per cent and 40 per cent, respectively, for the unskilled employees.

4. *Both sex and skill level are related statistically to attitude.* Suppose that relatively more males than females are satisfied with their jobs at each

skill level, and that relatively more skilled workers than unskilled workers are satisfied in each sex group. The relationships among the per cents might be as follows:

	Male		*Female*	
	Skilled	*Unskilled*	*Skilled*	*Unskilled*
Satisfied	80%	40%	60%	20%
Dissatisfied	20%	60%	40%	80%
	(350)	(150)	(100)	(200)

Note in particular how the per cent of employees satisfied with their jobs declines as the skilled and unskilled employees are compared in each sex group and also as the males and females are compared within each skill group.

QUESTIONS AND PROBLEMS

26.1. Explain briefly each of the following:
- **a.** Cross-classification
- **b.** Antecedent variable
- **c.** Base of a per cent distribution

26.2. Distinguish briefly between:
- **a.** Two-way cross-classification and three-way cross-classification
- **b.** Statistical relationship and causal relationship
- **c.** Antecedent variable and linking variable

26.3. The following question was included in a mail questionnaire sent to a sample of economists, and the tabulations were published as shown below: "Assuming that the objectives of maximum employment and price stability are not compatible, please indicate which objective should be given greater emphasis in the long run if you have a firm opinion on the subject."

Response	*Number*	*Per Cent*
Maximum employment	213	35
Price stability	108	18
Other response [1]	281	47
Total	602	100

[1] Includes, in addition to no response, essay-type responses.

- **a.** Do you encounter any difficulty in evaluating the data as presented? Why, or why not?
- **b.** What formal requirement concerning classification is suggested by your answer to part **a**?

26.4. Assume that we have two separate tables presenting data on the same group of employees. In one table the employees are classified by age only, while in the other table these same employees are classified by income only.
- **a.** Will the entry for "Total, All Ages" in the first table be identical to the entry for "Total, All Incomes" in the second table? Why, or why not?
- **b.** If we had only the information contained in the two tables, could we construct a

single table in which the employees are cross-classified by age and income? Why, or why not?

c. Suppose we began with only a single table in which the employees are cross-classified by age and income. Could we construct the two separate tables described above from the data in the cross-classified table? Explain fully.

26.5. The data below were compiled in a sample survey of the housing status of families in a large metropolitan area:

	Housing Status				
Age, Head of Family	*Owns House*	*Rents House*	*Other*	*Total Per Cent*	*No. of Families*
18–24	16	57	27	100	(150)
25–34	42	52	6	100	(534)
35–44	63	32	5	100	(625)
45–54	64	31	5	100	(513)
55–64	69	25	6	100	(431)
65 and over	66	24	10	100	(411)

a. Which is the dependent variable studied in the survey? Explain.

b. Which is the independent variable?

c. Were the per cent distributions calculated on the most appropriate bases for studying the relation between the independent and dependent variables? Discuss.

d. Recast the table so that the dependent variable is in the stub of the table.

e. Is there any evidence of a statistical relationship between age of family head and housing status? Explain.

***26.6.** As part of a detailed statistical analysis of operations, management of Huron Airlines compiled the following data on seat miles flown during a recent period on its "golden triangle" routes and its other routes. (A golden triangle route is one that lies entirely within the region bounded by Pittsburgh, Detroit, Boston, New York, and Washington.)

Loaded Seat Miles, in Millions:	
Golden triangle routes	177.4
Other routes	68.2
Empty Seat Miles, in Millions:	
Golden triangle routes	53.2
Other routes	30.7

a. Assume that you are studying factors affecting the proportion of loaded seat miles and empty seat miles flown by this airline. Convert the data to per cents and present them in a cross-classified table to facilitate the study of statistical relationships. Design your table so that the base of each per cent presented in the table can be identified.

b. Support your choice of the base or bases of the per cents presented in your table.

c. What are the two variables in the cross-classification of your table?

d. Is there any indication in your table of a statistical relationship between the variables indicated in part **c**? Explain.

26.7. In a sample survey of 984 male employees of the Banda Company, the respondents were asked (among other things) whether they preferred higher income or greater leisure as personal goals for the near future. The results of this question were published in the form of per cent distributions as follows:

	Preference			
Age of Employee	*Income*	*Leisure*	*Total Per Cent*	*Number of Employees*
18–24	38	62	100	(205)
25–34	53	47	100	(217)
35–44	89	11	100	(213)
45–54	83	17	100	(196)
55–64	41	59	100	(153)
Home Ownership Status of Employee				
Owns	62	38	100	(541)
Does not own	63	37	100	(443)

a. Recast these tabulations so that the dependent variable, preference, is in the stub of the table.

b. Is there any evidence of a statistical relationship between preference and age of employee? Between preference and home ownership? Explain.

c. Could sampling variation effects create the appearance of a relationship between the variables when actually there is none, or vice versa? Explain.

d. Can cause-and-effect relationships between preference, age of employee, and home ownership be studied from the data as presented? Why, or why not?

e. Can you study the statistical relationship, if any, between age of employee and home ownership from the data as presented? Discuss.

26.8. Refer to Problem 26.7.

a. Set up a table that would help you study relationships between preference, age of employee, and home ownership, assuming the data were available in the required cross-classifications. Show the basis of the per cents by filling in the appropriate cells representing 100 per cent.

b. Enter hypothetical per cents in the table constructed in part **a** illustrating a case where there is no statistical relationship between preference, age of employee, and home ownership, and explain briefly why this conclusion can be inferred from your table.

c. Using the same tabular format, construct a set of hypothetical per cents for the case where age of employee is an antecedent factor affecting preference, but in which home ownership has no effect. Explain briefly how your data illustrate this type of case.

26.9. A life insurance company analyst studied a random sample of group life insurance policies in force with the company to determine: (1) the relation between the size of the group and the average amount of life insurance per member of the group, and (2) the factors associated with any differences in these average amounts of insurance. The initial tabulations were as follows:

Number of Members in Group	*Average Amount of Insurance per Member*	*Number of Groups in Sample*
Under 25	$8,628	230
25–99	5,970	187
100–499	5,424	96
500 or more	7,806	40

The relationship evident in these data was tested by adding various third variables for which data had been collected. When the data were stratified by type of group (employment-based or not employment-based) the tabulations shown below were obtained. Analyze the tabulation below, state any findings that are relevant to the above-mentioned purposes of the study, and support your findings by explaining how you arrived at them. Note that it has not been feasible to place the dependent variable in the stub in this tabulation.

Size of Group, Average Amount of Policy, and Number of Groups in Sample

Type of Group	*Under 25*		*25–99*		*100–499*		*500 or More*	
	Am't	*No.*	*Am't*	*No.*	*Am't*	*No.*	*Am't*	*No.*
Emp.-based	$9,980	(187)	$9,963	(84)	$9,970	(36)	$9,966	(28)
Not emp.-based	2,750	(43)	2,713	(103)	2,697	(60)	2,767	(12)

26.10. An electric and gas company conducted a sample survey to determine customer attitudes toward the company and to study factors affecting these attitudes. The replies to a question on opinion of company service were as follows, cross-classified by nature of opinion and location of customer (data are number of customers falling into each opinion-location category):

	Location of Customer	
Opinion of Service	*Metropolitan Area*	*Other Area*
Excellent or Good	1,020	570
Fair or Poor	563	180

a. Is there any indication of a statistical relationship between opinion of service and location of customer? Explain concretely how you arrived at your answer.

b. The results of adding a third variable—class of customer—to the cross-classified data are shown below. Convert these data to per cents and present them in a table so that relationships between the dependent and independent variables can be studied readily. Be sure to set up the table in such a way that the base of each per cent can be ascertained.

	Location and Type of Customer			
	Metropolitan Area		*Other Area*	
Opinion of Service	*Residential*	*Commercial*	*Residential*	*Commercial*
Excellent or Good	862	158	525	45
Fair or Poor	75	488	45	135

c. Are any new insights obtained into factors affecting customer attitude when the third variable is added to the data? Explain, and relate your answer directly to your table constructed in part **b**.

d. Would sampling variation effects be likely to account for your conclusion based on the introduction of the third variable? Explain. What is the value of knowing the size of the base of each per cent in the table in this connection?

***26.11.** In a consumer research project in a test city, 850 housewives in a panel were asked to keep records of selected purchases for a two-month period. As part of the research project a new "triple action" detergent was introduced in the city at the beginning of the project and was advertised throughout the project. At the end of the period, each housewife in the panel was classified as a buyer or non-buyer of the detergent. The following results were obtained when the panel data were cross-classified by number of children under 18 living at home (none, one or more) and buying behavior of housewife (buyer, non-buyer):

No children: 88 buyers; 187 non-buyers
One or more children: 317 buyers; 258 non-buyers

a. Convert these data to per cents and present them in a table employing cross-classification, so that any statistical relationship between buying action and presence of children can be studied readily.

b. What base or bases did you use for the per cents calculated in part **a**? What was the reason for your choice?

c. Does there appear to be a statistical relationship between buying action and presence of children? Indicate the basis for your conclusion, and describe the relationship if there appears to be one.

d. The following results were obtained when the data given above were stratified by a third variable, namely, degree of concern of housewife with environmental pollution (concerned, unconcerned):

No children, concerned: 26 buyers; 56 non-buyers
No children, unconcerned: 62 buyers; 131 non-buyers
One or more children, concerned: 127 buyers; 103 non-buyers
One or more children, unconcerned: 190 buyers; 155 non-buyers

Convert these data to per cents and present them in a table employing cross-classification, so that relationships between the three variables can be studied.

e. Does the conclusion obtained previously in part **c** continue to hold when the third variable is added? Explain.

f. Is there an indication in your second table of a statistical relationship between degree of concern with environmental pollution and buying action? Explain the basis for your answer.

26.12. The Essex Optical Company studied factors affecting absenteeism of production workers in one of its plants. The following results were obtained when the data collected in the study were cross-classified by sex of employee and attendance record:

Number of Employees Having Satisfactory Records

Male	1,441
Female	991

Number of Employees Having Unsatisfactory Records

Male	811
Female	508

a. Convert these data to per cents and present them in a table employing cross-classification, so that any statistical relationship between the variables can be studied readily.

b. What base or bases did you use for the per cents calculated in part **a**? What was the reason for your choice?

c. Is there an indication of a statistical relationship between the variables in your table? Explain.

d. When a third variable, marital status, was added to the analysis, the following results were obtained:

Male, married and living with spouse: 1,298 satisfactory; 473 unsatisfactory
Male, other marital status: 143 satisfactory; 338 unsatisfactory
Female, married and living with spouse: 326 satisfactory; 461 unsatisfactory
Female, other marital status: 665 satisfactory; 47 unsatisfactory

Convert these data to per cents and present them in a table employing cross-classification, so that cause-and-effect relationships between the dependent and independent variables can be studied readily.

e. From your table constructed in part **d**, does there seem to be a statistical relationship between attendance record and employee's sex? Between attendance record and marital status? Discuss fully, and indicate what inferences the data suggest about cause-and-effect relationships between the variables.

Chapter

27

PRESENTATION

Statistical data must be presented effectively, both as an aid to analysis and for communicating the results of analysis. Without effective presentation, statistical data lose much of their value and impact. In this chapter, we shall study two basic, self-contained, and complementary techniques for presenting statistical data, namely statistical tables and graphs.

27.1 FUNCTIONAL PARTS AND CONSTRUCTION OF STATISTICAL TABLES

Analytical and reference tables

A statistical table is a method of presenting and arranging data that have been broken down by one or more systems of classification. One may distinguish, somewhat arbitrarily, between analytical tables and reference tables.

(27.1) An ***analytical table*** is designed to aid in a formal analysis of interrelationships between variables. A ***reference table*** is designed to serve as a repository of statistical information.

We employed analytical tables extensively in the preceding chapter on cross-classification. In turning to reference tables, we should first note that these tables are also called *source, repository,* or *general purpose* tables. Typically they are found in descriptive reports or studies, and also in appendices of analytical studies to show the source data on which the analytical tables are based. Reference tables often contain too much data to permit ready analysis of interrelationships between variables. Hence when

Table 27.1 Universal Oil Company, New Investment in Property, Plant, and Equipment, 1972, Classified by Location and Function (Millions of Dollars)

Function	*Location*		
	Total, All Locations	*United States*	*Foreign*
Total, all functions	1,046 [1]	484	562
Producing	414	306	108
Refining	223	35	188
Marketing	290	90	200
Transportation	64	27	37
Other	55	26	29

[1] Does not include $228 million in non-capitalized exploration expenses.

interrelationships are to be analyzed, simpler analytical tables are constructed to facilitate the study of particular relationships.

The distinction between analytical and reference tables lies primarily in their use, not in their construction. The basic structural features of both types of tables are the same. Consider Table 27.1, which is a reference table; it has the same structural features as the analytical tables already discussed. The major functional parts of Table 27.1, and of statistical tables in general, are shown in Figure 27.1. Let us study each part in turn.

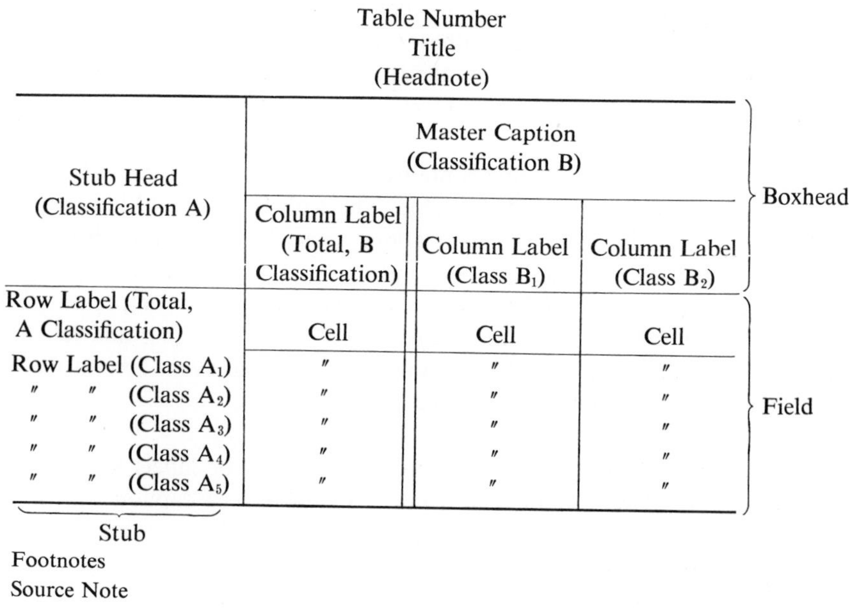

Figure 27.1. The major functional parts of a statistical table containing two classifications, cross-classified

Structural elements of tables

Table number. The table number permits one to cite a given table readily. For ease of reference, tables are numbered according to their order of appearance in a report or presentation. When only one table appears in a report or presentation, the table number is sometimes omitted.

Title. The title of a table indicates the table's contents. In general, the title should answer at least the following questions about the activity for which data in the table are presented: *What? Where? When?* Frequently, the question, *How classified?* is also answered in the title. In composing a title one should avoid two extremes: (1) over-elaborate description of the material presented in the table, and (2) extreme brevity in which not enough information is furnished about the table's contents. Sometimes it is helpful to present a title in two parts by placing a concise eyecatching phrase above an expanded statement of the contents of the table.

Headnote. A headnote appears near the title and provides information relating to the table as a whole or to a major part of the table. In some cases, headnotes provide additional title information that has been crowded out of the title in the interest of brevity; for example, a headnote may explain that the data in the table are based upon a sample. In other cases, a headnote will qualify or define something stated in the title; headnotes frequently are used in this way to indicate the units in which the data in the table are stated. Headnotes are not always needed; when they are used, they may be placed in parentheses immediately following the title, or with or without parentheses below the title, depending upon the style that is being followed.

Stub. The stub of a table contains: (1) the *stub head,* and (2) the labels to the individual rows of the table. The stub head should be used to indicate the classification or classifications appearing below it in the row labels.

Every row in a table should have a label that describes the data presented in that row. When more than one classification is presented in the stub of a table, special care must be taken in arranging and labeling the rows so that readers will know the relationship of every row to the overall classification scheme in the table.

Boxhead. The boxhead contains the *captions,* or labels to the columns, of a table. Every column in a table should have a caption describing the class for which the data in that column are presented. In addition, all columns presenting data for individual classes within a common classification may be spanned by a label indicating that classification.

Labels in the stub and boxhead of a table should be placed horizontally, not vertically, so that they can be read easily.

Footnote. Footnotes are most often used to explain or to qualify a *particular* item or group of items in a table. An example is found in Table 27.1, where the footnote qualifies the cell entry relating to total new investment.

Source note. The source note indicates the origin of the data presented in a table. This note serves two purposes. First, it gives proper recognition to the person or organization that compiled or published the data. Second, it is an aid in evaluating the reliability of the data, and it permits one to verify the data and obtain additional information by consulting the source of these data. Thus, a source note should be complete enough to serve both of these purposes. When the source of the data in a table is obvious—as, for example, in the case of financial data of a corporation included in that corporation's annual report—the source note is usually omitted. When a source note is included in a table, it generally is placed at the bottom of the table; less frequently, it appears in the form of a headnote below the title.

Field. The field or body of a table contains the statistical data presented in the table. Each entry is presented in a *cell,* the basic unit of presentation in the table. A cell consists of the intersection of a given column and a given row; hence the meaning of the data in this cell is indicated by the combined labels of the intersecting column and row. This framework is shown schematically in Figure 27.1, where each cell is related simultaneously to both systems of classification, A and B.

It is important that every cell should have an entry. If the proper entry for a cell is zero, this zero should be entered in the cell. If the information for a cell is not available, this fact should be indicated, preferably by entering the letters N.A. (not available) in the cell or by a footnote. When a cell is left blank, readers do not know whether the proper entry should have been zero, N.A., or some number that was inadvertently omitted.

Additional examples of tables

Cross-classified tables. The tables used in Chapter 26 were cross-classified tables. Figure 27.1 shows the general form of a table for presenting data cross-classified two ways. For a three-way cross-classification, the table may be constructed in two basic ways: (1) One variable is located in the stub and the other two variables are in the columns. (2) Two variables are located in the stub and one is in the columns.

We used the first method in Chapter 26, since we followed the standard practice of locating the dependent variable in the stub. Table 27.2 shows an example of the second method. Dollar sales data are presented for a company that operates a group of variety stores. The sales data are broken down simultaneously by three systems of classification: merchandise line, location of store, and ownership status of store. Two classifications are

Table 27.2 Ace Dry Goods Association,
Dollar Sales in Stores in 1971, Classified by Merchandise
Line, Store Location, and Store Ownership (Millions of Dollars)

Location and Ownership Status of Store	*Merchandise Line*		
	Total, Both Lines	*Line A*	*Line B*
Total, downtown districts and suburban centers			
Total, owned and franchised	264	143	121
Owned stores	240	130	110
Franchised stores	24	13	11
Downtown districts			
Total, owned and franchised	187	99	88
Owned stores	170	90	80
Franchised stores	17	9	8
Suburban centers			
Total, owned and franchised	77	44	33
Owned stores	70	40	30
Franchised stores	7	4	3

presented in the stub and one in the columns. The stub head indicates both classifications appearing below it. Indenting and spacing is used to help readers interrelate the classifications in the stub and to associate labels with appropriate rows. The classification as to merchandise line is presented straightforwardly in the columns.

If a four-way cross-classification must be presented in a table, two classifications could be placed in the columns and two in the stub. Alternatively, three classifications could be presented in the stub and one in the columns, or vice versa. When too many classifications are presented in one table, however, the resulting table may be too complex. Ordinarily it then is better to present the data in a series of simpler tables.

Tables not cross-classified. When there is but one system of classification, it usually is presented in the stub; the body of the table then can consist of a single column, showing the data for each class specified in the stub.

However, a table may contain many columns and rows without necessarily presenting cross-classified data. An example is presented in Figure 27.2, which shows a typical tabular format used by corporations in presenting reviews of operations in annual reports. Each column gives data on a particular item, such as capital expenditures, depreciation and depletion, and so on. The data in each column are classified by year, but note that there is no cross-classification. The arrangement in Figure 27.2 is useful for presenting data on diverse but related items, all classified individually by one common system of classification, such as time. Indeed, Figure 27.2 is merely a group of individual one-way tables that happen to have a common stub, hence are placed side-by-side to facilitate comparisons.

Year	Capital Expenditures	Depreciation and Depletion	Sales	Number of Employees
1967				
1966				
1965				
1964				
1963				

Figure 27.2. Example of format of a multiple-column table without cross-classification

27.2 ADDITIONAL CONCEPTS AND PROCEDURES IN TABULAR PRESENTATION

Emphasis on important comparisons

Tables should be set up in such a way that readers can make the important comparisons most easily. For example, in Table 27.2 it is easy to compare sales by merchandise line because the relevant data are located side-by-side in adjoining columns. On the other hand, it is more laborious to compare sales in owned stores in different locations and to compare sales in franchised stores in different locations, because the relevant data are not in adjoining rows. In tables that are relatively complex, all possible comparisons cannot be facilitated to the same degree. One must judge which comparisons are most important and design the table accordingly.

To be sure, there are times when purely mechanical considerations govern the arrangement of data in a table. For example, when a classification requires a lengthy list of classes, or requires long and detailed labels, it is most efficient to present this classification in the stub. Here more space is generally available for listing and labeling.

Order of classes

Various methods of arranging classes within their respective classifications are employed. Choice of method depends upon the nature of the data and the purpose of the table. In reference tables, classes are frequently arranged in alphabetical order, so that users can locate a particular figure easily. Another widely used method, employed when the variable is quantitative, is to arrange the classes in order of magnitude or size. For instance, income classes are usually listed from lowest to highest incomes. When data are classified chronologically—for example, by year—either the most recent or the most distant period is listed first, and the other periods are listed in appropriate chronology. In still other cases, convention determines the order of the classes.

Use of summary columns and rows

Summary columns and rows present totals, averages, or other summary data. Proper use of summary columns and rows is an important feature of effective tabular presentation. Columns or rows with labels such as "total" or "average" are particularly useful devices in reference tables, because they enable users to ascertain aggregate data at a glance for one or more classifications.

It is good practice to include all summary columns and rows for each classification within a table when first learning to make tables; later one can omit any that are not needed. In analytical tables, for instance, some of the summary columns or rows are frequently unnecessary and can be omitted without impairing the effectiveness of the table.

Summary columns and rows can be placed to the left and above, respectively, of the columns and rows whose data they summarize (as in Table 27.1), or to the right and below (as in Table 27.3). Placing summary data

Table 27.3 Tech-Systems Corporation, Distribution of Preferred and Common Shares by Class of Holder, as of December 31, 1972

Class of Holder	*Type of Stock*					
	Preferred		*Common*		*Total, All Stocks*	
	Thousands of Shares	*Per Cent*	*Thousands of Shares*	*Per Cent*	*Thousands of Shares*	*Per Cent*
Individuals	1,357	37.7	31,330	57.9	32,687	56.6
Nominees and brokers	1,229	34.1	17,892	33.1	19,121	33.1
Others	1,017	28.2	4,908	9.1	5,925	10.3
Total, all holders	3,603	100.0	54,130	100.0	57,733	100.0

Note: Details may not add to totals because of rounding.

to the left and above will generally lead readers to concentrate on them first, while placing the summary data to the right and below will subordinate them to the individual components. Summary data should be labeled specifically. The label "Total" used alone usually is not too helpful when the table contains several classifications. Rather, specific designations such as "Total, All Locations" or "Total, All Functions" give more help to readers. To help readers still further, summary columns and rows should be differentiated in some way from the individual columns and rows they summarize, as in the tables in this chapter, where special rules are used for this purpose.

In cases where the data in a table are averages or ratios, the summary columns and rows contain weighted averages of the measures in the constituent rows or columns.

Presentation of per cent data

Statistical tables frequently contain per cent data. Some tables contain only per cents, while others contain both per cent and absolute data. The construction of tables presenting per cent data follows the principles already discussed for tables in general. Hence, only two particular points need be added here.

Presentation of absolute and per cent data in same table. Some reference tables, and many analytical tables, contain both per cent and absolute data. Each type of data gives important information. Per cent data facilitate comparisons so that interrelationships between variables can be studied readily. Per cent data or other ratios do not, however, show in themselves the magnitude of the base from which the ratios were calculated. When knowledge of this magnitude is important for assessing the significance of per cents to be shown in tabular form, absolute data indicating the magnitude of the base also should be given.

There are various methods for doing this. Tables in the preceding chapter, in which the absolute data were given in parentheses, demonstrate a method widely used in setting up simple analytical tables. When tables are more complex, however, or when one intends to present the complete set of absolute data as well as the per cents, this simple procedure would be unwieldy. A more formal arrangement is then used, such as in Table 27.3, where each column is labeled to indicate the type of data contained. This method is most often followed in reference tables, but it is used in some analytical tables as well.

Reason for presenting summary "100 per cent" figures in columns and rows. At first thought it may seem pointless to include figures indicating "100 per cent," since users of the table already know that the components of a per cent distribution total 100 per cent. Actually, such figures can serve an important function for per cent data. They tell users the base of each per cent, or in other words, whether the per cent distributions are calculated over rows or columns. In Table 27.3, for instance, the 100 per cent figures inform us immediately that the per cent distributions are formed over the stockholder classes. When the bases are self-evident, the "100 per cent" figures may be omitted for simplification.

Often the per cents will not total 100 exactly in some columns or rows, because a fraction of a per cent is gained or lost as the net result of rounding when the per cent components are computed. In that event, one may include a note at the bottom of the table, explaining that details may not add to totals because of rounding. The problem of components that do not add exactly to their totals is not confined to the presentation of per cent data, but may arise whenever one presents rounded numbers. The type of note illustrated in Table 27.3 will cover all such cases.

Use of horizontal and vertical rules

Various ways of breaking up space in tables can be chosen, so that data can be related easily to the appropriate column and row labels. Horizontal rules, vertical rules, and blank space can all be used. We have employed two basic formats for illustrative purposes. In the tables in Chapter 26, blank space was used, in conjunction with spanning rules for headings. In the tables in this chapter, vertical and horizontal rules are the primary method.

27.3 GRAPHIC PRESENTATION

Graphic presentation is an important complement to tabular presentation. In graphs, statistical data are presented in terms of *visually interpreted magnitudes*. Here, essential facts and relationships that might be difficult to recognize in masses of statistical data can be brought out clearly. In this section, we shall briefly survey the uses of graphs, including the problems and limitations encountered. Then, in following sections, we shall examine the basic designs in which the majority of graphs serving a management function appear.

We may distinguish, somewhat arbitrarily to be sure, between two important ways in which graphs are employed. First, graphs are used to present conclusions or results of analysis. Second, graphs are used to present statistical data in a way that facilitates evaluation of the data. An example will best illustrate each method of use.

Presentation of results of analysis

Figure 27.3 shows how graphic presentation can provide a quick, simple, and effective picture of the results of analysis. Note how a set of graphs was employed to contrast changes in key monetary aggregates in commercial banks during the most recent year compared with the previous two years.

Aid in evaluation

Figure 27.4 shows how a graph can be used to present statistical information in a way that facilitates evaluation. Data on monthly and cumulative production of an item are presented together with a standard, cumulative planned production, in such a way that actual production can be compared readily with the standard. In Figure 27.4, management is quickly notified that cumulative actual production for May and June has fallen behind cumulative planned production.

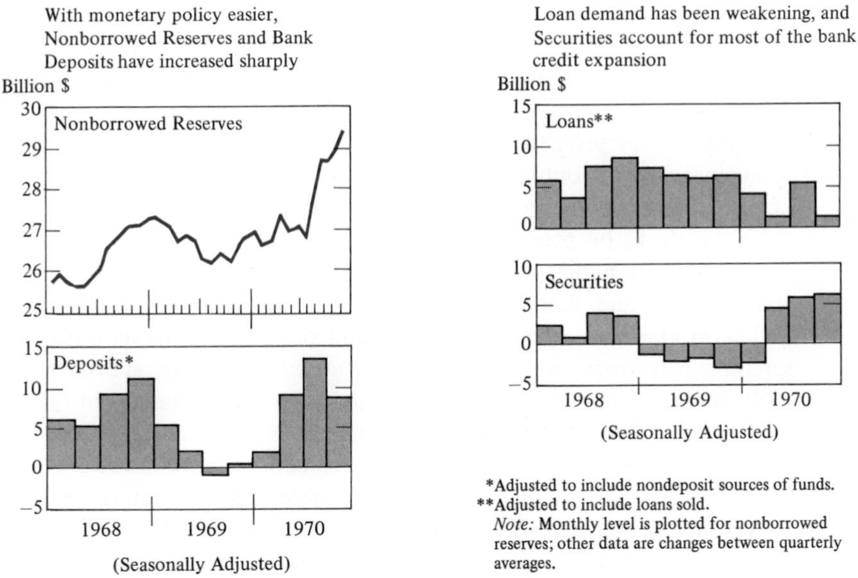

Adapted from: Survey of Current Business, January 1971, p. 19.

Figure 27.3. Example of a set of graphs presenting the results of analysis

Figure 27.4 is typical of graphs designed to aid management in evaluating and controlling operations. In graphs of this type, key variables such as measurements of performance or operating results are compared with relevant standards, forecasts, or other quantitatively defined objectives to determine whether actual operations are meeting the objectives. By periodi-

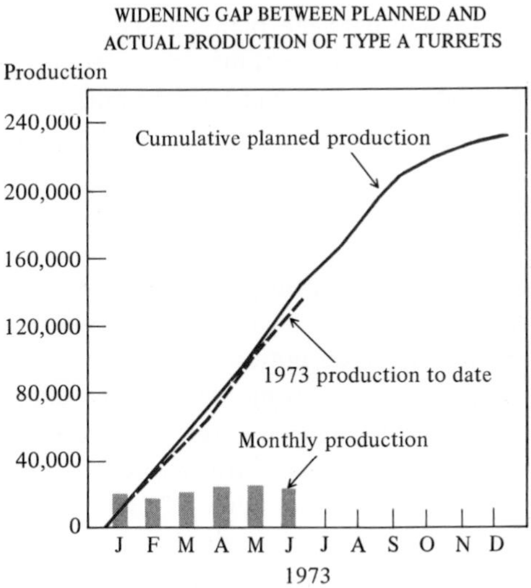

Figure 27.4. Example of a graph used in evaluation and control

cally reviewing an integrated series of such graphs, management obtains a quick and effective picture of operations. This review aids in evaluating performance and identifying potential trouble spots or causes of existing difficulties.

A number of problems are encountered when graphs are used as tools of evaluation and control. First, it must be decided which variables are the key ones to be reviewed periodically; this problem arises whether or not the data are to be presented graphically. In some firms the key variables are selected by management; in others, review and analysis is primarily a staff function and staff specialists select the variables. Some managements review production, sales, inventories, and other functions as more or less separate categories, while others focus attention on one special variable, such as rate of return on investment, and then study changes in other factors or areas in terms of their effect on the key variable. Obviously, the value of graphs when used as aids to evaluation and control depends on the usefulness and significance of the variables selected for review.

Another problem arises from the fact that the graphs must be simple and easily understood, yet meaningful for evaluation. Thus, when a complex situation is being studied, it is usually better to separate the data into component elements and to analyze them by means of a series of graphs rather than to overload one graph.

A third problem concerns the conclusion one can obtain from an analysis of graphs. Properly constructed graphs are a most useful device for presenting results of operations and relating these to objectives. Graphs seldom supply, however, the decision-making implications of the relationships shown. They display the relationships, so that these can be seen quickly by management, but management must then analyze the situation to determine the appropriate course of action. For example, Figure 27.4 does not indicate whether the lag between planned and actual cumulative production is substantial enough to require some special action. Management must make this analysis, and frequently will have to initiate a special study in cases of this kind to obtain further information on the problem.

Misuse of graphs

Unfortunately it is necessary to include some comments on misuse of graphs. Presenting data in terms of visually interpreted magnitudes offers great opportunities for deception.

Figure 27.5 illustrates some commonly encountered ways in which graphs are designed to mislead careless readers. The same set of sales data is plotted in all three graphs of this figure, yet notice how first impressions about each graph differ. In Figure 27.5a, the sales fluctuations appear to be moderate; Figure 27.5b gives the impression of substantial sales fluctuations, while Figure 27.5c gives the impression that sales scarcely fluctuated. Figure 27.5a has a conventional graphic format; in contrast, Figure 27.5c

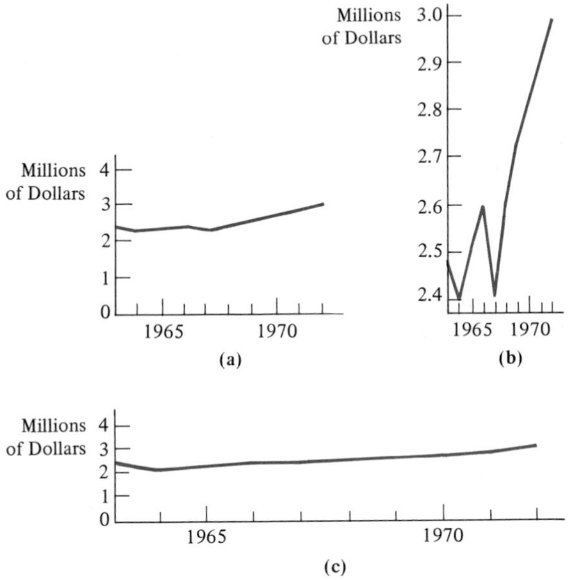

Figure 27.5. Three variations of a graph showing the same data

has substantially different proportions for the two scales, which flattens out the appearance of the sales fluctuations, as compared with that in Figure 27.5a. Figure 27.5b gives the impression of significant fluctuations in sales, with a sharp increase from 1967 to 1972, because the vertical scale begins arbitrarily at $2.4 million and is elongated relative to the horizontal scale.

If one takes a quick look at the three graphs in Figure 27.5 and does not pay much attention to the scales and other technical details, one will certainly receive different impressions of the fluctuations in sales. Yet this does not justify the view, taken by some, that graphs are worthless. Note that just a little study of any one of the graphs in Figure 27.5, including especially an examination of the scales, would make it possible to grasp the actual situation.

27.4 BAR CHARTS

Construction and interpretation of bar charts

A bar chart is easy to construct and can be readily interpreted, even by people who are not "chart-minded."

Figure 27.6 presents a bar chart, showing the Easton Glass Company's 1971 sales of different types of containers, each sales volume expressed as

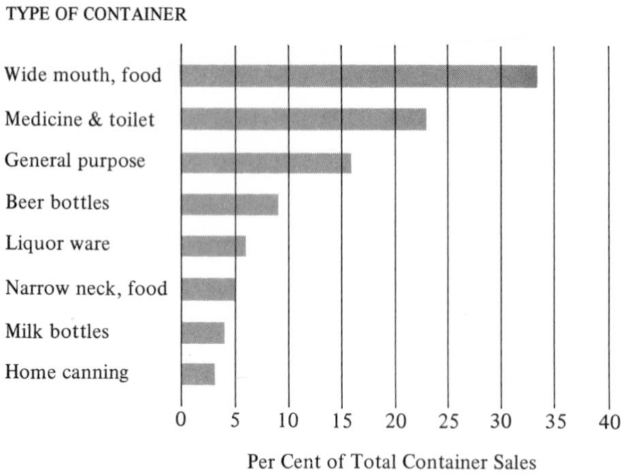

Figure 27.6. Sales of containers by type, expressed as a per cent of total container sales, Easton Glass, Inc., 1971

a per cent of total container sales. Note that magnitudes are shown by the lengths of the various bars, which have been laid out with reference to a horizontal *scale*. The scale markings are shown below the bottom bar and are carried up through the *grid,* or plotting surface of the chart, by *grid lines.* The bars are identified by labels in the *stub* of the chart. The stub has been kept as small as possible, in order to leave the greatest amount of space for the plotting surface.

Several aspects of the arrangement of the bars should be noted: (1) The bars differ only in length, not in width. (2) A space has been left between each bar to make it easier to identify each bar by its label. (3) The bars have been ranked by order of magnitude to facilitate analysis. The order may be a decreasing one, as it is here, or it may be an increasing one, in which case the shortest bar would be placed at the top. If an "all others" or "miscellaneous" category is present, it usually is shown as the lowest bar. Even though the lowest position may not be proper according to the ranking of magnitudes, it is appropriate, since this type of category most often is a collection of relatively unimportant classes. A bar representing an average is sometimes shown as the top bar for emphasis. Also, such a bar is often shaded or colored in a distinctive manner so that it will stand out as a basis for comparisons.

Importance of the zero line

A chart that has been designed to show absolute magnitudes should have a clearly defined zero line and an unbroken amount scale. The reason for this requirement can be understood by comparing the impressions given by Figures 27.7a and 27.7b. Each chart shows the net retail sales of the various outlets of Coastwise Stores, Inc., for the year ended February 6, 1971.

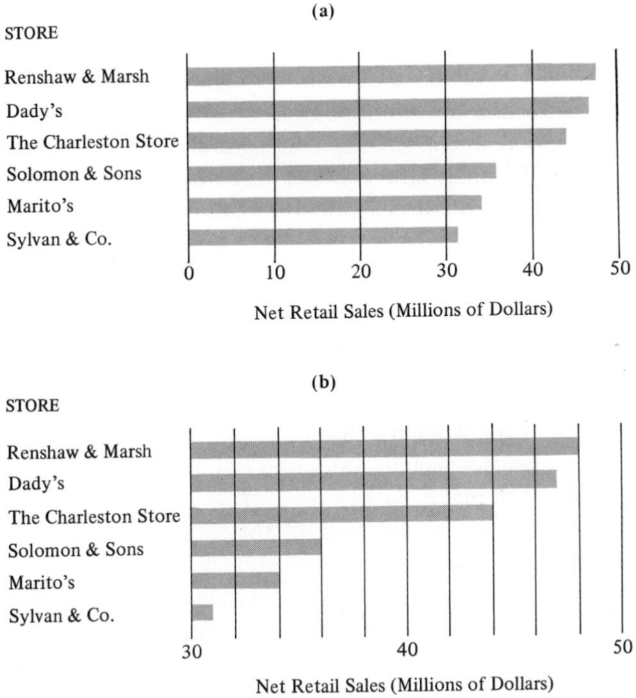

Figure 27.7. Net sales of outlets of Coastwise Stores, Inc., for the year ended February 6, 1971

Figure 27.7a clearly shows that sales were greater in certain stores than in others during this period; however, it also indicates that the differences in sales between the stores were not exceptionally large in view of the sales volumes involved. Figure 27.7b, on the other hand, suggests that the stores differed tremendously with respect to sales volume. The two charts give different impressions because the scale in Figure 27.7a begins at zero, while the scale in Figure 27.7b begins at $30 million. Thus, in Figure 27.7b, it is difficult to relate the differences in sales volumes between stores to the actual magnitudes of sales involved. If a graph is to permit comparisons of absolute magnitudes, the amount scale of the graph should begin at zero and continue without any break. This is true not only for bar charts, but also for other types of charts in which absolute magnitudes are to be compared.

An exception to the above principle sometimes is made when the data to be plotted are such that one bar would be very much longer than the others. If all the bars were to be plotted to a scale designed to accommodate the single very long bar, the other bars would be cramped into a restricted portion of the grid, and a comparison between their magnitudes could not be made readily. In this case, the long bar is sometimes broken, and the scale is set to accommodate the other bars.

Other types of horizontal bar charts

The bar charts discussed so far utilize individual, unsegmented bars measured in one direction along a horizontal axis. While this type of bar arrangement is the most basic one, several important adaptations are often employed. We shall now consider three of these: the component-part bar chart, the grouped bar chart, and the duo-directional bar chart.

Component-part bar chart. Figure 27.8a, a component-part bar chart, shows sales for major departments of J. Nicholby and Company during June 1972, broken down by account and cash sales. This chart is similar to those shown in our previous examples, except that each bar has been segmented into its component parts. For example, the top bar shows the total sales in the women's ready-to-wear department. This total consists of two components—account sales of $275,000 and cash sales of $150,000—which together make up the total of $425,000. This chart allows visual comparison of the relative size of the account and cash sales within each department, total sales by departments, and finally, account and cash sales by departments. Since the "cash" components in each bar do not all begin at the same point along the horizontal scale, it is more difficult to compare the cash sales than the account sales.

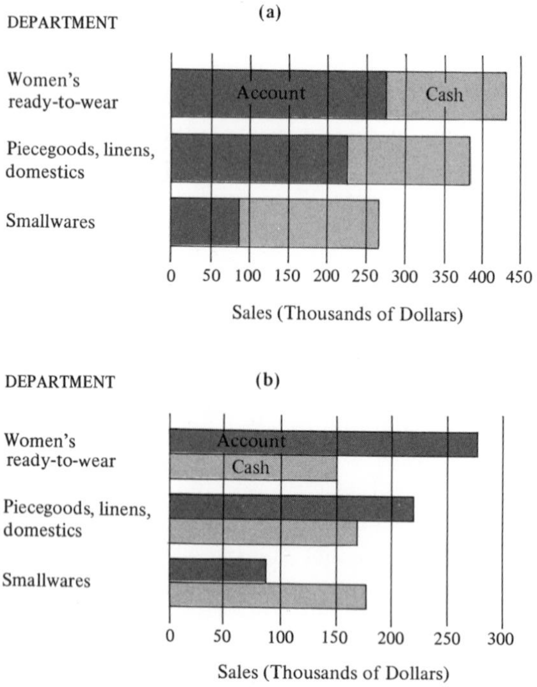

Figure 27.8. Sales by major departments, J. Nicholby and Co., June 1972

Grouped bar chart. If only comparisons between the account and cash sales within a department and between departments were important, a grouped bar chart such as that shown in Figure 27.8b could be constructed. This chart presents the same data as Figure 27.8a, except that the two types of sales are shown separately for ease in comparing sales by type within and between departments. The grouped bars do not enable one to compare total sales for each department readily.

Duo-directional bar chart. When one wishes to chart positive and negative quantities, such as gains and losses, percentage changes from one time period to the next, and positive and negative deviations around a norm, a duo-directional bar chart is a useful device. Figure 27.9, containing this kind of chart, indicates how bars can be plotted on either side of a vertical

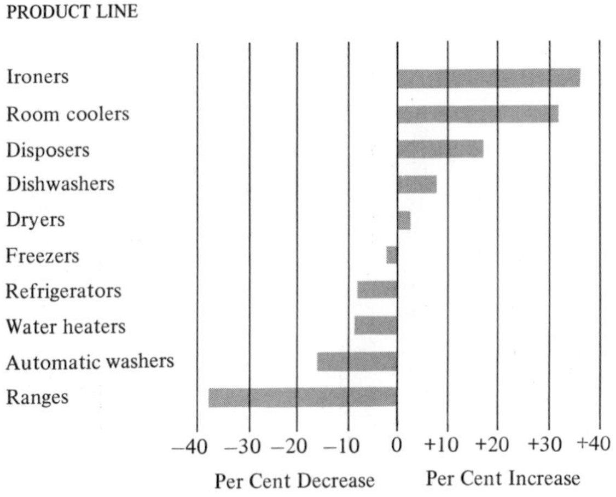

Figure 27.9. Per cent changes in sales of appliances, Dillingham-Smith, Inc., between fiscal years 1970 and 1971

base or zero line, enabling one to represent both positive and negative quantities on the same chart. Figure 27.9 utilizes simple bars, but component-part bars and grouped bars also can be used in duo-directional charts. Whenever possible, the bars are ranked in descending order. This arrangement aids in the analysis of the graph. Figure 27.9, for instance, enables one to see quickly which product lines indicated the largest relative increases or decreases in sales, and to compare these changes.

Vertical bar charts

We have now examined the three basic types of bar arrangements—the simple bar, the component-part bar, and the grouped bar. These bars have been plotted along a horizontal scale in the charts previously studied. Bars may also be plotted vertically, as in the charts shown in Figure 27.10; charts of this type sometimes are called *column charts.*

Our previous discussion of horizontal bar charts applies also to vertical bar charts. Only one point need be added here: Accompanying explanatory material, such as identifying labels for the bars, can be included far more conveniently when the bars are horizontal than vertical. Prove this point by attempting to recast Figure 27.7, for example, into columnar form.

Vertical bar charts are used chiefly for the presentation, analysis, and interpretation of time series data—for example, data as to sales, production,

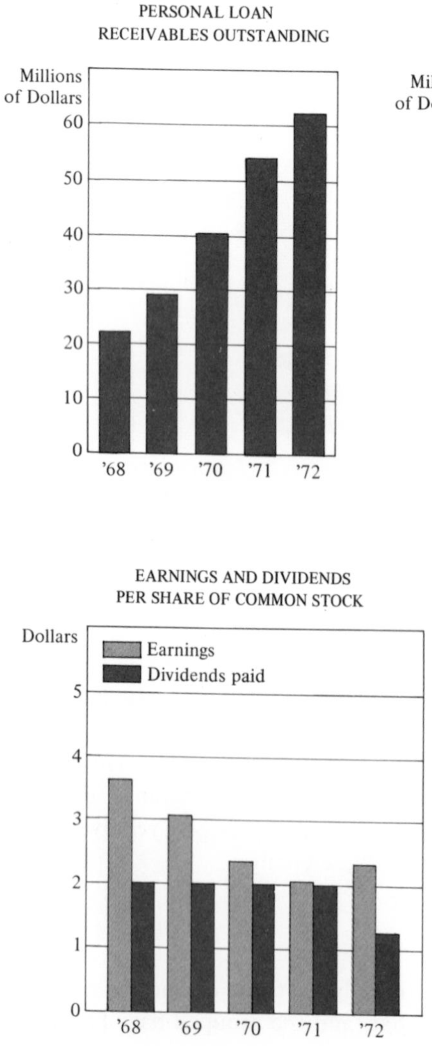

Figure 27.10. Some typical vertical bar charts appearing in annual reports of corporations

or inventories over successive periods of time. It is conventional to plot time along the horizontal axis of the chart, while magnitude is plotted along the vertical axis. A bar graph will present time series data effectively if the number of time periods plotted is not too great.

27.5 TIME SERIES LINE GRAPHS

Construction and interpretation of line graphs

When data covering a large number of time periods must be presented, bar graphs may become cluttered. Lines then are more effective than bars, especially when there are marked fluctuations in the data or when several series must be presented on the same chart.

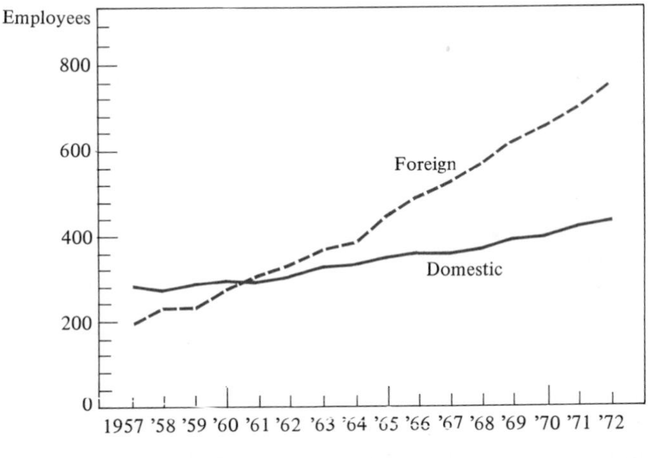

Figure 27.11. Computer Services, Inc., number of employees in domestic and foreign operations, 1957–1972

A typical line graph is presented in Figure 27.11 on number of employees in domestic and foreign operations of Computer Services, Inc. from 1957 to 1972 inclusive. The time scale is conventionally plotted on the *X* or horizontal axis, and the number of employees on the *Y* or vertical axis. Each series is plotted independently and the points connected by short straight lines. A line graph can contain one or more series, but of course too many series will tend to clutter the graph and make it ineffective.

Figure 27.12 contains some additional line graphs. Note the use of shading in Figure 27.12a to accentuate the impression given by the line. Note also that the labeling of the time scale in Figure 27.12a differs from that

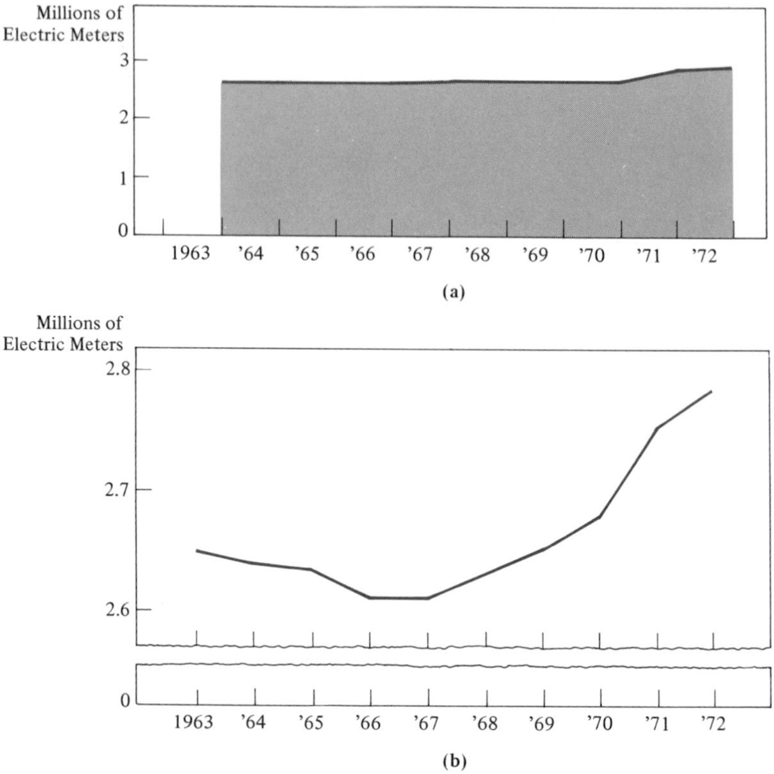

Figure 27.12. Metropolitan Gas and Electric Company, electric meters in operation, 1963–1972 (data as of December 31)

used in Figures 27.11 and 27.12b. In Figure 27.12a an *interval* on the *X* axis, rather than a *point,* is labeled to designate each year. Since the number of meters relates to the end of the year, the number for a given year is plotted at the right end of the interval for that year. If the number of meters had related to the beginning of the year, the number would be plotted at the left end of the interval, and so on. If the series does not relate to a specific point during the time period—for instance, if it shows average monthly number of meters in operation during the year—the data would be plotted by convention at the midpoint of the interval for each respective year.

Figure 27.12a shows that there has been some increase in the number of meters during the ten-year period, but that the increase has been relatively small. To interpret a line graph with an arithmetic *Y* scale—that is, the type of *Y* scale shown in Figures 27.11 and 27.12a—note that the scale begins at zero and that equal amounts of increase require equal vertical distances along this scale. Hence, if a point on Figure 27.12a is plotted twice as high as another, the amount represented by the first point is twice as great as that represented by the second. Furthermore, the steeper the slope of a line on the graph, the greater the *amount* of change that occurred during the period under consideration. Thus, Figure 27.12a shows that the annual increase in the number of meters in operation was greater during the latter part of the ten-year period than during the middle part because the slope of the curve is steeper.

Break in Y scale

Sometimes one is particularly interested in studying the *changes* that occur in a series, even at the sacrifice of some perspective on the relative importance of these changes in terms of the absolute magnitudes of the data. An ordinary line chart may not be effective for such a study of changes, as can be seen from Figure 27.12a. Here, a large amount of the plotting surface is used to indicate the absolute magnitudes of the data; hence the portrayal of year-to-year changes in the series is compressed into a small portion of the graph. In this situation, the Y scale can be broken and the appropriate portion elongated to utilize most of the plotting surface for accentuating the changes. Figure 27.12b, which shows the same data as Figure 27.12a, illustrates this procedure. Note that the break has been carried across the graph to alert the reader.

Sometimes a break in the Y scale is indicated only by a zigzag in the line denoting the Y axis, and at other times the Y scale shows no break but simply begins at some arbitrary value. Hence one must always check the scale before interpreting a line graph—or any graph. As a case in point, note how an unwary reader could make different interpretations of Figures 27.12a and 27.12b, although the same data are plotted in the two graphs.

Per cent change line graph

Figure 27.13 shows another adaptation of an arithmetic line chart designed to answer questions mainly about changes in one or more series.

The Lovejoy Toy Company wished to study the comparative behavior of unit production costs and selling prices for one of its products—a toy fire engine—from the second quarter of 1969, when the firm had substituted a plastic for a metal model, to the end of 1972. The unit production costs and selling prices during the second quarter of 1969 each were designated as 100 per cent, and subsequent quarterly costs and selling prices were expressed as percentages of the figures for the second quarter of 1969. In terms of this relationship, the per cent relative 105 for the selling price as of the last quarter of 1970 means that the selling price in that period was 105 per cent as great as that of the second quarter of 1969. Note on the chart that since fluctuations around the 100 per cent line—that is, around the level for the second quarter of 1969—are of chief interest, this line has become, in effect, the base line of the chart. Hence it is not necessary to

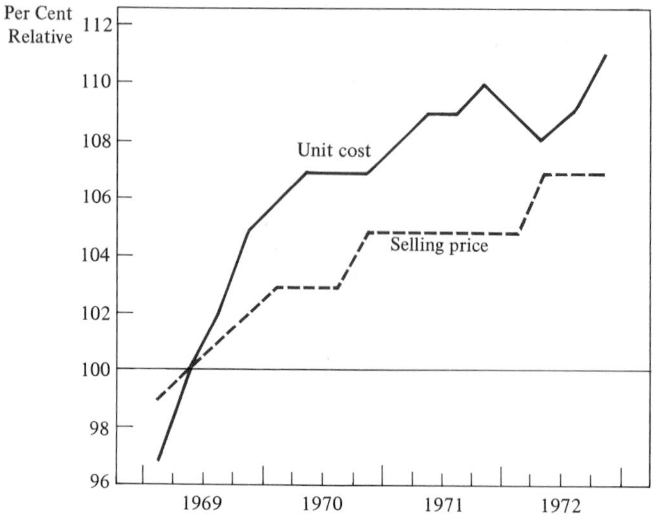

Figure 27.13. Selling prices and unit costs of toy fire engines produced by Lovejoy Toy Company, 1969–1972 (second quarter 1969 = 100)

extend the *Y* axis of Figure 27.13 downward to zero nor to show a break in the scale.

Figure 27.13 clearly indicates that the unit production cost of toy fire engines has increased, relatively, more than selling price since the base period, in spite of a temporary decline in costs early in 1972. Thus, this chart is an effective device for presenting and analyzing relative changes *since a given date.*

Component-part line graph

Corresponding to the subdivided or component-part bar graph is the component-part line graph. Figure 27.14a presents a component-part line graph showing annual sales of the Tech-Systems Corporation from 1963 to 1972, classified by type of sale. We can study changes in the total annual sales volume by examining the top line of the graph; in addition, we can study changes in each type of sale by examining the bands representing each component. The vertical distance covered by each band represents the magnitude of the component.

Note, then, how a component-part line graph differs from an ordinary line graph in which several series are plotted independently, such as Figure 27.11. In an ordinary line graph each series is plotted against the same base line. In a component-part line graph, in contrast, series are added cumulatively to each other and cumulative magnitudes are plotted. The top of each band becomes the base line, as it were, for plotting the magnitude of the next band. The graph is built up in layers; each layer represents a component of the total and is distinctively shaded and labeled. Note, for example, how readily the increase in annual sales of prefabricated structures between

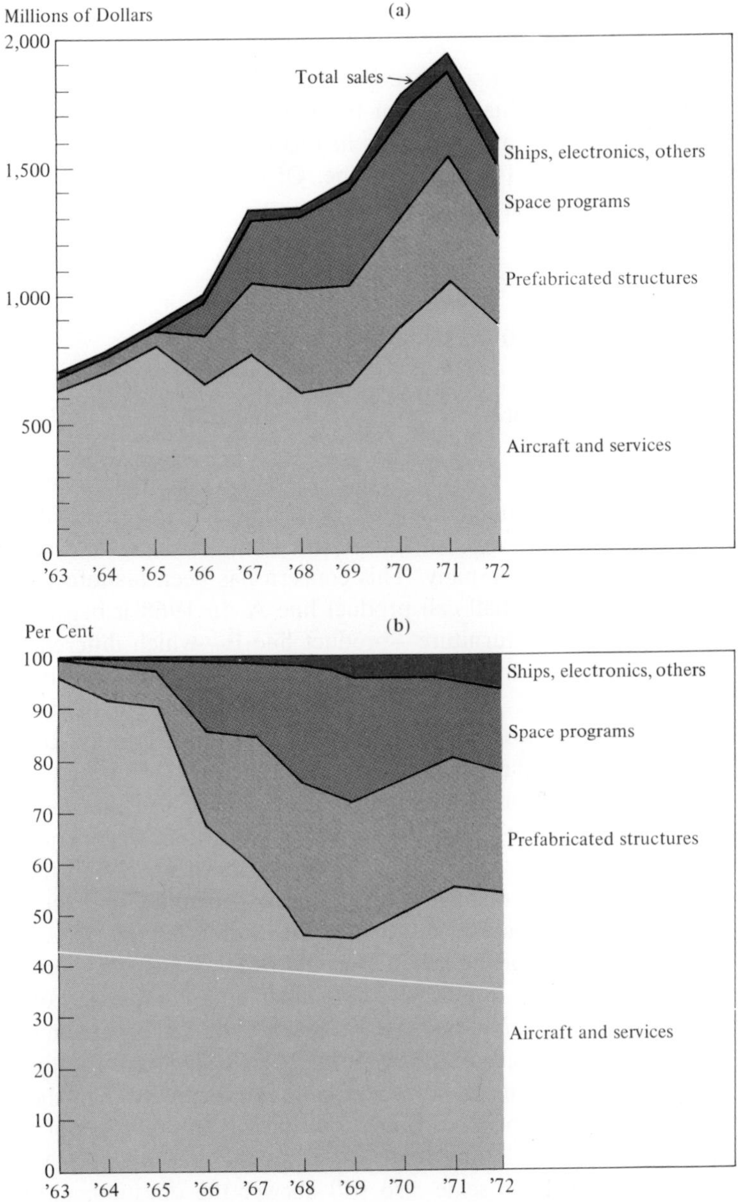

Figure 27.14. Tech-Systems Corporation, annual sales by type, 1963–1972

1967 and 1968 is conveyed by the widening of the band for this component, and how the constant width of the band during the remainder of the years covered by the graph indicates that annual sales in this component held roughly constant from 1968 onward.

If interest centers chiefly on changes in the *relative* importance of each type of sale, one can plot the per cent distributions rather than the actual dollar volumes. This is done in Figure 27.14b, for the sales data shown in Figure 27.14a. We see at once how sales of aircraft and services had declined in *relative* importance between 1963 and 1969, then gained somewhat during the final years of the ten-year period. Necessarily, when per cent distributions are plotted as in Figure 27.14b, the top of the graph will always be at the 100 per cent line. Of course, this graph tells us nothing about actual dollar sales volumes.

27.6
RATIO OR SEMILOGARITHMIC GRAPHS

The line graphs presented up to this point utilized an *arithmetic* scale on the *Y* axis—that is, a scale in which equal vertical distances represent equal amounts. Many types of problems are encountered, however, where a graph with an arithmetic vertical scale does not prove useful.

As a typical example of such a situation, consider the case of the Alexander Furniture Company. This concern has been manufacturing a line of furniture that we shall call product line A. In 1968 it began producing an additional line of furniture—product line B—which differed from the old line in both style and price range. Sales of both lines had been increasing during the period 1968–1972, as may be seen from Figure 27.15. This graph, which utilizes an arithmetic vertical scale, conveys the distinct impression that product line A performed much better during this period than product line B. Such an impression arises because the *absolute* increase in sales of product line A was much greater than that of product line B, and therefore the curve for line A climbs more steeply on the chart.

The company's management had no expectations that the sales volume of the new line would match that of the established one as yet, nor that the increases in sales of the new line would equal or surpass those of the established line. Hence, interest did not center on a comparison of the *absolute* sales or of the *absolute* increases as much as on a comparison of the *relative* increases in the sales of both lines. Specifically, the question was asked whether sales of line B were increasing more rapidly than those of line A. This question can be answered by calculating link relatives of sales for each product line and plotting these on arithmetic graph paper. A graph with a ratio or logarithmic scale also will answer the question, and without any intermediate calculations.

Before continuing the discussion relating to the Alexander Furniture Company, we shall discuss the characteristics of a ratio or logarithmic scale.

Ratio or logarithmic scale

Figure 27.16 shows a graph in which the horizontal, or time, scale is a conventional arithmetic scale. The vertical scale, however, is a *ratio* or

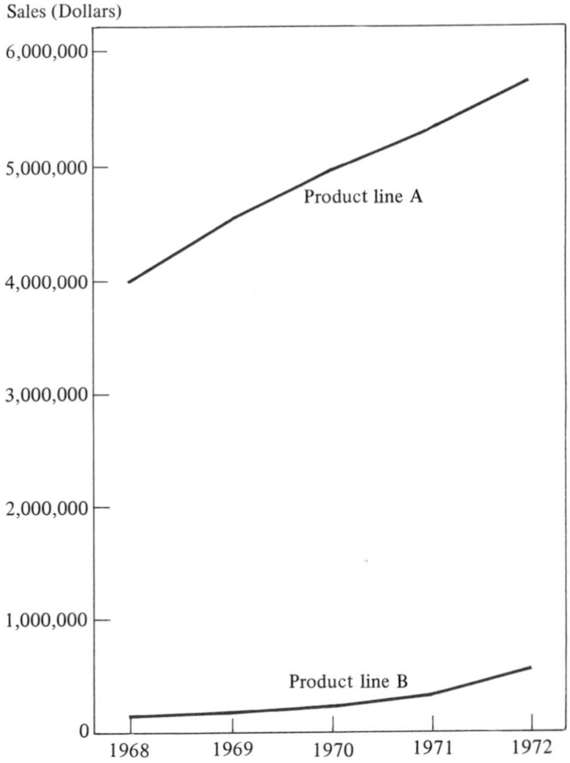

Figure 27.15. Sales of two product lines by Alexander Furniture Company, 1968–1972, arithmetic line graph

logarithmic scale—i.e., a scale in which equal intervals represent equal differences in the logarithms of numbers. Such a graph is called a *ratio* or *semilogarithmic graph.*

Note the graduated spacing of the tick marks on the vertical scale. Two sets of numbers are shown in the vertical scale. The inner numbers, consisting of 1, 2, etc., are not part of the scale proper, but are guide numbers found on semilogarithmic graph paper. Ordinarily these guide numbers are not reproduced with the graph, but we include them here to show how a ratio scale is set up.

The bottom guide number is 1 and serves as the starting point of the scale. Any positive scale number other than zero may be placed here. In the case of the Alexander Furniture Company, the smallest sales volume was $135,000; hence it is most convenient to begin the base line of the scale with $100,000. While we may begin with any positive value at the base line other than zero, it usually is easiest to start with 1, 10, or some multiple of 10 since the major horizontal divisions marked by ticks will then represent round numbers. Opposite guide number 2, we place the value that is twice that of the base line, or $200,000. Similarly, we write

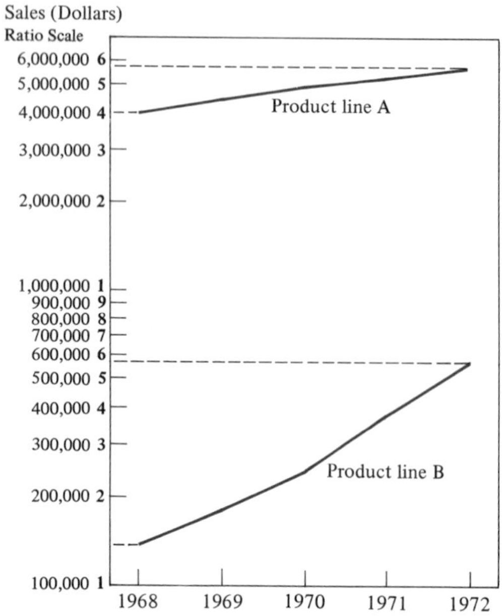

Figure 27.16. Sales of two product lines by Alexander Furniture Company, 1968–1972, ratio or semilogarithmic line graph

$300,000 corresponding to guide number 3, and so on. The guide number 1 that follows number 9 is assigned a value ten times that of the base line; in the present case it is given a value of $1,000,000. Note that the vertical distances between the guide numbers, which have been getting smaller up to this point, now become larger. In fact, the same sequence of graduations is starting all over again. Each full sequence of graduations is called a *cycle.* In labeling the next cycle we proceed as before. We must write $2,000,000 corresponding to the guide number 2 in the second cycle, since this is twice the value of the base of the second cycle. Note that the top of the first cycle has now become the base of the second one. Proceeding in this manner, we fill in the vertical scale in Figure 27.16. Note that the second cycle is not complete, since there is no need to carry the scale to $10,000,000.

Ratio or semilogarithmic graph paper is available in one, two, three, or even more, cycles. The number of cycles needed depends, of course, on the range of the data. Should a series be plotted in which the largest value is eight times the smallest, one-cycle paper would usually be used, since we know that the top of a cycle has a value ten times as great as that of the base line. On the other hand, a series whose largest value is, say, twelve times the smallest would require semilogarithmic graph paper with at least two cycles.

Once the vertical scale has been labeled, the plotting of the series proceeds in the usual manner. Semilogarithmic graph paper generally shows grid lines between the guide numbers on the vertical scale to aid in the plotting. If, say, there are 20 spaces between guide numbers 1 and 2 on the graph paper used to plot Figure 27.16, each of the spaces would represent \$5,000 in the first cycle and \$50,000 in the second cycle. These additional grid lines on the vertical scale enable one to plot the data quite accurately.

Interpretation of ratio or logarithmic scale

Having considered the mechanics of labeling the vertical scale and plotting points, we now discuss ways of interpreting a semilogarithmic graph. First, compare the distance on the vertical scale of Figure 27.16 between \$100,000 and \$300,000, and between \$300,000 and \$900,000. Note that in each instance the same distance has been covered on the vertical scale, despite the fact that the first case represents an increase of \$200,000 while the second represents an increase of \$600,000. Note also that the *relative* increase in each case is the same, namely 200 per cent. If the vertical distance for any other case in which there is a 200 per cent increase is measured, it will be found that the distance required for a 200 per cent increase on the vertical scale of Figure 27.16 is always the same.

In general, the ratio scale has the following important characteristics:

> Equal per cent changes require equal vertical distances on the ratio scale; the greater the relative change, the larger the vertical distance required.

We now return to our discussion of the sales of product lines A and B of the Alexander Furniture Company. In Figure 27.16, horizontal dashed lines have been superimposed on the graph to aid in comparing the vertical distances required to portray the increase in sales between 1968 and 1972 for each of the two product lines. Since the vertical distance is greater for product line B than for product line A, we conclude that the newer product line experienced a greater *relative* increase in sales between these two years.

The measurement of vertical distances in this way is not necessary in order to interpret the ratio graph. Note from Figure 27.16 that the curve for product line B is steeper than that for product line A, since the curve for B has to cover a larger vertical distance during the same time period. Hence we simply say that:

> The steeper the curve on a ratio chart, the larger the per cent change.

This means that one need only compare the slopes of the curves to draw conclusions about relative changes. If the two lines in Figure 27.16 had been parallel, equal rates of change would have been indicated, of course, because two parallel straight lines have the same slope.

In addition to comparing relative changes between two periods in several series on a ratio graph, one also can study relative changes from period to period in any given series. For instance, Figure 27.17a presents a ratio graph in which the series is represented by a straight line. It is at once

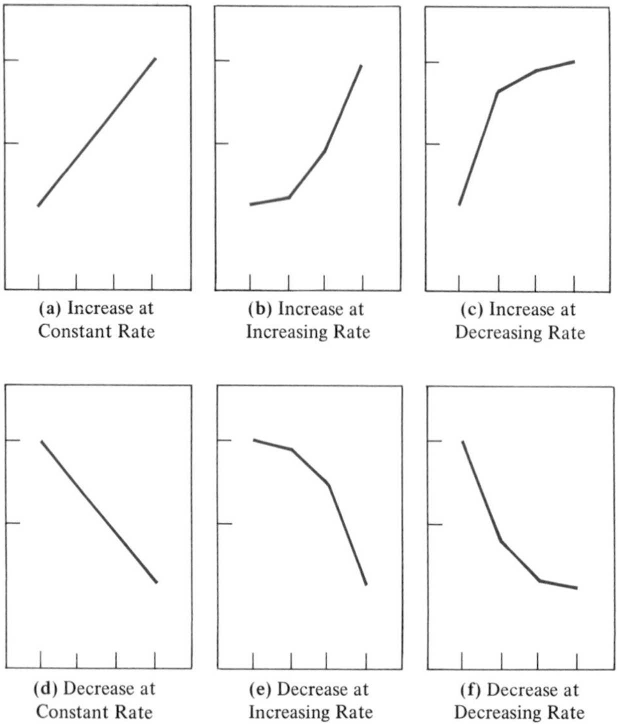

Figure 27.17. Examples of different patterns on ratio paper

evident that the per cent increase from period to period in this series is a constant one, because a straight line has a constant slope. While a straight line on an arithmetic chart indicates a constant *amount* of change, a straight line on a ratio chart indicates a constant *rate* of change.

Figure 27.17b presents on a ratio graph a series whose rate of increase is becoming greater and greater as each successive point is plotted. This is known because the curve becomes steeper and steeper. In short, one states that this series is increasing at an increasing rate.

Similarly, one can readily see that the series in Figure 27.17c is increasing at a decreasing rate because the curve is becoming less and less steep. Figure 27.17d presents a series that is decreasing at a constant rate, while Figures 27.17e and 27.17f present two series that are decreasing at increasing and decreasing rates respectively.

Let us now interpret Figure 27.16 more fully. While the sales of both product lines have been increasing, sales of the new product line have been increasing more rapidly. Indeed, sales of product line B have been increasing at an increasing rate while sales of product line A have been increasing at a decreasing rate. Thus, while sales of the new product line are still far less than those of the established line, and while the *absolute* increases in sales of the new line are far less than those of the established one, the ratio graph shows that the new product line has been catching on. Thus, the ratio graph provides ready answers to management's questions about the *relative* increases in sales of the two product lines.

Typical use of ratio graph in administration

We now present a typical instance in which the ratio graph is a most useful device for analyzing per cent changes in quantitative data. Figure 27.18 presents data on sales of the Pitman Manufacturing Company and of the entire industry from 1964 to 1972. Note that two vertical scales have

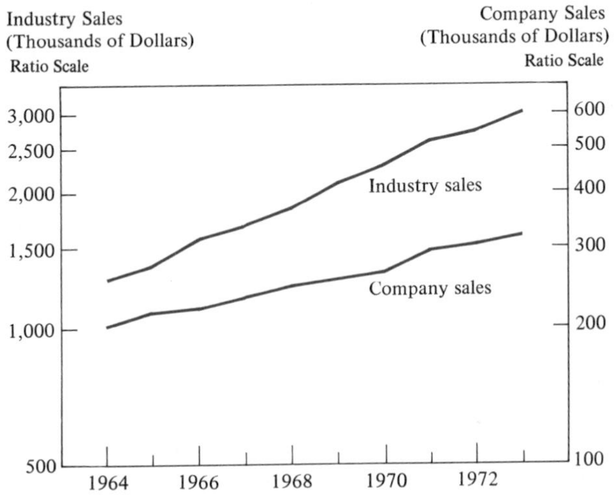

Figure 27.18. Sales of Pitman Manufacturing Company and of entire industry, 1964–1972

been used—one for company sales, the other for industry sales. By using two scales, the two curves can be brought closer together on the chart, so that their slopes can be compared more easily. It is customary to choose the two scales so that the line representing the aggregate—in this example, industry sales—will lie completely above the line representing one of its components—in this instance, company sales. The graph shows that sales both of the company and the industry have been increasing at fairly constant rates. However, the slope of the industry sales curve is steeper than that of the company's curve. Thus, the company's sales have not been increasing as rapidly as the industry's, or, to put this another way, the company's share of the market has been declining.

The use of two different dollar scales in Figure 27.18 does not prevent comparison of relative changes in company sales and industry sales. In any particular ratio graph, equal relative changes always are represented by the same vertical distance, no matter what scale is used. This means that in a ratio graph we also can readily compare relative changes in two or more series not expressed in the same units—for instance, number of automobiles sold and net profit.

Sometimes the reader will encounter *arithmetic* charts in which two series are plotted on *different scales*. These scales may or may not be in the same units. In either event, there is usually no consistent relationship between the two scales such as in a ratio graph. Hence, no meaning can be attached to the comparative heights and slopes of curves when different scales are used on arithmetic charts.

27.7
SOME GENERAL GUIDES FOR THE CONSTRUCTION OF GRAPHS

Effectiveness

There are no strict rules according to which graphs must be constructed, nor is there only one specific type of presentation that is right for a particular situation. Graphs can only be evaluated in terms of the effectiveness with which they present data and permit the user to pick out the most significant aspects of a situation. It is for this reason that one must bring imagination to the job of constructing an appropriate graph. In addition, though, one should be acquainted with the practices that make for a simple, effective, and self-contained graph.

Always remember that it is better to construct a series of graphs, each of which presents a single aspect of a situation effectively, than it is to prepare one graph in which so many relationships are shown that none of them can be studied effectively.

Procedures

We shall use Figure 27.19, which contains the technical names of the various parts of a typical graph, as a point of departure in discussing some useful procedures in constructing graphs.

Title and subtitle. The title may be placed either above or below the graph. If the graph is intended for use outside the organization in which it is prepared, the title should state succinctly but completely what is presented in the graph. Thus, the title of Figure 27.15 states the series plotted, the name of the company, and the time span covered. If the graph is used internally, or if it is part of a company report or of an article in a publication, the title simply may summarize the most significant aspects revealed by the graphic presentation. For example, the title at the top of Figure

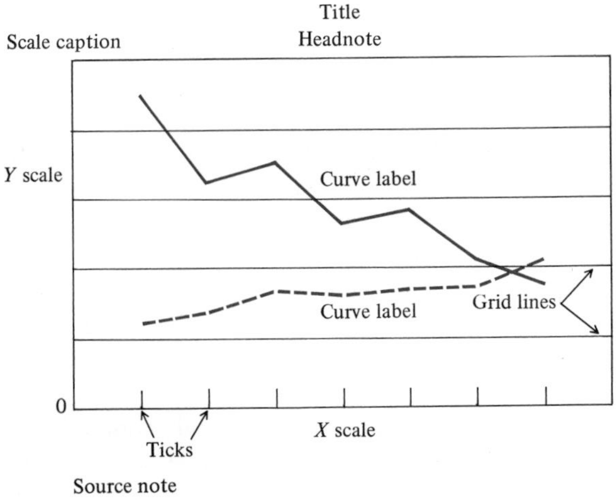

Figure 27.19. Arithmetic line graph with principal components labeled

27.4 calls attention to an increase in the gap between planned and actual production. Sometimes, the title merely identifies the series plotted, while a subtitle summarizes the most important features brought out in the graphic presentation. The purpose of the graph must govern the kind of title it should have.

Scale caption. The scale caption to the *Y* scale should state the units in which the data are expressed—for example, thousands of barrels, millions of dollars. If the chart is wide, it often is helpful to repeat the *Y* scale on the right. The user can then ascertain the approximate magnitudes more readily should he be concerned with the right side of the graph. A similar advantage exists in showing the amount scales of a horizontal bar chart both at the top and bottom of the plotting surface. If two different scales are used, as is frequently done in semilogarithmic graphs, the scale captions should identify the series that is plotted according to each scale.

Scales. The *X* and *Y* scales should be chosen in such a way that the height and width of the graph are in proportion. No rigid rule can be given as to appropriate proportions of height and width; judgment must be exercised in making this decision. When a chart is part of a written report, the proportions of the chart will be influenced by the general layout of the pages. Examination of the various charts in this chapter will indicate proportions in general use.

If interest centers on a comparison of absolute magnitudes, the amount scale should not be broken. Only if one needs to emphasize changes or fluctuations in a series may the amount scale be broken; in that event a clear break should be indicated to alert the reader.

Grid lines. As an aid to easier reading of a graph, grid lines may be used. They should be employed sparingly so that they will not obscure the plotted curves or bars and should be drawn more lightly than the bars or curves.

Ticks. These may be used in place of some or all of the grid lines.

Curves. If several curves are plotted on the same graph, a different type of line may be used for each. The most important curve is usually plotted with a heavy solid line, while the others may be plotted with light solid lines, broken lines, and the like. It is easier for the reader to analyze a graph if the curves are labeled directly than if a separate legend is used.

Bars. In a horizontal bar chart, the stub containing the labeling of the bars should be kept as narrow as possible so that adequate space is left for the bars. Judgment must be exercised in deciding upon the appropriate proportions of the bars. While space is usually left between individual bars to make the graph more readable, there are occasions when bars are joined so as to accentuate differences in magnitudes.

Cellulose tape with shading and cross-hatching can be purchased and cut for bar and component-part line graphs. The use of this tape facilitates the preparation of a graph and frequently improves its appearance.

Source. When the source of the data shown in a graph is obvious—for example, in the case of a graph presenting company data in an internal report—a source note may be omitted. When the source is not obvious, it is good practice to provide a complete reference to the source of the data, so that the reader can go to the source, if necessary.

Labeling. All labeling on the graph should be placed horizontally so that the labels will be easy to read.

Lettering. Whenever possible, variety in lettering should be used in order to avoid monotony and to emphasize important features. Lettering guides may be used to advantage.

Border. Graphs may be enclosed in a border to improve their appearance. The extent to which a graph should be "dressed up" depends upon the use to which it will be put.

Pictograms. When symbols are used to indicate magnitudes, the symbols should be uniform in size and should be arranged in the form of pictorial bars.

QUESTIONS AND PROBLEMS

27.1. For each of the following parts of a statistical table, indicate whether the part can be omitted from the table without making it incomplete and justify your position:

a. Headnote
b. Stub
c. Boxhead
d. Title
e. Table number
f. Field
g. Summary columns and/or rows

27.2. In which type of table, reference or analytical, would you be more likely to find classes presented alphabetically within a system of classification? Explain.

27.3. The format of a statistical table is shown below. Suggest improvements that can be made in it.

Expenditures [a] for New Plant and Equipment (Statistical Data)

	Manufacturing		*Mining*			
Activity	*Durable Goods*	*Non-Durable Goods*		*Railroad Transportation*	*Other Transportation*	*Other* [b]
1972						
1969						
1970						
1971						
Grand Total [c]						
1969						
1970						
1971						
1972						

[a] In billions of dollars.
[b] "Other"[d] includes public utilities, trade, service, finance, communications, and construction activity.
[c] "Grand totals" of data in each row above.
[d] Does not include agriculture.
Source: Washington, D.C.

27.4. The table below pertains to shares under option in a stock option plan initiated by a firm in 1967. Does this table illustrate cross-classification? Why or why not?

Shares Under Option as of October 31, 1972, Gerald Laboratories, Inc.

Year Granted	*Year Exercisable*	*Option Price*	*Shares Under Option as of Oct. 31, 1972*
1969	1971	\$52.38	224
1970	1972	68.88	1,066
1971	1973	60.19	812
1972	1974	51.41	1,638

27.5. Consider the following statement:

On page 81 of the *Statistical Abstract of the U.S.: 1970*, prepared by the Bureau of the Census and published in 1970 by the U.S. Government Printing Office, Washington, D.C., the following figures can be ascertained on cigarette smoking in the civilian noninstitutional population 17 years old and over in the United States (components may not add to totals because of rounding): In 1967, of 59.2 million males, 28.3 million were present smokers, 10.8 million were former smokers, 18.6 million had never smoked, and for 1.5 million it was unknown if they ever smoked. For 67.3 million females the corresponding figures were, in millions, 21.1, 4.7, 39.9, and 1.5. For the 126.5 million persons of both sexes in 1967, the corresponding figures were, in millions, 49.4, 15.5, 58.5, and 3.0. The comparable figures for 1968 were:

60.1 million males: 27.6, 11.5, 19.6, and 1.4
68.5 million females: 20.9, 5.4, 40.7, and 1.5
128.6 million of both sexes: 48.5, 16.9, 60.3, and 2.9

a. Present this information in a formal statistical table containing title, source note, etc. Be sure to design your table so that *all* the data given can be included.
b. Answer the following questions from an inspection of your table or, if necessary, from additional tables, and explain in each case how you arrived at your answer: (1) In 1967, was there any statistical relationship between sex and cigarette smoking status? Was there any statistical relationship in 1968? (2) During the period covered by your table, was there any statistical relationship between year and cigarette smoking status when sex is held constant?

27.6. The Courteous Finance Corporation, a consumer finance company, wishes to study for several years (1970, 1971, 1972) the distribution of its loans according to size of loan (under $100, $100–under $250, $250 and over) and purpose of the loan (home improvement, car purchase, consumer durable purchase, other).
a. Set up a formal table in which the data can be presented cross-classified by year, size of loan, and purpose of loan. Be sure to include summary rows and columns for *all* classifications given.
b. Test the completeness of your table by inserting the following figures in the appropriate cells: (1) In 1970, 43.9 per cent of all loans made for home improvements were for $100–under $250. (2) In 1971, 89.7 per cent of all loans made for purchase of cars were for $250 and over. (3) In 1972, 34.2 per cent of all loans were for under $100.

27.7. Management in the Hermes Equipment Company wishes to present data on the number of calls made by its salesmen, cross-classified by year (1971, 1972, 1973), sales territory (A, B, C), and type of call (call on prospect, call on customer).
a. Set up a formal table in which the data can be presented, cross-classified by year, sales territory, and type of call. For purposes of this problem, be sure to include summary rows or columns for *all* the classifications given.
b. Test the completeness of your table by inserting the following figures in the appropriate cells: (1) In 1972, the sales force made a total of 4,290 calls. (2) In 1971, 380 calls were made on prospects. (3) During the three-year period as a whole, a total of 1,820 calls were made on customers in territory B. (4) In 1971, 140 calls were made on prospects in territory C. (5) In 1972, a total of 1,125 calls were made in territory C. (6) During the three-year period as a whole, the sales force made a total of 13,119 calls.

27.8. Explain briefly each of the following:
a. Grouped bar chart
b. Component-part line graph
c. Duo-directional chart
d. Ratio scale
e. Grid line
f. Break in *Y* scale

27.9. For what types of applications are horizontal bar charts generally used? Vertical bar charts? Explain.

27.10. Discuss the similarities and differences for each of the following pairs of items:

a. Component-part bar graph and component-part line graph
b. Grouped bar graph and component-part bar graph
c. Semilogarithmic line graph and per cent change arithmetic line graph

27.11. The status of freight cars of the Trans-Missouri Railroad as of December 31, 1972 was:

Type of Car	*No. of Cars Leased*	*No. of Cars Owned*
Box	423	256
Refrigerator	209	384
Hopper	298	101
Gondola	80	237
Other types	127	86

a. Present these data in a component-part bar graph.
b. Present these data in a grouped bar graph.
c. Contrast the types of comparisons that can be made most readily with each type of graph.
d. What factors governed your choice between horizontal and vertical bars in constructing your graphs?

27.12. Two tables presenting data on operations of the Central Electronics Corporation follow:

Table I. Per Cent of Total Sales Billed by Product Markets, 1969–1973

Year	*Space and Defense*	*Consumer*	*Apparatus and General*	*Total*
1969	23	23	54	100
1970	23	25	52	100
1971	20	30	50	100
1972	17	25	58	100
1973	16	26	58	100

Table II. Utilization of Average Income Dollar, Fiscal Year 1973

Material, services, and other	49.1¢
Employee compensation and benefits	40.9¢
Taxes	3.6¢
Depreciation and amortization	2.5¢
Retained earnings	2.0¢
Dividends	1.9¢

a. Construct for each table a bar chart that effectively presents the data contained in the table.
b. Indicate the major points of difference between the two charts that you have constructed, and explain the reason or reasons for each point of difference.
c. Could line charts have been used to present effectively the data in Table I? In Table II? Explain.

27.13. The investment portfolio of a large bank was as follows on December 31, 1970 and on December 31, 1971 (data in millions of dollars):

Type of Security	*Dec. 31, 1970*	*Dec. 31, 1971*	*Increase (+) or Decrease (−)*
U.S. government obligations	1,166.2	1,205.7	+39.5
State and municipal securities	237.4	251.9	+14.5
Tax-exempt securities	92.6	67.8	−24.8
Stock of Federal Reserve Bank	10.4	9.9	−.5
Foreign securities payable in sterling	6.3	8.4	+2.1
Foreign securities payable in dollars	11.5	9.8	−1.7
Miscellaneous securities	59.0	46.1	−12.9
Total portfolio	1,583.4	1,599.6	+16.2

a. Construct a graph that effectively portrays the *changes* in the values of the different types of securities in the portfolio between December 31, 1970 and December 31, 1971.

b. Indicate an alternative graphic design that you might have used, and explain why your graph in part **a** is more effective than this alternative.

27.14. The Bureau of Labor Statistics' consumer price index and two components of this index were as follows for the period 1963–1970:

	Index, 1963 = 100		
Year	*All Items*	*Household Durables*	*All Services*
1963	100.0	100.0	100.0
1964	101.3	99.9	101.9
1965	103.0	98.4	104.2
1966	106.0	98.3	108.2
1967	109.0	99.7	113.0
1968	113.6	102.9	118.8
1969	119.7	107.1	127.2
1970	126.8	109.9	137.4

Source: U.S. Department of Labor, Bureau of Labor Statistics.

Each index number is a relative expressed on a base of 1963 average prices. Thus, the *All Items* index value of 126.8 for 1970 means that prices in 1970 of the items included in the index were, on the average, about 126.8 per cent as high as during the base period 1963.

a. Construct one line graph, using arithmetic scales, to present the three series.

b. Does your vertical scale begin at zero? Explain why or why not.

c. Analyze your graph, and present your findings in a paragraph. Be sure to include a discussion of the movements in the different components.

27.15. The stock of money in the United States for selected dates during the period 1966–1969 was as follows (in millions of dollars):

Date	*Stock of Money in U.S.*
June 30:	
1966	53,436
1967	54,357
1968	56,018
1969	60,872
Dec. 31:	
1968	60,435
1969	64,190

Source: U.S. Treasury Department.

a. In presenting these data in a line graph, would you use a point or an interval to designate a year on the time scale? Why?

b. Present the data in a line graph. Make your time scale simple, yet unambiguous.

27.16. The assets of the Tri-State Life Insurance Company during the period 1969–March 1973 inclusive were distributed as follows (data in billions of dollars):

Date	*Total*	*Bonds*	*Mortgage Loans*	*Stocks and Real Estate*	*Policy Loans and Other*
End of year:					
1969	5.90	3.07	1.68	.65	.50
1970	6.55	3.28	1.87	.74	.66
1971	6.89	3.38	1.97	.83	.71
1972	7.99	3.83	2.20	.96	1.00
End of month:					
1973–January	8.01	3.82	2.25	1.06	.88
February	8.03	3.83	2.28	1.07	.85
March	8.03	3.82	2.28	1.07	.86

a. Present the above data in an effective graph. Justify your choice of the type of graph used.

b. Calculate the per cent distribution of assets for each date, present these in a table, and plot the data in an effective graph. Justify your choice of the type of graph used.

c. Analyze your graphs and write a brief paragraph containing the chief findings of your analysis.

d. Did the shift from annual to monthly data cause any problems in constructing your graphs? Could it cause problems in interpreting your graphs? Discuss.

27.17. Refer to Problem 27.22.

a. Present the data on sales by type of equipment in a component-part line graph.

b. Indicate whether the lines that you plotted in part **a** cross each other, and explain whether or not this situation could change if different data were plotted in the same type of graph.

c. Write a brief paragraph interpreting your graph.

d. Compute the per cent distribution of sales by type of equipment for each year, present these distributions in a table, and plot the data in a component-part line graph.

e. What type of analysis can be made from your second graph that cannot be made from your first graph, and vice versa?

f. Write a brief paragraph interpreting your second graph.

27.18. Presented below are quarterly data (in millions of dollars) on military and commercial revenues of Golden Eagle Airlines, a charter airline, for the years 1969 through 1972. Questions concerning these data follow (see next page).

Year and Quarter	*Military Revenue*	*Commercial Revenue*	*Year and Quarter*	*Military Revenue*	*Commercial Revenue*
1969: 1st	2.0	1.5	1971: 1st	4.3	2.5
2d	2.3	1.6	2d	4.0	2.6
3d	2.4	1.8	3d	4.3	2.7
4th	2.8	1.8	4th	4.7	2.6
1970: 1st	2.9	1.9	1972: 1st	4.8	2.7
2d	3.4	2.1	2d	4.9	3.0
3d	3.6	2.3	3d	5.0	3.3
4th	3.8	2.4	4th	5.1	3.4

a. Plot the above two series in one arithmetic chart.

b. Plot the above two series in one semilogarithmic chart.

c. At the beginning of 1970, management in this airline had stated that its policy for the next several years would be to seek continued growth in both military and commercial business but to attain a higher rate of growth in the latter category. Analyze each chart and present your findings in a paragraph, making specific reference to this announced policy.

d. Did you represent each quarter by a point or by an interval on your horizontal scale? What governed your choice?

27.19. Explain why it would be misleading to plot a component-part line graph on a semilogarithmic grid.

27.20. Sales of refined products and natural gas by the Henney Oil Company during the period 1968–1973 were as follows:

Year	*Refined Products Sold (Million Barrels)*	*Natural Gas Sold (Billion Cubic Feet)*
1968	597	46
1969	627	133
1970	709	293
1971	779	460
1972	813	688
1973	826	889

a. Construct a graph from which a ready analysis of the *relative* growth of the two types of sales can be made.

b. Did sales of refined products or natural gas increase more rapidly from 1968 to 1973? Explain how you derived your answer from an analysis of your graph.

c. Did you use one or two vertical scales on your graph? Justify your choice.

d. How many cycles did you require in your graph paper? Could you have used paper with fewer cycles? Explain.

27.21. Some annual data on electric operations of the Tri-State Electric System for the period 1963–1972 are presented below:

Year	*Revenue From Residential Sales (Thousands of Dollars)*	*Residential Sales (Millions of Kilowatt-Hours)*	*Thousands of Residential Customers (Monthly Average for Year)*
1963	106.0	6,114	857
1964	114.6	6,514	868
1965	120.4	6,575	879
1966	125.2	6,794	887
1967	127.8	7,180	894
1968	133.0	7,507	904
1969	140.3	7,831	915
1970	147.1	8,305	924
1971	153.2	8,693	933
1972	163.4	9,782	944

a. Explain why it would be meaningful to plot these three series in one semilogarithmic graph, although it would not be meaningful to plot them in their above form in one arithmetic graph.

b. Plot these three series in one semilogarithmic graph. Note that you will require three different scales.

c. Examine your graph and describe the movements, if any, that took place over the ten-year period in the following three ratios: (1) kilowatt-hour sales per customer; (2) dollar revenue per kilowatt-hour sold; (3) revenue per customer. Explain how you can study such movements from an examination of your graph without actually having to calculate the ratios.

27.22. Annual sales by type of equipment of Hercules Wheeled Equipment, Inc., were as follows during the period 1965–1972 inclusive:

Type of Equipment	*Sales (Millions of Dollars)* 1965	'66	'67	'68	'69	'70	'71	'72
Highway	43	45	48	49	58	59	61	66
Airport	26	27	28	29	34	32	31	32
Farm	17	19	20	20	23	24	26	29
Lawn	14	16	17	15	18	19	19	20
Garden	30	34	34	28	24	26	22	20
Total	130	141	147	141	157	160	159	167

What type of graph would you use, what data would you present, and what would you plot on each scale:

a. To portray year-to-year changes in sales of each type of equipment, and to show the contribution of each to total sales?

b. To study the relative changes from year to year in total sales, as well as in sales of each type of equipment?

c. To compare year-to-year absolute changes in sales of each type of equipment?

d. To show year-to-year changes in the per cent distributions of total sales by type of equipment?

27.23. The following sales data (in thousands of dollars) were assembled in preparation for a management review meeting in which a corporation's operations for 1972 were to be evaluated:

Product Class	*Sales for 1971* Actual	*Sales for 1972* Actual	Forecast
Biological chemicals	93,962	83,370	90,000
Garden chemicals	84,777	71,204	80,000
Industrial chemicals	71,992	71,990	75,000
Polychemicals	57,846	62,216	60,000
Dyes	55,921	56,214	50,000
Pigments	61,835	65,331	65,000

a. Present these data in a graph designed to facilitate evaluation of the information.

b. Did you have any option in deciding between a bar graph and a line graph for presenting the data on actual sales? Explain.

c. Does your graph facilitate evaluation of *all* the information contained in the table? Specifically: (1) For each product class, is it easy to compare 1972 sales against both the forecast for 1972 and sales for that product class during the previous year? (2) Is it easy to compare sales between product classes for each year? Discuss.

27.24. One of the long-term objectives of management in a large hotel chain is to reduce the injury rate of the chain's hotel employees. However, for purposes of short-term evaluation and control, it is felt that rates within the range of 9.4 to 13.0 disabling work injuries per million employee-hours worked are "normal" under current conditions. Injury rates by month for the chain as a whole were as follows for the previous fiscal year and the first ten months of the current fiscal year:

	Disabling Work Injuries per Million Employee-Hours	
Month	*Previous Fiscal Year*	*Current Fiscal Year*
July	12.2	12.7
August	12.9	12.9
September	12.6	12.9
October	12.0	12.7
November	9.0	11.2
December	13.6	14.7
January	10.1	11.9
February	9.9	11.8
March	10.5	12.1
April	11.6	12.8
May	12.1	
June	12.9	

a. These data are to be presented graphically in a management report for May. Design a graph that will present the data so as to emphasize the significant relationships.

b. Interpret the relationships brought out in your graph and write a brief evaluation.

Unit

IX

INDEX NUMBERS AND TIME SERIES ANALYSIS

Chapter

28

INDEX NUMBERS

In Chapter 25 we noted that an index or index number is a ratio that typically is on a base of 100. In this chapter, we are concerned with price indexes and quantity indexes. Such indexes are often employed by administrators, economists, and engineers to obtain a quick overall picture of significant changes in such areas as prices of raw materials, prices of manufactured products, physical volume of production, and wage rates. First, we discuss the need for price and quantity index numbers, and explain calculational methods. Some typical uses of index numbers in administration and analysis are then presented, and finally, various considerations in the construction and use of index numbers are taken up.

28.1 COMPILATION OF PRICE INDEXES

To illustrate the concept of a price index, we shall consider some administrative problems involving highway construction, for which price index numbers provide information in a useful form.

Need for price indexes

Relatives for individual items. Government officials must have information on relative changes in the prices of construction materials, labor services, and other items used in highway construction to bring previous construction cost estimates up to date, to determine the effect of price changes on current construction costs, and to aid in the preparation of budgets.

The required figures can be calculated easily for individual highway construction items. For instance, the average bid prices per cubic yard of roadway excavation on federal-aid highway contracts between 1963 and 1970 are shown in Table 28.1, column 1. Relative changes in the average price of this item from a given base period can be studied by expressing each year's average price as a per cent relative. The calculation of per cent relatives was discussed in Chapter 25. Per cent relatives for the data in column 1 are shown in column 2, using 1963 as the base period. The 1970 relative, for instance, is 147, which means that the 1970 average price was 147 per cent as great as, or 47 per cent greater than, the 1963 average price. The per cent relatives in column 2 indicate clearly that the average bid price of roadway excavation on federal-aid highway contracts increased steadily during the period 1963–1970.

Table 28.1 Average Bid Prices and Price Relatives for Roadway Excavation on Federal-Aid Highway Contracts, 1963–1970

Year	(1) *Price per Cubic Yard*	(2) *Per Cent Relative (1963 = 100)*
1963	\$.45	100
1964	.46	102
1965	.47	104
1966	.52	116
1967	.54	120
1968	.56	124
1969	.59	131
1970	.66	147

Source: Engineering News-Record, June 17, 1971, p. 86.

Limitations in study of price relatives for individual items. In many cases, it is impractical to study price changes of individual items, such as those of roadway excavation above, because the number of items that have to be followed is so large. An administrator or economist requiring information on general price movements simply would not have time to keep abreast of price changes in dozens or even hundreds of items. Furthermore, studying price changes of individual items will not provide any direct information about the *composite* effect of these price changes on such related factors as aggregate costs or economic trends. For example, the unit price of roadway excavation used in federally-aided highway construction may rise 1 per cent and the unit price of reinforcing bar steel may fall 1 per cent. This does not mean, however, that the net effect of these two price changes upon costs is zero. To the extent that more money is spent for roadway excavation than for reinforcing bar steel, the net effect would be toward an increase in costs.

What is needed, then, is a technique for combining price changes in diverse items into a composite series that will reflect the net effect of these changes upon such factors as total costs or economic trends—in the present case, for instance, upon costs of federally-aided highway construction. A price index performs this task. Let us now examine the compilation of a highway construction price index that typifies the indexes constructed in some 28 states in the U.S.

Compilation of price index by method of aggregates

It is evident that we cannot study the effects of price changes on highway construction costs merely by comparing total costs in different years. To be sure, total costs will differ from one year to another partly because of shifts in prices, but they also will differ because of changes in the amount and nature of highway construction. We could adjust somewhat for changes in the amount of construction by calculating costs per unit of output in each year—for instance, cost per mile of highway. However, even this modification would not eliminate all non-price factors that affect total costs. The types of highway construction projects may change from one period to another with respect to such cost-affecting factors as kinds of highways, site locations, and job conditions, so that per-mile costs could change from year-to-year even if prices of the individual highway construction items remained fixed.

Description of procedure. To measure price-level changes only, all cost-affecting factors except prices should be held constant. This principle may be implemented operationally as follows in compiling a highway construction price index:

First, a list of sample items of work and material used in highway construction is drawn up, which is representative of all items of work and material used in this activity. The list that we use here to compile an index is shown in Table 28.2, and is typical of lists used to compile price indexes for highway construction. Note that the list shows the different items and the quantities consumed during a typical period. Important problems are encountered in constructing such a list of representative items and typical quantities, but we postpone a discussion of these until later.

Second, we determine how much it would have cost in different years to purchase the fixed list of items. Table 28.2 contains the prices of the items in 1968, 1969, and 1970. The calculation of the cost of the list of items in any year is straightforward. For instance, 250 million cubic yards of roadway excavation at the 1968 price of \$.56 per cubic yard would have cost $250(.56) = \$140.0$ million, while the same volume of excavation at 1969 and 1970 prices would have cost, respectively, \$147.5 million and \$165.0 million. These costs are entered in the top row of the last three columns in Table 28.2. In this same way, costs of the other typical quantities are calculated at the prices of the three years and entered in the appropriate columns.

Table 28.2 Computation of Highway Construction Price Index by Method of Weighted Aggregates

	Quantity Used During Typical Period	Unit Price (Average Unit Bid Price)			Cost of Indicated Quantity (Millions of Dollars)		
		1968	*1969*	*1970*	*1968*	*1969*	*1970*
Item	q_t	p_o	p_n	p_n	$p_o q_t$	$p_n q_t$	$p_n q_t$
Roadway excavation	250 mill cu yds	$ .56	$ .59	$ .66	$140.0	$147.5	$165.0
Portland cement	10 mill bbls	4.79	4.87	5.42	47.9	48.7	54.2
Bituminous surfacing	7 mill sq yds	6.77	7.01	8.04	47.4	49.1	56.3
Structural steel	360 mill lbs	.25	.32	.34	90.0	115.2	122.4
Structural concrete	.8 mill cu yds	71.81	81.34	92.73	57.4	65.1	74.2
				Total	$382.7	$425.6	$472.1

Index for 1968, on 1968 base: $\frac{\$382.7}{\$382.7} \cdot 100 = 100$

Index for 1969, on 1968 base: $\frac{\$425.6}{\$382.7} \cdot 100 = 111$

Index for 1970, on 1968 base: $\frac{\$472.1}{\$382.7} \cdot 100 = 123$

Next, we add the costs of the sample items for each year. The aggregate cost in each year is shown at the bottom of the appropriate column in Table 28.2. Note, for example, that the aggregate cost of the list of items is higher at 1969 prices than at 1968 prices. Since the same items and quantities are priced for each year, this difference in aggregate costs must be attributed to changes in the prices of the items.

Finally, at the bottom of Table 28.2, we find that the aggregate cost of the sample items at 1969 prices is 111 per cent as great as the cost of the same items at 1968 prices. The per cent relative 111 is called the 1969 price index on a 1968 base. In a similar manner, we find that the 1970 price index on a 1968 base is 123. Of course, the index value for the base year is 100.

A price index could be calculated for any other year by finding the cost of the list at the prices of that year and expressing the cost as a per cent of the base period (1968) cost. Note that we are calculating a *fixed base* index in that the cost of the list in every year is compared directly with the 1968 cost. We selected 1968 as the base period arbitrarily. If we had selected 1969 as the base, the cost of the list in each year would be expressed as a per cent of the 1969 cost. We leave until later a discussion of considerations in selecting the base period.

It is important to understand clearly that the indexes calculated in Table 28.2 must be interpreted as per cents, not as absolute magnitudes. The index of 111 for 1969 signifies that the cost at 1969 prices of the typical quantities consumed was 111 per cent as great as the cost of these same quantities at 1968 prices. Roughly speaking, we can say that the prices of the items represented by the index increased, on the average, by 11 per cent between 1968 and 1969.

This method of constructing a price index is called the *method of weighted aggregates*. The same method could be used to construct a price index that measures changes in the cost of a typical "market basket" of goods and services purchased by a family each week, a price index that measures changes in the cost of a list of typical quantities of raw materials purchased by a company, and so on. The weighted aggregate index is so named, because the costs of a list of typical quantities of items are added or aggregated for each period.

Formal representation of weighted aggregate price index. The formula for the weighted aggregate price index is:

$$\text{(28.1)} \qquad \text{Weighted aggregate price index} = \frac{\Sigma p_n q_t}{\Sigma p_o q_t} \cdot 100$$

Here, for each item, q_t is the typical number of units produced, consumed, or the like; p_o is the unit price of the item during the base period; and p_n is the unit price of the item during the current or given period.

The quantity data used in constructing a price index are called *quantity weights*. They enable us to give the appropriate importance to the period-to-period price changes occurring in each item.

Computation of price index by method of relatives

Description of procedure. Absolute price data were used in the previous computations of the weighted aggregate price index. Price indexes can also be computed from price data in the form of price relatives. The price relative of an item is its price during a current or given period expressed as a per cent of the base period price. In other words, a price relative is just a particular kind of per cent relative.

Price relatives, on a 1968 base, for the five highway construction items are shown in Table 28.3. They were calculated from the price data in Table 28.2. For example, the roadway excavation price relative of 105.4 for 1969 means that the price of this item in 1969 was 105.4 per cent as great as the price in the base year 1968.

Consider the five price relatives for 1969. These relatives show the magnitude of the price of each item in 1969 relative to its price in 1968. We wish to average these individual price changes in order to measure their composite effect upon highway construction costs. As was pointed out in Chapter 25, misleading results may be obtained if unweighted averages of ratios are calculated. Hence, it is necessary to take a weighted average of the price relatives. The question arises, then, as to appropriate weights to

Table 28.3 Computation of Highway Construction Price Index by Method of Weighted Average of Price Relatives

	Price Relatives (1968 = 100)				*Value Weight (Millions of Dollars)*	*Price Relative × Value Weight*		
	1968	*1969*	*1970*			*1968*	*1969*	*1970*
Item	$\frac{p_o}{p_o} \cdot 100$	$\frac{p_n}{p_o} \cdot 100$	$\frac{p_n}{p_o} \cdot 100$		$p_t q_t$	$\frac{p_o}{p_o} \cdot 100 \cdot p_t q_t$	$\frac{p_n}{p_o} \cdot 100 \cdot p_t q_t$	$\frac{p_n}{p_o} \cdot 100 \cdot p_t q_t$
Roadway excavation	100.0	105.4	117.9		$140.0	$14,000.00	$14,756.00	$16,506.00
Portland cement	100.0	101.7	113.2		47.9	4,790.00	4,871.43	5,422.28
Bituminous surfacing	100.0	103.5	118.8		47.4	4,740.00	4,905.90	5,631.12
Structural steel	100.0	128.0	136.0		90.0	9,000.00	11,520.00	12,240.00
Structural concrete	100.0	113.3	129.1		57.4	5,740.00	6,503.42	7,410.34
				Total	$382.7	$38,270.00	$42,556.75	$47,209.74

Index for 1968, on 1968 base: $\frac{\$38,270.00}{\$382.7} = 100$

Index for 1969, on 1968 base: $\frac{\$42,556.75}{\$382.7} = 111$

Index for 1970, on 1968 base: $\frac{\$47,209.74}{\$382.7} = 123$

be used in the present example. Typical quantities cannot be used here, unlike the case of the weighted aggregate index. Such quantities are not appropriate, because the physical units entering the index are not the same and it is not meaningful to add cubic yards of roadway excavation, barrels of portland cement, and so on. Instead, dollar expenditures on the items during some typical period are often used as weights. Such dollar expenditure weights, often called *value weights,* are shown in Table 28.3. We shall discuss shortly how such typical value weights are obtained.

Weighted averages of the price relatives in Table 28.3 can now be computed. The average for, say, 1969 is obtained by multiplying each 1969 price relative by its respective value weight. The products then are summed —in this case they total \$42,556.75 million—and finally the total is divided by the sum of the value weights—\$382.7 million. Thus the index for 1969, computed by the method of a *weighted average of price relatives,* is $42{,}556.75/382.7 = 111$. This index says that the prices of the items in 1969 were, on the average, 111 per cent as great as the prices in the base year 1968. The index for 1970 is computed in a similar manner. Clearly, these index numbers have been computed on a 1968 base, because all the price relatives were calculated with 1968 prices as the basis of comparison. The index for 1968 equals 100, of course, since a weighted average of five price relatives that are each 100 must equal 100.

Formal representation of weighted average of price relatives. The formula for the weighted average of price relatives index is:

$$\text{(28.2)} \qquad \text{Weighted average of price relatives} = \frac{\sum \frac{p_n}{p_o} \cdot 100 \cdot p_t q_t}{\Sigma p_t q_t}$$

Here, for each item, $(p_n/p_o)100$ is the price relative for a given period on the base period and $p_t q_t$ is the value weight.

Comparison between method of aggregates and method of relatives

When base period prices are used in the value weights in calculating a price index by the method of relatives, (28.2) reduces to:

$$\text{(28.2a)} \qquad \begin{array}{l}\text{Weighted average of price}\\ \text{relatives with base period}\\ \text{prices in value weights}\end{array} = \frac{\sum \frac{p_n}{p_o} \cdot 100 \cdot p_o q_t}{\Sigma p_o q_t} = \frac{\Sigma p_n q_t}{\Sigma p_o q_t} \cdot 100$$

Note that the p_o's cancel out in the numerator, so that the weighted average of price relatives with base period prices in the value weights is identical to the weighted aggregate price index. Our examples illustrate this point. Since we used base period prices in the value weights in Table 28.3, the same index number values were obtained as in Table 28.2.

When base period prices are not used in the value weights for the weighted average of price relatives, the index value will differ from that of the weighted aggregate price index even though both are computed from the same set of data. In general, though, the differences will not be great. In practice, the choice between the aggregate and relative methods depends in large part on whether only one overall index is needed, or whether separate indexes are required showing average movements in subgroups of prices before the data are combined into an overall index. Where only an overall index containing relatively few items is needed, the aggregate method is desirable, because it involves fewer calculations than the method of relatives and has a concrete meaning that is easy to grasp. When separate indexes are desired for subgroups of items entering the overall index, as with many of the major indexes compiled by the federal government, the method of relatives is more efficient with respect to calculations required. Price relatives can be calculated initially for individual items and then combined successively (with proper weighting, of course) into indexes for subgroups, groupings of subgroups, and finally into a comprehensive overall index. If this procedure is followed with base period prices in the value weights, one can in fact obtain the calculational efficiencies inherent in the method of relatives and still obtain an index by the method of aggregates with its concrete meaning.

28.2 COMPILATION OF QUANTITY INDEXES

Need for quantity indexes

A quantity index measures relative changes from one period to another in physical volume of production, physical quantities consumed, and the like. Suppose government officials want information on relative changes from period to period in the volume of highway construction. For some purposes, total miles of highway constructed or rebuilt in each period would be an adequate measure of quantity of construction. However, characteristics of construction jobs differ, and a mile of highway laid down on flat open ground involves considerably less construction than a mile of highway built in rocky, mountainous terrain or in an urban area. Hence it could be very misleading to measure the volume of highway construction simply in terms of miles of roadway built.

One way out of this problem is to compare the amounts of different items of work and material actually used in highway construction in different periods. If this procedure is followed, it does not matter whether a given amount of work and material is used to construct several miles of roadway under easy conditions, or a mile or less under difficult conditions.

In comparing these amounts of work and materials used in different periods, however, one encounters the same problems as those mentioned in connection with the study of period-to-period price changes of individual items. First, too many items would usually have to be studied. Second, the item-by-item study of changes in amounts of individual items does not provide a clear picture of changes in the overall volume of activity. Again an index number—this time, a quantity index—can help one to assess changes in the overall volume of activity.

A quantity index of highway construction may be calculated by a method analogous to that described for constructing a price index. The crux of the procedure for computing the price index was to hold quantities constant—by using typical quantities consumed of the five representative items of highway construction—and to price these quantities at prices of different years. To construct a quantity index by the analogous procedure, one holds prices constant—by using *typical prices* of representative items of highway construction—and then calculates the value at these typical prices of the actual quantities consumed in each year.

Computation of quantity index by weighted aggregate method

We illustrate here how this approach is used to construct a *weighted aggregate quantity index*. First, a list of representative items of work and materials used in highway construction must be collected. Such a list—the same one as used in constructing the price index—is shown in Table 28.4. Next, typical prices of these items must be ascertained; such typical prices

Table 28.4 Computation of Highway Construction Quantity Index by Method of Weighted Aggregates

	Typical Unit Price	*Quantity Used*			*Value of Quantity Used (Millions of Dollars)*		
		1968	*1969*	*1970*	*1968*	*1969*	*1970*
Item	p_t	q_0	q_n	q_n	q_0p_t	q_np_t	q_np_t
Roadway excavation	$ .60	70 mill cu yds	77	80	$ 42.00	$ 46.20	$ 48.00
Portland cement	5.03	3 mill bbls	4	4	15.09	20.12	20.12
Bituminous surfacing	7.27	2 mill sq yds	3	3	14.54	21.81	21.81
Structural steel	.30	100 mill lbs	125	140	30.00	37.50	42.00
Structural concrete	81.96	.2 mill cu yds	.3	.4	16.39	24.59	32.78
				Total	$118.02	$150.22	$164.71

Index for 1968, on 1968 base: $\frac{\$118.02}{\$118.02} \cdot 100 = 100$

Index for 1969, on 1968 base: $\frac{\$150.22}{\$118.02} \cdot 100 = 127$

Index for 1970, on 1968 base: $\frac{\$164.71}{\$118.02} \cdot 100 = 140$

are also shown in Table 28.4. As in the previous discussion of the price index, we postpone temporarily a discussion of the problems involved in constructing the list of representative items and typical prices.

Next, one must determine the values, at these typical prices, of the actual quantities of the representative items consumed in different years. Table 28.4 contains the quantities consumed in each of the years 1968 through 1970 inclusive. Note that the description of the units has been entered in the column for 1968.

The values, at the typical prices, of the quantities used in the different years are shown in the final three columns. We see that the aggregate value of the quantities consumed in 1969 was $(150.22/118.02) \cdot 100 = 127$ per cent as great as the aggregate value of the quantities consumed in 1968. This difference cannot be due to price changes, since prices were held constant by using typical prices. Hence the increase in total value must be due to an increase in the quantities of work and materials used in highway construction. The per cent relative 127 is the quantity index for 1969 on a 1968 base. We therefore state that the quantity of highway construction measured by the index was about 127 per cent as great in 1969 as in the base year 1968. Table 28.4 also shows that the quantity of construction in 1970 was about 140 per cent as great as the quantity in 1968.

Quantity indexes for other years are calculated in the same manner. The quantities actually consumed in each year are valued at the same typical prices, and the total value for each year then is expressed as a per cent of the value, at the same typical prices, of the quantities used in the base period.

Formulas for quantity indexes

Weighted aggregate quantity index. The procedure of calculating the weighted aggregate quantity index can be described by the following formula:

$$\text{(28.3)} \qquad \text{Weighted aggregate quantity index} = \frac{\Sigma q_n p_t}{\Sigma q_o p_t} \cdot 100$$

Here, for each item, p_t is the typical price per unit of the item (or man-hours expended per unit, value added per unit, or the like); q_o is the number of units produced, consumed, or the like during the base period; and q_n is the number of units produced, consumed, or the like during the given period.

Note that (28.3) is the quantity index counterpart to price index (28.1); both represent indexes calculated by the method of weighted aggregates.

Weighted average of quantity relatives. The formula for the quantity index constructed by the method of weighted average of quantity relatives is the counterpart to price index formula (28.2), and is as follows:

(28.4) $$\text{Weighted average of quantity relatives} = \frac{\sum \frac{q_n}{q_o} \cdot 100 \cdot q_t p_t}{\Sigma q_t p_t}$$

Here, for each item, q_o and q_n are as defined in (28.3) and $q_t p_t$ is the value weight.

28.3 SOME TYPICAL USES OF INDEX NUMBERS IN ADMINISTRATION AND ANALYSIS

General applications

The price indexes for highway construction that we compiled previously are one type of construction price index. Other specialized construction price indexes are compiled for bridges, sewers and sewer lines, and various classes of buildings. These construction indexes are used:

1. To indicate period-to-period changes in the physical volume of work obtainable from an expenditure of a given size,
2. To compare cost changes in one geographical region with changes in the costs of comparable activities in other regions,
3. To aid, in cases where an index is applicable, in estimating costs of prospective projects by determining the costs of completed similar projects and changes in the price index since completion of these projects,
4. To estimate current replacement costs of structures for insurance purposes.

Index numbers are utilized by private firms as well as by public agencies. In some firms, especially the larger ones, special company indexes, such as indexes of prices paid for raw materials, of hourly wages paid, and of company selling prices, are calculated from internal data. Indexes of this type provide descriptions of particular aspects of operations, and can be compared with corresponding indexes for the industry or the economy to help management evaluate company operations and assess the influence of external economic factors on these operations.

Index numbers play a major role in the study of price and quantity changes in key functional areas of the national economy. The statistical agencies of the federal government compile a wide variety of index numbers, which are invaluable sources of information for businessmen, economists, public administrators, and others who wish to keep informed on the latest developments in the economy. Among these index numbers are series describing the most recent movements in prices, such as the wholesale price index and the consumer price index; series measuring changes in production, such as the index of industrial production; and series on retail activity, such as the indexes of department store sales and stocks. Were it not for index numbers such as these, it would be very difficult and time-consuming to determine what is happening, in an overall sense, in the American economy. In Chapter 30 the use of index numbers as business indicators and forecasting aids is discussed further.

In addition to their general information function, index numbers also are used as a specialized tool in the analysis of certain types of business and economic problems. We now examine some typical illustrations of these specialized uses of index numbers.

Distinguishing between money values and real values

In many types of problems that arise in administration and in economic analysis, price movements obscure fundamental changes and developments in the activities being analyzed. Hence, it is desirable in these instances to express dollar values in terms of "constant dollars" or "constant prices." Price indexes can be utilized to this end. We now examine a typical problem that is complicated by price-level changes and observe how the use of price indexes contributes to the analysis.

Changes in money earnings and purchasing power of earnings. Between 1964 and 1969, average hourly earnings of employees in manufacturing industries in the United States increased by about 26 per cent, from $2.53 per hour in 1964 to $3.19 per hour in 1969. Data on hourly earnings for the entire period are shown in Table 28.5, column 1. These data have not been adjusted for price-level changes, and hence are said to be expressed in "current dollars." That is, average hourly earnings in 1964 are expressed in terms of the buying power of the dollar in 1964, earnings in 1965 are expressed in terms of the buying power of the dollar in 1965, and so on.

Current dollars are useful for period-to-period comparisons if one is interested only in changes in the "money value" of the average hourly

Table 28.5 Average Hourly
Earnings in Manufacturing, 1964–1969, Measured in Current and in 1969 Prices

Year	(1) *Average Hourly Earnings in Manufacturing (Current Prices)*	(2) *Consumer Price Index, All Items (1969 = 100)*	(3) *Average Hourly Earnings (1969 Prices) [(Col. 1 ÷ Col. 2) × 100]*
1964	$2.53	84.7	$2.99
1965	2.61	86.1	3.03
1966	2.71	88.6	3.06
1967	2.83	91.1	3.11
1968	3.01	94.9	3.17
1969	3.19	100.0	3.19

Source of data: U.S. Department of Labor, Bureau of Labor Statistics.

earnings—that is, in changes in the amount of dollars involved regardless of their purchasing power. In many problems, though, interest centers on comparing changes in the *purchasing power* represented by money values, such as changes in the quantities of things that an hour's earnings could buy. In a period of changing price levels, changes in money earnings are an inadequate measure of changes in the purchasing power of these earnings. Rather, data on "real" earnings—money earnings adjusted for price-level changes—are required.

The extent to which the prices of goods and services bought by wage earners changed during 1964 to 1969 is shown in Table 28.5, column 2, which contains the Bureau of Labor Statistics' consumer price index. The index, as presented here, is on a 1969 base; hence it shows the per cent relationship between consumer prices in 1969 and earlier years. For instance, the index value of 84.7 for 1964 means that prices paid by wage earners in 1964 were, on the average, 84.7 per cent of the 1969 level. To put this another way, a wage earner had to pay $1 in 1969, on the average, in the purchase of consumer items for every 84.7 cents that these items cost in 1964.

Given the data on money earnings in column 1 and the relevant price index in column 2, only simple calculations are required to obtain estimates of changes in real earnings—that is, estimates of changes measured in constant dollars. Let us illustrate these computations for 1964. Since consumer prices in 1964 were, on the average, 84.7 per cent of their 1969 level, one would require $1/.847 = 1.18$ times as much on the average in 1969 to buy the same items as in 1964. Thus average hourly earnings of $2.53 in 1964 are equivalent in purchasing power to $(2.53/.847) = \$2.99$ in 1969. Therefore, to express the 1964 average hourly earnings in terms of dollars of 1969 purchasing power, we simply divide the 1964 earnings by .847.

In the same way, we can adjust the average hourly earnings in other years by dividing each figure in column 1 by the corresponding value of the consumer price index in decimal form. Column 3 contains the average hourly earnings during the period 1964–1969, expressed in "1969 dollars." *Since each of these figures shows the amount that would have been required on the average in 1969 to buy as much as could have been bought in the given year with an hour's earnings of that year, changes from year to year in the constant-dollar data in column 3 indicate changes in the purchasing power of the average hourly "money" earnings shown in column 1.*

A comparison between columns 1 and 3 brings out the distinction between money values and real values. Money hourly earnings increased by about 26 per cent between 1964 and 1969, whereas real hourly earnings increased by about 7 per cent during the same period.

Some problems in using index numbers to obtain constant-dollar data. One of the main uses of price indexes is to adjust data into constant dollars, as we have just done. The adjustment process is so easy to perform that important considerations sometimes are overlooked. Before going on, therefore, we take up some basic considerations in using index numbers to convert money values into real values. Although these will be presented in the context of the example just discussed, they have general applicability.

1. The arithmetic operations just illustrated are meaningful only to the extent that the price index used is a valid measure of average changes in consumer prices paid by the types of employees whose average hourly earnings are studied. We used the consumer price index because it is designed to measure changes in prices of goods and services purchased by urban wage earners' and clerical workers' families, and it was the most relevant price index available for the illustration.
2. The earnings and price data shown in Table 28.5 are averages and therefore do not necessarily apply to particular individuals. Since the interpretation of averages was discussed in detail in Chapter 4, we need not elaborate on this point here.
3. Finally, note that the data in column 3 of Table 28.5 are in constant 1969 dollars, because 1969 was used as the base of the index. Suppose the consumer price index had been expressed on a 1964 base in the table. Then, the index values would have been 100.0 for 1964 and 118.1 for 1969. Dividing the hourly earnings by the appropriate index values, we would obtain:

Year	(1) *Average Hourly Earnings at Current Prices*	(2) *Consumer Price Index, All Items (1964 = 100)*	(3) *Average Hourly Earnings (1964 Prices)* [(*Col. 1* ÷ *Col. 2*) × *100*]
1964	$2.53	100.0	$2.53
1969	3.19	118.1	2.70

The earnings in column 3 are now expressed in constant 1964 dollars. If these hourly earnings in 1964 dollars are compared with the hourly earnings expressed in 1969 dollars in Table 28.5 ($2.99 in 1964, $3.19 in 1969), one can see that the magnitude of real earnings varies with the base in which the price index is expressed. Thus, real earnings are arbitrary magnitudes. However, note that the relative change between 1964 and 1969 in both the hourly earnings in 1964 dollars and in 1969 dollars is the same, namely a 6.7 per cent increase. This demonstrates the general rule that the *relative* period-to-period changes in constant-dollar data are of chief significance, because the absolute magnitudes are arbitrarily affected by the choice of the base period of the price index used.

Measuring quantity changes

The construction of the quantity index for measuring changes in the physical volume of highway construction, discussed previously, exemplifies a direct approach to measuring changes in the physical volumes of production and sales, when the units to be measured are not homogeneous. Often, however, an indirect approach can be used to measure quantity changes that provides reasonably accurate results and that may be simpler. We now examine an application in this area.

Analysis of company sales. Changes in the dollar volume of a company's sales reflect not only changes in the physical volume of goods sold, but changes in the selling prices as well. Dollar sales volumes cannot, therefore, be used as a measure of the physical volumes of goods sold, unless one is able to remove from the data the effect of changes in selling prices. This can be done by the use of an appropriate price index.

To illustrate the procedure, let us estimate year-to-year changes in the physical volume of sales of the General Electric Company between 1955 and 1964 by adjusting company dollar sales figures for price-level changes. The annual dollar sales of this company for the period 1955–1964 are presented in Table 28.6, column 1. The relative magnitudes of company price changes during this period are shown in column 2, which presents an index of General Electric product prices compiled by the company on a 1957–1959 base.

Table 28.6 Sales by General Electric Company in Current and in Constant Dollars, 1955–1964

Year	(1) *Net Sales Billed (Millions of Current Dollars)*	(2) *General Electric Orders Price Index (1957–1959 = 100)*	(3) *Net Sales Billed (Millions of 1957–1959 Dollars)* [(*Col. 1* ÷ *Col. 2*) × *100*]	(4) *Per Cent Relatives of Data in Column 3 (1957–1959 = 100)*
1955	$3,463.7	86	$4,027.6	94.3
1956	4,090.0	93	4,397.8	103.0
1957	4,335.7	99	4,379.5	102.6
1958	4,120.8	100	4,120.8	96.5
1959	4,349.5	101	4,306.4	100.9
1960	4,197.5	97	4,327.3	101.4
1961	4,456.8	92	4,844.3	113.5
1962	4,792.7	90	5,325.2	124.7
1963	4,918.7	87	5,653.7	132.4
1964	4,941.4	87	5,679.8	133.1

Source of basic data: General Electric, *1964 Annual Report,* pp. 32–33.

To the extent that the price index refers to the same group of products that is involved in the sales data, this index can be used to measure company sales in terms of constant 1957–1959 average prices. For example, the company price index indicates that company selling prices in 1964 were 87 per cent of their average 1957–1959 level. Thus, the company received, on the average, \$.87 for products in 1964 for which it received \$1 in 1957–1959. Hence, if the 1964 sales had been made at 1957–1959 average prices, the sales volume would have been (4,941.4/.87) = \$5,679.8 million. Thus, as usual, we adjust for price-level changes by dividing the price index into the current-dollar figure.

Dollar sales in the other years are expressed in terms of 1957–1959 prices in the same way, by dividing the sales figure for each year by the price index (in decimal form) for that year. The constant-dollar sales data thus obtained are shown in column 3 of Table 28.6. Year-to-year changes in these constant-dollar data are attributable to changes in the physical volumes of goods sold, since all the sales have now been valued at the same 1957–1959 average prices.

We pointed out earlier that the *relative* period-to-period changes in constant-dollar data are of chief significance, because the absolute magnitudes depend in part on the base period used for the price index. To bring out the relative changes most clearly in the present example, we have calculated per cent relatives of the constant-dollar sales data based on 1957–1959 = 100. These are shown in column 4 and were calculated by expressing the constant-dollar sales in any year as a per cent of the average yearly constant-dollar sales during the three-year period 1957–1959 inclusive. The data in column 4 can be interpreted as a derived quantity index of the company's sales on a 1957–1959 base. Note from Table 28.6 that the dollar sales data since 1959 do not fully reflect the increase in physical volume of goods sold, because of the decline in General Electric selling prices.

28.4
PROBLEMS AND PROCEDURES IN THE CONSTRUCTION AND USE OF INDEX NUMBERS

System of weights

We observed that the system of weights used in computing an index should reflect the relative importance of the individual items. We now consider some of the issues that arise in determining appropriate weights.

Type of weights. In price indexes, the most appropriate weights are based on quantity or value. In quantity indexes, unit prices often are appropriate as weights. However, in some situations price weights could be misleading in a quantity index. For example, in a production index, which is the most important type of quantity index, the weights should reflect the relative amounts of "production" entering each type of item. Consider a plant that assembles several kinds of items, principally from component parts purchased from vendors. The unit price of one type of assembled item might be much higher than that of another, because its component parts are much more expensive. Yet the assembly of a unit of each type might require approximately the same amount of productive effort in the plant. In such a case, weights derived from the number of manhours typically expended in assembling a unit of each type of item, or from the "value added" in the plant to a unit of each type of item, would be more appropriate. ("Value added" to a unit may be defined as its value when shipped from the plant, less cost of materials, supplies, containers, fuel, purchased electric energy, and work contracted out.) The most important production index currently compiled in the United States—the Federal Reserve Board index of industrial production—has "value added" weights in many of its segments.

Coverage of weights. In some indexes the purpose is to measure price or quantity changes only for the particular items included in the index. In these cases, the weights can reflect the importance of the individual items. Often, however, each item included in the index is intended to represent a whole class of related items. In that case, the weight assigned to an individual item in the index should reflect the importance of the entire class of items which that item represents.

Fixed versus changing weights. When a continuing time series of consistent price or quantity index values is compiled, the practice is to use "typical-period" weights that remain fixed from period to period covered by the index. A problem then arises, because a period that is typical under current conditions is usually not typical under future conditions. For instance, if the quantity weights used in a monthly index of prices paid by consumers have been determined in accordance with consumption patterns during a current typical year, and if these weights are then used in the future, they are liable to become out-of-date, because consumers' buying patterns do not remain fixed. Yet, if the weights are changed every year or two to conform to relatively small changes in these buying habits, the price index really will measure two sets of changes—variations in consumer prices and variations in the quantities consumed. In the great majority of problems arising in economic analysis and in business and public administration, such an ambiguous price-quantity index would be relatively useless.

In this dilemma the practical compromise taken most frequently is that of using fixed weights and revising these periodically. Thus the Bureau of Labor Statistics, in compiling the consumer price index, has made a number of major revisions in this index since it was first initiated in World War I and plans to review and revise the index systematically every decade or so. The weights are brought up-to-date as part of each major revision.

The base period

The base period of an index is the period against which comparisons of relative changes are made. The base period may be a month, a year, or several years. Whatever the base period may be, the index for that period is 100, by definition. To demonstrate the calculation of indexes for highway construction, we used the year 1968 as the base; hence, the index value was 100 for that year, regardless of the formula employed in calculating the index. When a base period covers several years, the indexes for these years average 100. The period chosen as the base should be the one from which it is desired to measure relative price or quantity changes. For example, if a company wanted to measure changes in the selling prices of its products since 1969, it would compute its selling price index on a 1969 base.

Criteria for base period selection. Since the base period of an index serves as the point from which changes are measured, it generally is best to select a base period that is not too remote in time. Most users of index numbers are interested in making comparisons with the recent past, rather than with more distant periods. Furthermore, many comparisons lose some of their meaning when made over a span of too many years. This happens partly because items change in efficiency, convenience, and useful life and new items are developed that replace or supplement old ones, and partly because fixed weights do not remain typical over a long period of time. In actual practice, most published indexes are put on an up-to-date base whenever their item coverage and system of weights are revised.

Often a period of several years' duration is chosen as the base, since a relatively long period is more likely to be average than a shorter one. Any short-run period of a few months may be marked by some atypical events, such as a crop failure affecting an important agricultural commodity or a work stoppage in a major industry. Thus, by selecting a base period of several years' duration one does not give undue importance to any one of the temporary, atypical events that may have occurred for brief times during this base period.

Relationship between base and weights. The base period of an index should not be confused with the period from which the index's system of weights is derived. The "typical" period from which the weights are derived may be any period that will give appropriate weights. In practice, such a period frequently falls within, or coincides with, the base period, but this is not always the case. When the period from which an index's weights are derived coincides with its base period, the index is said to contain *base period weights*. The term *weight base* sometimes is used to designate the period from which weights are taken, while the term *reference base* is used for the period from which relative changes are measured.

Shifting the base of an index. Various types of situations arise in which it is useful to shift the base of an index. In some cases a more recent base period is required. In other cases, one may wish to compare changes in two or more index series that have different bases; such comparisons will be facilitated if all the series are placed on a common base period. In still other cases, the base of an index is shifted in order to "splice" or join two index series that overlap in time.

For an illustration of how to shift the base of an index, consider the example discussed earlier in which average hourly earnings in current dollars were adjusted to constant 1964 dollars (p. 634). This required that the consumer price index be shifted from a 1969 base to a 1964 base. One way in which an index can be restated on a new base is to recompute the index, using the new base period. Such a procedure often will involve tedious and perhaps costly computations; furthermore, if the index has been taken from a published source, the basic data needed for recomputing the index may not be easily obtainable. Another way of shifting the base, which usually is employed in these circumstances, is a shortcut method that does not involve recomputation of the index.

In shifting the consumer price index from a 1969 base to a 1964 base by this shortcut method, one must adjust the series so that the index value for 1964 will equal 100. This calculation is to be done in such a way that the *relative* changes from year to year in the series are not affected by the shifting. We know from Table 28.5 that the value of the consumer price index in 1964 was 84.7 on a 1969 base. To change this value to 100, we merely divide it by .847. In order that we will not affect the relative changes from year to year in the series, we must divide every other value by .847 also. Thus:

Year	(1) *Consumer Price Index (1969 = 100)*	(2) *Consumer Price Index for 1964 (As decimal)*	(3) *Consumer Price Index (1964 = 100)*
1964	84.7	.847	100.0
1965	86.1	.847	101.7
.	.	.	.
.	.	.	.
.	.	.	.
1969	100.0	.847	118.1

Column 3 contains the values of the consumer price index on a 1964 base. Since every value in column 3 is a constant multiple (1/.847) of the corresponding value in column 1, the relative year-to-year changes in column 1 have been preserved in column 3.

Thus, all we must do to shift an index series to a new base is to divide each value in the series by an appropriate divisor that will shift the series upward or downward to make the index value for the new base period equal 100.

One technical point should be mentioned in connection with shifting bases by this shortcut method. When the base of an index series computed by the method of aggregates with fixed weights is shifted by the shortcut method described above, the results are identical with those that would be obtained if a new index were computed by this method on the new base. With most other index number formulas, however, shifting the base by the shortcut method will give results that only approximate those obtained if the index were recomputed.

Splicing. The procedure used in splicing two index series is akin to that used in shifting the base. For an illustration of splicing, consider two indexes of selling prices compiled by Barns' Foods, Inc. One index, computed on a 1968 base, was compiled between 1968 and 1970 inclusive. During 1970 the company revised its selling price index, placing the new index on a 1970 base. The old and new indexes are shown in Table 28.7, columns 1

Table 28.7 Method for Splicing Old and New Selling Price Indexes Compiled by Barns' Foods, Inc.

Year	(1) *Old Index* *(1968 = 100)*	(2) *New Index* *(1970 = 100)*	(3) *Old Index Shifted to 1970 Base* *(Col. 1 ÷ 1.16)*	(4) *Spliced Series* *(1970 = 100)* *(Col. 2 and Col. 3)*
1968	100		86	86
1969	108		93	93
1970	116	100	100	100
1971		109		109
1972		115		115

and 2 respectively. Note that the indexes overlap at 1970, but do not have a common value for that year. To splice the two index series together, so that a continuous picture of changes in the firm's selling prices since 1968 can be obtained, the company should shift one or both series to give them a common value for 1970. In the present case, it was decided to shift the old index from a 1968 to a 1970 base, so that both series would have the common value of 100 for 1970. The shortcut method was employed; each of the index numbers in column 1 was divided by 1.16, the decimal equivalent of the old index for 1970. The results are shown in column 3. Since the old and new series now have a common 1970 value, they can be combined into the single 1970-based series that is presented in column 4.

Had the company desired to obtain a combined series on a 1968 base, the new index could have been shifted upward so that its 1970 value would equal 116; this would be done by multiplying each year's value of the new index by 1.16. Since the two series then would have the common value of 116 for 1970, they could be joined. Incidentally, the procedures of base shifting and splicing show again why index numbers have significance only as relative, not as absolute, magnitudes.

Sampling in index number construction

Sampling of items. Frequently indexes are based on only a sample of all items on which interest centers. For instance, highway construction price indexes compiled by the various states are based on samples of from five to fifteen items. Some of the major indexes compiled by the federal government are based on larger samples, consisting of hundreds of items. The main reasons for basing an index only upon a sample of items are: (1) The index can be compiled more speedily if the number of items included is relatively small. This reason is of fundamental importance, since managers and public officials usually must have timely data in order to act effectively. (2) It is much more economical to work with only a relatively small number of items. These reasons presuppose, of course, that the sample results will be precise enough to be useful.

Needless to say, the sample of items selected for the index should be representative of the relevant population of items. The purposes for which an index is compiled will determine this population. The consumer price index, for example, is designed to measure average changes in prices of items purchased by urban wage earners' and clerical workers' families. Thus the population of items includes, in principle, all items purchased by such urban families. On the other hand, items that are used, though not purchased, such as goods and services furnished through fringe benefits in wage contracts, are excluded from the population. As another example, highway construction price indexes are designed to measure price level changes in materials used in highway construction, hence the items selected for the sample are chosen to be representative of all the materials used in this activity.

Collection of data for weights. Sampling is used in some instances to collect data for the weights. The consumer price index provides us with an outstanding example. In order to measure the average change in prices of goods and services customarily purchased by urban wage earners' and clerical workers' families, the Bureau of Labor Statistics has had to make sample surveys from time to time to determine the kinds and quantities of goods and services actually purchased by these families. An extensive sample survey in 1961 and 1962, for example, developed data on the purchasing patterns of wage earners' and clerical workers' families in 66 urban areas. The data collected in this sample survey were utilized in setting up the system of weights adopted in the revision of the consumer price index that became effective in January 1964.

In some instances, data for weights can be obtained from complete enumerations. For many internal company indexes—such as indexes of raw material prices, or indexes of company selling prices—relevant data on weights often can be obtained from a complete enumeration of the organization's records. The same applies to certain external indexes, such as the

Federal Reserve Board's indexes of industrial production and of department store sales, for which up-to-date weights are obtained from the periodic censuses of business, manufactures, and agriculture carried out by the federal government.

Collection of current data on price and quantity changes. No sampling problem may arise in the collection of current data on price or quantity changes for internal indexes, since such data are usually collected on a complete basis as part of the reporting system of the organization concerned. In most external indexes compiled by the federal government, however, data on current price and quantity changes necessarily must be collected by sampling. For instance, it would be impossible for the Bureau of Labor Statistics to obtain current price data from all retail outlets in the United States for its consumer price index; sampling of outlets is the only feasible solution.

Quality changes and product development

In some important applications of price indexes, price-level changes are measured in order to ascertain period-to-period cost changes involved in achieving some fixed level of welfare or output. Thus for purposes of financial management a firm may wish to have an index which measures year-to-year changes in the cost of replacing the productive capacity of a battery of machines operated in the plant, in contrast to changes in the cost of replacing the machines with more-or-less identical ones (replacement in kind). Under conditions of rapid product development and technological change, the distinction between these two types of replacement can be significant. Existing indexes tend to measure changes in costs of replacement in kind. Hence one of the goals of current index number research is to find practicable methods for compiling indexes that do measure cost changes involved in attaining, at minimum cost, a given objective or capability such as a level of productive capacity. Such indexes would be an important supplement to existing indexes.

QUESTIONS AND PROBLEMS

28.1. Contrast the construction and uses of a price index and a quantity index.

28.2. What information would you require in order to construct a cost-of-living index for undergraduates in a particular university?

28.3. Briefly describe or define each of the following:

a. Price relative
b. Distinction between money values and real values
c. Fixed weights
d. Distinction between weight base and reference base

***28.4.** The Home Appliance Division of the Universal Electric Company produces four types of fans for home use: desk, hassock, kitchen exhaust, and window ventilating. Average unit selling prices of these fans and quantities sold during the years 1970, 1971, and 1972 were as follows:

Type of Fan	*Average Unit Selling Price*			*Thousands of Fans Sold*		
	1970	*1971*	*1972*	*1970*	*1971*	*1972*
Desk	$17.00	$18.50	$19.25	600	600	610
Hassock	37.00	39.00	39.75	78	80	76
Kitchen	41.50	43.00	46.00	710	700	713
Window	43.50	45.00	48.00	503	500	506

a. Calculate an annual index of fan selling prices for the years 1970 through 1972 by the method of weighted aggregates. Use 1970 as the base year, and use base-period weights.

b. Explain, in words understandable to a layman, precisely what the value of the price index for 1972 means.

c. Does your index provide any information that could not be obtained just as readily from an examination of the data that entered the index?

d. The Universal Electric Company included all four types of fans in the index of fan prices. Is it always feasible to include in a price index all of the items whose price changes are to be measured by the index? Explain.

e. Late in 1971 the company improved its kitchen and window fans by adopting a more powerful electric motor. Would knowledge of this change be helpful in interpreting the meaning of the price index calculated in part **a**?

***28.5. a.** Utilizing the data presented in Problem 28.4, calculate an index of fan selling prices by the method of a weighted average of price relatives. Use 1970 as the base period, and use data on prices and quantities sold in 1970 in constructing your value weights.

b. Are the index values that you obtained in part **a** identical to those obtained in Problem 28.4**a** by the method of weighted aggregates? Is this situation typical for index values obtained by the method of weighted aggregates and by the method of a weighted average of relatives? Explain.

28.6. A firm that produces leather goods compiles an annual index of hourly wage rates for production employees. Relevant data for three years are as follows:

Job Title	*Average Hourly Wage Rate*			*Total Hours Worked During Year by Production Employees (Thousands of Hours)*		
	1970	*1971*	*1972*	*1970*	*1971*	*1972*
Plating press operator	$2.65	$2.71	$2.80	28.6	28.9	28.0
Measuring machine operator	2.56	2.66	2.69	31.4	31.4	31.0
Hand seasoner	2.60	2.68	2.69	40.0	41.5	35.5
Machine seasoner	2.68	2.73	2.83	45.5	45.5	45.6
Dry trimmer	2.55	2.57	2.60	41.0	41.0	38.1

a. Calculate an annual index of hourly wage rates for the three years by the method of weighted aggregates. Use 1971 as the base year, and assume that the year 1970 is a typical period for the purpose of obtaining weights. *(Continued)*

b. What type of weights did you use, and why? Could the average number of employees in each type of job have been used as weights, if these data had been available? Explain.

c. Explain the meaning of the index number for 1972.

d. The average hourly wage rate can be obtained for each year by dividing the total production payroll by the total number of hours worked by production employees. Why may the average hourly rates for successive years not serve as a precise indicator of changes in the hourly wage rates? Explain.

28.7. a. Utilizing the data presented in Problem 28.6, calculate an index of hourly wage rates, with 1971 as the base, by the method of a weighted average of relatives. Use the data on wages and hours worked in 1970 in constructing your value weights.

b. Does the index calculated in part **a** have as concrete a meaning as an index of hourly wage rates calculated from the same data by the method of weighted aggregates? Explain.

c. Under what conditions will the method of weighted average of relatives provide index values identical to those obtained by the method of weighted aggregates?

***28.8. a.** Utilize the data in Problem 28.4 to calculate a quantity index of fan production for 1970, 1971, and 1972 by the method of weighted aggregates. Use 1970 as the base year, and use base-period weights.

b. Explain, in words understandable to a layman, what the value of the index for 1972 means.

***28.9.** Utilize the data in Problem 28.4 to calculate a quantity index of fan production for 1970, 1971, and 1972 by the method of a weighted average of relatives. Use 1970 as the base period, and use data on quantities and prices in 1970 in constructing your value weights.

28.10. The J. Lost Company produces Lost Shirts in three price lines: Economy, Utility, and Austerity. Company data on shirt production and manhours expended in the years 1971–1973 inclusive are as follows:

	Production (Thousand Dozen Shirts)			*Manhours Expended per Dozen Shirts*		
Price Line	*1971*	*1972*	*1973*	*1971*	*1972*	*1973*
Economy	2.7	3.6	5.0	6.1	6.0	6.2
Utility	5.5	4.5	6.5	4.7	4.8	4.9
Austerity	8.0	8.0	8.5	4.4	4.4	4.4

a. Calculate a quantity index of shirt production for 1971, 1972, and 1973 by the method of weighted aggregates. Use 1972 as your base period, and use data on manhours expended per dozen shirts in 1971 for your weights.

b. The table indicates that the company produced 16.2 thousand dozen shirts in 1971, 16.1 thousand dozen in 1972, and 20.0 thousand dozen in 1973. Express these figures as relatives on a 1972 base and compare the results with your index calculated in part **a**. What is the advantage, if any, of measuring shirt production by a quantity index instead of relatives derived from a direct count of the total number of shirts produced each year?

28.11. Utilizing the data in Problem 28.10, calculate a quantity index of shirt production by the method of a weighted average of relatives. Use as weights the aggregate numbers of manhours expended on the price lines in 1971, and use 1972 as the base year.

28.12. In Congressional committee hearings on government price statistics conducted a number of years ago, a committee member asked whether the use of value weights in price indexes calculated by the method of a weighted average of relatives gives a double importance to prices, since data on prices are weighted by value weights that are themselves based on price and quantity data. Discuss.

28.13. Department of Labor data on average hourly earnings of production workers in manufacturing industries during 1967–1970 inclusive, and values of the consumer price index for this same period, are as follows:

Year	*Average Hourly Earnings*	*Consumer Price Index, All Items (1967 = 100)*
1967	\$2.83	100.0
1968	3.01	104.2
1969	3.19	109.8
1970	3.36	116.3

a. Utilizing the consumer price index, determine whether real average hourly earnings changed from year to year during this period, and if so, how. Answer explicitly.

b. Explain precisely what is measured by your data on real average hourly earnings obtained in part **a**.

c. Would your answer in part **a** still be the same if the base of the index were shifted to 1969 and real earnings were re-calculated with the 1969-based index? Would your answer in part **b** still be the same? Carry out the necessary calculations to support your answers. What are the implications of your answers? Discuss fully.

d. In view of the fact that federal income taxes are not included in the consumer price index, do changes in the real average hourly earnings obtained in part **a** necessarily measure changes in real average hourly earnings that are available for consumption expenditures? Explain.

e. If it were decided to include federal income taxes in the consumer price index, would you expect the new index numbers for each year to be necessarily higher than the corresponding original index numbers? Discuss.

28.14. The following data appeared in a corporation's report to stockholders:

Nature of Series	*1967*	*1969*	*1970*	*1971*
(1) Average hourly wage of company employees, excluding benefits	\$2.92	\$3.12	\$3.37	\$3.66
(2) Per cent increase in (1) since 1967	0	6.8	15.4	25.3
(3) Consumer price index, 1967 = 100	100.0	104.2	109.8	116.3
(4) Value of average hourly wage of company employees in 1967 dollars	\$2.92	\$2.99	\$3.07	\$3.15
(5) Per cent increase in (4) since 1967	0	2.4	5.1	7.9

a. How were the data in row 4 obtained? Explain in nontechnical language the meaning of the entry of \$3.15 for 1971.

b. Compare the data in rows 2 and 5, and explain fully what conclusion can be drawn from this comparison.

(Continued)

c. Would the results in row 4 have been the same if some other year, such as 1971, had been used as the base period of the consumer price index? Would the results in row 5 have been the same? Explain.

28.15. Data are presented below for 1966–1970 inclusive on annual sales revenues of the Organic Products Division of Diamond Chemicals, Inc. This division processes and sells various inedible oils and fats to industrial users. Also shown are values of the wholesale price index for inedible oils and fats compiled by the Bureau of Labor Statistics.

Year	*Sales Revenues, Organic Products Division (Thousand Dollars)*	*Wholesale Price Index, Inedible Oils and Fats (1967 = 100)*
1966	1,076.5	126.4
1967	853.4	100.0
1968	775.0	90.9
1969	931.7	109.1
1970	1,237.4	133.3

a. Restate the sales revenues for each year in terms of 1967 prices.

b. What type of information is disclosed by the time series of sales revenues at constant prices? Explain.

c. Plot on one graph the sales revenues at current and constant prices. Interpret your graph and write a brief paragraph that presents your chief findings.

28.16. Consider the situation in Problem 28.15.

a. What assumption is implicit in using the wholesale price index for inedible oils and fats compiled by the Bureau of Labor Statistics to express the Organic Products Division's sales revenues at constant prices? Discuss fully.

b. Suppose the sales revenues of the division include a substantial amount of income from sales of hides and skins. Would the wholesale price index for inedible oils and fats still be appropriate to express sales revenues at constant prices? Why or why not?

***28.17.** Consider the data in Problem 28.15.

a. Determine the per cent by which sales revenues at 1967 prices changed between 1969 and 1970.

b. Obtain the sales revenues for 1969 and 1970 at 1969 prices.

c. By what per cent did sales revenues at 1969 prices change between 1969 and 1970?

d. What generalization is suggested by your answers to parts **a** and **c**? Explain fully.

28.18. Shown below are annual data on U.S. gross national product in current dollars and in constant 1958 dollars.

	GNP in Billion Dollars	
Year	*Current Dollars*	*Constant 1958 Dollars*
1968	864.2	706.6
1969	929.1	724.7
1970	974.1	720.0

a. What can one infer, from the figures given above, about changes in the prices of goods and services included in GNP over the period as a whole?
b. The GNP data in constant dollars are obtained by adjusting each component of current-dollar GNP separately for price-level changes by a relevant price index. The adjusted components then are aggregated to obtain GNP in constant dollars. A special price index, called the *implicit price deflator*, can be derived from the corresponding current-dollar and constant-dollar figures. Obtain the value of the implicit price deflator for each of the three years shown.
c. Are the index values obtained in part **b** consistent with your answer in part **a**? Discuss.
d. What is the base period of the index values obtained in part **b**? Explain.

28.19. Effective with the January 1971 index, the reference base of the consumer price index has been shifted from 1957–1959 = 100 to 1967 = 100. The Bureau of Labor Statistics has published *conversion factors* to assist users in rebasing index values published prior to January 1971. An index value on a 1957–1959 base is converted to a 1967 base by multiplying the index value by the conversion factor.
a. Annual values of the fruits and vegetables component of the consumer price index on the base 1957–1959 = 100 were, for the years 1967 through 1970, 117.5, 126.8, 128.4, and 133.2 respectively. The published conversion factor for the fruits and vegetables component of the consumer price index is .8510638. Verify this published value.
b. Conversion factors can also be used to shift a 1967-based series to the base 1957–1959 = 100. The fruits and vegetables component of the consumer price index for July 1971 stood at 126.0 on the base 1967 = 100. Show how the conversion factor given in part **a** can be used to shift this index value to the base 1957–1959 = 100.

***28.20.** The Haskins Corporation has been constructing a price index for its raw materials since 1966. In 1969, the Research Department revised the index by improving the coverage of items included in the index, by bringing the weights up to date, and by shifting the base period. The old and new index series are:

Year	*Old Index (1966 = 100)*	*New Index (1969 = 100)*
1966	100.0	
1967	123.7	
1968	130.4	
1969	137.0	100.0
1970		96.8
1971		99.9
1972		102.1

a. Splice the two indexes on the new base 1969 = 100.
b. By what per cent have the prices of raw materials increased between 1966 and 1972?
c. Is a comparison of raw material prices between 1966 and 1972 as meaningful as a comparison of the prices between 1971 and 1972? Explain.
d. If you spliced the two indexes on the base 1966 = 100, would the indicated per cent increase between 1966 and 1972 be the same as in part **b**? Explain.

28.21. The following statement appeared in a business column in a newspaper:

If you compare the wholesale price index for all manufactured products with the wholesale price index for textiles only, you will find that the textile index tends to be consistently lower than the index for all manufactured products. This occurs because the textile industry typically operates at a profit level of about 2.5 per cent, while the average profit level in manufacturing industries as a whole is around 4.5 per cent.

a. Do you agree with the explanation given? Why or why not?

b. What important principle about the interpretation of index numbers is illustrated by this example?

28.22. a. A research analyst of the Masters Cement Company wishes to study the relationship between construction activity in the United States and the number of barrels of portland cement consumed in the United States annually. Data are available on annual construction expenditures measured in current dollars. Would you recommend that the analyst use these data without adjustment in his analysis, or that he first express them in constant dollars?

b. Assuming that the construction data are to be adjusted for price-level changes, explain *why* a relevant price index could be employed in making such adjustments.

c. If the series to be studied had been the annual dollar values of construction activity and the annual dollar values of portland cement consumption, would it have been meaningful to adjust both dollar series for price-level changes? Explain.

d. Assuming that both series in part **c** were to be adjusted for price-level changes, could the same price index be employed for adjusting both series? Explain.

28.23. The following evaluation of index numbers was presented in 1964 to a group of middle-management participants in an executive development program:

I call your attention to Table I, showing indexes of prices and earnings for alternate years between 1947 and 1963. The Bureau of Labor Statistics' consumer price index, calculated on a 1947 base, is in row 1. An index of average weekly earnings of production employees in manufacturing industries, also calculated on a 1947 base, is in row 2. Note that while consumer prices have admittedly increased since the base period, earnings in manufacturing increased relatively more. Similar gaps between earnings indexes and the consumer price index exist for employees in other sectors of the economy. These widening gaps show that during the last 15 years employees have had increases in earnings beyond the amounts needed to offset price increases and maintain basic levels of living. In other words, the period since 1947 has seen the emergence for the first time of a mass market for luxury goods in the United States that should be pondered over by the management of every firm serving the consumer market.

Do the data in Table I document the speaker's contention? Discuss.

TABLE I

Indexes, 1947 = 100	*1947*	*1949*	*1951*	*1953*	*1955*	*1957*	*1959*	*1961*	*1963*
(1) Consumer price index	100	107	116	120	120	126	130	134	137
(2) Average weekly earnings in manufacturing	100	110	129	143	154	166	179	188	203

28.24. The U.S. Department of Labor compiles U.S. Department of State indexes of living costs abroad. These indexes are calculated to establish post allowances for U.S. government employees assigned to foreign posts where living costs, based on an American pattern of living, are significantly higher than living costs in Washington, D.C. Thus the index for, say, Reykjavik, Iceland measures the cost of representative goods and services in Reykjavik relative to the costs of equivalent goods and services in Washington, D.C.

Why is it inappropriate to use this index to compare living costs of foreign nationals in their home countries with those of Americans living in Washington, D.C., that is, to compare, say, living costs of an Icelandic family in Reykjavik and an American family in Washington, D.C.?

28.25. Annual values of the consumer price index for the U.S., based on a sample of 56 areas, as well as index values for two of the sample areas, are presented below for 1967, 1968, and 1969:

	Consumer Price Index, 1967 = 100		
Area	*1967*	*1968*	*1969*
U.S. average	100.0	104.2	109.8
Atlanta	100.0	104.0	110.2
Houston	100.0	104.3	111.0

a. Do the above data indicate that in 1969 the prices of items entering the consumer price index were higher, on the average, in Houston than in Atlanta? Discuss.

b. Which area—the entire United States, Atlanta, or Houston—showed the greatest relative increase between 1968 and 1969 in the prices of items entering the consumer price index? Which area showed the smallest relative increase? Show your calculations.

28.26. For one index from the following list:

(a) B.L.S. Consumer Price Index
(b) B.L.S. Wholesale Price Index
(c) F.R.B. Index of Industrial Production
(d) Department of Agriculture Index of Prices Paid by Farmers
(e) *Engineering News-Record* Construction Cost Index

go to its primary source and study the most recent description of this index. Then write a brief paper on the index, covering the following points:

1. Description of items included in the index; if a sample, basis of selecting the sample items.
2. Choice of base period.
3. Method of calculating the index; reasons for choosing this method.
4. System of weights; way in which data on weights were obtained.
5. Method of obtaining current data for the index; if from a sample, describe the sample.
6. Information on the accuracy of the data collected.
7. Special problems in the construction of the index.

Chapter

29

TREND ANALYSIS

In this and following chapters, we shall examine "classical" procedures of business and economic time series analysis. This type of analysis is a technique for categorizing and studying movements in time series data—that is, movements in data consisting of successive values of a variable at monthly, yearly, or other regular time intervals. Examples of time series are weekly sales data for a firm, monthly production data for an industry, or yearly production worker employment data for the United States. A statistical analysis of the past movements of such data enables us: (1) to determine the past and current pattern of these movements in a given time series, and (2) to obtain clues about the pattern in the future. These clues can be used by management as an aid in forecasting, a prerequisite to planning and control.

The *classical* procedures of time series analysis, which we shall discuss, are basically descriptive in nature. They do not utilize formal probability models, such as the ones underlying regression analysis. *Econometric* procedures, which are based on formal probability models, also have been developed for analysis of time series data, but a discussion of these procedures is beyond the scope of this book.

In these chapters we first examine briefly the subject of forecasting, so that its place in company operations will be clear. Then we examine specific procedures of time series analysis and study their uses as aids to forecasting, planning, and control.

29.1
A BRIEF SURVEY OF FORECASTING

Forecasting: a management responsibility

The future is always uncertain to some degree, and no forecast is safe from error. Even so, management has no choice but to forecast constantly. Any decision based on an appraisal of the future involves a forecast of some type, and management must continually make such appraisals.

A forecast may be made wholly by hunch, "feel," or intuition, or it may be the product of a formal procedure. In recent years, management has come to rely more and more on formal forecasting systems rather than on informal assessments of future prospects. There are various reasons for this, among them the increasing complexity of modern business, the attenuation of direct contact between producer and user, gains in the amount and quality of data available for forecasting, and the improvement of data tabulation and forecasting techniques.

Companies generally make both long-term and short-term forecasts. Long-term forecasts usually deal with the probable direction of events from about 5 to perhaps 15 or 20 years into the future. Short-term forecasts are concerned with the more immediate future, from a few months to about 2 years ahead.

The most important type of company forecast, long-term or short-term, is the company sales forecast. Other types closely allied with the company sales forecast are the general business forecast and the industry sales forecast. Companies also forecast prices of their raw materials, prices of their finished goods, and their short- and long-term capital requirements.

The hazards of forecasting

The greatest single hazard in forecasting is that events that were unforeseen and unpredicted by the forecaster will arise to overturn a forecast. Thus, the possibility of serious error in a forecast increases, as a rule, with the length of the forecast. A forecast covering a period six months in the future is less likely to be in error because of the impact of unforeseen events than a comparable forecast projected five years ahead. Similarly, forecasts made during periods of relative business stability are more likely to be accurate than forecasts made during periods when unknown and unpredictable conditions may be encountered by the businessman.

We also may say broadly that one can make more accurate forecasts for larger aggregates than for smaller ones. In forecasting sales of large and expensive machinery of which a relatively small number of units are sold in any year, the forecasts can be rendered inaccurate by the loss or gain of a single order. But when many units of the item or product line are sold to a multitude of customers, no individual order has too pronounced an effect, and forecasting errors due to unique conditions with one or a few customers are not as likely to lead to substantial errors in the forecasts. This stabilizing factor permits industry sales to be forecast somewhat more accurately than company sales, and company sales somewhat more accurately than sales by specific product lines.

Forecasting accuracy varies from one industry to another. A forecast that proves to be 85 or 90 per cent accurate will be considered exceptionally good in some industries, but merely fair in others. In general, it is more difficult to make consistently accurate forecasts in durable goods than in non-durable goods industries, because patterns of demand for durable goods tend to fluctuate widely with changes in general business conditions, whereas patterns of demand for non-durable goods tend to be more stable.

The accuracy of a forecast must always be evaluated in terms of the uses that will be made of the forecast. A long-term forecast of company sales to be used as a basis for a program of plant expansion is not expected to pinpoint future sales volume, while a short-term operating forecast to be used as the basis for production planning will involve an attempt to make a precise projection.

Uses and limitations of time series analysis in forecasting

The techniques of time series analysis that are examined in this and following chapters have proved to be useful tools for forecasting. It should be recognized at the start, however, that these techniques cannot be applied mechanically; rather, subjective evaluations must play a key role in their use.

There are several reasons why subjective considerations are so important in time series analysis. First, a generally satisfactory probability approach to such analysis has not yet been found. Second, some purely subjective evaluations would be necessary in making forecasts even if a suitable probability approach to time series analysis were available. Whenever we examine the past to obtain clues about the future—as is the case when we use time series analysis as an aid to forecasting—the past is relevant only to the extent that causal conditions previously in effect continue to hold in the period ahead. In economic and business activity, causal conditions seldom remain constant from period to period. Rather, the complex of causal factors at work tends to be constantly shifting, so that the connection between the past, present, and the future must be continually evaluated.

While the techniques of time series analysis to be discussed do not eliminate the factor of subjective evaluations, they still make a useful contribution by providing a conceptual approach to forecasting in which forecasts are made with the aid of a set of specific formal procedures, and judgments are indicated explicitly.

Because of the particular limitations involved in any one method of forecasting, it is general practice to supplement a forecast based on time series analysis with independent analysis utilizing other methods. For example, the reasonableness of a statistical forecast of company sales may be examined through relevant business and economic analysis. In addition, other independent sales forecasts are often developed from opinions of the sales force, from the composite view of a panel of top executives, or from interviews with consumers and customers to ascertain their buying expectations and related matters. Incidentally, statistical sample survey methods, such as those discussed in Chapter 13, are being used increasingly to develop data on buying expectations.

29.2 SECULAR TREND

We have mentioned that companies make both long-term and short-term forecasts. We now turn our attention to a concept that is useful in long-term forecasting as well as in business and economic analysis—the concept of long-term, or secular, trend.

The meaning of secular trend

Figure 29.1 shows data on annual consumption of man-made fibers in the United States over five decades, plotted on a semilogarithmic graph. If we were asked to describe the essential features of the pattern of consumption, we could point out first that there has been a long-term upward movement in the series, and second, that this upward movement was not smooth and uninterrupted but was marked by fluctuations.

Thus, we can speak of two components in the pattern of annual consumption: (1) a long-term smooth component that corresponds to the general sweep of the series, and (2) a fluctuating component. This breaking up of a series into component parts is characteristic of the classical model of time series analysis. In this model:

(29.1) The smooth component, representing the general long-term sweep of the data, is called the ***long-term,*** or ***secular, trend*** of the series.

(29.2) The fluctuating component comprises a number of additional components—namely, ***cyclical fluctuations, seasonal variation,*** and ***irregular*** or ***random*** changes.

The trend concept, on which we now focus, has proved useful in the analysis of activities that are affected by such deep-seated, lasting, evolutionary factors as population growth, economic development, and gradual changes in habits of consumers. Where activities are not affected by long-term factors, the trend concept should not be applied. Consider, for example, the case of a copper mining company that happens by chance to strike

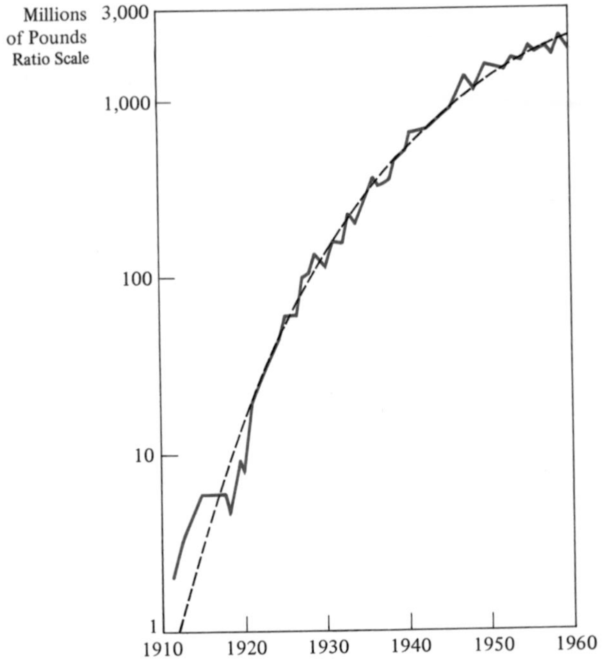

Figure 29.1. Fifty-year trend pattern of consumption of man-made fibers

silver from time to time in its copper mining operations. A time series on silver production by this company *might* show an upward or downward drift over a sequence of years, but if this pattern is due simply to short-term chance factors, it would not make sense to read a trend component into the silver production time series.

Since movements in the fluctuating component are chiefly of significance in short-term forecasting, we discuss these separately in later chapters.

Describing the secular trend: the trend curve

We represent the long-term tendency of our data by a trend curve. The trend curve in Figure 29.1 shows the general sweep of the data, which in this case has followed a long-term pattern of increase at a decreasing rate. Note that the trend curve is smooth, corresponding to the model wherein trend represents the continuous, gradual change due to the workings of long-term factors. For any one year, the trend curve in Figure 29.1 shows that year's "trend level" of consumption of man-made fibers.

The trend curve must cover a relatively long period if it is to be a good representation of the long-term sweep of the data. At a minimum it should extend beyond the duration of one cycle of fluctuation in the series. Note, for example, the restricted picture of secular movement that would be obtained from the data shown in Figure 29.1 if a period covered by only a portion of a cycle of fluctuation were examined—for example, the period in the early 1950's. Also, note the distorted picture of long-term trend that would be obtained had we chosen a period beginning at, say, the high point of one cycle and ending at the low point of the following cycle.

Of course, even when the period is relatively long, the trend pattern based on a particular time period tends to be affected by the years covered. In Figure 29.1, if a trend curve were based on just that part of the series beginning in 1946 and ending in 1960, a different type of trend pattern and different trend values would be obtained than in the graph, since the trend curve in the graph was constructed to give a good fit to the series for the longer period 1911–1960. Since different relatively long periods can lead to varying descriptions of the long-term trend in an activity, it is important that the period chosen for trend analysis be the most meaningful one for the problem at hand. We shall say more about this later.

Uses of the trend concept

Now that we have examined the concept of secular trend, we consider the two principal uses of the trend concept in problems of economics and business.

Study of past pattern. The nature of the secular trend in a time series may be studied as a matter of intrinsic interest, or for the historical record, or in order to obtain a better picture of the other components in a series. In each of these uses, interest centers on the trend for some period that is wholly in the past.

Projection of secular trend. Frequently, however, the past pattern of secular trend in a series is studied to obtain a clue about the *future* direction this pattern may reasonably be expected to take. In this case, one wishes to *extrapolate* or *project* the trend curve to estimate its level for some future period on the basis of its pattern of past behavior.

Examples of trend curve projections are shown in Figures 29.4a and 29.4b (p. 659). Here the trend curves of gross national product, fitted to the series for the period 1910–1970, are projected ahead 10 years.

29.3
PATTERNS OF SECULAR TREND IN ECONOMIC AND BUSINESS ACTIVITY

We now examine some typical patterns of secular trend in economic and business activity. Such an examination will provide insights that can be applied to long-term forecasting as well as to business and economic analysis in general.

Growth curves

Studies of long-term trend patterns for many industries in the American economy have indicated that industries generally tend to undergo a period of rapid expansion after they are once established. As the size of the industry increases, however, the *rate* of expansion slackens, and eventually a saturation point is approached.

Thus the trend curve in Figure 29.1 is typical of those for many activities, in that the long-term pattern of change indicates the activity is increasing at a decreasing rate. Figure 29.2 presents another trend pattern of this same type, for bituminous coal production. The bituminous coal industry

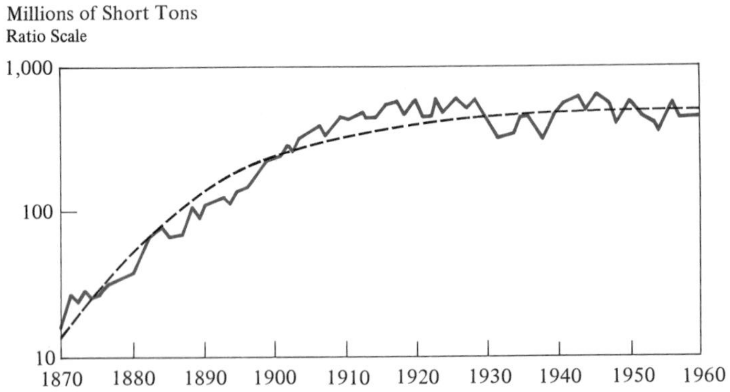

Source: National Industrial Conference Board, Inc.

Figure 29.2. Ninety-year trend pattern of bituminous coal production

shows a pattern of increase at a decreasing rate that is well advanced. The trend pattern of consumption of man-made fibers, in contrast, indicates that this activity is still in a stage of relatively rapid expansion. While long-term trend patterns for many business and economic activities are similar to those shown in that they follow patterns of increase at a decreasing rate, the patterns differ as to rates of increase and duration of the period of relatively rapid increase before a leveling-off sets in.

Trend patterns of increase at a decreasing rate can be described mathematically by *growth curves*. Two representative families of growth curves—there are others—are the *Gompertz curve* and the *logistic,* or *Pearl-Reed, curve*. Examples of these curves are plotted on arithmetic and semilogarithmic grids in Figure 29.3. Note that on arithmetic grids these curves take the shape of an elongated S; they are, in fact, sometimes called S curves. These elongated S shapes indicate a pattern of *absolute* growth as

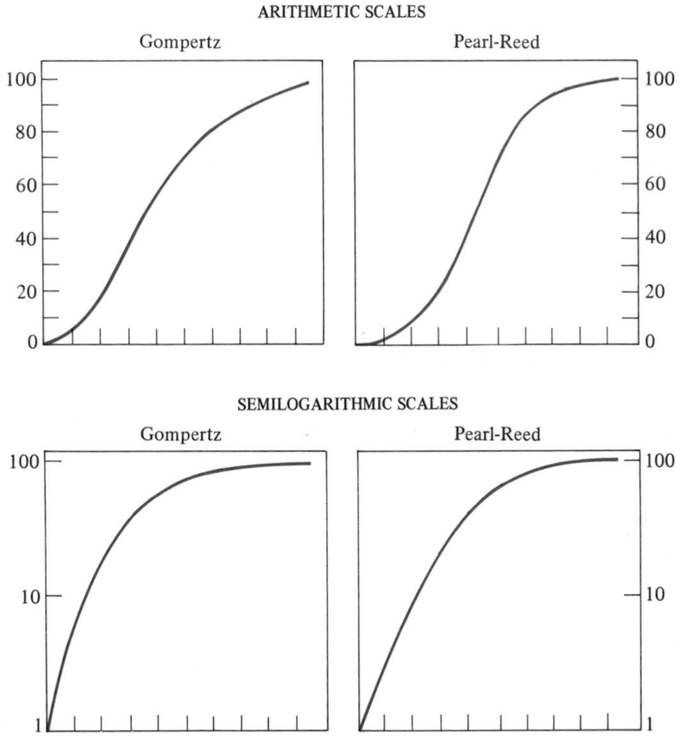

Figure 29.3. Characteristics of growth curves

follows: (1) an initial introduction period during which absolute increments of growth are small, (2) a period of rapid absolute growth, and (3) an approach to maturity. At the same time, the *relative* growth, that is, the rate of increase, is a constantly declining one throughout the duration of these curves. Thus, the mathematical properties of these curves conform to the pattern of increase at a decreasing rate that we have noted to be a basic pattern of long-term change in business and economic activities. As may be seen in Figure 29.3, the Gompertz curve is most applicable to situations in which the approach to maturity is relatively gradual, whereas the logistic curve is applicable when the approach is relatively rapid.

It is important to note that when one uses a Gompertz or logistic growth curve, one implicitly assumes that there is an upper limit, determinable from the past data, that the growth of the activity is approaching. This assumption arises from the mathematical properties of these curves, and is often a reasonable one for an activity in a closed system where there is a limitation on some key resource. An example of such a situation would be the growth in tea production in a certain country where the government has encouraged domestic tea-growing to cut down on imports. The shrubs can be grown only in a narrow region near one part of the sea coast. This limitation in suitable land imposes a fixed upper limit on the number of shrubs that eventually can be brought into cultivation and on the volume of tea production that can be achieved.

The assumption of a fixed upper limit would not be reasonable, on the other hand, for many forms of business and economic activity in an open and expanding economy where levels of resources and demand continue to rise. Even in an open economy, to be sure, many individual business and economic activities show declines in their rates of growth as time passes, but it does not follow that these activities are approaching *fixed* upper limits of expansion implied in Gompertz, logistic, and similar curves. Hence, we must interpret such curves with great care, reinterpret them as new data and insights become available, and revise the trend calculations by using a different time period or trend curve when circumstances indicate that the fixed upper limit in the growth curve exerts an unrealistic influence when the curve is projected for forecasting purposes.

Straight-line trends

Not all business and economic time series show long-term tendencies that are of the growth-curve type. We now consider two types of straight-line trend patterns, the *semilogarithmic straight-line trend* and the *arithmetic straight-line trend.*

Semilogarithmic straight-line trends. A semilogarithmic straight-line trend —a straight line on semilogarithmic graph paper—is appropriate when the long-term pattern of change in the series is deemed to be more or less constant in rate. Figure 29.4a shows a semilogarithmic straight-line trend curve fitted to constant-dollar data on gross national product in the United States from 1910 to 1970 inclusive. The trend curve has been projected to 1980, as shown by the dotted portion. Figure 29.4b shows the same data plotted on an arithmetic graph. Note that here the long-term pattern bends upward, since a constant *rate* of increase is associated with larger and larger *absolute amounts* of increase as the level of a series becomes higher.

A curve that changes in value at a constant rate is called an *exponential* curve. Thus a semilogarithmic straight-line trend pattern is an exponential pattern. The exponential pattern of continual change at a constant rate contrasts with the basic pattern in growth curves in which the trend values approach an imputed upper limit and the rate of increase declines continually as time passes and the limit is approached ever more closely.

The constant rate of long-term growth in the series on gross national product in Figure 29.4 is roughly 3 per cent per year. For individual products and industries, in contrast, initial rates of growth tend to be higher than 3 per cent but taper off in time, often to less than 3 per cent. The more or less constant rate of growth in general economic activity and declining growth rates for individual products and industries go hand-in-hand in the

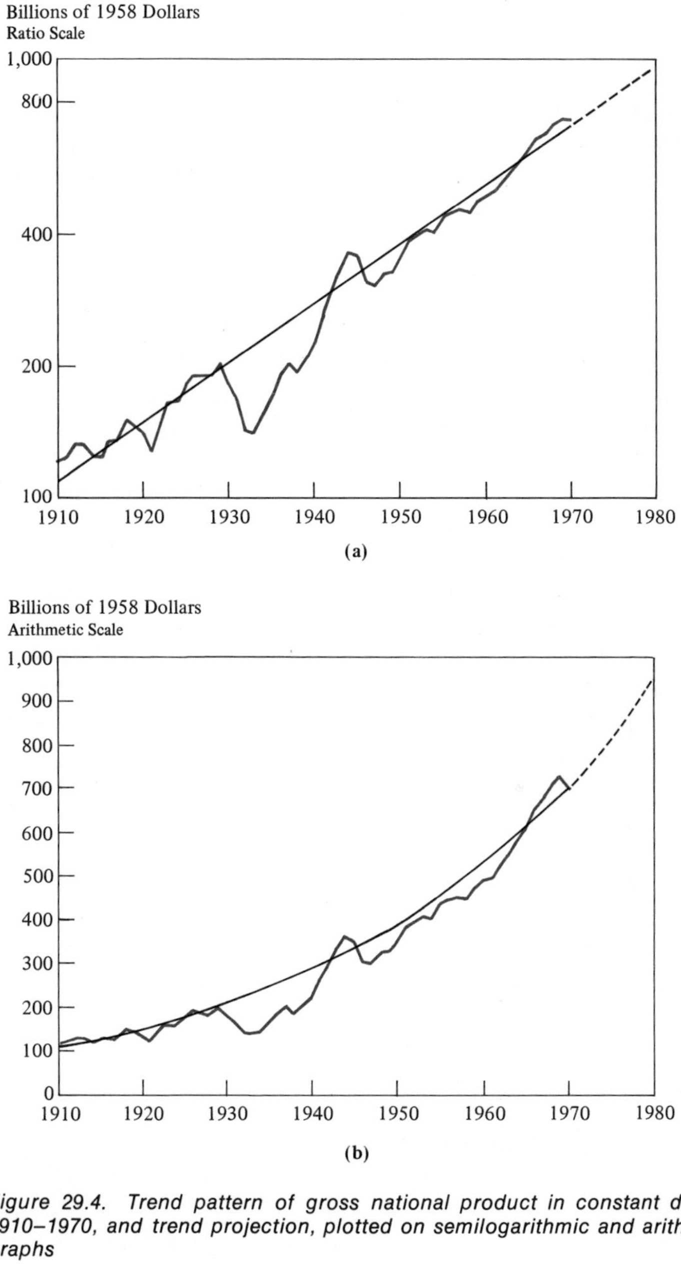

Figure 29.4. Trend pattern of gross national product in constant dollars, 1910–1970, and trend projection, plotted on semilogarithmic and arithmetic graphs

American economy because of the continuing introduction of new, rapidly growing lines of activity.

A constant long-term rate of growth is, of course, not confined to aggregate economic activity. Some individual industries, as well as some firms, show such a pattern of long-term growth. More frequently, however, industry and company series show retardation in the long-term rate of growth, so that a semilogarithmic straight-line trend is not appropriate if a sufficiently long period of time is considered. Often, though, semilogarithmic straight-line trends will fit such series over more limited time periods—perhaps 10 to 20 years. A number of such periods can be identified in the series in Figures 29.1 and 29.2. In practice, then, semilogarithmic straight-line trends tend to be applicable to individual activities when the period covered is not too long and the trend is projected only into the near future.

Arithmetic straight-line trends. Occasionally a time series will be encountered whose long-term trend pattern can be best described by a straight line on arithmetic graph paper. Such a trend line reflects a constant absolute amount of change in the long-term trend. Figure 29.6a (p. 663) shows a fitted trend pattern of this type.

Arithmetic straight-line trends tend to be applicable mainly over restricted periods of a few decades, when a segment of a long-term S curve of the type in Figure 29.3 may appear roughly as a straight line. Thus, both the arithmetic and semilogarithmic straight-line trends tend as a rule to be applicable over relatively restricted time periods. The semilogarithmic straight-line trend is applicable to situations in which period-to-period changes are, on the average, constant in rate; arithmetic straight-line trends are applicable to situations in which period-to-period changes are, on the average, constant in absolute amount.

Discontinuities in trend patterns

Sometimes the basic long-term factors affecting an activity change sharply, to an extent that it is more reasonable to break the overall time period into segments for trend analysis than to attempt to apply a single pattern to the period as a whole. An example is shown in Figure 29.5 on oleomargarine production in the United States since 1909. In a study of the

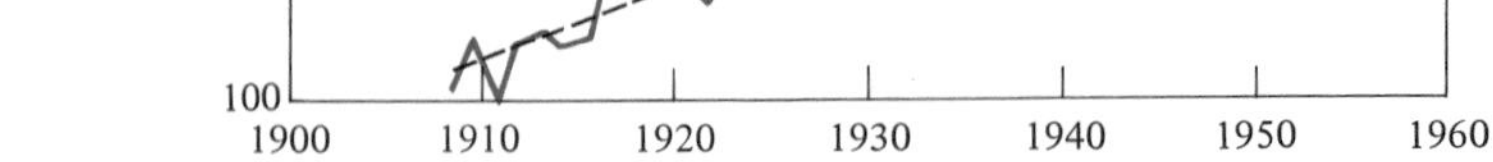

Source: National Industrial Conference Board, Inc.

Figure 29.5. Trend patterns of oleomargarine production

trend pattern in this activity, the period was broken into two parts, 1909–1939 and 1940 onward, and a separate growth curve was fitted to each part. The reason for this break is that the period beginning around 1940 saw the removal of legislative restrictions that had hampered consumption in many states, and a new long-term pattern began to develop (Ref. 29.1, pp. 62–63). Examples of breaks in trend patterns are often encountered in economies in which new technological and other developments are common.

29.4 CALCULATIONS IN TIME SERIES ANALYSIS

Linear trend curves—that is, arithmetic and semilogarithmic straight lines—can be readily fitted to time series data by the method of least squares introduced in Chapter 22. In the present section we fit such trends by this method, and then use the trend as a basis for isolating and measuring the fluctuating component in the series. This latter procedure is useful in economic analysis and short-term forecasting.

The examples used here are simple ones, and the time periods included in the trend calculations are rather short, to facilitate the illustration of the computational procedures.

Calculations for arithmetic straight-line trends

Fitting trend curve. We will fit an arithmetic straight-line trend curve to the data in Table 29.1 on the number of used textbooks sold during the period 1963–1972 inclusive by a Student Union book exchange.

As in Chapter 22, we write the general equation of an arithmetic straight line calculated from sample data as follows:

$$\overline{Y}_X = a + bX \tag{29.3}$$

In time series analysis, X represents the time period—in this case, year—and $\overline{Y}_X$ is the trend value for period X. The constant a represents the value of $\overline{Y}_X$ when $X = 0$, and b is the slope of the trend line—that is, b indicates the amount of increase or decrease in $\overline{Y}_X$ for each unit change in X. The constants a and b, according to the method of least squares, were given in (22.3c) and (22.3a):

$$b = \frac{\Sigma XY - \dfrac{\Sigma X \Sigma Y}{n}}{\Sigma X^2 - \dfrac{(\Sigma X)^2}{n}} \tag{29.4a}$$

$$a = \frac{1}{n}(\Sigma Y - b\Sigma X) \tag{29.4b}$$

Table 29.1 Computations for Fitting Arithmetic Straight-Line Trend to Data on Used Textbooks Sold

Year	Year in Transformed Units X	Used Textbooks Sold (No. of Volumes) Y	XY	X^2
1963	0	800	0	0
1964	1	700	700	1
1965	2	800	1,600	4
1966	3	1,200	3,600	9
1967	4	1,400	5,600	16
1968	5	1,500	7,500	25
1969	6	1,600	9,600	36
1970	7	2,000	14,000	49
1971	8	1,900	15,200	64
1972	9	2,300	20,700	81
Total	45	14,200	78,500	285

$$b = \frac{\Sigma XY - \dfrac{\Sigma X \Sigma Y}{n}}{\Sigma X^2 - \dfrac{(\Sigma X)^2}{n}} = \frac{78{,}500 - \dfrac{(45)(14{,}200)}{10}}{285 - \dfrac{(45)^2}{10}} = 177$$

$$a = \frac{1}{n}(\Sigma Y - b\Sigma X) = \frac{1}{10}[14{,}200 - (177)(45)] = 624$$

$$\overline{Y}_X = 624 + 177X$$
$$X = 0 \text{ at } 1963$$

With time series data the computational work will be reduced if the values of the X variable (time) are transformed to values of smaller magnitude. This can be done without any complications. In the case at hand, we simply designate 1963 as year 0, 1964 as year 1, and so on, as shown in Table 29.1. The computational work may be reduced still further, though sometimes at the cost of minor complications in method, if the X values are chosen in such a way that the middle of the period to which the trend is fitted is designated as zero. (See Section 32.1.)

The basic calculations for fitting an arithmetic straight-line trend to the data are performed in Table 29.1. The results are $b = 177$ and $a = 624$. The trend equation is $\overline{Y}_X = 624 + 177X$, where $X = 0$ at 1963.

This equation indicates that the trend value for 1963 ($\overline{Y}_{1963}$) is 624 books ($a = 624$), and that $\overline{Y}_X$ increases by 177 units for each increase of one unit in X—that is, for each year. Note that the year for which $X = 0$ is shown with the trend equation. It is good practice to give this information whenever the original X values are transformed.

The trend curve is plotted in Figure 29.6a by calculating $\overline{Y}_X$ for several transformed values of X (for example, $X = 0, 4, 9$), plotting the appropriate points, and connecting the points with a straight line.

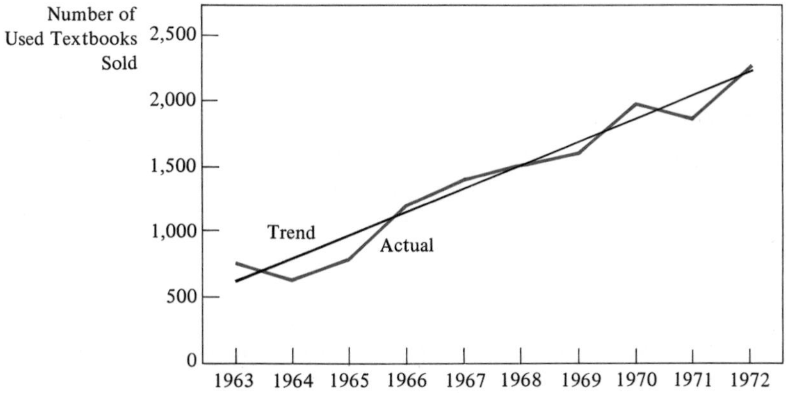

(a) Actual and Trend

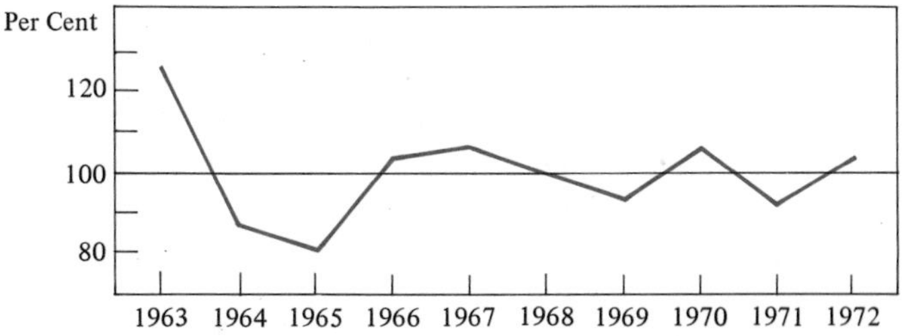

(b) Per Cent of Trend

Figure 29.6. Sales of used textbooks, Student Union Book Exchange, 1963–1972, trend and per cent of trend

Projecting trend curve. To project the trend curve obtained previously, one need compute only the value of $\overline{Y}_X$ for future values of X. If the original X values have been transformed, remember to maintain this transformation in making the computations. For example, if one wants to compute the trend value of book sales for, say, 1983, one would use $X = 20$ since this is the transformed X value for 1983 when $X = 0$ in 1963. The calculations are as follows:

$$\overline{Y}_{1983} = 624 + 177(20) = 4{,}164$$

The projected trend value for, say, 1987 is:

$$\overline{Y}_{1987} = 624 + 177(24) = 4{,}872$$

Of course, one could also obtain the approximate trend values for 1983 and 1987 by extending the linear trend curve on a graph and reading the trend values from the graph.

Per cent of trend

We mentioned earlier that it is useful in short-term statistical forecasting to be able to isolate and measure the fluctuating component in a time series. The fluctuating component may be measured in terms of its deviations from the smooth component, or trend curve, of the series. The most widely used and generally applicable procedure is to express this deviation in per cent, or relative, terms. That is, the fluctuating component may be measured as a *per cent of trend,* or as a *per cent deviation from trend.*

Measuring fluctuating component as per cent of trend. We utilize the earlier example on used textbook sales to illustrate how the fluctuating component is measured as a per cent of trend. For instance, the number of used textbooks sold in 1963 by the Student Union book exchange was 800. The trend value for that year is 624 books. The fluctuating component for that year, measured as a per cent of trend, therefore is $(800/624)100 = 128.2$ per cent. Measured as a per cent deviation from trend, the magnitude of this component is +28.2 per cent. In other words, actual sales were 28.2 per cent greater than the trend level in 1963.

In the same manner, the fluctuating component may be measured for the other years, once the trend values have been obtained. These calculations are shown in Table 29.2, and a graph of the fluctuating component measured as per cent of trend is presented in Figure 29.6b. We shall discuss the role of the fluctuating component in short-term forecasting in the next chapter.

Table 29.2 Computations for Measurement of Fluctuating Component in Sales of Used Textbooks as Per Cent of Arithmetic Straight-Line Trend

(1) Year	(2) *Number of Used Textbooks Sold*	(3) *Trend Value*	(4) *Per Cent of Trend* [(*Col. 2* ÷ *Col. 3*) × *100*]
1963	800	624	128.2
1964	700	801	87.4
1965	800	978	81.8
1966	1,200	1,155	103.9
1967	1,400	1,332	105.1
1968	1,500	1,509	99.4
1969	1,600	1,686	94.9
1970	2,000	1,863	107.4
1971	1,900	2,040	93.1
1972	2,300	2,217	103.7

Calculations for semilogarithmic straight-line trends

Fitting trend curve. To show the computations involved in fitting a semilogarithmic straight-line trend by mathematical methods, we shall fit a trend line to annual data on the number of subscribers belonging to a "Food of the Month" plan sponsored by a mail order food specialty house. These data are presented in Table 29.3.

Table 29.3 Computations for Fitting Semilogarithmic Straight-Line Trend to Data on Membership of "Food of the Month" Plan

Year	*Year in Transformed Units* X	*Number of Members* Y	$\log Y$	$X \log Y$	X^2
1962	0	97	1.98677	0	0
1963	1	110	2.04139	2.04139	1
1964	2	147	2.16732	4.33464	4
1965	3	165	2.21748	6.65244	9
1966	4	230	2.36173	9.44692	16
1967	5	258	2.41162	12.05810	25
1968	6	406	2.60853	15.65118	36
1969	7	452	2.65514	18.58598	49
1970	8	615	2.78888	22.31104	64
1971	9	970	2.98677	26.88093	81
1972	10	1,100	3.04139	30.41390	100
Total	55		27.26702	148.37652	385

$$b = \frac{\Sigma X \log Y - \dfrac{\Sigma X \Sigma \log Y}{n}}{\Sigma X^2 - \dfrac{(\Sigma X)^2}{n}} = \frac{148.37652 - \dfrac{(55)(27.26702)}{11}}{385 - \dfrac{(55)^2}{11}} = .10947$$

$$a = \frac{1}{n}(\Sigma \log Y - b\Sigma X) = \frac{1}{11}[27.26702 - (.10947)(55)] = 1.93147$$

$$\log \overline{Y}_X = 1.93147 + .10947X$$

$$X = 0 \text{ at } 1962$$

The general equation of a semilogarithmic straight line calculated from sample data can be written as:

(29.5) $$\log \overline{Y}_X = a + bX$$

It will be observed that this equation is identical in form to (29.3) for an arithmetic straight line, except that in (29.5) the logarithms of the Y variable are used rather than the actual values of this variable.

The constants a and b may be calculated as before by the method of least squares; the appropriate equations in this case are:

(29.6a) $$b = \frac{\Sigma X \log Y - \dfrac{\Sigma X \Sigma \log Y}{n}}{\Sigma X^2 - \dfrac{(\Sigma X)^2}{n}}$$

(29.6b) $$a = \frac{1}{n}(\Sigma \log Y - b\Sigma X)$$

Note the similarity between (29.6a) and (29.4a) and between (29.6b) and (29.4b); in the formulas for the semilogarithmic straight-line constants, log Y simply replaces the Y that appeared in the earlier formulas for the arithmetic straight-line constants.

As before, computational work can be reduced by designating the first year in our series—in this case 1962—as year 0, 1963 as year 1, and so on. The basic calculations for fitting a semilogarithmic straight-line trend to the data are performed in Table 29.3. Note that once the logarithms of the Y values have been obtained, the arithmetic procedure in Table 29.3 follows that of Table 29.1. The results are $b = .10947$ and $a = 1.93147$. The trend equation is $\log \overline{Y}_X = 1.93147 + .10947X$, where $X = 0$ at 1962.

Projecting trend curve. To obtain a trend value from a semilogarithmic straight-line trend equation, we first compute the value of $\log \overline{Y}_X$ corresponding to the appropriate value of X. We then find $\overline{Y}_X$ by obtaining the antilogarithm of $\log \overline{Y}_X$. If the original X values have been transformed, this transformation must be maintained when substituting into the trend equation to obtain $\log \overline{Y}_X$. The calculation of the projected semilogarithmic trend value for 1979, for instance, is as follows:

$$\log \overline{Y}_{1979} = 1.93147 + .10947(17) = 3.79246$$
$$\overline{Y}_{1979} = \text{antilog } 3.79246 = 6{,}201$$

Measuring fluctuating component as per cent of trend. The fluctuating component of a series to which a semilogarithmic straight-line trend has been fitted can be isolated and measured by expressing it as a per cent of trend or as a per cent deviation from trend. Thus, no new problems arise in measuring the fluctuating component when the trend is represented by a semilogarithmic straight line. It is necessary simply to remember that the trend value is represented by $\overline{Y}_X$, that is, by the antilogarithm of the value of $\log \overline{Y}_X$.

Calculating rate of growth. The constant rate of growth implicit in a semilogarithmic straight-line trend curve often is measured for descriptive and analytical purposes. This rate of growth can be determined from the following relationship:

$$\log(1 + g) = b \qquad (29.7)$$

where b is the slope of the semilogarithmic straight-line trend equation, and g represents the rate of growth.

Continuing with the "Food of the Month" plan example, we have $b = .10947$, so that $\log(1 + g) = .10947$ and $(1 + g) = \text{antilog } .10947 = 1.287$. Finally, we have $g = .287$. Thus, we calculate that the rate of growth in this case is about 29 per cent per year.

29.5 TREND PROJECTIONS AND FORECASTING

In applications of time series analysis, trend projections are useful primarily as an aid in long-term forecasting. Such projections relate only to the smooth, long-term component of a time series. Thus if the trend projection of sales of a product indicates a sales volume of 1.2 million units by 1983, this figure should not be taken as a precise forecast of sales for that year. To pinpoint future sales, one must forecast not only the trend component of the series but also the position of the fluctuating component around this trend.

It is generally impossible to project the fluctuating component of a business or economic time series very far into the future with accuracy. But this limitation is seldom serious in *long-term forecasting,* which assists management in making decisions about long-range programs such as plant expansion and related financing. In planning such long-range programs, management is interested in the general prospects for an extended period in the future rather than in the specific prospect for any one year. For example, in deciding whether to build a new plant, management may wish to obtain the general sales prospects for the period 1978–1985 rather than a forecast for a specific year such as 1981. Thus, management is concerned with the average or trend level of sales around which actual sales will fluctuate during the period 1978–1985; if this forecast of the trend is fairly accurate, it may be adequate for purposes of long-term planning even though actual sales during this period will differ somewhat from the projected trend level of sales.

Prediction intervals for forecasts

It would be helpful to set prediction intervals for forecasts. We then could state with a specified confidence coefficient that, for instance, the annual sales of a given product five years hence will be 1.2 million units plus or minus a certain amount. Such prediction intervals can be obtained in some cases, but a probability model and quite advanced statistical techniques are needed. Even without computing prediction intervals, however, we still can obtain a clue about the usefulness of the trend level as an indicator of the average actual level in a future period by examining the nature and causes of the fluctuating component in the data. If this component consists of cycles that are of relatively small amplitude and short duration, and if we believe that this fluctuating component will continue to have these attributes in the future and that the trend curve is an appropriate one, we may conclude that a trend projection will be a fairly good indicator of the actual level of activity in the period ahead. Figure 29.1, for instance, displays a trend pattern in which the fluctuating component in the series consists of cycles of relatively small amplitude and short duration.

In contrast, if the amplitude of the fluctuating component is relatively large, or if the duration of the cycles is long, the trend projection generally will be less meaningful for forecasting. Figure 29.2 shows a trend pattern in which the duration of the cycles is relatively long, so that the level of the fluctuating component is entirely above or below the trend level for extended periods of time. Indeed, in some series the cycles in the fluctuating component will be so extreme in amplitude or duration, or the effect of the long-term factors so difficult to isolate, that the trend projection will be of little or no use in making a long-term forecast.

Note that any analysis based on the extent of divergence between the actual levels and the fitted trend levels of an activity during a past period can be used in forecasting only if it can be assumed that the fluctuating component will behave in the future as it has in the past. Furthermore, this analysis does not indicate whether the particular trend curve employed is really a good representation of the past long-term pattern of the series, or whether it appropriately may be projected into the future.

Important considerations in projecting trend curves

A forecaster must know more than the mechanics of trend fitting and trend projection. Other elements of trend analysis—many of which are largely subjective—are most important in forecasting. We now examine the major considerations that are crucial when trend analysis is used for long-term forecasting.

The time period. Before a historical trend pattern is projected into the future for forecasting purposes, one must determine that the past pattern is relevant to the period ahead. It cannot be assumed automatically that a long-term trend pattern will continue without a break. As we noted, long-term trends of many activities in the American economy actually have broken out of one pattern into another. In Figure 29.5 it was evident that an established long-term pattern of oleomargarine production was broken by the effects of legislative changes. Other important causes of breaks in trend patterns are technological innovations and changes in consumers' habits and preferences. Of course, when a shift in the trend pattern of an activity has taken place during some time in the past, only that portion of the series still relevant to the future should be used as a basis for trend projection.

Choice of appropriate trend curve. In addition to determining the particular past time period that is relevant to the future, it also is necessary to determine the type of trend curve—a growth curve, semilogarithmic straight line, arithmetic straight line, or other type of curve—that will serve best *as the basis for trend projection.* This determination, like the choice of the time period, generally is made by judgment and requires analysis of the past pattern of the activity as well as assumptions about the future. Competing types of trend curves can be fitted to ascertain which type gives the best fit (in some defined sense) to a historical time series, but comparisons of fit do not necessarily indicate which type best expresses the effects of the long-term factors nor which type is most reasonable as a basis for trend projection.

The problem of choosing an appropriate trend curve for making projections into the future is illustrated in Figure 29.7. This graph presents data on annual sales of residential patio swimming pools by the Mermaid Pool Corporation between 1960, the first full year the firm operated, and 1971 inclusive. Two trend curves have been fitted mathematically to the sales data—a semilogarithmic straight line and a logistic curve. The logistic curve bends only slightly within the range of the past data. Both curves fit the data well, and there is little to choose between the two representations of the smooth long-term pattern in the series. However, when the trends are projected beyond the range of the actual data, the inherent mathematical characteristics of the curves cause the projections to diverge increasingly. Still other types of trend curves would give good representations of the long-term pattern in the series, and yet provide differing projections. Thus a Gompertz curve would give a good fit to the data, but yield a projection that falls roughly midway between the two shown in Figure 29.7.

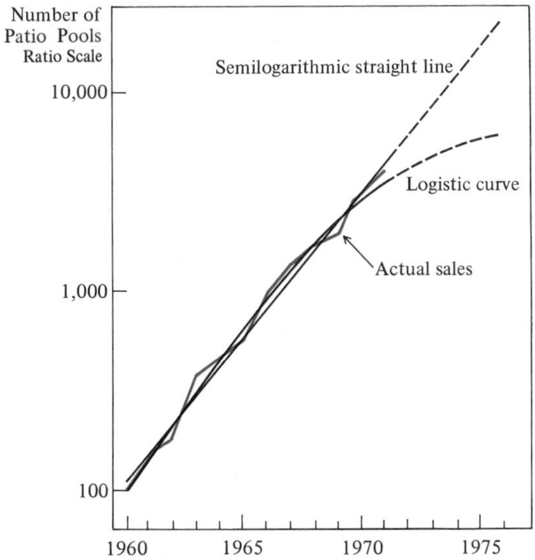

Figure 29.7. Alternative trends and trend projections of sales of patio pools by Mermaid Pool Corporation

Assume that management in the firm wants to project the trend of patio-pool sales as an aid in planning long-term capital requirements. Which trend curve is the appropriate one to project? The data on past sales have helped to narrow the choice of trends that are possibly useful, but cannot give direct help in choosing, for projection into the future, one of the several types of trend curves that provide a good representation of the growth pattern in the past. This final selection must depend on analysis of the factors affecting the course of sales in the future. If it is believed that the firm's patio-pool sales will continue to grow at the same rate as in the past, and that no significant retardation will set in over the period of the forecast, a projection of the semilogarithmic straight-line trend would be appropriate. On the other hand, if management believes that sales are approaching a saturation point and that retardation in sales growth will become an increasingly significant factor, it may be appropriate to employ some type of growth curve. The choice of growth curve then follows from close evaluation of the activity under study. If it is believed that the period of relatively rapid growth is coming to an end and that significant retardation will begin soon, a logistic curve might be chosen. But if relatively rapid growth is expected to continue, with retardation setting in gradually, a Gompertz curve might be appropriate. In any case, a curve should be chosen whose mathematical properties express the nature of the growth pattern believed to exist in the activity under study.

Thus, in choosing the appropriate trend curve for projection into the future, the analyst studies the long-term pattern of change in the activity to obtain insights about the effects of long-term factors in the past, evaluates the extent to which these past long-term effects will be modified in the future, and then consolidates the results of his analysis in his choice of the appropriate trend curve to project for long-term forecasting.

Assumptions. As will have been recognized from the previous discussion, the choices of a relevant time period and of the appropriate type of trend curve are greatly affected by the assumptions that are made—explicitly or implicitly—regarding the future course of events. These assumptions underlying a forecast are in themselves a forecast of conditions in a given future period. In a forecast of industry sales, the assumptions involve such elements as the state of the economy, political decisions that will affect the industry, and technological developments. In a forecast of company sales, additional factors become important, such as the extent and strength of future competition, and any probable changes in company policy concerning products, distribution, pricing, sales promotion, and advertising.

In some organizations, the standard procedure is to develop a long-term forecast on the basis of a single set of assumptions. These assumptions may be made by the forecasting specialists, or they may be prescribed by management. In other organizations, two or more alternative forecasts are made on the basis of alternative sets of assumptions, so that management may choose the most likely alternative in the light of additional study and unfolding events. Sometimes forecasts made under alternative sets of assumptions agree closely. In other cases, different assumptions lead to widely divergent forecasts; in these situations, management may be well advised to undertake a detailed analysis of the alternative sets of assumptions to determine which is most reasonable. No matter how carefully the assumptions are prepared, however, long-term forecasts are provisional at best and are subject to frequent revisions as new, unforeseen contingencies arise.

Note, incidentally, how important it is for management to require that the assumptions underlying a forecast be listed explicitly as part of the forecast when these assumptions are made by the forecasting specialists rather than by management. Such a listing enables management both to evaluate the assumptions at the time the forecast is made and to check them against future events as these events unfold.

29.6 CASE ILLUSTRATIONS OF LONG-TERM FORECASTING

Now that the concept of secular trend and the uses and limitations of this concept as a forecasting tool have been discussed, some examples of actual statistical forecasting procedures will be presented.

Long-term forecasting by gas and electric companies

Long-term forecasting and planning is of special importance to gas and electric companies. These firms are public utilities and are protected by law from direct competition within their franchise areas; in return, they are obliged to supply adequate service to all customers. As it may take a gas and electric company several years to design, construct, and install a new plant, the need for such a plant must be anticipated well in advance. Thus, the long-range forecasts made by gas and electric companies are necessary for the preparation of programs involving new construction, as well as for programs for improvement, replacement, and retirement of existing property. In addition, forecasts are needed to develop operating budgets—that is, to estimate revenues, expenses, and net income arising from future operations.

The Long Island Lighting Company.[1] This company forecasts monthly sales 18 months ahead, and annual sales 5 years ahead (Ref. 29.2). In doing so, the company studies the trends of four related factors: population, meters or customers, consumption, and revenue. Each factor is studied separately and in relation to the others. Since population is the prime factor affecting company sales, much effort is devoted to forecasting population

[1] This account is based in part upon material kindly provided by Mr. Fred C. Eggerstedt, Jr., of the Long Island Lighting Company.

trends in the areas served by the company. These forecasts take into account birth and death rates, migration of people into and out of each area, and other developments. The company studies the relationships between the four primary factors affecting revenues by the use of ratios measuring the number of people per meter, sales per meter, revenue per meter, and revenue per unit of power sold versus consumption per meter. Changes in the values of these ratios are forecast with the aid of trend projections. Through the use of statistical techniques supplemented by judgment, the company has been able to make useful long-term forecasts.

A company officer has pointed out that the use of statistical techniques alone will not produce a reasonable forecast. However, their use tends to "reduce the area in which judgment must act and thus sharpens it by directing it to a few points rather than requiring it to encompass the whole field" (Ref. 29.3, p. 21).

Use of electronic computers in forecasting: Monsanto Chemical Company

In recent years, company forecasters have had increasing access to electronic computers. As a consequence formal quantitative methods—including time series analysis—have become more readily available to the forecaster. In long-term forecasting specifically, electronic computers have been programmed to fit trend curves to series and to make trend projections. Often several curves are fitted to the same series and the results compared, to aid in identifying the trend pattern to employ in the current forecast.

In the Monsanto Chemical Company, as a case in point, a computer fits several types of trend curves to annual data on major products and product groups, and projects trend values 5 and 10 years ahead. The trend patterns principally used are straight-line trends, the Gompertz curve, and the logistic curve. For each trend projection, the computer prints out an error band based on analysis of deviations from the trend curve in the series. This error band widens as the projection is extended into the future. The trend projections made by the computer are reviewed by company researchers, and modified if warranted in the light of information not reflected in the historical series on which the trend projections are based (Ref. 29.4).

Cited references

29.1 *Growth Patterns in Industry: A Reexamination,* Studies in Business Economics No. 75. New York: National Industrial Conference Board, Inc., 1961.

29.2 *Forecasting in Industry,* Studies in Business Policy No. 77. New York: National Industrial Conference Board, Inc., 1956.

29.3 *Forecasting Sales,* Studies in Business Policy No. 25. New York: National Industrial Conference Board, Inc., 1947.

29.4 *Forecasting Sales,* Studies in Business Policy No. 106. New York: National Industrial Conference Board, Inc., 1963.

QUESTIONS AND PROBLEMS

29.1. Explain briefly each of the following:

a. Time series
b. Secular trend
c. Growth curve
d. Trend value
e. Trend projection
f. Per cent of trend

29.2. **a.** The Manager of Business Research of the Triumph Paperboard Company wished to study the trend of the company's monthly sales. Before fitting the trend curve, he first divided each month's dollar sales by an index number measuring the selling prices of the company's products.

(1) Why would he take this preliminary step before fitting the trend curve to the company's monthly sales?

(2) Is it always necessary to divide dollar sales figures by a relevant price index before studying the trend of these sales?

(3) If the manager were interested in obtaining a projection for the company's actual dollar sales, would he have to make any other predictions in addition to the projection of the trend curve mentioned above? If so, explain what other trend he would have to study.

(4) Would the procedure discussed in (3) be less preferable to a trend projection based only on the company's actual dollar sales if the manager wished to obtain an indication of the level of actual dollar sales some years ahead?

b. The Manager of Business Research also wanted to study the trend of the company's monthly production volume. Before fitting any trend curves, however, he divided each month's production by the number of working days in that month.

(1) Why would he take this preliminary step before fitting the trend curve to the company's monthly production figures?

(2) Is it always necessary to divide production data by the number of working days during the relevant period before studying the trend of this production?

(3) Should the manager have divided the sales data mentioned in part **a** by the number of working days in each respective month before fitting a trend curve to the company sales?

29.3. The following excerpt is taken from a letter that once appeared in a news magazine:

If one examines projections of manhour productivity for our economy made by various economic research groups, one finds that increases ranging from 2.3 to 2.7 per cent per year were used in the projections. Invariably, it is claimed that these are reasonable long-term goals for our economy, and are in line with the past trend of manhour productivity during this century. Yet if one looks closely at the supporting data, one notes that manhour productivity increased at an average annual rate of 4.2 per cent between 1917–1925 inclusive, 4.8 per cent between 1933–1941 inclusive, and 5.2 per cent from 1947 to 1950 inclusive. Therefore, for this composite long-term period of 22 years, the trend of manhour productivity shows a rate of increase of over 4.6 per cent per year. The economists in the research groups are too conservative. The evidence I have just presented shows that they can use annual increases of at least 4.6 per cent, not 2.5 per cent, in their trend projections.

In assembling his evidence, did the writer of this letter employ the trend concept in the same sense that it is used in the classical approach to time series analysis discussed in the text? Explain.

29.4. A firm received a letter from a job applicant presenting the following idea:

A scientific approach to forecasting is within the reach of any firm that has an electronic computer programmed to fit trend curves. The trend curve gives the long-term pattern of a series. The series may stray above or below the trend at intervals, but will always snap back. Therefore, when a trend curve has been fitted scientifically to a series, one should be able to extrapolate the trend into the future to obtain a long-term forecast that is foolproof. The actual level of the activity may depart temporarily from the trend projection, but the activity must inevitably snap back to the trend because this effect is inherent in the behavior of business and economic time series and in the trend concept.

Present a concise, but complete, evaluation of this statement.

29.5. The following statement has been made: "Certain potentially troublesome problems are solved objectively whenever mathematical methods are used to fit trend curves to time series data. Mathematical fitting assures that one will obtain the best possible fit to the data for a given type of curve. Even more important, the difficult problem of what type of curve to fit as a basis for a trend projection is solved neatly, since mathematical fitting will yield automatically the curve of the most appropriate type."

a. Indicate whether you agree with all, part, or none of this statement and support your opinion.

b. What are the implications of your answer in part **a** for the use of trend analysis in forecasting?

29.6. The arithmetic straight-line trend equation of annual sales of a product, in millions of dollars, during a 15-year period was:

$$\bar{Y}_X = 150.6 + 6.4X, \quad \text{where} \quad X = 0 \text{ at } 1957$$

a. Explain precisely what interpretation in terms of the product's sales should be given to the number 150.6 in this trend equation.

b. Explain what interpretation should be given to the number +6.4 in this trend equation; include the sign of this number in your explanation.

***29.7.** Annual personal consumption expenditures (in billions of dollars) were as follows in the United States between 1963 and 1970 inclusive:

Year	*Personal Consumption Expenditures*	*Year*	*Personal Consumption Expenditures*
1963	375	1967	492
1964	401	1968	536
1965	433	1969	580
1966	466	1970	616

Source: U.S. Department of Commerce.

a. Plot the data on an arithmetic graph.

b. Fit an arithmetic straight-line trend to the series by the method of least squares. Show your basic calculations systematically in a table, and the final results in the form of a trend equation.

c. Utilizing the trend equation obtained in part **b**, plot the trend curve on your graph. Show the calculations made in order to plot the trend curve from the equation.

d. If another person were to fit an arithmetic straight-line trend to the series by the method of least squares, would his trend curve differ from yours? Explain.

Assume in your explanation that all calculations would be free of arithmetic and rounding errors.

e. Calculate the projected trend value of personal consumption expenditures for 1985. Assuming that your trend equation accurately describes the trend in the series, and assuming that this trend pattern will continue to hold until 1985, would you predict then that the actual consumption expenditures in 1985 will be identical to your trend projection for that year? Explain.

f. Calculate the per cents of trend for the series. Plot these per cents on a graph similar to Figure 29.6b in the text.

g. In the classical method of time series analysis, one speaks of "decomposing" a time series. Explain with reference to the original annual data given in this problem how the time series was decomposed in steps **b** and **f** and what information is derived from each of these steps.

29.8. Data are presented below on annual sales of products and of services by Servodata, Inc. between 1965 and 1972 inclusive:

	Sales (Millions of Dollars)	
Year	*Products*	*Services*
1965	6.0	32.9
1966	7.2	30.6
1967	10.8	29.0
1968	11.9	30.8
1969	12.1	28.1
1970	16.8	28.9
1971	17.6	27.8
1972	18.2	27.2

a. If arithmetic straight-line trend equations were computed mathematically for these two series, how would their a constants differ? How would their b constants differ? Explain.

b. Fit an arithmetic straight-line trend to each series by the method of least squares and state the trend equations. Show your basic calculations systematically in a table.

c. Calculate the trend value for 1982 for each series. What is the precise meaning of these trend projections?

d. Plot the data for the two series on an arithmetic graph, together with the corresponding trend curves and trend projections obtained in parts **b** and **c**, respectively. Do arithmetic straight-line trends give good fits to the series? How would you proceed in determining whether these straight-line trends give reasonable projections to 1982 for sales of products and of services? Discuss.

29.9. For the data in Problem 29.8, obtain the straight-line trend equations for the two series (if you have not already done so).

a. Calculate the per cents of trend for each series.

b. Plot the per cents of trend on graphs similar to Figure 29.6b in the text.

c. Can the fluctuating components of the respective series be compared as readily from the plots in Problem 29.8**d** as from the plots in part **b** above? Would your answer change if one or both of the two trend curves were not linear? Discuss.

***29.10.** Total U.S. domestic production and imports for private sale of firearms were as follows during the years 1962–1968 inclusive:

Year	Total Production and Imports (Thousand Units)
1962	2,066
1963	2,232
1964	2,523
1965	3,121
1966	3,522
1967	4,087
1968	5,266

Source: U.S. Department of Commerce, *Statistical Abstract of the U.S.: 1970,* p. 143.

a. Calculate the semilogarithmic straight-line trend equation for the above series by the method of least squares. Show your basic calculations systematically in a table.

b. On semilogarithmic graph paper, plot the actual data and also the calculated trend line.

c. Do you believe that the semilogarithmic straight line provides a good description of the trend component in the series? Explain.

d. Would an arithmetic straight line provide a good description of the trend component in the series? Explain.

e. Explain the meaning of the b coefficient that you obtained in part **a**. Include the sign of the coefficient in your explanation.

f. Calculate the trend value for 1980. Does this calculated trend value automatically represent a forecast of total domestic production and imports for private sale of firearms in the United States in the year 1980? Discuss fully.

g. Do you believe that the semilogarithmic trend line is a reasonable description of the pattern of long-term change in this activity for, say, the next 50 years? Explain.

***29.11.** For the series in Problem 29.10, obtain the semilogarithmic straight-line trend equation (if you have not yet already done so).

a. Express the total production and imports between 1962 and 1968 as per cents of their respective trend values.

b. Plot the fluctuating component obtained in part **a** on a chart similar to Figure 29.6b in the text. What time series components are represented in the fluctuating component in your chart?

c. Calculate the average rate of growth in total production and imports of firearms for private sale as indicated by the trend curve for the period covered by the data.

29.12. Gross national product in the United States was as follows (in billions of current dollars) during the years 1961–1970 inclusive:

Year	Gross National Product	Year	Gross National Product
1961	520	1966	750
1962	560	1967	794
1963	590	1968	864
1964	632	1969	929
1965	685	1970	974

Source: U.S. Department of Commerce.

a. Calculate by the method of least squares the semilogarithmic straight-line trend equation for gross national product during the years 1961–1970 inclusive. Show your calculations systematically in a table.
b. Plot the actual gross national product and your calculated trend line on semilogarithmic graph paper.
c. Does your semilogarithmic straight line provide a good description of the trend component in the series? Explain.
d. Explain the meaning of the *b* coefficient that you obtained in part **a**.
e. Is a period of ten years long enough to serve as a reliable basis for trend projection? Discuss.
f. Calculate the trend value for 1985. Is this value a forecast of gross national product in 1985? Discuss fully.
g. Do you believe that the semilogarithmic trend line is a reasonable description of the pattern of long-term change in gross national product for, say, the next 50 years? Explain.

29.13. Obtain the semilogarithmic straight-line trend equation for the gross national product data in Problem 29.12 (if you have not already done so).
a. Calculate the per cents of trend for the series. Plot these per cents on a chart similar to Figure 29.6b in the text. What time series components are represented in the fluctuating component in your chart?
b. Calculate the average rate of growth in annual gross national product between 1961 and 1970 inclusive.

Chapter

30

CYCLICAL FLUCTUATIONS

In the previous chapter, we briefly surveyed the place of forecasting in administration, examined the concept of secular trend, and studied the uses and limitations of this concept as an aid to long-term forecasting. We now examine the fluctuating component of a time series with reference to short-term forecasting. This fluctuating component may be divided, in terms of the conceptual framework of "classical" time series analysis, into three constituent elements: cyclical fluctuations, seasonal variation, and irregular or random changes. The first of these, cyclical fluctuations, will be discussed in this chapter, the other two in the following chapter.

30.1
CYCLICAL FLUCTUATIONS AND SHORT-TERM FORECASTING

Companies not only make long-term forecasts but also must forecast their business situation in the more immediate time span of the next month, quarter, year, or perhaps two years. Short-term forecasts are used in determining operating budgets, scheduling production, controlling inventory, and establishing sales goals. In short, these forecasts are used in planning and controlling day-to-day business operations of the near future.

Required precision of short-term forecasts

Short-term forecasts usually must be more precise than long-term ones. As a case in point, consider two forecasts of titanium oxide sales—a long-term forecast and a short-term one—made by the Bessing Chemical Corporation in 1970. These forecasts are shown as broken lines in Figure 30.1.

The long-term forecast, required in developing a long-term construction and financing program, involved a projection of the trend of company sales of titanium oxide to 1980. It was not necessary, for purposes of long-term planning, that management should attempt to predict precisely what the sales of this product would be during each year of the period 1971–1980; rather, it was sufficient to know that yearly sales by 1975 would be in the neighborhood of 53 thousand short tons and by 1980 in the neighborhood of 57 thousand short tons, as indicated by Figure 30.1.

The short-term operating forecast for 1971 involved different considerations. In this forecast it was necessary to estimate fairly precisely the volume of titanium oxide sales during the one-year period covered by the

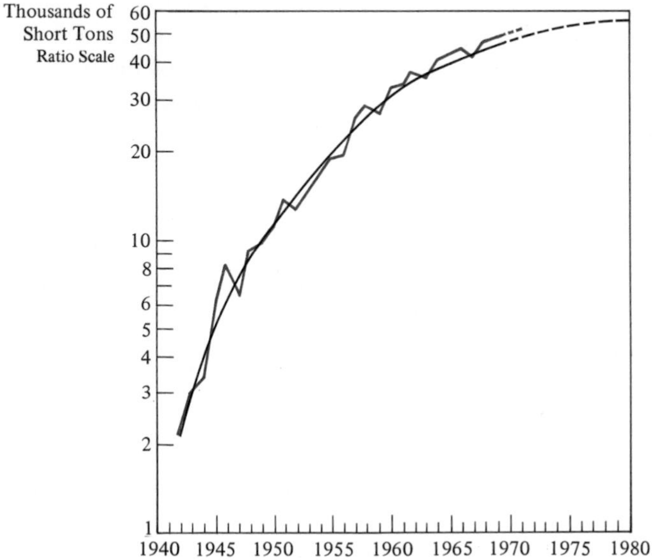

Figure 30.1. Bessing Chemical Corporation, sales of titanium oxide, 1942–1970, and sales forecasts (indicated by broken lines)

short-term forecast. A precise estimate was needed, because company planning and control for the year—for instance, scheduling production and setting sales goals—had to meet the specific day-to-day needs of the year 1971. Projections of trend generally are inadequate for such short-term forecasting needs. Figure 30.1 indicates why this is so. The trend curve fitted to the sales data describes the long-term pattern of the company's titanium oxide sales. Actual sales during most years, however, were not equal to their corresponding trend values. Rather, these actual sales fluctuated around the trend pattern in the manner shown in the chart. Thus, to estimate actual sales in 1971, management had to consider not merely the trend in sales, but also the fluctuating movement of actual sales around this trend.

When fluctuations around the trend curve are relatively minor, as in the case of some products of the petroleum industry, management can often make usable short-term operating forecasts on the basis of secular trend projections alone. In the typical case, however, the situation is similar to that presented in Figure 30.1, in which fluctuations around the trend curve are a predominant feature of the data.

A key problem in short-term forecasting

To make a short-term forecast of titanium oxide sales, the Bessing Chemical Corporation uses a procedure analogous to trend projection. It simply projects, on the basis of past experience, the short-term movement of sales. This projection is shown as the short dotted line in Figure 30.1. The projection of the short-term movement, unlike that of the trend, generally is made from the current actual level of the time series rather than from the trend level. It is based on movements in the series during the recent past only, and is modified according to evaluations concerning the immediate future.

Projection of the short-term movement of titanium oxide sales by the Bessing Chemical Corporation will give a satisfactory short-term forecast as long as sales are moving up or down at a fairly steady rate. The company's major short-term forecasting problem is to predict changes in the direction of the movement of sales. Should the company's short-term forecast fail to predict a downturn in sales such as occurred in 1966–1967, severe operating losses could result; should it fail to predict an upturn such as occurred in 1967–1968, the result could be lost sales opportunities and revenues.

It is precisely in predicting such upturns and downturns in sales and related activities that the most serious forecasting problems are encountered. The Director of Business Research for a large metal fabricating firm has stated: "Good forecasting is not particularly difficult when business is improving at a fairly steady rate. In fact, if a forecaster always predicts that sales will go up or down in line with what happened the preceding year, he will usually be right. Calling the turns is the difficult part, and that is where forecasting most commonly misses the mark" (Ref. 30.1, p. 156). Let us see why this is so.

Characteristics of cyclical fluctuations

If the reader examines the shapes of the fluctuating components in the time series presented in Chapter 29, he will see that this component might be defined as follows:

(30.1) The *cyclical component* of a time series consists of a series of irregular wave-like fluctuations or cycles of more than one year's duration, varying in length and amplitude.

The general cyclical patterns emerge fairly clearly in the graphs in Chapter 29, though information on the timing of changes in direction of the cyclical movements is not too precise because all the graphs were based on annual data.

For short-term forecasting purposes, it is usually desirable to utilize weekly, monthly, quarterly, or semiannual time series to enable the analyst to study the behavior of the cyclical movements in some detail. A problem arises here because cyclical and seasonal movements are entangled in such time series data. (Seasonal movements are not present in annual data, because these movements balance out within a year.) To analyze more readily the cyclical movements in weekly, monthly, quarterly, or semiannual time series, such data are usually *deseasonalized* first. Deseasonalizing of time series, and the measurement of cyclical movements afterwards, will be discussed in the next chapter.

At this point, we simply examine a typical business or economic time series based on monthly data that have been deseasonalized, so that we can observe the typical characteristics of cyclical fluctuations. Such a time series, value of new orders received monthly by the durable goods industries, is presented in Figure 30.2. We can visually trace the cyclical pattern in this series and, with some arbitrariness, identify cyclical turning points.

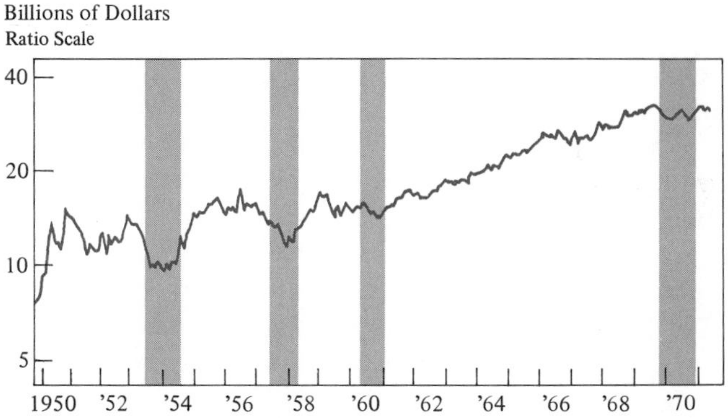

Source: U.S. Department of Commerce.

Figure 30.2. Value of new orders received by durable goods industries, monthly deseasonalized data, 1950–1970

Figure 30.2 has been divided into clear and shaded intervals, to correspond to the identified periods of cyclical expansion and contraction in the series.

Figure 30.2 shows, first of all, that the cycles in an economic time series are composed of successive short-term phases of expansion and contraction. A time interval corresponding to a clear area and the following shaded one in Figure 30.2 covers one complete cycle. Secondly, Figure 30.2 shows that the cycles in an economic time series are, in accordance with the definition of cyclical fluctuations, of more than a year's duration. Finally, this figure illustrates the great variability in the pattern of cyclical movements that is typically present in a business or economic time series. Some periods of expansion and contraction were long, others were quite short; some expansions and contractions were of substantial magnitude, others were mild.

Implications for short-term forecasting

In short-term forecasting, the main objective in studying the cyclical component is, of course, to *identify* the current status of the cyclical pattern and to *predict* future behavior. It is tempting to seek a regular, or average, pattern in the cyclical fluctuations in a series so that this pattern can be projected ahead mechanically for purposes of identification and prediction. Unfortunately, mechanical projection of an average cyclical pattern is not a useful forecasting aid in the same sense that projection of secular trend can be. There is simply too much variability from cycle to cycle in most activities for any idealized or average cycle to be meaningful for the period at hand. This is generally true for cycles at all economic levels, from the overall economy to the individual firm. Thus, with few exceptions, reliable predictions of cyclical movements at industry or company levels cannot be obtained by projecting cycles ahead mechanically.

Identification of the current state of the cyclical movements is hindered also by the presence of irregular movements. Note, in this connection, the saw-tooth appearance of the series in Figure 30.2. This is due to short-term irregular movements and is found in many business and economic series. When a series contains these movements, it becomes virtually impossible to identify current cyclical behavior from inspection of the data alone. Only with hindsight is one able to ascertain whether, say, a downward dip is merely an irregular movement or the beginning of a cyclical decline.

In practice it is of the greatest importance to determine quickly whether a turn in direction in a series signifies a cyclical turning point. At the present stage of knowledge of business cycles, analysts have found that only by a comprehensive study of many economic factors is it possible even to hope to make timely identifications of cyclical turns and reasonably reliable predictions of cyclical movements in business activities or economic sectors. Evaluation of *business indicators* frequently plays an important role in analysis of cyclical movements and hence in short-term forecasting, and we discuss these next.

30.2 BUSINESS INDICATORS

Development of business indicators

Business or economic indicators are statistical time series measuring activities in key sectors of the economy. Many businessmen and economists systematically follow the movements of such statistical series to obtain economic and business information in the form of an unfolding picture that is up-to-date, comprehensive, relatively objective, and capable of being read and understood with a minimum expenditure of time.

The concept of a business indicator has been broadened considerably since the term was first coined. Originally, the most widely followed indicators were series felt to be representative of movements in general business activity. Many businessmen, for example, followed the latest changes in statistical series on such business and industrial activities as freight carloadings, steel ingot production, or bank debits to obtain an *indication* of movements in general business activity; in fact, the term "business indicator" arose to describe series that could be interpreted as indicating such movements.

As knowledge of business cycles increased, it became possible to define types of transactions and areas of activity in which changes had important and relatively predictable effects on broad segments of the economy. Concurrently, advances in the techniques and scope of data collection made it possible for governmental and private agencies to measure changes in these key types of transactions and areas of activity. As a result, the concept of a business indicator now includes a large variety of series measuring selected activities in key functional economic areas, such as national income and product, production and prices, plant and equipment expenditures, retail sales, and manufacturers' sales, inventories, and orders.

In addition, attention has been directed further toward identifying and developing statistical series that *foreshadow* economic movements. Some of these series do not measure activity as such, but rather the *plans* and *intentions* of businessmen and consumers that precede actual transactions. Surveys of capital-expenditures intentions, of capital appropriations, and of consumer finances and expectations provide expectational data that are a most useful complement to the data on actual activity available to the businessman and economist.

Some widely used business indicators

Many of the widely used business indicators are series issued by the statistical agencies of the federal government. Among these are important series based upon the national income concept, such as series dealing with gross national product, national income, and disposable personal income. Production is covered by such series as the Federal Reserve Board index of industrial production, the Department of Agriculture series on volume of farm marketings, and various Department of Commerce series on manufacturers' orders, shipments, and inventories. Current price movements can be watched through the wholesale price index and the consumer price index compiled by the Bureau of Labor Statistics. Department of Labor data on labor force size, employment, and unemployment cover this important functional sector of the economy. Information on wholesale and retail sales is available through series issued under the auspices of the Department of Commerce.

Other series that are highly regarded as business indicators are issued by private organizations. For example, information on business failures is issued by Dun & Bradstreet, Inc., and information on construction contracts is compiled by F. W. Dodge Company. Still other indicators are published by trade associations—for instance, railroad freight carloadings compiled by the Association of American Railroads.

All of these series, governmental and nongovernmental, receive wide distribution and can be found in governmental publications, newspapers, business periodicals and trade journals. Frequently they are presented in graphic as well as in tabular form.

Uses of statistical business indicators

Statistical intelligence system. Business indicators are often used as a network of statistical intelligence—that is, a large number of these series are studied as an entity. In this fashion, valuable information about the activities of the economy and various sectors can be obtained that would not be revealed by one or two business indicators alone.

Too often an administrator will follow only a single business indicator, such as freight carloadings or electric power production, and suppose that he is obtaining a reliable picture of what is happening in the economy. The weakness of such a procedure has been summed up as follows: "Its users . . . [find] . . . themselves with, first, an increasingly inadequate picture of total activity and, second, with too little insight into the causative factors underlying the change recorded in their favorite index" (Ref. 30.2, p. 44).

The series to be followed should be picked carefully for relevance to the needs and problems of the organization involved. A government economist attempting to predict tax revenues, for example, might pay most attention to series measuring changes in aggregate economic activity. On the other hand, an economist working for an individual firm would have to consider not only aggregate economic indicators, but also business indicators for the specific sectors of the economy in which the firm does its business.

A network of statistical intelligence may be used without formally applying statistical techniques. Many forecasters, for example, use large amounts of statistical data in subjectively analyzing demand and supply factors at work in various economic sectors. Business indicators also are employed with various formal analytical techniques to provide information about cyclical changes in the economy as a whole and in key sectors. To illustrate this use, we shall examine two approaches developed by the National Bureau of Economic Research, in which statistical series are systematically studied to provide direct indications of cyclical turning points in general business activity.

Statistical indicators of business expansions and contractions. The National Bureau of Economic Research has found that certain statistical time series may be useful as direct indicators of cyclical expansions and contractions in business activity. This organization is engaged in a continuous study of business cycles; from this study it has learned that all areas of the economy do not expand simultaneously during expansions in the business cycle, nor do all contract concurrently during periods of contraction. Actually, the business cycle has been a loosely coordinated movement whose net effect is that of relative cyclical expansion or contraction in the economy during a given period of time. A study of individual economic time series and their relation to this general cyclical movement indicates that the timing of most series conforms only loosely—and in some series not at all—to that of the business cycle in aggregate economic activity. Exceptions to this general statement, however, do exist. The National Bureau has identified some 80 series that have proven to be definitely useful as indicators of business conditions. These series are presented on a timely basis and analyzed in a special-purpose periodical, *Business Conditions Digest,* published monthly by the U.S. Department of Commerce.

For the guidance of forecasters and other users, each series in the National Bureau list has been evaluated and scored by the Bureau in terms of the following elements: (1) extent to which the series measures or represents an activity having a key role in the cyclical process; (2) statistical accuracy and dependability of the series; (3) degree of conformity of the series to historical business cycles; (4) consistency with which the series has moved in some specific phase (leading, coincident, lagging) with cyclical movement in the economy; (5) degree of smoothness—i.e., relative absence of persistent major irregular fluctuations; (6) timeliness of publication (Ref. 30.3).

Some 26 series have been culled from the larger list by the National Bureau and assembled into a short list as shown in Table 30.1. Occasional revisions are made in this list as experience dictates. The series selected for the short list all have high scores and involve little duplication in coverage. These series are divided into three groups as Table 30.1 shows. The first group consists of series whose turning points typically have preceded turns in aggregate economic activity, while the second and third groups contain series whose turning points have tended respectively to coincide with, and lag behind, cyclical turns in the economy.

In practice, the leading series are studied to help in anticipating cyclical turning points. The coincident and lagging series are studied to help in recognizing a cyclical turn once it has occurred. Like other forecasting tools, cyclical indicators cannot be used mechanically for forecasting; when they are used, several knotty problems are encountered.

One of the major difficulties is to tell when an indicator has reached a cyclical turning point. As we have mentioned, the fluctuating component of economic and business series contains short-term irregular movements in

Table 30.1 Cyclical Indicators (NBER Short List)

Leading Indicators
Average hourly workweek, production workers, manufacturing
Average weekly initial claims, state unemployment insurance
Index of net business formation
New orders, durable goods industries
Contracts and orders, plant and equipment
Index of new building permits, private housing units
Change in book value, manufacturing and trade inventories
Index of industrial materials prices
Index of stock prices, 500 common stocks
Corporate profits after taxes (quarterly)
Index: ratio, price to unit labor cost, manufacturing
Change in consumer installment debt
Roughly Coincident Indicators
GNP in current dollars
GNP in 1958 dollars
Index of industrial production
Personal income
Manufacturing and trade sales
Sales of retail stores
Employees on nonagricultural payrolls
Unemployment rate, total
Lagging Indicators
Unemployment rate, persons unemployed 15 weeks or over
Business expenditures, new plant and equipment
Book value, manufacturing and trade inventories
Index of labor cost per unit of output in manufacturing
Commercial and industrial loans outstanding in large commercial banks
Bank rates on short-term business loans

Source: U.S. Department of Commerce.

addition to cyclical ones. Thus weekly, monthly, or quarterly data plotted on a chart typically have the ragged, saw-tooth appearance that was evident in Figure 30.2. Consequently, it is difficult to identify cyclical turning points *near the time they occur*. Remember that the turning points come into existence only as the consequence of a *following* decline or gain in the cyclical component. Hence, several months may go by before a genuine cyclical upturn or downturn in a leading series is finally identified with any assurance.

Another problem in using the cyclical-indicator approach arises because no uniformity occurs in the length of time by which a given leading indicator precedes cyclical turns in the economy; instead, considerable variability can be noted in the lead time from cycle to cycle. Consequently, the leading indicators may signal that a recession or recovery can be expected some time in the future, but they provide less help in establishing the timing of the turn. Analysis of the coincident and lagging indicators is frequently helpful in this connection; for instance, if leading indicators have signaled a cyclical downturn, analysts will begin to look very carefully for signs of weakening in the coincident indicators. In practice, then, effective use of the cyclical-indicator approach requires continuous evaluation of series in all three timing groups.

Still another difficulty is that the indicators occasionally give "false signals"—that is, they signal a turning point that does not materialize. Sometimes such signals are due to factors that can be identified in advance, such as a major strike, so that the signals are discounted, but in other cases it has been impossible to distinguish false signals from accurate ones until after the fact.

Diffusion indexes. Diffusion indexes, like the list of cyclical indicators, are meaningful when business cycles are loosely coordinated movements extending through the economy. While there are various ways in which diffusion indexes can be expressed, we discuss them in their basic form, in which the index is simply the per cent of individual series expanding *cyclically* at a given time in a group of series.

To understand the behavior and economic meaning of a diffusion index, consider a group of ten time series constituting some aggregate. Suppose that all ten series are expanding cyclically; a diffusion index calculated for this group would equal 100 (per cent). Suppose now that two of the ten series turn downward cyclically; the diffusion index then is 80, as eight of the ten series are still expanding. Note that the index has begun to decline, although the majority of the series in the aggregate, and in the usual case the aggregate itself, is still expanding.

Suppose the cyclical contraction becomes diffused through more series, so that two additional series turn downward cyclically. The index will decline to 60; note, however, that the majority of the series is still expanding. If three additional series begin declining cyclically, the index now will fall to 30.

In the usual case, the aggregate will begin to decline at roughly the time that the index falls below 50; in other words, the turning point for the aggregate generally is reached several stages after the index itself began to decline.

Let us assume that the situation now becomes stable for several periods —in other words, that the diffusion index remains at 30. The aggregate, however, would normally continue to decline cyclically, because most of the series are declining. If, now, one of the declining series turns cyclically upward, the index will move upward correspondingly, heralding an upturn in the aggregate should the movement spread to more series.

Notice that the diffusion index we have described will serve as an advance indicator of cyclical turning points in aggregate activity only if certain conditions are met. First, all the series must move more or less together, with some series lagging behind others in turning cyclically. In other words, the turning points of the different series must be loosely clustered when arrayed in time. If the individual series reach cyclical turning points at random, the diffusion index would fluctuate erratically; on the other hand, if all the series turn cyclically in simultaneous fashion, the index would jump from 0 to 100, or vice versa, whenever a turn occurs.

Further, it was assumed implicitly that all series have equal importance with respect to the aggregate, or that differences in importance cancel out. Otherwise, the simple index of per cent of series expanding would not be an appropriate measure.

The conditions just described are met in practice sufficiently well so that a large variety of diffusion indexes have led the corresponding aggregates in empirical studies of past business cycles made by the National Bureau. Since the mid-1950's, economists have experimented with a variety of groups of component series and with alternative methods of calculating diffusion indexes, some of which do not require explicit identification of cyclical turning points in each component series.

Of course, diffusion indexes are summarizing devices and cannot be expected to bring out all significant facts. They indicate nothing, for example, about which particular activities are expanding and which are contracting, the relative economic importance of the expanding and contracting groups, whether the same or different series are expanding during successive periods, and the rates and amplitude of expansion or contraction in each series. Another limitation of diffusion indexes is that indexes that perform reasonably well in turning upward or downward ahead of business-cycle turns are prone to giving false signals also, whereas indexes that give reliable signals tend to do so concurrently with business-cycle turns instead of ahead of them.

Forecasting based on statistical relationships. Another use of business indicators is to serve as a basis for predicting activity for a firm or industry, by means of statistical relationships between the business indicator and the activity to be forecast. Regression analysis is frequently employed in this type of use, and we shall discuss it next.

30.3 USE OF REGRESSION ANALYSIS IN FORECASTING

Regression analysis was discussed in Chapters 22 through 24. In the present section we will illustrate the use of regression analysis when the independent variable is a business indicator.

uses regression analysis to forecast its dollar sales on the basis of disposable personal income. Annual data on company sales and disposable personal income in the U.S. for the years 1963 through 1970 are presented in Table 30.2 and shown in a scatter diagram in Figure 30.3.

The scatter diagram indicates that there may be a linear regression rela-

Table 30.2 Calculations for Castle Company Example

Year	*Disposable Personal Income (Billions of Dollars)* X	*Castle Company Sales (Millions of Dollars)* Y	XY	X^2
1963	405	69.4	28,107.0	164,025
1964	438	70.5	30,879.0	191,844
1965	473	73.0	34,529.0	223,729
1966	512	74.1	37,939.2	262,144
1967	546	78.2	42,697.2	298,116
1968	591	79.3	46,866.3	349,281
1969	634	79.5	50,403.0	401,956
1970	687	82.4	56,608.8	471,969
	4,286	606.4	328,029.5	2,363,064

$$b = \frac{\Sigma XY - \dfrac{\Sigma X \Sigma Y}{n}}{\Sigma X^2 - \dfrac{(\Sigma X)^2}{n}} = \frac{328{,}029.5 - \dfrac{(4{,}286)(606.4)}{8}}{2{,}363{,}064 - \dfrac{(4{,}286)^2}{8}} = .047138$$

$$a = \frac{1}{n}(\Sigma Y - b\Sigma X) = \frac{1}{8}\left[606.4 - (.047138)(4{,}286)\right] = 50.5458$$

Linear regression equation is: $\overline{Y}_X = 50.55 + .04714X$

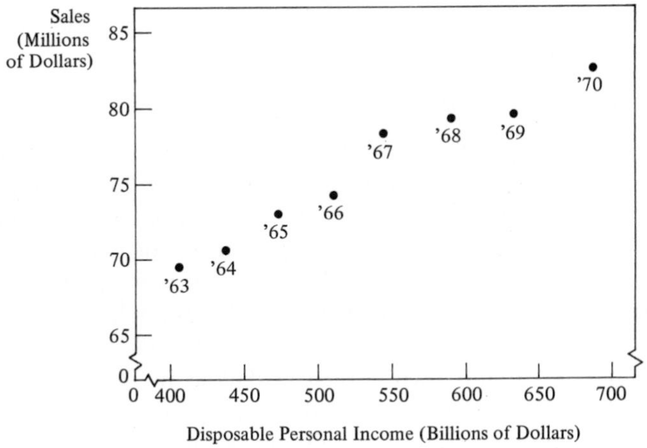

Figure 30.3. Scatter diagram of disposable personal income and Castle Company sales, 1963–1970

tionship between the two series. It will be recalled that the sample estimate of such a relationship is of the form $\overline{Y}_X = a + bX$, and that a and b can be obtained by the method of least squares explained in Chapter 22. The computations for a and b are performed in Table 30.2. Here, we simply note that the linear regression equation estimated in Table 30.2 is:

$$\overline{Y}_X = 50.55 + .04714X$$

Early in 1971, the company obtained a forecast that disposable personal income for that year would be \$745 billion. The point estimate of mean company sales when disposable personal income is \$745 billion is:

$$\overline{Y}_{745} = 50.55 + .04714(745) = 85.7$$

or \$85.7 million. This point estimate was used as a forecast since it was believed that the 1963–1970 regression relationship was applicable to 1971 and that the forecast of the indicator series (disposable personal income in 1971) was reasonably reliable.

Precision of forecast

As noted, the sales estimate of \$85.7 million is a point estimate of the average annual volume of company sales when disposable personal income is \$745 billion. As will be recognized from our discussion in Chapter 23, it would be useful to calculate a prediction interval for actual sales during a particular year when disposable personal income is at the indicated level. Unfortunately, the prediction interval calculations explained in Chapter 23 usually do not have a direct application to regression problems involving business and economic time series data, because they are based on assumptions that generally are too simple for this type of data. More advanced mathematical-statistical techniques must be used to obtain estimates for which probability statements can be made.

Predicting beyond the range of past data

The dangers in predicting from a regression relationship beyond the limits of past data were pointed out in Chapter 23. We mentioned there that the shape of the regression curve becomes more and more doubtful beyond the limits of the data. During periods of expansion in a growing economy, however, it will often be necessary to forecast beyond the range of past information. This happened in the example just discussed, where the forecast of disposable personal income for 1971 exceeded all the past levels of that variable used in the calculations in Table 30.2. In short-term forecasting, extrapolations beyond the range of past data ordinarily are moderate, however, and are usually not a cause for special concern unless there is doubt about the shape of the regression curve as it approaches the upper reach of the observed data.

Spurious correlations

Sometimes we wish to measure the "closeness of relationship" between fluctuations in two (or more) time series, and we frequently use the coefficient of correlation as such a measure. This coefficient can be computed for time series data as it is done for other data; however, special precautions then must be observed in interpreting the meaning of *r*, since trends that exist in time series will often dominate this statistical measure. For example, short-term year-to-year movements in two time series may show little or no statistical relationship, but if both series have pronounced trends of similar slope the computed value of *r* may be relatively high. In the same way, dissimilar trends may mask a really close relationship between short-term movements of two time series.

When interest centers upon the "closeness of relationship" between the *short-term* fluctuations in two series, it is generally best to remove the effect of trend from the data before computing the correlation coefficient. The fluctuating component of a time series can be separated from the trend, as was explained in Section 29.4, by expressing it as a per cent of trend. The per cent of trend values then can be used in the correlation analysis.

Forecasting with lead-lag relationships

Note that any success with the technique of forecasting by utilizing a business indicator variable in regression analysis depends in part upon an accurate forecast of the indicator series. It may be possible to avoid this forecast of the indicator variable if a suitable lead-lag relationship between the indicator series and the series to be forecast can be found.

An idealized example of a lead-lag relationship is shown in Figure 30.4, where movements of the indicator series precede, in point of time, corresponding movements of the other series. Actually, lead-lag relationships seldom will stand out as clearly as in Figure 30.4. However, regression and

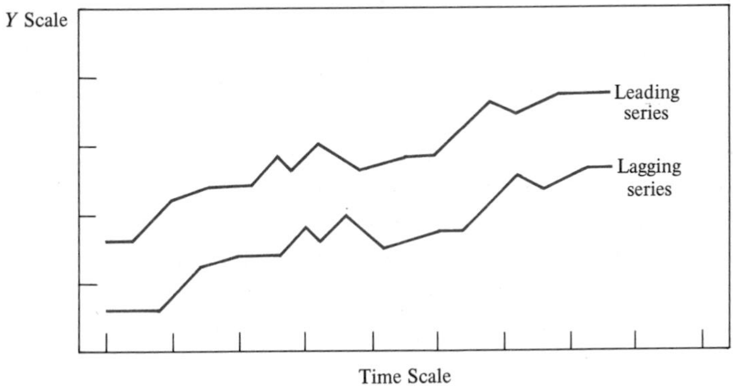

Figure 30.4. An example of a lead-lag relationship

correlation analysis can readily be used to investigate whether lead-lag relationships, anticipated on logical grounds, do in fact hold between pairs of series. When a lead-lag relationship is found, regression analysis can be used for forecasting without requiring an additional forecast of the indicator variable. For instance, the dependent variable may be current period sales and the independent variable preceding period disposable personal income. If current period disposable personal income is substituted into such a regression model, the predicted variable will be next period's sales.

An example of the use of a lead-lag relationship in forecasting is found in the American Radiator and Standard Sanitary Corporation (Ref. 30.4). Years ago this company discovered that sales of its plumbing supplies lagged construction contracts awarded by four months. The company, therefore, could use the latest construction data as a direct indicator of future sales of its plumbing supplies. Another application of lead-lag relationships is found in SKF Industries, Inc. (Ref. 30.5). This firm manufactures ball and roller bearings. Using a computer to analyze movements in sales over a ten-year period, the company found that lead-lag relationships exist among sales of various groups of bearings. Knowledge of these relationships has proved useful in forecasting sales. Note that in this case the lead-lag relationhips are based entirely on internal series.

In multiple regression analysis a combination of "lagged" and "current" independent variables may be used. Thus, in a multiple regression analysis of company sales for quarter-year periods, the regression equation might contain the following variables: company sales (during current quarter) as dependent variable, and company advertising expenditure (during current quarter) and disposable personal income (during previous quarter) as independent variables. In this case, the income variable is lagged one time period—that is, by one quarter.

Of course, the same common-sense precautions apply in projecting lead-lag relationships as in projecting any past relationship between time series for forecasting purposes. It always is necessary to evaluate the extent to which future developments might modify or terminate lead-lag or other statistical relationships in past series. Also, an observed lead-lag relationship should be employed only if it is meaningful structurally. A lead-lag relationship that arose merely by coincidence is not a reliable basis for forecasting.

Special considerations in using business indicators for forecasting

We have seen how the indicator series is a key element in forecasting by regression analysis. Widely used indicator series include gross national product, national income, disposable personal income, and subindexes of the Federal Reserve Board index of industrial production. Indicators such as these measure aspects of general economic activity that directly condition the activity of many industries and companies.

When the indicator must itself be predicted, the forecasting problem is shifted from a direct forecast for the industry or company to a prior forecast of the indicator as a basis for the industry or company forecast. Thus, industry or company forecasts with this approach are conditional on the indicator series being at its predicted value. Many forecasters follow this roundabout procedure simply because it tends to work better than direct projections. Obviously, though, the indicator series must be one for which relatively accurate forecasts can be obtained.

Subjective considerations discussed for statistical long-term forecasting apply equally to short-term forecasting. Thus the historical time period on which the regression relationship is based should be relevant to the period ahead for which the forecast is being made. Assumptions should be stated explicitly, and the regression-based forecast should be compared with forecasts made independently by other methods before a final forecast is developed.

30.4 SOME ADDITIONAL FORECASTING EXAMPLES

We conclude our discussion of cyclical fluctuations and their implications for short-term statistical forecasting by examining some specific applications of the concepts and procedures discussed above.

Forecasting methods of a producer of ball bearings

Two basic techniques for sales forecasting are used in the New Departure Division, General Motors Corporation (Ref. 30.6). They are independent of each other and are performed by different people, so that each provides a check on the other. One method, sometimes called the "grass-roots" approach, involves obtaining information about future sales from customers and salesmen in direct touch with the customers. The other approach involves economic and statistical analysis, and has been outlined as follows by a company officer:

> The first step is to find some indicator of the nation's economy—generally a regularly published government or trade association statistic—which past sales of the company have roughly paralleled. Then the past relationship between the selected statistical bench mark and company sales must be established.
>
> An indicator whose activity "leads" the company's sales is very desirable, because the current activity of such a bench mark indicates the future activity of the company's sales. Leading indicators that may be helpful are new orders for various industries, and the composite of . . . early-moving economic indicators based on . . . series selected by the National Bureau of Economic Research.
>
> The past relationship of sales to the selected indicator may be established

statistically by employing correlation analysis, or arithmetically by using the average ratio of sales to bench mark; also, it may be done by the simple technique of graphing.

Next, in order to prepare the company sales forecast, a forecast of business as represented by the economic indicator must be made. Then the historical relationship of company sales to statistical indicator can be applied to estimate future company sales.

It may be necessary to modify the sales estimate after carefully considering the following: changes in the general marketability of the company's products; changes in the competitive position of the company or its customers; and changes in prices.

Finally, all these statistical results should be tempered by judgment and experience. (Ref. 30.6, pp. 135, 137)

Oakite Products, Inc.

Forecasting in Oakite Products, Inc., illustrates the blending of judgment and statistical analysis that typifies forecasting in many companies. This firm produces cleaning compounds used in a wide variety of industries (Ref. 30.5). Movements in company dollar sales have been found to be related statistically to movements in three general economic indicators, namely gross national product in current dollars, manufacturers' dollar sales, and the Federal Reserve Board index of industrial production. A separate regression analysis is maintained for company sales and each indicator. The company purchases forecasts of the three indicators from an economic consulting service and uses these to derive a company sales forecast from each regression analysis. The marketing research director then develops a single sales forecast from the three separate statistical forecasts, using judgment and insights into current economic conditions.

Regression analysis is used also to develop sales forecasts for the company's five divisions. Usable regression relationships have been found between quantity indexes of division sales and appropriate segments of the Federal Reserve Board index of industrial production. From forecasts of the segments of the industrial production index, a forecast is made of the index of sales for each division, and a dollar sales forecast is derived in turn from the sales-index forecast. The sum of the dollar sales forecasts for the five divisions is checked against the forecast of total dollar sales based on the three general indicators, and any significant difference between the two figures is resolved.

Each division head independently prepares his own forecast of dollar sales. These forecasts are purely subjective and are based on knowledge of market factors and information obtained from personal contacts with large customers. It is reported that the forecasts prepared by the division heads often tend to be over-optimistic (Ref. 30.5, p. 45). These forecasts are compared against, and reconciled with, the forecasts of divisional sales derived from regression analysis.

Cited references

30.1 MacGowan, A. C., "Techniques in Forecasting Consumer Durable Goods Sales," *The Journal of Marketing,* October 1952, pp. 156–162.

30.2 Gainsbrugh, Martin R. (contributor), "The Best Business and Financial Indicators," *Banking,* October 1952, pp. 41–50.

30.3 Moore, Geoffrey H., and Julius Shiskin, *Indicators of Business Expansions and Contractions.* New York: National Bureau of Economic Research, Inc., 1967.

30.4 *Forecasting in Industry,* Studies in Business Policy No. 77. New York: National Industrial Conference Board, Inc., 1956.

30.5 *Forecasting Sales,* Studies in Business Policy No. 106. New York: National Industrial Conference Board, Inc., 1963.

30.6 *Sales Forecasting: Uses, Techniques, and Trends,* Special Report No. 16. New York: American Management Association, Inc., 1956.

QUESTIONS AND PROBLEMS

30.1. Briefly describe or define each of the following:

a. Business indicator

b. Lead-lag relationship

c. Cyclical turning point

d. Diffusion index

e. Cyclical indicators

30.2. Discuss the following statement, indicating whether you agree or disagree and why: "In many industries, the most adequate forecasts can be made for the period immediately ahead, such as the next one or two quarters, and for the long-term future, such as a period ten years ahead. Forecasts made for the intermediate period, such as six to eighteen months ahead, are most liable to prove inadequate or even positively misleading in retrospect."

30.3. A writer stated, in the financial section of a leading newspaper, that "the bulges and recessions of business cycles cancel themselves out over the years." Discuss the validity of this statement.

30.4. The following point was made in a panel discussion on uses of statistical data in forecasting: "Long-term forecasting and short-term forecasting involve different problems and serve different requirements. This distinction is germane to any discussion of statistical indicators. We cannot assume that a statistical series will be applicable in long-term forecasting simply because it has proven to be useful as a business indicator in short-term forecasting, and vice versa."

Do you agree with this statement? Explain why or why not, and cite specific statistical series in support of your point of view.

30.5. Contrast the following series with respect to their use as business indicators:

(1) Number of railroad cars of freight loaded weekly by major railroads in the United States.

(2) Quarterly appropriations for new plant and equipment in manufacturing firms in the United States.

(3) F.R.B. monthly index of industrial production (combined index for all manufactures and minerals).

(*Continued*)

Consider such factors as scope and coverage of the series, relationships between the series and aggregate economic activity, and expected timing of movements in the series compared with movements in aggregate activity.

30.6. The following statement appeared in a newsletter sent to clients by a firm of consulting economists: "The most recent data have supported our preliminary findings, reported in a previous letter, that our diffusion index of the National Bureau's leading indicators is definitely tending to move in a downward direction, having fallen in successive months from 83 to 75 to 67. Moreover, our analysis gives strong reason to believe that in the next two or three months the index will fall below 50."

Assume that the diffusion index mentioned in the statement is calculated by the method described in the text. In a short essay, interpret the statement for readers who are not familiar with the specialized terminology that has been employed. Be sure to cover the following points in your discussion, as well as any others that you believe are relevant: (1) meaning of diffusion index; (2) meaning of leading group of cyclical indicators; (3) manner in which these two concepts have been combined in the statement; (4) possible reasons, if any, for hedging in the description of recent movements in the index; (5) statement's implications to recipients of the newsletter.

30.7. **a.** Assume a hypothetical economic system in which movements in all economic time series are identical in magnitude and timing. Would the cyclical-indicator concept be applicable to forecasting in such a system? Would the diffusion-index concept be applicable to forecasting? Explain.

b. Assume a system in which there are no relations between movements in economic time series. Would your answers in part **a** still apply under this assumption? Explain fully.

c. What characteristic of economic time series movements in the American economy makes the cyclical-indicator and diffusion-index concepts useful in forecasting? Explain, relating your discussion to your answers in parts **a** and **b** above.

30.8. A business newsletter contained the following statement: "Most observers agree that the economy is now in a low phase of the business cycle. Immediate improvement cannot be expected. The average duration between upturns in peacetime business cycles since 1854 has been 45 months. It has been only 33 months since the last upturn, thus another upturn will not occur until 12 more months." Evaluate the forecasting approach implicit in this statement.

30.9. A consulting economist remarked as follows in an address to a group of businessmen: "I believe we have entered the next recession. It is not surprising that the signs of decline are generally unrecognized as yet. In the recession of three years ago the decline began in July but was not generally recognized until late in the year. Similarly, the recovery began in the following spring but was not recognized until late summer." What basic forecasting problem is illustrated in these comments? What are some of the factors that are responsible for this problem? Discuss.

***30.10.** Between 1961 and 1970, the Canadian index of industrial production, and domestic sales of aluminum ingot by Victoria Extraction, Ltd., were as given below.

a. Plot these data as a scatter diagram.

b. Does there appear to be a statistical relationship between the two series? Explain.

c. Estimate the linear regression equation by the method of least squares. Show your basic calculations systematically in a table.

d. What relationship is described by the regression equation obtained in part **c**?

e. In 1970, the company had obtained a forecast indicating that the index would be at 116 in 1971. On the average, what is the volume of the company's domestic sales of aluminum ingot when the index is at 116? Make a point estimate on the basis of the regression equation obtained in part **c**.

f. What are some of the important factors that would have had to be considered in deciding whether the estimate made in part **e** could be used as a forecast of the company's domestic sales of aluminum ingot in 1971?

g. Why would one be willing to first obtain a forecast of the index and then use regression analysis to forecast sales as above, rather than forecast sales directly by projecting the sales trend? Discuss.

Year	*Index (1967 = 100)*	*Domestic Sales (Thousands of Tons)*
1961	66	162
1962	72	169
1963	76	170
1964	84	176
1965	91	188
1966	97	190
1967	100	197
1968	106	205
1969	111	208
1970	114	211

30.11. The annual values of new orders received by manufacturers in producers' capital goods industries, and new orders received by Marshall Machinery, Inc., were as follows between 1959 and 1970:

Year	*New Orders, Producers' Capital Goods Industries (Billions of Dollars)*	*New Orders, Marshall Machinery (Millions of Dollars)*
1959	34.6	59.0
1960	33.5	56.2
1961	34.2	57.7
1962	37.0	63.7
1963	41.0	63.8
1964	47.3	72.5
1965	53.2	75.9
1966	63.2	90.3
1967	59.4	82.6
1968	63.6	90.9
1969	72.9	98.1
1970	69.5	94.1

a. Plot these data as a scatter diagram.

b. Does there appear to be a statistical relationship between the two series? Explain.

c. Estimate the linear regression equation by the method of least squares. Show your basic calculations systematically in a table.

d. What relationship is described by the regression equation obtained in part **c**?

e. In 1970, Marshall Machinery, Inc. obtained a forecast that the value of new orders received by manufacturers in producers' capital goods industries would be \$62.5 billion in 1971. On the average, what is the dollar volume of new orders received by Marshall Machinery, Inc. when the value of new orders received by manufacturers in producers' capital goods industries is $62.5 billion? Make a point estimate on the basis of the regression equation obtained in part **c**.

f. Suppose the point estimate made in part **e** was taken by Marshall Machinery as a forecast of the dollar volume of new orders to be received in 1971. Discuss the major assumptions and limitations implicit in using this point estimate as a forecast.

g. In practice, is there any advantage in forecasting sales or other activity for an industry or firm by first forecasting some relevant economic indicator and then using regression analysis as above, rather than directly projecting the trend of sales or other activity of the industry or firm? Discuss.

30.12. In a survey of company forecasting methods, one firm submitted the following reply:

We produce cigars under several brand names. For many years, our annual sales forecasts have been made by a panel of top executives in collaboration with the field sales staff and with key distributors in different sections of the country. This method has yielded forecasts that have seldom been in error by more than plus or minus 5 per cent. Early this year we decided to supplement our executive-panel forecast with an objective, statistical forecast. We looked for a business indicator that had proven to be closely related to our sales during the past 15 years. Using an electronic computer, we systematically measured statistical relationships, as indicated by the coefficient of correlation, between our sales and every series that had any standing as a business indicator. The computer then automatically selected the series having the closest statistical relationship to our sales. It proved to be a series on new business incorporations in the United States, and the statistical relationship between this series and our sales was amazingly close. We plan now to base our annual forecast for next year on the combined results of the subjective executive-panel forecast and the objective statistical forecast based on the known relationship between our sales and the indicator.

a. Discuss the problems involved in the firm's approach to an "objective, statistical forecast."

b. On the basis of the firm's statement, can you conclude that the executive-panel forecasting method is a useful one for the company? Discuss.

Chapter

31

SEASONAL VARIATION

31.1

NATURE AND CAUSES OF SEASONAL VARIATION

Cyclical fluctuations and their significance for short-term forecasting were discussed in the previous chapter. We now conclude our study of time series analysis by examining another component of many time series that is also pertinent for short-term forecasting, planning, and control—namely, seasonal variation.

An example of a time series containing seasonal variation is shown in Figure 31.1. This chart presents the number of revenue passenger miles flown monthly in domestic scheduled operations of the trunk air carriers in the United States between 1957 and 1962 inclusive. *Year-to-year* changes in air travel during this period are evident. They are mainly the result—according to the conceptual framework of "classical" time series analysis—of trend and cyclical forces. In addition, however, there is a pattern of *month-to-month* variation in the series. This type of variation has not been observed in the previous time series consisting of annual data or deseasonalized monthly data.

The monthly variation in air travel during any year follows roughly a set pattern, in which travel tends to be relatively high during the middle months of each year and relatively low during the early and late months. This pattern of peak travel around mid-year repeats itself year after year. Such recurrent patterns of change within the year are indicative of seasonal variation. In this particular case, we would say that air travel is seasonally high during the mid-year months, and seasonally low during the early and late months of the year. Other economic activities, of course, have other seasonal patterns.

Seasonal patterns and their causes

A year-long pattern of seasonal variation is connected with climatic changes or other changes that accompany the seasons of the year. Thus, the seasonal pattern of airline travel shown in Figure 31.1 is determined partly by weather conditions and partly by customs and conventions that influence the character and timing of holidays, vacation periods, and so forth. The calendar also is a source of seasonal variation, since there is a pattern of variation in the lengths of successive months. This pattern leads in some cases to corresponding variation in monthly time series data on economic activities.

There are also "seasonal" patterns that unfold in periods of less than a year. Some examples of these are daily recurrent patterns of hourly productivity rates in a plant, or weekly recurrent patterns of daily demand for public transportation in a city.

Thus:

(31.1) ***Seasonal variation*** is a more or less recurrent pattern of change in an economic time series, where the duration of a full cycle of change is a year or less.

In this chapter, we concern ourselves with yearly seasonal patterns, but only minor changes would be necessary in applying our comments to seasonal patterns that run their course in such periods as days, weeks, months, or quarters.

Problems arising from seasonal variation

Seasonal variation creates two classes of special problems for analysts and managers, namely: (1) problems in analyzing past or current per-

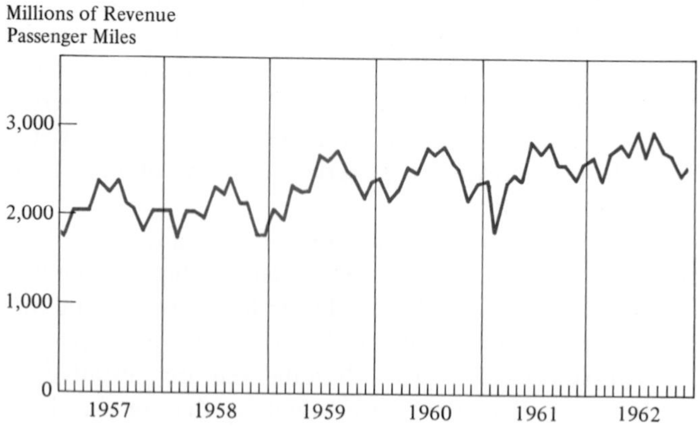

Figure 31.1. Revenue passenger miles in the domestic scheduled operations of the trunk air carriers in the United States, as reported by month, 1957–1962

formance or conditions to determine which course of action now is appropriate; (2) problems in developing operating forecasts, schedules, and goals for the future.

For an example of the first class of problems, suppose that sales of a department store begin to increase markedly in October and November. Store officials would need to know, for guidance in various areas of operations, whether this increase reflects normal seasonal variation or whether it is greater than, or not as great as, could be expected from seasonal factors alone.

An example of the second class of problems would be the breaking down of an annual sales forecast for a major commodity line in the department store into a set of monthly forecasts in order to ascertain working-capital requirements. Seasonal variation causes substantial month-to-month movements in sales of many products, and these seasonal movements have to be incorporated into monthly forecasts.

The first class of problems requires that the seasonal pattern be removed from the data for periods in the recent past so that a clearer picture can be obtained of the other types of movements, especially cyclical fluctuations. The second class of problems requires that the relevant seasonal pattern be incorporated into the projection of activity for the year ahead. In either case, one needs to obtain measures of the seasonal pattern to handle the problems properly.

31.2
A CONCEPTUAL FRAMEWORK FOR MEASURING STABLE PATTERNS OF SEASONAL VARIATION

Key features of seasonal patterns

Since seasonal forces are recurrent, it is not surprising that seasonal patterns tend to be repetitive from period to period. But even a repetitive seasonal pattern, such as the one in Figure 31.1 on air travel, is not perfectly regular. Rather, the successive cycles of seasonal change in business and economic series typically show a certain amount of variation. This, after all, is what one would expect, since events in the real world are seldom perfectly repetitive.

The most commonly used methods of measuring a repetitive seasonal pattern in a business or economic activity have been developed in terms of a model in which a given time series is considered to contain two components in addition to trend and cyclical fluctuations: (1) an underlying seasonal pattern arising from the existence of recurrent seasonal factors, and (2) irregular or random fluctuations that arise from a wide variety of events not occurring in any stable pattern.

A crude method of isolating seasonal and random components

To amplify these comments and suggest how a seasonal index is interpreted and used, we consider a simple but crude method of measuring seasonal variation that minimizes calculational details, yet preserves the essential ideas involved in more refined methods. *This crude procedure illustrates the basic problems involved in measuring seasonal variation when the seasonal pattern is relatively stable from year to year, and trend and cyclical movements are negligible.* Later we will incorporate refinements into our measuring technique.

Quarterly sales of a large retail store for a three-year period, together with total yearly sales and average quarterly sales, are shown in Table 31.1, columns 1, 2, and 3. In columns 4, 5, and 6, we compare the *actual* quarterly sales for each year with the *average* quarterly sales for the same year by expressing the actual sales as per cents of the average quarterly sales. We thereby find, for instance, that sales for the first quarter of 1969 ($13.1 million) were 119 per cent as great as average quarterly sales for 1969 ($11.0 million).

Table 31.1 Simplified Calculation of Seasonal Index

	(1)	(2)	(3)	(4)	(5)	(6)	(7)
	Actual Quarterly Sales (Millions of Dollars)			*Actual Quarterly Sales as Per Cent of Average Quarterly Sales for Year*			*Seasonal Index (Average of Percentages)*
Quarter	*1969*	*1970*	*1971*	*1969*	*1970*	*1971*	
1	13.1	12.3	15.4	119	123	118	120
2	10.0	8.8	11.8	91	88	91	90
3	8.6	8.2	10.4	78	82	80	80
4	12.3	10.7	14.4	112	107	111	110
Total	44.0	40.0	52.0				
Quarterly average	11.0	10.0	13.0				

At this point, it is useful to ask why the volume of first-quarter sales in 1969 was that far above the quarterly average. To answer this question, one must recognize that annual data contain the results of a *complete* cycle of seasonal variation. This means that seasonal variation is not associated with the level of annual sales for the year as a whole, since seasonal variation affects only the distribution of sales within the year. Consequently, in our comparison the actual sales for the quarter have been affected by seasonal and random variations, but the average quarterly sales for the year, which are calculated from the annual total, do not contain any effects of seasonal variation and only small effects of short-term random variation.

Hence, two possible reasons why the first-quarter sales in 1969 were so high relative to the average quarterly sales for the year are: (1) First-quarter sales are seasonally high during every year. (2) Short-term random influences may have caused sales to increase substantially during the first quarter of 1969. From this comparison of actual sales for a quarter with the average quarterly sales for the year, therefore, we are able to gauge crudely the impact of seasonal and random forces on sales during that particular quarter. In columns 4, 5, and 6 of Table 31.1, similar per cents are calculated for the other quarters of the three-year period, and each of these reflects the influence of seasonal and random forces.

Let us now consider the three first-quarter percentages—namely, 119, 123, and 118. Each percentage reflects the same seasonal forces—those affecting sales during every first quarter—plus short-term random influences peculiar to the first quarter of the given year. If we were to use the percentage for any particular first quarter as a measure of first-quarter seasonal variation, we would not be able to separate the seasonal from the random effects. Therefore, an average of the first-quarter percentages is taken to balance out the random influences as much as possible and to leave a measure of the first-quarter seasonal variation in sales for the years 1969–1971 inclusive. In the same way, the seasonal variation during the other quarters is estimated. These estimates for the four quarters are presented in column 7 of Table 31.1, and constitute a rough index of seasonal variation.

The crude method of measuring seasonal variation just explained indicates the approximate meaning of a seasonal index. For example, the first-quarter seasonal index of 120 indicates that, on the average, first-quarter sales during 1969–1971 were 120 per cent as great as average quarterly sales for the year.

31.3 APPLICATIONS OF SEASONAL INDEXES

Deseasonalizing data

Meaning of deseasonalizing. Let us continue with our retail store sales illustration. Suppose that actual sales during the first quarter of 1972 were \$12.0 million. We wish to determine the deseasonalized level of sales on the basis of the seasonal index calculated in Table 31.1. The index value of 120 for the first quarter indicates that if all factors other than seasonal ones remain constant throughout the year, the \$12.0 million first-quarter sales will be 120 per cent as great as average quarterly sales for the year; consequently, average quarterly sales for the year will be $(12.0/120)100 =$ \$10.0 million, and total sales for the year will be $10.0(4) =$ \$40.0 million. The magnitude \$10.0 million represents the *deseasonalized* or *seasonally adjusted* level of sales for the first quarter, and the \$40.0 million represents the *seasonally adjusted annual rate* of first-quarter sales.

It may be helpful to examine the meaning of deseasonalized data in another way. Table 31.2a contains the seasonal index of sales, and also shows the actual first-quarter sales of \$12.0 million. Now, if only seasonal changes take place during the year, second-quarter sales should be in the same proportion to first-quarter sales as the second-quarter index is to the first-quarter index. Thus, second-quarter sales should be $(90/120)100 = 75$ per cent as great as first-quarter sales, or $12.0(.75) = \$9.0$ million. In the same way, we calculate that sales during the third quarter should be $(80/90)100 = 88.9$ per cent as great as second-quarter sales if only the regular seasonal changes occur between the second and third quarters. Therefore, third-quarter sales should be $9.0(.889) = \$8.0$ million. Finally, we calculate that sales during the fourth quarter will be \$11.0 million if only the regular seasonal changes take place between the third and fourth quarters.

Table 31.2 Actual Sales and Equivalent Sales Rates for Text Example

Quarter	(1) *Index of Seasonal Variation*	(2) *Per Cent Change in Sales From Preceding Quarter Expected From Seasonal Factors*	(3) *Sales if Only Seasonal Changes Occur (Millions of Dollars)*	
		(a)		
1	120		\$12.0	(actual)
2	90	−25.0	9.0	(expected)
3	80	−11.1	8.0	"
4	110	+37.5	11.0	"
		Total	\$40.0	"
		Quarterly average	\$10.0	"
		(b)		
2	90		\$11.0	(actual)
3	80	−11.1	9.8	(expected)
4	110	+37.5	13.5	"
1	120	+9.1	14.7	"
		Total	\$49.0	"
		Quarterly average	\$12.2	"

Note from Table 31.2a that the annual sales to be expected from first-quarter sales of \$12.0 million are \$40.0 million, and that the expected average quarterly sales are \$10.0 million, if no changes except seasonal ones occur during the year. These are the seasonally adjusted annual rate of first-quarter sales and the seasonally adjusted first-quarter sales, respectively, which we obtained earlier.

To emphasize the mechanics of deseasonalizing and the meaning of deseasonalized data, we continue our previous example one more step. Suppose that actual second-quarter sales are \$11.0 million. Second-quarter sales typically are 90 per cent of average quarterly sales for the year. Hence, if no changes occur from the second-quarter level of sales except regular seasonal variations, the average quarterly sales for a year will be about $(11.0/90)100 = \$12.2$ million, and the equivalent seasonally adjusted annual rate will be approximately $12.2(4) = \$49$ million. Table 31.2b shows the meaning of the seasonally adjusted annual rate and the seasonally adjusted quarterly sales for the second quarter in terms of the sales in each quarter to be expected from second-quarter sales of \$11.0 million if no changes except seasonal ones take place during the year.

To summarize our discussion so far: Seasonally adjusted sales are obtained by dividing the actual sales for a time period by the corresponding seasonal index (expressed in decimal form). The equivalent seasonally adjusted annual rate of sales for a given time period is obtained by multiplying the seasonally adjusted sales by 4 if quarterly data are involved, by 12 if monthly data are involved, and so on. The seasonally adjusted annual rate of sales is the annual sales that would be expected in a period of a year if only the regular seasonal changes occur from the level of actual sales in a given month, quarter, or other time period. Seasonally adjusted sales are the average sales per month, quarter, or the like that would be expected for the year if only the regular seasonal changes occur from the level of actual sales in the given time period.

Interpretation of deseasonalized data. Naturally, changes other than seasonal ones constantly take place in actual business and economic data. How, then, are deseasonalized figures useful in analyzing events in the real world?

To study this question, we take the case of a department store whose monthly transactions volume during the final quarter of 1971 is shown in Table 31.3. Note that the number of transactions increased during each month of the quarter. Management wants to know, so that it can advise its buyers, whether the increase is purely a seasonal one, or whether the change is greater or less than could be expected from the action of seasonal factors alone. The answer to this question yields vital information on the current behavior of other factors, especially cyclical ones.

The past pattern of seasonal variation in the store's transactions during the final quarter of the year is presented in column 2 of Table 31.3. These figures are part of a complete monthly seasonal index cálculated by the store from transactions data covering the period 1965–1970.

We assume that management believes this seasonal index is applicable to 1971. The transactions data in column 1 then are divided by the corresponding seasonal indexes in column 2 (in decimal form) to yield the deseasonalized data in column 3. The deseasonalized number of transac-

Table 31.3 Actual and Deseasonalized Number of Department Store Transactions, Fourth Quarter, 1971 (Thousands of Transactions)

Month	(1) *Number of Transactions*	(2) *Seasonal Index*	(3) *Deseasonalized Number of Transactions* [(*Col. 1* ÷ *Col. 2*) × *100*]	(4) *Seasonally Adjusted Annual Rate of Transactions* [(*Col. 3*) × *12*]
Oct.	1,204	140	860.0	10,320
Nov.	1,426	178	801.1	9,613
Dec.	1,565	209	748.8	8,986

tions for October is 860.0 thousand, and the equivalent seasonally adjusted annual rate is 10.3 million. If all forces but seasonal ones remain constant, we would expect the seasonally adjusted annual rates for November and December to be 10.3 million also. Naturally, we would not expect the actual numbers of transactions to remain the same, because as the index shows, November and December are more active periods seasonally than October.

Table 31.3 shows that the equivalent seasonally adjusted annual rates for November and December declined to 9.6 and 9.0 million respectively. This indicates that actual transactions shown in column 1 increased by less than would be expected from seasonal forces alone, or in other words that *other factors did not remain constant* during the quarter. The seasonal upswing in the last quarter actually hides an underlying contraction, possibly cyclical in nature, that should receive careful attention from management.

Analysis of deseasonalized data versus similar-period comparisons. Businessmen frequently follow the intuitive approach of comparing activity in a given week, month, quarter, or other period with activity for the same period of the previous year, rather than deseasonalizing the data by means of a seasonal index as we have just explained. For example, management may compare sales for November 1972 with sales for November 1971. In this comparison, any purely seasonal variation is assumed to be held constant; thus, differences between these two periods can be attributed wholly to non-seasonal factors.

This approach suffers from the disadvantage that the periods compared are a year apart. Consequently, the user does not receive an unfolding picture of underlying movements in the series during the intervening months, such as can be obtained with deseasonalized data. This limitation is often critical when a cyclical decline or upturn occurs, because in such cases the cyclical contraction or upturn usually must continue for some time before a comparison of the current level with the previous year's level will lead to the recognition of this change. For example, suppose sales were expanding cyclically during the last part of 1971 and continued to do so until the summer of 1972, at which time a cyclical downturn occurred. Sales for November 1972 might well be higher than those for November 1971, although a contraction had been under way for several months, because the expansion during the months immediately after November 1971 had not yet been offset by November 1972.

Measuring seasonal variation was a time-consuming and relatively costly procedure before electronic computers revolutionized data processing. Seasonal indexes were maintained, and deseasonalized data published, for only a handful of the most important statistical series on economic activity in the United States. Few firms compiled seasonal indexes for their own activities. As a result, similar-period comparisons were widely used in the absence of quantitative information on seasonal variation. Today, however, seasonal variation is regularly measured for thousands of business and economic series by electronic computers. Businessmen therefore need to understand the use of deseasonalized data and the meaning of seasonally adjusted annual rates in order to interpret published data correctly and to cope on the most effective terms with seasonal variation at the company level.

Study of cyclical or trend-cyclical components. Deseasonalizing also is undertaken if one wishes to study cyclical changes or trend-cyclical changes in monthly or quarterly data. To study cyclical changes, the data are first expressed as per cents of trend (see Chapter 29) to remove the trend component. This requires that the trend equation be on a monthly or quarterly basis. Such a trend equation may be calculated from monthly or quarterly data, or a trend equation calculated from annual data may be converted to a monthly or quarterly basis. The conversion of an annual trend equation to a monthly or quarterly one is illustrated in Section 32.2.

The monthly or quarterly per cents of trend then are deseasonalized in the usual way. The deseasonalized per cents of trend reflect principally the influence of cyclical and random forces, and may be used for studies of cyclical characteristics. An illustration of these calculations for one year is shown in Table 31.4. The deseasonalized per cents of trend sometimes are smoothed by taking an appropriate moving average that will level out the irregular component and leave only the cyclical one. The procedure for taking a moving average will be discussed later.

Table 31.4 Procedure for Calculating Deseasonalized Per Cents of Trend

	(1)	(2)	(3)	(4)	(5)
1972 Quarter	*Actual Sales*	*Trend Value*	*Per Cent of Trend [(Col. 1 ÷ Col. 2) × 100]*	*Seasonal Index*	*Deseasonalized Per Cent of Trend [(Col. 3 ÷ Col. 4) × 100]*
1	100,000	90,000	111	80	139
2	150,000	95,000	158	130	122
3	120,000	100,000	120	110	109
4	110,000	105,000	105	80	131

If one wishes to study the trend and cyclical components jointly, the monthly or quarterly series is first deseasonalized. The resultant series, containing trend, cyclical, and irregular components, then can be smoothed, if desired, to eliminate the irregular component.

Forecasting

With a relevant seasonal index, seasonal variation can be incorporated routinely into forecasts. For example, the Ellis Company estimates that 240,000 units of a certain product will be sold next year. On the basis of past experience and analysis of the near future, the company concludes that trend-cyclical influences on sales will be only minor during the coming year. Hence, seasonal variations in sales of this product are the only type of movement that has to be considered in converting the annual forecast into the monthly ones that management requires.

The annual forecast of 240,000 units is the equivalent of a forecast of average monthly sales of 20,000 units, and is shown in Table 31.5, column 1. The index of seasonal variation for sales of this product was computed by the company and is given in column 2 (computations not shown here). Since January sales are, on the average, only about 89 per cent as great as average monthly sales during a complete 12-month period and since the latter are expected to be 20,000 units during next year, the expected sales during January would be about $20{,}000(.89) = 17{,}800$ units. Similarly, the forecast of sales for April is $20{,}000(1.17) = 23{,}400$ units. Column 3 of Table 31.5 presents the forecast of sales for each month.

Table 31.5 Construction of Monthly Sales Forecasts for Ellis Company

Month	(1) *Forecast Average Monthly Sales*	(2) *Index of Seasonal Variation in Sales of Product*	(3) *Forecast Monthly Sales* [(*Col. 1* × *Col. 2*) ÷ *100*]
Jan.	20,000	89	17,800
Feb.	20,000	100	20,000
March	20,000	104	20,800
April	20,000	117	23,400
May	20,000	111	22,200
June	20,000	98	19,600
July	20,000	92	18,400
Aug.	20,000	89	17,800
Sept.	20,000	97	19,400
Oct.	20,000	106	21,200
Nov.	20,000	100	20,000
Dec.	20,000	97	19,400
Total	240,000	1,200	240,000

31.4 COMPUTATIONS FOR ESTIMATING INDEXES OF SEASONAL VARIATION BY THE METHOD OF RATIO TO MOVING AVERAGE

Limitations of crude method

Earlier we discussed a crude method by which a seasonal pattern in a series could be isolated from the other movements. This method illustrates, without refinements, the basic approach to measuring seasonal variation. It is adequate when trend and cyclical movements are of small consequence. However, when these movements are present to a significant extent, the crude method does a relatively poor job of isolating the seasonal pattern as compared with more refined methods that are available.

To see one reason why this is so, consider again the pattern in air travel. The data in Figure 31.1 are presented in Table 31.6, column 1, but on a quarterly instead of a monthly basis. Note that the series shows an upward trend-cyclical movement in addition to the repetitive yearly seasonal pattern. This trend-cyclical movement affects our comparison of actual travel during any quarter with average quarterly travel for the year. For instance, first-quarter travel during any year is less than the average quarterly travel during that year. We could infer from the pattern in the series that seasonal and perhaps random influences were in part responsible for this difference. Another reason, however, is that first-quarter travel in any year shows fewer effects of the upward trend-cyclical movement than does travel during the later quarters. Consequently, this upward trend-cyclical movement will lead to distortions in the seasonal index if seasonal variation is measured in this series by the crude method previously discussed. Air travel then would tend to appear seasonally lower during the early quarters of any year than it actually is, and seasonally higher during the later quarters. If the direction of the trend-cyclical movement had been downward, the opposite effect would occur.

Advantages of moving seasonal average

What is the situation for the middle period of any year? If the trend-cyclical movement is approximately linear within a year, as is the case in Figure 31.1 on air travel, then this component is at its average level for the year at the middle of the year. Hence, a comparison of the actual level of the activity at the middle of the year with the average level of the activity for the year would not contain much bias due to trend-cyclical movements within the year. This suggests that the crude procedure explained previously could be refined if each quarter were treated as the middle of its own particular "year" or four-quarter period. Thus, under the more refined approach, travel in the first quarter of 1960, for instance, would be compared to average quarterly travel during a four-quarter period for

TABLE 19.6 Computation of Specific Seasonal Relatives by Method of Ratio to Moving Average, Quarterly Data

Year and Quarter		(1) Revenue Passenger Miles Flown (Millions)	(2) 4-Quarter Moving Total of Col. 1	(3) 4-Quarter Moving Average [(Col. 2) ÷ 4]	(4) 2-Quarter Moving Total of Col. 3	(5) Centered 4-Quarter Moving Average [(Col. 4) ÷ 2]	(6) Specific Seasonal Relative [(Col. 1 ÷ Col. 5) × 100]
1957	1	5,604					
	2	6,357					
			24,499	6,124.75			
	3	6,702			12,296.25	6,148.12	109.01
			24,686	6,171.50			
	4	5,836			12,321.50	6,160.75	94.73
			24,600	6,150.00			
1958	1	5,791			12,303.75	6,151.88	94.13
			24,615	6,153.75			
	2	6,271			12,262.75	6,131.38	102.28
			24,436	6,109.00			
	3	6,717			12,335.50	6,167.75	108.91
			24,906	6,226.50			
	4	5,657			12,672.25	6,336.12	89.28
			25,783	6,445.75			
1959	1	6,261			13,159.75	6,579.88	95.15
			26,856	6,714.00			
	2	7,148			13,746.00	6,873.00	104.00
			28,128	7,032.00			
	3	7,790			14,199.00	7,099.50	109.73
			28,668	7,167.00			
	4	6,929			14,453.75	7,226.88	95.88
			29,147	7,286.75			

1960	1	6,801			14,611.00	7,305.50	93.09
			29,297	7,324.25			
	2	7,627			14,632.50	7,316.25	104.25
			29,233	7,308.25			
	3	7,940			14,549.25	7,274.62	109.15
			28,964	7,241.00			
	4	6,865			14,480.75	7,240.38	94.82
			28,959	7,239.75			
1961	1	6,532			14,486.50	7,243.25	90.18
			28,987	7,246.75			
	2	7,622			14,630.25	7,315.12	104.20
			29,534	7,383.50			
	3	7,968			15,036.00	7,518.00	105.99
			30,610	7,652.50			
	4	7,412			15,480.75	7,740.38	95.76
			31,313	7,828.25			
1962	1	7,608			15,722.25	7,861.12	96.78
			31,576	7,894.00			
	2	8,325			15,850.00	7,925.00	105.05
			31,824	7,956.00			
	3	8,231					
	4	7,660					

Note: Data for February 1956 and February 1960 adjusted to 28-day basis.
Source of basic data: Civil Aeronautics Board.

which the first quarter of 1960 is the center. The calculation of consecutive four-quarter averages under the more refined procedure leads to a *four-quarter moving average.*

The calculation of air travel in each quarter as a per cent of a four-quarter average centered around that quarter is shown in Table 31.6. It is the first step in constructing a seasonal index by the *ratio-to-moving-average* method. This is the most widely used of several alternative methods that have been developed for the measurement of seasonal patterns. Here, we shall describe the basic method suitable for use with desk calculators, without additional refinements that have been developed in connection with electronic-computer programs for calculating seasonal indexes.

Isolation of seasonal and random effects

The first steps in the ratio-to-moving-average method are designed to isolate the seasonal and random effects in the series. It will be easiest for the reader to follow the logic and procedure of the method if we tie our discussion to the successive columns in Table 31.6.

Column 1 presents quarterly data on air travel between 1957 and 1962 inclusive.

Next, we compute a series of four-quarter averages, each of which is to be related to the quarter in the center of its four-quarter period. To do this systematically, we have computed in column 2 successive four-quarter totals for the data in column 1. For example, the revenue passenger miles flown during the four quarters of 1957 totaled 24,499 million. This sum is placed midway in the four-quarter interval; thus it is placed between the second and third quarters of 1957. The four-quarter total for the period beginning with the second quarter of 1957 and ending with the first quarter of 1958 is 24,686 million; this figure is placed between the third and fourth quarters of 1957, which is the midpoint of that four-quarter period. In obtaining successive four-quarter totals, it is not necessary to sum four figures each time; the computation can be made by subtracting, from the four-quarter total, the figure for the earliest quarter of the preceding period and adding the figure for the latest quarter of the new period. For example, the four-quarter total for the period beginning with the third quarter of 1957 and ending with the second quarter of 1958 is 24,686 minus 6,357 (second quarter, 1957) plus 6,271 (second quarter, 1958), or 24,600 million. This figure is placed midway between the fourth quarter of 1957 and the first quarter of 1958.

In column 3, each of the four-quarter totals is divided by 4 to obtain *four-quarter moving averages.*

We now wish to express actual travel during each quarter as a per cent of the average quarterly travel for the "year"—that is, for the four-quarter period centered at that quarter. Before this can be done, however, an additional step must be taken. Note that the averages in column 3 are placed between quarters; hence they do not correspond precisely in point of time with the actual data in column 1. The two sets of data are made comparable in point of time by averaging, in groups of two, the successive four-quarter averages of column 3. To do this systematically, successive two-quarter totals of the data in column 3 are placed in column 4 and are converted to quarterly averages in column 5. For example, 12,296.25, the first figure in column 4, represents the sum of 6,124.75 and 6,171.50 and is placed *between* the two figures. The two-quarter totals then are divided by 2 and the results shown in column 5.

A shortcut, which will give the results in column 5 with one less step, is to omit calculation of the four-quarter averages in column 3. Instead, eight-quarter moving totals are calculated directly from the data in column 2 and are divided by 8 to give the averages shown in column 5.

In either case, the operations resulting in column 5 will have centered the four-quarter averages so that they now coincide in point of time with the data in column 1.[1] The first figure in column 5—6,148.12—represents average quarterly travel during the four-quarter period of which the third quarter of 1957 is the center; the second figure—6,160.75—represents average quarterly travel during the four-quarter period of which the fourth quarter of 1957 is the center, and so on.

In column 6, the seasonal and short-term random movements finally are isolated by dividing the actual air travel during any quarter by the corresponding centered four-quarter average. Each resulting quotient is expressed as a per cent and is called a *specific seasonal relative*. For example, the specific seasonal relative for the third quarter of 1957 is 109.01. It means that actual travel during that quarter was 109.01 per cent as great as average quarterly travel for the four-quarter period centered at that quarter. Note, incidentally, that the procedure used does not enable us to obtain specific seasonal relatives for the first or last two quarters of the period.

Examination of the stability of the seasonal pattern

A seasonal pattern in a business or economic series may be fairly stable, or it may be shifting from year to year. Before we can separate the seasonal from the irregular movements in a series, we first must determine whether the seasonal pattern is stable or shifting.

To study the stability of the seasonal pattern, it is helpful to assemble the specific seasonal relatives for each month into individual time series. The series may be presented in either tabular or graphic form. Table 31.7 (p. 716), the tabular presentation, has one column for all the first-quarter

[1] The centered four-quarter averages really are based on data for five quarters, in which the first and fifth quarters are each given half weight and the other quarters are given full weight. Thus each of the quarters in any "year" is given equal weight.

specific seasonal relatives, a second column for all the second-quarter specific seasonal relatives, and so on.

Figure 31.2 contains the information of Table 31.7 in graphic form. Note that each grid shows successive specific seasonal relatives for a particular quarter. For example, in the top left grid the specific seasonal relatives are plotted for the first quarter of 1958, the first quarter of 1959, and so on. From an examination of the four grids, one can obtain a comprehensive picture of the year-to-year movements in each quarter's specific seasonal relatives.

If the seasonal pattern in the series were perfectly stable and the irregular movements negligible, the successive specific seasonal relatives in each grid would fall along horizontal straight lines—in other words, for any one quarter they would have values that are approximately the same from year to year.

Suppose, on the other hand, that the seasonal pattern were gradually changing—say, flattening out—while irregular movements were negligible. In this case, the relatives for the seasonally active quarters would decline over the period of several years, while the relatives for the quarters that had been relatively slack would increase. A chart such as Figure 31.2 would show these interrelated declines and gains.

When there are marked irregular movements, it becomes more difficult to determine whether the seasonal pattern is stable or changing. Such is the case in Figure 31.2. The successive relatives for some quarters show an erratic upward drift, while others correspondingly show a downward drift.

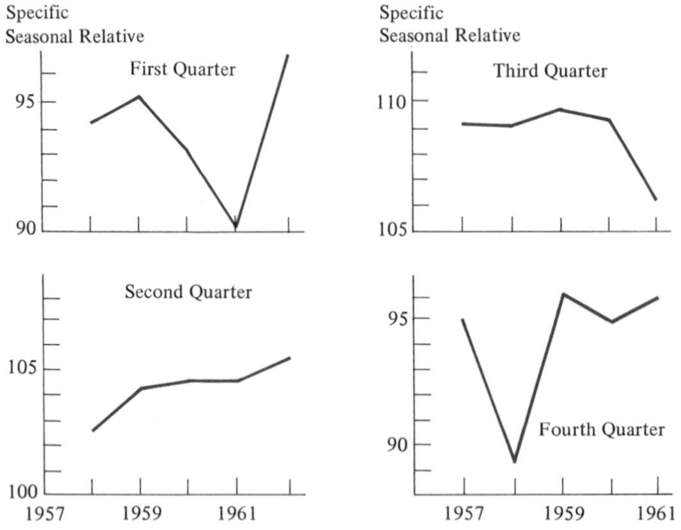

Source of data: Table 31.7.

Figure 31.2. Specific seasonal relatives for air travel, quarterly, 1957–1962

However, there seems to be no systematic change in the group as a whole, so that these patterns may be due merely to the random, irregular movements in the series.

To determine whether the seasonal pattern is stable or shifting, we would have to supplement our visual examination of Figure 31.2 with a careful analysis of the character of the forces causing seasonal variation in air travel. Statistical techniques could be employed in this analysis to aid in deciding whether the seasonal pattern is stable and the changes in the specific seasonal relatives are only random, or whether the seasonal pattern is not stable. We will not digress to make such a detailed analysis here, but will assume for our purposes that the seasonal pattern in air travel is stable and that any net upward or downward movement in each quarter's successive relatives is due simply to erratic fluctuations arising from random effects.

Isolation of seasonal component when seasonal pattern is stable

If the seasonal pattern is stable, it is customary to isolate the seasonal component by averaging the specific seasonal relatives for each of the four quarters—that is, by determining an average of all the first-quarter relatives, an average of all the second-quarter relatives, and so on. The idea behind this procedure is that the irregular movements in the relatives for each particular quarter should more or less balance out during the period as a whole; by so doing, the averages, or *typical seasonal relatives,* will indicate the underlying seasonal pattern.

Naturally, we must use a type of average for which there is a reasonable chance that the irregular movements will roughly cancel out. Thus, it would not be good to use an arithmetic mean here, since the number of specific seasonal relatives to be averaged is generally small and an average of this type then can be particularly affected by extreme values. As any extreme specific seasonal relative is usually "extreme" because of irregular influences, the use of an arithmetic mean could transmit a good deal of this influence to our final estimate of seasonal variation. For this reason, an average such as the median, which is not affected by extreme values, usually is chosen. We employ the median in our illustration. The median values for the columns in Table 31.7 can be obtained readily by inspection, and are shown at the bottom of this table. If more years had been used in the calculations, it might have been helpful to array the data in each column before obtaining the medians.

As an alternative to using the median as the average, we could have employed a *modified mean,* which is an arithmetic average of an arbitrary number of central items when the items are arranged in an array. For instance, in each column in Table 31.7 we could have arrayed the data and

Table 31.7 Specific
Seasonal Relatives and Seasonal Index for Air Travel, Quarterly, 1957–1962

Year	Quarter 1	2	3	4	Total
1957	—	—	109.01	94.73	
1958	94.13	102.28	108.91	89.28	
1959	95.15	104.00	109.73	95.88	
1960	93.09	104.25	109.15	94.82	
1961	90.18	104.20	105.99	95.76	
1962	96.78	105.05	—	—	
Median (Adjusted typical seasonal relative)	94.13	104.20	109.01	94.82	402.16
Seasonal index	93.6	103.7	108.4	94.3	400.0

Source: Table 31.6.

computed an arithmetic mean of the central three items. By excluding extreme items, the modified mean, like the median, tends to avoid the inclusion of irregular influences in the final measure of seasonal variation. Another possibility is to exclude only those specific seasonal relatives known to be strongly affected by important irregular factors, such as strikes and build-ups and depletions of inventories, and take a mean of the remaining items.

Adjustment of typical seasonal relatives

Since a yearly seasonal pattern completes itself, by definition, within a year, the typical seasonal relatives should balance out at 100; in other words, their average should be 100 and the four relatives should total 400. The ratio-to-moving-average method does not contain a built-in feature to assure that the typical seasonal relatives will average out to 100, though in practice their average usually will be close to this figure.

Consequently, a minor adjustment generally is required in these relatives to bring their total to 400. In our illustration, the unadjusted seasonal relatives sum to 402.16, as shown in Table 31.7. Thus they must be reduced by the overall amount of 2.16 index points. This reduction can be accomplished, without changing the relative seasonal pattern during the year, simply by multiplying each unadjusted relative by the ratio 400.00/402.16 or .9946290. Each relative is reduced slightly so that the relatives now total 400. Of course, had the unadjusted relatives added to less than 400 they would be multiplied by a factor slightly greater than 1. Note that in any case the ratio used to adjust the relatives has the value 400.00 as its numerator and the sum of the unadjusted relatives as its denominator. The adjusted typical seasonal relatives, which constitute the index of seasonal variation, are shown in the bottom row of Table 31.7.

Seasonal indexes for monthly time periods

Monthly seasonal indexes are calculated by the ratio-to-moving-average method through procedures directly comparable to those we have demonstrated for quarterly data.

Moving seasonal patterns

Causes of shifts in seasonal patterns. We now have explained how seasonal variation can be measured when the pattern is stable from year to year. Often, however, the forces causing seasonal variation in business or economic series change over time, so that the resulting seasonal patterns are not stable. Some seasonal patterns undergo modification slowly, with year-to-year continuity and predictability, while others shift suddenly in a complete break with the past. There are various causes of these modifications in seasonal patterns, such as changes in consumer buying habits, impact of technological innovations, and deliberate management actions.

As we pointed out earlier, the stability of a seasonal pattern can be studied from the specific seasonal relatives. It is helpful to organize the data into a graph such as that of Figure 31.2 or, to take another example, that of Figure 31.3. This latter graph was used in the Eastman Kodak Company to study seasonal movements in sales of a major consumer product. This graph differs from Figure 31.2 in that 13 periods (of 28 days each) are shown, rather than four quarters. Also, a logarithmic vertical scale is used for each grid rather than an arithmetic one.[2] These differences do not affect our discussion.

Note that the seasonal pattern shown in Figure 31.3 was changing in a consistent manner. The specific seasonal relatives for periods 1, 2, 10, 11, 12, 13—that is, the early and final periods for any year—were increasing. Correspondingly, the specific seasonal relatives for the middle periods were decreasing. Since these movements were consistent with technological developments during the period that would lead to increased consumer purchases of the product in the fall and winter periods, it is reasonable to conclude that Figure 31.3 shows a real shift in a seasonal pattern, rather than merely the results of chance fluctuations.

Measurement and projection of moving seasonal pattern. When the seasonal pattern is modified gradually, it is called a *moving seasonal pattern.*

[2] In order to obtain specific seasonal relatives for the last 6 periods of the range of the data, which are now of particular importance for projecting future seasonal movements, we may project the 13-period moving average for those final 6 periods. The specific seasonal relatives then can be calculated in the usual manner. It also may be noted that in the particular example illustrated in Figure 31.3, a special step is not necessary to center the moving totals and averages; since there are 13 periods instead of 12 months or four quarters, the 13-period totals immediately are associated with specific periods rather than initially placed halfway between two periods.

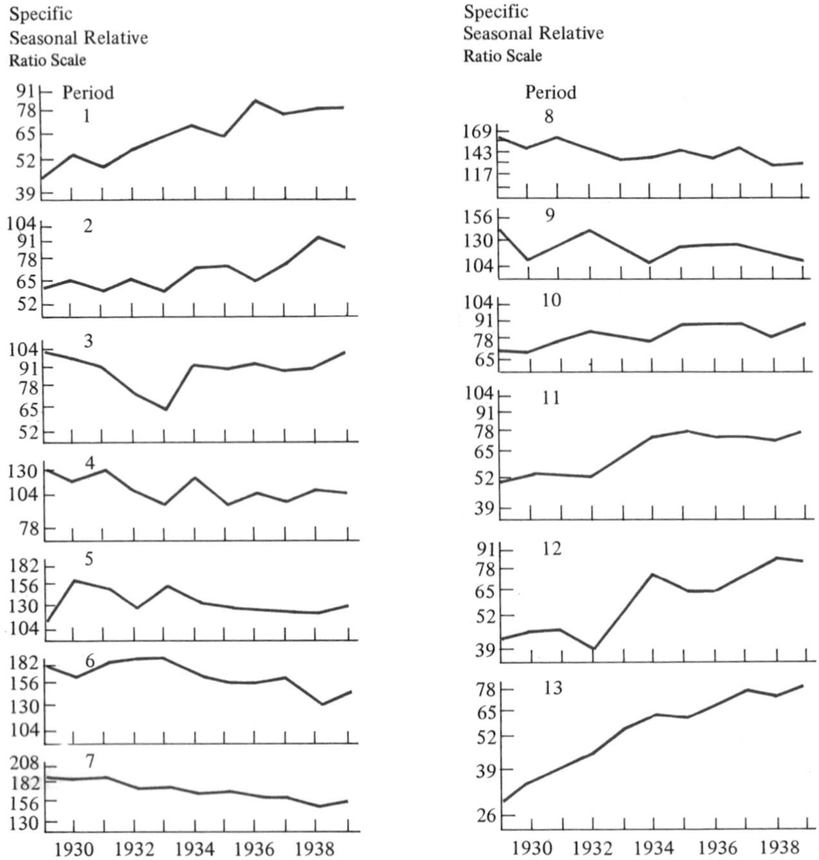

Source: Eastman Kodak Company.

Figure 31.3. Moving seasonal pattern in sales of a major semidurable good by Eastman Kodak Company, 1929–1939 (data plotted are specific seasonal relatives)

In this case, a single seasonal index for a period of some years would not be appropriate, since the seasonal pattern differs from year to year.

To measure seasonal variation when the pattern is gradually shifting, we utilize the underlying tendency or "trend" in the shifting pattern to arrive at measures of seasonal variation for each year. In effect, we fit a "trend" curve to each set of specific seasonal relatives. If, for instance, a quarterly seasonal index were being developed, we would fit a trend curve to the first-quarter specific seasonal relatives. The seasonal index for the first quarter of a particular year would then be the ordinate of the trend curve for that year. In the same way, the seasonal index values for the other quarters in the year would be determined. The latest values of the trends indicate the current rates of seasonal activity; projections of the trends will show the rates to be expected in the next year or two.

Since the fluctuations in each set of specific seasonal relatives tend to balance out around the set's trend curve, the above procedure is analogous to that for stable seasonal patterns in which the seasonal indexes are obtained by averaging out the specific seasonal relatives. In determining the moving seasonal indexes by the method just described, it is also generally necessary to make minor arbitrary adjustments so that the final index of seasonal variation averages out to 100 for a year.

Precautions in using seasonal indexes

As was shown, a seasonal index is derived empirically from past movements in a time series. To avoid influencing current indexes by old seasonal effects that may no longer be operative, many organizations recompute their seasonal indexes periodically, incorporating the latest data and dropping the data for the period furthest in the past. Often, the seasonal indexes are based upon experience during the most recent six or seven years. Needless to say, even an index based on relatively recent data must be employed with care and judgment when applied to the present or future.

It is well to keep in mind that irregular movements can cause significant errors in measuring seasonal variation. Major irregular fluctuations due to identifiable causes such as strikes can be adjusted for in the basic data before a seasonal index is calculated, but as a practical matter most irregular movements cannot be identified and removed before the calculations. To be sure, the procedures for measuring seasonal variation contain steps designed to average out the irregular effects. However, in any given series it is always possible that the irregular effects are distributed in such a way that they will not average out. Thus, when a seasonal index is calculated, it should be reviewed by a competent analyst to make sure that the index values are reasonable in light of the seasonal factors known to be operating on the activity. This is especially true when the irregular movements are known to be relatively large, as is frequently the case in activities at the level of the individual firm.

If one obtains a seasonal index in which the index values for the different months or quarters are all close to 100 or cannot be explained by known seasonal factors, it may be that there is no real seasonal pattern in the series and that the index figures reflect only irregular movements. Statistical techniques are available for helping to decide whether a series really contains a pattern of seasonal variation. For example, the test for means of several populations discussed in Chapter 19 could be employed with the data of Table 31.7 to test whether a stable seasonal pattern is present. This table contains five sample observations for each of the four quarters. If the four population means μ_1, μ_2, μ_3, and μ_4, corresponding to the stable quarterly effects, are all equal, there is no seasonal variation. On the other hand, if the population means are unequal, there is seasonal variation. Thus the two alternative conclusions are:

C_1 $\quad \mu_1 = \mu_2 = \mu_3 = \mu_4$; there is no seasonal variation

C_2 $\quad$ The means μ_j are not all equal; there is seasonal variation

QUESTIONS AND PROBLEMS

31.1. Give an example (not used in the text) of each type of seasonal pattern listed below:

a. Year-long pattern of seasonal variation

b. Month-long pattern of seasonal variation

c. Weekly pattern of seasonal variation

d. Daily pattern of seasonal variation

e. A seasonal pattern for some period other than those specified in parts **a** through **d.**

31.2. Contrast each of the following:

a. Deseasonalized monthly sales and seasonally adjusted annual rate of sales

b. Seasonal movements and irregular movements

c. Specific seasonal relative and typical seasonal relative

d. Stable seasonal pattern and moving seasonal pattern

31.3. Which are usually more difficult to predict—cyclical fluctuations discussed in Chapter 30, or seasonal variations? Why?

31.4. A newspaper printed an advertisement in which the monthly seasonal indexes for grocery store sales and for the circulation of this newspaper were presented graphically. Both indexes showed little monthly variation from the 100 per cent line. The following point then was made:

The acid test of whether a commodity is essential is the test of actual use. Naturally there are certain exceptions, but in general the really essential commodity is used regularly, month in and month out, with little variation over the year. The graph shows that grocery store sales fluctuate very little seasonally; this is to be expected, since groceries are essential and are bought and used regularly. The seasonal index of our circulation shows negligible fluctuation for the same reason. This objective test of actual use is the clearest possible proof that this newspaper must be considered an essential commodity in this city.

Evaluate the idea that a seasonal index showing little variation from the 100 per cent line can be interpreted as an indicator of the essentialness of a commodity.

31.5. An automobile dealer last October set a goal of 800 new cars to be sold by his agency during the next 12 months. As of the following January 31st, his agency had sold 270 new cars. Could the dealer tell from this fact alone whether sales were progressing at a satisfactory rate? Explain.

31.6. **a.** During World War II, the production of passenger cars in the United States was almost completely curtailed. What influence would you expect this curtailment to have had on the seasonal pattern of automobile sales during the first few postwar years?

b. Would the seasonal index of passenger car sales, based on pre-World War II years, have been applicable to these first few postwar years? Explain.

c. Suppose that the seasonal pattern changed sharply frcm one year to the next; this happened, for instance, when the introduction of new passenger car models was moved up by several months. Of what relevance then is the seasonal index based upon the earlier conditions? What can be done in this case to obtain a measure of the new pattern of seasonal variation in sales of passenger cars? Explain.

31.7. A large clothing store, adjacent to a university campus and catering mainly to students, engaged a marketing student to study factors affecting its dollar volume of clothing sales. As part of his study the student calculated a seasonal index based on the store's monthly dollar sales volume during the past five years.

The student then decided to calculate another seasonal index. For the same five-year period, he divided the dollar volume of sales for each month by the number of days that month when the store was open. He then calculated a seasonal index, by the same method as before, based upon the mean dollar volume per business day for each month. The two seasonal indexes were not identical.

a. How do you explain the difference in the two seasonal indexes? Discuss fully.

b. Which of the two indexes, in your opinion, is the more meaningful one?

c. Does the second index take account of the fact that one month may contain more Saturdays than another? Is this of any relevance?

d. Could a weekly seasonal index have been computed in this instance?

e. Could an additional seasonal index, for some other period than a month or week, also be meaningful in this study? Discuss.

f. Six years previously the university had shifted from a two-semester system to a trimester system. Could this have affected the student's choice of data on which his seasonal indexes were based? Explain.

31.8. Several years ago a seasonal index of monthly revenues was calculated for the ABA Taxi Company, which operates in a large metropolitan area. Since then, monthly revenues for the spring and summer months have declined, but revenues for the rest of the year have remained unchanged.

a. If a new seasonal index were calculated, based only on the data of the past several years since this change took place, would the reduction in revenues during the spring and summer change the seasonal-index values for these months only, or the values for all months? Explain fully.

b. An analyst for the company suggested that the revised seasonal index be based on the years before this change took place as well as on the more recent years. He argued that there would be a better chance of eliminating irregular influences from the measure of seasonal variation if the seasonal index were based on a longer time period. Discuss fully.

31.9. Data reported by the U.S. Department of Commerce indicated that personal consumption expenditures in the United States were at a seasonally adjusted annual rate of $620.9 billion in the third quarter of 1970, and at a seasonally adjusted annual rate of $624.7 billion in the fourth quarter of that year.

a. Does this mean that personal consumption expenditures in the United States totaled $624.7 billion in 1970? Explain.

b. Do these figures indicate that actual personal consumption expenditures in the third quarter of 1970 were necessarily lower than in the fourth quarter? If so, explain why. If not, explain why not and indicate what additional information you would need before you could estimate the actual magnitudes of personal consumption expenditures for these periods from the data as given.

c. Is it preferable to report personal consumption expenditures and other national income data in the form of seasonally adjusted annual rates rather than as deseasonalized quarterly data? Discuss.

d. Is it preferable to report national income data adjusted for seasonal variation, unadjusted for seasonal variation, or both ways? Explain.

***31.10.** Quarterly sales (in millions of dollars) of the Neely Company during the year 1972, together with the seasonal index pertinent to these sales, were as follows:

Quarter	*Sales*	*Seasonal Index*
1st	7.13	103
2d	7.09	98
3d	6.43	87
4th	8.37	112

a. Analyze these data to determine the influence of factors other than seasonal ones upon the changes in the quarterly sales volume, and present your findings.

b. Suppose that no changes in sales other than seasonal ones were expected between the fourth quarter of 1972 and the first quarter of 1973. What would be the expected sales volume for the first quarter of 1973, assuming that the seasonal pattern is a stable one? Show how you arrived at your answer.

31.11. Describe three types of business problems for which annual forecasts are inadequate—in other words, for which monthly forecasts, quarterly forecasts, or the like are needed.

***31.12.** The Business Research Department of the Woodrow Corporation forecasts that sales next year will be about $18.4 million. It also is expected that no sharp cyclical fluctuations will occur during the year, that the effect of trend during the year will be minute, and that the past pattern of quarterly seasonal variation will continue. This pattern is as follows:

Quarter	*Seasonal Index*
1st	76
2d	115
3d	118
4th	91

a. Prepare a forecast of quarterly sales from the above information.

b. Does the sum of the forecast quarterly sales equal the forecast sales volume of the entire year? Why?

c. What step or steps in your procedure for making the forecast in part **a** depended specifically on the assumption that no sharp cyclical fluctuations will occur during next year and that the effect of trend will be minute? What step or steps depended specifically on the assumption that the past pattern of seasonal variation will continue? Explain.

31.13. The Traders' National Bank estimates that it will make commercial loans aggregating about $70 million during the coming year. Trend and cyclical movements in the volume of commercial loans made by this bank are expected to be negligible in the coming year; however, a marked seasonal pattern is expected as in past years. A seasonal index of the quarterly volumes of commercial loans made by the bank has been calculated and is as follows:

Quarter	*Seasonal Index*
1st	88
2d	71
3d	125
4th	116

a. Estimate, on the basis of the above data, the dollar volume of commercial loans that is expected to be made by the bank during each quarter of the coming year. Show your calculations.

b. Would your procedure in answering part **a** have to be modified if the assumption as to negligibility of trend and cyclical movements were dropped? If no, explain why not. If yes, explain specifically what modifications you would have to make and what additional information, if any, you would require.

31.14. Data are presented below on new orders for a product (in thousands of dollars) received by a firm during July, August, and September 1972, and a seasonal index of orders received for this product calculated by the firm's research department from data for the period 1965–1970 inclusive:

Month	*New Orders Received*
July 1972	78.4
Aug. 1972	84.9
Sept. 1972	90.5

Seasonal Index					
Jan.	72	May	114	Sept.	106
Feb.	79	June	121	Oct.	100
March	83	July	127	Nov.	94
April	105	Aug.	118	Dec.	81

a. Was the increase in orders received during these three months greater than, about equal to, or less than the increase that could be expected on seasonal grounds alone? Show your calculations and explain.

b. What implicit assumptions did you make in your calculations in part **a** when you used a seasonal index based on 1965–1970 data to analyze seasonal movements in new orders received in 1972?

c. Suppose that the assumptions described in part **b** are still appropriate and that the only changes in new orders received between September and October 1972 are expected to be the regular seasonal ones; what then is the expected volume of new orders for October 1972? Show how you arrived at your answer.

31.15. Several years ago two members of an investment club assessed the current short-term sales outlook for the electrical machinery industry, but came to different conclusions. Member A felt that the outlook was favorable and based his case in part on the industry sales data for the previous year and the most recent data available for the current year, as shown below. He emphasized that sales for each month of

	Member A's Data (Monthly Sales, in Millions of Dollars)		*Member B's Data (Deseasonalized Monthly Sales, in Millions of Dollars)*
Month	*Previous Year*	*Current Year*	*Current Year*
January	1,408	1,665	1,785
February	1,431	1,738	1,827
March	1,501	1,797	1,711
April	1,527	1,709	1,765
May	1,643	1,796	1,833
June	1,718	1,843	1,763
July	1,474	1,659	1,890
August	1,657	1,774	1,823
September	1,684	1,838	1,760
October	1,820	1,938	1,795
November	1,749	1,776	1,743
December	1,882	N.A.	N.A.

the current year were higher than sales for the same month of the year before, that this month-to-month comparison was a widely used method of holding seasonal variation constant so that trend-cyclical movements could be ascertained, and that it showed the underlying trend-cyclical movements to be currently upward.

a. According to the conceptual framework of time series analysis, is seasonal variation held constant when sales for each month in the current year are compared with sales for the corresponding month of the previous year? Explain why, or why not. Does your answer hold regardless of whether the seasonal pattern is stable or moving? Explain.

b. Member B supplemented A's data with the seasonally adjusted figures for the current year, also tabulated, and contended that the almost uninterrupted decline in these figures since July contradicted A's evaluation of the current direction of the trend-cyclical movements in sales. Do you agree with B's contention? Explain fully, and indicate how you account for the contradictory conclusions obtained by A and B.

31.16. Cyclical indicators were discussed in Chapter 30. When a series such as new orders received by durable goods industries is studied specifically as a cyclical indicator, is it better that the series be studied unadjusted for seasonal variation or adjusted for seasonal variation? Discuss.

31.17. An economic analyst in a firm received a phone call from the vice president for sales, who requested an up-to-date quarterly or monthly seasonal index of new plant and equipment expenditures in the United States for immediate use in a meeting. The analyst could not locate an index in a search of his sources of published data, but he did obtain the Department of Commerce figures for new U.S. plant and equipment expenditures during the most recent year, shown below.

a. Show the steps by which the analyst could quickly derive a suitable quarterly index from these data, and derive the index.

b. Suppose that the analyst's data had not covered a calendar year, but instead that the data had been for the third and fourth quarters of last year and the first and second quarters of this year. Would your calculations described in part **a** still have yielded a complete seasonal index? Discuss.

New Plant and Equipment Expenditures

Quarter	*Unadjusted Quarterly Totals (Billions of Dollars)*	*Seasonally Adjusted Quarterly Totals at Annual Rates (Billions of Dollars)*
1st	17.47	78.22
2d	20.33	80.22
3d	20.26	81.88
4th	21.66	78.63

31.18. An agricultural economist measured seasonal variation in monthly holdings of salt pork in the meat packing industry between 1950 and 1970 inclusive. He presented his results in the following form (most of the months have been omitted for conciseness):

Month	*Unadjusted Seasonal Index (T = Time in Years; $T = 0$ at 1950)*
January	$88.88 + .504T$
February	$99.20 + .784T$
.	.
.	.
.	.
December	$80.28 - .044T$

a. Why would the economist present the information in this form rather than in the simpler form used in the bottom row of Table 31.7?

b. Why did the economist label his seasonal indexes "unadjusted"?

c. What is the unadjusted seasonal index of salt pork holdings for January 1975, based on the economist's findings?

d. On the basis of the data provided, could you "adjust" the unadjusted index obtained in part **c**? If yes, explain how, and make the adjustment. If no, explain why not.

e. Do you think it would be appropriate to project the formulas for the seasonal index values to, say, 1990? Discuss.

31.19. List and explain the steps by which you would obtain an index of monthly seasonal variation by the method of ratio to moving average. You may wish to set up illustrative work sheets that do not yet contain data but that show the appropriate labels for the columns and rows.

31.20. A company uses a 13-period calendar for internal planning and control, instead of the usual 12-month calendar. List and explain the steps by which you would obtain an index of 13-period seasonal variation in company sales by the method of ratio to moving average. You may wish to set up illustrative work sheets that do not yet contain data but that show the appropriate labels for the columns and rows.

31.21. An analyst measured quarterly seasonal variation in prices charged by a certain supermarket chain for large grade A eggs during the years 1967–1972 inclusive. He obtained the following specific seasonal relatives:

	Quarter			
Year	*1*	*2*	*3*	*4*
1967	—	—	100.8	106.5
1968	100.1	92.9	100.5	106.3
1969	101.5	93.3	99.3	106.4
1970	101.4	93.2	98.9	106.2
1971	102.1	93.4	98.1	106.4
1972	101.9	93.6	—	—

a. To determine whether the seasonal pattern is stable or shifting, would you compare the relatives within columns or within rows? Explain.

b. Examine the data and give your interpretation as to whether the seasonal pattern is stable or shifting. Support your conclusions with specific evidence. You may wish to construct a chart of the relatives to help you study the stability of the seasonal pattern.

c. Is there evidence of irregular movements in the data? Explain fully. Did this evidence or lack of it raise any difficulties for you in answering part **b**? Explain why or why not.

31.22. You have been asked to deseasonalize a firm's quarterly profits for several quarters of the current year, using a seasonal index calculated by the method of ratio to moving average from data on quarterly profits for earlier periods. You find, however, that during the most recent quarter the firm showed a loss for the first time. Would it be all right to use the index nevertheless and deseasonalize the current data by the method explained in the text? Explain why or why not, and cite hypothetical figures to support your point of view.

***31.23.** Quarterly exports of goods and services from the United States (in billions of dollars) were as follows between 1965 and 1969 inclusive:

Quarter	*1965*	*1966*	*1967*	*1968*	*1969*
1st	8.6	10.3	11.3	11.8	11.8
2d	10.4	11.0	11.8	13.0	14.7
3d	9.5	10.4	11.0	12.6	13.9
4th	10.7	11.7	12.2	13.2	15.3

Source: U.S. Department of Commerce.

a. Plot the exports data as a line graph on arithmetic graph paper.
b. Describe the pattern of seasonal variation in the data. Is there also evidence of trend and/or cyclical movements? Explain.
c. As a first step in obtaining a seasonal index, calculate specific seasonal relatives of the quarterly exports by the method of ratio to moving average.
d. Plot the relatives calculated in part **c** on a graph similar to Figure 31.2.
e. Does the seasonal pattern appear to be stable or shifting? Support your conclusion by specific references to your graph constructed in part **d**.
f. Is there evidence of a random or irregular component in the relatives plotted in part **d**? Does a random component make it easier or more difficult to identify and measure a seasonal pattern in a series? Discuss.
g. Regardless of your answer in part **e**, assume for purposes of this problem that the seasonal pattern is stable. Calculate typical seasonal relatives by arranging the specific seasonal relatives in arrays and taking modified means based on the central two items in the arrays. Adjust the typical seasonal relatives, if necessary, to obtain an index of seasonal variation.
h. What is the value of the specific seasonal relative for the third quarter of 1967? Why can it differ from the specific seasonal relative for the third quarter of 1968? From the typical seasonal relative for the third quarter? From the specific seasonal relative for the fourth quarter of 1967? Explain.
i. Why is it appropriate to average specific seasonal relatives, as in part **g**, when the seasonal pattern is stable? Why is a modified mean an appropriate average to use? Would the ordinary arithmetic mean be appropriate? Explain.
j. When typical seasonal relatives are adjusted, as in the last step in part **g**, is the seasonal pattern within the year affected? Why, or why not? What is the purpose of the adjustment?

***31.24.** Refer to Problem 31.23. During 1970, quarterly exports of goods and services from the United States (in billions of dollars) were as follows:

Quarter	*Exports*
1st	15.0
2d	16.3
3d	15.2
4th	16.3

a. Using the seasonal index obtained in Problem 31.23, calculate deseasonalized quarterly exports for 1970. Show your calculations.
b. What effect, if any, did factors other than seasonal ones have on exports in 1970? Discuss.
c. How does the seasonally adjusted annual rate of exports in the fourth quarter of 1970 compare with annual exports in 1969? Show the appropriate calculations.
d. What assumption did you implicitly make in using the seasonal index obtained in Problem 31.23 for analyzing exports data for 1970?

e. Suppose it is estimated that exports next year will total $70 billion. Assume that the seasonal index calculated in Problem 31.23 is applicable and that trend-cyclical movements in exports will be negligible next year. Convert the forecast of annual exports into forecasts of quarterly exports. Show your calculations.

***31.25.** Refer to Problem 31.23. The linear trend equation of quarterly exports for the years 1965 to 1969 inclusive is as follows: $\overline{Y}_X = 9.2886 + .26015X$, where $X = 0$ for the first quarter of 1965 and is in units of one quarter and $\overline{Y}_X$ is in units of billion dollars.

a. Using this trend equation and appropriate data and results obtained in Problem 31.23, calculate deseasonalized per cents of trend from 1965 to 1969 inclusive.

b. On one sheet of graph paper, set up a series of four small graphs containing: (1) the original exports data for 1965–1969, and the following components of the classical time series model: (2) trend, (3) cyclical-irregular, and (4) seasonal. Assume for purposes of this problem that a period of five years is long enough to enable the components to be separated satisfactorily. Be sure to identify each component.

c. From your graph constructed in part **b**, which component would you conclude was chiefly responsible for variation in quarterly exports within each year? Which component was chiefly responsible for variation in exports from one year to another? Explain the basis for your answers.

31.26. Net quarterly sales of Oasis Stores, Inc. (in millions of dollars) were as follows during 1967–1972 inclusive:

Quarter	*1967*	*1968*	*1969*	*1970*	*1971*	*1972*
1st	119	115	79	86	89	91
2d	108	104	70	74	74	82
3d	131	126	86	95	98	98
4th	194	166	115	120	122	125

a. Plot the sales data as a line graph on arithmetic graph paper.

b. What evidence do you find of a seasonal pattern in the series?

c. Is there evidence of movements other than seasonal ones in the data? Explain.

d. As a first step in obtaining an index of seasonal variation, calculate specific seasonal relatives for the data by the method of ratio to moving average.

e. Plot the specific seasonal relatives calculated in part **d** on a graph similar to Figure 31.2.

f. Is there evidence of a random or irregular component in the relatives plotted in part **e**? Does a random component make it easier or more difficult to identify and measure a seasonal pattern in a time series? Discuss.

g. Does the seasonal pattern appear to be stable or shifting? Explain.

h. Regardless of your answer in part **g**, assume for purposes of this problem that the seasonal pattern is stable. Calculate typical seasonal relatives from the specific seasonal relatives obtained in part **d**. Use the median to average the specific seasonal relatives. Adjust the typical seasonal relatives, if necessary, to obtain an index of seasonal variation.

i. What is the value of the specific seasonal relative for the second quarter of 1970? Why can it differ from the specific seasonal relative for the second quarter of 1971? From the typical seasonal relative for the second quarter? From the specific seasonal relative for the third quarter of 1970?

j. Why is it appropriate to average specific seasonal relatives, as in part **h**, when the seasonal pattern is stable? Why is the median an appropriate average to use? Would the arithmetic mean be appropriate? Explain.

k. When typical seasonal relatives are adjusted, as in the last step in part **h**, is the seasonal pattern within the year affected? Why, or why not? What is the purpose of the adjustment?

31.27. Refer to Problem 31.26. During 1973, quarterly sales of the firm (in millions of dollars) were as follows:

Quarter	*Net Sales*
1st	100
2d	90
3d	113
4th	135

a. Using the seasonal index obtained in Problem 31.26, convert these quarterly sales data into seasonally adjusted annual rates.

b. What is the meaning of the seasonally adjusted annual rate for the first quarter? How does this rate of sales compare with the previous year's sales? Discuss.

c. Was the decline in actual sales between the first and second quarters greater, about equal to, or less than could be expected from seasonal factors? Explain how this question can be answered directly from the seasonally adjusted annual rates calculated in part **a**.

d. Assume that the corporation's management forecasts that sales will total $500 million during the coming fiscal year, and that trend-cyclical movements during the year will be negligible. Using your seasonal index obtained in Problem 31.26, convert this forecast into quarterly forecasts.

e. Was any other important assumption, not mentioned in part **d**, implicitly made when you used the seasonal index obtained in Problem 31.26 to derive quarterly forecasts from the annual forecast?

31.28. Refer to Problem 31.26. The linear trend equation of quarterly sales of the firm for the years 1967–1972 inclusive is as follows: $\bar{Y}_X = 125.18 - 1.5848X$, where $X = 0$ for the first quarter of 1967 and is in units of one quarter, and $\bar{Y}_X$ is in units of million dollars.

a. Using this trend equation and appropriate data and results obtained in Problem 31.26, calculate deseasonalized per cents of trend for the quarterly sales from 1967 to 1972 inclusive.

b. On one sheet of graph paper, set up a series of four small graphs containing: (1) the original sales data for 1967–1972, and the following components of the classical time series model: (2) trend, (3) cyclical-irregular, and (4) seasonal. Assume for purposes of this problem that a period of six years is long enough to enable the components to be separated satisfactorily. Be sure to identify each component.

c. From your graph in part **b**, which component would you conclude was chiefly responsible for variation in quarterly sales within each year? Which component was chiefly responsible for variation in sales from one year to another? Explain the basis for your answers.

Chapter

32

ADDITIONAL TOPICS IN TIME SERIES ANALYSIS

In this chapter, we discuss some helpful methods for fitting linear trends. In addition, we consider alternative time series models, as well as exponential smoothing.

32.1 SHORTCUT METHOD OF FITTING LINEAR TREND

The calculations for fitting linear trend curves to time series data by the method of least squares can be reduced if the middle of the time period to which the trend is fitted is designated as zero. In this case, $\Sigma X = 0$ and (29.4a) and (29.4b) become:

$$b = \frac{\Sigma XY}{\Sigma X^2} \tag{32.1a}$$

$$a = \frac{\Sigma Y}{n} \tag{32.1b}$$

When the period for which the trend curve is calculated contains an *odd* number of months, years, or the like, the middle X is transformed to zero and the other X's are transformed accordingly. Table 32.1 shows the calculations for fitting a linear trend curve by the least-squares short method for this type of case.

When the period contains an *even* number of months, years, or the like, the point between the two middle periods is assigned a value of zero, and the other X's are transformed accordingly. Calculations are shown in Table 32.2 for fitting a trend curve by the least-squares short method for this type of case.

Table 32.1 Calculations for Fitting a Linear Trend Curve by the Least-Squares Short Method, Odd Number of Years

Year	*Year in Transformed Units* X	*Company Sales (Millions of Dollars)* Y	XY	X^2
1964	−4	4	−16	16
1965	−3	7	−21	9
1966	−2	7	−14	4
1967	−1	8	−8	1
1968	0	9	0	0
1969	+1	11	+11	1
1970	+2	13	+26	4
1971	+3	14	+42	9
1972	+4	17	+68	16
Total	0	90	+88	60

$$b = \frac{\Sigma XY}{\Sigma X^2} = \frac{88}{60} = 1.47 \qquad \bar{Y}_X = 10.0 + 1.47X$$

$$a = \frac{\Sigma Y}{n} = \frac{90}{9} = 10.0 \qquad X = 0 \text{ at } 1968$$

Table 32.2 Calculations for Fitting a Linear Trend Curve by the Least-Squares Short Method, Even Number of Years

Year	*Year in Transformed Units* X	*Company Production (Thousands of Units)* Y	XY	X^2
1963	−4.5	3	−13.5	20.25
1964	−3.5	5	−17.5	12.25
1965	−2.5	6	−15.0	6.25
1966	−1.5	6	−9.0	2.25
1967	−.5	8	−4.0	.25
1968	+.5	10	+5.0	.25
1969	+1.5	11	+16.5	2.25
1970	+2.5	12	+30.0	6.25
1971	+3.5	13	+45.5	12.25
1972	+4.5	15	+67.5	20.25
Total	0	89	+105.5	82.50

$$b = \frac{\Sigma XY}{\Sigma X^2} = \frac{105.5}{82.5} = 1.28 \qquad \bar{Y}_X = 8.9 + 1.28X$$

$$a = \frac{\Sigma Y}{n} = \frac{89}{10} = 8.9 \qquad X = 0 \text{ at Jan. 1, 1968}$$

32.2
ADAPTATION OF ANNUAL LINEAR TREND EQUATION

Annual totals

A linear trend equation in the form $\overline{Y}_X = a + bX$ calculated from annual totals, such as annual sales data, can be reduced to a monthly basis by dividing a by 12 and b by 144. The a term then represents the trend value of monthly sales ($\overline{Y}_X$) in the month for which $X = 0$, and b represents the month-to-month increment in the trend of monthly sales. For instance:

Annual Trend Equation	*Monthly Trend Equation*
$\overline{Y}_X = 12 + 28.8X$	$\overline{Y}_X = 1.0 + .2X$
$X = 0$ at 1970	$X = 0$ at July 1, 1970
X in one-year units	X in one-month units

The monthly trend equation above is centered at July 1, 1970. For comparisons with monthly data, trend values must usually be centered on mid-months. This may be done by adding half of the monthly trend increment to a. In the present example, the monthly trend equation is centered on July 15, 1970, by adding .1 to a:

$$\overline{Y}_X = 1.1 + .2X$$
$$X = 0 \text{ at July 15, 1970}$$
$$X \text{ in one-month units}$$

A linear trend equation calculated from annual totals is reduced to a quarterly basis by dividing a by 4 and b by 16, and centering the equation appropriately.

Monthly or quarterly averages

An annual linear trend equation calculated from monthly or quarterly averages is reduced to a monthly or quarterly basis by dividing b by 12 or 4, respectively, and centering the equation appropriately.

32.3
ALTERNATIVE MODELS IN TIME SERIES ANALYSIS

Multiplicative and additive forms of the classical model

In our discussion of time series analysis we have employed a model in which the current level of a time series is determined by the levels of four components that respectively embody trend, cyclical, seasonal, and irregular factors. A basic assumption in this model is that the four components are independent—for example, that the current magnitude of the cyclical component is not affected by that of the trend component. Consequently, we were able to isolate and measure the components separately. This approach, in which a time series is broken down into these four components one at a time, has become known as the "classical" method of time series analysis.

The classical time series model has two basic forms, which can be written as follows:

(32.2) $$Y = T \cdot C \cdot S \cdot I$$

(32.3) $$Y = T + C + S + I$$

Here Y is the current level of a series and T, C, S, and I are, respectively, the current levels of the trend, cyclical, seasonal, and irregular components. The two forms are called *multiplicative* and *additive* models respectively. Most analysts believe that the multiplicative form generally is more appropriate than the additive one for analysis of business and economic time series. For this reason, we have framed our discussion around the multiplicative model.

Under either form, the trend component is isolated by fitting a trend curve, and is measured in terms of absolute magnitudes. In the multiplicative form, the other components are measured in terms of ratios, usually per cents. In the additive model, on the other hand, the other components are measured in terms of positive or negative deviations. Thus, with the multiplicative model we measured the seasonal component by a method that gave per cent seasonal indexes that averaged to 100. Under the additive model we would use a procedure that gives positive or negative seasonal deviations that sum to zero. Similarly, the cyclical-random component is isolated under the multiplicative model by calculating per cents of trend (using deseasonalized data for a monthly or quarterly series), whereas positive or negative deviations from trend would be used with the additive form. For either model, a moving average of the cyclical-random component may be taken in an attempt to isolate the purely cyclical fluctuations.

Limitations of classical method. The classical method of time series analysis has proved to be a relatively practical and useful one for the solution of many types of problems that arise in administration and in economics, especially ones relating to long-term analysis or to short-term analysis involving seasonal fluctuations.

In the search for alternative conceptual approaches to time series analysis, however, the classical method has come under criticism. Many economists find this method to be unsatisfying because it is based on the study of movements in economic series rather than on the explicit application of economic concepts. Also, some critics point out that the classical method of isolating and measuring the components of a time series one by one is not the best conceptual approach to the problem of time series analysis. It has long been observed that the components of a time series are usually interrelated. For instance, the forces that determine long-term movements affect cyclical fluctuations also; forces that determine cyclical fluctuations also affect seasonal movements. Hence, it is felt that components of a time series should be estimated simultaneously instead of individually.

Econometric methods

Methods are available by which analysis of time series data can be related to explicit economic concepts, and components estimated simultaneously in systems of equations. These methods involve the *econometric* approach. Econometrics combines mathematical model building based on economic theory with statistical methodology for estimating the parameters of mathematical-economic models from observed data. Generally the estimation procedures are more complex than those discussed in this text.

Econometric methods have been employed to analyze time series data on growth, business-cycle behavior, and other phenomena in which changes are measured over time. In some areas of study, econometric methods offer an alternative to the classical method of time series analysis. In forecasting, specifically, econometric methods have been applied with some success to produce forecasts at the level of the aggregate economy, and in a few cases, an individual industry. Forecasting by econometric methods is rare at the level of the individual firm. At all levels, however, the classical method that we have discussed continues to be the method most widely used in day-to-day analysis of business and economic time series data.

32.4 EXPONENTIAL SMOOTHING

Statistical forecasting by either classical time series analysis or by econometric methods requires time and professional skill for good results. In certain instances, however, it does not pay to make forecasts for individual items or activities by means of these relatively costly procedures. Inventory management offers a case in point. Many companies must stock thousands of different types of spare parts, raw materials, components, and finished products. It could be prohibitively expensive, and impractical for other reasons as well, to employ the above-mentioned forecasting methods to predict demand or use for each of the thousands of items in inventory. Yet some type of forecasting approach is desirable so that carrying costs on the one hand, and out-of-stock costs on the other, can be controlled at reasonably low levels.

Analysts in recent years have experimented with a variety of mechanical forecasting methods that are fast, easy to apply, and capable of being handled routinely by electronic computers with a minimum of attention. One such method is *exponential smoothing.* It has been receiving increasing attention in business, and we discuss it briefly here.

The basic formula of exponential smoothing

In the basic method of exponential smoothing, the forecast of use or demand for an item in the period ahead is derived from two factors: (1) the forecast of use or demand applicable to the current period; (2) the extent to which actual use or demand in the current period differs from the forecast for this period.

The basic forecasting formula of exponential smoothing can be written as follows:

New forecast = Current forecast + w (Current demand − Current forecast)

where w is a weight that has a value somewhere between 0 and 1. By "new forecast" we mean the forecast made in the current period and applicable to the forthcoming period, and by "current forecast" we mean the forecast made in the previous period and applicable to the current period. Note that the new forecast is equal to current forecast plus an adjustment based on some fraction of the error in the current forecast.

Let F denote a forecast of demand and let D denote the actual demand. Suppose we denote the current period as period 0; the preceding period will then be designated as period −1, and the forthcoming period as period 1, and so on. Let F_0 be the forecast of demand in period 0; this forecast would be made in period −1. Similarly, F_1 stands for the forecast for period 1 (made in period 0). In the same fashion, let D_0 be the actual demand in the current period (0), D_{-1} the demand in the preceding period, and so on.

We now write the basic exponential smoothing formula as follows:

$$F_1 = F_0 + w(D_0 - F_0) \tag{32.4}$$

or:

$$F_1 = (1 - w)F_0 + wD_0 \tag{32.4a}$$

Note from (32.4a) that the only information required to calculate F_1 is the current level of demand, D_0, and the forecast F_0 that was calculated in the previous period for the current one.

The only information carried over from the previous period, then, is F_0. In turn, only the new value F_1, calculated in the current period, needs to be stored and carried over to the next period to calculate F_2. Thus, for each of the thousands of items covered by the forecasting system, only one number needs to be stored in the system at any one time. In operations where tens of thousands of different kinds of items are carried in inventory, this minimal requirement for data storage is a key advantage of exponential smoothing over alternative computer-oriented forecasting systems that require more data storage.

This is not to say, however, that past use or demand for an item is ignored in forecasting by exponential smoothing. Suppose that the exponential smoothing system had been applied for some time. Then, F_0 in (32.4a) was obtained by the same process whereby we obtained F_1, so that we obtain by changing subscripts in (32.4a):

$$F_0 = (1 - w)F_{-1} + wD_{-1}$$

but then we can write:

$$\begin{aligned} F_1 &= (1 - w)F_0 + wD_0 \\ &= (1 - w)[(1 - w)F_{-1} + wD_{-1}] + wD_0 \\ &= (1 - w)^2 F_{-1} + (1 - w)(w)D_{-1} + wD_0 \qquad (32.4b) \end{aligned}$$

In turn, F_{-1} was based on F_{-2}, so that we obtain:

$$\begin{aligned} F_1 &= (1 - w)^2[(1 - w)F_{-2} + wD_{-2}] + (1 - w)(w)D_{-1} + wD_0 \\ &= (1 - w)^3 F_{-2} + (1 - w)^2(w)D_{-2} + (1 - w)(w)D_{-1} + wD_0 \qquad (32.4c) \end{aligned}$$

Of course, F_{-2} consolidates experience represented by D_{-3}, D_{-4}, and so on, and these demand terms would appear explicitly if (32.4c) were expanded still further. Thus, the forecast for period 1 is based on the actual demand for all of the earlier periods; in fact, it is a weighted average of all of the earlier demands. Note, however, that the further the period is in the past, the smaller is the weight assigned to demand in that period with exponential smoothing. This can be recognized by recalling that $(1 - w)$ is a number between 0 and 1; hence, $(1 - w)^k$ becomes smaller as k increases. The speed of decline in the weights depends upon w. The higher the value of w, the more quickly do the weights become smaller for periods further in the past. To put this another way, the higher the value of w, the more the forecast depends upon demand experience in the most recent periods. The term *exponential smoothing* refers to the fact that the weight factor $(1 - w)$ receives a successively higher exponent, the further the period is in the past.

One of the problems of applying exponential smoothing is to determine the best value of w for each item. If w is too high, the forecast becomes overly sensitive to random movements in demand during the most recent periods. If w is too low, on the other hand, the forecasting system responds sluggishly to changes in the demand for the item. It has been suggested that in practice $w = .10$ is satisfactory for many items (Ref. 32.1). Of course, w can be changed from time to time as conditions warrant. Thus if management believes that a change in demand is occurring because of a special promotion, w can be increased temporarily so that the forecasting system will become more responsive to current movements in demand and less affected by demand in periods further in the past.

Example

To illustrate exponential smoothing, consider the case of an industrial adhesives manufacturer. Weekly demand for a certain glue is to be forecast by means of the basic exponential-smoothing formula (32.4), with $w = .10$. Suppose the forecast of demand for the current week is $F_0 = 875.9$ gallons.

If actual demand in the current week is $D_0 = 910$ gallons, the demand forecast for the next week is:

$$F_1 = F_0 + w(D_0 - F_0) = 875.9 + .10(910 - 875.9)$$
$$= 879.3 \text{ or } 879 \text{ gallons}$$

Similarly, if actual demand in the next week is $D_1 = 895$ gallons, then the demand forecast for the following week is:

$$F_2 = F_1 + w(D_1 - F_1) = 879.3 + .10(895 - 879.3)$$
$$= 880.9 \text{ or } 881 \text{ gallons}$$

The procedure is followed in this manner in subsequent weeks.

Extension of basic formula

The basic forecasting procedure represented by (32.4) is appropriate when trend and seasonal movements are negligible. However, if these movements are too important to overlook in forecasting demand for an item, the basic formula can be expanded, at an increase in data-storage requirements, so that trend and seasonal movements are taken into account in calculating the forecast of demand applicable to the period ahead.

Cited reference

32.1 Brown, Robert G., *Statistical Forecasting for Inventory Control.* New York: McGraw-Hill Book Company, Inc., 1959.

QUESTIONS AND PROBLEMS

***32.1. a.** Using formulas (32.1a) and (32.1b), calculate the linear trend equation for the personal consumption expenditures data in Problem 29.7 by the method of least squares.

b. For the trend equation obtained in part **a**, calculate the projected trend value for 1985. Must your projected trend value necessarily equal the projected trend value in Problem 29.7e? Discuss.

32.2. a. Using formulas (32.1a) and (32.1b), calculate the linear trend equation for the products series in Problem 29.8 by the method of least squares.

b. For the trend equation obtained in part **a**, calculate the projected trend value for 1982. Must this value be equal to the corresponding value in Problem 29.8**c**? Discuss.

32.3. In reducing an annual trend equation based on annual totals to a quarterly basis, a in the annual trend equation is divided by 4 but b is divided by 16. Why is b divided by 16 instead of by 4? Explain.

***32.4.** The linear trend equation for the annual personal consumption expenditures data in Problem 29.7 is: $\bar{Y}_X = 365.83 + 34.726X$, where $X = 0$ at 1963 and is in units of one year. Reduce this trend equation:

a. To the corresponding monthly trend equation centered on July 15, 1963.

b. To the corresponding quarterly trend equation centered at the middle of the third quarter, 1963.

32.5. Refer to Problem 32.4. How would the required calculations for converting the linear trend equation differ if the trend equation were based on average monthly personal consumption expenditures for the years 1963–1970? Explain.

32.6. Refer to Problem 31.25**b**. Suppose the series had been broken down into components in terms of the additive time series model instead of the multiplicative model. What features of the graphs would now be different? Be specific.

***32.7.** An inventory manager wishes to compare the forecasts that would have been developed for an item under different mechanical forecasting systems. Demand for this item had shifted downward last March because of a price increase. The following numbers of units were demanded in the past eight months:

Month	Jan.	Feb.	March	April	May	June	July	Aug.
Units	450	454	432	417	396	387	389	385

a. Obtain the monthly forecasts of demand for February through September inclusive that would be developed by the basic exponential-smoothing formula. Assume the forecast of demand for January—that is, $F_{\text{Jan.}}$—was 454.0 units, and that the weight factor is to be $w = .30$.

b. In calculating the forecasts in part **a**, what information did you have to carry over from one month to the next? What does this imply with respect to data-storage requirements in forecasting by the basic formula of exponential smoothing?

c. Suppose the weight factor had been set at $w = .10$ instead of at .30 as in part **a**. Obtain the forecasts with this weight factor and compare them with those in part **a**. Does a decrease in the weight factor make the forecasting system more sensitive or less sensitive to a basic shift in demand? Explain why, referring specifically to the basic exponential-smoothing formula.

d. If erratic or random movements in monthly demand are relatively large, would it be better to set the weight factor relatively low or relatively high? Explain.

e. If demand in March had been 442 units, the demand for all other months being the same, would the forecast of demand for April (using $w = .10$) be the same as that obtained in part **c**? Would the forecast of demand for September be the same as that in part **c**? Explain, referring specifically to the exponential-smoothing forecasting formula.

32.8. Refer to Problem 32.7. Answer all parts, but assume that demand for the item had shifted upward, starting in March, because of the unavailability of a substitute product. The following numbers of units were demanded:

Month	Jan.	Feb.	March	April	May	June	July	Aug.
Units	450	454	486	490	482	491	484	486

APPENDIX TABLES

Table A-1 Table of Areas for Standard Normal Probability Distribution

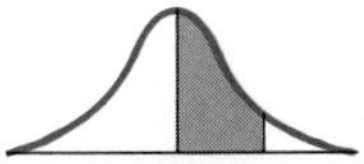

z	.00	.01	.02	.03	.04	.05	.06	.07	.08	.09
0.0	.0000	.0040	.0080	.0120	.0160	.0199	.0239	.0279	.0319	.0359
0.1	.0398	.0438	.0478	.0517	.0557	.0596	.0636	.0675	.0714	.0753
0.2	.0793	.0832	.0871	.0910	.0948	.0987	.1026	.1064	.1103	.1141
0.3	.1179	.1217	.1255	.1293	.1331	.1368	.1406	.1443	.1480	.1517
0.4	.1554	.1591	.1628	.1664	.1700	.1736	.1772	.1808	.1844	.1879
0.5	.1915	.1950	.1985	.2019	.2054	.2088	.2123	.2157	.2190	.2224
0.6	.2257	.2291	.2324	.2357	.2389	.2422	.2454	.2486	.2518	.2549
0.7	.2580	.2612	.2642	.2673	.2704	.2734	.2764	.2794	.2823	.2852
0.8	.2881	.2910	.2939	.2967	.2995	.3023	.3051	.3078	.3106	.3133
0.9	.3159	.3186	.3212	.3238	.3264	.3289	.3315	.3340	.3365	.3389
1.0	.3413	.3438	.3461	.3485	.3508	.3531	.3554	.3577	.3599	.3621
1.1	.3643	.3665	.3686	.3708	.3729	.3749	.3770	.3790	.3810	.3830
1.2	.3849	.3869	.3888	.3907	3925	.3944	.3962	.3980	.3997	.4015
1.3	.4032	.4049	.4066	.4082	.4099	.4115	.4131	.4147	.4162	.4177
1.4	.4192	.4207	.4222	.4236	.4251	.4265	.4279	.4292	.4306	.4319
1.5	.4332	.4345	.4357	.4370	.4382	.4394	.4406	.4418	.4429	.4441
1.6	.4452	.4463	.4474	.4484	.4495	.4505	.4515	.4525	.4535	.4545
1.7	.4554	.4564	.4573	.4582	.4591	.4599	.4608	.4616	.4625	.4633
1.8	.4641	.4649	.4656	.4664	.4671	.4678	.4686	.4693	.4699	.4706
1.9	.4713	.4719	.4726	.4732	.4738	.4744	.4750	.4756	.4761	.4767
2.0	.4772	.4778	.4783	.4788	.4793	.4798	.4803	.4808	.4812	.4817
2.1	.4821	.4826	.4830	.4834	.4838	.4842	.4846	.4850	.4854	.4857
2.2	.4861	.4864	.4868	.4871	.4875	.4878	.4881	.4884	.4887	.4890
2.3	.4893	.4896	.4898	.4901	.4904	.4906	.4909	.4911	.4913	.4916
2.4	.4918	.4920	.4922	.4925	.4927	.4929	.4931	.4932	.4934	.4936
2.5	.4938	.4940	.4941	.4943	.4945	.4946	.4948	.4949	.4951	.4952
2.6	.4953	.4955	.4956	.4957	.4959	.4960	.4961	.4962	.4963	.4964
2.7	.4965	.4966	.4967	.4968	.4969	.4970	.4971	.4972	.4973	.4974
2.8	.4974	.4975	.4976	.4977	.4977	.4978	.4979	.4979	.4980	.4981
2.9	.4981	.4982	.4982	.4983	.4984	.4984	.4985	.4985	.4986	.4986
3.0	.49865	.4987	.4987	.4988	.4988	.4989	.4989	.4989	.4990	.4990
4.0	.4999683									

Illustration: For $z = 1.93$, shaded area is .4732 out of total area of 1.

Table A-2 **Poisson Probabilities**

	μ_X									
X	0.1	0.2	0.3	0.4	0.5	0.6	0.7	0.8	0.9	1.0
0	.9048	.8187	.7408	.6703	.6065	.5488	.4966	.4493	.4066	.3679
1	.0905	.1637	.2222	.2681	.3033	.3293	.3476	.3595	.3659	.3679
2	.0045	.0164	.0333	.0536	.0758	.0988	.1217	.1438	.1647	.1839
3	.0002	.0011	.0033	.0072	.0126	.0198	.0284	.0383	.0494	.0613
4		.0001	.0002	.0007	.0016	.0030	.0050	.0077	.0111	.0153
5				.0001	.0002	.0004	.0007	.0012	.0020	.0031
6							.0001	.0002	.0003	.0005
7										.0001

	μ_X									
X	1.5	2.0	2.5	3.0	3.5	4.0	4.5	5.0	6.0	7.0
0	.2231	.1353	.0821	.0498	.0302	.0183	.0111	.0067	.0025	.0009
1	.3347	.2707	.2052	.1494	.1057	.0733	.0500	.0337	.0149	.0064
2	.2510	.2707	.2565	.2240	.1850	.1465	.1125	.0842	.0446	.0223
3	.1255	.1804	.2138	.2240	.2158	.1954	.1687	.1404	.0892	.0521
4	.0471	.0902	.1336	.1680	.1888	.1954	.1898	.1755	.1339	.0912
5	.0141	.0361	.0668	.1008	.1322	.1563	.1708	.1755	.1606	.1277
6	.0035	.0120	.0278	.0504	.0771	.1042	.1281	.1462	.1606	.1490
7	.0008	.0034	.0099	.0216	.0385	.0595	.0824	.1044	.1377	.1490
8	.0001	.0009	.0031	.0081	.0169	.0298	.0463	.0653	.1033	.1304
9		.0002	.0009	.0027	.0066	.0132	.0232	.0363	.0688	.1014
10			.0002	.0008	.0023	.0053	.0104	.0181	.0413	.0710
11				.0002	.0007	.0019	.0043	.0082	.0225	.0452
12				.0001	.0002	.0006	.0016	.0034	.0113	.0264
13					.0001	.0002	.0006	.0013	.0052	.0142
14						.0001	.0002	.0005	.0022	.0071
15							.0001	.0002	.0009	.0033
16									.0003	.0014
17									.0001	.0006
18										.0002
19										.0001

Example: If $\mu_X = 1$, $P(X = 2) = .1839$.

Source: Abridged from E. C. Molina, *Poisson's Exponential Binomial Limit*. New York: D. Van Nostrand Company, Inc., 1949, by permission of the author and publishers.

Table A-3 Probabilities in Right Tail of Exponential Probability Distribution

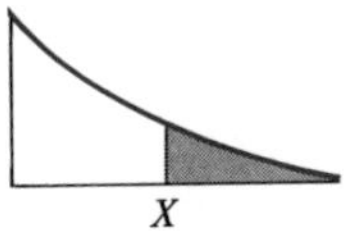

$\frac{X}{\mu_X}$	*Prob.*	$\frac{X}{\mu_X}$	*Prob.*	$\frac{X}{\mu_X}$	*Prob.*	$\frac{X}{\mu_X}$	*Prob.*
0.0	1.000	2.5	0.082	5.0	0.0067	7.5	0.00055
0.1	0.905	2.6	0.074	5.1	0.0061	7.6	0.00050
0.2	0.819	2.7	0.067	5.2	0.0055	7.7	0.00045
0.3	0.741	2.8	0.061	5.3	0.0050	7.8	0.00041
0.4	0.670	2.9	0.055	5.4	0.0045	7.9	0.00037
0.5	0.607	3.0	0.050	5.5	0.0041	8.0	0.00034
0.6	0.549	3.1	0.045	5.6	0.0037	8.1	0.00030
0.7	0.497	3.2	0.041	5.7	0.0033	8.2	0.00028
0.8	0.449	3.3	0.037	5.8	0.0030	8.3	0.00025
0.9	0.407	3.4	0.033	5.9	0.0027	8.4	0.00022
1.0	0.368	3.5	0.030	6.0	0.0025	8.5	0.00020
1.1	0.333	3.6	0.027	6.1	0.0022	8.6	0.00018
1.2	0.301	3.7	0.025	6.2	0.0020	8.7	0.00017
1.3	0.273	3.8	0.022	6.3	0.0018	8.8	0.00015
1.4	0.247	3.9	0.020	6.4	0.0017	8.9	0.00014
1.5	0.223	4.0	0.018	6.5	0.0015	9.0	0.00012
1.6	0.202	4.1	0.017	6.6	0.0014	9.1	0.00011
1.7	0.183	4.2	0.015	6.7	0.0012	9.2	0.00010
1.8	0.165	4.3	0.014	6.8	0.0011	9.3	0.00009
1.9	0.150	4.4	0.012	6.9	0.0010	9.4	0.00008
2.0	0.135	4.5	0.011	7.0	0.0009	9.5	0.00008
2.1	0.122	4.6	0.010	7.1	0.0008	9.6	0.00007
2.2	0.111	4.7	0.009	7.2	0.0007	9.7	0.00006
2.3	0.100	4.8	0.008	7.3	0.0007	9.8	0.00006
2.4	0.091	4.9	0.007	7.4	0.0006	9.9	0.00005

Illustration: If $\mu_X = 600$, the probability of exceeding $X = 900$ is .223.

Table A-4 Binomial Probabilities

n	$\bar{p}$	p = .05	.10	.15	.20	.25	.30	.35	.40	.45	.50
2	0	.9025	.8100	.7225	.6400	.5625	.4900	.4225	.3600	.3025	.2500
	$\frac{1}{2}$	.0950	.1800	.2550	.3200	.3750	.4200	.4550	.4800	.4950	.5000
	1	.0025	.0100	.0225	.0400	.0625	.0900	.1225	.1600	.2025	.2500
3	0	.8574	.7290	.6141	.5120	.4219	.3430	.2746	.2160	.1664	.1250
	$\frac{1}{3}$	.1354	.2430	.3251	.3840	.4219	.4410	.4436	.4320	.4084	.3750
	$\frac{2}{3}$	.0071	.0270	.0574	.0960	.1406	.1890	.2389	.2880	.3341	.3750
	1	.0001	.0010	.0034	.0080	.0156	.0270	.0429	.0640	.0911	.1250
4	0	.8145	.6561	.5220	.4096	.3164	.2401	.1785	.1296	.0915	.0625
	$\frac{1}{4}$	.1715	.2916	.3685	.4096	.4219	.4116	.3845	.3456	.2995	.2500
	$\frac{2}{4}$	.0135	.0486	.0975	.1536	.2109	.2646	.3105	.3456	.3675	.3750
	$\frac{3}{4}$	.0005	.0036	.0115	.0256	.0469	.0756	.1115	.1536	.2005	.2500
	1		.0001	.0005	.0016	.0039	.0081	.0150	.0256	.0410	.0625
5	0	.7738	.5905	.4437	.3277	.2373	.1681	.1160	.0778	.0503	.0312
	$\frac{1}{5}$	.2036	.3280	.3915	.4096	.3955	.3602	.3124	.2592	.2059	.1562
	$\frac{2}{5}$	.0214	.0729	.1382	.2048	.2637	.3087	.3364	.3456	.3369	.3125
	$\frac{3}{5}$	.0011	.0081	.0244	.0512	.0879	.1323	.1811	.2304	.2757	.3125
	$\frac{4}{5}$		.0004	.0022	.0064	.0146	.0284	.0488	.0768	.1128	.1562
	1			.0001	.0003	.0010	.0024	.0053	.0102	.0185	.0312
6	0	.7351	.5314	.3771	.2621	.1780	.1176	.0754	.0467	.0277	.0156
	$\frac{1}{6}$	.2321	.3543	.3993	.3932	.3560	.3025	.2437	.1866	.1359	.0938
	$\frac{2}{6}$	.0305	.0984	.1762	.2458	.2966	.3241	.3280	.3110	.2780	.2344
	$\frac{3}{6}$	.0021	.0146	.0415	.0819	.1318	.1852	.2355	.2765	.3032	.3125
	$\frac{4}{6}$	.0001	.0012	.0055	.0154	.0330	.0595	.0951	.1382	.1861	.2344
	$\frac{5}{6}$		.0001	.0004	.0015	.0044	.0102	.0205	.0369	.0609	.0938
	1				.0001	.0002	.0007	.0018	.0041	.0083	.0156
7	0	.6983	.4783	.3206	.2097	.1335	.0824	.0490	.0280	.0152	.0078
	$\frac{1}{7}$	.2573	.3720	.3960	.3670	.3115	.2471	.1848	.1306	.0872	.0547
	$\frac{2}{7}$	.0406	.1240	.2097	.2753	.3115	.3177	.2985	.2613	.2140	.1641
	$\frac{3}{7}$	.0036	.0230	.0617	.1147	.1730	.2269	.2679	.2903	.2918	.2734
	$\frac{4}{7}$	.0002	.0026	.0109	.0287	.0577	.0972	.1442	.1935	.2388	.2734
	$\frac{5}{7}$		.0002	.0012	.0043	.0115	.0250	.0466	.0774	.1172	.1641
	$\frac{6}{7}$			.0001	.0004	.0013	.0036	.0084	.0172	.0320	.0547
	1					.0001	.0002	.0006	.0016	.0037	.0078
8	0	.6634	.4305	.2725	.1678	.1001	.0576	.0319	.0168	.0084	.0039
	$\frac{1}{8}$	.2793	.3826	.3847	.3355	.2670	.1977	.1373	.0896	.0548	.0312
	$\frac{2}{8}$	.0515	.1488	.2376	.2936	.3115	.2965	.2587	.2090	.1569	.1094
	$\frac{3}{8}$	.0054	.0331	.0839	.1468	.2076	.2541	.2786	.2787	.2568	.2188
	$\frac{4}{8}$	.0004	.0046	.0185	.0459	.0865	.1361	.1875	.2322	.2627	.2734
	$\frac{5}{8}$		.0004	.0026	.0092	.0231	.0467	.0808	.1239	.1719	.2188
	$\frac{6}{8}$			.0002	.0011	.0038	.0100	.0217	.0413	.0703	.1094
	$\frac{7}{8}$				.0001	.0004	.0012	.0033	.0079	.0164	.0312
	1						.0001	.0002	.0007	.0017	.0039

Example: If $p = .25$, $n = 5$, $P(\bar{p} = 3/5) = .0879$.

Table A-5 Table of *t*-Distribution

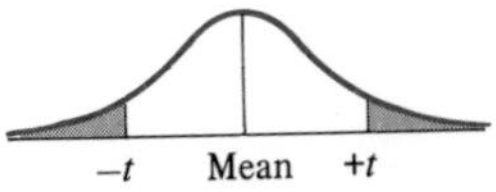

Degrees of Freedom	Total Area in Both Tails .10	.05	.02	.01
1	6.314	12.706	31.821	63.657
2	2.920	4.303	6.965	9.925
3	2.353	3.182	4.541	5.841
4	2.132	2.776	3.747	4.604
5	2.015	2.571	3.365	4.032
6	1.943	2.447	3.143	3.707
7	1.895	2.365	2.998	3.499
8	1.860	2.306	2.896	3.355
9	1.833	2.262	2.821	3.250
10	1.812	2.228	2.764	3.169
11	1.796	2.201	2.718	3.106
12	1.782	2.179	2.681	3.055
13	1.771	2.160	2.650	3.012
14	1.761	2.145	2.624	2.977
15	1.753	2.131	2.602	2.947
16	1.746	2.120	2.583	2.921
17	1.740	2.110	2.567	2.898
18	1.734	2.101	2.552	2.878
19	1.729	2.093	2.539	2.861
20	1.725	2.086	2.528	2.845
21	1.721	2.080	2.518	2.831
22	1.717	2.074	2.508	2.819
23	1.714	2.069	2.500	2.807
24	1.711	2.064	2.492	2.797
25	1.708	2.060	2.485	2.787
26	1.706	2.056	2.479	2.779
27	1.703	2.052	2.473	2.771
28	1.701	2.048	2.467	2.763
29	1.699	2.045	2.462	2.756
30	1.697	2.042	2.457	2.750
40	1.684	2.021	2.423	2.704
Normal Distribution	1.645	1.960	2.326	2.576

Illustration: The *t*-value for 9 degrees of freedom corresponding to area of .05 in both tails is 2.262.

Source: Abridged from Table III of Fisher and Yates, *Statistical Tables for Biological, Agricultural, and Medical Research*, 4th ed., 1953, published by Oliver and Boyd Ltd., Edinburgh, by permission of the authors and publishers.

Table A-6 Table of χ^2 Distribution

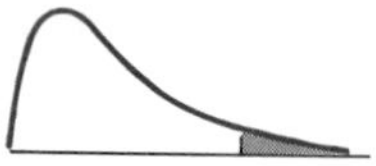

Degrees of Freedom δ	*Area in Right Tail* .10	.05	.02	.01
1	2.706	3.841	5.412	6.635
2	4.605	5.991	7.824	9.210
3	6.251	7.815	9.837	11.345
4	7.779	9.488	11.668	13.277
5	9.236	11.070	13.388	15.086
6	10.645	12.592	15.033	16.812
7	12.017	14.067	16.622	18.475
8	13.362	15.507	18.168	20.090
9	14.684	16.919	19.679	21.666
10	15.987	18.307	21.161	23.209
11	17.275	19.675	22.618	24.725
12	18.549	21.026	24.054	26.217
13	19.812	22.362	25.472	27.688
14	21.064	23.685	26.873	29.141
15	22.307	24.996	28.259	30.578
16	23.542	26.296	29.633	32.000
17	24.769	27.587	30.995	33.409
18	25.989	28.869	32.346	34.805
19	27.204	30.144	33.687	36.191
20	28.412	31.410	35.020	37.566
21	29.615	32.671	36.343	38.932
22	30.813	33.924	37.659	40.289
23	32.007	35.172	38.968	41.638
24	33.196	36.415	40.270	42.980
25	34.382	37.652	41.566	44.314
26	35.563	38.885	42.856	45.642
27	36.741	40.113	44.140	46.963
28	37.916	41.337	45.419	48.278
29	39.087	42.557	46.693	49.588
30	40.256	43.773	47.962	50.892

Illustration: The value on the χ^2 scale for $\delta = 4$ associated with an area .02 in the right tail is 11.668.

Source: Abridged from Table IV of Fisher and Yates, *Statistical Tables for Biological, Agricultural, and Medical Research*, 6th ed., 1963, published by Oliver and Boyd Ltd., Edinburgh, by permission of the authors and publishers.

Table A-7 Table of *F*-Distribution

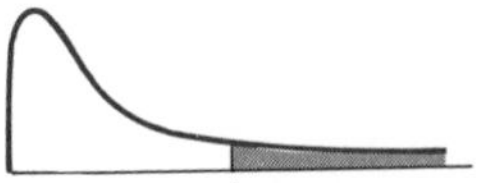

F–scale value corresponding to area .05 in right tail in light-face type
F–scale value corresponding to area .01 in right tail in bold-face type

δ_1 = Degrees of Freedom of MS_1	δ_2 = Degrees of Freedom of MS_2									
	1	2	3	4	5	6	7	8	9	10
1	161	200	216	225	230	234	237	239	241	242
	4,052	**4,999**	**5,403**	**5,625**	**5,764**	**5,859**	**5,928**	**5,981**	**6,022**	**6,056**
2	18.51	19.00	19.16	19.25	19.30	19.33	19.36	19.37	19.38	19.39
	98.49	**99.00**	**99.17**	**99.25**	**99.30**	**99.33**	**99.34**	**99.36**	**99.38**	**99.40**
3	10.13	9.55	9.28	9.12	9.01	8.94	8.88	8.84	8.81	8.78
	34.12	**30.82**	**29.46**	**28.71**	**28.24**	**27.91**	**27.67**	**27.49**	**27.34**	**27.23**
4	7.71	6.94	6.59	6.39	6.26	6.16	6.09	6.04	6.00	5.96
	21.20	**18.00**	**16.69**	**15.98**	**15.52**	**15.21**	**14.98**	**14.80**	**14.66**	**14.54**
5	6.61	5.79	5.41	5.19	5.05	4.95	4.88	4.82	4.78	4.74
	16.26	**13.27**	**12.06**	**11.39**	**10.97**	**10.67**	**10.45**	**10.27**	**10.15**	**10.05**
6	5.99	5.14	4.76	4.53	4.39	4.28	4.21	4.15	4.10	4.06
	13.74	**10.92**	**9.78**	**9.15**	**8.75**	**8.47**	**8.26**	**8.10**	**7.98**	**7.87**
7	5.59	4.74	4.35	4.12	3.97	3.87	3.79	3.73	3.68	3.63
	12.25	**9.55**	**8.45**	**7.85**	**7.46**	**7.19**	**7.00**	**6.84**	**6.71**	**6.62**
8	5.32	4.46	4.07	3.84	3.69	3.58	3.50	3.44	3.39	3.34
	11.26	**8.65**	**7.59**	**7.01**	**6.63**	**6.37**	**6.19**	**6.03**	**5.91**	**5.82**
9	5.12	4.26	3.86	3.63	3.48	3.37	3.29	3.23	3.18	3.13
	10.56	**8.02**	**6.99**	**6.42**	**6.06**	**5.80**	**5.62**	**5.47**	**5.35**	**5.26**
10	4.96	4.10	3.71	3.48	3.33	3.22	3.14	3.07	3.02	2.97
	10.04	**7.56**	**6.55**	**5.99**	**5.64**	**5.39**	**5.21**	**5.06**	**4.95**	**4.85**
11	4.84	3.98	3.59	3.36	3.20	3.09	3.01	2.95	2.90	2.86
	9.65	**7.20**	**6.22**	**5.67**	**5.32**	**5.07**	**4.88**	**4.74**	**4.63**	**4.54**

(Continued)

Table A-7 Table of *F*-Distribution (Continued)

δ_1 = *Degrees of Freedom of* MS_1	δ_2 = *Degrees of Freedom of* MS_2									
	1	2	3	4	5	6	7	8	9	10
12	4.75	3.88	3.49	3.26	3.11	3.00	2.92	2.85	2.80	2.76
	9.33	**6.93**	**5.95**	**5.41**	**5.06**	**4.82**	**4.65**	**4.50**	**4.39**	**4.30**
13	4.67	3.80	3.41	3.18	3.02	2.92	2.84	2.77	2.72	2.67
	9.07	**6.70**	**5.74**	**5.20**	**4.86**	**4.62**	**4.44**	**4.30**	**4.19**	**4.10**
14	4.60	3.74	3.34	3.11	2.96	2.85	2.77	2.70	2.65	2.60
	8.86	**6.51**	**5.56**	**5.03**	**4.69**	**4.46**	**4.28**	**4.14**	**4.03**	**3.94**
15	4.54	3.68	3.29	3.06	2.90	2.79	2.70	2.64	2.59	2.55
	8.68	**6.36**	**5.42**	**4.89**	**4.56**	**4.32**	**4.14**	**4.00**	**3.89**	**3.80**
16	4.49	3.63	3.24	3.01	2.85	2.74	2.66	2.59	2.54	2.49
	8.53	**6.23**	**5.29**	**4.77**	**4.44**	**4.20**	**4.03**	**3.89**	**3.78**	**3.69**
17	4.45	3.59	3.20	2.96	2.81	2.70	2.62	2.55	2.50	2.45
	8.40	**6.11**	**5.18**	**4.67**	**4.34**	**4.10**	**3.93**	**3.79**	**3.68**	**3.59**
18	4.41	3.55	3.16	2.93	2.77	2.66	2.58	2.51	2.46	2.41
	8.28	**6.01**	**5.09**	**4.58**	**4.25**	**4.01**	**3.85**	**3.71**	**3.60**	**3.51**
19	4.38	3.52	3.13	2.90	2.74	2.63	2.55	2.48	2.43	2.38
	8.18	**5.93**	**5.01**	**4.50**	**4.17**	**3.94**	**3.77**	**3.63**	**3.52**	**3.43**
20	4.35	3.49	3.10	2.87	2.71	2.60	2.52	2.45	2.40	2.35
	8.10	**5.85**	**4.94**	**4.43**	**4.10**	**3.87**	**3.71**	**3.56**	**3.45**	**3.37**
21	4.32	3.47	3.07	2.84	2.68	2.57	2.49	2.42	2.37	2.32
	8.02	**5.78**	**4.87**	**4.37**	**4.04**	**3.81**	**3.65**	**3.51**	**3.40**	**3.31**
22	4.30	3.44	3.05	2.82	2.66	2.55	2.47	2.40	2.35	2.30
	7.94	**5.72**	**4.82**	**4.31**	**3.99**	**3.76**	**3.59**	**3.45**	**3.35**	**3.26**
23	4.28	3.42	3.03	2.80	2.64	2.53	2.45	2.38	2.32	2.28
	7.88	**5.66**	**4.76**	**4.26**	**3.94**	**3.71**	**3.54**	**3.41**	**3.30**	**3.21**
24	4.26	3.40	3.01	2.78	2.62	2.51	2.43	2.36	2.30	2.26
	7.82	**5.61**	**4.72**	**4.22**	**3.90**	**3.67**	**3.50**	**3.36**	**3.25**	**3.17**
25	4.24	3.38	2.99	2.76	2.60	2.49	2.41	2.34	2.28	2.24
	7.77	**5.57**	**4.68**	**4.18**	**3.86**	**3.63**	**3.46**	**3.32**	**3.21**	**3.13**

Illustration: The *F*-scale value for $\delta_2 = 3$, $\delta_1 = 10$ corresponding to area .01 in right tail is 6.55.

Source: Abridged from Table 10.5.3 of George W. Snedecor, *Statistical Methods*, 5th ed., Iowa State University Press, Ames, Iowa, 1956, by permission of the author and publisher.

Table A-8 Table of Unit Normal Loss

D	.00	.01	.02	.03	.04	.05	.06	.07	.08	.09
.0	.3989	.3940	.3890	.3841	.3793	.3744	.3697	.3649	.3602	.3556
.1	.3509	.3464	.3418	.3373	.3328	.3284	.3240	.3197	.3154	.3111
.2	.3069	.3027	.2986	.2944	.2904	.2863	.2824	.2784	.2745	.2706
.3	.2668	.2630	.2592	.2555	.2518	.2481	.2445	.2409	.2374	.2339
.4	.2304	.2270	.2236	.2203	.2169	.2137	.2104	.2072	.2040	.2009
.5	.1978	.1947	.1917	.1887	.1857	.1828	.1799	.1771	.1742	.1714
.6	.1687	.1659	.1633	.1606	.1580	.1554	.1528	.1503	.1478	.1453
.7	.1429	.1405	.1381	.1358	.1334	.1312	.1289	.1267	.1245	.1223
.8	.1202	.1181	.1160	.1140	.1120	.1100	.1080	.1061	.1042	.1023
.9	.1004	.09860	.09680	.09503	.09328	.09156	.08986	.08819	.08654	.08491
1.0	.08332	.08174	.08019	.07866	.07716	.07568	.07422	.07279	.07138	.06999
1.1	.06862	.06727	.06595	.06465	.06336	.06210	.06086	.05964	.05844	.05726
1.2	.05610	.05496	.05384	.05274	.05165	.05059	.04954	.04851	.04750	.04650
1.3	.04553	.04457	.04363	.04270	.04179	.04090	.04002	.03916	.03831	.03748
1.4	.03667	.03587	.03508	.03431	.03356	.03281	.03208	.03137	.03067	.02998
1.5	.02931	.02865	.02800	.02736	.02674	.02612	.02552	.02494	.02436	.02380
1.6	.02324	.02270	.02217	.02165	.02114	.02064	.02015	.01967	.01920	.01874
1.7	.01829	.01785	.01742	.01699	.01658	.01617	.01578	.01539	.01501	.01464
1.8	.01428	.01392	.01357	.01323	.01290	.01257	.01226	.01195	.01164	.01134
1.9	.01105	.01077	.01049	.01022	$.0^{2}9957$	$.0^{2}9698$	$.0^{2}9445$	$.0^{2}9198$	$.0^{2}8957$	$.0^{2}8721$
2.0	$.0^{2}8491$	$.0^{2}8266$	$.0^{2}8046$	$.0^{2}7832$	$.0^{2}7623$	$.0^{2}7418$	$.0^{2}7219$	$.0^{2}7024$	$.0^{2}6835$	$.0^{2}6649$
2.1	$.0^{2}6468$	$.0^{2}6292$	$.0^{2}6120$	$.0^{2}5952$	$.0^{2}5788$	$.0^{2}5628$	$.0^{2}5472$	$.0^{2}5320$	$.0^{2}5172$	$.0^{2}5028$
2.2	$.0^{2}4887$	$.0^{2}4750$	$.0^{2}4616$	$.0^{2}4486$	$.0^{2}4358$	$.0^{2}4235$	$.0^{2}4114$	$.0^{2}3996$	$.0^{2}3882$	$.0^{2}3770$
2.3	$.0^{2}3662$	$.0^{2}3556$	$.0^{2}3453$	$.0^{2}3352$	$.0^{2}3255$	$.0^{2}3159$	$.0^{2}3067$	$.0^{2}2977$	$.0^{2}2889$	$.0^{2}2804$
2.4	$.0^{2}2720$	$.0^{2}2640$	$.0^{2}2561$	$.0^{2}2484$	$.0^{2}2410$	$.0^{2}2337$	$.0^{2}2267$	$.0^{2}2199$	$.0^{2}2132$	$.0^{2}2067$
2.5	$.0^{2}2004$	$.0^{2}1943$	$.0^{2}1883$	$.0^{2}1826$	$.0^{2}1769$	$.0^{2}1715$	$.0^{2}1662$	$.0^{2}1610$	$.0^{2}1560$	$.0^{2}1511$
3.0	$.0^{3}3822$	$.0^{3}3689$	$.0^{3}3560$	$.0^{3}3436$	$.0^{3}3316$	$.0^{3}3199$	$.0^{3}3087$	$.0^{3}2978$	$.0^{3}2873$	$.0^{3}2771$
3.5	$.0^{4}5848$	$.0^{4}5620$	$.0^{4}5400$	$.0^{4}5188$	$.0^{4}4984$	$.0^{4}4788$	$.0^{4}4599$	$.0^{4}4417$	$.0^{4}4242$	$.0^{4}4073$
4.0	$.0^{5}7145$	$.0^{5}6835$	$.0^{5}6538$	$.0^{5}6253$	$.0^{5}5980$	$.0^{5}5718$	$.0^{5}5468$	$.0^{5}5227$	$.0^{5}4997$	$.0^{5}4777$

Illustration: The value of $L(D)$ for $D = 3.01$ is $.0^{3}3689 = .0003689$.

Source: These Tables of "Unit Normal Loss Integral" appear in *Introduction to Statistics for Business Decisions* by Robert Schlaifer, published by McGraw-Hill Book Company, Inc., 1961. They are reproduced here by specific permission of the copyright holder, The President and Fellows of Harvard College.

Table A-9 Five-Place Logarithms

N	0	1	2	3	4	5	6	7	8	9
0	$-\infty$	00000	30103	47712	60206	69897	77815	84510	90309	95424
10	00000	00432	00860	01284	01703	02119	02531	02938	03342	03743
11	04139	04532	04922	05308	05690	06070	06446	06819	07188	07555
12	07918	08279	08636	08991	09342	09691	10037	10380	10721	11059
13	11394	11727	12057	12385	12710	13033	13354	13672	13988	14301
14	14613	14922	15229	15534	15836	16137	16435	16732	17026	17319
15	17609	17898	18184	18469	18752	19033	19312	19590	19866	20140
16	20412	20683	20952	21219	21484	21748	22011	22272	22531	22789
17	23045	23300	23533	23805	24055	24304	24551	24797	25042	25285
18	25527	25768	26007	26245	26482	26717	26951	27184	27416	27646
19	27875	28103	28330	28556	28780	29003	29226	29447	29667	29885
20	30103	30320	30535	30750	30963	31175	31387	31597	31806	32015
21	32222	32428	32634	32838	33041	33244	33445	33646	33846	34044
22	34242	34439	34635	34830	35025	35218	35411	35603	35793	35984
23	36173	36361	36549	36736	36922	37107	37291	37475	37658	37840
24	38021	38202	38382	38561	38739	38917	39094	39270	39445	39620
25	39794	39967	40140	40312	40483	40654	40824	40993	41162	41330
26	41497	41664	41830	41996	42160	42325	42488	42651	42813	42975
27	43136	43297	43457	43616	43775	43933	44091	44248	44404	44560
28	44716	44871	45025	45179	45332	45484	45637	45788	45939	46090
29	46240	46389	46538	46687	46835	46982	47129	47276	47422	47567
30	47712	47857	48001	48144	48287	48430	48572	48714	48855	48996
31	49136	49276	49415	49554	49693	49831	49969	50106	50243	50379
32	50515	50651	50786	50920	51055	51188	51322	51455	51587	51720
33	51851	51983	52114	52244	52375	52504	52634	52763	52892	53020
34	53148	53275	53403	53529	53656	53782	53908	54033	54158	54283
35	54407	54531	54654	54777	54900	55023	55145	55267	55388	55509
36	55630	55751	55871	55991	56110	56229	56348	56467	56585	56703
37	56820	56937	57054	57171	57287	57403	57519	57634	57749	57864
38	57978	58092	58206	58320	58433	58546	58659	58771	58883	58995
39	59106	59218	59329	59439	59550	59660	59770	59879	59988	60097
40	60206	60314	60423	60531	60638	60746	60853	60959	61066	61172
41	61278	61384	61490	61595	61700	61805	61909	62014	62118	62221
42	62325	62428	62531	62634	62737	62839	62941	63043	63144	63246
43	63347	63448	63548	63649	63749	63849	63949	64048	64147	64246
44	64345	64444	64542	64640	64738	64836	64933	65031	65128	65225
45	65321	65418	65514	65610	65706	65801	65896	65992	66087	66181
46	66276	66370	66464	66558	66652	66745	66839	66932	67025	67117
47	67210	67302	67394	67486	67578	67669	67761	67852	67943	68034
48	68124	68215	68305	68395	68485	68574	68664	68753	68842	68931
49	69020	69108	69197	69285	69373	69461	69548	69636	69723	69810

(*Continued*)

Table A-9 Five-Place Logarithms (Continued)

N	0	1	2	3	4	5	6	7	8	9
50	69897	69984	70070	70157	70243	70329	70415	70501	70586	70672
51	70757	70842	70927	71012	71096	71181	71265	71349	71433	71517
52	71600	71684	71767	71850	71933	72016	72099	72181	72263	72346
53	72428	72509	72591	72673	72754	72835	72916	72997	73078	73159
54	73239	73320	73400	73480	73560	73640	73719	73799	73878	73957
55	74036	74115	74194	74273	74351	74429	74507	74586	74663	74741
56	74819	74896	74974	75051	75128	75205	75282	75358	75435	75511
57	75587	75664	75740	75815	75891	75967	76042	76118	76193	76268
58	76343	76418	76492	76567	76641	76716	76790	76864	76938	77012
59	77085	77159	77232	77305	77379	77452	77525	77597	77670	77743
60	77815	77887	77960	78032	78104	78176	78247	78319	78390	78462
61	78533	78604	78675	78746	78817	78888	78958	79029	79099	79169
62	79239	79309	79379	79449	79518	79588	79657	79727	79796	79865
63	79934	80003	80072	80140	80209	80277	80346	80414	80482	80550
64	80618	80686	80754	80821	80889	80956	81023	81090	81158	81224
65	81291	81358	81425	81491	81558	81624	81690	81757	81823	81889
66	81954	82020	82086	82151	82217	82282	82347	82413	82478	82543
67	82607	82672	82737	82802	82866	82930	82995	83059	83123	83187
68	83251	83315	83378	83442	83506	83569	83632	83696	83759	83822
69	83885	83948	84011	84073	84136	84198	84261	84323	84386	84448
70	84510	84572	84634	84696	84757	84819	84880	84942	85003	85065
71	85126	85187	85248	85309	85370	85431	85491	85552	85612	85673
72	85733	85794	85854	85914	85974	86034	86094	86153	86213	86273
73	86332	86392	86451	86510	86570	86629	86688	86747	86806	86864
74	86923	86982	87040	87099	87157	87216	87274	87332	87390	87448
75	87506	87564	87622	87679	87737	87795	87852	87910	87967	88024
76	88081	88138	88195	88252	88309	88366	88423	88480	88536	88593
77	88649	88705	88762	88818	88874	88930	88986	89042	89098	89154
78	89209	89265	89321	89376	89432	89487	89542	89597	89653	89708
79	89763	89818	89873	89927	89982	90037	90091	90146	90200	90255
80	90309	90363	90417	90472	90526	90580	90634	90687	90741	90795
81	90849	90902	90956	91009	91062	91116	91169	91222	91275	91328
82	91381	91434	91487	91540	91593	91645	91698	91751	91803	91855
83	91908	91960	92012	92065	92117	92169	92221	92273	92324	92376
84	92428	92480	92531	92583	92634	92686	92737	92788	92840	92891
85	92942	92993	93044	93095	93146	93197	93247	93298	93349	93399
86	93450	93500	93551	93601	93651	93702	93752	93802	93852	93902
87	93952	94002	94052	94101	94151	94201	94250	94300	94349	94399
88	94448	94498	94547	94596	94645	94694	94743	94792	94841	94890
89	94939	94988	95036	95085	95134	95182	95231	95279	95328	95376
90	95424	95472	95521	95569	95617	95665	95713	95761	95809	95856
91	95904	95952	95999	96047	96095	96142	96190	96237	96284	96332
92	96379	96426	96473	96520	96567	96614	96661	96708	96755	96802
93	96848	96895	96942	96988	97035	97081	97128	97174	97220	97267
94	97313	97359	97405	97451	97497	97543	97589	97635	97681	97727
95	97772	97818	97864	97909	97955	98000	98046	98091	98137	98182
96	98227	98272	98318	98363	98408	98453	98498	98543	98588	98632
97	98677	98722	98767	98811	98856	98900	98945	98989	99034	99078
98	99123	99167	99211	99255	99300	99344	99388	99432	99476	99520
99	99564	99607	99651	99695	99739	99782	99826	99870	99913	99957

Table A-10 Squares, Square Roots, and Reciprocals 1–1000

N	N^2	$\sqrt{N}$	$\sqrt{10N}$	$1/N$
1	1	1.000 000	3.162 278	1.0000000
2	4	1.414 214	4.472 136	.5000000
3	9	1.732 051	5.477 226	.3333333
4	16	2.000 000	6.324 555	.2500000
5	25	2.236 068	7.071 068	.2000000
6	36	2.449 490	7.745 967	.1666667
7	49	2.645 751	8.366 600	.1428571
8	64	2.828 427	8.944 272	.1250000
9	81	3.000 000	9.486 833	.1111111
10	100	3.162 278	10.00000	.1000000
11	121	3.316 625	10.48809	.09090909
12	144	3.464 102	10.95445	.08333333
13	169	3.605 551	11.40175	.07692308
14	196	3.741 657	11.83216	.07142857
15	225	3.872 983	12.24745	.06666667
16	256	4.000 000	12.64911	.06250000
17	289	4.123 106	13.03840	.05882353
18	324	4.242 641	13.41641	.05555556
19	361	4.358 899	13.78405	.05263158
20	400	4.472 136	14.14214	.05000000
21	441	4.582 576	14.49138	.04761905
22	484	4.690 416	14.83240	.04545455
23	529	4.795 832	15.16575	.04347826
24	576	4.898 979	15.49193	.04166667
25	625	5.000 000	15.81139	.04000000
26	676	5.099 020	16.12452	.03846154
27	729	5.196 152	16.43168	.03703704
28	784	5.291 503	16.73320	.03571429
29	841	5.385 165	17.02939	.03448276
30	900	5.477 226	17.32051	.03333333
31	961	5.567 874	17.60682	.03225806
32	1 024	5.656 854	17.88854	.03125000
33	1 089	5.744 563	18.16590	.03030303
34	1 156	5.830 952	18.43909	.02941176
35	1 225	5.916 080	18.70829	.02857143
36	1 296	6.000 000	18.97367	.02777778
37	1 369	6.082 763	19.23538	.02702703
38	1 444	6.164 414	19.49359	.02631579
39	1 521	6.244 998	19.74842	.02564103
40	1 600	6.324 555	20.00000	.02500000
41	1 681	6.403 124	20.24846	.02439024
42	1 764	6.480 741	20.49390	.02380952
43	1 849	6.557 439	20.73644	.02325581
44	1 936	6.633 250	20.97618	.02272727
45	2 025	6.708 204	21.21320	.02222222
46	2 116	6.782 330	21.44761	.02173913
47	2 209	6.855 655	21.67948	.02127660
48	2 304	6.928 203	21.90890	.02083333
49	2 401	7.000 000	22.13594	.02040816
50	2 500	7.071 068	22.36068	.02000000

N	N^2	$\sqrt{N}$	$\sqrt{10N}$	$1/N$ .0
50	2 500	7.071 068	22.36068	2000000
51	2 601	7.141 428	22.58318	1960784
52	2 704	7.211 103	22.80351	1923077
53	2 809	7.280 110	23.02173	1886792
54	2 916	7.348 469	23.23790	1851852
55	3 025	7.416 198	23.45208	1818182
56	3 136	7.483 315	23.66432	1785714
57	3 249	7.549 834	23.87467	1754386
58	3 364	7.615 773	24.08319	1724138
59	3 481	7.681 146	24.28992	1694915
60	3 600	7.745 967	24.49490	1666667
61	3 721	7.810 250	24.69818	1639344
62	3 844	7.874 008	24.89980	1612903
63	3 969	7.937 254	25.09980	1587302
64	4 096	8.000 000	25.29822	1562500
65	4 225	8.062 258	25.49510	1538462
66	4 356	8.124 038	25.69047	1515152
67	4 489	8.185 353	25.88436	1492537
68	4 624	8.246 211	26.07681	1470588
69	4 761	8.306 624	26.26785	1449275
70	4 900	8.366 600	26.45751	1428571
71	5 041	8.426 150	26.64583	1408451
72	5 184	8.485 281	26.83282	1388889
73	5 329	8.544 004	27.01851	1369863
74	5 476	8.602 325	27.20294	1351351
75	5 625	8.660 254	27.38613	1333333
76	5 776	8.717 798	27.56810	1315789
77	5 929	8.774 964	27.74887	1298701
78	6 084	8.831 761	27.92848	1282051
79	6 241	8.888 194	28.10694	1265823
80	6 400	8.944 272	28.28427	1250000
81	6 561	9.000 000	28.46050	1234568
82	6 724	9.055 385	28.63564	1219512
83	6 889	9.110 434	28.80972	1204819
84	7 056	9.165 151	28.98275	1190476
85	7 225	9.219 544	29.15476	1176471
86	7 396	9.273 618	29.32576	1162791
87	7 569	9.327 379	29.49576	1149425
88	7 744	9.380 832	29.66479	1136364
89	7 921	9.433 981	29.83287	1123596
90	8 100	9.486 833	30.00000	1111111
91	8 281	9.539 392	30.16621	1098901
92	8 464	9.591 663	30.33150	1086957
93	8 649	9.643 651	30.49590	1075269
94	8 836	9.695 360	30.65942	1063830
95	9 025	9.746 794	30.82207	1052632
96	9 216	9.797 959	30.98387	1041667
97	9 409	9.848 858	31.14482	1030928
98	9 604	9.899 495	31.30495	1020408
99	9 801	9.949 874	31.46427	1010101
100	10 000	10.00000	31.62278	1000000

(Continued)

Table A-10 Squares, Square Roots, and Reciprocals 1–1000 (Continued)

N	N^2	$\sqrt{N}$	$\sqrt{10N}$	$1/N$ .0
100	10 000	10.00000	31.62278	10000000
101	10 201	10.04988	31.78050	09900990
102	10 404	10.09950	31.93744	09803922
103	10 609	10.14889	32.09361	09708738
104	10 816	10.19804	32.24903	09615385
105	11 025	10.24695	32.40370	09523810
106	11 236	10.29563	32.55764	09433962
107	11 449	10.34408	32.71085	09345794
108	11 664	10.39230	32.86335	09259259
109	11 881	10.44031	33.01515	09174312
110	12 100	10.48809	33.16625	09090909
111	12 321	10.53565	33.31666	09009009
112	12 544	10.58301	33.46640	08928571
113	12 769	10.63015	33.61547	08849558
114	12 996	10.67708	33.76389	08771930
115	13 225	10.72381	33.91165	08695652
116	13 456	10.77033	34.05877	08620690
117	13 689	10.81665	34.20526	08547009
118	13 924	10.86278	34.35113	08474576
119	14 161	10.90871	34.49638	08403361
120	14 400	10.95445	34.64102	08333333
121	14 641	11.00000	34.78505	08264463
122	14 884	11.04536	34.93850	08196721
123	15 129	11.09054	35.07136	08130081
124	15 376	11.13553	35.21363	08064516
125	15 625	11.18034	35.35534	08000000
126	15 876	11.22497	35.49648	07936508
127	16 129	11.26943	35.63706	07874016
128	16 384	11.31371	35.77709	07812500
129	16 641	11.35782	35.91657	07751938
130	16 900	11.40175	36.05551	07692308
131	17 161	11.44552	36.19392	07633588
132	17 424	11.48913	36.33180	07575758
133	17 689	11.53256	36.46917	07518797
134	17 956	11.57584	36.60601	07462687
135	18 225	11.61895	36.74235	07407407
136	18 496	11.66190	36.87818	07352941
137	18 769	11.70470	37.01351	07299270
138	19 044	11.74734	37.14835	07246377
139	19 321	11.78983	37.28270	07194245
140	19 600	11.83216	37.41657	07142857
141	19 881	11.87434	37.54997	07092199
142	20 164	11.91638	37.68289	07042254
143	20 449	11.95826	37.81534	06993007
144	20 736	12.00000	37.94733	06944444
145	21 025	12.04159	38.07887	06896552
146	21 316	12.08305	38.20995	06849315
147	21 609	12.12436	38.34058	06802721
148	21 904	12.16553	38.47077	06756757
149	22 201	12.20656	38.60052	06711409
150	22 500	12.24745	38.72983	06666667

N	N^2	$\sqrt{N}$	$\sqrt{10N}$	$1/N$ .00
150	22 500	12.24745	38.72983	6666667
151	22 801	12.28821	38.85872	6622517
152	23 104	12.32883	38.98718	6578947
153	23 409	12.36932	39.11521	6535948
154	23 716	12.40967	39.24283	6493506
155	24 025	12.44990	39.37004	6451613
156	24 336	12.49000	39.49684	6410256
157	24 649	12.52996	39.62323	6369427
158	24 964	12.56981	39.74921	6329114
159	25 281	12.60952	39.87480	6289308
160	25 600	12.64911	40.00000	6250000
161	25 921	12.68858	40.12481	6211180
162	26 244	12.72792	40.24922	6172840
163	26 569	12.76715	40.37326	6134969
164	26 896	12.80625	40.49691	6097561
165	27 225	12.84523	40.62019	6060606
166	27 556	12.88410	40.74310	6024096
167	27 889	12.92285	40.86563	5988024
168	28 224	12.96148	40.98780	5952381
169	28 561	13.00000	41.10961	5917160
170	28 900	13.03840	41.23106	5882353
171	29 241	13.07670	41.35215	5847953
172	29 584	13.11488	41.47288	5813953
173	29 929	13.15295	41.59327	5780347
174	30 276	13.19091	41.71331	5747126
175	30 625	13.22876	41.83300	5714286
176	30 976	13.26650	41.95235	5681818
177	31 329	13.30413	42.07137	5649718
178	31 684	13.34166	42.19005	5617978
179	32 041	13.37909	42.30839	5586592
180	32 400	13.41641	42.42641	5555556
181	32 761	13.45362	42.54409	5524862
182	33 124	13.49074	42.66146	5494505
183	33 489	13.52775	42.77850	5464481
184	33 856	13.56466	42.89522	5434783
185	34 225	13.60147	43.01163	5405405
186	34 596	13.63818	43.12772	5376344
187	34 969	13.67479	43.24350	5347594
188	35 344	13.71131	43.35897	5319149
189	35 721	13.74773	43.47413	5291005
190	36 100	13.78405	43.58899	5263158
191	36 481	13.82027	43.70355	5235602
192	36 864	13.85641	43.81780	5208333
193	37 249	13.89244	43.93177	5181347
194	37 636	13.92839	44.04543	5154639
195	38 025	13.96424	44.15880	5128205
196	38 416	14.00000	44.27189	5102041
197	38 809	14.03567	44.38468	5076142
198	39 204	14.07125	44.49719	5050505
199	39 601	14.10674	44.60942	5025126
200	40 000	14.14214	44.72136	5000000

(*Continued*)

Table A-10 Squares, Square Roots, and Reciprocals 1–1000 (Continued)

N	N^2	$\sqrt{N}$	$\sqrt{10N}$	$1/N$ .00
200	40 000	14.14214	44.72136	5000000
201	40 401	14.17745	44.83302	4975124
202	40 804	14.21267	44.94441	4950495
203	41 209	14.24781	45.05552	4926108
204	41 616	14.28286	45.16636	4901961
205	42 025	14.31782	45.27693	4878049
206	42 436	14.35270	45.38722	4854369
207	42 849	14.38749	45.49725	4830918
208	43 264	14.42221	45.60702	4807692
209	43 681	14.45683	45.71652	4784689
210	44 100	14.49138	45.82576	4761905
211	44 521	14.52584	45.93474	4739336
212	44 944	14.56022	46.04346	4716981
213	45 369	14.59452	46.15192	4694836
214	45 796	14.62874	46.26013	4672897
215	46 225	14.66288	46.36809	4651163
216	46 656	14.69694	46.47580	4629630
217	47 089	14.73092	46.58326	4608295
218	47 524	14.76482	46.69047	4587156
219	47 961	14.79865	46.79744	4566210
220	48 400	14.83240	46.90416	4545455
221	48 841	14.86607	47.01064	4524887
222	49 284	14.89966	47.11688	4504505
223	49 729	14.93318	47.22288	4484305
224	50 176	14.96663	47.32864	4464286
225	50 625	15.00000	47.43416	4444444
226	51 076	15.03330	47.53946	4424779
227	51 529	15.06652	47.64452	4405286
228	51 984	15.09967	47.74935	4385965
229	52 441	15.13275	47.85394	4366812
230	52 900	15.16575	47.95832	4347826
231	53 361	15.19868	48.06246	4329004
232	53 824	15.23155	48.16638	4310345
233	54 289	15.26434	48.27007	4291845
234	54 756	15.29706	48.37355	4273504
235	55 225	15.32971	48.47680	4255319
236	55 696	15.36229	48.57983	4237288
237	56 169	15.39480	48.68265	4219409
238	56 644	15.42725	48.78524	4201681
239	57 121	15.45962	48.88763	4184100
240	57 600	15.49193	48.98979	4166667
241	58 081	15.52417	49.09175	4149378
242	58 564	15.55635	49.19350	4132231
243	59 049	15.58846	49.29503	4115226
244	59 536	15.62050	49.39636	4098361
245	60 025	15.65248	49.49747	4081633
246	60 516	15.68439	49.59839	4065041
247	61 009	15.71623	49.69909	4048583
248	61 504	15.74802	49.79960	4032258
249	62 001	15.77973	49.89990	4016064
250	62 500	15.81139	50.00000	4000000

N	N^2	$\sqrt{N}$	$\sqrt{10N}$	$1/N$ .00
250	62 500	15.81139	50.00000	4000000
251	63 001	15.84298	50.09990	3984064
252	63 504	15.87451	50.19960	3968254
253	64 009	15.90597	50.29911	3952569
254	64 516	15.93738	50.39841	3937008
255	65 025	15.96872	50.49752	3921569
256	65 536	16.00000	50.59644	3906250
257	66 049	16.03122	50.69517	3891051
258	66 564	16.06238	50.79370	3875969
259	67 081	16.09348	50.89204	3861004
260	67 600	16.12452	50.99020	3846154
261	68 121	16.15549	51.08816	3831418
262	68 644	16.18641	51.18594	3816794
263	69 169	16.21727	51.28353	3802281
264	69 696	16.24808	51.38093	3787879
265	70 225	16.27882	51.47815	3773585
266	70 756	16.30951	51.57519	3759398
267	71 289	16.34013	51.67204	3745318
268	71 824	16.37071	51.76872	3731343
269	72 361	16.40122	51.86521	3717472
270	72 900	16.43168	51.96152	3703704
271	73 441	16.46208	52.05766	3690037
272	73 984	16.49242	52.15362	3676471
273	74 529	16.52271	52.24940	3663004
274	75 076	16.55295	52.34501	3649635
275	75 625	16.58312	52.44044	3636364
276	76 176	16.61325	52.53570	3623188
277	76 729	16.64332	52.63079	3610108
278	77 284	16.67333	52.72571	3597122
279	77 841	16.70329	52.82045	3584229
280	78 400	16.73320	52.91503	3571429
281	78 961	16.76305	53.00943	3558719
282	79 524	16.79286	53.10367	3546099
283	80 089	16.82260	53.19774	3533569
284	80 656	16.85230	53.29165	3521127
285	81 225	16.88194	53.38539	3508772
286	81 796	16.91153	53.47897	3496503
287	82 369	16.94107	53.57238	3484321
288	82 944	16.97056	53.66563	3472222
289	83 521	17.00000	53.75872	3460208
290	84 100	17.02939	53.85165	3448276
291	84 681	17.05872	53.94442	3436426
292	85 264	17.08801	54.03702	3424658
293	85 849	17.11724	54.12947	3412969
294	86 436	17.14643	54.22177	3401361
295	87 025	17.17556	54.31390	3389831
296	87 616	17.20465	54.40588	3378378
297	88 209	17.23369	54.49771	3367003
298	88 804	17.26268	54.58938	3355705
299	89 401	17.29162	54.68089	3344482
300	90 000	17.32051	54.77226	3333333

(*Continued*)

Table A-10 Squares, Square Roots, and Reciprocals 1–1000 (Continued)

N	N^2	$\sqrt{N}$	$\sqrt{10N}$	$1/N$ .00
300	90 000	17.32051	54.77226	3333333
301	90 601	17.34935	54.86347	3322259
302	91 204	17.37815	54.95453	3311258
303	91 809	17.40690	55.04544	3300330
304	92 416	17.43560	55.13620	3289474
305	93 025	17.46425	55.22681	3278689
306	93 636	17.49286	55.31727	3267974
307	94 249	17.52142	55.40758	3257329
308	94 864	17.54993	55.49775	3246753
309	95 481	17.57840	55.58777	3236246
310	96 100	17.60682	55.67764	3225806
311	96 721	17.63519	55.76737	3215434
312	97 344	17.66352	55.85696	3205128
313	97 969	17.69181	55.94640	3194888
314	98 596	17.72005	56.03570	3184713
315	99 225	17.74824	56.12486	3174603
316	99 856	17.77639	56.21388	3164557
317	100 489	17.80449	56.30275	3154574
318	101 124	17.83255	56.39149	3144654
319	101 761	17.86057	56.48008	3134796
320	102 400	17.88854	56.56854	3125000
321	103 041	17.91647	56.65686	3115265
322	103 684	17.94436	56.74504	3105590
323	104 329	17.97220	56.83309	3095975
324	104 976	18.00000	56.92100	3086420
325	105 625	18.02776	57.00877	3076923
326	106 276	18.05547	57.09641	3067485
327	106 929	18.08314	57.18391	3058104
328	107 584	18.11077	57.27128	3048780
329	108 241	18.13836	57.35852	3039514
330	108 900	18.16590	57.44563	3030303
331	109 561	18.19341	57.53260	3021148
332	110 224	18.22087	57.61944	3012048
333	110 889	18.24829	57.70615	3003003
334	111 556	18.27567	57.79273	2994012
335	112 225	18.30301	57.87918	2985075
336	112 896	18.33030	57.96551	2976190
337	113 569	18.35756	58.05170	2967359
338	114 244	18.38478	58.13777	2958580
339	114 921	18.41195	58.22371	2949853
340	115 600	18.43909	58.30952	2941176
341	116 281	18.46619	58.39521	2932551
342	116 964	18.49324	58.48077	2923977
343	117 649	18.52026	58.56620	2915452
344	118 336	18.54724	58.65151	2906977
345	119 025	18.57418	58.73670	2898551
346	119 716	18.60108	58.82176	2890173
347	120 409	18.62794	58.90671	2881844
348	121 104	18.65476	58.99152	2873563
349	121 801	18.68154	59.07622	2865330
350	122 500	18.70829	59.16080	2857143

N	N^2	$\sqrt{N}$	$\sqrt{10N}$	$1/N$ .00
350	122 500	18.70829	59.16080	2857143
351	123 201	18.73499	59.24525	2849003
352	123 904	18.76166	59.32959	2840909
353	124 609	18.78829	59.41380	2832861
354	125 316	18.81489	59.49790	2824859
355	126 025	18.84144	59.58188	2816901
356	126 736	18.86796	59.66574	2808989
357	127 449	18.89444	59.74948	2801120
358	128 164	18.92089	59.83310	2793296
359	128 881	18.94730	59.91661	2785515
360	129 600	18.97367	60.00000	2777778
361	130 321	19.00000	60.08328	2770083
362	131 044	19.02630	60.16644	2762431
363	131 769	19.05256	60.24948	2754821
364	132 496	19.07878	60.33241	2747253
365	133 225	19.10497	60.41523	2739726
366	133 956	19.13113	60.49793	2732240
367	134 689	19.15724	60.58052	2724796
368	135 424	19.18333	60.66300	2717391
369	136 161	19.20937	60.74537	2710027
370	136 900	19.23538	60.82763	2702703
371	137 641	19.26136	60.90977	2695418
372	138 384	19.28730	60.99180	2688172
373	139 129	19.31321	61.07373	2680965
374	139 876	19.33908	61.15554	2673797
375	140 625	19.36492	61.23724	2666667
376	141 376	19.39072	61.31884	2659574
377	142 129	19.41649	61.40033	2652520
378	142 884	19.44222	61.48170	2645503
379	143 641	19.46792	61.56298	2638522
380	144 400	19.49359	61.64414	2631579
381	145 161	19.51922	61.72520	2624672
382	145 924	19.54483	61.80615	2617801
383	146 689	19.57039	61.88699	2610966
384	147 456	19.59592	61.96773	2604167
385	148 225	19.62142	62.04837	2597403
386	148 996	19.64688	62.12890	2590674
387	149 769	19.67232	62.20932	2583979
388	150 544	19.69772	62.28965	2577320
389	151 321	19.72308	62.36986	2570694
390	152 100	19.74842	62.44998	2564103
391	152 881	19.77372	62.52999	2557545
392	153 664	19.79899	62.60990	2551020
393	154 449	19.82423	62.68971	2544529
394	155 236	19.84943	62.76942	2538071
395	156 025	19.87461	62.84903	2531646
396	156 816	19.89975	62.92853	2525253
397	157 609	19.92486	63.00794	2518892
398	158 404	19.94994	63.08724	2512563
399	159 201	19.97498	63.16645	2506266
400	160 000	20.00000	63.24555	2500000

(Continued)

Table A-10 Squares, Square Roots, and Reciprocals 1–1000 (Continued)

N	N^2	$\sqrt{N}$	$\sqrt{10N}$	$1/N$ .00
400	160 000	20.00000	63.24555	2500000
401	160 801	20.02498	63.32456	2493766
402	161 604	20.04994	63.40347	2487562
403	162 409	20.07486	63.48228	2481390
404	163 216	20.09975	63.56099	2475248
405	164 025	20.12461	63.63961	2469136
406	164 836	20.14944	63.71813	2463054
407	165 649	20.17424	63.79655	2457002
408	166 464	20.19901	63.87488	2450980
409	167 281	20.22375	63.95311	2444988
410	168 100	20.24846	64.03124	2439024
411	168 921	20.27313	64.10928	2433090
412	169 744	20.29778	64.18723	2427184
413	170 569	20.32240	64.26508	2421308
414	171 396	20.34699	64.34283	2415459
415	172 225	20.37155	64.42049	2409639
416	173 056	20.39608	64.49806	2403846
417	173 889	20.42058	64.57554	2398082
418	174 724	20.44505	64.65292	2392344
419	175 561	20.46949	64.73021	2386635
420	176 400	20.49390	64.80741	2380952
421	177 241	20.51828	64.88451	2375297
422	178 084	20.54264	64.96153	2369668
423	178 929	20.56696	65.03845	2364066
424	179 776	20.59126	65.11528	2358491
425	180 625	20.61553	65.19202	2352941
426	181 476	20.63977	65.26868	2347418
427	182 329	20.66398	65.34524	2341920
428	183 184	20.68816	65.42171	2336449
429	184 041	20.71232	65.49809	2331002
430	184 900	20.73644	65.57439	2325581
431	185 761	20.76054	65.65059	2320186
432	186 624	20.78461	65.72671	2314815
433	187 489	20.80865	65.80274	2309469
434	188 356	20.83267	65.87868	2304147
435	189 225	20.85665	65.95453	2298851
436	190 096	20.88061	66.03030	2293578
437	190 969	20.90454	66.10598	2288330
438	191 844	20.92845	66.18157	2283105
439	192 721	20.95233	66.25708	2277904
440	193 600	20.97618	66.33250	2272727
441	194 481	21.00000	66.40783	2267574
442	195 364	21.02380	66.48308	2262443
443	196 249	21.04757	66.55825	2257336
444	197 136	21.07131	66.63332	2252252
445	198 025	21.09502	66.70832	2247191
446	198 916	21.11871	66.78323	2242152
447	199 809	21.14237	66.85806	2237136
448	200 704	21.16601	66.93280	2232143
449	201 601	21.18962	67.00746	2227171
450	202 500	21.21320	67.08204	2222222

N	N^2	$\sqrt{N}$	$\sqrt{10N}$	$1/N$ .00
450	202 500	21.21320	67.08204	2222222
451	203 401	21.23676	67.15653	2217295
452	204 304	21.26029	67.23095	2212389
453	205 209	21.28380	67.30537	2207506
454	206 116	21.30728	67.37952	2202643
455	207 025	21.33073	67.45369	2197802
456	207 936	21.35416	67.52777	2192982
457	208 849	21.37756	67.60178	2188184
458	209 764	21.40093	67.67570	2183406
459	210 681	21.42429	67.74954	2178649
460	211 600	21.44761	67.82330	2173913
461	212 521	21.47091	67.89698	2169197
462	213 444	21.49419	67.97058	2164502
463	214 369	21.41743	68.04410	2159827
464	215 296	21.54066	68.11755	2155172
465	216 225	21.56386	68.19091	2150538
466	217 156	21.58703	68.26419	2145923
467	218 089	21.61018	68.33740	2141328
468	219 024	21.63331	68.41053	2136752
469	219 961	21.65641	68.48357	2132196
470	220 900	21.67948	68.55655	2127660
471	221 841	21.70253	68.62944	2123142
472	222 784	21.72556	68.70226	2118644
473	223 729	21.74856	68.77500	2114165
474	224 676	21.77154	68.84766	2109705
475	225 625	21.79449	68.92024	2105263
476	226 576	21.81742	68.99275	2100840
477	227 529	21.84033	69.06519	2096436
478	228 484	21.86321	69.13754	2092050
479	229 441	21.88607	69.20983	2087683
480	230 400	21.90890	69.28203	2083333
481	231 361	21.93171	69.35416	2079002
482	232 324	21.95450	69.42622	2074689
483	233 289	21.97726	69.49820	2070393
484	234 256	22.00000	69.57011	2066116
485	235 225	22.02272	69.64194	2061856
486	236 196	22.04541	69.71370	2057613
487	237 169	22.06808	69.78539	2053388
488	238 144	22.09072	69.85700	2049180
489	239 121	22.11334	69.92853	2044990
490	240 100	22.13594	70.00000	2040816
491	241 081	22.15852	70.07139	2036660
492	242 064	22.18107	70.14271	2032520
493	243 049	22.20360	70.21396	2028398
494	244 036	22.22611	70.28513	2024291
495	245 025	22.24860	70.35624	2020202
496	246 016	22.27106	70.42727	2016129
497	247 009	22.29350	70.49823	2012072
498	248 004	22.31591	70.56912	2008032
499	249 001	22.33831	70.63993	2004008
500	250 000	22.36068	70.71068	2000000

(Continued)

Table A-10 Squares, Square Roots, and Reciprocals 1–1000 (Continued)

N	N^2	$\sqrt{N}$	$\sqrt{10N}$	$1/N$ .00
500	250 000	22.36068	70.71068	2000000
501	251 001	22.38303	70.78135	1996008
502	252 004	22.40536	70.85196	1992032
503	253 009	22.42766	70.92249	1988072
504	254 016	22.44994	70.99296	1984127
505	255 025	22.47221	71.06335	1980198
506	256 036	22.49444	71.13368	1976285
507	257 049	22.51666	71.20393	1972387
508	258 064	22.53886	71.27412	1968504
509	259 081	22.56103	71.34424	1964637
510	260 100	22.58318	71.41428	1960784
511	261 121	22.60531	71.48426	1956947
512	262 144	22.62742	71.55418	1953125
513	263 169	22.64950	71.62402	1949318
514	264 196	22.67157	71.69379	1945525
515	265 225	22.69361	71.76350	1941748
516	266 256	22.71563	71.83314	1937984
517	267 289	22.73763	71.90271	1934236
518	268 324	22.75961	71.97222	1930502
519	269 361	22.78157	72.04165	1926782
520	270 400	22.80351	72.11103	1923077
521	271 441	22.82542	72.18033	1919386
522	272 484	22.84732	72.24957	1915709
523	273 529	22.86919	72.31874	1912046
524	274 576	22.89105	72.38784	1908397
525	275 625	22.91288	72.45688	1904762
526	276 676	22.93469	72.52586	1901141
527	277 729	22.95648	72.59477	1897533
528	278 784	22.97825	72.66361	1893939
529	279 841	23.00000	72.73239	1890359
530	280 900	23.02173	72.80110	1886792
531	281 961	23.04344	72.86975	1883239
532	283 024	23.06513	72.93833	1879699
533	284 089	23.08679	73.00685	1876173
534	285 156	23.10844	73.07530	1872659
535	286 225	23.13007	73.14369	1869159
536	287 296	23.15167	73.21202	1865672
537	288 369	23.17326	73.28028	1862197
538	289 444	23.19483	73.34848	1858736
539	290 521	23.21637	73.41662	1855288
540	291 600	23.23790	73.48469	1851852
541	292 681	23.25941	73.55270	1848429
542	293 764	23.28089	73.62065	1845018
543	294 849	23.30236	73.68853	1841621
544	295 936	23.32381	73.75636	1838235
545	297 025	23.34524	73.82412	1834862
546	298 116	23.36664	73.89181	1831502
547	299 209	23.38803	73.95945	1828154
548	300 304	23.40940	74.02702	1824818
549	301 401	23.43075	74.09453	1821494
550	302 500	23.45208	74.16198	1818182

N	N^2	$\sqrt{N}$	$\sqrt{10N}$	$1/N$ .00
550	302 500	23.45208	74.16198	1818182
551	303 601	23.47339	74.22937	1814882
552	304 704	23.49468	74.29670	1811594
553	305 809	23.51595	74.36397	1808318
554	306 916	23.53720	74.43118	1805054
555	308 025	23.55844	74.49832	1801802
556	309 136	23.57965	74.56541	1798561
557	310 249	23.60085	74.63243	1795332
558	311 364	23.62202	74.69940	1792115
559	312 481	23.64318	74.76630	1788909
560	313 600	23.66432	74.83315	1785714
561	314 721	23.68544	74.89993	1782531
562	315 844	23.70654	74.96666	1779359
563	316 969	23.72762	75.03333	1776199
564	318 096	23.74868	75.09993	1773050
565	319 225	23.76973	75.16648	1769912
566	320 356	23.79075	75.23297	1766784
567	321 489	23.81176	75.29940	1763668
568	322 624	23.83275	75.36577	1760563
569	323 761	23.85372	75.43209	1757469
570	324 900	23.87467	75.49834	1754386
571	326 041	23.89561	75.56454	1751313
572	327 184	23.91652	75.63068	1748252
573	328 329	23.93742	75.69676	1745201
574	329 476	23.95830	75.76279	1742160
575	330 625	23.97916	75.82875	1739130
576	331 776	24.00000	75.89466	1736111
577	332 929	24.02082	75.96052	1733102
578	334 084	24.04163	76.02631	1730104
579	335 241	24.06242	76.09205	1727116
580	336 400	24.08319	76.15773	1724138
581	337 561	24.10394	76.22336	1721170
582	338 724	24.12468	76.28892	1718213
583	339 889	24.14539	76.35444	1715266
584	341 056	24.16609	76.41989	1712329
585	342 225	24.18677	76.48529	1709402
586	343 396	24.20744	76.55064	1706485
587	344 569	24.22808	76.61593	1703578
588	345 744	24.24871	76.68116	1700680
589	346 921	24.26932	76.74634	1697793
590	348 100	24.28992	76.81146	1694915
591	349 281	24.31049	76.87652	1692047
592	350 464	24.33105	76.94154	1689189
593	351 649	24.35159	77.00649	1686341
594	352 836	24.37212	77.07140	1683502
595	354 025	24.39262	77.13624	1680672
596	355 216	24.41311	77.20104	1677852
597	356 409	24.43358	77.26578	1675042
598	357 604	24.45404	77.33046	1672241
599	358 801	24.47448	77.39509	1669449
600	360 000	24.49490	77.45967	1666667

(Continued)

Table A-10 Squares, Square Roots, and Reciprocals 1–1000 (Continued)

N	N^2	$\sqrt{N}$	$\sqrt{10N}$	$1/N$ .00
600	360 000	24.49490	77.45967	1666667
601	361 201	24.51530	77.52419	1663894
602	362 404	24.53569	77.58866	1661130
603	363 609	24.55606	77.65307	1658375
604	364 816	24.57641	77.71744	1655629
605	366 025	24.59675	77.78165	1652893
606	367 236	24.61707	77.84600	1650165
607	368 449	24.63737	77.91020	1647446
608	369 664	24.65766	77.97435	1644737
609	370 881	24.67793	78.03845	1642036
610	372 100	24.69818	78.10250	1639344
611	373 321	24.71841	78.16649	1636661
612	374 544	24.73863	78.23043	1633987
613	375 769	24.75884	78.29432	1631321
614	376 996	24.77902	78.35815	1628664
615	378 225	24.79919	78.42194	1626016
616	379 456	24.81935	78.48567	1623377
617	380 689	24.83948	78.54935	1620746
618	381 924	24.85961	78.61298	1618123
619	383 161	24.87971	78.67655	1615509
620	384 400	24.89980	78.74008	1612903
621	385 641	24.91987	78.80355	1610306
622	386 884	24.93993	78.86698	1607717
623	388 129	24.95997	78.93035	1605136
624	389 376	24.97999	78.99367	1602564
625	390 625	25.00000	79.05694	1600000
626	391 876	25.01999	79.12016	1597444
627	393 129	25.03997	79.18333	1594896
628	394 384	25.05993	79.24645	1592357
629	395 641	25.07987	79.30952	1589825
630	396 900	25.09980	79.37254	1587302
631	398 161	25.11971	79.43551	1584786
632	399 424	25.13961	79.49843	1582278
633	400 689	25.15949	79.56130	1579779
634	401 956	25.17936	79.62412	1577287
635	403 225	25.19921	79.68689	1574803
636	404 496	25.21904	79.74961	1572327
637	405 769	25.23886	79.81228	1569859
638	407 044	25.25866	79.87490	1567398
639	408 321	25.27845	79.93748	1564945
640	409 600	25.29822	80.00000	1562500
641	410 881	25.31798	80.06248	1560062
642	412 164	25.33772	80.12490	1557632
643	413 449	25.35744	80.18728	1555210
644	414 736	25.37716	80.24961	1552795
645	416 025	25.39685	80.31189	1550388
646	417 316	25.41653	80.37413	1547988
647	418 609	25.43619	80.43631	1545595
648	419 904	25.45584	80.49845	1543210
649	421 201	25.47548	80.56054	1540832
650	422 500	25.49510	80.62258	1538462

N	N^2	$\sqrt{N}$	$\sqrt{10N}$	$1/N$ .00
650	422 500	25.49510	80.62258	1538462
651	423 801	25.51470	80.68457	1536098
652	425 104	25.53429	80.74652	1533742
653	426 409	25.55386	80.80842	1531394
654	427 716	25.57342	80.87027	1529052
655	429 025	25.59297	80.93207	1526718
656	430 336	25.61250	80.99383	1524390
657	431 649	25.63201	81.05554	1522070
658	432 964	25.65141	81.11720	1519757
659	434 281	25.67100	81.17881	1517451
660	435 600	25.69047	81.24038	1515152
661	436 921	25.70992	81.30191	1512859
662	438 244	25.72936	81.36338	1510574
663	439 569	25.74879	81.42481	1508296
664	440 896	25.76820	81.48620	1506024
665	442 225	25.78759	81.54753	1503759
666	443 556	25.80698	81.60882	1501502
667	444 889	25.82634	81.67007	1499250
668	446 224	25.84570	81.73127	1497006
669	447 561	25.86503	81.79242	1494768
670	448 900	25.88436	81.85353	1492537
671	450 241	25.90367	81.91459	1490313
672	451 584	25.92296	81.97561	1488095
673	452 929	25.94224	82.03658	1485884
674	454 276	25.96151	82.09750	1483680
675	455 625	25.98076	82.15838	1481481
676	456 976	26.00000	82.21922	1479290
677	458 329	26.01922	82.28001	1477105
678	459 684	26.03843	82.34076	1474926
679	461 041	26.05763	82.40146	1472754
680	462 400	26.07681	82.46211	1470588
681	463 761	26.09598	82.42272	1468429
682	465 124	26.11513	82.58329	1466276
683	466 489	26.13427	82.64381	1464129
684	467 856	26.15339	82.70429	1461988
685	469 225	26.17250	82.76473	1459854
686	470 596	26.19160	82.82512	1457726
687	471 969	26.21068	82.88546	1455604
688	473 344	26.22975	82.94577	1453488
689	474 721	26.24881	83.00602	1451379
690	476 100	26.26785	83.06624	1449275
691	477 481	26.28688	83.12641	1447178
692	478 864	26.30589	83.18654	1445087
693	480 249	26.32489	83.24662	1443001
694	481 636	26.34388	83.30666	1440922
695	483 025	26.36285	83.36666	1438849
696	484 416	26.38181	83.42661	1436782
697	485 809	26.40076	83.48653	1434720
698	487 204	26.41969	83.54639	1432665
699	488 601	26.43861	83.60622	1430615
700	490 000	26.45751	83.66600	1428571

(*Continued*)

Table A-10 Squares, Square Roots, and Reciprocals 1–1000 (Continued)

N	N^2	$\sqrt{N}$	$\sqrt{10N}$	$1/N$ .00	N	N^2	$\sqrt{N}$	$\sqrt{10N}$	$1/N$ .00
700	490 000	26.45751	83.66600	1428571	750	562 500	27.38613	86.60254	1333333
701	491 401	26.47640	83.72574	1426534	751	564 001	27.40438	86.66026	1331558
702	492 804	26.49528	83.78544	1424501	752	565 504	27.42262	86.71793	1329787
703	494 209	26.51415	83.84510	1422475	753	567 009	27.44085	86.77557	1328021
704	495 616	26.53300	83.90471	1420455	754	568 516	27.45906	86.83317	1326260
705	497 025	26.55184	83.96428	1418440	755	570 025	27.47726	86.89074	1324503
706	498 436	26.57066	84.02381	1416431	756	571 536	27.49545	86.94826	1322751
707	499 849	26.58947	84.08329	1414427	757	573 049	27.51363	87.00575	1321004
708	501 264	26.60827	84.14274	1412429	758	574 564	27.53180	87.06320	1319261
709	502 681	26.62705	84.20214	1410437	759	576 081	27.54995	87.12061	1317523
710	504 100	26.64583	84.26150	1408451	760	577 600	27.56810	87.17798	1315789
711	505 521	26.66458	84.32082	1406470	761	579 121	27.58623	87.23531	1314060
712	506 944	26.68333	84.38009	1404494	762	580 644	27.60435	87.29261	1312336
713	508 369	26.70206	84.43933	1402525	763	582 169	27.62245	87.34987	1310616
714	509 796	26.72078	84.49852	1400560	764	583 696	27.64055	87.40709	1308901
715	511 225	26.73948	84.55767	1398601	765	585 225	27.65863	87.46428	1307190
716	512 656	26.75818	84.61678	1396648	766	586 756	27.67671	87.52143	1305483
717	514 089	26.77686	84.67585	1394700	767	588 289	27.69476	87.57854	1303781
718	515 524	26.79552	84.73488	1392758	768	589 824	27.71281	87.63561	1302083
719	516 961	26.81418	84.79387	1390821	769	591 361	27.73085	87.69265	1300390
720	518 400	26.83282	84.85281	1388889	770	592 900	27.74887	87.74964	1298701
721	519 841	26.85144	84.91172	1386963	771	594 441	27.76689	87.80661	1297017
722	521 284	26.87006	84.97058	1385042	772	595 984	27.78489	87.86353	1295337
723	522 729	26.88866	85.02941	1383126	773	597 529	27.80288	87.92042	1293661
724	524 176	26.90725	85.08819	1381215	774	599 076	27.82086	87.97727	1291990
725	525 625	26.92582	85.14693	1379310	775	600 625	27.83882	88.03408	1290323
726	527 076	26.94439	85.20563	1377410	776	602 176	27.85678	88.09086	1288660
727	528 529	26.96294	85.26429	1375516	777	603 729	27.87472	88.14760	1287001
728	529 984	26.98148	85.32292	1373626	778	605 284	27.89265	88.20431	1285347
729	531 441	27.00000	85.38150	1371742	779	606 841	27.91057	88.26098	1283697
730	532 900	27.01851	85.44004	1369863	780	608 400	27.92848	88.31761	1282051
731	534 361	27.03701	85.49854	1367989	781	609 961	27.94638	88.37420	1280410
732	535 824	27.05550	85.55700	1366120	782	611 524	27.96426	88.43076	1278772
733	537 289	27.07397	85.61542	1364256	783	613 089	27.98214	88.48729	1277139
734	538 756	27.09243	85.67380	1362398	784	614 656	28.00000	88.54377	1275510
735	540 225	27.11088	85.73214	1360544	785	616 225	28.01785	88.60023	1273885
736	541 696	27.12932	85.79044	1358696	786	617 796	28.03569	88.65664	1272265
737	543 169	27.14774	85.84870	1356852	787	619 369	28.05352	88.71302	1270648
738	544 644	27.16616	85.90693	1355014	788	620 944	28.07134	88.76936	1269036
739	546 121	27.18455	85.96511	1353180	789	622 521	28.08914	88.82567	1267427
740	547 600	27.20294	86.02325	1351351	790	624 100	28.10694	88.88194	1265823
741	549 081	27.22132	86.08136	1349528	791	625 681	28.12472	88.93818	1264223
742	550 564	27.23968	86.13942	1347709	792	627 264	28.14249	88.99438	1262626
743	552 049	27.25803	86.19745	1345895	793	628 849	28.16026	89.05055	1261034
744	553 536	27.27636	86.25543	1344086	794	630 436	28.17801	89.10668	1259446
745	555 025	27.29469	86.31338	1342282	795	632 025	28.19574	89.16277	1257862
746	556 516	27.31300	86.37129	1340483	796	633 616	28.21347	89.21883	1256281
747	558 009	27.33130	86.42916	1338688	797	635 209	28.23119	89.27486	1254705
748	559 504	27.34959	86.48699	1336898	798	636 804	28.24889	89.33085	1253133
749	561 001	27.36786	86.54479	1335113	799	638 401	28.26659	89.38680	1251564
750	562 500	27.38613	86.60254	1333333	800	640 000	28.28427	89.44272	1250000

(Continued)

Table A-10 Squares, Square Roots, and Reciprocals 1–1000 (Continued)

N	N^2	$\sqrt{N}$	$\sqrt{10N}$	$1/N$ .00
800	640 000	28.28427	89.44272	1250000
801	641 601	28.30194	89.49860	1248439
802	643 204	28.31960	89.55445	1246883
803	644 809	28.33725	89.61027	1245330
804	646 416	28.35489	89.66605	1243781
805	648 025	28.37252	89.72179	1242236
806	649 636	28.39014	89.77750	1240695
807	651 249	28.40775	89.83318	1239157
808	652 864	28.42534	89.88882	1237624
809	654 481	28.44293	89.94443	1236094
810	656 100	28.46050	90.00000	1234568
811	657 721	28.47806	90.05554	1233046
812	659 344	28.49561	90.11104	1231527
813	660 969	28.51315	90.16651	1230012
814	662 596	28.53069	90.22195	1228501
815	664 225	28.54820	90.27735	1226994
816	665 856	28.56571	90.33272	1225490
817	667 489	28.58321	90.38805	1223990
818	669 124	28.60070	90.44335	1222494
819	670 761	28.61818	90.49862	1221001
820	672 400	28.63564	90.55385	1219512
821	674 041	28.65310	90.60905	1218027
822	675 684	28.67054	90.66422	1216545
823	677 329	28.68798	90.71935	1215067
824	678 976	28.70540	90.77445	1213592
825	680 625	28.72281	90.82951	1212121
826	682 276	28.74022	90.88454	1210654
827	683 929	28.75761	90.93954	1209190
828	685 584	28.77499	90.99451	1207729
829	687 241	28.79236	91.04944	1206273
830	688 900	28.80972	91.10434	1204819
831	690 561	28.82707	91.15920	1203369
832	692 224	28.84441	91.21403	1201923
833	693 889	28.86174	91.26883	1200480
834	695 556	28.87906	91.32360	1199041
835	697 225	28.89637	91.37833	1197605
836	698 896	28.91366	91.43304	1196172
837	700 569	28.93095	91.48770	1194743
838	702 244	28.94823	91.54234	1193317
839	703 921	28.96550	91.59694	1191895
840	705 600	28.98275	91.65151	1190476
841	707 281	29.00000	91.70605	1189061
842	708 964	29.01724	91.76056	1187648
843	710 649	29.03446	91.81503	1186240
844	712 336	29.05168	91.86947	1184834
845	714 025	29.06888	91.92388	1183432
846	715 716	29.08608	91.97826	1182033
847	717 409	29.10326	92.03260	1180638
848	719 104	29.12044	92.08692	1179245
849	720 801	29.13760	92.14120	1177856
850	722 500	29.15476	92.19544	1176471

N	N^2	$\sqrt{N}$	$\sqrt{10N}$	$1/N$ .00
850	722 500	29.15476	92.19544	1176471
851	724 201	29.17190	92.24966	1175088
852	725 904	29.18904	92.30385	1173709
853	727 609	29.20616	92.35800	1172333
854	729 316	29.22328	92.41212	1170960
855	731 025	29.24038	92.46621	1169591
856	732 736	29.25748	92.52027	1168224
857	734 449	29.27456	92.57429	1166861
858	736 164	29.29164	92.62829	1165501
859	737 881	29.30870	92.68225	1164144
860	739 600	29.32576	92.73618	1162791
861	741 321	29.34280	92.79009	1161440
862	743 044	29.35984	92.84396	1160093
863	744 769	29.37686	92.89779	1158749
864	746 496	29.39388	92.95160	1157407
865	748 225	29.41088	93.00538	1156069
866	749 956	29.42788	93.05912	1154734
867	751 689	29.44486	93.11283	1153403
868	753 424	29.46184	93.16652	1152074
869	755 161	29.47881	93.22017	1150748
870	756 900	29.49576	93.27379	1149425
871	758 641	29.51271	93.32738	1148106
872	760 384	29.52965	93.38094	1146789
873	762 129	29.54657	93.43447	1145475
874	763 876	29.56349	93.48797	1144165
875	765 625	29.58040	93.54143	1142857
876	767 376	29.59730	93.59487	1141553
877	769 129	29.61419	93.64828	1140251
878	770 884	29.63106	93.70165	1138952
879	772 641	29.64793	93.75500	1137656
880	774 400	29.66479	93.80832	1136364
881	776 161	29.68164	93.86160	1135074
882	777 924	29.69848	93.91486	1133787
883	779 689	29.71532	93.96808	1132503
884	781 456	29.73214	94.02127	1131222
885	783 225	29.74895	94.07444	1129944
886	784 996	29.76575	94.12757	1128668
887	786 769	29.78255	94.18068	1127396
888	788 544	29.79933	94.23375	1126126
889	790 321	29.81610	94.28680	1124859
890	792 100	29.83287	94.33981	1123596
891	793 881	29.84962	94.39280	1122334
892	795 664	29.86637	94.44575	1121076
893	797 449	29.88311	94.49868	1119821
894	799 236	29.89983	94.55157	1118568
895	801 025	29.91655	94.60444	1117318
896	802 816	29.93326	94.65728	1116071
897	804 609	29.94996	94.71008	1114827
898	806 404	29.96665	94.76286	1113586
899	808 201	29.98333	94.81561	1112347
900	810 000	30.00000	94.86833	1111111

(*Continued*)

Table A-10 Squares, Square Roots, and Reciprocals 1–1000 (Continued)

N	N^2	$\sqrt{N}$	$\sqrt{10N}$	$1/N$ .00
900	810 000	30.00000	94.86833	1111111
901	811 801	30.01666	94.92102	1109878
902	813 604	30.03331	94.97368	1108647
903	815 409	30.04996	95.02631	1107420
904	817 216	30.06659	95.07891	1106195
905	819 025	30.08322	95.13149	1104972
906	820 836	30.09983	95.18403	1103753
907	822 649	30.11644	95.23655	1102536
908	824 464	30.13304	95.28903	1101322
909	826 281	30.14963	95.34149	1100110
910	828 100	30.16621	95.39392	1098901
911	829 921	30.18278	95.44632	1097695
912	831 744	30.19934	95.49869	1096491
913	833 569	30.21589	95.55103	1095290
914	835 396	30.23243	95.60335	1094092
915	837 225	30.24897	95,65563	1092896
916	839 056	30.26549	95.70789	1091703
917	840 889	30.28201	95.76012	1090513
918	842 724	30.29851	95.81232	1089325
919	844 561	30.31501	95.86449	1088139
920	846 400	30.33150	95.91663	1086957
921	848 241	30.34798	95.96874	1085776
922	850 084	30.36445	96.02083	1084599
923	851 929	30.38092	96.07289	1083424
924	853 776	30.39737	96.12492	1082251
925	855 625	30.41381	96.17692	1081081
926	857 476	30.43025	96.22889	1079914
927	859 329	30.44667	96.28084	1078749
928	861 184	30.46309	96.33276	1077586
929	863 041	30.47950	96.38465	1076426
930	864 900	30.49590	96.43651	1075269
931	866 761	30.51229	96.48834	1074114
932	868 624	30.52868	96.54015	1072961
933	870 489	30.54505	96.59193	1071811
934	872 356	30.56141	96.64368	1070664
935	874 225	30.57777	96.69540	1069519
936	876 096	30.59412	96.74709	1068376
937	877 969	30.61046	96.79876	1067236
938	879 844	30.62679	96.85040	1066098
939	881 721	30.64311	96.90201	1064963
940	883 600	30.65942	96.95360	1063830
941	885 481	30.67572	97.00515	1062699
942	887 364	30.69202	97.05668	1061571
943	889 249	30.70831	97.10819	1060445
944	891 136	30.72458	97.15966	1059322
945	893 025	30.74085	97.21111	1058201
946	894 916	30.75711	97.26253	1057082
947	896 809	30.77337	97.31393	1055966
948	898 704	30.78961	97.36529	1054852
949	900 601	30.80584	97.41663	1053741
950	902 500	30.82207	97.46794	1052632

N	N^2	$\sqrt{N}$	$\sqrt{10N}$	$1/N$ .00
950	902 500	30.82207	97.46794	1052632
951	904 401	30.83829	97.51923	1051525
952	906 304	30.85450	97.57049	1050420
953	908 209	30.87070	97.62172	1049318
954	910 116	30.88689	97.67292	1048218
955	912 025	30.90307	97.72410	1047120
956	913 936	30.91925	97.77525	1046025
957	915 849	30.93542	97.82638	1044932
958	917 764	30.95158	97.87747	1043841
959	919 681	30.96773	97.92855	1042753
960	921 600	30.98387	97.97959	1041667
961	923 521	31.00000	98.03061	1040583
962	925 444	31.01612	98.08160	1039501
963	927 369	31.03224	98.13256	1038422
964	929 296	31.04835	98.18350	1037344
965	931 225	31.06445	98.23441	1036269
966	933 156	31.08054	98.28530	1035197
967	935 089	31.09662	98.33616	1034126
968	937 024	31.11270	98.38699	1033058
969	938 961	31.12876	98.43780	1031992
970	940 900	31.14482	98.48858	1030928
971	942 841	31.16087	98.53933	1029866
972	944 784	31.17691	98.59006	1028807
973	946 729	31.19295	98.64076	1027749
974	948 676	31.20897	98.69144	1026694
975	950 625	31.22499	98.74209	1025641
976	952 576	31.24100	98.79271	1024590
977	954 529	31.25700	98.84331	1023541
978	956 484	31.27299	98.89388	1022495
979	958 441	31.28898	98.94443	1021450
980	960 400	31.30495	98.99495	1020408
981	962 361	31.32092	99.04544	1019368
982	964 324	31.33688	99.09591	1018330
983	966 289	31.35283	99.14636	1017294
984	968 256	31.36877	99.19677	1016260
985	970 225	31.38471	99.24717	1015228
986	972 196	31.40064	99.29753	1014199
987	974 169	31.41656	99.34787	1013171
988	976 144	31.43247	99.39819	1012146
989	978 121	31.44837	99.44848	1011122
990	980 100	31.46427	99.49874	1010101
991	982 081	31.48015	99.54898	1009082
992	984 064	31.49603	99.59920	1008065
993	986 049	31.51190	99.64939	1007049
994	988 036	31.52777	99.69955	1006036
995	990 025	31.54362	99.74969	1005025
996	992 016	31.55947	99.79980	1004016
997	994 009	31.57531	99.84989	1003009
998	996 004	31.59114	99.89995	1002004
999	998 001	31.60696	99.94999	1001001
1000	1 000 000	31.62278	100.00000	1000000

ANSWERS TO SELECTED PROBLEMS

Chapter 3

3.18. f. (1) 4.9; (2) 5.2; (3) 8.9

Chapter 4

4.9. a. 1,151.2 **b.** 1,202.5 **d.** Yes **e.** No
4.10. a. 749 **b.** 213.7 **c.** No **e.** 18.6%
4.20. a. 3 **b.** No **c.** 5 **d.** 2
4.22. a. 1941: 5.8; 1968: 5.6 **c.** Yes
4.23. a. 1941: 5.3; 1968: 4.9 **c.** 1941: 5.3; 1968: 5.5 **d.** 1941: 11.6; 1968: 11.5
4.24. b. 1941: 3.7; 1968: 4.0 **c.** 1941: 64%; 1968: 71%
e. 1941: +.41; 1968: +.52
4.32. a. 21.9 **b.** 6.3, 28.8% **d.** Yes **e.** 0 **f.** 12.0
4.34. a. 45.4 **b.** 37.6

Chapter 5

5.1. a. 5.8, 3.7
5.3. a. .16 **b.** 0

Chapter 6

6.14. a. (1) $P(A_1 \text{ and } B_5)$; (2) $P(A_2 \text{ and } B_3)$; (3) $P(B_2)$; (4) $P(A_1 \text{ or } A_2)$; (5) $P(B_4|A_2)$
c. (1) .024; (2) .064; (3) .160; (4) .30; (5) .18 **d.** (1) .28; (2) .028; (3) .10
g. Bivariate

	B_1	B_2	B_3	B_4	B_5
A_1	.012	.020	.024	.020	.024
A_2	.020	.044	.064	.036	.036
A_3	.116	.048	.012	.028	.096
A_4	.252	.048	.040	.016	.044

h.

A_1	A_2	A_3	A_4
.10	.20	.30	.40

i.

B_1	B_2	B_3	B_4	B_5
.39	.16	.04	.09	.32

6.18. a. .072 **b.** .708 **c.** .103
d. Not independent

	B_1	B_2	B_3
A_1	.228	.400	.072
A_2	.222	.070	.008

6.20. a. .016 **b.** .008, yes
6.23. a. .37 **b.** .75, .87 **d.** 7.40 **e.** 300
6.24. b. .74, no **c.** 1.50, yes **d.** 14.8, 600
6.27. a. \$0.26 **b.** Yes, expected gain becomes \$0.2775

Chapter 7

7.2. **a.** .1, .09 **b.** Yes
7.7. **a.** .1246, .0181 **b.** 11
7.12. **a.** 50% **b.** 15.87% **c.** 81.85% **d.** 13.59% **e.** Yes **f.** 3,438 **g.** No **h.** .004
7.17. **a.** Less than .001 **b.** 1.6 **c.** Optimum location 31.39, average waste 1.39 **d.** Yes **e.** Optimum location 30.92, average waste reduction .47
7.19. **a.** .220 **b.** .713 **c.** .472

Chapter 8

8.1. **a.** .19 **b.** .034
8.4. **a.** $\int_0^5 f(X)dX$ **b.** $\int_5^{10} f(X)dX$ **c.** $\int_3^5 f(X)dX$ **d.** $\int_3^5 f(X)dX \Big/ \int_3^8 f(X)dX$ **e.** $\int_0^{10} Xf(X)dX$
8.6. **c.** (1) .4; (2) .3; (3) .6 **d.** 5 **e.** 8.33, 2.89 **f.** .5

Chapter 9

9.10. .01, .001

Chapter 10

10.6. **a.** 4, 4.43
b.

$\bar{X}$	1.00	1.67	2.67	4.00	5.00	5.67	6.67
Prob.	.1	.1	.2	.1	.2	.2	.1

c. (1) .2; (2) .8 **d.** .3 **e.** 4, yes, yes **f.** 1.81, yes
10.7. **a.**

M_e	0	3	5
Prob.	.3	.4	.3

b. 2.7, 1.95 **c.** No **f.** 3, no
10.10. **a.** .79 **b.** 48.7 to 51.3 **c.** (1) .99; (2) .99 **d.** No
10.13. **a.** .60 **b.** .86 **c.** 333 **d.** Yes

Chapter 11

11.3. **a.** .6 **b.**

$\bar{p}$	0	.5	1
Prob.	.1	.6	.3

c. (1) .3; (2) .1 **d.** .6 **e.** .6, yes, yes **f.** .3, yes **g.** No
11.7. **a.** .6 **b.** .4
11.10. **a.**

X	0	1
Prob.	.55	.45

b.

$\bar{p}$	0	$\frac{1}{7}$	$\frac{2}{7}$	$\frac{3}{7}$	$\frac{4}{7}$	$\frac{5}{7}$	$\frac{6}{7}$	1
Prob.	.0152	.0872	.2140	.2918	.2388	.1172	.0320	.0037

c. (1) .2388; (2) .3164 **d.** .45, yes **e.** .188, yes

11.14. **a.** .1211 **b.** .0580
11.18. **a.** .15, .0357 **b.** Yes **c.** .8384, .7187 **d.** .091 to .209
e. .121 to .179 **f.** .5

Chapter 12

12.9. **a.** .85 **b.** No **c.** .48 to 1.22 **f.** No
12.13. **a.** 86 **b.** (1) 342; (2) 342; (3) 342 **c.** Yes **e.** No
12.20. 10, 2.764; 23, 2.500; 2, 6.965; 119, 2.326
12.21. **a.** 330 to 404 **c.** 306 to 428

Chapter 14

14.1. **a.** 20.1 to 41.5 **c.** Yes **e.** No **f.** No
14.3. **a.** .10 **b.** No **c.** .065 to .135
14.6. **a.** (1) .5, 471; (2) .7, 396; (3) .8, 301
14.11. **a.** −.012 to +.168
14.14.

Stratum	1	2	3
Sample Size	99	18	3

14.17. **a.** Proportional allocation **b.** 29.62 **c.** 28.73 to 30.51
d.

Stratum	1	2	3	4
Optimal Sample Size	64	70	72	44

Chapter 15

15.5. **a.** A: $120 thousand; B: $165 thousand; C: $165 thousand; D: $0
15.7. **b.**

	Outcome			
Act	*Win*	*Place*	*Show*	*Lose*
Win	0	6	5	2
Place	8	0	5	2
Show	9	1	0	2
No bet	10	4	3	0

15.10. **a.** Yes **c.** (1) Low; (2) Medium or high; (3) High
15.12. **a.** 920
15.16. **a.**

	Outcome				
Act	*0*	*1*	*2*	*3*	*4 or more*
0	0	0	0	0	0
1	−10	20	20	20	20
2	−20	10	40	40	40
3	−30	0	30	60	60

b.

Act	0	1	2	3
Expected Payoff	0	8.96 (Best act)	6.89	−0.70

Chapter 16

16.4. **a.** No, B is not **b.** D **c.** A

16.7. **a.** 30.8

b. C_1: $\mu_X \geq 30.8$; C_2: $\mu_X < 30.8$

c.

μ_X	$P(C_1)$	$P(C_2)$	P (error)
30.6	.0228	.9772	.0228
30.7	.1587	.8413	.1587
30.8	.5000	.5000	.5000
30.9	.8413	.1587	.1587
31.0	.9772	.0228	.0228
31.1	.9986	.0014	.0014
31.2	1	0	0
31.3	1	0	0

d.

μ_X	$P(C_1)$	$P(C_2)$	P (error)
30.6	0	1	0
30.7	0	1	0
30.8	.0014	.9986	.9986
30.9	.0228	.9772	.9772
31.0	.1587	.8413	.8413
31.1	.5000	.5000	.5000
31.2	.8413	.1587	.1587
31.3	.9772	.0228	.0228

e. (1) No; (2) Rule in **c**, rule in **d**

16.9. **a.**

μ_X	14	15	16	17	18	19	20	21
$P(C_2)$	1	.9986	.9772	.8413	.5000	.1587	.0228	.0014

b. .1587

d.

μ_X	14	15	16	17	18	19	20	21
$P(C_2)$	.9986	.9772	.8413	.5000	.1587	.0228	.0014	0

Chapter 17

17.3. **a.** C_1: $\mu_X \geq 19$; C_2: $\mu_X < 19$.
If $\overline{X} \geq 17.37$, conclude C_1; otherwise, conclude C_2.
Conclude C_2.

b. No **c.** .3557

e. If $\overline{X} \geq 18.63$, conclude C_1; otherwise, conclude C_2.
Conclude C_2.

17.5. **a.** 218 **b.** (1) 54; (2) 54

17.6. **a.** 172

b. If $\overline{X} \geq 18$, conclude C_1; otherwise, conclude C_2.

17.9. **b.**

μ_X	$P(C_2)$
−1.0	.9901
−.6	.8426
−.4	.6392
−.2	.4182
0	.3174
+.2	.4182
+.4	.6392
+.6	.8426
+1.0	.9901

c. .3174

e.

μ_X	$P(C_2)$
−1.0	.9525
−.6	.6294
−.4	.3720
−.2	.1686
0	.0950
+.2	.1686
+.4	.3720
+.6	.6294
+1.0	.9525

17.12. **a.** C_1: $\mu_X = .5$; C_2: $\mu_X \neq .5$.
If $.19 \leq \overline{X} \leq .81$, conclude C_1; otherwise, conclude C_2.
Conclude C_2.

b. No **c.** 95 per cent **d.** .54 to 1.16 **e.** .8869

17.14. **a.** 182 **b.** 81 **c.** 117

Chapter 18

18.4. **a.** C_1: $\mu_X \leq 350$; C_2: $\mu_X > 350$.
If $\overline{X} \leq 378.0$, conclude C_1; otherwise, conclude C_2.
Conclude C_1.
b. Yes **c.** Yes

18.5. **b.** C_1: $\mu_{X_1} \leq \mu_{X_2}$; C_2: $\mu_{X_1} > \mu_{X_2}$.
If $D \leq 696$, conclude C_1; otherwise, conclude C_2. ($D = \overline{X}_1 - \overline{X}_2$.)
Conclude C_2.
c. No **d.** .7088 **e.** No

18.8. **a.**

p	.01	.02	.03	.05	.07	.08	.09
$P(C_2)$	1	.9236	.5000	.0658	.5008	.7705	.9192

e.

p	.02	.05	.09
$P(C_2)$	.9979	.3576	.9823

f.

p	.02	.05	.09
$P(C_2)$	.9838	.4902	.9462

18.9. **a.** C_1: $p = .7$; C_2: $p \neq .7$.
If $.663 \leq \bar{p} \leq .737$, conclude C_1; otherwise, conclude C_2.
Conclude C_2.
c. Yes, 97.5 per cent **d.** .739 to .808 **e.** .9998

18.12. **a.** 364
b. C_1: $p \leq .15$; C_2: $p > .15$.
If $\bar{p} \leq .179$, conclude C_1; otherwise, conclude C_2.
c. 473

18.15. **a.** C_1: $p_1 = p_2$; C_2: $p_1 \neq p_2$.
If $-.028 \leq d \leq +.028$, conclude C_1; otherwise, conclude C_2.
($d = \bar{p}_1 - \bar{p}_2$).
Conclude C_2.
b. Yes, 98 per cent **c.** .057 to .117

18.18. **a.** .0091, .0168, .0030 **c.** 496, 2,228, 4,852

Chapter 19

19.3. **c.** 21.064, 29.141 **d.** .05, .02
e. If $V_1 \leq 29.141$, conclude C_1; if $V_1 > 29.141$, conclude C_2.
f. Yes **g.** 15

19.5. **a.** C_1: Population Poisson; C_2: Population not Poisson.
b.

X	0	1	2	3	4	5 or more
f_e	13.53	27.07	27.07	18.04	9.02	5.26

c. 2.21, 4 **d.** If $V_1 \leq 7.779$, conclude C_1; if $V_1 > 7.779$, conclude C_2.
Conclude C_1.

19.10. **a.** C_1: Variables are independent; C_2: Variables are not independent.
b.

	Did Know	*Did Not Know*
Wage earner or clerical worker	55	55
Managerial or professional worker	20	20
Other	25	25

c. 10.41, 2 **e.** If $V_1 \leq 7.824$, conclude C_1; if $V_1 > 7.824$, conclude C_2.
Conclude C_2.

g. No

19.14. **a.** 15, 4 **b.** 3.06, 4.89 **c.** 16, 3; 3.24, 5.29

19.15. **a.** C_1: $\mu_A = \mu_B = \mu_C$; C_2: all μ's not equal. **b.** 14, 12, 2

c.

Component	*Sum of Squares*	*Degrees of Freedom*	*Mean Square*
Between	.90	2	.4500
Within	.70	12	.0583
Total	1.60	14	

$V_2 = 7.71$

f. If $V_2 \leq 3.88$, conclude C_1; if $V_2 > 3.88$, conclude C_2.

g. Conclude C_2. **h.** .0583

Chapter 20

20.3. **a.** .135

b.

	Prior	*Posterior (Given Charged Purchase)*
Return	.10	.135
No return	.90	.865

c. .938 **d.** .133

20.5. **a.**

Act	*Expected Payoff*
C_1	23
C_2	26

C_2 is the Bayes act.

b.

Columns Requiring Cleaning	*Posterior Probability*
0	0
1	.143
2	.857

c.

Act	*Expected Payoff*
C_1	11.43
C_2	2.86

C_1 is the Bayes act.

d. If $X = 0$, select act C_2; if $X = 1$, select act C_1. (X = number of columns in the sample requiring cleaning and maintenance.)

e. 28 **f.** 27, optimal $n = 1$ **g.** Yes

20.6. **a.** 29 **c.** 3

20.11. **a.**

Act	*Expected Payoff*
Modernize now	1,375
Delay modernization	1,400

Delay modernization is the Bayes act.

c. 1,600; 200 **d.** 200 **e.** Yes

Chapter 21

21.4. **a.** No **b.** 530, 39

21.5. **a.** 26.5

b.

Act	*Expected Payoff*
C_1	4,600
C_2	4,800

C_2 is the Bayes act.

c. 26.41, .0877, yes

d.

Act	*Expected Payoff*
C_1	4,890
C_2	4,800

C_1 is the Bayes act.

e. Yes

21.7. **a.** Yes; $t = 1{,}000$ **b.** 115.2 **c.** 112.6; 4,912.6 **d.** Yes **e.** 115

f.

n	EVSI	cn	ENGS
0	0	0	0
25	109.6	25	84.6
50	112.6	50	62.6
100	113.7	100	13.7

g. 25

Chapter 22

22.9. **b.** $\bar{Y}_X = 323.05 + .26505\,X$ **f.** 456 **g.** 4.655 **h.** .965, +.983

22.11. **a.** $\bar{Y}_X = -49.374 + .35123\,X$ **c.** 56.0, no **e.** 3.019, cars **f.** .847, no units **g.** +.920

Chapter 23

23.6. **a.** 457.3 to 467.1 **c.** 476.4 to 503.7; no, width = ±2.8 per cent **f.** .224 to .306 **g.** Yes

23.8. **a.** 54.5 to 57.5 **c.** 90.0 to 106.2 **e.** No **f.** .329 to .374 **h.** Yes

Chapter 24

24.4. **a.** $\bar{Y}_{X_1X_2} = 244.17 + .18272\,X_1 + 19.951\,X_2$ **c.** 483.5 **d.** 2.722 **e.** .990 **f.** .995

24.6. **a.** $\bar{Y}_X = 246.27 + .61187\,X - .00037814\,X^2$ **b.** 477.3

Chapter 25

25.4. **a.**

Year	*Rate of Return on Investment (Per Cent)*
1970	6.97
1971	6.16
1972	5.93

c.

Year	*Profit (Per Cent of Sales)*	*Turnover Rate*
1970	3.71	1.88
1971	3.60	1.71
1972	3.43	1.73

25.6. **a.**

1971	*1970*
100.0	100.0
66.2	65.4
8.9	9.2
5.8	8.2
1.8	1.5
1.5	1.1
84.2	85.3
15.8	14.7
9.1	7.8
6.6	6.9

25.8. a.

Year	*Disposable Personal Income per Capita*
1965	2,763
1966	2,881
1967	2,965
1968	3,057
1969	3,099

b.

Year	*Disposable Personal Income*	*Per Capita Disposable Personal Income*
1965	100.0	100.0
1966	105.5	104.3
1967	109.8	107.3
1968	114.4	110.6
1969	117.1	112.2

c.

Year	*Disposable Personal Income*	*Per Capita Disposable Personal Income*
1965	–	–
1966	105.5	104.3
1967	104.1	102.9
1968	104.2	103.1
1969	102.4	101.4

25.10. **a.** 2.8 **b.** 180 **c.** 35.7 **d.** 28 **e.** 280 **f.** 35.7

25.18. **a.** 5 **b.** 25

25.19. **a.** 109.4, 55.2 **b.** 102.3, yes

Chapter 26

26.6. a.

	Routes	
Seat-mile Status	*Golden Triangle*	*Other*
Loaded	77	69
Empty	23	31
Total (%)	100	100
(Million Seat Miles)	(230.6)	(98.9)

d. Yes

26.11. a.

	Children under 18	
Action	*None*	*One or More*
Buy	32	55
Not buy	68	45
Total (%)	100	100
(Cases)	(275)	(575)

c. Yes

d.

	None		*One or More*	
Action	*Concerned*	*Unconcerned*	*Concerned*	*Unconcerned*
Buy	32	32	55	55
Not buy	68	68	45	45
Total (%)	100	100	100	100
(Cases)	(82)	(193)	(230)	(345)

e. Yes **f.** No

Chapter 28

28.4. **a.** 1970: 100.0; 1971: 104.5; 1972: 110.9 **c.** Yes **d.** No **e.** Yes
28.5. **a.** 1970: 100.0; 1971: 104.5; 1972: 110.9 **b.** Yes, no
28.8. **a.** 1970: 100.0; 1971: 99.3; 1972: 100.5
28.9. 1970: 100.0; 1971: 99.3; 1972: 100.5
28.17. **a.** +8.7 **b.** 1969: 931.7; 1970: 1,012.8 **c.** +8.7
28.20. **a.**

Year	*Index*	*Year*	*Index*
1966	73.0	1970	96.8
1967	90.3	1971	99.9
1968	95.2	1972	102.1
1969	100.0		

b. 39.9 **c.** No **d.** Yes

Chapter 29

29.7. **b.** $X = 0$ at 1963, X in years $\overline{Y}_X = 365.83 + 34.726\,X$
d. No **e.** 1,129.8, no
f.

Year	*Per Cent of Trend*	*Year*	*Per Cent of Trend*
1963	102.5	1967	97.5
1964	100.1	1968	99.4
1965	99.5	1969	101.0
1966	99.1	1970	101.2

29.10. **a.** $X = 0$ at 1962, X in years $\log \overline{Y}_X = 3.2890 + .067475X$
f. 31,890
29.11. **a.**

Year	*Per Cent of Trend*	*Year*	*Per Cent of Trend*
1962	106.2	1966	97.3
1963	98.2	1967	96.6
1964	95.1	1968	106.6
1965	100.7		

c. 16.8%

Chapter 30

30.10. **b.** Yes **c.** $\overline{Y}_X = 91.59 + 1.0470\,X$ **e.** 213.0

Chapter 31

31.10. **a.**

Quarter	1st	2d	3d	4th
Seasonally Adjusted Sales	6.92	7.23	7.39	7.47

b. 7.69
31.12. **a.**

Quarter	1st	2d	3d	4th
Forecast	3.5	5.3	5.4	4.2

b. Yes

31.23. c.

Year	*Quarter* *1st*	*2d*	*3d*	*4th*
1965	–	–	94.88	103.88
1966	98.21	102.56	94.76	104.46
1967	99.34	102.50	94.52	102.95
1968	96.72	103.79	99.60	102.62
1969	89.14	107.59	–	–

g.

Quarter	*Index*
1st	97.7
2d	103.5
3d	95.1
4th	103.7

h. 94.52

31.24. a.

Quarter	*Deseasonalized Exports*
1st	15.4
2d	15.7
3d	16.0
4th	15.7

c. Seasonally adjusted annual rate of exports in the 4th quarter: 62.9; annual exports in 1969: 55.7

e.

Quarter	1st	2d	3d	4th
Forecast	17.1	18.1	16.6	18.1

31.25. a.

Year and Quarter		*Deseasonalized Per Cent of Trend*
1965	1	94.8
	2	105.2
	3	101.8
	4	102.5
1966	1	102.1
	2	100.4
	3	100.8
	4	101.6
1967	1	101.7
	2	98.0
1967	3	97.3
	4	96.8
1968	1	97.3
	2	99.1
	3	102.5
	4	96.5
1969	1	89.8
	2	103.6
	3	104.6
	4	103.7

Chapter 32

32.1. a. $\overline{Y}_X = 487.38 + 34.726\,X$ ($X = 0$ at January 1, 1967; X in years)

b. 1,129.8; yes

32.4. a. $\overline{Y}_X = 30.606 + .24115\,X$ **b.** $\overline{Y}_X = 92.543 + 2.1704\,X$

32.7. a.

Month	*Forecast*	*Month*	*Forecast*
Feb.	452.8	Jun.	425.3
Mar.	453.2	Jul.	413.8
Apr.	446.8	Aug.	406.4
May	437.9	Sep.	400.0

c.

Month	*Forecast*	*Month*	*Forecast*
Feb.	453.6	Jun.	442.8
Mar.	453.6	Jul.	437.2
Apr.	451.4	Aug.	432.4
May	448.0	Sep.	427.7

e. No, no

INDEX

Acceptance sampling, 403–405
Act, 303
  admissible, 313
  dominated, 313
  inadmissible, 313
Action limit, of decision rule, 344
  effect of change on power curve, 344–345
Act probability, 335–338
Addition theorem, 123–125
Admissible act, 313
Aggregates, method of, 623–625, 629–630
Alden's, Inc., 403
Alexander Furniture Company, 602
American Radiator and Standard Sanitary Corporation, 692
Analysis of variance, 425–434
  degrees of freedom, 429
  mean squares, 429–430
  test statistic, 430–433
  total variation and components, 426–429
Analytical table, 580
Antecedent independent variable, 567–570
Area sampling, 268–269
Arithmetic average (*see also* Mean):
  calculation of:
    from grouped data, 79–81, 101–102
    from ungrouped data, 79
  as measure of location, 71–75
  modified, 715
  moving, 712
  weighted, 81, 550–551
Arithmetic straight-line trend, 660
  fitting trend curve, 661–663, 729–730
  per cent of trend, 664
  projecting trend curve, 663
  shift from annual to monthly or quarterly basis, 731
Array, 55
Assignable cause, 399
Association of American Railroads, 684
Average (*see* Arithmetic average; Median; Mode)

Bar charts, 591–597
Base period, for index numbers, 637–638
  shifting of, 637–640
Base period weights, 638
Basic outcome, in random experiment, 116–117
Bayes act, 448
Bayes decision rule, 453
  expected payoff of, 453–454
Bayesian inference:
  determining optimal sample size, 454–455
  with normal prior, 462–464
  with normal prior and sampling, 464–467
  no-sample case, 446–449
  sample case, 449–454
  with subjective probabilities, 457–458
Bayes procedure, 448–449
Bayes' theorem, 443–445
Bernoulli probability distribution, 141–143
Bessing Chemical Corporation, 678–680
Between-treatments sum of squares, 428
Bias, in questionnaire or schedule, 30
Binomial probability distribution, 213–217
  table of probabilities, 744
Bivariate probability distribution, 120–122
Bivariate sample space, 117
Boxhead, of table, 582
Bristol Laboratories, 49–51
Business Conditions Digest, 685
Business indicator, 682–688
  cyclical indicator, 685–687
  diffusion index, 687–688

Calumet and Hecla Consolidated Copper Company, 275
Caption:
  to scale of graph, 609
  in table, 582

Cell, in table, 583
Census, 16–17
Central limit theorem, 196–198, 219
Chart (*see* Graph)
Chebyshev inequality, 102–103, 166
Check question, 31
Chesapeake and Ohio Railroad, 271–273
Chi-square probability distribution, 416–417
  table of areas, 746
Chunk, 263–264
Classification of data, 33–34
Class limits, of frequency distribution, 54–55
Cluster, 269
Coding, 34–35
Coefficient of correlation, 499–500
  from time series data, 691
Coefficient of determination, 498–499
Coefficient of multiple correlation, 531–532
Coefficient of multiple determination, 531
Coefficient of skewness, 90
Coefficient of variation, 89
Coincidental method of audience research, 24
Collection of statistical data:
  construction of schedules and questionnaires, 27–30
  observation, 22
  personal interview, 22–24
  registration, 27
  self-enumeration, 25–27
  telephone interview, 24–25
Complementary event, 119–120
Component-part bar chart, 594
Component-part line graph, 600–602
Conditional mean, 486
  confidence interval, 508–511
  point estimation, 493–494
Conditional probability distribution, 122–123, 484–486
Conditional standard deviation, 486
  estimation of, 496–497, 530–531
Confidence coefficient, 238
  choice of, 244
  meaning of, 242
Confidence interval, 236–244
  analytical development, 238–239, 241–242
  choice of confidence coefficient, 244
  confidence coefficient, 242
  half-width of, 246
  relation to statistical decision-making, 374–375
  usefulness of, 242–243
Confidence limits, 243 (*see also* Confidence interval)
Consequence, 303
Consistency, 233–234
Constant cause system, 48–49
Constant dollars, 632–633
Consumer price index (*see* U.S. Bureau of Labor Statistics)
Contingency table, 421–425
Continuity, correction for, 425
Continuous probability distribution, 111, 166–169
Control chart, 398–403
Control limits, 399
Correlation analysis:
  applications, 524–527
  coefficient of correlation, 499–500
  coefficient of determination, 498–499
  coefficient of multiple correlation, 531–532
  coefficient of multiple determination, 531
  spurious correlations with time series data, 691
Criterion, for decision-making, 304
  expected payoff, 318–320
  maximax, 314
  maximization of payoff, 306
  minimax or maximin, 309–310, 314
  minimax regret, 314–316
Critical path analysis, 155–156
Cross-classification of data, 560–561
  study of causes and effects, 567–574
  study of statistical relationships, 562–567
  in table, 583–584
Cumulative frequency distribution, 58–62
Curvilinear regression analysis, 532–534
Cyclical fluctuations:
  business indicators, 682–687
  case illustrations, 693–694
  characteristics of, 680–682
  diffusion indexes, 687–688
  forecasting of, 688–693
  measurement of, 664, 666
Cyclical indicator, 685–688

Data, statistical:
  classification of, 33–34
  coding of, 34–35
  experimental, 15–16
  external, 13–14
  internal, 11–13

survey, 15–16
tabulation of, 35–38
Decision-making, statistical:
applications, 398–405
classical, 332–347, 353–378
nature of, 329–331
relation to confidence intervals, 374–375
statistical decision rules, 331–332
with use of prior probabilities, 446–473
Decision-making under certainty, 304–307
Decision-making under competitive conditions, 307–311
Decision-making under risk, 316–317
expected payoff criterion, 318–320
need for utility measure, 320–321
use of subjective probabilities, 321
Decision-making under uncertainty, 311–316
Decision rule, statistical, 331–332
inadmissible, 343
Degrees of freedom, 250, 416, 429, 431
Department of the Army:
Office of Director of Civilian Personnel, 526–527
Transportation Corps, 245
Dependent variable, 32–33
Deseasonalizing, of data, 703–706
Dichotomous question, 28
Diffusion index, 687–688
Discrete probability distribution, 111
Distribution (*see* Frequency distribution; Probability distribution)
Dodge Company, F. W., 684
Dominance, 313
Dun and Bradstreet, Inc., 546, 684
Duo-directional bar chart, 595

Eastman Kodak Company, 717
Econometrics, 733
Editing, of schedules and questionnaires, 30–31
Efficiency:
of estimator, 233
of sampling procedure, 264–265
Eggerstedt, Fred C., Jr., 671n.
Electronic data processing, 36–37
Elementary unit, 269
Equal complete coverage, 20–21
Equilibrium point, 310
Erie Railroad, 179
Error curve, 342
Error probability, 338–340
Errors:
in statistical data, 20–22
Type I and II, 334–335
Estimate, 231
Estimation, statistical:
case studies, 271–275
interval estimation, 235
point estimation, 230–231
consistency, 233–234
efficiency, 233
unbiasedness, 232–233
Estimator, 231
Event, 119–120
Exeter Corporation, 45–49
Expectation, of random variable, 129–131, 168–169
Expected net gain from sampling, 471
Expected payoff, 318–320
with perfect information, 455–456
Expected payoff criterion, 318–320
Expected value of perfect information, 457, 467–470
Expected value of sample information, 470
Experiment, 15–16, 18–19
design of, 434
experimental unit, 18
planning of, 19–20
randomization, 18–19
treatment, 18
Experimental data, 15–16
collection of, 22–27
errors in, 22
Experimental unit, 18
Exponential curve, 658
Exponential probability distribution, 153–155
table of areas, 743
Exponential smoothing, 733–736
External data, 13–14

F-distribution, 431–432
table of areas, 747–748
Federal Products Corporation, 402–403
Federal Reserve Board:
index of department store sales, 642
index of industrial production, 637, 642, 683, 692, 694
Field:
in punchcard, 36
of table, 583
Financial reports, 12
Finite correction factor, 196

Finite population, 107–109, 176
  interpreted as probability distribution, 112–113
Footnote, of table, 583
Forecasting, 651–653 (*see also* Cyclical fluctuations; Seasonal variation; Trend)
  long-term, 667–671
    case illustrations, 671–672
  short-term, 678–682, 708
    case illustrations, 693–694
    exponential smoothing, 733–736
Frame, 16
Free-answer question, 28–29
Frequency, of class, 47
Frequency distribution:
  construction of, 53–56
  cumulative, 58–62
  definition of, 51–52
  graphic presentation of, 57–58
Frequency polygon, 47, 57
Functional relation, 480–481

Game theory, 308–311
General Electric Company, 635–636
General Motors Corporation, 693–694
Gompertz curve, 656–658
Goodness of fit, tests of, 412–421
Graph, statistical:
  bar chart, 591–597
  construction of, 608–610
  frequency polygon, 47, 57
  histogram, 57–58
  line graph, 597–608
  ogive, 60–62
  scatter diagram, 483, 490–491
Grid lines, of graph, 592, 610
Grouped bar chart, 595
Grouped data, 79
Growth curve, 656–658

Half-width, of confidence interval, 246
Hansen, Morris H., 264
Harold Aircraft Company, 329–330
Headnote, of table, 582
Hi-Ace Company, 484
Histogram, 57–58
Hooper, Inc., C. E., 24
Hurwitz, William N., 264
Hypergeometric probability distribution, 212–213
Hypothesis testing, 334

Inadmissible act, 313
Inadmissible decision rule, 343
Independence, statistical:
  of events, 127
  of variables, 127–128
    test of, 421–425
Independent variable, 32–33
  antecedent, 567–570
  linking, 570–572
Index numbers:
  base period, 637–640
  price index, 621–628
  quantity index, 628–631
  splicing, 640
  use of sampling, 641–642
  uses of, 631–636
  weights, 636–637
Indifference point, 469
Infinite population, 109–110, 176
  as probability distribution, 110
Internal data, 11–13
Internal records, 12
Internal report, 12–13
Interquartile range, 85
Interstate Commerce Commission, 183
Interval estimate, 235 (*see also* Confidence interval)
Interview:
  personal, 22–24
  telephone, 24–25
Irregular changes, in time series data, 653, 702–703, 707, 712–713

Joint probability, 121
Judgment sample, 262–263

Leading question, 30
Lead-lag relationship, 691–692
Least squares, method of estimation, 492–496, 527–528
"Less than" distribution, 58–59
Level of significance, 355
Linear programming, 304–307
Linear regression analysis (*see* Regression analysis)
Linear trend (*see* Arithmetic straight-line trend; Semilogarithmic straight-line trend)
Line graph:
  arithmetic scale, 597–602
  ratio scale, 602–608

Linking variable, 570–572
Link relative, 547–548
Logarithmic scale, 602–603
Logistic curve, 656–658
Long, Clarence D., 3
Long Island Lighting Company, 671–672
Lower-tail decision problem, 364

Machine tabulation, 35–36
Mail questionnaire, 25–27
Manual tabulation, 37–38
Marginal probability distribution, 122
Maximax criterion, 314
Maximin criterion, 309–310, 314
Mean:
  as measure of location, 71–75
  modified, 715
  of population, 108, 129–131
    decision-making concerning, 353–378, 385–389, 425–434
    estimation of, 230–254, 278–283
  of sample, calculation of, 79–81, 101–102
    sampling distribution of, 192–198
Mean, conditional (*see* Conditional mean)
Mean square, 429–430
Mechanical editing, 31
Median:
  calculation of:
    from grouped data, 82–84
    from ungrouped data, 82
  definition of, 75
  interpretation as percentile, 84
Midpoint of class, of frequency distribution, 54–55
Mills, Frederick C., 3
Minimax criterion, 309–310
Minimax regret criterion, 314–316
Mixed strategy, 311
Mode, 76
Modified mean, 715
Monsanto Chemical Company, 672
"More than" distribution, 59–60
Moving average, 712
  centering of, 713
Moving seasonal pattern, 717–719
Multiple-choice question, 28
Multiple regression analysis, 528–532
Multiplication theorem, 125–128
Multistage sampling, 270
Multivariate sample space, 117
Mutually exclusive events, 119

National Bureau of Economic Research, 684–687
Nestlé's Chocolate Company, 524–525
Net operating profit as a per cent of sales, 544
Non-sampling error, 20–22
Normal equations, 492, 528, 529, 533
Normal probability distribution, 146–153
  sum or difference of two normal variables, 156
  table of areas, 741
Null hypothesis, 334

Oakite Products, Inc., 694
Objective probability, 114–115
Observational method, 22
Ogive, 60–62
One-sided alternative, in decision-making, 358
One-way analysis of variance (*see* Analysis of variance)
Open-end interval, of frequency distribution, 54
Open-end question, 28–29
Operating-characteristic curve, 341–342
Operating report, 12
Opportunity loss, 315, 468
Opportunity loss function, 468–469
Optimal allocation, stratified sampling, 293–294
Outcome state, 313

Parameter, of population, 109
Payoff, 306
  probability distribution of, 318
Payoff function, 330, 463
Pearl-Reed curve, 656
Pearson's coefficient of skewness, 90
Per cent change line graph, 599–600
Per cent changes, 548–550
Per cent distribution, 544–546, 562–563
Per cent frequency distribution, 52
Percentile, 84–85
Per cent points of change, 549–550
Per cent relative, 546–547
Personal interview, 22–24
Personal probability, 115–116
  used in decision-making under risk, 321
  used in statistical decision-making, 457–458
Pictogram, 610

Point estimation, 230–235
  consistency, 233–234
  efficiency, 233
  unbiasedness, 232–233
Poisson probability distribution, 143–146
  table of probabilities, 742
  test concerning, 413–419
Population, 16, 176
  finite, 107–109, 176
  infinite, 109–110, 176
  sampled, 21
  target, 21
Population mean:
  confidence interval:
    for large sample, 235–248
    for small sample, 248–254
  decision-making:
    for large sample, 353–378
    for small sample, 385–387
  decision-making for difference between two means, 387–389
  decision-making for several means, 425–434
  definition of, 108, 129–131
  estimating difference between two means, 281–283
  point estimation, 230–235
Population proportion, 211
  confidence interval, 284–286
  decision-making, 389–395
  decision-making for difference between two proportions, 395–398
  estimating difference between two proportions, 287–289
  point estimation, 283
Population standard deviation, 108, 131
  estimation of, 85–89
Population variance, 131, 132, 169
  estimation of, 87
Posterior probability, 445
Posterior probability distribution, 451
Power curve, 340–341
Precision, of sample estimate, 235
Pre-coding, 35
Prediction interval, for next observation, 512–516
  with time series data, 667–668
Pre-testing, of schedule or questionnaire, 30
Price index, 621–628 (*see also* Index numbers)
Primary source of data, 13
Prior probability, 445
Prior probability distribution, 446
Probability:
  conditional, 122–123
  of event, 119
  joint, 121
  marginal, 122
  objective, 114–115
  personal, 115–116
  posterior, 445
  postulates, 118
  prior, 445
  theorems, 123–128
Probability distribution:
  Bernoulli, 141–143
  bivariate, 120–122
  conditional, 122–123
  continuous, 111, 166–169
  discrete, 111
  exponential, 153–155
  marginal, 122
  mean of, 129–131
  normal, 146–153
  of payoffs, 318
  Poisson, 143–146
  qualitative, 111
  standard deviation of, 131
  tests about nature of, 412–421
  univariate, 120
  variance of, 131, 132
Probability distribution of $\bar{p}$ (*see* Sampling distribution of $\bar{p}$)
Probability distribution of $\bar{X}$ (*see* Sampling distribution of $\bar{X}$)
Probability sample, 261–262 (*see also* Sampling)
Projective techniques, 29
Proportion:
  in population, 211
    decision-making concerning, 389–398
    estimation of, 283–289
  in sample, 211
    sampling distribution of, 212–217
Proportional allocation, stratified sampling, 293
Punchcard, 35–36

Qualitative distribution, 52
Qualitative variable, 32
Quantitative variable, 32
Quantity index, 628–631 (*see also* Index numbers)

Quartile, 85
Questionnaire, 25–27
  construction of, 27–30
  editing of, 30–31
Quota sample, 263

Rand Corporation, 183
Random changes (*see* Irregular changes)
Random digits, table of, 183–185
Random experiment, 116
Randomization, 18–19
Randomized strategy, 311
Random sample, 180–182 (*see also* Probability sample; Sampling; Simple random sampling)
Random variable:
  definition of, 128
  expectation of, 129–131, 168–169
  functions of, 128–129
  standard deviation of, 131
  sum or difference of two random variables, 132–133
  variance of, 131, 132, 169
Range, 78
Rate of return on investment, 542–544
Ratio:
  averaging of, 550–551
  construction of, 539–542, 551–553
  link relative, 547–548
  per cent change, 548–550
  per cent distribution, 544–546
  per cent relative, 546–547
Ratio graph, 602–608
Ratio to moving average, method of, 709–716
Redundancy, 157
Reference base, 638
Reference table, 580
Registration, 27
Regression analysis:
  applications, 524–527
  curvilinear, 532–534
  estimation of conditional mean, 493–494, 508–511
  estimation of parameters, 491–493, 496–497, 527–528
  model, 484–488
  multiple, 528–532
  prediction of next observation, 512–516
Regression curve, 486–488
  estimation of conditional mean, 493–494, 508–511
  estimation of parameters, 491–493, 496–497
Regret, 315
Relatives, method of, 625–627, 630–631
Reliability engineering, 156–157
Report:
  financial, 12
  operating, 12
  special, 12–13

Saddle point, 310
Sample, 17, 176 (*see also* Sampling)
  changing, 17–18
  continuous, 17–18
  judgment, 262–263
  probability, 261–262
Sampled population, 21
Sample mean, 78–81
  sampling distribution of, 192–198
Sample proportion, 211
  sampling distribution of, 192, 211–217
Sample size:
  determination for decision-making:
    population mean, 361–364, 375–377
    population proportion, 393–395
  determination for estimating:
    population mean, 245–248
    population proportion, 285–286
Sample space, 116–117
Sample standard deviation, 85–89
Sample statistic, 109
Sample variance, 87
Sampling:
  applications, 271–275
  area, 268–269
  multistage, 270
  reasons for, 177–180
  simple random, 180–186
  stratified random, 265–267
  systematic, 267–268
  with unequal probabilities, 269
Sampling distribution, 189–192
Sampling distribution of b, 516
Sampling distribution of d, 287–288
Sampling distribution of D, 280–281
Sampling distribution of M_e, 192
Sampling distribution of $\overline{p}$, 192, 211–217
  approach to normal distribution, 219
  binomial distribution, 213–217
  estimation of standard deviation, 284
  hypergeometric distribution, 212–213
  mean of, 217–218
  standard deviation of, 218–219

Sampling distribution of $\overline{X}$, 192, 193
approach to normal distribution, 196–198
effect of population variability, 201–202
effect of sample size, 200–201
estimation of standard deviation, 239–240
mean of, 194–195
standard deviation of, 195–196
use of table of normal areas, 199–200
Sampling error, 20–22
Sampling unit, 268–269
Scale, of graph, 592, 609
Scatter diagram, 483, 490–491
Schedule, 22–24
construction of, 27–30
editing of, 30–31
Seasonal index, 703, 716 (*see also* Seasonal variation)
Seasonal relative:
specific, 713
typical, 715
Seasonal variation, 700–701
crude method of measurement, 702–703
deseasonalizing, 703–708
forecasting, 708
measurement by method of ratio to moving average, 709–716
moving seasonal patterns, 717–719
Secondary source of data, 13–14
Secular trend (*see* Trend)
Self-enumeration, 25–27
Semilogarithmic graph, 602–608
Semilogarithmic straight-line trend, 658–660
fitting trend curve, 664–666
per cent of trend, 666
projecting trend curve, 666
rate-of-growth determination, 666
Shewhart, W. A., 197–198
Significance level, 355
Simple random sampling:
from infinite population, 181, 185–186
use of table of random digits, 183–185
without replacement, 180
with replacement, 180–181
Skewness, in frequency distribution, 74, 76–77, 90
SKF Industries, Inc., 692
Slope, of regression curve, 487
inferences concerning, 516–518
Smith Company, R. L., 543
Source note:
of graph, 610
of table, 583
Source of statistical data:
external, 13–14
primary, 13
secondary, 13–14
internal, 11–13
Special report, 12–13
Specific seasonal relative, 713
Splicing, of index numbers, 640
Split-ballot technique, 30
Spurious relationship, 568–570, 691
Standard deviation:
as measure of variation, 77–78
of population, 108, 131
of sample, calculation of, 85–89, 102
Standard deviation, conditional (*see* Conditional standard deviation)
Standard deviation of $\overline{X}$, 195
Standard error of the mean, 195
Standardized variable, 132
Standard normal deviate, 148
Standard normal distribution, 148–150
table of, 741
Standard Register Company, 405
State of nature, 313
Statistic, from sample, 109
Statistical Abstract of the United States, 14
Statistical decision-making (*see* Decision-making, statistical)
Statistical decision rule, 331–332
Statistical estimation (*see* Estimation, statistical)
Statistical independence, 127–128
test of, 421–425
Statistical indicator (*see* Business indicator)
Statistical relation, 481–484
Statistics, meaning of, 1
Stewart-Warner Corporation, 404–405
Straight-line trend (*see* Arithmetic straight-line trend; Semilogarithmic straight-line trend)
Stratified random sampling, 265–267
estimation of population mean, 291–292
optimal allocation, 293–294
proportional allocation, 293
setting up strata, 290
Stratum, 266
Stub:
of graph, 592
of table, 582

Stub head, in table, 582
Subjective probability (*see* Personal probability)
Summary columns and rows, in tables, 586
Superior Canning Company, 366–367
Survey, statistical, 15–18
  planning of, 19–20
Survey data, 15–16
  collection of, 22–27
  errors in, 20–22
Sylvania Electric Products, Inc., 74
Systematic sampling, 267–268

Table, statistical:
  analytical, 580
  construction of, 585–588
  cross-classified, 583–584
  per cent data, 587
  reference, 580
  structural elements of, 582–583
Table number, 582
Tabulating machine, 36
Tabulation of data:
  by electronic computer, 36–37
  by machine, 35–36
  manual, 37–38
Target population, 21
t-distribution, 249–251
  approach to normality, 253
  table of areas, 745
Telephone interview, 24–25
Testing hypotheses, 334
The New Yorker, 553
Thurston Corporation, 230–231
Tick, on graph, 610
Time series analysis, 650–736 (*see also* Cyclical fluctuations; Irregular changes; Seasonal variation; Trend)
  alternative models, 731–733
  exponential smoothing, 733–736
Title:
  of graph, 608–609
  of table, 582
Total sum of squares, 427
Treatment, 18
Trend, 653–655
  arithmetic straight-line, 661–664
  case illustrations, 671–672
  patterns of, 655–661
  projection of trend curve, 663, 666, 667–671
  semilogarithmic straight-line, 664–666
Turnover rate, 544

Two-person, zero-sum game, 310
*Two-sided alternative, in decision-making, 367
Two-way question, 28
Type I error, 334–335
Type II error, 334–335

Unbiased estimator, 195, 232–233
Ungrouped data, 79
Unimodal distribution, 76
Unit normal loss function, 469–470
  table of, 749
Univariate probability distribution, 120
Univariate sample space, 117
Upper-tail decision problem, 358
U.S. Bureau of Labor Statistics, consumer price index, 633, 637, 641, 642
U.S. Bureau of the Census, 179
U.S. Department of Agriculture, 683
U.S. Department of Commerce, 683
U.S. Food and Drug Administration, 312
Utility measure, 320–321
Utilization factor, 158

Value added, 637
Value weight, 627
Variable, 31–33
  antecedent, 567–570
  dependent, 32–33, 490
  independent, 32–33, 490
  linking, 570–572
  qualitative, 32
  quantitative, 32
  random, 128
  standardized, 132
Variance:
  of population, 131, 132, 169
  of sample, 87

Waiting line problems, 157–159
Weight base, 638
Weighted aggregate index (*see* Aggregates, method of)
Weighted arithmetic average, 81
  of means, 81
  of ratios, 550–551
Weighted average of relatives index (*see* Relatives, method of)
Weights, for index numbers, 636–637
Wilson Metals Corporation, 278–280
Within-treatments sum of squares, 428
Work sampling, 273–274